**AAPC**

MEMBERSHIP

Join over 170,000 Professionals in the Business of Healthcare

 UNMATCHED NETWORKING OPPORTUNITIES

Meet other industry professionals at any of our local and national events.

Connect with seasoned experts in thousands of online forum discussions.

 NATIONAL RECOGNITION

Take advantage of opportunities for leadership, authorship, interviews, speaking and more.

Earn internationally recognized certifications.

 BIG SAVINGS

Save on hundreds of national brands through Member Savings.

Get exclusive discounts on AAPC products and educational events, including workshops, webinars, and conferences.

 INVALUABLE ACCESS TO JOBS

Find thousands of industry jobs in our healthcare employment database.

Network at local chapter meetings, workshops, conferences, and in member-only forums.

 COMPREHENSIVE EDUCATION

Get the latest training you can trust whether you are preparing for certification or staying up-to-date on industry changes.

Advance your career with continuing education opportunities online or at local, regional, or national events.

 HEALTHCARE BUSINESS RESOURCES

Get the latest industry information with AAPC's Healthcare Business Monthly magazine.

Keep up-to-date with industry news, trends, and tips in specialized eNewsletters.

Learn more at www.AAPC.com

Where will YOU be next spring?

AAPC

HEALTHCON.com

2018

HCPCS
EXPERT
LEVEL II

AAPC
Advancing the Business of Healthcare

Table of Contents

NOTES

Introduction

This Healthcare Common Procedure Coding System (HCPCS) Level II manual goes beyond the basics to help you to code accurately and efficiently. In addition to including a customized Alphabetic Index and Tabular List for services, supplies, durable medical equipment, and drugs which the Centers for Medicare and Medicaid Services (CMS) developed.

Features

We've crafted a select set of bonus features based on requests from coders in the field as well as the recommendations of our core group of veteran coding educators. Features that you'll benefit from page after page include:

- HCPCS Coding Procedures guide from CMS to help you to better understand HCPCS codes
- Comprehensive list of new/revised/deleted codes for 2018
- G codes to CPT® Crosswalk
- Deleted Codes Crosswalk
- Symbols showing which codes have restrictions based on age or sex of the patient
- Medicare and carrier coverage and reimbursement alerts
- APC status indicators
- HCPCS code modifiers
- Full illustrations of body systems at the front of the book so you don't have to search the manual for these large color images of body systems
- Highlighted coding instructional and informational notes help you recognize important code usage guidance for specific sections
- Intuitive color-coded symbols and alerts identify critical coding and reimbursement issues quickly
- A user-friendly page design, including dictionary-style headers, color bleed tabs, and legend keys

Additionally, our dedicated team drew on their years of experience using coding manuals to develop this manual's user friendly symbols, highlighting, color coding, and tabs, all designed to help you find the information you need quickly.

Let Us Know What You Think

Our goal for this manual is to support those involved in the business side of healthcare, helping them to do their jobs and do them well. We'd appreciate your feedback, including your suggestions for what you'll need in a HCPCS resource, so we can be sure our manuals serve your needs.

Symbols and Conventions

Citations to AHA's *Coding Clinic®* for HCPCS

AHA's *Coding Clinic®*, a quarterly newsletter, is the official publication for coding guidelines and advice as designated by the four Cooperating Parties (American Hospital Association, American Health Information Management Association, Centers for Medicare and Medicaid Services (CMS), and National Center for Health Statistics) and the Editorial Advisory Board.

We've marked codes with related *Coding Clinic®* articles with a citation that includes the year, quarter, and page number(s) of the issue.

Symbols & Conventions used in the manual include:

2018 HCPCS code updates:

- ●   New code
- ▲   Revised Code

Symbols and Alerts Related to Medicare or Carrier Coverage and Reimbursement

When relevant, you'll see the following symbols and alerts to the left of a code or beside or under the code descriptor:

C	Carrier judgment
D	Special coverage instructions apply
I	Not payable by Medicare
M	Non-covered by Medicare
S	Non-covered by Medicare statute

A2 - Z3 = ASC Payment Indicator

A - Y =   APC Status Indicator

ASC =   ASC Approved Procedure

Service not separately priced by Part B

Other carrier priced

Reasonable charge

Price established using national RVUs

Price subject to national limitation amount

Price established by carriers

Statute references

BETOS code and descriptor

Paid under the DME fee schedule

Pub 100 references

Modifier Alerts Showing Applicable Modifiers for a HCPCS Code

DME Modifier - Alert appears under the code descriptor

References to Pub 100 (non-dental codes) – Alert appears under the code descriptor

Symbols for Age and Sex Codes

When relevant, you'll see the following symbols to the right of a code descriptor. We based symbol use on Medicare's Outpatient Code Editor (OCE).

♀	Female code symbol
♂	Male code symbol
A	Age

Symbols and Alerts Related to Services, Supplies, or Equipment

When relevant, you'll see the following symbols to the right of code descriptors:

DME	Paid under the DME fee schedule
MIPS	Merit-based Incentive Payment System (MIPS)

MIPS data in this manual is from the latest updates from CMS at the time this book went to print. Refer to the CMS website for the latest updates on MIPS reporting.

Instructions for Using This Manual

Understand Code Structure to Choose the Most Specific Code

HCPCS codes are made up of five alphanumeric characters, starting with a letter that represents a category of similar codes, followed by four numbers.

The Tabular List arranges codes in alphanumeric order, starting with codes beginning with the letter A.

Code descriptors identify a category of like items or services and typically do not identify specific products or brand/trade names.

Code Services, Supplies, Equipment, and Drugs With Confidence Following This Approach

➤ The first step in choosing the proper HCPCS code is reading the medical documentation to identify the service, supply, equipment, or drug that the provider documents and confirms.

- Be sure to check online or hard copy references, such as medical dictionaries and anatomy resources, to look up unfamiliar terms.

➤ Next, decide which main term you will search in the Index based on the patient's specific case. You can look under the name of the service (magnetic resonance angiography, EMG), supply (dialysis drain bag, filler), equipment (bathtub, cane), or drug (hydrocortisone, ipratropium bromide), the body site involved (hip, knee), or the type of service (laboratory tests, oncology).

➤ When searching the Table of Drugs and Biologicals, search for the name of the drug, then the unit and route to find the drug code to cross-reference to the Tabular List.

➤ Once you find the term in the Index, note the recommended code. Start with the main term and review any available subterms. Cross-reference all codes listed, whether it is one code, a series of codes separated by commas, or a code range separated by a hyphen. Pay attention to the "*see*" convention that directs you to look elsewhere to find the code or the "*see also*" convention that directs you to look in an additional place to find the code.

➤ Turn to that code in the Tabular List, and read the full code descriptor for correct code assignment.

➤ Before making your final code decision, review the surrounding codes to be sure there isn't a more appropriate code available. Pay attention to the "*see*" convention that directs you to look elsewhere to find the code or the "*see also*" convention that directs you to look in an additional place to find the code.

➤ Finally, take a moment to confirm that your code choice complies with the philosophy of ethical coding. Never report a HCPCS code simply because it will support reimbursement from a payer. Report only those codes the documentation supports.

HEALTHCARE COMMON PROCEDURE CODING SYSTEM (HCPCS) LEVEL II CODING PROCEDURES

This information provides a description of the procedures CMS follows in making coding decisions.

FOR FURTHER INFORMATION CONTACT:

Jennifer Carver (410) 786-6610 or Cindy Hake (410) 786-3404 for HCPCS level II coding issues.

A. HCPCS BACKGROUND INFORMATION

Each year, in the United States, health care insurers process over 5 billion claims for payment. For Medicare and other health insurance programs to ensure that these claims are processed in an orderly and consistent manner, standardized coding systems are essential. The HCPCS Level II Code Set is one of the standard code sets used for this purpose. The HCPCS is divided into two principal subsystems, referred to as level I and level II of the HCPCS. Level I of the HCPCS is comprised of CPT® (Current Procedural Terminology), a numeric coding system maintained by the American Medical Association (AMA). The CPT® is a uniform coding system consisting of descriptive terms and identifying codes that are used primarily to identify medical services and procedures furnished by physicians and other health care professionals. These health care professionals use the CPT® to identify services and procedures for which they bill public or private health insurance programs. Decisions regarding the addition, deletion, or revision of CPT® codes are made by the AMA. The CPT® codes are republished and updated annually by the AMA. Level I of the HCPCS, the CPT® codes, does not include codes needed to separately report medical items or services that are regularly billed by suppliers other than physicians.

Level II of the HCPCS is a standardized coding system that is used primarily to identify products, supplies, and services not included in the CPT® codes, such as ambulance services and durable medical equipment, prosthetics, orthotics, and supplies (DMEPOS) when used outside a physician's office. Because Medicare and other insurers cover a variety of services, supplies, and equipment that are not identified by CPT® codes, the level II HCPCS codes were established for submitting claims for these items. The development and use of level II of the HCPCS began in the 1980's. Level II codes are also referred to as alpha-numeric codes because they consist of a single alphabetical letter followed by 4 numeric digits, while CPT® codes are identified using 5 numeric digits.

In October of 2003, the Secretary of HHS delegated authority under the HIPAA legislation to CMS to maintain and distribute HCPCS Level II Codes. As stated in 42 CFR Sec. 414.40 (a) CMS establishes uniform national definitions of services, codes to represent services, and payment modifiers to the codes. Within CMS there is a CMS HCPCS Workgroup which is an internal workgroup comprised of representatives of the major components of CMS, as well as other consultants from pertinent Federal agencies. Prior to December 31, 2003, Level III HCPCS were developed and used by Medicaid State agencies, Medicare contractors, and private insurers in their specific programs or local areas of jurisdiction. For purposes of Medicare, level III codes were also referred to as local codes. Local codes were established when an insurer preferred that suppliers use a local code to identify a service, for which there is no level I or level II code, rather than use a

"miscellaneous or not otherwise classified code." The Health Insurance Portability and Accountability Act of 1996 (HIPAA) required CMS to adopt standards for coding systems that are used for reporting health care transactions. We published, in the Federal Register on August 17, 2000 (65 FR 50312), regulations to implement this part of the HIPAA legislation. These regulations provided for the elimination of level III local codes by October 2002, at which time, the level I and level II code sets could be used. The elimination of local codes was postponed, as a result of section 532(a) of BIPA, which continued the use of local codes through December 31, 2003.

B. HCPCS LEVEL II CODES

The regulation that CMS published on August 17, 2000 (45 CFR 162.10002) to implement the HIPAA requirement for standardized coding systems established the HCPCS level II codes as the standardized coding system for describing and identifying health care equipment and supplies in health care transactions that are not identified by the HCPCS level I, CPT® codes. The HCPCS level II coding system was selected as the standardized coding system because of its wide acceptance among both public and private insurers. Public and private insurers were required to be in compliance with the August 2000 regulation by October 1, 2002. The purpose of this section is to provide a general description of the current HCPCS level II coding system.

The HCPCS level II coding system is a comprehensive and standardized system that classifies similar products that are medical in nature into categories for the purpose of efficient claims processing. For each alphanumeric HCPCS code, there is descriptive terminology that identifies a category of like items. These codes are used primarily for billing purposes. For example, suppliers use HCPCS level II codes to identify items on claim forms that are being billed to a private or public health insurer.

HCPCS is a system for identifying items and services. It is not a methodology or system for making coverage or payment determinations, and the existence of a code does not, of itself, determine coverage or non-coverage for an item or service. While these codes are used for billing purposes, decisions regarding the addition, deletion, or revision of HCPCS codes are made independent of the process for making determinations regarding coverage and payment.

Currently, there are national HCPCS codes representing over 4,000 separate categories of like items or services that encompass millions of products from different manufacturers. When submitting claims, suppliers are required to use one of these codes to identify the items they are billing. The descriptor that is assigned to a code represents the definition of the items and services that can be billed using that code.

In summary, the HCPCS level II coding system has the following characteristics:

- This system ensures uniform reporting on claims forms of items or services that are medical in nature. Such a standardized coding system is needed by public and private insurance programs to ensure the uniform reporting of services on claims forms by suppliers and for meaningful data collection.
- The descriptors of the codes identify a category of like items or services and typically do not identify specific products or brand/trade names.

- The coding system is not a methodology for making coverage or payment determinations. Each payer makes determinations on coverage and payment outside this coding process.

C. TYPES OF HCPCS LEVEL II CODES

There are several types of HCPCS level II codes depending on the purpose for the codes and who is responsible for establishing and maintaining them.

Permanent National Codes

National permanent HCPCS level II codes are maintained by the CMS HCPCS Workgroup. The Workgroup is responsible for making decisions about additions, revisions, and deletions to the permanent national alpha-numeric codes. These codes are for the use of all private and public health insurers. Since HCPCS is a national coding system all payers will be represented in the Workgroup including representatives from private insurance agencies, the Pricing, Data Analysis, and Coding (PDAC), and Medicaid will participate in the workgroup meetings and provide input as to what is necessary to meet each party's program operating needs.

The permanent national codes serve the important function of providing a standardized coding system that is managed jointly by private and public insurers. This standardized approach to developing a set of uniform codes provides a stable environment for claims submission and processing.

Dental Codes

The dental codes are a separate category of national codes. The Current Dental Terminology (CDT®) is a publication copyrighted by the American Dental Association (ADA) that lists codes for billing for dental procedures and supplies. While the CDT® codes are considered HCPCS level II codes, decisions regarding the revision, deletion, or addition of CDT® codes are made by the ADA and not the CMS HCPCS Workgroup, and CDT® codes are published by the ADA and not by CMS.

Miscellaneous Codes

National codes also include "miscellaneous/not otherwise classified" codes. These codes are used when a supplier is submitting a bill for an item or service and there is no existing national code that adequately describes the item or service being billed. The importance of miscellaneous codes is that they allow suppliers to begin billing immediately for a service or item as soon as it is allowed to be marketed by the Food and Drug Administration (FDA) even though there is no distinct code that describes the service or item. A miscellaneous code can be used during the period of time a request for a new code is being considered under the HCPCS review process. The use of miscellaneous codes also helps us to avoid the inefficiency and administrative burden of assigning distinct codes for items or services that are rarely furnished or for which we expect to receive few claims.

Because of miscellaneous codes, the absence of a specific code for a distinct category of products does not affect a supplier's ability to submit claims to private or public insurers and does not affect patient access to products. Claims with miscellaneous codes are manually reviewed, the item or service being billed must be clearly described, and pricing information must be provided along with documentation to explain why the item or service is needed by the beneficiary.

Ordinarily, before using a miscellaneous code on a claim form, a supplier should check with the entity that will receive the payment claim to determine whether there is a specific code that should be used rather than a miscellaneous code. In the case of claims that are to be submitted to one of the four Durable Medical Equipment Medicare Administrative Contractors (DME MACs), suppliers that have coding questions should check with the pricing, data analysis, and coding (PDAC), contractor to CMS. The PDAC is responsible for providing suppliers and manufacturers with assistance in determining which HCPCS code should be used to describe DMEPOS items for the purpose of billing Medicare. The PDAC has a toll free helpline for this purpose, (877) 735-1326. In addition, the PDAC publishes a product classification list on its website that lists individual items to code categories. More information about the PDAC and the PDAC's product classification list can be found at http://www.dmepdac.com.

If no code exists that describes the product category to which the item belongs, and if the item fits a Medicare Benefit Category, the PDAC may instruct the supplier to submit claims using a "miscellaneous/not otherwise classified" code. If an item does not fit a Medicare Benefit Category, the PDAC might assign a code that indicates that the product is not covered by Medicare for example, code A9270, NON-COVERED ITEM OR SERVICE. If an item is included or bundled into another code and not separately reimbursed by Medicare, the PDAC may assign the code that includes the item or a code that indicates that the item is included as a component of another code. In those cases in which a supplier or manufacturer has been advised to use a miscellaneous code because there is no existing code that describes a given product, and the supplier or manufacturer believes that the code is needed, it should submit a request to modify the HCPCS in accordance with the established process. The process for requesting a revision to the HCPCS level II codes is explained below.

Temporary National Codes

Temporary codes are for the purpose of meeting, within a short time frame, the national program operational needs of a particular insurer that are not addressed by an already existing national code. The CMS HCPCS Workgroup has set aside certain sections of the HCPCS code set to allow the Workgroup to develop temporary codes. Decisions regarding the number and type of temporary codes and how they are used are also made by the CMS HCPCS Workgroup. These codes are used at the discretion of CMS. This means that if, before the next scheduled annual update for permanent codes, the CMS HCPCS Workgroup needs a code in order to meet specific operating needs that pertain to its particular programs, it may establish a national temporary code. In the case of Medicare, decisions regarding temporary codes are made by the CMS HCPCS workgroup. For example, Medicare may need additional codes before the next scheduled annual HCPCS update to implement newly issued coverage policies or legislative requirements. Although we establish temporary codes to meet our specific operational needs, the temporary codes we establish can be used by other insurers. Temporary codes allow insurers the flexibility to establish codes that are needed before the next January 1 annual update for permanent national codes or until consensus can be achieved on a permanent national code. Permanent national codes are only updated once a year on January 1.

The CMS HCPCS Workgroup may decide to replace temporary codes with permanent codes. However, temporary codes do not have established expiration dates. Whenever a permanent code is established by the CMS HCPCS Workgroup to replace a temporary code, the temporary code is deleted and cross-referenced to the new permanent code.

Types of temporary HCPCS codes:

The C codes were established to permit implementation of section 201 of the Balanced Budget Refinement Act of 1999. HCPCS C codes are utilized to report drugs, biologicals, magnetic resonance angiography (MRA), and devices that must be used by OPPS hospitals. HCPCS C codes are reported for device categories, new technology procedures, and drugs, biologicals and radiopharmaceuticals that do not have other HCPCS code assignments. Non-OPPS hospitals, Critical Access Hospitals (CAHs), Indian Health Service Hospitals (IHS), hospitals located in American Samoa, Guam, Saipan, or the Virgin Islands, and Maryland waiver hospitals may report these codes at their discretion. More information regarding HOPPS can be found at http://www.cms.gov/HospitalOutpatientPPS/.

- The G codes are used to identify professional health care procedures and services that would otherwise be coded in CPT®-4 but for which there are no CPT®-4 codes. The Q codes are used to identify services that would not be given a CPT®-4 code, such as drugs, biologicals, and other types of medical equipment or services, and which are not identified by national level II codes but for which codes are needed for claims processing purposes.

- The K codes were established for use by the DME MACs when the currently existing permanent national codes do not include the codes needed to implement a DME MAC medical review policy. For example, codes other than the permanent national codes may be needed by the DME MACs to identify certain product categories and supplies necessary for establishing appropriate regional medical review coverage policies.

- The S codes are used by private insurers to report drugs, services, and supplies for which there are no national codes but for which codes are needed by the private sector to implement policies, programs, or claims processing. They are for the purpose of meeting the particular needs of the private sector. These codes are also used by the Medicaid program, but they are not payable by Medicare.

- Certain H codes are used by those State Medicaid agencies that are mandated by State law to establish separate codes for identifying mental health services such as alcohol and drug treatment services.

- The T codes are designated for use by Medicaid State agencies to establish codes for items for which there are no permanent national codes and for which codes are necessary to meet a national Medicaid program operating need. T codes are not used by Medicare but can be used by private insurers.

Code Modifiers

In some instances, insurers instruct suppliers that a HCPCS code must be accompanied by code modifier to provide additional information regarding the service or item identified by the HCPCS code. Modifiers are used when the information provided by a HCPCS code descriptor needs to be supplemented to identify specific circumstances that may apply to an item or service. For example, a UE modifier is used when the item identified by a HCPCS code is "used equipment," a NU modifier is used for "new equipment." The level II HCPCS modifiers are either alpha-numeric or two letters.

C. REQUESTING A REVISION TO THE HCPCS LEVEL II CODES

Anyone can submit a request for modifying the HCPCS level II national code set. A document explaining the HCPCS revision process, as well as a detailed format for submitting a request, is available on the HCPCS website at http://www.cms.hhs.gov/medicare/hcpcs. Besides the information requested in this format, a requestor should also submit any additional descriptive material, including the manufacturer's product literature and information, that it thinks would be helpful in furthering our understanding of the medical features of the item for which a coding revision is being recommended. The HCPCS coding review process is an ongoing continuous process. Requests may be submitted at any time throughout the year. Requests that are received and complete by January 4 of the current year will be considered for inclusion in the next annual update (January 1st of the following year). Requests received on or after January 5, and requests received earlier that require additional evaluation, will be included in a later HCPCS update. There are three types of coding revisions to the HCPCS that can be requested:

1. That a permanent code be added
   When there is not a distinct code that describes a product, a code may be requested (1) if the FDA allows the product to be marketed in the United States and (2) if the product is not a drug, the product has been on the market for at least 3 months; if the product is a drug, there is no requirement to submit marketing data; and (3) the product represents 3 percent or more of the outpatient use for that type of product in the national market. If a request for a new code is approved, the addition of a new HCPCS codes does not mean that the item is necessarily covered by any insurer. Whether an item identified by a new code is covered is determined by the Medicare law, regulations, and medical review policies and not by the assignment of a code.

2. That the language used to describe an existing code be changed when there is an existing code, a recommendation to modify the code can be made when an interested party believes that the descriptor for the code needs to be modified to provide a better description of the category of products represented by the code.

3. That an existing code be deleted

When an existing code becomes obsolete or is duplicative of another code, a request can be made to delete the code.

When there is no currently existing code to describe a product, a miscellaneous code/not otherwise classified code may be appropriate. The use of a miscellaneous code permits a claims history to be established for an item that can be used to support the need for a national permanent code.

Requests for coding revisions should be sent to the following:
Alpha-Numeric HCPCS Coordinator,
Center for Medicare Management,
Centers for Medicare and Medicaid Services,
C5-08-27,
7500 Security Boulevard,
Baltimore, MD 21244-1850.

CMS HCPCS Workgroup

The CMS HCPCS Workgroup is an internal workgroup comprised of representatives of the major components of CMS, the Medicaid State agencies, and the PDAC. The PDAC represents Medicare program operating needs with input from the four DME MACs which have responsibility for processing Durable Medical Equipment, Prosthetics, Orthotics and Supplies (DMEPOS) claims for the Medicare program. Coding decisions are coordinated with both public and private insurers. The CMS HCPCS workgroup considers each coding request, and beginning with the 2006 cycle, will determine whether HCPCS coding requests warrant a change to the national permanent codes. Prior to the 2006 cycle, the National Panel was responsible for final decisions.

When a recommendation for a revision to the HCPCS is received, it is reviewed at a regularly scheduled meeting of the CMS HCPCS Workgroup. Ordinarily, the CMS HCPCS Workgroup meets monthly to discuss whether coding requests warrant a change to the national permanent codes.

Evaluating HCPCS Coding Requests

The CMS HCPCS workgroup applies the following criteria to determine whether there is a demonstrated need for a new or modified code or the need to remove a code:

1. When an existing code adequately describes the item in a coding request, then no new or modified code is established. An existing code adequately describes an item in a coding request when the existing code describes products with the following:

   - Functions similar to the item in the coding request.
   - No significant therapeutic distinctions from the item in the coding request.

2. When an existing code describes products that are almost the same in function with only minor distinctions from the item in the coding request, the item in the coding request may be grouped with that code and the code descriptor modified to reflect the distinctions.

3. A code is not established for an item that is used only in the inpatient setting or for an item that is not diagnostic or therapeutic in nature.

4. A new or modified code is not established for an item unless the FDA allows the item to be marketed. FDA approval documentation is required to be submitted with the coding request application for all non-drug items. For drugs, FDA approval documentation will be accepted up to March 31 following the application deadline as long as the application is otherwise complete and submitted by the deadline.

5. There must be sufficient claims activity or volume, as evidenced by 3 months of marketing activity for non-drug products, so that the adding of a new or modified code enhances the efficiency of the system and justifies the administrative burden of adding or modifying a code. Applications for products/services that are not yet available on the U.S. market will be considered incomplete and will not be processed.

6. The determination to remove a code is based on the consideration of whether a code is obsolete (for example, products no longer are used, other more specific codes have been added) or duplicative

and no longer useful (for example, new codes are established that better describe items identified by existing codes). In developing its decisions, the HCPCS Workgroup uses the criteria mentioned above. In deciding upon a recommendation, the workgroup does not include cost as a factor.

Opportunity for Public Input/Public Meeting Process for HCPCS

On December 21, 2000, the Congress passed the Medicare, Medicaid, and SCHIP Benefits Improvement and Protection Act of 2000 (BIPA), Pub. L. 106-554. Section 531(b) of BIPA mandated that we establish procedures that permit public consultation for coding and payment determinations for new DME under Medicare Part B of title XVIII of the Social Security Act (the Act). As part of HCPCS reform, CMS expanded the public meeting forum to include all public requests as of the 2005-2006 coding cycle. Accordingly, CMS hosts annual public meetings that provide a forum for interested parties to make oral presentations and/or to submit written comments in response to preliminary coding and pricing recommendations for new durable medical equipment that have been submitted using the Healthcare Common Procedure Coding System coding revision process. Agenda items for the meetings will be published in advance of the public meeting on the HCPCS website at http://www.cms.gov/medhcpcsgeninfo. The agenda will include descriptions of the coding requests, the requestor, and the name of the product or service. This change will provide more opportunities for the public to become aware of coding changes under consideration, as well as opportunities for public input into decision-making.

The HCPCS coordinator schedules meetings with interested parties, at their request, as time permits, to discuss their recommendations regarding possible changes to the HCPCS level II codes. These meetings are held at the Central Office of CMS. In addition to representatives from the CMS HCPCS Workgroup, staff from Medicaid and Medicare coverage, payment and operations are invited to attend these meetings. These meetings are not related to the meetings mandated by section 531(b) of BIPA, they are also not decision making meetings or CMS HCPCS Workgroup meetings.

Final Decisions

The CMS HCPCS Workgroup is responsible for making the final decisions pertaining to additions, deletions, and revisions to the HCPCS codes. The CMS HCPCS Workgroup reviews all requests for coding changes and makes final decisions regarding the annual update to the national codes. The Workgroup sends letters to those who requested coding revisions to inform them of the Workgroup's decision regarding their coding requests. The decision letters include, but may not be limited to, the following types of responses:

1. A change to the national codes has been approved that reflects, completely or in part, your coding request.

2. Your request for a coding revision to this year's update has not been approved because the scope of your request necessitates that additional consideration be given to your request before the CMS HCPCS Workgroup reaches a final decision.

3. Your reported sales volume was insufficient to support your request for a revision to the national codes. To determine whether there is sufficient sales volume to warrant a permanent code, we ask requestors to submit 3 months of the most recent sales volume for

non-drug items. There is not a requirement to submit marketing data for drugs.

4. Your request for a new national code has not been approved because there already is an existing permanent or temporary code that describes your product.

5. Your request for a code has not been approved because your product is not used by health care providers for diagnostic or therapeutic purposes.

6. Your request for a code has not been approved because the code you requested is for capital equipment.

7. Your request for a code has not been approved because your product is an integral part of another service and payment for that service includes payment for your product; therefore, your product may not be billed separately to Medicare.

8. Your request for a revision to the language that describes the current code has not been approved because it does not improve the code descriptor.

9. Your request for a new code has not been approved because your product is not primarily medical in nature (for example, generally not useful in the absence of an illness or injury).

10. Your request for a code has not been approved because your product is used exclusively in the inpatient hospital setting.

11. Your request for a code has not been approved because it is inappropriate for inclusion in the HCPCS Level II code set and request should be submitted independently to another coding authority (e.g. AMA for CPT® coding, ADA for CDT® coding, etc.)

Decision letters also inform the requestors that they may contact the entity in whose jurisdiction a claim is filed for assistance in answering any coding questions. For Medicare, contact the PDAC. Contractor to CMS, the PDAC is responsible for providing suppliers and manufacturers with assistance in determining which HCPCS code should be used to describe DMEPOS items for the purpose of billing Medicare. The PDAC has a toll free helpline for this purpose, (877) 735-1326, which is operational during the hours of 9 AM to 4 PM (EST). For Medicaid, contact the state Medicaid agency. For private insurance, contact the individual insurer. A requestor who is dissatisfied with the final decision may submit a new request asking the CMS HCPCS Workgroup to reconsider and re-evaluate the code request. At that time, the requestor should include new information or additional explanations to support the request.

Reconsideration Process

CMS management is considering pilot-testing, a process by which denied applicants would be allowed an opportunity to have their application reconsidered during the same coding cycle. The basis for denial will be clearly delineated in a notice to the applicant and provided in a timely fashion.

D. HCPCS Updates
Permanent National Codes

The national codes are updated annually, according to the following schedule:

1. Coding requests have to be received by January 3 of the current year to be considered for the next January 1 update of the subsequent year. This means that completed requests must be received by no later than January 3 of the current year to be considered for inclusion in the January update of the following year unless January 3 falls on a weekend; then the due date is extended to the following Monday.

2. Computer tapes and instructions, that include an updated list of codes and identify which codes have been changed or deleted, are updated and sent to our contractors and Medicaid State agencies at least 60 days in advance of the January 1 implementation date for the annual update. In addition, the CMS HCPCS Workgroup's final decisions on all public requests for changes to the HCPCS coding system will be published on the official HCPCS web site at www.cms.gov/medhcpcsgeninfo in November of each year.

Temporary Codes

Temporary codes can be added, changed, or deleted on a quarterly basis. Once established, temporary codes are usually implemented within 90 days, the time needed to prepare and issue implementation instructions and to enter the new code into CMS's and the contractors' computer systems and initiate user education. This time is needed to allow for instructions such as bulletins and newsletters to be sent out to suppliers to provide them with information and assistance regarding the implementation of temporary CMS codes.

HCPCS/Medicare Website

Our website, http://www.cms.gov/medhcpcsgeninfo lists all of the current HCPCS codes, an alphabetical index of HCPCS codes by type of service or product, and an alphabetical table of drugs for which there are level II codes. The HCPCS Public Meeting Agendas (separated by product category) published on this website list applications submitted in the current coding cycle. Interested parties can submit comments regarding the agenda items to the CMS HCPCS Workgroup by sending an e-mail to CMS through this website. These comments are included as part of the Workgroup's review as it considers the coding requests.

The newly established temporary codes and effective dates for their use are also posted on the HCPCS website at http://www.cms.gov/medhcpcsgeninfo. This website enables us to quickly disseminate information on coding requests and decisions.

Code Assignment Following Medicare National Coverage Determination

Pursuant to Sec. 1862 (l) (3) (C) (iv) of the Social Security Act (added by Section 731 (a) of the Medicare Modernization Act), the Centers for Medicare and Medicaid Services (CMS), has developed a process by which the CMS HCPCS Workgroup will identify an appropriate existing code category and/or establish a new code category to describe the item that is the subject of a National Coverage Determination (NCD). If the item is considered Durable Medical Equipment, Prosthetic, Orthotic or Supply (DMEPOS), the CMS will defer to the Pricing, Data Analysis and Coding (PDAC) to determine the appropriate code category. Contractor to the CMS, the (PDAC) assigns individual DMEPOS products to HCPCS code categories for the purpose of billing Medicare.

As a matter of meeting on-going Medicare program operating needs, processes have existed for some time by which items and services that are newly covered by Medicare are assigned to a new or existing code category. Effective July 1, 2004, the process outlined below has been used by CMS to comply with the requirements of Sec. 1862 (l).

1. Assignment of an Existing "Temporary" or "Permanent" Code: When the CMS determines that an item is already identified by an existing "temporary" or "permanent" (as described in A and B above) HCPCS code category, but was previously not covered, the CMS will assign the item to the existing code category, and ensure that the coverage indicator assigned to the code category accurately reflects Medicare policy regarding payment for the item. Sec. 731 of the MMA does not require that a new code category or a product specific code be created for an item simply because a new coverage determination was made, without regard to codes available in the existing code set.

2. Assignment of a New "Temporary" or "Permanent" Code: When the CMS determines that a new code category is appropriate, CMS will make every effort to establish, publish, and implement the new code at the time the final coverage determination is made.

3. Assignment of an Unclassified Code: Under certain circumstances, the assignment of an item to an unclassified code may be necessary. A number of unclassified codes already exist under various headings throughout the HCPCS Level II code set. When an item is newly covered, but usage is narrow and the item would be billed infrequently, it may be more of an administrative burden to revise the code set than to use an unclassified code along with other, existing processing methods. When a new "temporary" or "permanent" code is appropriate, but the change cannot be implemented and incorporated into billing and claims processing systems at the time the final NCD decision memorandum is released, an unclassified code may be assigned in the interim, until a new code can be implemented, in order to ensure that claims can be processed for the item. The timing of implementation of new "temporary" or "permanent" codes relative to the date of the coverage determination depends on a variety of factors, some of which are not within the direct control of the code set maintainers, for example:

   • coding alternatives may require extensive research;
   • the timing of the coverage determination may be such that the publication deadline for the next Quarterly Update is missed;
   • there is insufficient time between NCD and Quarterly Update to incorporate new codes into new policy and accompanying billing instructions, and into claims processing systems along with any edits needed to operationalize the new code.

New/Revised/Deleted Codes for 2018

NEW CODES

Code	Code Descriptor
C9014	Injection, cerliponase alfa, 1 mg
C9015	Injection, C-1 esterase inhibitor (human), haegarda, 10 units
C9016	Injection, triptorelin extended release, 3.75 mg
C9024	Injection, liposomal, 1 mg daunorubicin and 2.27 mg cytarabine
C9028	Injection, inotuzumab ozogamicin, 0.1 mg
C9029	Injection, guselkumab, 1 mg
C9488	Injection, conivaptan hydrochloride, 1 mg
C9492	Injection, durvalumab, 10 mg
C9493	Injection, edaravone, 1 mg
C9738	Adjunctive blue light cystoscopy with fluorescent imaging agent (list separately in addition to code for primary procedure)
C9745	Nasal endoscopy, surgical; balloon dilation of eustachian tube
C9746	Transperineal implantation of permanent adjustable balloon continence device, with cystourethroscopy, when performed and/or fluoroscopy, when performed
C9747	Ablation of prostate, transrectal, high intensity focused ultrasound (HIFU), including imaging guidance
C9748	Transurethral destruction of prostate tissue; by radiofrequency water vapor (steam) thermal therapy
E0953	Wheelchair accessory, lateral thigh or knee support, any type including fixed mounting hardware, each
E0954	Wheelchair accessory, foot box, any type, includes attachment and mounting hardware, each foot
G0511	Rural health clinic or federally qualified health center (RHC or FQHC) only, general care management, 20 minutes or more of clinical staff time for chronic care management services or behavioral health integration services directed by an RHC or FQHC practitioner (physician, NP, PA, or CNM), per calendar month
G0512	Rural health clinic or federally qualified health center (RHC or FQHC) only, psychiatric collaborative care model (psychiatric COCM), 60 minutes or more of clinical staff time for psychiatric COCM services directed by an RHC or FQHC practitioner (physician, NP, PA, or CNM) and including services furnished by a behavioral health care manager and consultation with a psychiatric consultant, per calendar month
G0513	Prolonged preventive service(s) (beyond the typical service time of the primary procedure), in the office or other outpatient setting requiring direct patient contact beyond the usual service; first 30 minutes (list separately in addition to code for preventive service)
G0514	Prolonged preventive service(s) (beyond the typical service time of the primary procedure), in the office or other outpatient setting requiring direct patient contact beyond the usual service; each additional 30 minutes (list separately in addition to code G0513 for additional 30 minutes of preventive service)
G0515	Development of cognitive skills to improve attention, memory, problem solving (includes compensatory training), direct (one-on-one) patient contact, each 15 minutes

Code	Code Descriptor
G0516	Insertion of non-biodegradable drug delivery implants, 4 or more (services for subdermal rod implant)
G0517	Removal of non-biodegradable drug delivery implants, 4 or more (services for subdermal implants)
G0518	Removal with reinsertion, non-biodegradable drug delivery implants, 4 or more (services for subdermal implants)
G9890	Dilated macular exam performed, including documentation of the presence or absence of macular thickening or geographic atrophy or hemorrhage and the level of macular degeneration severity
G9891	Documentation of medical reason(s) for not performing a dilated macular examination
G9892	Documentation of patient reason(s) for not performing a dilated macular examination
G9893	Dilated macular exam was not performed, reason not otherwise specified
G9894	Androgen deprivation therapy prescribed/administered in combination with external beam radiotherapy to the prostate
G9895	Documentation of medical reason(s) for not prescribing/administering androgen deprivation therapy in combination with external beam radiotherapy to the prostate (e.g., salvage therapy)
G9896	Documentation of patient reason(s) for not prescribing/administering androgen deprivation therapy in combination with external beam radiotherapy to the prostate
G9897	Patients who were not prescribed/administered androgen deprivation therapy in combination with external beam radiotherapy to the prostate, reason not given
G9898	Patient age 65 or older in institutional special needs plans (SNP) or residing in long-term care with POS code 32, 33, 34, 54, or 56 any time during the measurement period
G9899	Screening, diagnostic, film, digital or digital breast tomosynthesis (3D) mammography results documented and reviewed
G9900	Screening, diagnostic, film, digital or digital breast tomosynthesis (3D) mammography results were not documented and reviewed, reason not otherwise specified
G9901	Patient age 65 or older in institutional special needs plans (SNP) or residing in long-term care with POS code 32, 33, 34, 54, or 56 any time during the measurement period
G9902	Patient screened for tobacco use and identified as a tobacco user
G9903	Patient screened for tobacco use and identified as a tobacco non-user
G9904	Documentation of medical reason(s) for not screening for tobacco use (e.g., limited life expectancy, other medical reason)
G9905	Patient not screened for tobacco use, reason not given

Code	Code Descriptor
G9906	Patient identified as a tobacco user received tobacco cessation intervention (counseling and/or pharmacotherapy)
G9907	Documentation of medical reason(s) for not providing tobacco cessation intervention (e.g., limited life expectancy, other medical reason)
G9908	Patient identified as tobacco user did not receive tobacco cessation intervention (counseling and/or pharmacotherapy), reason not given
G9909	Documentation of medical reason(s) for not providing tobacco cessation intervention if identified as a tobacco user (eg, limited life expectancy, other medical reason)
G9910	Patients age 65 or older in institutional special needs plans (SNP) or residing in long-term care with POS code 32, 33, 34, 54 or 56 anytime during the measurement period
G9911	Clinically node negative (T1N0M0 or T2N0M0) invasive breast cancer before or after neoadjuvant systemic therapy
G9912	Hepatitis B virus (HBV) status assessed and results interpreted prior to initiating anti-TNF (tumor necrosis factor) therapy
G9913	Hepatitis B virus (HBV) status not assessed and results interpreted prior to initiating anti-TNF (tumor necrosis factor) therapy, reason not given
G9914	Patient receiving an anti-TNF agent
G9915	No record of HBV results documented
G9916	Functional status performed once in the last 12 months
G9917	Documentation of medical reason(s) for not performing functional status (e.g., patient is severely impaired and caregiver knowledge is limited, other medical reason)
G9918	Functional status not performed, reason not otherwise specified
G9919	Screening performed and positive and provision of recommendations
G9920	Screening performed and negative
G9921	No screening performed, partial screening performed or positive screen without recommendations and reason is not given or otherwise specified
G9922	Safety concerns screen provided and if positive then documented mitigation recommendations
G9923	Safety concerns screen provided and negative
G9924	Documentation of medical reason(s) for not providing safety concerns screen or for not providing recommendations, orders or referrals for positive screen (e.g., patient in palliative care, other medical reason)
G9925	Safety concerns screening not provided, reason not otherwise specified
G9926	Safety concerns screening positive screen is without provision of mitigation recommendations, including but not limited to referral to other resources
G9927	Documentation of system reason(s) for not prescribing warfarin or another FDA-approved anticoagulation due to patient being currently enrolled in a clinical trial related to af/atrial flutter treatment
G9928	Warfarin or another FDA-approved anticoagulant not prescribed, reason not given
G9929	Patient with transient or reversible cause of AF (e.g., pneumonia, hyperthyroidism, pregnancy, cardiac surgery)
G9930	Patients who are receiving comfort care only

Code	Code Descriptor
G9931	Documentation of CHA2DS2-VASc risk score of 0 or 1
G9932	Documentation of patient reason(s) for not having records of negative or managed positive TB screen (e.g., patient does not return for mantoux (PPD) skin test evaluation)
G9933	Adenoma(s) or colorectal cancer detected during screening colonoscopy
G9934	Documentation that neoplasm detected is only diagnosed as traditional serrated adenoma, sessile serrated polyp, or sessile serrated adenoma
G9935	Adenoma(s) or colorectal cancer not detected during screening colonoscopy
G9936	Surveillance colonoscopy - personal history of colonic polyps, colon cancer, or other malignant neoplasm of rectum, rectosigmoid junction, and anus
G9937	Diagnostic colonoscopy
G9938	Patients age 65 or older in institutional special needs plans (SNP) or residing in long-term care with POS code 32, 33, 34, 54, or 56 any time during the measurement period
G9939	Pathologists/dermatopathologists is the same clinician who performed the biopsy
G9940	Documentation of medical reason(s) for not on a statin (e.g., pregnancy, in vitro fertilization, clomiphene Rx, ESRD, cirrhosis, muscular pain and disease during the measurement period or prior year)
G9941	Back pain was measured by the visual analog scale (VAS) within three months preoperatively and at three months (6 - 20 weeks) postoperatively
G9942	Patient had any additional spine procedures performed on the same date as the lumbar discectomy/laminotomy
G9943	Back pain was not measured by the visual analog scale (VAS) within three months preoperatively and at three months (6 - 20 weeks) postoperatively
G9944	Back pain was measured by the visual analog scale (VAS) within three months preoperatively and at one year (9 to 15 months) postoperatively
G9945	Patient had cancer, fracture or infection related to the lumbar spine or patient had idiopathic or congenital scoliosis
G9946	Back pain was not measured by the visual analog scale (VAS) within three months preoperatively and at one year (9 to 15 months) postoperatively
G9947	Leg pain was measured by the visual analog scale (VAS) within three months preoperatively and at three months (6 to 20 weeks) postoperatively
G9948	Patient had any additional spine procedures performed on the same date as the lumbar discectomy/laminotomy
G9949	Leg pain was not measured by the visual analog scale (VAS) within three months preoperatively and at three months (6 to 20 weeks) postoperatively
G9954	Patient exhibits 2 or more risk factors for post-operative vomiting
G9955	Cases in which an inhalational anesthetic is used only for induction
G9956	Patient received combination therapy consisting of at least two prophylactic pharmacologic anti-emetic agents of different classes preoperatively and/or intraoperatively

Code	Code Descriptor
G9957	Documentation of medical reason for not receiving combination therapy consisting of at least two prophylactic pharmacologic anti-emetic agents of different classes preoperatively and/or intraoperatively (e.g., intolerance or other medical reason)
G9958	Patient did not receive combination therapy consisting of at least two prophylactic pharmacologic anti-emetic agents of different classes preoperatively and/or intraoperatively
G9959	Systemic antimicrobials not prescribed
G9960	Documentation of medical reason(s) for prescribing systemic antimicrobials
G9961	Systemic antimicrobials prescribed
G9962	Embolization endpoints are documented separately for each embolized vessel and ovarian artery angiography or embolization performed in the presence of variant uterine artery anatomy
G9963	Embolization endpoints are not documented separately for each embolized vessel or ovarian artery angiography or embolization not performed in the presence of variant uterine artery anatomy
G9964	Patient received at least one well-child visit with a PCP during the performance period
G9965	Patient did not receive at least one well-child visit with a PCP during the performance period
G9966	Children who were screened for risk of developmental, behavioral and social delays using a standardized tool with interpretation and report
G9967	Children who were not screened for risk of developmental, behavioral and social delays using a standardized tool with interpretation and report
G9968	Patient was referred to another provider or specialist during the performance period
G9969	Provider who referred the patient to another provider received a report from the provider to whom the patient was referred
G9970	Provider who referred the patient to another provider did not receive a report from the provider to whom the patient was referred
G9974	Dilated macular exam performed, including documentation of the presence or absence of macular thickening or geographic atrophy or hemorrhage and the level of macular degeneration severity
G9975	Documentation of medical reason(s) for not performing a dilated macular examination
G9976	Documentation of patient reason(s) for not performing a dilated macular examination
G9977	Dilated macular exam was not performed, reason not otherwise specified
J0565	Injection, bezlotoxumab, 10 mg
J0604	Cinacalcet, oral, 1 mg, (for ESRD on dialysis)
J0606	Injection, etelcalcetide, 0.1 mg
J1428	Injection, eteplirsen, 10 mg
J1555	Injection, immune globulin (CuVitru™), 100 mg
J1627	Injection, granisetron, extended-release, 0.1 mg
J1726	Injection, hydroxyprogesterone caproate, (Makena®), 10 mg
J1729	Injection, hydroxyprogesterone caproate, not otherwise specified, 10 mg
J2326	Injection, nusinersen, 0.1 mg
J2350	Injection, ocrelizumab, 1 mg

Code	Code Descriptor
J3358	Ustekinumab, for intravenous injection, 1 mg
J7210	Injection, factor VIII, (antihemophilic factor, recombinant), (AFSTYLA), 1 I.U.
J7211	Injection, factor VIII, (antihemophilic factor, recombinant), (Kovaltry®), 1 I.U.
J7296	Levonorgestrel-releasing intrauterine contraceptive system, (Kyleena™), 19.5 mg
J7345	Aminolevulinic acid HCl for topical administration, 10% gel, 10 mg
J9022	Injection, atezolizumab, 10 mg
J9023	Injection, avelumab, 10 mg
J9203	Injection, gemtuzumab ozogamicin, 0.1 mg
J9285	Injection, olaratumab, 10 mg
K0553	Supply allowance for therapeutic continuous glucose monitor (CGM), includes all supplies and accessories, 1 month supply = 1 Unit Of Service
K0554	Receiver (monitor), dedicated, for use with therapeutic glucose continuous monitor system
L3761	Elbow orthosis (EO), with adjustable position locking joint(s), prefabricated, off-the-shelf
L7700	Gasket or seal, for use with prosthetic socket insert, any type, each
L8625	External recharging system for battery for use with cochlear implant or auditory osseointegrated device, replacement only, each
L8694	Auditory osseointegrated device, transducer/actuator, replacement only, each
P9073	Platelets, pheresis, pathogen-reduced, each unit
P9100	Pathogen(s) test for platelets
Q0477	Power module patient cable for use with electric or electric/pneumatic ventricular assist device, replacement only
Q2040	Tisagenlecleucel, up to 250 million car-positive viable T cells, including leukapheresis and dose preparation procedures, per infusion
Q4176	Neopatch, per square centimeter
Q4177	Floweramnioflo, 0.1 cc
Q4178	Floweramniopatch, per square centimeter
Q4179	Flowerderm™, per square centimeter
Q4180	Revita®, per square centimeter
Q4181	Amnio wound, per square centimeter
Q4182	Transcyte® , per square centimeter

REVISED CODES

Code	Code Descriptor
G8442	Pain assessment not documented as being performed, documentation the patient is not eligible for a pain assessment using a standardized tool at the time of the encounter
G8535	Elder maltreatment screen not documented; documentation that patient is not eligible for the elder maltreatment screen at the time of the encounter
G8540	Functional outcome assessment not documented as being performed, documentation the patient is not eligible for a functional outcome assessment using a standardized tool at the time of the encounter
G8808	Trans-abdominal or trans-vaginal ultrasound not performed, reason not given
G8869	Patient has documented immunity to hepatitis B and initiating anti-TNF therapy
G8880	Documentation of reason(s) sentinel lymph node biopsy not performed (e.g., reasons could include but not limited to; non-invasive cancer, incidental discovery of breast cancer on prophylactic mastectomy, incidental discovery of breast cancer on reduction mammoplasty, pre-operative biopsy proven lymph node (LN) metastases, inflammatory carcinoma, stage 3 locally advanced cancer, recurrent invasive breast cancer, clinically node positive after neoadjuvant systemic therapy, patient refusal after informed consent)
G8939	Pain assessment documented as positive, follow-up plan not documented, documentation the patient is not eligible at the time of the encounter
G8941	Elder maltreatment screen documented as positive, follow-up plan not documented, documentation the patient is not eligible for follow-up plan at the time of the encounter
G8967	Warfarin or another FDA approved oral anticoagulant is prescribed
G8968	Documentation of medical reason(s) for not prescribing warfarin or another FDA-approved anticoagulant (e.g., atrial appendage device in place)
G8969	Documentation of patient reason(s) for not prescribing warfarin or another FDA-approved oral anticoagulant that is FDA approved for the prevention of thromboembolism (e.g., patient choice of having atrial appendage device placed)
G9227	Functional outcome assessment documented, care plan not documented, documentation the patient is not eligible for a care plan at the time of the encounter
G9263	Documentation of patient discharged alive following endovascular AAA repair
G9313	Amoxicillin, with or without clavulanate, not prescribed as first line antibiotic at the time of diagnosis for documented reason
G9348	CT scan of the paranasal sinuses ordered at the time of diagnosis for documented reasons
G9504	Documented reason for not assessing hepatitis B virus (HBV) status (e.g., patient not initiating anti-TNF therapy, patient declined) prior to initiating anti-TNF therapy
G9607	Documented medical reasons for not performing intraoperative cystoscopy (e.g., urethral pathology precluding cystoscopy, any patient who has a congenital or acquired absence of the urethra) or in the case of patient death

Code	Code Descriptor
G9624	Patient not screened for unhealthy alcohol use using a systematic screening method or patient did not receive brief counseling if identified as an unhealthy alcohol user, reason not given
G9637	At least two orders for the same high-risk medication
G9638	At least two orders for the same high-risk medications not ordered
G9656	Patient transferred directly from anesthetizing location to PACU or other non-ICU location
G9758	Patient in hospice at any time during the measurement period
G9762	Patient had at least two HPV vaccines (with at least 146 days between the two) or three HPV vaccines on or between the patient's 9th and 13th birthdays
G9763	Patient did not have at least two HPV vaccines (with at least 146 days between the two) or three HPV vaccines on or between the patient's 9th and 13th birthdays
G9764	Patient has been treated with an oral systemic or biologic medication for psoriasis vulgaris
G9765	Documentation that the patient declined therapy change or alternative therapies were unavailable, has documented contraindications, or has not been treated with an oral systemic or biologic for at least six consecutive months (e.g., experienced adverse effects or lack of efficacy with all other therapy options) in order to achieve better disease control as measured by PGA, BSA, PASI, or DLQI
G9785	Pathology report diagnosing cutaneous basal cell carcinoma or squamous cell carcinoma (to include in situ disease) sent from the pathologist/dermatopathologist to the biopsying clinician for review within 7 days from the time when the tissue specimen was received by the pathologist
G9786	Pathology report diagnosing cutaneous basal cell carcinoma or squamous cell carcinoma (to include in situ disease) was not sent from the pathologist/dermatopathologist to the biopsying clinician for review within 7 days from the time when the tissue specimen was received by the pathologist
G9794	Documentation of medical reason(s) for not on a daily aspirin or other antiplatelet (e.g., history of gastrointestinal bleed, intra-cranial bleed, idiopathic thrombocytopenic purpura (ITP), gastric bypass or documentation of active anticoagulant use during the measurement period)
G9814	Death occurring during the index acute care hospitalization
G9815	Death did not occur during the index acute care hospitalization
G9816	Death occurring after discharge from the hospital but within 30 days post procedure
G9817	Death did not occur after discharge from the hospital within 30 days post procedure
G9840	RAS (KRAS and NRAS) gene mutation testing performed before initiation of anti-EGFR MOAB
G9841	RAS (KRAS and NRAS) gene mutation testing not performed before initiation of anti-EGFR MOAB
G9843	RAS (KRAS and NRAS) gene mutation
J7321	Hyaluronan or derivative, Hyalgan®, Supartz or Visco-3™, for intra-articular injection, per dose

Code	Code Descriptor
L3760	Elbow orthosis (EO), with adjustable position locking joint(s), prefabricated, item that has been trimmed, bent, molded, assembled, or otherwise customized to fit a specific patient by an individual with expertise
L8618	Transmitter cable for use with cochlear implant device or auditory osseointegrated device, replacement
L8624	Lithium ion battery for use with cochlear implant or auditory osseointegrated device speech processor, ear level, replacement, each
L8691	Auditory osseointegrated device, external sound processor, excludes transducer/actuator, replacement only, each
Q4132	Grafix® CORE and GrafixPL® CORE, per square centimeter
Q4133	Grafix® prime and GrafixPL® prime, per square centimeter
Q4148	Neox® CORD 1K, Neox® CORD RT, or Clarix™ CORD 1K, per square centimeter
Q4156	Neox® 100 or Clarix™ 100, per square centimeter
Q4158	Kerecis™ Omega3, per square centimeter
Q4162	WoundEx® Flow, BioSkin Flow, 0.5 cc
Q4163	WoundEx®, BioSkin, per square centimeter

DELETED CODES

Code	Code Descriptor
A9599	Radiopharmaceutical, diagnostic, for beta-amyloid positron emission tomography (PET) imaging, per study dose, not otherwise specified
C9140	Injection, factor viii (antihemophilic factor, recombinant) (AFSTYLA®), 1 i.u.
C9483	Injection, atezolizumab, 10 mg
C9484	Injection, eteplirsen, 10 mg
C9485	Injection, olaratumab, 10 mg
C9486	Injection, granisetron extended release, 0.1 mg
C9487	Ustekinumab, for intravenous injection, 1 mg
C9489	Injection, nusinersen, 0.1 mg
C9490	Injection, bezlotoxumab, 10 mg
C9491	Injection, avelumab, 10 mg
C9494	Injection, ocrelizumab, 1 mg
G0202	Screening mammography, bilateral (2-view study of each breast), including computer-aided detection (CAD) when performed
G0204	Diagnostic mammography, including computer-aided detection (CAD) when performed; bilateral
G0206	Diagnostic mammography, including computer-aided detection (CAD) when performed; unilateral
G0364	Bone marrow aspiration performed with bone marrow biopsy through the same incision on the same date of service
G0502	Initial psychiatric collaborative care management, first 70 minutes in the first calendar month of behavioral health care manager activities, in consultation with a psychiatric consultant, and directed by the treating physician or other qualified health care professional, with the following required elements: outreach to and engagement in treatment of a patient directed by the treating physician or other qualified health care professional; initial assessment of the patient, including administration of validated rating scales, with the development of an individualized treatment plan; review by the psychiatric consultant with modifications of the plan if recommended; entering patient in a registry and tracking patient follow-up and progress using the registry, with appropriate documentation, and participation in weekly caseload consultation with the psychiatric consultant; and provision of brief interventions using evidence-based techniques such as behavioral activation, motivational interviewing, and other focused treatment strategies

Code	Code Descriptor
G0503	Subsequent psychiatric collaborative care management, first 60 minutes in a subsequent month of behavioral health care manager activities, in consultation with a psychiatric consultant, and directed by the treating physician or other qualified health care professional, with the following required elements: tracking patient follow-up and progress using the registry, with appropriate documentation; participation in weekly caseload consultation with the psychiatric consultant; ongoing collaboration with and coordination of the patient's mental health care with the treating physician or other qualified health care professional and any other treating mental health providers; additional review of progress and recommendations for changes in treatment, as indicated, including medications, based on recommendations provided by the psychiatric consultant; provision of brief interventions using evidence-based techniques such as behavioral activation, motivational interviewing, and other focused treatment strategies; monitoring of patient outcomes using validated rating scales; and relapse prevention planning with patients as they achieve remission of symptoms and/or other treatment goals and are prepared for discharge from active treatment
G0504	Initial or subsequent psychiatric collaborative care management, each additional 30 minutes in a calendar month of behavioral health care manager activities, in consultation with a psychiatric consultant, and directed by the treating physician or other qualified health care professional (list separately in addition to code for primary procedure); (use G0504 in conjunction with G0502, G0503)
G0505	Cognition and functional assessment using standardized instruments with development of recorded care plan for the patient with cognitive impairment, history obtained from patient and/or caregiver, in office or other outpatient setting or home or domiciliary or rest home
G0507	Care management services for behavioral health conditions, at least 20 minutes of clinical staff time, directed by a physician or other qualified health care professional, per calendar month, with the following required elements: initial assessment or follow-up monitoring, including the use of applicable validated rating scales; behavioral health care planning in relation to behavioral/psychiatric health problems, including revision for patients who are not progressing or whose status changes; facilitating and coordinating treatment such as psychotherapy, pharmacotherapy, counseling and/or psychiatric consultation; and continuity of care with a designated member of the care team
G8696	Antithrombotic therapy prescribed at discharge
G8697	Antithrombotic therapy not prescribed for documented reasons (e.g., patient had stroke during hospital stay, patient expired during inpatient stay, other medical reason(s)); (e.g., patient left against medical advice, other patient reason(s))
G8698	Antithrombotic therapy was not prescribed at discharge, reason not given
G8879	Clinically node negative (T1N0M0 or T2N0M0) invasive breast cancer

Code	Code Descriptor
G8947	One or more neuropsychiatric symptoms
G8971	Warfarin or another oral anticoagulant that is fda approved not prescribed, reason not given
G8972	One or more high risk factors for thromboembolism or more than one moderate risk factor for thromboembolism
G9381	Documentation of medical reason(s) for not offering assistance with end of life issues (e.g., patient in hospice care, patient in terminal phase) during the measurement period
G9496	Documentation of reason for not detecting adenoma(s) or other neoplasm. (e.g., neoplasm detected is only diagnosed as traditional serrated adenoma, sessile serrated polyp, or sessile serrated adenoma
J1725	Injection, hydroxyprogesterone caproate, 1 mg
J9300	Injection, gemtuzumab ozogamicin, 5 mg
P9072	Platelets, pheresis, pathogen reduced or rapid bacterial tested, each unit
Q9984	Levonorgestrel-releasing intrauterine contraceptive system (Kyleena®), 19.5 mg
Q9985	Injection, hydroxyprogesterone caproate, not otherwise specified, 10 mg
Q9986	Injection, hydroxyprogesterone caproate, (Makena®), 10 mg
Q9987	Pathogen(s) test for platelets
Q9988	Platelets, pheresis, pathogen-reduced, each unit
Q9989	Ustekinumab, for intravenous injection, 1 mg

Deleted Codes Crosswalk

Deleted Code	Crosswalk Code
A9599	A9597
C9140	J7210
C9483	J9022
C9484	J1428
C9485	J9285
C9486	J1627
C9487	Q9989
C9489	J2326
C9490	J0565

Deleted Code	Crosswalk Code
C9491	J9023
C9494	J2350
Q9984	J7296
Q9985	J1729
Q9986	J1726
Q9987	P9100
Q9988	P9073
Q9989	J3358

G Codes to CPT® Codes Crosswalk

G Codes	CPT® Codes
G0008	90460
	90461
	90471
	90472
	90473
	90474
	90630
	90647
	90648
	90653
	90654
	90655
	90656
	90657
	90658
	90660
	90661
	90662
	90664
	90666
	90667
	90668
	90672
	90673
	90682
	90685
	90686
	90687
	90688
	90697
	90749
G0009	90460
	90461
	90471
	90472
	90670
	90732
	90749
G0010	90460
	90461
	90471
	90472
	90636

G Codes	CPT® Codes
G0010 – Cont.	90697
	90723
	90739
	90740
	90743
	90744
	90746
	90747
	90748
	90749
G0027	89310
	89320
	89321
	89322
	89331
G0101	99384
	99385
	99386
	99387
	99394
	99395
	99396
	99397
G0103	84152
	84153
	84154
G0104	45330
	45331
	45332
	45333
	45334
	45335
	45337
	45338
	45340
	45341
	45342
	45346
	45347
	45349
	45350
	91299

G Codes	CPT® Codes
G0105	45378
	45379
	45380
	45381
	45382
	45384
	45385
	45386
	45388
	45389
	45390
	45391
	45392
	45393
	45398
	91299
G0106	45330
	45331
	45332
	45333
	45334
	45335
	45337
	45338
	45340
	45341
	45342
	45346
	45347
	45349
	45350
	74270
	91299
G0108	97535
	97802
	98960
	98961
	98962
G0109	0403T
	97535
	97802
	98960
	98961
	98962

G Codes	CPT® Codes
G0117	92100
	92285
G0118	92100
	92285
G0120	45378
	45379
	45380
	45381
	45382
	45384
	45385
	45386
	45388
	45389
	45390
	45391
	45392
	45393
	45398
	91299
G0121	45378
	45379
	45380
	45381
	45382
	45384
	45385
	45386
	45388
	45389
	45390
	45391
	45392
	45393
	45398
	91299
G0122	74270
	91299
G0123	88141
	88142
	88143
	88147
	88148

G Codes	CPT® Codes	G Codes	CPT® Codes	G Codes	CPT® Codes	G Codes	CPT® Codes
G0123 – Cont.	88150	G0128 – Cont.	99310	G0143 – Cont.	88162	G0147 – Cont.	88147
	88152		99315		88164		88148
	88153		99316		88165		88152
	88155	G0129	97127		88166		88155
	88160		97165		88167		88166
	88161		97166		88172		88167
	88162		97167		88173		88172
	88164		97168		88174		88173
	88165		97799		88175		88174
	88166	G0130	76977		88177		88175
	88167		77078		88199		88177
	88172		78350	G0144	88141		88199
	88173	G0141	88141		88147	G0148	88141
	88174		88142		88148		88142
	88175		88143		88152		88143
	88177		88147		88155		88147
	88199		88148		88166		88148
G0124	88141		88150		88167		88150
	88142		88152		88172		88152
	88143		88153		88173		88153
	88147		88155		88174		88155
	88148		88160		88175		88160
	88150		88161		88177		88161
	88152		88162		88199		88162
	88153		88164	G0145	88141		88164
	88155		88165		88142		88165
	88160		88166		88143		88166
	88161		88167		88147		88167
	88162		88172		88148		88172
	88164		88173		88150		88173
	88165		88174		88152		88174
	88166		88175		88153		88175
	88167		88177		88155		88177
	88172		88199		88164		88199
	88173	G0143	88141		88165	G0151	97110
	88174		88142		88166	G0152	97530
	88175		88143		88167		97535
	88177		88147		88172		97537
	88199		88148		88173		99509
G0128	99304		88150		88174	G0153	92507
	99305		88152		88175		92508
	99306		88153		88177	G0156	99374
	99307		88155		88199		99375
	99308		88160	G0147	88141	G0157	97110
	99309		88161		88142	G0158	97530
					88143		

G Codes	CPT® Codes	G Codes	CPT® Codes	G Codes	CPT® Codes	G Codes	CPT® Codes
G0158 – Cont.	97535		12055	G0237 – Cont.	94799		90964
	97537		12056		97139		90965
G0159	97161		12057		94667	G0257 – Cont.	90966
	97162		13100		94668		90967
	97163		13101	G0238	94799		90968
	97164		13102		97139		90969
	97799		13120		97530		90970
G0160	97165	G0168 – Cont.	13121		94799		90999
	97166		13122	G0239	97139	G0259	27096
	97167		13131		97150	G0260	27096
	97168		13132		11719	G0268	69209
G0161	92522		13133		11720		69210
	92523		13151	G0247	11721		97802
G0166	92971		13152		97597		97803
	93799		13153		97598		97804
	12001		13160		97602	G0270	98960
	12002	G0175	99366		93792		98961
	12004		0364T		99347		98962
	12005		0365T		99348		99509
	12006		0366T	G0248	99349		97803
	12007		0367T		99350		97804
	12011		0368T		99374		98960
	12013		0369T		99375	G0271	98961
	12014	G0176	0370T	G0250	99374		98962
	12015		0371T		99375		99509
	12016		0372T	G0252	78811	G0276	62287
	12017		0373T		95907	G0277	99183
	12018		0374T		95908		73706
	12020		90847		95909	G0278	73719
	12021		90849	G0255	95910		73720
G0168	12031		97530		95911		77061
	12032	G0179	99374		95912	G0279	77062
	12034		99375		95913		77063
	12035	G0180	99374		90951		64550
	12036		99375		90952	G0281	97014
	12037	G0181	99374		90953		97032
	12041		99375		90954		64550
	12042	G0182	99377		90955	G0282	97014
	12044		99378		90956		97032
	12045	G0219	78813	G0257	90957		64550
	12046		78816		90958	G0283	97014
	12047	G0235	78811		90959		97032
	12051		78814		90960		74174
	12052	G0237	94667		90961	G0288	74175
	12053		94668		90962		75635
	12054				90963		

G Codes	CPT® Codes	G Codes	CPT® Codes	G Codes	CPT® Codes	G Codes	CPT® Codes
G0289	29874	G0299	96370	G0300	90962	G0337	99377
	29875		96371		90963		99378
	29876		96372		90964	G0339	61796
	29877		96373		90965		61797
	29879		96374		90966		61798
	29880		96375		90967		61799
	29881		96376		90968		63620
	29882		96379		90969		63621
	29883		99341		90970		77372
G0295	97014		99342		96360	G0340	61796
	97032		99343		96361		61797
G0296	99401		99344		99341		61798
	99402		99345		99342		61799
	99403		99347		99343		63620
	99404		99348		99344		63621
G0297	71250		99349		99345		77372
	71260	G0299 – Cont.	99350		99347	G0341	48160
	76497		99374		99348		48999
G0299	90951		99375		99349	G0342	48160
	90952		99500	G0300 – Cont.	99350		48999
	90953		99501		99374		60659
	90954		99502		99375	G0343	48160
	90955		99503		99500		48999
	90956		99504		99501		49002
	90957		99505		99502		60659
	90958		99506		99503	G0365	93970
	90959		99507		99504		93971
	90960		99509		99505	G0372	97542
	90961		99510		99506		97755
	90962		99511		99507	G0378	99218
	90963		99512		99509		99219
	90964		99600		99510		99220
	90965		99601		99511		99224
	90966		99602		99512		99225
	90967	G0300	90951		99600		99226
	90968		90952		99601		99234
	90969		90953		99602		99235
	90970		90954	G0306	85025		99236
	96360		90955	G0307	85027		99356
	96361		90956	G0328	82274		99357
	96365		90957	G0329	64550	G0379	99218
	96366		90958		97014		99219
	96367		90959		97024		99220
	96368		90960		97032		99224
	96369		90961				99225

G Codes	CPT® Codes	G Codes	CPT® Codes	G Codes	CPT® Codes	G Codes	CPT® Codes
G0379 – Cont.	99226		99384		93010		93797
	99234		99385		93042	G0422	93798
	99235		99386		99381		93799
	99236		99387		99382		93797
	99356		99401		99383	G0423	93798
	99357	G0402 – Cont.	99402		99384		93799
G0380	99281		99403	G0405	99385	G0424	94799
	99282		99404		99386	G0428	29868
	99283		99406		99387		11950
	99284		99407		99401	G0429	11951
	99285		99408		99402		11952
G0381	99281		99409		99403		11954
	99282		99411		99404		86701
	99283		99412		99429		86702
	99284		99429		99251		86703
	99285		93000		99252		87389
G0382	99281		93010	G0406	99253	G0432	87390
	99282		93040		99254		87391
	99283		93042		99255		87449
	99284		99381		99251		87450
	99285		99382		99252		87451
G0383	99281		99383	G0407	99253		86701
	99282	G0403	99384		99254		86702
	99283		99385		99255		86703
	99284		99386		99251		87389
	99285		99387		99252	G0433	87390
G0384	99281		99401	G0408	99253		87391
	99282		99402		99254		87449
	99283		99403		99255		87450
	99284		99404		99510		87451
	99285		99429	G0409	99600		86689
G0390	99199		93005	G0410	90853		86701
	99291		93041		90899		86702
	99292		99381	G0411	90853		86703
G0396	99408		99382		90899		87389
G0397	99409		99383	G0412	27215	G0435	87390
G0398	95800		99384	G0413	27216		87391
	95801	G0404	99385	G0414	27217		87449
	95806		99386	G0415	27218		87450
G0399	95800		99387	G0416	88305		87451
	95801		99401	G0420	97799		96160
	95806		99402		98960		96161
G0400	95801		99403		98961	G0438	99381
G0402	99381		99404	G0421	98962		99382
	99382		99429		99078		99383
	99383						

G Codes	CPT® Codes	G Codes	CPT® Codes	G Codes	CPT® Codes	G Codes	CPT® Codes
G0438 – Cont.	99384	G0445	99402	G0468	99384	G0471	36400
	99385	G0446	99401		99385		36405
	99386	G0447	99401		99386		36406
	99387	G0448	33230		99387		36410
	99401		33231		99394		36415
	99402		33240		99395		51701
	99403		33241		99396	G0472	80074
	99404		33249		99397		86803
	99406		33262	G0469	90791		86804
	99407		33263		90792		87520
	99408		33264		90832		87521
	99409		33270		90833		87522
	99411		33999		90834		87902
	99412	G0451	96110		90836	G0473	99411
	99429		96111		90837	G0475	86689
G0439	96160	G0453	95941		90838		86701
	96161	G0454	97542		90839		86702
	99391		97755		90840		86703
	99392	G0455	44705		90845	G0476	0500T
	99393		44799		90846		87624
	99394	G0458	55875		90847	G0480	80320
	99395		77778		90849		80321
	99396	G0460	86890		90853		80322
	99397	G0463	99201		90875		80323
	99401		99202		90876		80324
	99402		99203		90885		80325
	99403		99204	G0470	90791		80326
	99404		99205		90792		80327
	99406		99211		90832		80328
	99407		99212		90833		80329
	99408		99213		90834		80330
	99409		99214		90836		80331
	99411		99215		90837		80332
	99412	G0466	99201		90838		80333
	99429		99202		90839		80334
G0442	99408		99203		90840		80335
	99409		99204		90845		80336
	99401		99205		90846		80337
G0443	99408	G0467	99211		90847		80338
	99409		99212		90849		80339
G0444	96150		99213		90853		80340
	96151		99214		90875		80341
	96152		99215		90876		
	96160				90885		
	96161						
	99401						

G Codes	CPT® Codes	G Codes	CPT® Codes	G Codes	CPT® Codes	G Codes	CPT® Codes
	80342		80328		80373		80359
	80343		80329		80374		80360
	80344		80330	**G0481** – Cont.	80375		80361
	80345		80331		80376		80362
	80346		80332		80377		80363
	80347		80333		82542		80364
	80348		80334		80320		80365
	80349		80335		80321		80366
	80350		80336		80322		80367
	80351		80337		80323	**G0482** – Cont.	80368
	80352		80338		80324		80369
	80353		80339		80325		80370
	80354		80340		80326		80371
	80355		80341		80327		80372
	80356		80342		80328		80373
	80357		80343		80329		80374
	80358		80344		80330		80375
	80359		80345		80331		80376
G0480 – Cont.	80360		80346		80332		80377
	80361		80347		80333		82542
	80362		80348		80334		80320
	80363		80349		80335		80321
	80364	**G0481** – Cont.	80350		80336		80322
	80365		80351		80337		80323
	80366		80352		80338		80324
	80367		80353	**G0482**	80339		80325
	80368		80354		80340		80326
	80369		80355		80341		80327
	80370		80356		80342		80328
	80371		80357		80343		80329
	80372		80358		80344		80330
	80373		80359		80345		80331
	80374		80360		80346	**G0483**	80332
	80375		80361		80347		80333
	80376		80362		80348		80334
	80377		80363		80349		80335
	82542		80364		80350		80336
	80320		80365		80351		80337
	80321		80366		80352		80338
	80322		80367		80353		80339
	80323		80368		80354		80340
G0481	80324		80369		80355		80341
	80325		80370		80356		80342
	80326		80371		80357		80343
	80327		80372		80358		80344

G Codes	CPT® Codes
G0483 – Cont.	80345
	80346
	80347
	80348
	80349
	80350
	80351
	80352
	80353
	80354
	80355
	80356
	80357
	80358
	80359
	80360
	80361
	80362
	80363
	80364
	80365
	80366
	80367
	80368
	80369
	80370
	80371
	80372
	80373
	80374
	80375
	80376
	80377
	82542
G0491	90935
	90937
	90945
	90947
	90999
G0492	90935
	90945
	90989
	90993
	90997
	90999

G Codes	CPT® Codes
G0493	99307
	99308
	99309
	99310
G0494	99307
	99308
	99309
	99310
G0495	98960
	99600
G0496	98960
	99600
G0499	86704
	86705
	86706
	87340
	87341
G0500	99152
G0501	99201
	99202
	99203
	99204
	99205
	99211
	99212
	99213
	99214
	99215
	99354
	99355
	99415
	99416
G0506	99487
	99490
G0508	99449
G0511	99487
	99489
	99490
G0512	90837
	90838
	90839
G0513	99354
G0514	99354
G0515	97127

G Codes	CPT® Codes
G0516	11981
G0517	11982
G0518	11983
G6001	77387
G6002	77387
G6003	77402
G6004	77402
G6005	77402
G6006	77402
G6007	77407
G6008	77407
G6009	77407
G6010	77407
G6011	77412
G6012	77412
G6013	77412
G6014	77412
G6015	77385
G6016	77385
G6017	77387
G9143	81355
G9147	82947
	82948
	82950
	84132
	84133
	84540
	94681
	96365
	96366
	99199
G9156	97161
	97162
	97163
	97164
	97165
	97166
	97167
	97168
	97169
	97170
	97171
	97172
	97542
G9157	76999

G Codes	CPT® Codes
G9474	97802
	97803
G9475	99374
	99375
	99377
	99378
	99510
G9477	99347
	99348
	99349
	99350
	99374
	99375
	99377
	99378
G9478	99374
	99375
	99377
	99378
	99503
	99504
	99505
	99506
	99507
	99509
	99510
	99511
	99512
	99600
G9479	99605
	99606
	99607
G9481	99324
	99325
	99326
	99327
	99328
	99334
	99341
	99342
	99343
	99344
	99345
	99600

G Codes	CPT® Codes	G Codes	CPT® Codes	G Codes	CPT® Codes	G Codes	CPT® Codes
G9482	99324	G9486	99334	G9686	99367	G9937	44388
	99325		99335		99368		44389
	99326		99336	G9770	64450		44390
	99327		99337		64520		44391
	99328		99347	G9890	2019F		44392
	99341		99348		2021F		44394
	99342		99349	G9899	77063		44401
	99343		99350	G9900	77063		44402
	99344		99600	G9902	4004F		44403
	99345	G9487	99334	G9903	4004F		44404
	99600		99335	G9906	99406		44405
G9483	99324		99336		99407		44406
	99325		99337		4004F		44407
	99326		99347	G9912	87516		44408
	99327		99348		87517	G9964	99381
	99328		99349		87912		99382
	99341		99350	G9922	97165		99383
	99342		99600		97166		99391
	99343	G9488	99334		97167		99392
	99344		99335		97168		99393
	99345		99336	G9923	97165	G9966	96110
	99600		99337		97166	G9974	2019F
G9484	99324		99347		97167		2021F
	99325		99348		97168		
	99326		99349	G9926	97165		
	99327		99350		97166		
	99328		99600		97167		
	99341	G9489	99334		97168		
	99342		99335	G9933	3775F		
	99343		99336	G9935	3776F		
	99344		99337	G9936	44388		
	99345		99347		44389		
	99600		99348		44390		
G9485	99324		99349		44391		
	99325		99350		44392		
	99326		99600		44394		
	99327	G9490	97535		44401		
	99328		98960		44402		
	99341		99509		44403		
	99342		99600		44404		
	99343	G9497	99406		44405		
	99344		99407		44406		
	99345	G9635	96160		44407		
	99600		96161		44408		
			99429				

Anatomical Illustrations

Circulatory System — Arteries and Veins

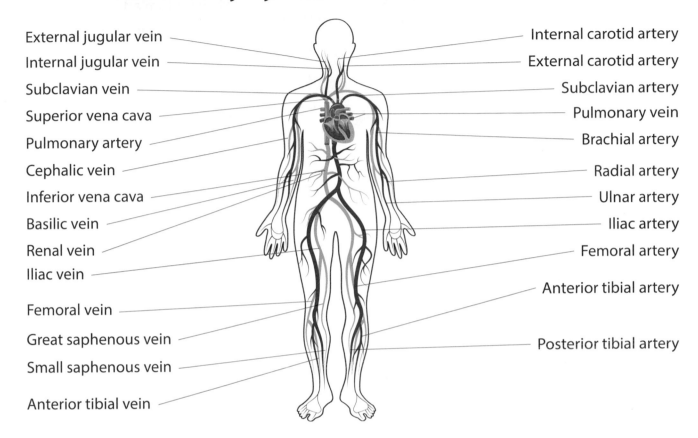

External jugular vein
Internal jugular vein
Subclavian vein
Superior vena cava
Pulmonary artery
Cephalic vein
Inferior vena cava
Basilic vein
Renal vein
Iliac vein
Femoral vein
Great saphenous vein
Small saphenous vein
Anterior tibial vein

Internal carotid artery
External carotid artery
Subclavian artery
Pulmonary vein
Brachial artery
Radial artery
Ulnar artery
Iliac artery
Femoral artery
Anterior tibial artery
Posterior tibial artery

Circulatory System — Artery and Vein Anatomy

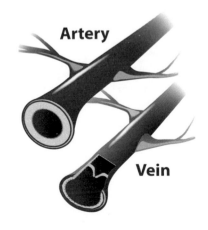

Artery

Vein

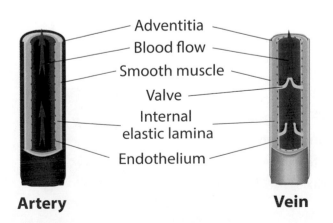

Adventitia
Blood flow
Smooth muscle
Valve
Internal elastic lamina
Endothelium

Artery

Vein

Circulatory System — Heart Anatomy and Cardiac Cycle

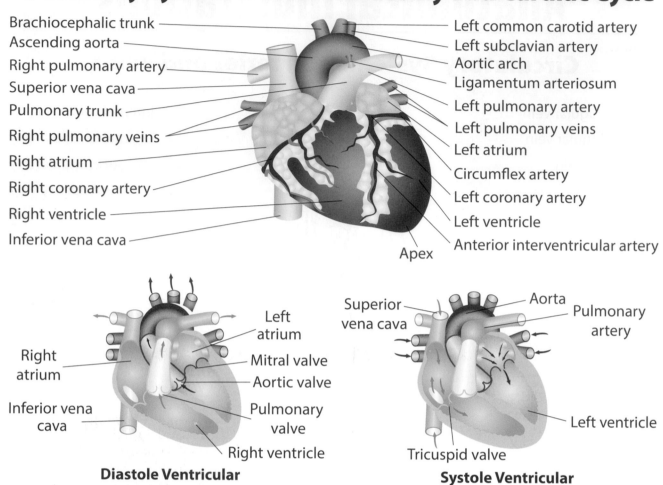

Brachiocephalic trunk
Ascending aorta
Right pulmonary artery
Superior vena cava
Pulmonary trunk
Right pulmonary veins
Right atrium
Right coronary artery
Right ventricle
Inferior vena cava

Left common carotid artery
Left subclavian artery
Aortic arch
Ligamentum arteriosum
Left pulmonary artery
Left pulmonary veins
Left atrium
Circumflex artery
Left coronary artery
Left ventricle
Anterior interventricular artery
Apex

Right atrium
Inferior vena cava

Left atrium
Mitral valve
Aortic valve
Pulmonary valve
Right ventricle

**Diastole Ventricular
Relaxation and Filling**

Superior vena cava

Aorta
Pulmonary artery

Tricuspid valve

Left ventricle

**Systole Ventricular
Contraction and Ejection**

Digestive System — Digestive Organs

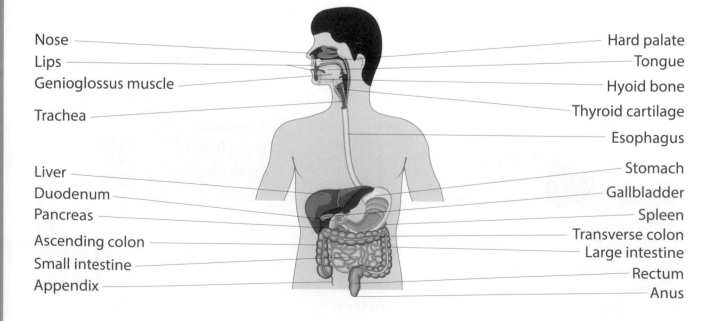

Nose
Lips
Genioglossus muscle
Trachea
Liver
Duodenum
Pancreas
Ascending colon
Small intestine
Appendix

Hard palate
Tongue
Hyoid bone
Thyroid cartilage
Esophagus
Stomach
Gallbladder
Spleen
Transverse colon
Large intestine
Rectum
Anus

Digestive System — Large Intestine Anatomy

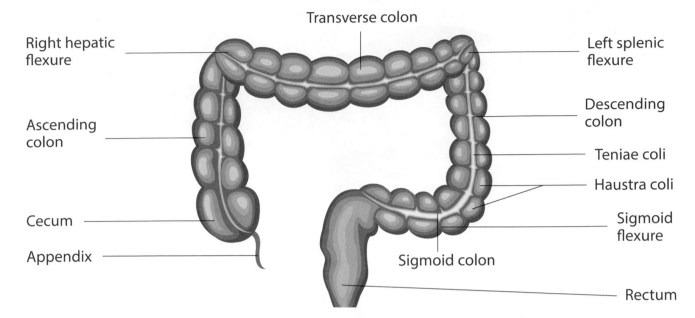

Transverse colon

Right hepatic flexure

Left splenic flexure

Descending colon

Ascending colon

Teniae coli

Haustra coli

Cecum

Sigmoid flexure

Appendix

Sigmoid colon

Rectum

Digestive System — Rectum Anatomy

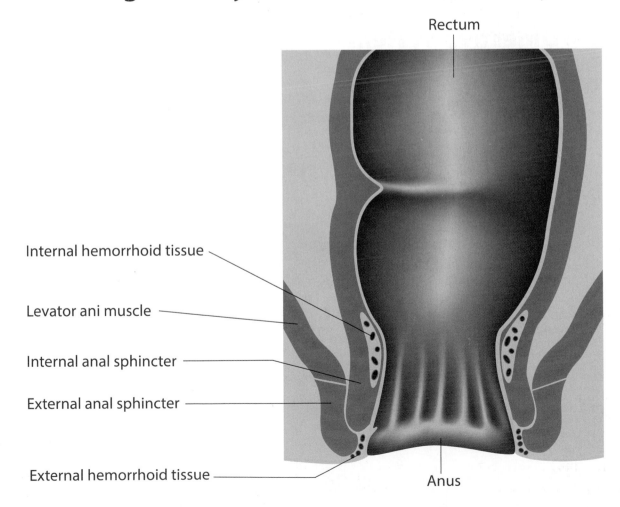

Rectum

Internal hemorrhoid tissue

Levator ani muscle

Internal anal sphincter

External anal sphincter

External hemorrhoid tissue

Anus

Digestive System — Liver Anatomy

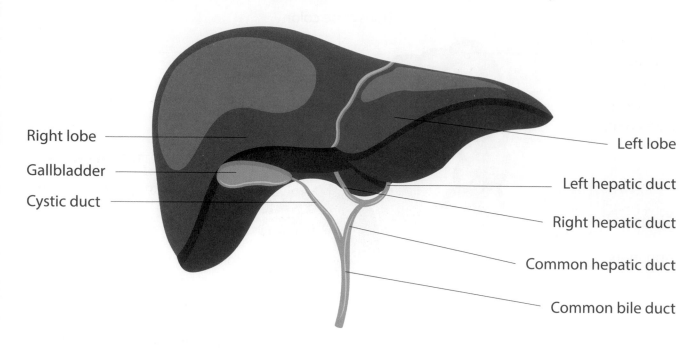

Right lobe

Gallbladder

Cystic duct

Left lobe

Left hepatic duct

Right hepatic duct

Common hepatic duct

Common bile duct

Digestive System — Pancreas Anatomy

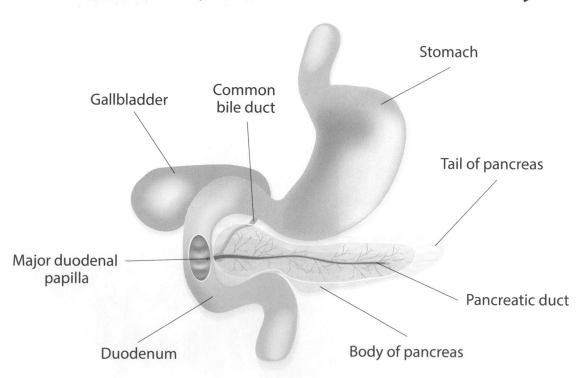

Gallbladder

Common bile duct

Stomach

Tail of pancreas

Major duodenal papilla

Pancreatic duct

Duodenum

Body of pancreas

Digestive System — Mouth Anatomy

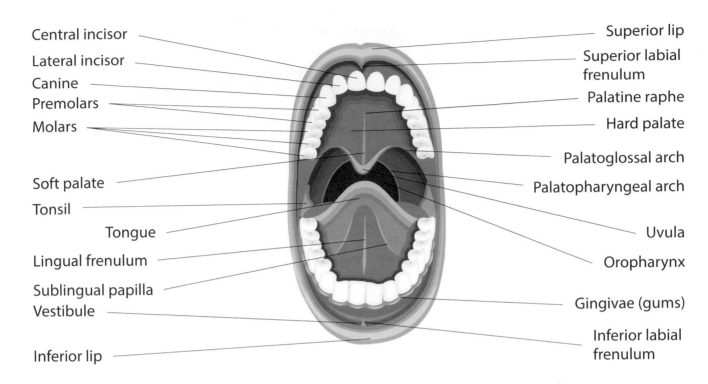

Central incisor
Lateral incisor
Canine
Premolars
Molars
Soft palate
Tonsil
Tongue
Lingual frenulum
Sublingual papilla
Vestibule
Inferior lip

Superior lip
Superior labial frenulum
Palatine raphe
Hard palate
Palatoglossal arch
Palatopharyngeal arch
Uvula
Oropharynx
Gingivae (gums)
Inferior labial frenulum

Digestive System — Tongue Anatomy

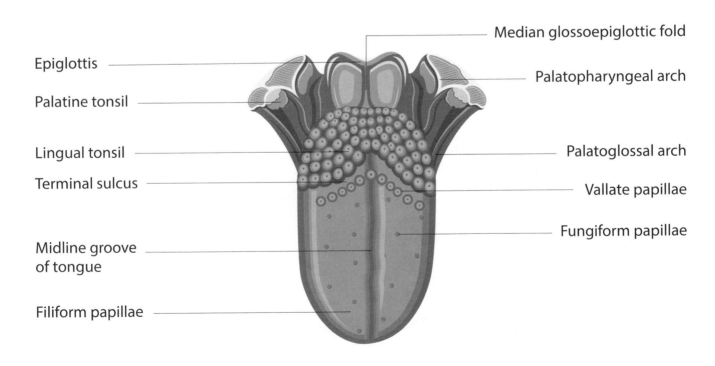

Epiglottis
Palatine tonsil
Lingual tonsil
Terminal sulcus
Midline groove of tongue
Filiform papillae

Median glossoepiglottic fold
Palatopharyngeal arch
Palatoglossal arch
Vallate papillae
Fungiform papillae

Digestive System — Small Intestine Anatomy

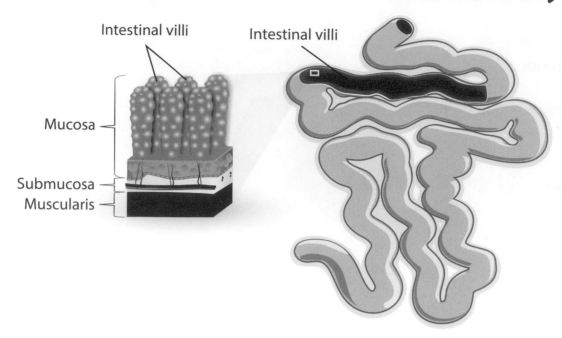

Intestinal villi

Intestinal villi

Mucosa

Submucosa

Muscularis

Digestive System — Stomach Anatomy

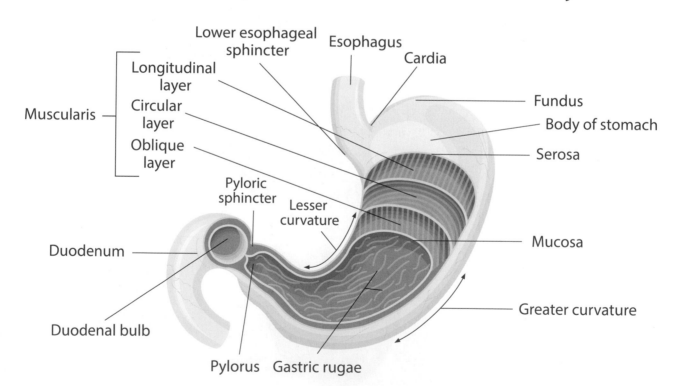

Lower esophageal
sphincter

Esophagus

Cardia

Longitudinal
layer

Muscularis

Circular
layer

Fundus

Oblique
layer

Body of stomach

Pyloric
sphincter

Serosa

Lesser
curvature

Duodenum

Mucosa

Duodenal bulb

Greater curvature

Pylorus

Gastric rugae

Ear Anatomy

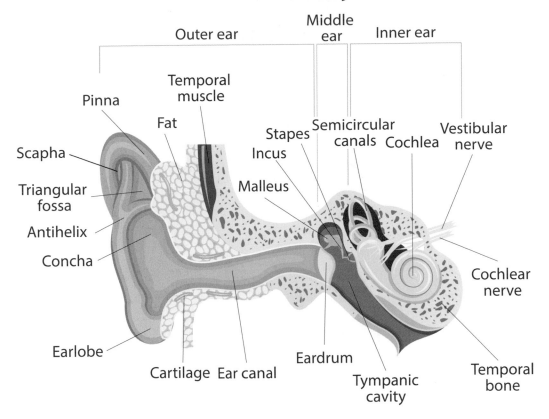

Outer ear Middle ear Inner ear

Pinna
Temporal muscle
Fat
Scapha
Triangular fossa
Antihelix
Concha
Earlobe
Cartilage Ear canal
Stapes
Incus
Malleus
Semicircular canals
Cochlea
Vestibular nerve
Cochlear nerve
Eardrum
Tympanic cavity
Temporal bone

Cochlea Anatomy (Inner Ear)

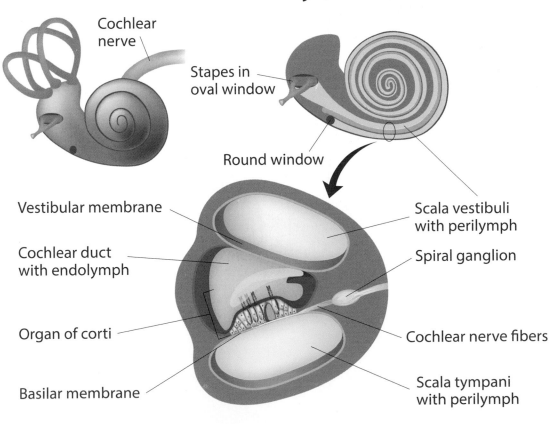

Cochlear nerve
Stapes in oval window
Round window
Vestibular membrane
Cochlear duct with endolymph
Organ of corti
Basilar membrane
Scala vestibuli with perilymph
Spiral ganglion
Cochlear nerve fibers
Scala tympani with perilymph

Endocrine System Anatomy

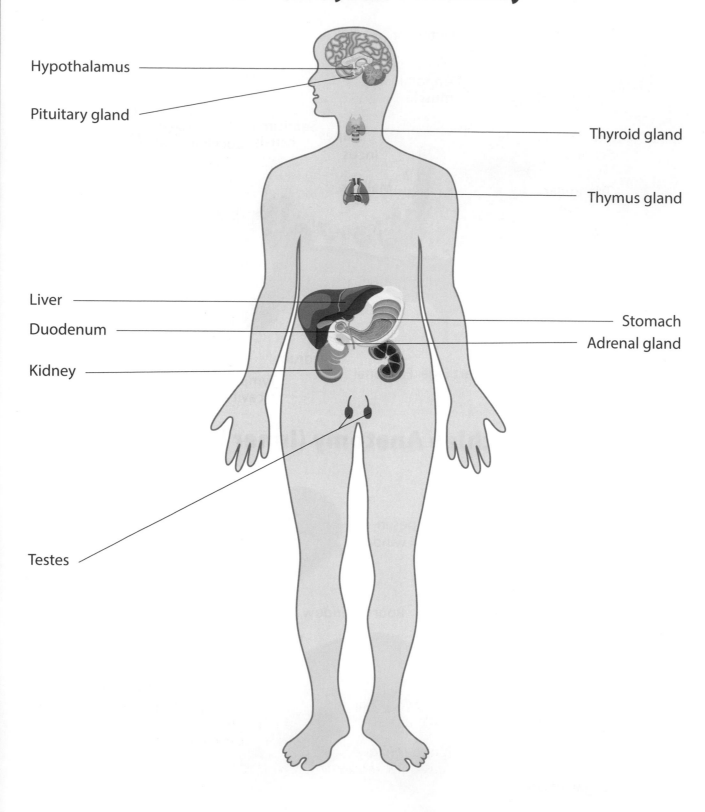

Hypothalamus

Pituitary gland

Thyroid gland

Thymus gland

Liver

Duodenum

Stomach

Adrenal gland

Kidney

Testes

Eye Anatomy

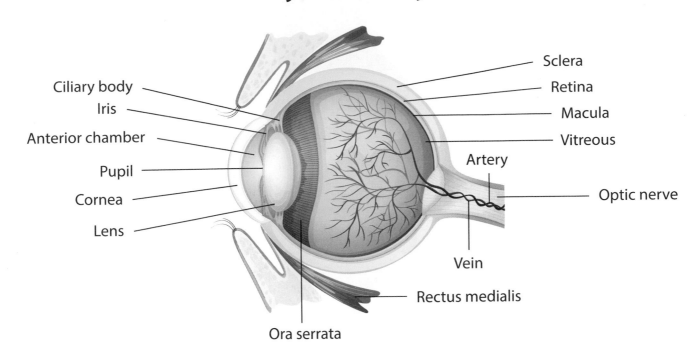

Muscles of the Eye

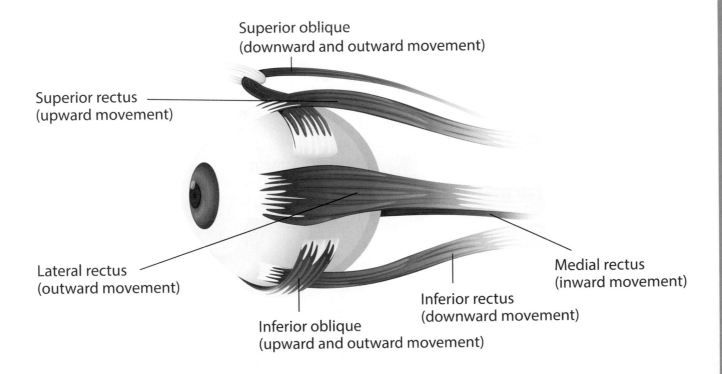

Female Reproductive System Anatomy

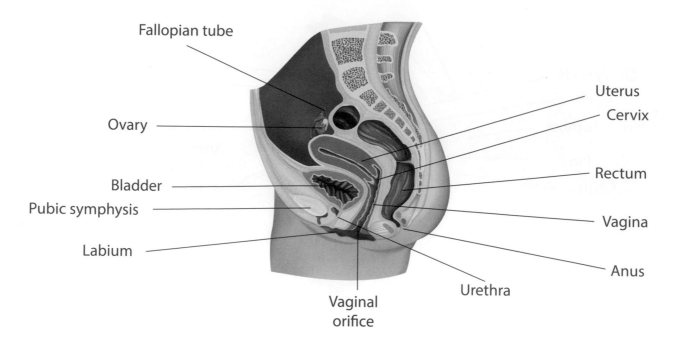

Fallopian tube

Ovary

Bladder

Pubic symphysis

Labium

Uterus

Cervix

Rectum

Vagina

Anus

Urethra

Vaginal orifice

Female Reproductive System — Uterus and Adnexa Anatomy

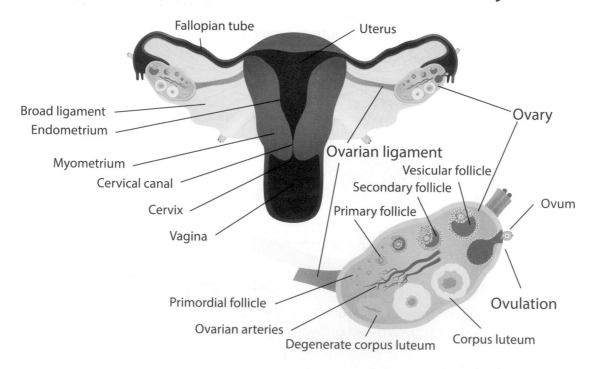

Fallopian tube

Uterus

Broad ligament

Endometrium

Myometrium

Cervical canal

Cervix

Vagina

Ovarian ligament

Ovary

Vesicular follicle

Secondary follicle

Primary follicle

Ovum

Primordial follicle

Ovarian arteries

Degenerate corpus luteum

Corpus luteum

Ovulation

Female Reproductive System — Breast Anatomy

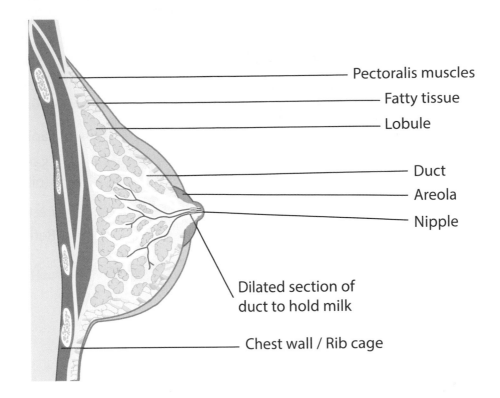

- Pectoralis muscles
- Fatty tissue
- Lobule
- Duct
- Areola
- Nipple
- Dilated section of duct to hold milk
- Chest wall / Rib cage

Female Reproductive System — Perineum Anatomy

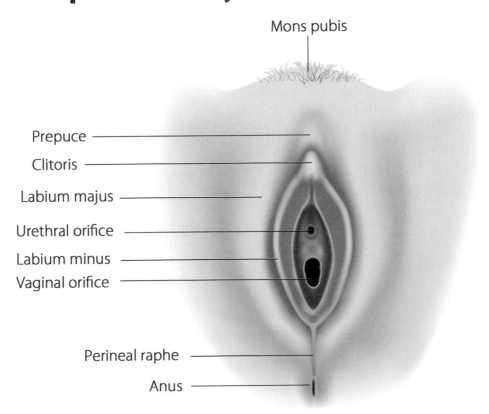

- Mons pubis
- Prepuce
- Clitoris
- Labium majus
- Urethral orifice
- Labium minus
- Vaginal orifice
- Perineal raphe
- Anus

Integumentary System Anatomy

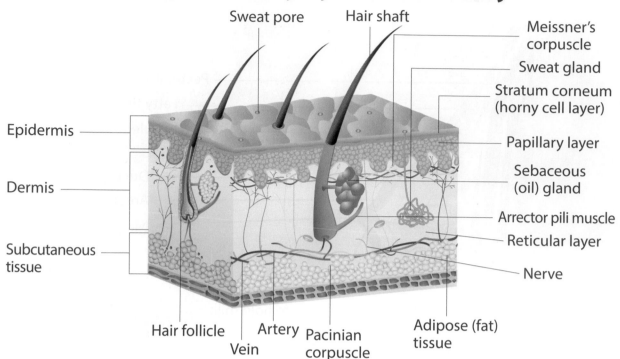

Sweat pore

Hair shaft

Meissner's corpuscle

Sweat gland

Stratum corneum (horny cell layer)

Papillary layer

Sebaceous (oil) gland

Arrector pili muscle

Reticular layer

Nerve

Epidermis

Dermis

Subcutaneous tissue

Hair follicle

Vein

Artery

Pacinian corpuscle

Adipose (fat) tissue

Lymphatic System Anatomy

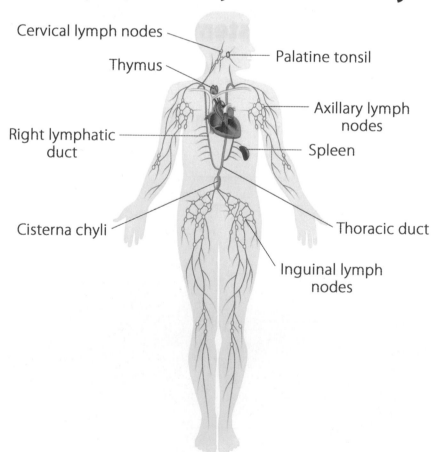

Cervical lymph nodes

Palatine tonsil

Thymus

Axillary lymph nodes

Right lymphatic duct

Spleen

Cisterna chyli

Thoracic duct

Inguinal lymph nodes

Lymphatic System — Humoral Immunity

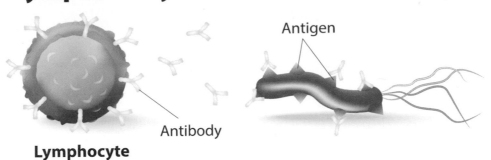

Antigen

Antibody

Lymphocyte

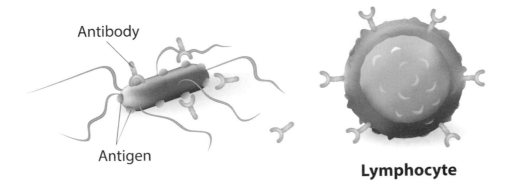

Antibody

Antigen

Lymphocyte

Lymph Node Anatomy

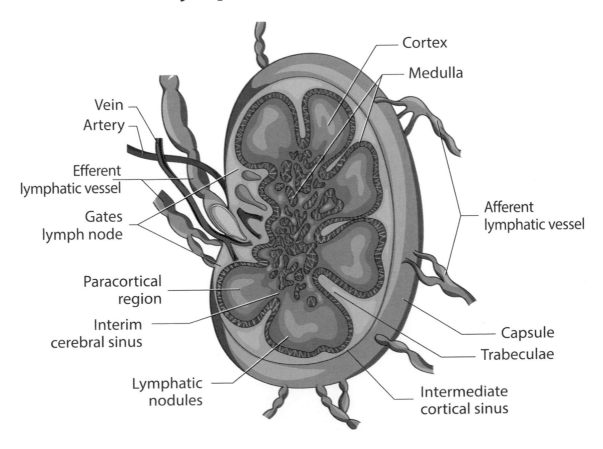

Cortex

Medulla

Vein

Artery

Efferent
lymphatic vessel

Gates
lymph node

Paracortical
region

Interim
cerebral sinus

Lymphatic
nodules

Afferent
lymphatic vessel

Capsule

Trabeculae

Intermediate
cortical sinus

Male Reproductive System Anatomy

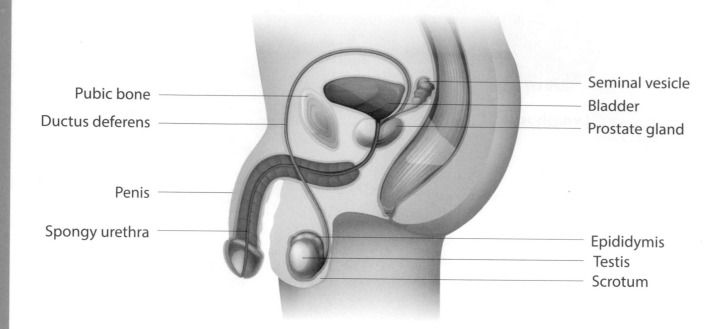

Pubic bone

Ductus deferens

Penis

Spongy urethra

Seminal vesicle

Bladder

Prostate gland

Epididymis

Testis

Scrotum

Male Reproductive System — Testicle Anatomy

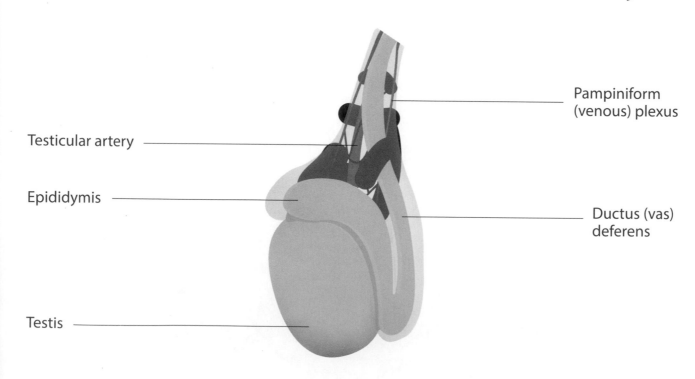

Testicular artery

Epididymis

Testis

Pampiniform (venous) plexus

Ductus (vas) deferens

Male Reproductive System — Penis Anatomy

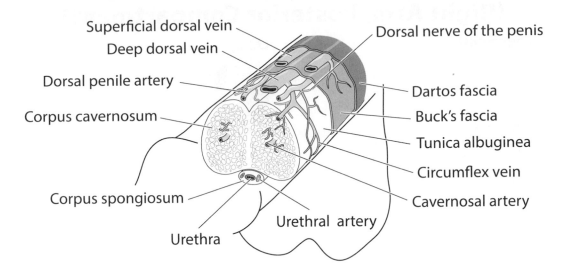

Superficial dorsal vein
Deep dorsal vein
Dorsal penile artery
Corpus cavernosum
Corpus spongiosum
Urethra
Urethral artery
Dorsal nerve of the penis
Dartos fascia
Buck's fascia
Tunica albuginea
Circumflex vein
Cavernosal artery

Muscular System Anatomy

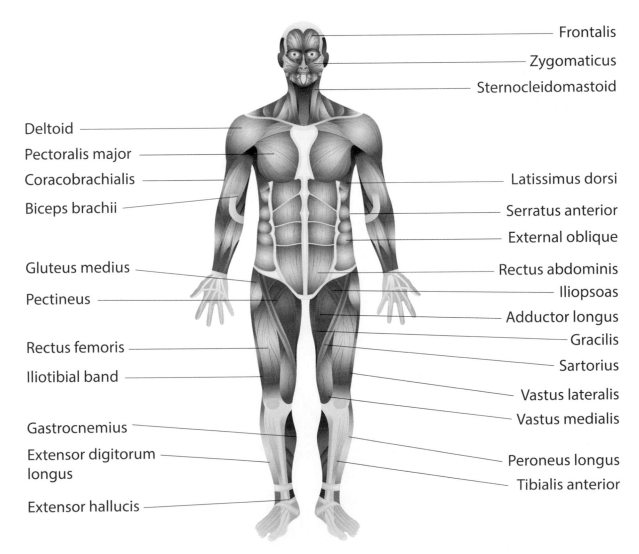

Frontalis
Zygomaticus
Sternocleidomastoid
Deltoid
Pectoralis major
Coracobrachialis
Biceps brachii
Latissimus dorsi
Serratus anterior
External oblique
Gluteus medius
Rectus abdominis
Pectineus
Iliopsoas
Adductor longus
Gracilis
Rectus femoris
Sartorius
Iliotibial band
Vastus lateralis
Vastus medialis
Gastrocnemius
Extensor digitorum longus
Peroneus longus
Tibialis anterior
Extensor hallucis

Muscular System — Forearm Muscles (Right Arm, Posterior Compartment)

Superficial

- Triceps brachii
- Brachioradialis
- Anconeus
- Extensor carpi radialis longus
- Flexor carpi ulnaris
- Extensor carpi radialis brevis
- Extensor carpi ulnaris
- Abductor pollicis longus
- Extensor digit minimi
- Extensor pollicis brevis
- Extensor digitorum
- Extensor pollicis longus
- Extensor retinaculum

Deep

- Triceps brachii
- Anconeus
- Brachioradialis
- Extensor carpi radialis longus
- Extensor carpi radialis brevis
- Flexor carpi
- Supinator
- Abductor pollicis longus
- Extensor pollicis brevis
- Extensor pollicis longus
- Extensor indicis
- Tendons of extensor carpi radialis longus and brevis

Muscular System — Knee Joint Anatomy

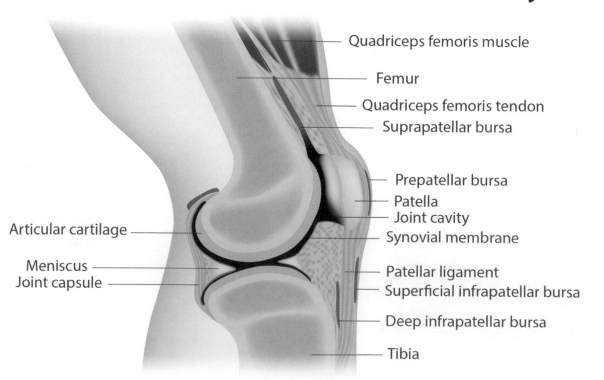

- Quadriceps femoris muscle
- Femur
- Quadriceps femoris tendon
- Suprapatellar bursa
- Prepatellar bursa
- Patella
- Joint cavity
- Articular cartilage
- Synovial membrane
- Meniscus
- Patellar ligament
- Joint capsule
- Superficial infrapatellar bursa
- Deep infrapatellar bursa
- Tibia

Muscular System — Shoulder (Rotator Cuff) Muscles

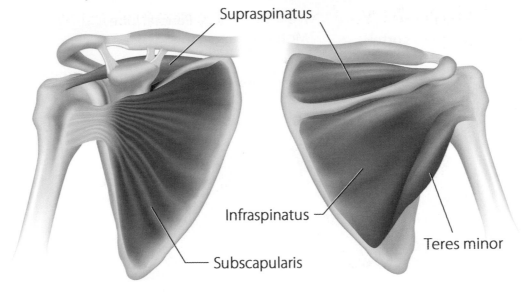

Supraspinatus

Infraspinatus

Teres minor

Subscapularis

Anterior view   **Posterior view**

Nervous System Anatomy

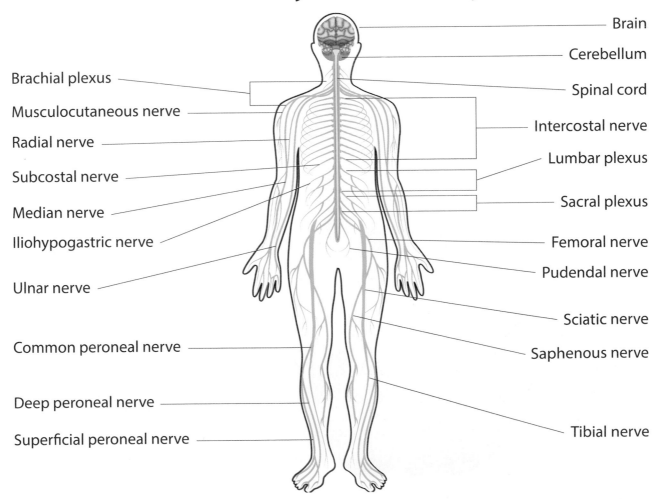

Brachial plexus

Musculocutaneous nerve

Radial nerve

Subcostal nerve

Median nerve

Iliohypogastric nerve

Ulnar nerve

Common peroneal nerve

Deep peroneal nerve

Superficial peroneal nerve

Brain

Cerebellum

Spinal cord

Intercostal nerve

Lumbar plexus

Sacral plexus

Femoral nerve

Pudendal nerve

Sciatic nerve

Saphenous nerve

Tibial nerve

Nervous System — Brain Anatomy

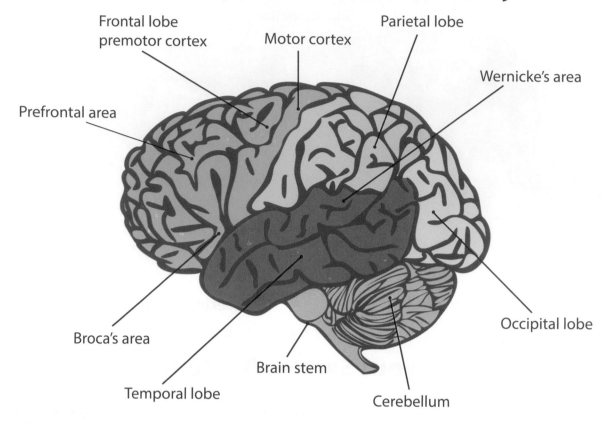

Frontal lobe premotor cortex

Motor cortex

Parietal lobe

Prefrontal area

Wernicke's area

Broca's area

Occipital lobe

Temporal lobe

Brain stem

Cerebellum

Nervous System — Cranial Nerves

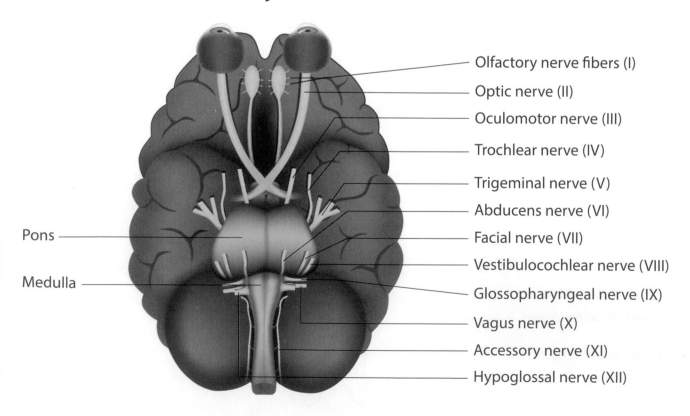

Pons

Medulla

Olfactory nerve fibers (I)

Optic nerve (II)

Oculomotor nerve (III)

Trochlear nerve (IV)

Trigeminal nerve (V)

Abducens nerve (VI)

Facial nerve (VII)

Vestibulocochlear nerve (VIII)

Glossopharyngeal nerve (IX)

Vagus nerve (X)

Accessory nerve (XI)

Hypoglossal nerve (XII)

Nervous System — Nerve Anatomy

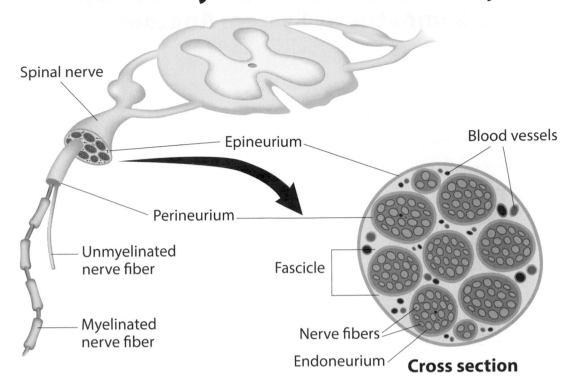

Spinal nerve

Epineurium

Blood vessels

Perineurium

Unmyelinated nerve fiber

Myelinated nerve fiber

Fascicle

Nerve fibers

Endoneurium

Cross section

Nervous System — Parasympathetic System Anatomy

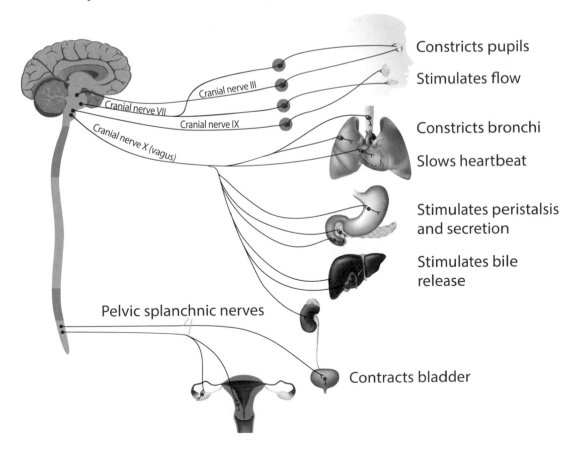

Constricts pupils

Stimulates flow

Cranial nerve III

Cranial nerve VII

Cranial nerve IX

Cranial nerve X (vagus)

Constricts bronchi

Slows heartbeat

Stimulates peristalsis and secretion

Stimulates bile release

Pelvic splanchnic nerves

Contracts bladder

Nervous System — Sympathetic System Anatomy

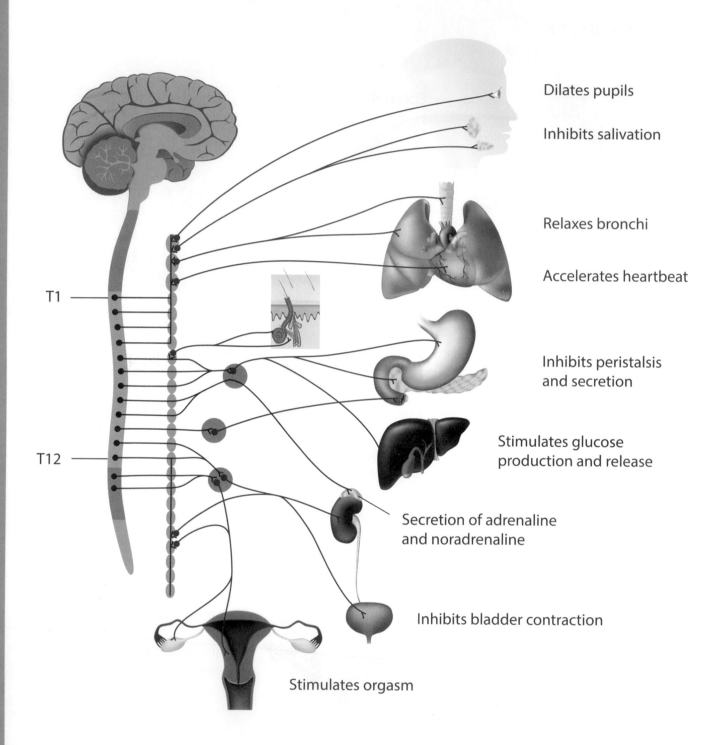

Dilates pupils

Inhibits salivation

Relaxes bronchi

Accelerates heartbeat

Inhibits peristalsis and secretion

Stimulates glucose production and release

Secretion of adrenaline and noradrenaline

Inhibits bladder contraction

Stimulates orgasm

T1

T12

Respiratory System Anatomy

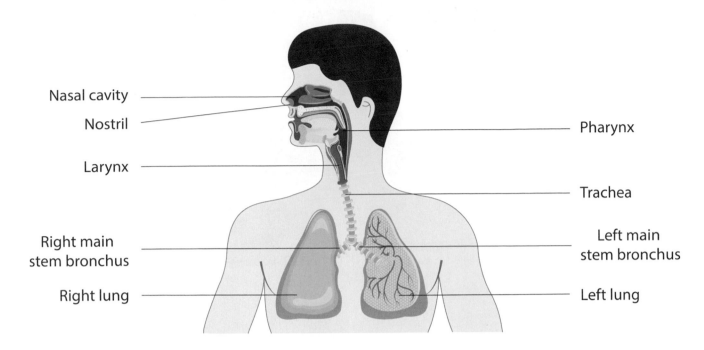

Nasal cavity

Nostril

Larynx

Right main
stem bronchus

Right lung

Pharynx

Trachea

Left main
stem bronchus

Left lung

Respiratory System — Larynx Anatomy

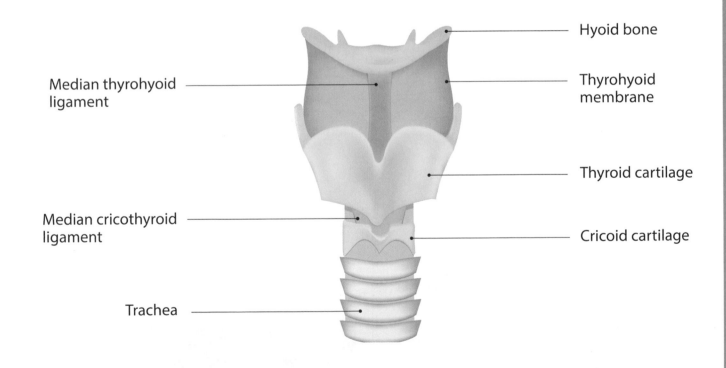

Median thyrohyoid
ligament

Median cricothyroid
ligament

Trachea

Hyoid bone

Thyrohyoid
membrane

Thyroid cartilage

Cricoid cartilage

Respiratory System — Lung Anatomy

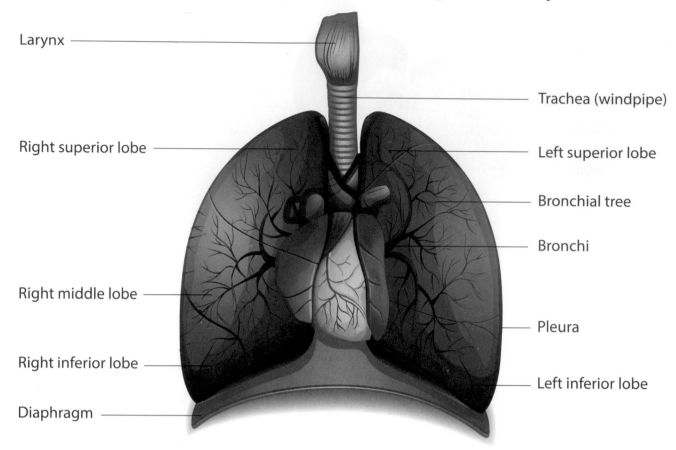

Larynx

Right superior lobe

Trachea (windpipe)

Left superior lobe

Bronchial tree

Bronchi

Right middle lobe

Right inferior lobe

Pleura

Left inferior lobe

Diaphragm

Respiratory System Function

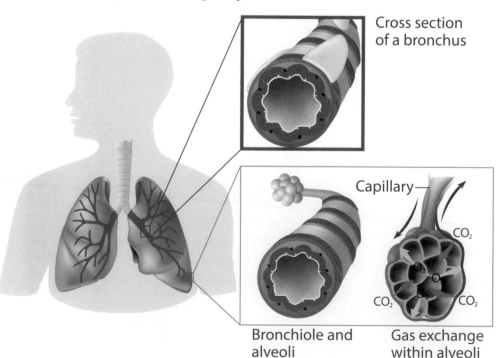

Cross section
of a bronchus

Capillary

CO_2

CO_2

CO_2

Bronchiole and
alveoli

Gas exchange
within alveoli

Respiratory System — Nose Anatomy

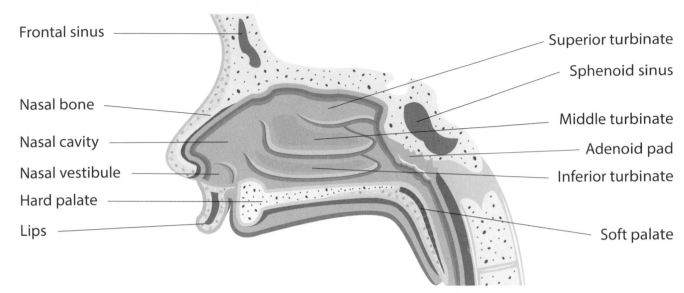

Frontal sinus

Nasal bone

Nasal cavity

Nasal vestibule

Hard palate

Lips

Superior turbinate

Sphenoid sinus

Middle turbinate

Adenoid pad

Inferior turbinate

Soft palate

Respiratory System — Sinus Anatomy

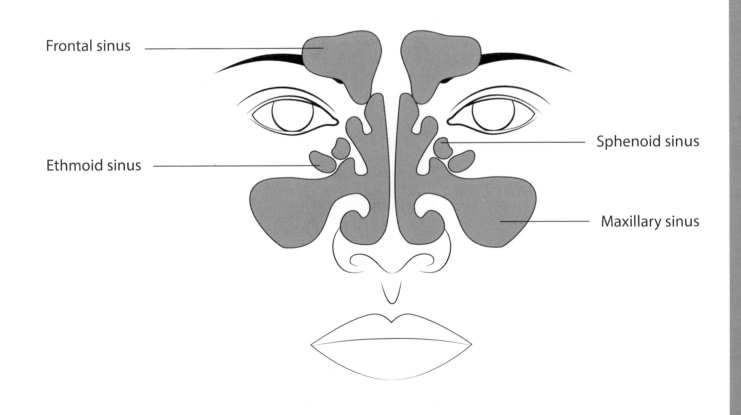

Frontal sinus

Ethmoid sinus

Sphenoid sinus

Maxillary sinus

Respiratory System — Throat Anatomy

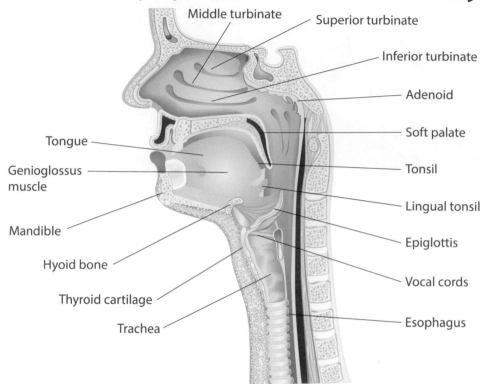

Middle turbinate
Superior turbinate
Inferior turbinate
Adenoid
Soft palate
Tongue
Genioglossus muscle
Tonsil
Lingual tonsil
Mandible
Epiglottis
Hyoid bone
Vocal cords
Thyroid cartilage
Esophagus
Trachea

Skeletal System Anatomy

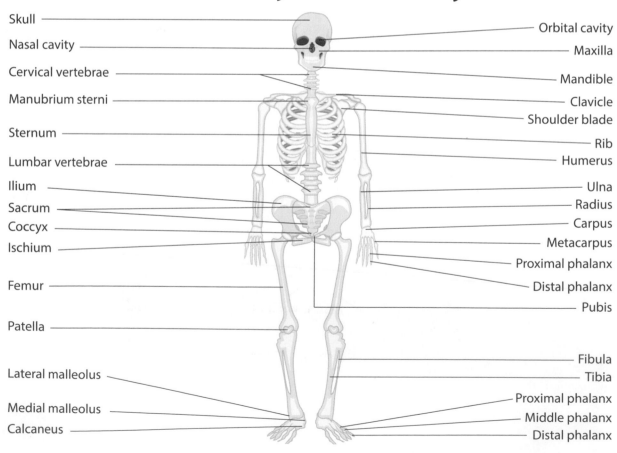

Skull
Orbital cavity
Nasal cavity
Maxilla
Cervical vertebrae
Mandible
Manubrium sterni
Clavicle
Shoulder blade
Sternum
Rib
Lumbar vertebrae
Humerus
Ilium
Ulna
Sacrum
Radius
Coccyx
Carpus
Ischium
Metacarpus
Proximal phalanx
Femur
Distal phalanx
Pubis
Patella
Fibula
Lateral malleolus
Tibia
Medial malleolus
Proximal phalanx
Middle phalanx
Calcaneus
Distal phalanx

Skeletal System — Bone Structure

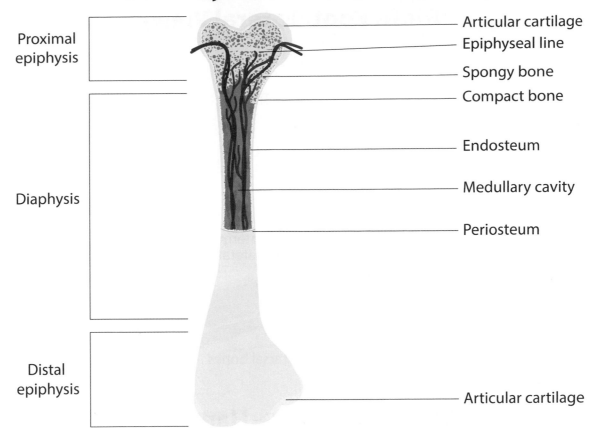

Proximal epiphysis

Diaphysis

Distal epiphysis

Articular cartilage
Epiphyseal line
Spongy bone
Compact bone

Endosteum

Medullary cavity

Periosteum

Articular cartilage

Skeletal System — Cervical, Thoracic, and Lumbar Spine

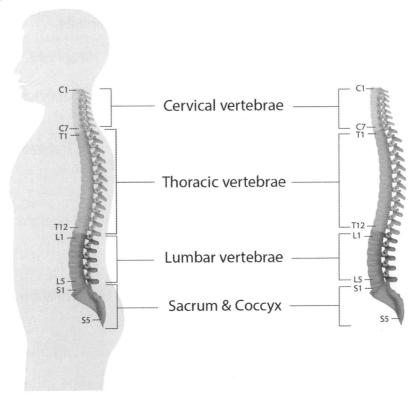

C1

C7
T1

T12
L1

L5
S1

S5

Cervical vertebrae

Thoracic vertebrae

Lumbar vertebrae

Sacrum & Coccyx

C1

C7
T1

T12
L1

L5
S1

S5

Skeletal System — Foot Bones
(Right Foot, Lateral View)

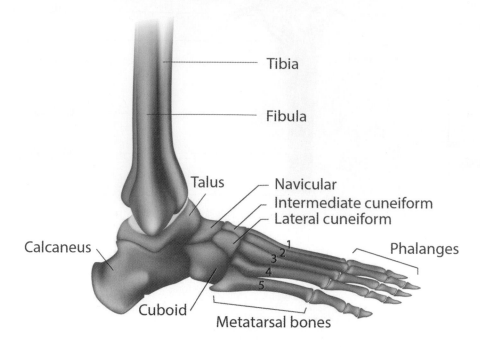

- Tibia
- Fibula
- Talus
- Navicular
- Intermediate cuneiform
- Lateral cuneiform
- Calcaneus
- 1
- 2
- 3
- 4
- 5
- Phalanges
- Cuboid
- Metatarsal bones

Skeletal System — Hand Bones

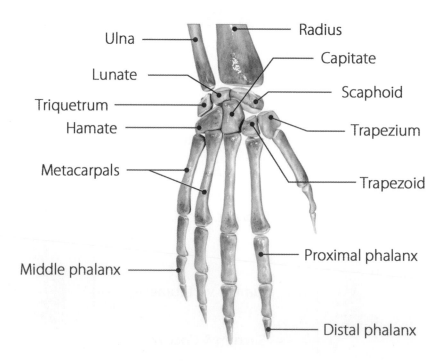

- Ulna
- Radius
- Lunate
- Capitate
- Triquetrum
- Scaphoid
- Hamate
- Trapezium
- Metacarpals
- Trapezoid
- Middle phalanx
- Proximal phalanx
- Distal phalanx

Skeletal System — Skull Anatomy

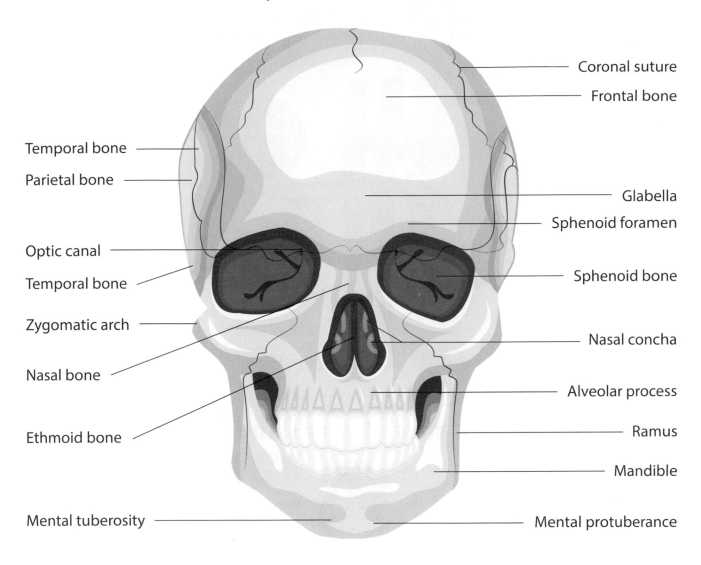

Coronal suture

Frontal bone

Temporal bone

Parietal bone

Glabella

Sphenoid foramen

Optic canal

Temporal bone

Sphenoid bone

Zygomatic arch

Nasal concha

Nasal bone

Alveolar process

Ethmoid bone

Ramus

Mandible

Mental tuberosity

Mental protuberance

Urinary System — Kidney Anatomy

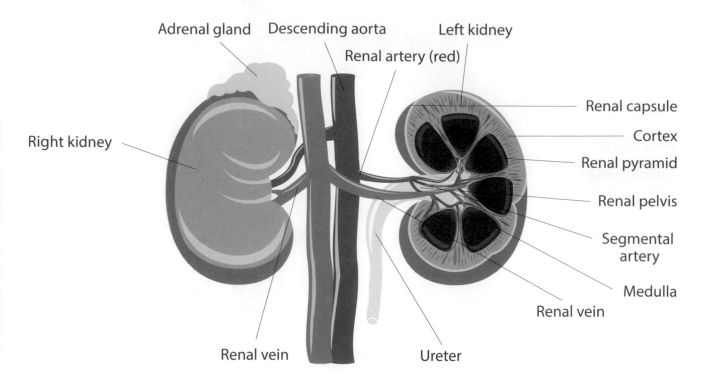

Adrenal gland Descending aorta Left kidney

Renal artery (red)

Right kidney

Renal capsule

Cortex

Renal pyramid

Renal pelvis

Segmental artery

Medulla

Renal vein

Renal vein Ureter

Urinary System — Organs and Structures

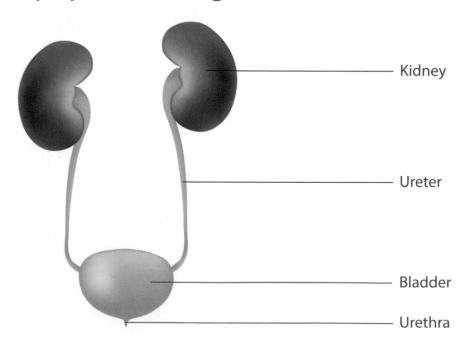

Kidney

Ureter

Bladder

Urethra

Index to Services, Supplies, Equipment, Drugs

A

A-Hydrocort® J1710
Abatacept J0129
Abciximab J0130
Abdominal pad, TLSO L1270
Abduction
  Control, hip orthosis, hip joint
    Dynamic, adjustable L1680
    Flexible
      Frejka type L1600, L1610
      Pavlik harness L1620
    Semi-flexible, Van Rosen type L1630
    Static
      Adjustable, Ilfeld type, prefabricated L1650
      Pelvic band or spreader bar L1640
      Plastic, prefabricated L1660
  Control, lower extremity orthosis, hip joint L2624
  Pillow (miscellaneous durable medical equipment) E1399
  Restrainer, shoulder L3650
    Canvas and webbing L3660
    Vest type L3675
  Rotation bar
    Foot L3150
      Adjustable shoe-styled positioning device L3160
      Including shoes L3140
      Prefabricated, off-the-shelf, each L3170
    Lower extremity
      Hip involvement, jointed, adjustable L2300
      Straight L2310
Ablation
  Prostate C9747
Ablation catheter
  Electrophysiological
    3D or vector mapping C1732
    Other than 3D or vector mapping or cool-tip C1733
  Endovascular, noncardiac C1888
  Extravascular, any modality C1886
  Tissue, extravascular C1886
  Ultrasound, focused C9734
Abobotulinumtoxin type A J0586
Abortion, induced
  17 to 24 weeks S2260
  25 to 28 weeks S2265
  29 to 31 weeks S2266
  32 or greater S2267
  Drug induced, with other services S0199
Absorption dressing A6251-A6256
Access system A4301
Accessories
  Ambulation devices E0153-E0159
  Artificial kidney, *see also* Dialysis
    Machines E1510-E1699
  Beds E0271-E0280, E0300-E0316
  Wheelchairs E0950-E1030, E2201-E2397, E2626-E2633, K0001-K0108, K0669
Accu-Chek® or similar product
  Blood glucose meter E0607
  Test strips, box of 50 A4253
Acetaminophen J0131
Acetate concentrate for hemodialysis A4708
Acetazolamide sodium J1120
Acetylcysteine
  Inhalation solution J7604, J7608
  Injection J0132

Acid concentrate for hemodialysis A4709
Activated carbon filter for hemodialysis A4680
Activity therapy
  45 minutes or more G0176
  Per 15 minutes H2032
Acute myocardial infarction
  Discharge G9798
Acyclovir J0133
Adalimumab J0135
Adapter
  Breast pump A4282
  Electric/pneumatic ventricular assist device Q0478
  Neurostimulator C1883
  Oxygen accessory E1358
  Pacing lead C1883
  Pneumatic ventricular assist device Q0504
Addition, *see also* **orthotic devices**
  Cushion socket
    Above knee L5648
    Below knee L5646
  Harness upper extremity
    Dual cable L6676
    Single cable L6675
  Interface replacement for halo procedure L0861
  Orthotic components, lower extremity K0672, L2750, L2760, L2780-L2861
  Prosthesis components
    Adjustable heel height L5990
    SACH foot L5970
  Torsion mechanism, upper extremity joint orthotic L3891
  Wrist unit, flexion, extension L6620
Adenosine J0153
Adhesive
  Bandage A6413
    Conforming A6442-A6447
    Padding A6441
    Self-adherent A6453, A6454, A6455
    Zinc paste impregnated A6456
  Barrier C1765
  Disc or foam pad A5126
  Dressing
    Composite
      16 sq. in. or less A6203
      More than 16 sq. in. but less than or equal to 48 sq. in. A6204
      More than 48 sq. in A6205
    Foam A6214
    Gauze
      16 sq. in. or less A6219
      More than 16 sq. in. but less than or equal to 48 sq. in. A6220
      More than 48 sq. in. A6221
    Hydrocolloid
      16 sq. in. or less A6234
      More than 16 sq. in. but less than or equal to 48 sq. in. A6238
      More than 48 sq. in. A6239
    Hydrogel
      16 sq. in. or less A6245
      More than 16 sq. in. but less than or equal to 48 sq. in. A6246
      More than 48 sq. in. A6247
    Specialty
      16 sq. in. or less A6254

More than 16 sq. in. but less than or equal to 48 sq. in. A6255
More than 48 sq. in. A6256
Liquid A4364
Remover A4455, A4456
Support for breast prosthesis A4280
Tape
Nonwaterproof A4450
Waterproof A4452
Tissue (wound closure) G0168
Adjustment, gastric band S2083
Administration
Aerosolized drug therapy S9061
Medication
Direct observation H0033
Oral, intramuscular and/or subcutaneous medication T1502
Other than oral and/or injectable T1503
Trastuzumab
Administered G9835
Not administered G9837
Not administered, doc reason G9836
Vaccine
Hepatitis B G0010
Influenza virus G0008
Pneumococcal G0009
Administrative, miscellaneous and investigational A9150-A9999
Adoptive immunotherapy S2107
Ado-trastuzumab J9354
Adrenal tissue transplant S2103
Adrenalin J0171
Advance directive S0257
Advanced brain imaging G9534, G9535, G9536, G9537, G9538
Aerosol
Compressor E0572
Compressor filter A7013, A7014
Mask A7015
Aflibercept J0178
AF, transient or reversible cause G9929
AFO (ankle foot orthosis) L1900-L1990
Dynamic adjustable E1815, E1830, L4397
Fracture L2106-L2116
Replace L4392, L4396
Walking boot L4631
Agalsidase beta J0180
Aggrastat J3246
Air bubble detector, dialysis E1530
Air fluidized bed E0194
Air pressure pad/mattress E0186, E0197
Air travel and nonemergency transportation A0140
Alarm, pressure, dialysis E1540
Alatrofloxacin mesylate J0200
Albumin, human
5%, 50 mL P9041
5%, 250 mL P9045
25%, 20 mL P9046
25%, 50 mL P9047
Albuterol, all formulations, inhalation solution
Concentrated
Compounded J7610
Noncompounded J7611
Unit dose
Compounded J7609
Noncompounded J7613, J7620
Alcohol (and drug)
Abuse and prevention services G0443, H0001-H2037, T1006-T1012

Not otherwise specified (NOS) H0047
Screening G9621, G9622, G9623, G9624
Structured, with intervention
15-20 minutes G0396
Greater than 30 minutes G0397
Per pint A4244
Testing collection and handling only H0048
Wipes A4245
Aldesleukin (IL2) J9015
Alefacept J0215
Alemtuzumab J0202
Alert device A9280
Alginate dressing A6196, A6197, A6198, A6199
Alglucerase J0205
Alglucosidase J0220
Alglucosidase alfa J0221
Alkaline battery
Blood glucose monitor
J cell A4234
Other than J cell A4233
Cochlear implant device replacement L8622
External infusion pump owned by patient, alkaline K0603
AlloDerm® Q4116
Allogeneic cord blood harvest S2140
Allograft, small intestine and liver S2053
AlloSkin™ Q4115
Alpha-1-proteinase inhibitor, human J0256, J0257
Alphanate J7186
Alprostadil
Injection J0270
Urethral suppository J0275
ALS (advanced life support)
Disposable supplies service
Esophageal intubation A0396
IV drug therapy A0394
Level 2 A0433
Mileage A0390
Routine disposable supplies A0398
Alteplase recombinant J2997
Alternating pressure mattress/pad replacement pad A4640
Air mattress E0277
Powered pressure reducing mattress overlay/pad E0181
Replacement only E0182
Alternative communication device board E1902
Ambulance A0021-A0999
Air A0430, A0431, A0435, A0436
Basic life support (BLS) A0428
Disposable supplies A0382-A0398
Fixed wing S9960
Mileage A0425
Nonemergency transport A0080-A0160, A0180-A0200, A0426, A0428, S0215
Oxygen A0422
Response and treatment A0998
Rotary wing S9961
Unlisted service A0999
Ambulation device E0100-E0159
Amifostine J0207
Amikacin sulfate J0278
Aminocaproic acid S0017
Aminolevulinate J7309
Aminolevulinic acid HCl J7308, J7345
Aminophylline J0280
Amiodarone HCl J0282
Amitriptyline HCl J1320
Ammonia N-13 A9526
Ammonia test paper A4774
Amnio wound Q4181

Amniotic membrane V2790
Amobarbital J0300
Amphotericin B J0285
Amphotericin B injection
    Cholesteryl sulfate complex J0288
    Lipid complex J0287
    Liposome J0289
Ampicillin sodium J0290
Ampicillin sodium/sulbactam sodium J0295
Amputation after revascularization procedure G9639, G9640, G9641
Amputee
    Adapter, wheelchair E0959
    Prosthesis L5000-L7520, L7900, L8400-L8465
    Stump sock L8470-L8485
    Wheelchair E1170-E1190, E1200
Analysis
    Dose optimization S3722
    Gene analysis S3866
    Gene sequence, hypertrophic cardiomyopathy S3865
    Semen G0027
Anastrozole, oral S0170
Anchor/screw C1713
Anesthesia
    Care services G9654, G9655, G9656, G9658
    Preop no smoking instructions given G9497
Angiography
    Fluorescent, nonophthalmic C9733
    Iliac and/or femoral artery G0278
    Magnetic resonance
        Abdomen C8901
            Followed by/with contrast C8902
        Chest C8910
            With contrast C8909
            Without contrast followed by with contrast C8911
        Lower extremity C8913
            With contrast C8912
            Without contrast followed by with contrast C8914
        Pelvis C8919
            With contrast C8918
            Without contrast followed by with contrast C8920
    Reconstruction, aorta, CT, for vascular surgery G0288
Anidulafungin J0348
Ankle-foot orthosis (AFO) L1900-L1990
    Dynamic, adjustable E1815
    Fabricated L2112, L2114, L2116
    Fracture custom-fabricated L2106, L2108
    Replace replacement, static AFO L4392
    Static or dynamic ankle foot orthosis L4396
    Toe E1830
Annual
    Gynecological examination
        Clinical breast examination without pelvic evaluation S0613
        Established patient S0612
        New patient S0610
    Wellness visit
        Initial G0438
        Subsequent G0439
Antenna, nerve stimulation device L8696
Anti-emetic J8498, Q0161-Q0181
Anti-platelet agents G9609, G9610, G9611
Anti-sperm antibodies test, immunobead S3655
Antibiotic
    Child taking 30 days prior dx estab G9701
    Child taking 30 days prior dx phary G9703
    Home infusion therapy S9494
        Every 3 hours S9497
        Every 4 hours S9504
        Every 6 hours S9503
        Every 8 hours S9502
        Every 12 hours S9501
        Every 24 hours S9500
    Regimen G9498, G9505
        Not prescribed within specified time period G9287
        Prescribed within specified time period G9286
Anticoagulation clinic S9401
Antimicrobial prophylaxis
    Not documented G9198
    Not ordered G9196
    Ordered G9197
Antiseptic
    Chlorhexidine A4248
    Solution used to clean dialysis equipment A4674
Antiviral
    Home infusion therapy S9494-S9504
Aortic aneurysm G9598, G9599, G9600
Apheresis, low density lipid (LDL) S2120
Apligraf® Q4101
Apnea monitor E0618
    Electrodes A4556
    Lead wires A4557
    With recording feature E0619
Apomorphine hydrochloride J0364
Application
    Low cost skin substitute
        Other areas C5275, C5276, C5277, C5278
        Trunk, arms, legs C5271, C5272, C5273, C5274
    Tantalum ring(s) scleral S8030
Aprotinin J0365
AquaPedic® sectional gel flotation E0196
Arbutamine HCl J0395
Arformoterol, inhalation solution J7605
Argatroban injection J0883, J0884
Aripiprazole J0400, J0401
Aripiprazole lauroxi injection J1942
Arm, wheelchair E0973
Arsenic trioxide J9017
Arthroereisis, subtalar S2117
Arthroscopy
    Knee
        Harvesting of cartilage S2112
        Removal foreign body G0289
    Shoulder, with capsulorrhaphy S2300
Artificial
    Cornea L8609
    Kidney, *see also* Dialysis
        Machines and accessories E1510-E1699
    Larynx L8500
    Pancreas device system
        Low glucose suspend feature S1034
        Receiver S1037
        Sensor S1035
        Transmitter S1036
    Saliva A9155
Asparaginase J9019, J9020
Assembly
    Footrest, complete, replacement K0045
    Ratchet, replacement K0050
Assertive community treatment
    Per 15 minutes H0039
    Per diem H0040
Assessment
    Alcohol and/or substance G0397
    Alcohol or drug H0001
    Audiologic
        Conformity evaluation V5020

Hearing aid V5010
  Fitting/orientation/checking V5011
  Repair/modification V5014
Hearing screening V5008
Comp assess care plan ccm svc G0506
Family H1011
Functional outcome G9227
Geriatric S0250
Mental health H0031
Nursing assessment/evaluation T1001
Pain, not documented G8442
Preoperative G9615, G9616, G9617
Psychiatric symptoms G9742, G9743
Speech services
  Dysphagia screening V5364
  Language screening V5363
  Screening V5362
  Wellness S5190

Assisted living
Per diem T2031
Per month T2030

Assistive listening device
Alerting V5269
Cochlear implant assistive V5273
FM/DM
  Accessories
    Direct audio input receiver V5285
    Ear level receiver V5284
    Neck loop induction receiver V5283
    Not otherwise specified (NOS) V5287
    Personal adapter/boot coupling V5289
    Personal Bluetooth® receiver V5286
    Personal transmitter V5288
    Transmitter microphone V5290
  System
    Binaural V5282
    Monaural V5281
Not otherwise specified (NOS) V5274
Supplies and accessories not otherwise specified (NOS)
  V5267
TDD V5272
Telephone amplifier V5268
Television amplifier V5270
Television caption decoder V5271

Asthma
Education S9441
Kit S8097
Medication event G9799
Reporting
  Not well-controlled based
  Reason not given G9434
  Result documented G9432
  Well-controlled based G9432, G9434

Atezolizumab injection J9022
Atropine sulfate J0461
Atropine, inhalation solution
Concentrated J7635
Unit dose J7636
Attendant care
Per 15 min S5125
Per diem S5126
Audiologic assessment
Conformity evaluation V5020
Fitting/orientation/checking, hearing aid V5011
Hearing aid V5010
  Repair/modification V5014
Hearing screening V5008
Audiometry S0618

Auditory osseointegrated device
Abutment length replacement L8693
Batteries L8624
External sound processor
  Headband or other external attachment L8692
  Replacement L8691
Internal and external components L8690
Transducer/actuator replacement L8694
Transmitting cable L8618
Aurothioglucose J2910
Autologous cultured chondrocytes, implant J7330
Avelumab injection J9023
Azacitidine J9025
Azathioprine J7500, J7501
Azithromycin J0456
Azithromycin dihydrate Q0144
Aztreonam S0073

B

Back supports L0621-L0861
Baclofen J0475, J0476
Bacterial sensitivity study P7001
Bag
Bedside drainage A4357
Ostomy irrigation supply A4398
Urinary latex A5112
Urinary suspensory covering A5105
Urinary, vinyl A4358
With or without tube A4357-A4358
Ballistocardiogram S3902
Balloon
Dilatation C1726
Tissue dissector C1727
Bandage A6413
By type
  Compression A6448, A6449, A6450, A6451, A6452
  Conforming A6442-A6447
  Gauze A6216-A6230, A6402, A6403, A6404
  Padding A6441, S8430
  Self-adherent A6453, A6454, A6455
  Zinc paste impregnated A6456
Barrier adhesion C1765
Basiliximab J0480
Bathtub
Chair E0240
Rail
  Floor base E0242
  Wall E0241
Stool or bench E0245
Transfer bench E0247
  Heavy duty E0248
Transfer rail E0246
Battery
Charger
  Oxygen accessory E1357
  Power wheelchair accessory
    Dual mode E2367
    Single mode E2366
  Six volt L7362
  Twelve volt L7366
  Ventilator, patient owned A4613
External infusion pump
  Alkaline 1.5 volt K0603
  Lithium 1.5 volt A4602
  Silver oxide
    1.5 volt K0601
    3 volt K0602

3.6 volt K0604
4.5 volt K0605
Hearing device V5266
Lithium
  Electric and/or pneumatic ventricular assist Q0495
    Replacement Q0506
  External infusion pump
    1.5 volt A4602
    3.6 volt K0604
    4.5 volt K0605
  Nonprosthetic use A4601
  Replacement L7367
Power wheelchair accessory
  Lead acid
    12 to 24 amp hour sealed K0733
    22 NF nonsealed E2360
    22 NF sealed lead E2361
    24 nonsealed E2362
    24 sealed lead E2363
    27 nonsealed E2372
    27 sealed E2371
    34 nonsealed E2358
    34 sealed E2359
    U-1 nonsealed E2364
    U-1 sealed E2365
  Lithium-based E2397
Replacement
  Auditory osseointegrated device L8624
  Automated external defibrillator K0607
  Blood glucose monitor
  Cochlear implant device L8623, L8624
  Home
    Alkaline, J cell, each A4234
    Lithium, each A4235
    Other than J cell, each A4233
    Silver oxide, each A4236
Six volt L7360
TENS A4630
Twelve volt L7364
Ventilator, patient owned
  Battery cables A4612
  Battery charger A4613
  Battery, heavy duty A4611
BCG live, intravesical J9031
Becaplermin gel S0157
Beclomethasone inhalation solution J7622
Bed
Air fluidized E0194
Cradle, any type E0280
Hospital
  Fixed height E0250, E0291
    With mattress E0251, E0290
  Heavy-duty capacity, any type
    350 pounds to 600 pounds E0301
      With mattress E0303
    Greater than 600 pounds E0302
      With mattress E0304
  Institutional type E0270
  Pediatric E0328, E0329
  Semi-electric E0261, 295
    With mattress E0260, E0294
  Total electric E0266, E0297
    With mattress E0265, E0296
  Variable height E0256, E0293
    With mattress E0255, E0292
Pan
  Fracture E0276
  Standard E0275
Rail E0305, E0310

Full length E0310
Half length E0305
Safety enclosure frame/canopy E0316
Bedside
Drainage bag A4357
Drainage bottle A5102
Behavioral health services G0177, G0445-G0447, G0473, H0001-H2037, S9480, S9482
Belatacept J0485
Belimumab J0490
Belinostat J9032
Belt
Extremity E0945
Ostomy A4367
Pelvic E0944
Wheelchair E0978
Bench, bathtub E0245
Bendamustine HCl J9033, J9034
Benesch boot L3212, L3213, L3214
Benztropine J0515
Betadine A4246, A4247
Beta-lactam antibiotic treatment G9558, G9559, G9560
Betamethasone acetate and betamethasone sodium phosphate J0702
Betamethasone inhalation solution J7624
Bethanechol chloride J0520
Bevacizumab J9035
Bezlotoxumab injection J0565
Bifocal, glass or plastic V2200-V2299
Bilirubin (phototherapy) light E0202
Binder A4465
Bio-ConneKt® Q4161
Biofeedback device E0746
Biologic immune response modifier G9506
Biologicals and skin substitutes Q4100-Q4175
Biperiden lactate J0190
Bitolterol mesylate, inhalation solution
Concentrated J7628
Unit dose J7629
Bivalirudin J0583
Bladder injury G9625, G9626, G9627, G9628, G9629, G9630
Blinatumomab J9039
Blinded procedure for lumbar stenosis G0276
Blood
Fresh frozen plasma P9017
Glucose monitor E0607, E2100, E2101
Glucose test A4253
Granulocytes, pheresis P9050
Ketone test A4252
Leak detector, dialysis E1560
Leukocyte poor P9016
Leukocytes reduced P9031
Mucoprotein P2038
Platelets P9019
  Irradiated P9032
  Leukocytes reduced, irradiated P9033
  Pheresis P9034
    Irradiated P9036
    Leukocytes reduced P9035
    Leukocytes reduced, irradiated P9037
    Pathogen-reduced P9073
  Pathogen(s) test P9100
Pressure monitor A4660, A4663, A4670
Pump, dialysis E1620
Red blood cells
  Deglycerolized P9039
  Irradiated P9038
  Leukocytes reduced P9016
  Leukocytes reduced, irradiated P9040
  Washed P9022

Cellular therapy M0075
Cement, ostomy A4364
Centrifuge E1500
Centruroides immune F(ab) J0716
Cephalin flocculation, blood P2028
Cephalothin sodium J1890
Cephapirin sodium J0710
Cerliponase alfa C9014
Certolizumab pegol J0717
Cerumen removal G0268
Cervical
    Halo L0810-L0830
    Head harness/halter E0942
    Orthosis L0112-L0200
    Traction E0855, E0856
Cervical cap contraceptive A4261
Cervical-thoracic-lumbar-sacral orthosis (CTLSO) L0700
    With interface material L0710
Cetuximab J9055
Chair
    Adjustable, dialysis E1570
    Bath/shower E0240
    Lift E0627
    Rollabout E1031
    Sitz bath E0160, E0161, E0162
Chamber
    Pacemaker, dual C1785
    Pacemaker, single C1786
Chelation therapy M0300
Chemical endarterectomy M0300
Chemistry and toxicology tests P2028-P3001
Chemodenervation S2340, S2341
Chemotherapy, *see also* **Appendix A: Table of Drugs**
    Administration (hospital reporting only) Q0083, Q0084, Q0085
    Drug, oral, not otherwise classified J8999
    Drugs J9000-J9999
    Office/clinic setting G0498
Chest
    Drain A7040, A7041
    Shell (cuirass) E0457
    Wall oscillation system E0483
        Hose, replacement A7026
        Vest, replacement A7025
    Wrap E0459
Chin cup, cervical L0150
Chlorambucil, oral S0172
Chloramphenicol sodium succinate J0720
Chlordiazepoxide HCl J1990
Chloromycetin sodium succinate J0720
Chloroprocaine HCl J2400
Chloroquine HCl J0390
Chlorothiazide sodium J1205
Chlorpromazine HCl J3230, Q0161
Choline c-11 A9515
Chorionic gonadotropin J0725
Choroid lesion destruction G0186
Christian Science practitioner services S9900, S9901
Chromic phosphate P32 suspension A9564
Chromium CR-51 sodium chromate A9553
Cidofovir J0740
Cilastatin sodium, imipenem J0743
Cimetidine hydrochloride S0023
Cinacalcet, oral J0604
Ciprofloxacin for intravenous infusion J0744
Ciprofloxacin otic suspension J7342
Cisplatin J9060
Cladribine J9065

Clamp
    Dialysis A4918
    External urethral A4356
Clarix™ Q4148, Q4156
Cleanser, wound A6260
Cleansing agent, dialysis equipment A4674
Clindamycin phosphate S0077
Clinic visit
    All-inclusive T1015
    Hospital outpatient G0463
Clinical trial services S9988, S9990, S9991, S9992, S9994, S9996
Clofarabine J9027
Clonidine J0735
Clotting time tube A4771
Clozapine S0136
Clubfoot wedge L3380
Cochlear prosthetic implant L8614
    Batteries L8621, L8622, L8623, L8624
    Headset L8615
    Replacement L8619, L8627, L8628, L8629
    Transmitting coil/cable L8617, L8618
Codeine phosphate J0745
Cognitive skills development G0515
Coil, insertable, MRI C1770
Cold pad, water circulating E0218
Colistimethate sodium J0770, S0142
Collagen
    Skin test Q3031
    Urinary tract implant L8603
    Wound dressing A6021, A6022, A6023, A6024
Collagenase, Clostridium histolyticum J0775
Collar, cervical
    Multiple post L0180-L0200
    Nonadjustable (foam) L0120
Colonoscopy
    Advanced age G9659, G9660, G9661
    Consultation S0285
    Diagnostic G9937
    Flexible sigmoidoscopy G0104
    Screening
        Barium enema G0120
        Fecal occult blood test G0328
        Individual at high risk G0105
        Not meeting criteria for high risk G0121
    Surveillance G9936
Coly-Mycin M® J0770
Coma stimulation S9056
Commode E0160-E0175
    Chair, mobile or stationary E0163-E0165
        With lift mechanism E0170-E0171
    Lift E0172, E0625
    Pail E0167
    Seat, wheelchair E0968
Communication device, augmentative V5336
Compensator-based beam modulation treatment G6016
Complete blood count (CBC) G0306, G0307
Composite dressing A6203, A6204, A6205
Compounded drug, not otherwise classified J7999
Compressed gas system E0424-E0480
Compression
    Bandage A6448, A6449, A6450, A6451, A6452
        Padding S8430
    Burn garment A6501-A6513
    Device, limb A4600, E0676
Compression stockings A6530-A6549
Compressor E0565, E0570, E0572, E0650, E0651, E0652
Conduction
    Glasses, air V5070
    Hearing aid V5030

Cystourethroscopy
With insertion of transprostatic implant
1 to 3 implants C9739
4 or more implants C9740
With ureteroscopy and or pyeloscopy S2070
Cytarabine J9100
Cytarabine liposome J9098
Cytomegalovirus immune globulin (human) J0850

D

Dacarbazine J9130
Daclizumab J7513
Dactinomycin J9120
Dalalone J1100
Dalbavancin J0875
Dalteparin sodium J1645
Daptomycin J0878
Daratumumab injection J9145
Darbepoetin alfa
ESRD on dialysis J0882
Non-ERSD use J0881
Daunorubicin citrate J9151
Daunorubicin HCl J9150
DaunoXome® (daunorubicin citrate) J9151
Day care services S5100, S5101, S5102, S5105
Decitabine J0894
Decompression procedure, intervertebral disc S2348
Decubitus care equipment E0181-E0199
Deferoxamine mesylate J0895
Defibrillator, external E0617, K0606
Battery K0607
Electrode K0609
Garment K0608
Degarelix J9155
Deionizer, water purification system E1615
Delivery or service to high risk area S9381
Delivery, home, supplies S8415
Delivery, set-up, dispensing A9901
Deluxe item S1001
Demonstration project
ESRD G9013, G9014
Frontier extended stay clinic G9140
MAPCP G9151, G9152, G9153
Medications G9017-G9036
Oncology G9050-G9139
Denileukin diftitox J9160
Denosumab J0897
Depo-estradiol cypionate J1000
Dermagraft® Q4106
Desmopressin acetate J2597
Destruction
Prostate tissue C9748
Detector, blood leak, dialysis E1560
Development testing G0451
Device
Balloon continence C9746
Closure, vascular C1760
Cochlear with headset L8614, L8615
Other cochlear accessories L8616-L8629
Dexamethasone
Inhalation solution
Concentrated J7637
Unit dose J7638
Intravitreal implant J7312
Oral J8540

Dexamethasone acetate J1094
Dexamethasone sodium phosphate J1100
Dexrazoxane hydrochloride J1190
Dextran J7100, J7110
Dextroamphetamine sulfate S0160
Dextrose S5010, S5012, S5013, S5014
5% LR J7121
Saline (normal) J7042
Water J7060, J7070
Dextrostix® or similar product A4772
Diabetes
Home management of gestational diabetes S9214
Management program G0245, G0246, S9140, S9141, S9455, S9460, S9465, S9470
Self-management training
Group G0109
Individual G0108
Diagnostic radiology/EKG services R0070-R0076
Dialysate concentrate additives A4765
Dialysate solution A4728
Dialysate testing solution A4760
Dialysis, *see also* **ESRD**
Access system (implantable) C1881
Air bubble detector E1530
Bath conductivity, meter E1550
Chemicals/antiseptics solution A4674
Discontinued G9523
Disposable cycler set A4671
Emergency/unscheduled G0257
Equipment E1510-E1699
Extension line A4672, A4673
Filter A4680
Fluid barrier E1575
Pressure alarm E1540
Shunt A4740
Supplies A4653-A4932
Unipuncture control system E1580
Venous pressure clamp A4918
Diaper T4521-T4540, T4543, T4544
Adult incontinence garment A4520
Diazepam J3360
Diazoxide J1730
Diclofenac sodium injection J1130
Dicyclomine HCl J0500
Didanosine (DDI) S0137
Diethylstilbestrol diphosphate J9165
Digoxin immune fab (ovine) J1162
Digoxin J1160
Dihydroergotamine mesylate J1110
Dimenhydrinate J1240
Dimercaprol J0470
Dimethyl sulfoxide (DMSO) J1212
Diphenhydramine HCl J1200, Q0163
Dipyridamole J1245
Direct admission/refer for hospital observation care G0379
Directional, transluminal, atherectomy C1714
Disarticulation
Lower extremities, prosthesis L5000-L5999
Upper extremities, prosthesis L6000-L6692
Disease management program S0315, S0316, S0317
Telephone calls by RN S0320
Diskectomy, anterior S2350, S2351
Dispensing fee
BiCROS V5240
Bilateral V5110
Binaural V5160
CROS V5200
Monaural hearing aid, any type V5241

Pharmacy
Anti-cancer, antiemetics Q0510, Q0511, Q0512
Compounding S9430
Immunosuppressives Q0510
Inhalation drug(s) G0333, Q0513, Q0514
Unspecified hearing aid V5090
Disposable supplies, ambulance A0382, A0384, A0392-A0398
DMSO J1212
DNA analysis, multiple endocrine neoplasia type 2 S3840
Dobutamine HCl J1250
Docetaxel J9171
Dolasetron mesylate J1260, S0174
Dome and mouthpiece (for nebulizer) A7016
Donor
Lobectomy, living donor S2061
Solid organs, global definition S2152
Door to puncture time G9580, G9582
Dopamine HCl J1265
Doripenem J1267
Dornase alpha, inhalation solution, unit dose form J7639
Doxercalciferol J1270
Doxorubicin HCl J9000, Q2049, Q2050
Drainage
Bag
Bedside A4357
Urinary, latex A5112
Urinary, vinyl A4358
With or without tube A4357-A4358
Board, postural E0606
Bottle, bedside A5102
Catheter C1729
Dressing, *see also* **bandage by type**
Alginate A6196, A6197, A6198, A6199
Collagen A6021, A6022, A6023, A6024
Composite A6203, A6204, A6205
Contact layer A6206-A6208
Foam A6209-A6215
Gauze A6216-A6230, A6402, A6403, A6404
Gel sheet A6025
Holder/binder A4461, A4463, A4465
Hydrocolloid A6234-A6241
Hydrogel A6242-A6248
Nonreusable A4461
Packing strips A6407
Reusable A4463
Specialty absorptive A6251-A6256
Transparent film A6257, A6258, A6259
Tubular A6457
Dronabinol Q0167
Droperidol J1790
With fentanyl citrate J1810
Dropper A4649
Drug abuse G9518
Drugs, *see also* **Appendix A: Table of Drugs**
Administered through metered dose inhaler J3535
Chemotherapy J8501-J9999
Antiemetic Q0161-Q0181
Compounded, not otherwise classified (NOC) J7999
Controlled dose inhalation drug delivery system K0730
Disposable delivery system
5 mL or less per hour A4306
50 mL or greater per hour A4305
Immunosuppressive J7500-J7599
Infusion supplies A4221, A4222, A4224, A4225, A4230, A4231, A4232
Inhalation solutions J7608-J7699

Non-biodegradable delivery implants
Insertion G0516
Removal G0517
Removal and reinsertion G0518
Nonprescription A9150
Not otherwise classified (NOC) J3490, J7699, J7799, Q4082
Prescription S5000, S5001
Testing, definitive
1-7 classes G0480
8-14 classes G0481
15-21 classes G0482
22 or more classes G0483
Perf w/o rec standards, any number of classes G0659
Dry pressure pad/mattress E0184, E0199
Durable medical equipment (DME) E0100-E8002, K codes
Duraclon® (clonidine) J0735
Durvalumab C9492
Dyphylline J1180

E

Ear mold V5264
Early periodic screening diagnosis and treatment (EPSDT) S0302
Ecallantide J1290
Echocardiography injectable contrast material A9700
Echosclerotherapy S2202
Eculizumab J1300
Edaravone C9493
Edetate calcium disodium J0600
Edetate disodium J3520
Eggcrate dry pressure pad/mattress E0184, E0199
Elbow
Disarticulation, endoskeletal L6450
Orthosis (EO) E1800, L3702-L3740, L3760, L3761, L3762
Protector E0191
Elbow-wrist-hand-finger orthosis L3763, L3764, L3765, L3766
Electrical stimulation
Auricular acupuncture points S8930
Device for cancer treatment E0766
Treatment G0281, G0282, G0283
Electrical work, dialysis equipment A4870
Electrocardiogram (ECG), routine G0403, G0404, G0405
Electrodes A4555, A4556
Electromagnetic stimulation E0761, E0769, G0295, G0329
Electron beam CT (ultrafast CT) S8092
Electronic medication compliance management device T1505
Electrophysiology
3D or vector mapping C1730, C1731
Diagnostic, other than 3D mapping C1730, C1731
Diagnostic/ablation with 3D mapping C1732
Other than 3D or vector mapping and cool-tip C1733
Elevating leg rest
Lower extension tube, replacement, each K0046
Pair K0195
Upper hanger bracket, replacement, each K0047
Elliotts B solution J9175
Elosulfase alfa J1322
Elotuzumab injection J9176
Embolectomy catheter C1757
Emergency department visit G9521, G9522
Level 1 G0380
Level 2 G0381
Level 3 G0382
Level 4 G0383
Level 5 G0384
Emergency response system S5160, S5161, S5162
Emergency stat laboratory charge S3600, S3601

EMG (electromyography) E0746, S3900
Eminase® J0350
Endarterectomy, chemical M0300
Endoscope
   Retrograde imaging colonoscope device C1749
   Sheath (disposable), each A4270
Endoskeletal system, addition L5848, L5856, L5857, L5925, L5969
Enfuvirtide J1324
Enoxaparin sodium J1650
Enteral
   Feeding supply kit
      Gravity fed B4036
      Pump fed B4035
      Syringe fed B4034
   Formula
      Blenderized natural foods with intact nutrients B4149
      Complete with intact nutrients B4150
      Complete, calorically dense B4152
      Fluid and electrolyte replacement B4102
      Hydrolyzed proteins B4153
      Incomplete/modular nutrients B4155
      Pediatrics
         Complete calorically dense B4160
         Complete soy-based, intact nutrients B4159
         Complete with intact nutrients B4158
         Fluid and electrolyte replacement B4103
         Hydrolyzed/amino acids B4161
         Special metabolic needs for inherited disease of metabolism B4162
      Special metabolic needs B4154
      Special metabolic needs for inherited disease of metabolism B4157
   Nutrition infusion pump B9002
   Supplies, not otherwise classified B9998
Enterostomal therapy S9474
Enuresis alarm S8270
Envarsus XR® J7503
Eosinophil count S3630
Epinephrine J0171
Epirubicin HCl J9178
Epoetin alpha
   ESRD on dialysis 100 units Q4081
   Non-ERSD use J0885
Epoetin beta J0887, J0888
Epoprostenol J1325
Eptifibatide J1327
Equestrian/hippotherapy S8940
Ergonovine maleate J1330
Eribulin mesylate J9179
Ertapenem sodium J1335
Erythromycin lactobionate J1364
ESRD (end-stage renal disease), *see also* **Dialysis**
   Emergency dialysis G0257
   Machines and accessories E1500-E1699
   Plumbing A4870
   Supplies A4651-A4929
Estradiol valerate J1380
Estrogen conjugated J1410
Estrone (5, aqueous) J1435
Etanercept J1438
Etelcalcetide injection J0606
Eteplirsen injection J1428
Ethanolamine oleate J1430
Etidronate disodium J1436
Etonogestrel implant system J7307
Etoposide J9181
Etoposide, oral J8560

Euflexxa J7323
Everolimus J7527
Exemestane S0156
Exercise equipment A9300
External
   Ambulatory infusion pump E0781, E0784
   Ambulatory insulin delivery system A9274
   Counterpulsation treatment G0166
   Drug infusion pump, non-insulin K0552
   Power, battery components L7360-L7368
   Power, elbow L7170-L7191
   Urinary supplies A4356, A4357, A4358, A5105
Extracorporeal shockwave lithotripsy S9034
   Global fee S0400
Extremity belt/harness E0945
Eye
   Case V2756
   Exam, routine S0620, S0621
   Lens, contact or spectacle V2100-V2615
   Miscellaneous items and services V2700-V2799
   Other miscellaneous item or service V2799
   Pad A6410, A6411
   Prosthetic
      Custom V2623
      Other type V2629
   Surgery S0800, S0810, S0812
Eye patch, occlusive A6412

F

Face tent, oxygen A4619
Faceplate, ostomy A4361
Factor VIIA coagulation factor, recombinant J7189
Factor VIII, anti-hemophilic factor J7182, J7185, J7188, J7190, J7191, J7192, J7205, J7207, J7209, J7210, J7211
Factor IX J7193, J7194, J7195, J7200, J7201
Factor XIII, A-subunit J7181
Factor XIII, anti-hemophilic factor J7180
Family planning education H1010
Famotidine S0028
Fecal microbiota preparation G0455
Federally qualified health center services G0466, G0467, G0468, G0469, G0470
Fentanyl citrate and droperidol J1810
Fentanyl citrate J3010
Fern test Q0114
Ferric carboxymaltose J1439
Ferric pyrophosphate citrate solution J1443
Ferumoxytol Q0138, Q0139
Fetoscopic laser therapy S2411
Filgrastim (G-CSF) J1442, Q5101
Filler
   Dermal, injection G0429
   Wound
      Alginate dressing A6199
      Collagen based A6011
      Foam dressing A6215
      Hydrocolloid dressing A6240, A6241
      Hydrogel dressing A6248
      Not elsewhere classified (NEC) A6261, A6262
Film, transparent (for dressing) A6257, A6258, A6259
Filter
   Aerosol compressor A7014
   Dialysis carbon A4680
   Ostomy A4368
   Placement G9539, G9540, G9541, G9542, G9543, G9544
   Tracheostoma A4481

Ultrasonic generator A7014
Vena cava C1880
Finasteride S0138
Fistula cannulation set A4730
Flebogamma J1572
Florbetaben Q9983
Florbetapir F18 A9586
Floweramnioflo Q4177
Floweramniopatch Q4178
Flowerderm™ Q4179
Flowmeter E0440, E0555, E0580
Floxuridine J9200
Fluciclovine f-18 A9588
Fluconazole, injection J1450
Fludarabine phosphate J8562, J9185
Fluid barrier, dialysis E1575
Flunisolide inhalation solution J7641
Fluocinolone J7311, J7313
Fluorodeoxyglucose F-18 FDG A9552
Fluorouracil J9190
Fluphenazine decanoate J2680
Flutamide, oral S0175
Flutemetamol Q9982
Flutter device S8185
Foam dressing A6209-A6215
Foam pad adhesive A5126
Folding walker E0135, E0143
Foley catheter A4312-A4316, A4338-A4346
Follitropin alfa S0126
Follitropin beta S0128
Fomepizole J1451
Fomivirsen sodium intraocular J1452
Fondaparinux sodium J1652
Foot
Arch support
Nonremovable L3070-L3090
Removable L3040-L3060
Exam G9502
Insert
Formed to patient foot L3030
High strength, lightweight material L3031
Longitudinal/ metatarsal support L3020
Plastazote or equal L3002
Silicone gel L3003
Spenco® L3001
UCB type, Berkeley shell L3000
Footdrop splint L4398
Footplate E0175, E0970, L3031
Footrest
Complete assembly, replacement K0045
High mount flip-up, replacement K0037
Lower extension tube, replacement, each K0043
Footwear
Diabetic
Compression molded A5510
Custom with fitting A5501
Inserts A5512, A5513
Orthopedic
Custom molded shoe L3250
Custom shoe L3230
Ladies shoe L3215, L3216, L3217, L3224
Men's shoe L3219, L3221, L3222, L3225
Forearm crutches E0110, E0111
Formoterol J7640
Formoterol fumarate J7606
Formula, additive, enteral B4104
Fosaprepitant J1453
Foscarnet sodium J1455
Fosphenytoin Q2009

Fosphenytoin sodium S0078
Foster care
Adult S5140, S5141
Child S5145, S5146
Fracture
Bedpan E0276
Frame E0920, E0930, E0946, E0947, E0948
Orthosis L2106-L2136, L3980-L3984
Orthotic additions L2180-L2192, L3995
Fragmin® (dalteparin sodium) J1645
Frames (spectacles) V2020, V2025
Fresh frozen plasma
Between 8-24 hours of collection P9059
Donor retested P9060
Single donor, frozen within 8 hours of collection P9017
Frontier extended stay clinic G9140
Fulvestrant J9395
Functional
Electrical stimulator, any type E0770
Limitation
Carrying, moving, and handling objects G8984, G8985, G8986
Changing/maintaining position G8981,G8982, G8983
Motor speech G8999
Other primary G8990, G8991, G8992
Other subsequent G8993, G8994, G8995
Self-care G8987, G8988, G8989
Swallowing G8996, G8997, G8998
Furosemide J1940

G

Gadobutrol A9585
Gadofosveset trisodium A9583
Gadoxetate disodium A9581
Gait trainer E8000, E8001, E8002
Gallium (Ga67) A9556
Gallium ga-68 A9587
Gallium nitrate J1457
Galsulfase J1458
Gamma globulin J1460, J1560
Gammagard® liquid J1569
Gammaplex® J1557
Gamunex® J1561
Ganciclovir sodium J1570
Ganciclovir, implant J7310
Ganirelix acetate S0132
Garamycin® J1580
Gas system
Compressed E0424, E0425
Gaseous E0430, E0431, E0441, E0443
Liquid E0434-E0440, E0442, E0444
Gastrointestinal fat absorption study S3708
Gauze, *see also* **bandage by type**
Impregnated A6222-A6233, A6266
Nonimpregnated A6402, A6403, A6404
Gefitinib J8565
Gel
Conductive A4558
Pressure pad E0185, E0196
Gel-syn® J7328
Gelatin capsule application device L8515
Gemcitabine HCl J9201
Gemtuzumab ozogamicin injection J9203
General care management, RHC/FQHC G0511
Generator, ultrasonic with nebulizer E0574
Genetic
Counseling S0265

Testing S3800-S3870
    Warfarin responsiveness G9143
Gentamicin sulfate J1580
Glasses
    Air conduction V5070
    Binaural V5120-V5150
    Bone conduction V5080
    Frames V2020, V2025
    Hearing aid V5230
Glatiramer acetate J1595
Gloves A4927, A4930
Glucagon HCl J1610
Glucose testing
    Continuous noninvasive monitoring S1030, S1031
    Disposable monitor A9275
    Monitor with lancing/blood sample collection E2101
    Monitor with voice synthesizer E2100
    Test strips
        Dialysis A4772
        Home blood glucose monitor A4253
Gluteal pad L2650
Glycopyrrolate, inhalation solution
    Concentrated J7642
    Unit dose J7643
Gold sodium thiomalate J1600
Golimumab J1602
Gonadorelin HCl J1620
Goserelin acetate implant J9202
Grab bar, trapeze E0910, E0940
Grade-aid, wheelchair E0974
Gradient pressure aid supplies S8420-S8429
Grafix®/Grafixpl®
    Core Q4132
    Prime Q4133
Graft, vascular catheter C1768
Granisetron, extended release J1627
Granisetron HCl J1626, Q0166, S0091
Granulocyte colony stimulating factor (G-CSF) J1442, Q5101
Gravity traction device E0941
Gravlee jet washer A4470
Group psychotherapy G0410, G0411
Guidewire C1769
Guselkumab C9029

H

Haberman feeder, cleft palate S8265
Habilitation
    Day T2020, T2021
    Educational T2012, T2013
    Prevocational T2014, T2015
    Residential T2016, T2017
    Supported employment T2018, T2019
Hair analysis (excluding arsenic) P2031
Hallus valgus dynamic splint L3100
Hallux prosthetic implant L8642
Halo procedures L0810, L0820, L0830, L0859, L0861
Haloperidol J1630
Haloperidol decanoate J1631
Halter, cervical head E0942
Hand finger orthosis, prefabricated L3923
Hand restoration L6900-L6915
    Orthosis (WHFO) E1805, E1825, L3763-L3809, L3900-L3956
    Partial prosthesis L6000-L6020
    Rims, wheelchair, replacement E0967
Handgrip (cane, crutch, walker) A4636
Harness E0942, E0944, E0945

Harvesting of donor multivisceral organs S2055
Health club membership S9970
Health-related quality of life assessment G9634, G9635, G9636
Hearing aid
    BiCROS, glasses V5230
    BiCROS, in the ear V5210
    Binaural
        Analog V5248, V5249
            CIC V5248
            ITC V5249
        Digital
            BTE V5261
            CIC V5258
            ITC V5259
            ITE V5260
        Digitally programmable
            BTE V5253
            ITC V5251
            ITE V5252
        Disposable V5263
    CROS, glasses V5190
    CROS, in the ear V5170
    Monaural
        Analog
            CIC (completely in ear canal) V5242
            ITC (in the canal) V5243
        Digital
            BTE V5257
            CIC V5254
            ITC V5255
            ITE V5256
        Digitally programmable
            BTE V5247
            CIC V5244
            ITC V5245
            ITE V5246
        Disposable V5262
Hearing services L8614, V5008-V5299, V5336
Heat
    Application E0200-E0239
    Infrared heating pad system A4639, E0221
    Lamp E0200, E0205
    Pad A9273, E0210, E0215, E0249
Heater (nebulizer) E1372
Heel
    Elevator, air E0370
    Protector E0191
    Shoe L3430-L3485
    Stabilizer L3170
Helicoll™ Q4164
Helicopter, ambulance A0431
Helmet, head A8000, A8001, A8002, A8003, A8004
Hemin J1640
Hemi-pelvectomy prosthesis L5280
Hemi-wheelchair E1083, E1084, E1085, E1086
Hemodialysis
    Discontinued G9523
    Machine E1590
    Short-term C1752
Hemodialyzer, portable E1635
Hemofil M J7190
Hemophilia clotting factor J7190-J7198
    Not elsewhere classified (NEC) J7199
Hemostick® and similar products A4773
Hep-lock (heparin lock) J1642
HepaGam B® J1571, J1573
Heparin infusion pump, dialysis E1520
Heparin lock flush J1642

Heparin sodium J1644
Hep b screen high risk indiv G0499
Hepatitis B status G9504
Hexalite® A4590
High osmolar contrast material Q9958-Q9964
High risk area, delivery or service S9381
High risk medication
    Not ordered G9638
    Ordered G9637
Hip
  Core decompression S2325
  Disarticulation prosthesis L5250, L5270
  Orthosis (HO) L1600-L1690
  Total resurfacing, metal on metal S2118
Hip-knee-ankle-foot orthosis (HKAFO) L2040-L2090
History and physical, outpatient, presurgical S0260
Histrelin acetate J1675
Histrelin implant J9225
HIV antigen/antibody screening G0475, S3645
HKAFO (hip-knee-ankle-foot orthosis) L2040-L2090
Holding chamber or spacer S8100, S8101
Home care services S9097, S9098, S9110, S9122-S9131
  Chore S5120-S5121
  Companion care S5135, S5136
  Foster care S5145, S5146
  Homemaker S5130, S5131
  Infusion therapy S9490
  Injection therapy S9537, S9542, S9558, S9559, S9560, S9562
  INR monitoring G0248, G0249, G0250
  Irrigation therapy S9590
  Nurse practitioner S0274
  Other services S5165, S5170, S5175
  Pharmacy S9810
  Respiratory therapy S5180, S5181
  Respite care S5150, S5151, T1005
  RN, LPN visit by RHC/FQHC G0490
  Training S5108-S5116
  Transfusion S9538
Home health agency services T1022
Home therapy and management services S0270-S0272, S0280, S0281, S5522, S5523, S9208-S9379
Home uterine monitor S9001
Hospice and/or home health services
  Aide G0156, T1004
  Assisted-living facility Q5002
  Care coordinator G9477
  Chaplain G9473
  Clinical social worker G0155
  Dietary counselor G9474
  Hospice facility Q5010
  Inpatient hospice facility Q5006
  Inpatient hospital Q5005
  Inpatient psychiatric facility Q5008
  Long term care facility Q5007
  Long-term care facility Q5003
  Not otherwise specified (NOS) Q5009
  Nursing G0128, G0162, G0299, G0300, G0493, G0494, G0495, G0496, T1000, T1002, T1003
  Occupational therapy G0129, G0152, G0158, G0160
  Other counselor G9475
  Patient's home Q5001
  Pharmacist G9479
  Physical therapy G0151, G0157, G0159
  Physician S0270, S0272, S0272, S0273
  Referral G9524, G9525, G9526, S0255
  Services T2042- T2048
  Skilled nursing facility Q5004
  Speech and language G0153, G0161
  Therapist G9478
  Volunteer G9476
Hospital services
  Inpatient admissions G9521, G9522
  Observation/ED visit G0378-G0384
Hospitalist services S0310
Hot water bottle A9273
Hotline service, behavioral health H0030
Human breast milk processing T2101
Human fibrinogen concentrate J7178
Humidifier A7046, E0550-E0562
Hyalgan® J7321
Hyaluronan or derivative J7320, J7322, J7326, J7327, J7328
Hyaluronidase J3470
  Ovine J3471, J3472, J3473
Hydralazine HCl J0360
Hydraulic patient lift E0630
Hydrocollator E0225, E0239
Hydrocolloid dressing A6234-A6241
Hydrocortisone
  Acetate J1700
  Sodium phosphate J1710
  Sodium succinate J1720
Hydrogel dressing A6231, A6232, A6233, A6242-A6248
Hydromorphone J1170
Hydromorphone hydrochloride S0092
Hydroxyprogesterone caproate injection
  Makena® J1726
  NOS J1729
Hydroxyurea, oral S0176
Hydroxyzine HCl J3410
Hydroxyzine pamoate Q0177
Hygienic item, device, any A9286
Hylan G-F 20 J7325
Hyoscyamine sulfate J1980
Hyperbaric oxygen treatment
  Full body chamber G0277
  Topical A4575
Hypertonic saline solution J7131

I

Ibandronate sodium J1740
Ibuprofen J1741
Ibutilide fumarate J1742
Icatibant J1744
Ice cap or collar A9273
Idarubicin HCl J9211
Idursulfase J1743
Ifosfamide J9208
Iloprost Q4074
Imaging
  Angiography G0278
  Cardiac stress G8961-G8966
  Computed tomography (CT) S8092
  Echocardiography C8923-C8930
  Magnetic resonance (MRI) C1770, C8903-C8908, S8042
  Magnetic source S8035
  PET scan G0219, G0235, G0252, S8085
  Ultrasound C1753, C9744, G8806, S8055, S9024
Imatinib S0088
Imiglucerase J1786
Immune globulin
  Bivigam™ J1556
  Cuvitru™ J1555
  Flebogamma® J1572
  Gammagard® liquid J1569

Gammaplex® J1557
Gamunex® J1561
HepaGam® B J1571
Hizentra® J1559
HyQvia® J1575
Intravenous services, supplies and accessories Q2052
Nonlyophilized, not otherwise specified (NOS) J1599
Not otherwise specified (NOS) J1566
Octagam® J1568
Privigen® J1459
Rho(D) J2788, J2790
Rhophylac® J2791
Subcutaneous J1562
With hyaluronidase J1575

Implant
Access system A4301
Aqueous shunt L8612
Auditory brain stem S2235
Autologous cultured chondrocytes J7330
Breast L8600
Buprenorphine J0570
Cochlear L8614, L8619
Collagen
    Meniscus G0428
    Urinary tract L8603
Device for intensive procedure, noc C1889
Dextranomer/hyaluronic acid copolymer L8604
Ganciclovir J7310
Hallux L8642
Infusion pump, programmable E0783, E0786
Joint L8630, L8641, L8658
Lacrimal duct A4262, A4263
Magnetic component, hearing device S2230
Metacarpophalangeal joint L8630
Metatarsal joint L8641
Mometasone furoate sinus S1090
Neurostimulator pulse generator L8679, L8681, L8685,
    L8686, L8687, L8688
    Inner ear A4638, E2120
Not otherwise specified (NOS) L8699
Ocular L8610
Ossicular L8613
Osteogenesis stimulator E0749
Percutaneous access system A4301
Replacement implantable intraspinal catheter E0785
Synthetic, urinary L8606
Urinary tract L8603, L8606
Vascular graft L8670
Implantable radiation dosimeter A4650
Impregnated gauze dressing A6222-A6230
Impression casting, foot S0395
Incobotulinumtoxin A J0588
Incontinence appliances and supplies
Bedside drainage bottle A5102
Catheter insertion tray A4310
Disposable urethral clamp A4360
Extension drainage tubing A4331
Leg strap A5113, A5114
Lubricant A4332
Male external catheter A4349
Pelvic floor electrical stimulator system E0740
Rectal insert A4337
Urinary drainage bag, leg or abdomen A5112
Urinary ostomy A5071, A5072, A5073
Urinary suspensory with leg bag A5105
Incontinence products
Disposable brief/diaper
    Adult

Above extra large T4543
Extra large T4524
Large T4523
Medium T4522
Small T4521
Pediatric T4529, T4530
    Large T4530
    Small/ medium T4529
Youth T4533
Disposable underpad T4541, T4542
    Large T4521
    Small T4542
Protective brief/diaper T4543, T4544
Protective underpad
    Bed T4537
    Chair T4540
Protective underwear
    Adult
        Above extra large T4543
        Extra large T4524
        Large T4523
        Medium T4522
        Small T4521
    Pediatric T4531, T4532
        Large T4532
        Small/ medium T4531
    Youth T4534
Reusable diaper/brief, any size T4539
Indium IN-111 capromab pendetide A9507
Indium IN-111 ibritumomab tiuxetan A9542
Indium IN-111 labeled autologous platelets A9571
Indium IN-111 labeled autologous white blood cells A9570
Indium IN-111 oxyquinoline A9547
Indium IN-111 pentetate A9548
Indium IN-111 pentetreotide A9572
Indium IN-111 satumomab A4642
Induction, medical indication G9361
Infection control supplies S8301
Infectious agent antibody detection
Enzyme immunoassay (EIA) technique G0432
Enzyme-linked immunosorbent assay (ELISA) technique
    G0433
Nucleic acid (DNA or RNA) G0476
Rapid antibody test G0435
Infliximab injection J1745, Q5102
Influenza virus vaccine
Afluria® Q2035
Agriflu® Q2034
FluLaval® Q2036
Fluvirin® Q2037
Fluzone® Q2038
Not otherwise specified (NOS) Q2039
Infusion
Catheter
    Intravenous, OPPS C8957
    Other than hemodialysis C1751
Normal saline solution
    250 cc J7050
    500 mL J7040
    1000 cc J7030
Pump
    Ambulatory E0779-E0786
    External K0552
    Insulin E0784
    Intravenous-pole E0776
    Mechanical, reusable E0779, E0780
    Nonprogrammable, permanent C1891
    Nonprogrammable, temporary C2626

Parenteral E0791
Programmable C1772
Refill kit A4220
Supplies A4221, A4222, A4224, A4225, A4230, A4231, A4232
Uninterrupted parenteral administration of medication K0455
Sipuleucel-T, autologous CD54+cell Q2043
Supplies A4222, A4223, S1015
Therapy
Home
Alpha-1-proteinase inhibitor S9346
Anti-emetic infusion, continuous or intermittent S9351
Anti-hemophilic agent infusion S9345
Anti-spasmodic S9363
Anti-tumor necrosis factor S9359
Antibiotic, antiviral, or antifungal S9494-S9504
Anticoagulant infusion S9336
Catheter care/maintenance S5497, S5498, S5501, S5502
Catheter repair kit S5518
Chelation S9355
Chemotherapy infusion S9329
Continuous (24 hours or more) S9330
Intermittent S9331
Declotting kit S5517
Diuretic S9361
Enzyme replacement intravenous therapy S9357
Hydration therapy S9373, S9374, S9375, S9376, S9377
Immunotherapy S9338
Insulin infusion S9353
Midline catheter insert kit S5521
Pain management infusion S9328
PICC insert kit S5520
Repair of infusion device S5036
Routine device maintenance S5035
Sympathomimetic/inotropic agent infusion S9349
Total parenteral nutrition S9364, S9365, S9366, S9367, S9368
Other than chemotherapeutic drugs Q0081
Inhalation solution, *see* **Appendix A: Table of Drugs**
Inhaler holding chamber or spacer S8100, S8101
Injection, *see also* **Appendix A: Table of Drugs**
Blood Factor J7175-J7209
Sacroiliac joint G0259, G0260
Supplies A4206-A4232
Self-administered A4211
Inotuzumab ozogamicin C9028
INR monitoring G0248, G0249, G0250
Insertion tray
With drainage bag
With indwelling catheter, Foley-type
Three-way, for continuous irrigation A4316
Two-way, all silicone A4315
Two-way, latex with coating A4314
Without catheter A4354
With indwelling catheter, Foley-type
Three-way, for continuous irrigation A4313
Two-way, all silicone A4312
Two-way, latex with coating A4311
Without catheter A4310
Without drainage bag
Insulin
Medication and supplies J1815, J1817, S5550-S5571
Outpatient intravenous treatment (OIVIT) G9147
Pump initiation S9145
Syringes S8490

Integrated keratoprosthesis C1818
Interdisciplinary team conference G0175, G9686, S0221
Interferential current stimulator S8130, S8131
Interferon
Alpha J9212, J9213, J9214, J9215
Beta-1a J1826, Q3027, Q3028
Beta-1b J1830
Gamma J9216
Interim labor facility, global S4005
Intermittent
Assist device with CPAP device E0470, E0471, E0472
Limb compression device A4600, E0676
Peritoneal dialysis system E1592
Positive pressure breathing (IPPB) machine E0500
Interphalangeal joint, prosthetic implant L8658, L8659
Interscapular thoracic prosthesis
Endoskeletal L6570
Upper limb L6350-L6370
Intracardiac echocardiography (catheter) C1759
Intradiscal catheter C1754
Intragastric hypothermia M0100
Intraocular lens
Category 4 Q1004
Category 5 Q1005
New technology C1780
Phakic S0596
Telescopic C1840
Intraoperative
Cystoscopy G9606, G9607, G9608
Neurophysiology monitoring G0453
Intrapulmonary percussive ventilation system E0481
Intraspinal catheter C1755
Intrauterine copper contraceptive J7300
Intravenous admin set, non-PVC, for unstable drugs S1016
Introducer sheaths
Guiding C1766, C1892, C1893
Other than guiding C1894, C2629
Inversion eversion corr device A9285
Iodine I-123 iobenguane A9582
Iodine I-123 ioflupane A9584
Iodine I-123 sodium iodide A9509, A9516
Iodine I-125 serum albumin A9532
Iodine I-125 sodium iodide A9527
Iodine I-125 sodium iothalamate A9554
Iodine I-131 iodinated serum albumin A9524
Iodine I-131 sodium iodide capsule A9517, A9528
Iodine I-131 sodium iodide solution A9529, A9530, A9531
Iodine iobenguane sulfate I-131 A9508
Iodine swabs/wipes A4247
IPD system E1592
Ipilimumab J9228
IPPB machine E0500
Ipratropium bromide, inhalation solution J7644, J7645
Irinotecan J9206
Irinotecan liposome injection J9205
Iron dextran J1750
Iron sucrose J1756
Irrigation solution for bladder calculi Q2004
Irrigation supplies A4320, A4321, A4322, A4355, A4397-A4400
Ostomy
Bag A4398
Cone/catheter, with or without brush A4399
Set A4400
Sleeve A4397
Syringe, bulb or piston A4322
Therapeutic agent for urinary catheter irrigation A4321
Three-way indwelling Foley catheter A4355

Tray with bulb or piston syringe A4320
Tubing set for continuous bladder A4355
Irrigation/evacuation system, bowel
Control unit E0350
Disposable supplies for E0352
Manual pump enema A4459
Isavuconazonium J1833
Isoetharine HCl, inhalation solution
Concentrated J7647, J7648
Unit dose J7649, J7650
Isolates B4150, B4152
Isoproterenol HCl, inhalation solution
Concentrated J7657, J7658
Unit dose J7659, J7660
Isosulfan blue Q9968
Itraconazole J1835
IV pole, each E0776, K0105
Ixabepilone J9207

J

Jacket, scoliosis L1300, L1310
Jenamicin J1580

K

Kanamycin sulfate J1840, J1850
Kartop® patient lift, toilet, or bathroom E0625
Keramatrix® Q4165
Kerecis™ Q4158
Ketorolac tromethamine J1885
Kidney
ESRD supply A4653-A4932
System E1510
Wearable artificial E1632
Kits
Enteral feeding supply
Gravity fed B4036
Pump fed B4035
Syringe fed B4034
Fistula cannulation (set) A4730
Parenteral nutrition B4220-B4224
Surgical dressing (tray) A4550
Tracheostomy A4625
Knee
Disarticulation, prosthesis L5150, L5160
Joint, miniature L5826
Orthosis (KO) E1810, L1810-L1860
Knee-ankle-foot orthosis (KAFO) L2000-L2038, L2126-L2136
Addition, high strength L2755
Replace components L4070-L4110
Kyphosis pad L1020, L1025

L

Laboratory tests
Chemistry P2028-P2038
Cytopathology P3000, P3001, Q0091
Microbiology P7001
Miscellaneous P9010-P9615, Q0111, Q0112, Q0113, Q0114, Q0115
Lacrimal duct implant
Permanent A4263
Temporary A4262
Lactated Ringer's infusion J7120
Laetrile J3570

Lancet spring-powered device
Each A4258
Per box 100 A4259
Lanreotide J1930
Laparoscopic esophagomyotomy S2079
Laronidase J1931
Larynx, artificial L8500
Laser blood collection device and accessory A4257, A4652, E0620
Laser treatment, low level S8948
Laser-assisted uvulopalatoplasty S2080
Lead investigation T1029
Lead wires, per pair A4557
Lead, endocardial single coil C1777
Leg
Bag A4358, A5105, A5112
Extensions for walker E0158
Rest, elevating K0195
Rest, wheelchair E0990
Strap, replacement A5113, A5114
Legg Perthes orthosis L1700-L1755
Lens supplies and services
Aniseikonic V2118, V2318
Contact V2500-V2599
Eye S0504-S0510, S0516-S0590, S0595, V2100-V2615, V2700-V2799
Intraocular V2630, V2631, V2632
Low vision V2600-V2615
Progressive V2781
Lepirudin J1945
Leucovorin calcium J0640
Leukocyte poor blood, each unit P9016
Leuprolide acetate
1 mg J9218
3.75 mg J1950
7.5 mg J9217
65 mg (implant) J9219
Levalbuterol and albuterol, all formulations J7612, J7613, J7614, J7615
Levalbuterol, all formulations, inhalation solution
Compounded product J7607
Noncompounded J7612
Levamisole hydrochloride, oral S0177
Levetiracetam J1953
Levocarnitine J1955
Levofloxacin J1956
Levoleucovorin J0641
Levonorgestrel, implants and supplies J7296, J7297, J7298, J7301, J7306
Levorphanol tartrate J1960
Lexidronam A9604
Lidocaine HCl J2001
Lidocaine/tetracaine patch C9285
Lifestyle modification program, cardiac S0340, S0341, S0342
Lift
Patient (includes seat type) E0621-E0642
Shoe L3300-L3334
Lincomycin HCl J2010
Linezolid J2020
Lipid microspheres Q9950, Q9955, Q9957
Liposomal
Daunorubicin and cytarabine C9024
Liquid barrier, ostomy A4363
Lithium ion
Battery, rechargeable
Auditory Osseointegrated device L8624
Cochlear implant speech processor L8623, L8624

Nonprosthetic use A4601
Prosthetic use L7367
Charger L7368
Lobectomy, living donor S2061
Lodging, recipient, escort nonemergency transport A0180, A0200
Lomustine, oral S0178
Lorazepam J2060
Low osmolar contrast material
100-199 mg/mL Q9965
200-299 mg/mL Q9966
300-399 mg/mL Q9967
Lubricant A4332, A4402
Lumbar-sacral orthosis (LSO) L0621-L0640
Lung
Biopsy plug with delivery system C2613
Cancer screening, low dose CT G0296, G0297
Volume reduction surgery (LVRS)
Postdischarge services G0305
Preoperative services G0302, G0303, G0304
Lymphedema therapy S8431, S8950
Lymphocyte immune globulin J7504, J7511

M

Magnesium sulphate, injection J3475
Magnetic resonance angiography
Abdomen C8901
With contrast C8900
Without contrast followed with contrast C8902
Chest C8910
With contrast C8909
Without contrast followed with contrast C8911
Lower extremity C8913
With contrast C8912
Without contrast followed with contrast C8914
Pelvis C8919
With contrast C8918
Without contrast followed with contrast C8920
Spinal canal and contents C8932
With contrast C8931
Without contrast followed with contrast C8933
Upper extremity C8935
With contrast C8934
Without contrast followed with contrast C8936
Magnetic resonance imaging (MRI), breast
Bilateral C8907
With contrast C8906
Without contrast followed by with contrast C8908
Unilateral C8904
With contrast C8903
Without contrast followed by with contrast C8905
Maintenance contract, ESRD A4890
Mannitol
Inhaler J7665
Injection J2150
MAPCP demonstration project G9151, G9152, G9153
Mask, oxygen A4620
Mastectomy
Bra L8000
Camisole S8460
Form L8020
Prosthesis L8030, L8600
Sleeve L8010
Masters two step S3904
Mattress
Air pressure E0186
Pad E0197
Alternating pressure E0277

Dry pressure E0184
Pad E0199
Gel pressure E0196
Pad E0185
Hospital bed E0271, E0272
Nonpowered, pressure reducing E0373
Overlay E0371, E0372
Powered, pressure reducing E0277
Water pressure E0187
Mecasermin, injection J2170
Mechlorethamine HCl, injection J9230
Medicaid certified community beh hlth clinic srvcs
Per diem T1040
Per month T1041
Medical and surgical supplies A4206-A8004
Medical conference S0220, S0221
Medical food S9433, S9434, S9435, T1999
Medical records copying fee S9981, S9982
Medicare Care Choice Model (MCCM) program admission G9480
Medication, *see also* **Appendix A: Table of Drugs**
Reminder service S5185
Medroxyprogesterone acetate J1050
Megestrol acetate, oral S0179
Melphalan HCl, injection J9245
Melphalan, oral J8600
Menotropins S0122
Meperidine and promethazine HCl, injection J2180
Meperidine hydrochloride J2175
Mepivacaine HCl J0670
Mepolizumab injection J2182
Mercaptopurine, oral S0108
Merit-based Incentive Payment System (MIPS)
AF, transient or reversible cause G9929
Amoxicillin as first-line antibiotic
Not prescribed at the time of diagnosis
Medical reason G9313
Reason not documented G9314
Prescribed at the time of diagnosis G9315
Androgen deprivation therapy
Not prescribed/administered, medical reason G9895
Not prescribed/administered, patient reason G9896
Not prescribed/administered, reason not given G9897
Prescribed/administered G9894
Anesthetic Inhalation G9955
Angiotensin converting enzyme (ACE) or angiotensin receptor blocker (ARB) therapy
Not prescribed
Reason documented G8474, G8936
Reason not documented G8475, G8937
Prescribed G8473, G8506, G8935
Antibiotic therapy
Documented med reason G9712
Not prescribed or dispensed G8708, G8712
Prescribed or dispensed G8709, G8710, G8711
Anticoagulation (warfarin or another oral anticoagulant)
Not prescribed
Medical reason G8968
Patient reason G8969
Prescribed G8967
Anti-epidermal growth factor receptor monoclonal antibodies G9839-G9845
Antimicrobial prophylaxis
Not ordered, medical reasons G9196
Ordered
Documented G9197
Not documented G9198
Antithrombotic/aspirin therapy

Merit-based Incentive Payment System (MIPS)

Medical reason G9384
Patient reason G9385
Reason not documented G9386
Received G9383
Hearing loss
No verification and documentation G8567
Verification and documentation G8565
Hemodialysis (maintenance) G8956
Greater than or equal to 90 days
With catheter G9265
Reason documented G9264
Without catheter G9266
Initiating with catheter G9239
Mode at initiation
With catheter G9240
Without catheter G9241
Hemoglobin (Hgb) level
Greater than or equal to 10 g/dL G8976
Less than 10 g/dL G8973
Medical reason G8975
Not documented G8974
Hepatitis C
Treatment options not discussed G9400
Hepatocellular cancer screening (HCC)
Abdominal imaging G9455
Not performed G9457
Not ordered or performed
Medical or patient reason G9456
High risk medication
Not ordered G9366
At least two different medications G9368
Ordered G9365
At least two different medications G9367
History
Blood transfusion before 1992 G9449
Colectomy or colorectal cancer G9711
Hypercholesterolemia, familial or pure dx G9782
Injection drug use G9450
Pre-op posterior capsule rupture G9759
Home health agency (HHA) specimen collection G0471
Hospice
Services used during measurement pd G9687,
G9688, G9690-G9694, G9700, G9702, G9707,
G9709, G9710, G9713-G9715, G9718, G9720,
G9723, G9725, G9740, G9741, G9758, G9760,
G9761, G9768, G9802, G9805, G9809, G9819,
G9856-G9861
Hospital readmission
No unplanned G9309
Unplanned G9310
Human epidermal growth factor receptor 2 (HER2/neu)
Neg/unknown G9825
Positive G9830
Therapy
Administered G9828
Not administered G9827
HPV (human papillomavirus) vaccine G9806, G9807
Did not receive three G9763
Received three G9762
Hypertension
Active diagnosis G9744
Follow-up documented G8950, G9745
Follow-up not documented
Reason not given G8952
Hysterectomy G9774
Influenza vaccination
Administered G8482
Not administered G8483, G8484

Institutional special needs plans (SNP) G9898, G9901,
G9910, G9938
Intensive care unit (ICU)
Admit G9853
Not admitted G9854
Intervention, anastomosis leak
Not required G9305
Required G9306
Joint replacement G9481-G9489, G9490
Left ventricular ejection fraction (LVEF)
Greater than or equal to 40% G8395
Less than 40% G8451, G8694, G8923, G8934
Not documented or performed G8396
Leg pain
Measured G9947
Not measured G9949
Liver lesion G9547, G9548, G9549, G9550, G9551
Lymph node biopsy
Not performed G8880
Reason not documented G8882
Performed G8878
Major depressive disorder
Clinician to clinician, for comorbid condition
Communication G8959
No communication G8960
Patient reason G9232
DSM-IVTM criteria
Documented G9212
Not documented G9213
Mastectomy G9708
Medical visit
1 medical visit/6 month period
Had visit G9247
No visit G9246
Hospital outpatient clinic visit G0463
Medication list updated or reviewed
Documented G8427
Patient not eligible G8430
Not documented G8428
Melanoma
Cancer stage G8944
No signs or symptoms G8749
Meningococcal vaccine dose G9414, G9415
Mitotic rate
Patient category included G9294, G9428
Patient category not included G9293, G9431
Medical reason G9292, G9429
Mitral Stenosis G9746
Nerve block, peripheral (PNB) G9770
Non-small-cell lung cancer
Classification documented G9283, G9289, G9422
Classification not documented G9284, G9290, G9425
Medical reason G9423
Specimen site, Other than lung G9285
Not non-small-cell lung cancer G9291, G9424
Not primary non-small-cell lung cancer G9420
Oncology G9050-G9139, G9678
Osteoporosis
DXA ordered and documented G8861
Therapy not prescribed G8635
Otology
Patient
Not eligible for referral G8561, G8566, G8857
Not referred G8563, G8568
Referred G8559, G8564
Referral
Not performed G8858
Performed G8856

Pain
  Assessment
    Documented
      Negative G8731
      Positive G8509
        Follow-up G8730
    Not documented G8442
  Level within 48 hours
    Comfortable G9250
    Not comfortable G9251
Palliative dialysis G9747, G9749
Paranasal sinus CT
  At diagnosis
    Not ordered G9350
    Ordered G9348
    Received within 28 days G9349
  Within 90 days of diagnosis
    Not ordered G9354
    Ordered or received G9351
      Reason documented G9353
      Reason not given G9352
Patient care survey, not completed G0914
Patient death G9751, G9812, G9814, G9816, G9846, G9849, G9852, G9855, G9859
  Documented cause
    AAA (abdominal aortic aneurysm) G9262
    CAS (carotid artery stenting) G9256
    CEA (carotid endarterectomy) G9260
Patient decision making
  Documented G9296
  Not documented G9297
Patient discharged alive
  AAA (abdominal aortic aneurysm) G9263
Patient health questionnaire (PHQ) G9393, G9395, G9396
Patient not ambulatory G9719, G9721
Patient referral oth provider/specialist
  Referred G9968
  Referred/report not received G9970
  Referred/report received G9969
Patient refuse to participate G9726, G9728, G9730, G9732, G9734, G9736, G9738
Patient stroke, following
  CAS (carotid artery stenting) G9257
  CEA (carotid endarterectomy) G9258
Patient survival G9787, G9813, G9815, G9817
  In hospital, following
    CAS (carotid artery stenting) G9259
    CEA (carotid endarterectomy) G9261
Patient-specific risk assessment G9316, G9317
Pharmacological therapy
  Not prescribed G8635
  Prescribed G8633
Pneumococcal vaccine
  Administered G8864
  Not administered G8866
    Medical reason G8865
    Reason not given G8867
Pneumocystis jiroveci G9223
Positive airway pressure therapy
  Not prescribed
    Reason given G8849
    Reason not given G8850
  Objective measurement G8851
    Not performed G8855
      Reason given G8854
  Prescribed G8845, G8852
Posterior capsule rupture

No unplanned G9390
  Unplanned G9389
Postpartum
  Evaluation/screening not performed G9358
  Evaluation/screening performed G9357
Pregnancy Dx G9778
Pregnancy, transabdominal/transvaginal ultrasound G8806
Preoperative order for IV antibiotic
  Initiated on time G8916
  Not documented G8918
  Not initiated on time G8917
Primary non-small cell lung cancer
  Classification documented G9418
  Classification not documented G9421
    Medical reason G9419
Prolonged intubation
  Not required G8570
  Required G8569
Prostate cancer recurrence risk G8465, G9706
Prosthetic implant specifications
  Identified G9304
  Not identified G9303
Reexploration, postoperative mediastinal bleeding
  Not required G8578
  Required G8577
Renal failure/dialysis
  Acute kidney no ESRD G0491
  Development postoperatively G8575
  Md/oth eval acut kid no ESRD G0492
  No development postoperatively G8576
Renal transplant documentation G9231
Respiratory disturbance/apnea hypopnea index
  Obstructive sleep apnea, moderate to severe G8846
Retina
  Dilated macular or fundus exam performed G8397
    Not performed G8398
  Postsurgery for retinal detachment G8627, G8628
Return to the operating room
  No return G9307
  Unplanned return G9308
Rh immune globulin (RhoGAM)
  Not ordered
    Reason documented G8810
    Reason not given G8811
  Ordered G8809
Risk factor evaluation (venous thromboembolic and cardiovascular)
  Evaluated G9298
  Not evaluated G9299
Safety concern
  Negative G9923
  No screen, medical reasons G9924
  No screen, reason NOS G9925
  Positive with no recommendations, medical reasons G9924
  Positive with recommendations G9922
  Positive w/o recommendations G9926
Screening
  Negative G9920
  Not performed G9921
  Partial G9921
  Positive no recommendations G9921
  Positive with recommendations G9919
Sexual activity
  Documented G9818
Sexually transmitted disease

Chlamydia screen G9820, G9821
Not screened
Reason not given G9230
Screened
Results documented G9228
Results not documented G9229
Sinusitis
Due to bacterial infection G9364
Skilled nursing facility (SNF) specimen collection G0471
Sleep apnea measures group
Sleep symptoms
Assessed G8839
Not documented G8840
Not assessed G8841
Specimen site, other than
Cutaneous location G9430
Other than PQRS G9295
Esophagus G8797
Prostate G8798
Speech and language G9158-G9186
Spine
Additional procedure(s) same date as lumbar discectomy/laminotomy G9942, G9948
Lumbar
Cancer G9945
Fracture G9945
Infection G9945
Scoliosis G9945
Spirometry
FEV1 >= 60%, FEV1/FVC >= 70%, predicted G8925
FEV1/FVC less than 70%, FEV < 60% predicted G8924
Not performed or documented G8926
Standard nomenclature for imaging study
Named G9318
Not named G9319
Statin not prescribed, medical reasons G9940
Statin therapy G8815, G8816, G8817, G9507, G9508, G9796, G9797
Stroke
Following CABG G8573
Following CAS G9257
Following CEA G9258
No stroke
Following CABG G8574
Following CAS G9259
Following CEA G9261
Surgical site infection G9311, G9312
Systemic antimicrobials
Not prescribed G9959
Prescribed G9961
Prescribed, medical reasons documented G9960
Talimogene laherparepvec J9325
TB, no record, patient reasons G9932
Tetanus, diphtheria, pertussis vaccine (Tdap)
No vaccine G9417
One vaccine G9416
Thromboembolism risk factor
None or one moderate risk factor G8970
Tobacco use G9642, G9643, G9644, G9645, G9791, G9792
Current nonuser G9459
Documented G9275
Current user G9276
Tobacco cessation intervention
Not performed G9460
Received G9458
Tobacco user screen
Not screened, medical reason G9904

Not screened, reason not given G9905
Screen Identified Non-user G9903
Screen Identified User G9902
Total knee replacement
Prophylactic antibiotic completely infused G9301
Not completely infused G9300, G9302
tPA G8600, G8601, G8602
Transfer, non-acute care G9801
Transplant program
Pt approv for live donor kidney G9748, G9750
Treatment choices
DICOM format image data available G9340
Documentation of discussion G9399
No documentation of discussion G9401
Tuberculosis screen negative or managed positive
Documentation G9359
Not documented G9360
Tumor
Category documented G8721
Not included in pathology report
Medical reason G8722
Reason not given G8724
Specimen site
Other than anatomic location G8723
Ultrasound, transabdominal or transvaginal
Not performed, no reason given G8808
Not performed, reason documented G8807
Vaccination
Pneumococcal screening and vaccination performed G9279
Pneumococcal vaccination not administered G9280
Screening performed G9281
Viral load G9242, G9243
Visual function
Achieved G0913
Not achieved G0915
Volume management G8955, G8958
Vomiting
Post-operative G9954
Warfarin or other anticoagulant
Not prescribed, reason documented G9927
Not prescribed, reason not given G9928
Well-child visit
Not received G9965
Received G9964
Wheelchair evaluation G9156
Wound
No sternal infection G8572
Sternal infection G8571
Meropenem, injection J2185
Mesh (implantable) C1781
Mesna, injection J9209
Metacarpophalangeal joint, prosthetic implant L8630, L8631
Metaproterenol sulfate, inhalation solution
Concentrated J7667, J7668
Unit dose J7669, J7670
Metaraminol bitartrate, injection J0380
Metastatic disease G9834, G9838, G9842
Metatarsal joint, prosthetic implant L8641
Meter, bath conductivity, dialysis E1550
Methacholine chloride J7674
Methadone HCl, injection J1230
Methadone, oral S0109
Methocarbamol, injection J2800
Methotrexate sodium J9250, J9260
Methotrexate, oral J8610
Methyldopate HCl, injection J0210
Methylene blue Q9968
Methylergonovine maleate J2210

Methylnaltrexone, injection J2212
Methylprednisolone
    Acetate, injection
        20 mg J1020
        40 mg J1030
        80 mg J1040
    Oral J7509
    Sodium succinate J2920, J2930
Methylprednisolone acetate, injection
Metoclopramide HCl, injection J2765
Metronidazole S0030
Micafungin sodium J2248
Microbiology test P7001
Midazolam HCl J2250
Mifepristone, oral S0190
Mileage, ambulance A0380, A0390
Milrinone lactate J2260
Mini-bus, nonemergency transportation A0120
Minocycline hydrochloride J2265
Minoxidil S0139
Miscellaneous therapeutic items and supplies T1999
Misoprostol, oral S0191
Mitomycin J7315, J9280
Mitoxantrone HCl J9293
Mobility, see also Wheelchairs
    Device, power operated K0800-K0812, K0899
    Functional limitation G8978, G8979, G8980
    Resource-inten svc during office visit G0501
Moderate sedation endo serv >5yrs G0500
Moisture exchanger, mechanical ventilation A4483
Moisturizer, skin A6250
Molecular pathology G0452
Monitor
    Blood glucose E0607
    Blood pressure A4670
    Pacemaker E0610, E0615
Monitoring feature/device A9279
Morcellator C1782
Morphine sulfate J2270, S0093
    Epidural or intrathecal use J2274
Mouthpiece (for respiratory equipment) A4617
Moxifloxacin, injection J2280
MRCP (magnetic resonance cholangiopancreatography)
    S8037
MRS score G9646, G9647, G9648
Mucoprotein, blood P2038
Mucus trap S8210
Multiaxial ankle prothesis L5986
Multidisciplinary services H2000-H2001, T1023-T1028
Multiple post collar, cervical L0180-L0200
Multi Podus® type AFO L4396
Muromonab-CD3 J7505
Mycophenolate mofetil J7517
Mycophenolic acid J7518
Myringotomy, laser-assisted S2225

N

Nabilone J8650
Nafcillin sodium S0032
Nail trimming S0390
    Dystrophic G0127
Nalbuphine HCl, Injection J2300
Naloxone HCl J2310
Naltrexone J2315
Nandrolone decanoate J2320
Narrowing device, wheelchair E0969
Nasal application device A7034

Nasal endoscopy C9745
Nasal endoscopy, postop debridement S2342
Nasal pillows/seals (for nasal application device) A7035
Nasal vaccine inhalation J3530
Nasogastric tubing B4081, B4082
Natalizumab J2323
National committee for quality assurance G9148, G9149,
    G9150
Nebulizer
    Aerosol compressor E0572
    Aerosol mask A7015
    Corrugated tubing, disposable A7010
    Filter, disposable A7013
    Filter, nondisposable A7014
    Glass or autoclavable plastic bottle E0580
    Heater E1372
    Large volume, disposable, prefilled A7008
    Large volume, disposable, unfilled A7007
    Not used with oxygen, durable, glass A7017
    Pneumatic, administration set A7003, A7005, A7006
    Pneumatic, nonfiltered A7004
    Small volume A7003-A7005
    Ultrasonic
        Dome and mouthpiece A7016
        Large volume E0575
        Reservoir bottle, nondisposable A7009
    Ultrasonic/electronic E0574
    Water collection device, large volume nebulizer A7012
    With compressor and/or heater E0570, E0575, E0585
Necitumumab injection J9295
Needle A4215
    Biopsy, prostate, pathology G0416
    Localization, not amenable to imaging G8873
    Noncoring A4212
    With syringe A4206-A4209
Negative pressure wound therapy pump E2402
    Accessories A6550
Nelarabine, injection J9261
Neonatal transport, ambulance, base rate A0225
Neopatch™ Q4176
Neostigmine methylsulfate, injection J2710
Neox® Q4148, Q4156
Nerve stimulator with batteries E0765
Nesiritide injection J2325
Netupitant and palonosetron J8655
Neurological examination, lower extremity G8404, G8405
Neuromuscular
    Stimulation E0764, L8680
    Stimulator E0745
Neurostimulator
    Battery recharging system
        Replacement only L8695
    Generator, nonrechargeable C1767
        With rechargeable battery and charging system C1820,
            C1822
    Lead (implantable) C1778
        Test kit C1897
    Patient programmer C1787
    Pulse generator replacement L8681
    Receiver and/or transmitter C1816, L8682, L8683, L8684
Nitrogen N-13 ammonia, diagnostic A9526
Nivolumab J9299
Nonchemotherapy drug, not otherwise specified (NOS)
    J8499
Noncovered
    Item or services A9270
    Procedure G0293, G0294
Nonemergency transportation A0080-A0210

Nonimpregnated gauze dressing A6216-A6221, A6402-A6404
Nonprescription drug A9150
Not medically necessary service S9986
Not otherwise classified (NOC) drug J3490, J7599, J7699, J7799, J9999, Q0181
NPH insulin J1815
NTIOL (new technology intraocular lens)
    Category 4 Q1004
    Category 5 Q1005
Nursing care, in home T1030, T1031
NuShield® Q4160
Nusinersen injection J2326
Nutrition
    Enteral infusion pump B9002
    Parenteral infusion pump B9004, B9006
    Parenteral solution B4164-B5200
    Therapy G0270, G0271

O

O&P (orthotics and prosthetics) L0112-L9900
    Component L9900
Obizur® J7188
Observation service G0378, G0379
Occipital/mandibular support, cervical L0160
Occlusive device placement G0269
Ocrelizumab injection J2350
Ocriplasmin J7316
Octafluoropropane Q9956
Octagam® J1568
Octreotide acetate J2353, J2354
Ocular
    Device, intraoperative, detached retina C1784
    Implant, aqueous drainage assist device C1783
    Prosthetic implant L8610
Ocularist evaluation S9150
Ofatumumab, injection J9302
Ofloxacin S0034
Olanzapine, injection J2358, S0166
Olaratumab injection J9285
Omacetaxine mepesuccinate J9262
Omalizumab J2357
Omnicardiogram/cardiointegram S9025
Onabotulinumtoxin A J0585
Oncology G9050-G9139
Ondansetron HCI J2405
Ondansetron oral Q0162, S0119
One arm drive attachment, manual wheelchair E0958
Opioid therapy G9561, G9562, G9563, G9577, G9578, G9579, G9583, G9584, G9585
Oprelvekin, injection J2355
Oral device/appliance E0485, E0486
Oral interface A7047
Oral/nasal mask A7027
    Nasal pillows A7029
    Oral cushion A7028
Oritavancin J2407
Oropharyngeal suction catheter A4628
Orphenadrine citrate, injection J2360
Orthopedic shoes
    Arch support L3040-L3090
    Footwear L3201-L3265
    Insert L3000-L3030
    Joint L3956
    Lift L3300-L3334
    Miscellaneous additions L3500-L3595, L3649
    Positioning device L3140-L3170
    Transfer L3600-L3649
    Wedge L3340-L3420
Orthotic additions
    Carbon/graphite lamination L2755
    Fracture
        Lower extremity L2180-L2192
        Upper extremity L3995
    Halo L0859
    Lower extremity L2200-L2999
    Ratchet lock L2430
    Scoliosis L1010-L1120, L1210-L1290
    Shoe L3300-L3595, L3649
    Spinal L0970-L0984
    Upper limb E2631, E2632, E2633, L3995
Orthotic devices, *see also* **Orthopedic shoes**
    Ankle-foot (AFO) E1815, E1816, E1830, L1900-L1990, L2106-L2116, L3160, L4361
    Anterior-posterior-lateral L0700, L0710
    Cervical L0120-L0200
    Cervical-thoracic-lumbar-sacral (CTLSO) L0700, L0710
    Elbow (EO) E1801, L3710-L3762
    Finger L3925, L3927, L3935
    Fracture L2106-L2136, L3917, L3980-L3999
    Halo L0810-L0830
    Hand L3917, L3919
    Hand-finger L3921, L3923, L3924, L3929, L3930
    Hip (HO) L1600-L1690
    Hip-knee-ankle-foot (HKAFO) L2040-L2090
    Interface material, replacement E1820
    Knee (KO) L1810-L1860
    Knee-ankle-foot (KAFO) L2000-L2038, L2126-L2136
    Legg Perthes L1700-L1755
    Multiple post collar, cervical L0180-L0200
    Not otherwise specified (NOS) L0999, L1499, L2999, L3999, L5999, L7499, L8039
    Pneumatic splint L4350-L4370
    Pronation/supination E1818
    Repair or replacement L4000-L4210
    Replacement, soft interface material L4392, L4394
    Scoliosis L1000-L1499
    Shoulder (SO) L3650, L3674
    Shoulder-elbow-wrist-hand (SEWHO) L3960-L3978
    Side bar disconnect L2768
    Spinal, cervical L0120-L0200
    Toe E1830, E1831
    Wrist-hand L3905-L3908, L3915, L3916
    Wrist-hand-finger (WHFO) E1805, E1825, L3807-L3904, L3913
Orthovisc® J7324
Ossicular prosthetic implant L8613
Osteogenesis stimulator E0747-E0749, E0760
Osteotomy, periacetabular S2115
Ostomy
    Absorbent material sheet A4422
    Belt A4396
    Convex insert, accessory A5093
    Incontinence supply, miscellaneous A4335
    Miscellaneous supply A4421
    Pouches A4416-A4419, A4423-A4435
    Skin barrier A4405-A4435
    Supplies A4361-A4435, A5051-A5093
Outpatient PPS hospital services C1713-C9899
    Magnetic resonance angiography/imaging C8901-C8914
    Pelvis C8918-C8920
Oxacillin sodium, injection J2700
Oxaliplatin, injection J9263
Oximeter device A4606, E0445

Oxygen
Ambulance supply A0422
Battery charger E1357
Battery pack/cartridge E1356
Chamber, hyperbaric, topical A4575
Concentrator E1390, E1391, E1392
Contents S8120, S8121
DC power adapter E1358
Liquid oxygen system, portable, rental E0433
Mask A4620
Portable K0738
Rack/stand E1355
Regulator E1352, E1353
Respiratory equipment/supplies A4611-A4627, E0424-E0480
Tent E0455
Tubing, per foot A4616
Water vapor enriching system E1405, E1406
Wheeled cart E1354
Oxymorphone HCl, injection J2410
Oxytetracycline HCl, injection J2460
Oxytocin, injection J2590

P

Pacemaker
Lead
Combination (implantable) C1899
Transvenous VDD C1779
Monitor
Audible and visible check systems E0610
Digital/visible check systems E0615
Non-rate-responsive (implantable)
Dual chamber C2619
Single chamber C2620
Other than single or dual chamber (implantable) C2621
Rate-responsive (implantable)
Dual chamber C1785
Single chamber C1786
Pacemaker monitor E0610, E0615
Paclitaxel protein-bound particles, injection J9264
Paclitaxel, injection J9267
Pad
Cold, water circulating with pump E0218
Gel pressure E0185, E0196
Heat
Electric E0210, E0215
Replacement E0249
Water circulating with pump E0217
Orthotic device interface E1820
Sheepskin E0188, E0189
Pail or pan, for use with commode chair E0167
Palifermin, injection J2425
Paliperidone palmitate, injection J2426
Palonosetron HCl, injection J2469
Pamidronate disodium, injection J2430
Panitumumab, injection J9303
Pantoprazole sodium S0164
Papanicolaou (Pap) screening smear P3000, P3001, Q0091
Papaverine HC, injection J2440
Paraffin bath unit E0235
Paraffin, per pound A4265
Paramedic intercept A0432, S0207, S0208
Parenteral nutrition B4164-B5200
Additives B4216
Administration kit B4224
Infusion pump
Enteral nutrition, any type B9002
Portable B9004
Stationary B9006

Solution B4164-B4199, B5000-B5200
Amino acid
3.5% B4168
5.5% through 7% B4172
7% through 8.5% B4176
Greater than 8.5% B4178
Carbohydrates
50% or less B4164
Greater than 50% B4180
Compounded amino acid and carbohydrates
10 to 51 grams B4189
52 to 73 grams B4193
74 to 100 grams B4197
Hepatic B5100
Renal B5000
Stress B5200
Lipids B4185
Supplies, not otherwise classified (NOC) B9999
Supply kit
Home mix, per day B4222
Premix, per day B4220
Paricalcitol, injection J2501
Parking fee, nonemergency transport A0170
Partial hospitalization services S0201
Pasireotide J2502
Paste, conductive A4558
Pathology and laboratory
Services P2028-P9615
Tests, miscellaneous P9010-P9615
Patient education
Back school S9117
Classes S9436-S9454
Face-to-face for CKD G0420,G0421
Patient support system E0636
Patient survey G0917, G9603, G9604, G9605
Patient transfer system E1035, E1036
PDC G9512, G9513
PEFR (peak expiratory flow rate)
Meter A4614, S8096
Physician services S8110
Pegademase bovine, injection J2504
Pegaptanib, injection J2503
Pegaspargase, injection J9266
Pegfilgrastim, injection J2505
Peginesatide, injection J0890
Pegloticase, injection J2507
Pegylated interferon alfa-2a S0145
Pegylated interferon alfa-2b S0148
Pelvic
Belt/harness/boot E0944
Bone fracture treatment G0412, G0413, G0414, G0415
Pembrolizumab J9271
Pemetrexed, injection J9305
Penicillin G
Benzathine J0561
Benzathine and procaine J0558
Potassium J2540
Procaine, aqueous J2510
Penile prosthesis
Inflatable C1813
Noninflatable C2622
Pentamidine isethionate
Inhalation solution J2545, J7676
Injection S0080
Pentastarch, 10% solution, injection J2513
Pentazocine HCl, injection J3070
Pentobarbital sodium, injection J2515
Pentostatin, injection J9268
Peramivir J2547

Physician Quality Reporting System (PQRS)

PHYSICIAN QUALITY REPORTING SYSTEM (PQRS)

INDEX TO SERVICES, SUPPLIES, EQUIPMENT, DRUGS

Medical reason G8865
Reason not given G8867
Pneumocystis jiroveci G9223
Positive airway pressure therapy
Not prescribed
Reason given G8849
Reason not given G8850
Objective measurement G8851
Not performed G8855
Reason given G8854
Prescribed G8845, G8852
Posterior capsule rupture
No unplanned G9390
Unplanned G9389
Postpartum
Evaluation/screening not performed G9358
Evaluation/screening performed G9357
Pregnancy Dx G9778
Pregnancy, transabdominal/transvaginal ultrasound G8806
Preoperative order for IV antibiotic
Initiated on time G8916
Not documented G8918
Not initiated on time G8917
Primary non-small cell lung cancer
Classification documented G9418
Classification not documented G9421
Medical reason G9419
Prolonged intubation
Not required G8570
Required G8569
Prostate cancer recurrence risk G8465, G9706
Prosthetic implant specifications
Identified G9304
Not identified G9303
Reexploration, postoperative mediastinal bleeding
Not required G8578
Required G8577
Renal failure/dialysis
Acute kidney no ESRD G0491
Development postoperatively G8575
Md/oth eval acut kid no ESRD G0492
No development postoperatively G8576
Renal transplant documentation G9231
Respiratory disturbance/apnea hypopnea index
Obstructive sleep apnea, moderate to severe G8846
Retina
Dilated macular or fundus exam performed G8397
Not performed G8398
Postsurgery for retinal detachment G8627, G8628
Return to the operating room
No return G9307
Unplanned return G9308
Rh immune globulin (RhoGAM)
Not ordered
Reason documented G8810
Reason not given G8811
Ordered G8809
Risk factor evaluation (venous thromboembolic and cardiovascular)
Evaluated G9298
Not evaluated G9299
Safety concern
Negative G9923
No screen, medical reasons G9924
No screen, reason NOS G9925
Positive with no recommendations, medical reasons G9924
Positive with recommendations G9922
Positive w/o recommendations G9926

Screening
Negative G9920
Not performed G9921
Partial G9921
Positive no recommendations G9921
Positive with recommendations G9919
Sexual activity
Documented G9818
Sexually transmitted disease
Chlamydia screen G9820, G9821
Not screened
Reason not given G9230
Screened
Results documented G9228
Results not documented G9229
Sinusitis
Due to bacterial infection G9364
Skilled nursing facility (SNF) specimen collection G0471
Sleep apnea measures group
Sleep symptoms
Assessed G8839
Not documented G8840
Not assessed G8841
Specimen site, other than
Cutaneous location G9430
Other than PQRS G9295
Esophagus G8797
Prostate G8798
Speech and language G9158-G9186
Spine
Additional procedure(s) same date as lumbar discectomy/laminotomy G9942, G9948
Lumbar
Cancer G9945
Fracture G9945
Infection G9945
Scoliosis G9945
Spirometry
FEV1 >= 60%, FEV1/FVC >= 70%, predicted G8925
FEV1/FVC less than 70%, FEV < 60% predicted G8924
Not performed or documented G8926
Standard nomenclature for imaging study
Named G9318
Not named G9319
Statin not prescribed, medical reasons G9940
Statin therapy G8815, G8816, G8817, G9507, G9508, G9796, G9797
Stroke
Following CABG G8573
Following CAS G9257
Following CEA G9258
No stroke
Following CABG G8574
Following CAS G9259
Following CEA G9261
Surgical site infection G9311, G9312
Systemic antimicrobials
Not prescribed G9959
Prescribed G9961
Prescribed, medical reasons documented G9960
Talimogene laherparepvec J9325
TB, no record, patient reasons G9932
Tetanus, diphtheria, pertussis vaccine (Tdap)
No vaccine G9417
One vaccine G9416
Thromboembolism risk factor
None or one moderate risk factor G8970

Preparatory prosthesis L5510-L5595
Prescription, *see also* **Appendix A: Table of Drugs**
    Chemotherapeutic, not otherwise specified (NOS) J8999
    Nonchemotherapeutic, not otherwise specified (NOS) J8499
Pressure
    Alarm, dialysis E1540
    Pad A4640, E0181, E0196-E0199
        Pump E0182
Preventive services, prolonged G0513, G0514
Privigen® J1459
Procainamide HCl J2690
Procarbazine hydrochloride, oral S0182
Prochlorperazine J0780
Prochlorperazine maleate Q0164
    Non-Medicare S0183
Procuren® or similar product S9055
Progestasert® IUD S4989
Progesterone, injection J2675
Prolonged preventive services G0513, G0514
Prolotherapy M0076
Promazine HCl J2950
Promethazine and meperidine J2180
Promethazine HCl
    Injection J2550
    Oral Q0169
Propofol J2704
Propranolol HCl J1800
Prosthesis
    Artificial larynx battery/accessory L8505
    Breast L8000-L8035, L8600
    Donning sleeve L7600
    Eye L8610, V2623-V2629
    Fitting L5400-L5460, L6380-L6388
    Foot/ankle one piece system L5979
    Hand L6000-L6020
        Electric L7007, L7008
    Hook, electric L7009, L7045
    Implants L8600-L8690
    Larynx L8500
    Lower extremity L5700-L5999, L8641, L8642
    Maxillofacial, provided by a nonphysician L8040-L8048
    Miscellaneous service L8499
    Repair L7510, L7520, L8049
    Socks (shrinker, sheath, stump sock) L8400-L8485
    Tracheo-esophageal L8507, L8509
    Upper extremity L6000-L6055
    Vacuum erection system L7900
Prosthetic additions
    Lower extremity L5610-L5999
    Upper extremity L6600-L7405
Prosthetic socket insert, gasket or seal L7700
Protamine sulfate J2720
Protectant, skin A6250
Protector, heel or elbow E0191
Protein C concentrate J2724
Protirelin J2725
Psoriasis G9649, G9651, G9764
Psychiatric collaborative care model, RHC/FQHC G0512
Psychotherapy, group G0410, G0411
Pulmonary nodule, incidental G9754
Pulmonary rehabilitation G0424, S9473
Pulse generator system, inner ear A4638, E2120
Pump
    Alternating pressure pad E0182
    Ambulatory infusion E0779, E0781
    Ambulatory insulin E0784
        Supplies A4230, A4232

    Blood, dialysis E1620
    Breast E0602-E0604
    Enteral infusion B9002
    Heparin infusion E1520
    Implantable infusion E0782, E0783
        Refill kit A4220
    Negative pressure wound therapy E2402
    Parenteral infusion B9004, B9006
    Suction, respiratory E0600
    Water circulating pad E0236
Purification system, water E1610, E1615
Pyridoxine HCl J3415

Q

Quad cane E0105
Quality of life assessment G9634, G9635, G9636
Quinupristin/dalfopristin J2770

R

Rack/stand, oxygen E1355
Radiation
    Exposure G9500, G9501
    Intesity modulated G6015
    Intra-fraction localization and tracking G6017
    Treatment delivery
        1 area G6003, G6004, G6005, G6006
        2 areas G6007, G6008, G6009, G6010
        3 or more areas G6011, G6012, G6013, G6014
Radiesse® Q2026
Radioelements for brachytherapy Q3001
Radiology, portable equipment transport R0070-R0076
Radiopharmaceuticals A4642, A9500-A9606
    Not otherwise classified A4641, A9698
Rail
    Bathtub E0241, E0242, E0246
    Bed side, full length E0310
    Bed side, half length E0305
    Toilet E0243
Ramucirumab J9308
Ranibizumab J2778
Ranitidine hydrochloride J2780
Rasburicase J2783
Ras Testing G9843
    Not performed G9841
    Performed G9840
Reaching/grabbing device A9281
Reagent strip
    Blood glucose A4253
    Blood ketone A4252
    Urine A4250
Reciprocating peritoneal dialysis system E1630
Recorder, event, cardiac C1764
Red blood cells P9021, P9022
Red congo, blood P2029
Regadenoson J2785
Regular insulin J1815
Regulator, oxygen E1353
Rehabilitation
    Cardiac G0422, G0423, S9472
    Program H2001
    Psychosocial rehabilitation services H2017, H2018
    Pulmonary G0424, S9473
    Vestibular S9476
Remission G9509, G9510

Repair
   Contract, ESRD A4890
   Device, urinary A4890
      With sling graft C1771
   DME (durable medical equipment)
      Other than oxygen equipment K0739
      Oxygen equipment K0740
   Fetal
      In utero procedures S2400, S2401, S2402, S2403, S2404, S2409
      Sacrococcygeal teratoma S2405
   Maxillofacial prosthesis
      Labor component L8049
Replacement
   Battery A4630
   Orthotic components L4000-L4130
   Pad (alternating pressure) A4640
   Temporary K0462
   Tip for cane, crutches, walker A4637
   Underarm pad for crutches A4635
Reproductive medicine services S4011-S4042
Reslizumab injection J2786
Respiratory procedures, therapeutic G0237, G0238, G0239
Restraint, any type E0710
Resuscitation bag S8999
Reteplase J2993
Retinal
   Diabetic indicator eye exam S3000
   Prosthesis C1841
   Tamponade device C1814
Retrieval device, insertable C1773
Return to the operating room G9514, G9515, G9516, G9517
Revita® Q4180
Rhabdomyolysis dx G9780
Rho(D) immune globulin, human J2788, J2790, J2791, J2792
Rib belt, thoracic L0220
Rilonacept J2793
RimabotulinumtoxinB J0587
Ring, ostomy A4404
Ringers lactate infusion J7120
Risperidone J2794
Rituximab J9310
Robin-Aids® hand L6000, L6010, L6020, L6708, L6709
Robotic surgical system techniques S2900
Rocking bed E0462
Rolapitant oral J8670
Rollabout chair E1031
Romidepsin J9315
Romiplostim J2796
Ropivacaine HCl J2795
Routine foot care S0390
   Diabetic patient G0247
   Exam G9502
Rubidium-82 (Rb-82) A9555
Rural Health Clinic or Federally Qualified Health Center (RHC/FQHC) only G0511, G0512

S

Sacral nerve stimulation test lead A4290
Safety equipment E0700
   Vest, wheelchair E0980
Sales tax S9999
Saline solution A4216, J7030-J7050
   Metered dose dispenser A4218
Saliva
   Artificial A9155
   Test, hormone level S3650, S3652

Samarium SM 153 lexidronam A9604
Saquinavir S0140
Sargramostim (GM-CSF) J2820
School-based education program T1018
Scintimammography S8080
Scoliosis, orthoses and procedures L1000-L1499
   Additions L1010-L1290
Score
   MRS G9646, G9647, G9648
   PHQ-9 score G9509, G9510, G9511, G9573, G9574
Screening
   Alcohol misuse G0442
   Cancer
      Abdominopelvic G0101-G0105
      Cervical or vaginal G0101
      Colorectal
         Barium enema G0106, G0120, G0122
         Colonoscopy G0105, G0121
         Fecal occult blood test G0328
         Flexible sigmoidoscopy G0104
         Proctoscopy S0601
      Lung, computed tomography G0296, G0297
      Prostate, rectal, digital exam G0102
         PSA (prostate specific antigen) test G0103
      Uterine G9618, G9620
   Cytopathology, cervical/vaginal G0123, G0124, G0141, G0143, G0144, G0145, G0147, G0148
   Depression G0444
   Dysphagia V5364
   Glaucoma G0117, G0118
   Hearing V5008
   HIV G0475
   Language V5363
   Lung cancer G0296, G0297
   Newborn metabolic panel S3620
   Papanicolaou smear Q0091
      Performed under physician supervision P3000
      Requiring interpretation by physician P3001
   Preadmission
      Level I T2010
      Level II T2011
   Speech V5362
   Tobacco user
      Identified Non-user G9903
      Identified User G9902
      Not screened, medical reason G9904
      Not screened, reason not given G9905
Sculptra® Q2028
Sealant, skin A6250
Seat
   Attachment, walker E0156
   Insert, wheelchair E0992
   Lift E0621, E0627-E0629
   Upholstery E0981, E1297
Sebelipase alfa injection J2840
Secretin J2850
Semen analysis G0027
Sensitivity study, urinary tract infection P7001
Sensory nerve conduction test (SNCT) G0255
Septal defect implant system, intracardiac C1817
Sermorelin acetate Q0515
Serum clotting time tube A4771
Services provided outside the USA S9989
SEWHO (shoulder, elbow, wrist, hand orthosis) L3960-L3967
SEXA (bone density study) G0130
Sheepskin pad E0188, E0189
Shoes
   Arch support

Nonremovable
    Longitudinal L3070
    Longitudinal/metatarsal L3090
    Metatarsal L3080
Removable
    Longitudinal L3040
    Longitudinal/metatarsal L3060
    Metatarsal L3050
Diabetic
    Deluxe feature A5508
    Fitting A5500, A5501
    Modification A5503, A5504, A5505, A5506
    Not otherwise specified (NOS) modification A5507
Insert, removable
    Formed to patient foot L3030
    Longitudinal arch support, each L3010
    Longitudinal/metatarsal support, each L3020
    Plastazote or equal, each L3002
    Silicone gel, each L3003
    Spenco®, each L3001
    UCB type, Berkeley shell, each L3000
Lift L3300-L3334
Orthopedic L3201-L3265
    Additions
        Shoes L3500-L3595
    High-top
        Child L3206
        Infant L3204
        Junior L3207
    Oxford
        Child L3202
        Infant L3201
        Junior L3203
Positioning device L3140, L3150, L3160, L3170
Transfer, orthosis L3600-L3649
Shoulder
    Disarticulation, prosthetic L6300-L6320, L6550
    Orthosis (SO) L3650-L3674, L3677, L3678
    Spinal, cervical L0120-L0200
Shoulder sling A4566
Shoulder-elbow-wrist-hand orthosis (SEWHO) L3960-L3967
Shunt
    Accessory for dialysis A4740
    Aqueous, for glaucoma L8612
Sigmoidoscopy, cancer screening G0104, G0106
Sign language/oral interpretive services T1013
Sildenafil citrate S0090
Siltuximab J2860
Sincalide J2805
Sipuleucel-T Q2043
Sirolimus J7520
Sitz bath
    Chair E0162
    With or without commode E0160
        With faucet attachment E0161
Skills training and development H2014
Skin
    Barrier, ostomy A4362, A4363, A4369-A4373, A4385, A5120
        Adhesive, liquid or equal A4364
    Sealant, protectant, moisturizer A6250
    Substitutes and biologics J3590, Q4100-Q4165
Sleep study test, home (HST) G0398, G0399, G0400
Sling A4565
    Patient lift E0621, E0630, E0635
Smoking cessation services and supplies
    Counseling G9016
    Supplies S4990, S4991, S4995
Social work and psychological services G0409

Sock
    Body L0984
    Prosthetic
        Above knee L8430
        Below knee L8420
        Upper limb L8435
    Stump
        Above knee L8480
        Below knee L8470
        Upper limb L8485
Sodium
    Ferric gluconate complex in sucrose J2916
    Fluoride F-18 A9580
    Hyaluronan J7325
        Synvisc®, Synvisc One® J7325
    Hyaluronate
        Euflexxa® J7323
        Hyalgan® J7321
        Orthovisc® J7324
        Supartz® J7321
        VISCO-3™ J7321
    Phosphate P32 A9563
    Succinate J1720
Solution
    Calibrator A4256
    Dialysate, test kit A4760
    Elliotts B J9175
    Enteral formulae B4149-B4155
    Parenteral nutrition B4164-B5200
Somatrem J2940
Somatropin J2941
Sorbent cartridge, ESRD E1636
Sotalol hydrochloride IV C9482
Specialty absorptive dressing A6251-A6256
Spectinomycin HCl J3320
Speech assessment V5362, V5363, V5364
Speech generating device
    Accessory
        Mounting system E2512
        Not otherwise classified E2599
    Digitized speech, pre-recorded messages
        Less than or equal to 8 minutes E2500
        More than 8 minutes, less than or equal to 20 minutes E2502
        More than 20 minutes but less than or equal to 40 minutes E2504
        More than 40 minutes E2506
    Synthesized speech
        Message formulation by spelling E2508
        Multiple methods of message formulation E2510
Speech generating software program E2511
Speech therapy
    In home S9128
    Re-evaluation S9152
Sperm procurement and cryopreservation S4030, S4031
Spinal orthosis
    Cervical L0120-L0200
        Multiple post collar L0180-L0200
    Cervical-thoracic-lumbar-sacral (CTLSO) L0700, L0710
    Halo L0810-L0830
    Scoliosis L1000-L1499
Spirometer, electronic E0487
Splint A4570
    Dynamic adjustable extension/flexion device
        Ankle E1815
        Elbow/forearm E1800, E1802
        Finger E1825
        Knee E1810, E1812

Pentetate A9539, A9567
Pertechnetate A9512
Pyrophosphate A9538
Sestamibi A9500
Sodium gluceptate A9550
Succimer A9551
Sulfur colloid A9541
Teboroxime A9501
Tetrofosmin A9502
Tilmanocept A9520
Tedizolid phosphate J3090
Telavancin J3095
Telehealth services
Consultation G0425, G0426, G0427, G0508, G0509
Inpatient pharmacologic management G0459
Originating site fee Q3014
Transmission T1014
Temozolomide
Injection J9328
Oral J8700
Temsirolimus J9330
Tenecteplase J3101
Teniposide Q2017
TENS (transcutaneous electric nerve stimulation) A4595, E0720-E0749
Tension ring, vacuum erection device L7902
Tent, oxygen E0455
Terbutaline sulfate
Inhalation solution, concentrated J7680
Inhalation solution, unit dose J7681
Injection J3105
Teriparatide J3110
Terminal devices
Hook or hand, heavy duty L6721, L6722
Hook, mechanical, voluntary closing L6707, L6709
Pediatric L6712, L6714
Hook, mechanical, voluntary opening L6706, L6708
Pediatric L6711, L6713
Multiple articulating digit L6715
Passive hand/mitt L6703
Sport/recreational/work attachment L6704
Testosterone
Cypionate and estradiol cypionate J1071
Enanthate J3121
Pellet S0189
Undecanoate J3145
Tetanus immune globulin, human J1670
Tetracycline J0120
Thallous chloride TI-201 A9505
Theophylline J2810
Therapeutic lightbox A4634, E0203
TheraSkin® Q4121
Thermometer A4931, A4932
Thiamine HCl J3411
Thickener, food B4100
Thiethylperazine maleate J3280, Q0174
Thiotepa J9340
Thoracic rib belt L0220
Thoracic-lumbar-sacral orthosis (TLSO) L1200
Additions L1210-L1290
Spinal L0450, L0452-L0492
Thrombectomy catheter C1757
Thymol turbidity, blood P2033
Thyroid nodule G9552, G9553, G9554, G9555, G9556, G9557
Thyrotropin alfa J3240
Ticarcillin disodium and clavulanate potassium S0040
Tigecycline J3243
Tinzaparin sodium J1655
Tip (cane/crutch/walker) replacement A4637

Tire, wheelchair, pneumatic E2381-E2385
Tirofiban J3246
Tisagenlecleucel, infusion Q2040
Tissue marker A4648
Tissue, connective
Human C1762
Nonhuman C1763
TLSO (thoracic-lumbar-sacral orthosis) L0452-L0492, L1200-L1290
Tobacco cessation intervention
Identified user G9906
Identified user, not provided, medical reason G9909
Not provided, medical reason G9907
Not provided, reason not given G9908
Tobramycin sulfate J3260
Tobramycin, inhalation solution, unit dose J7682, J7685
Tocilizumab J3262
Toilet and accessories
Commode chair
Electric E0170
Extra wide E0168
Nonelectric E0171
With integrated lift E0170-E0171
Foot rest E0175
Pan/pail E0167
Patient lift E0625
Rail E0243
Raised seat E0244
Seat lift E0172
Tolazoline HCl J2670
Toll, nonemergency transport A0170
Tomosynthesis, breast G0279
Topical hyperbaric oxygen chamber A4575
Topographic brain mapping S8040
Topotecan
Injection J9351
Oral J8705
Torsemide J3265
Trabectedin injection J9352
Tracheostoma heat moisture exchange system A7501-A7509
Tracheostomy
Care kit A4629
Filter A4481
Speaking valve L8501
Supplies A4623, A4629, A7523, A7524, A7527, S8189
Tube A7520-A7522
Tracheotomy mask or collar A7525, A7526
Traction device, ambulatory E0830
Traction equipment E0840-E0948
Training
Alcohol and/or drug training service H0021
Medication training and support H0034
Skills training and development H2014
Transcatheter occlusion or embolization S2095
Transcutaneous electrical nerve stimulator (TENS)
Conductive garment E0731
Electrical stimulator supplies A4595
Four-lead or more E0730
Two-lead E0720
Transcyte Q4182
Transducer protector, dialysis E1575
Transesophageal
Doppler measurement G9157
Echocardiography
For congenital cardiac anomalies C8926
For monitoring purposes C8927
Real time with 2D image documentation C8925
Pacing (catheter) C1756

Transfer (shoe orthosis) L3600-L3640
Transfer system with seat E1035
Transluminal angioplasty
    Laser catheter C1885
    Nonlaser catheter C1725, C2623
Transluminal, atherectomy
    Directional catheter C1714
    Rotational catheter C1724
Transparent film (for dressing) A6257-A6259
Transperineal implantation balloon continence device
  C9746
Transplant
    Bone marrow S2150
    Islet cell S2102
        Laparoscopy G0342
        Laparotomy G0343
        Percutaneous G0341
    Kidney and pancreas, simultaneous S2065
    Lobar lung S2060
    Multiple visceral organs S2054
    Related lodging, meals, transportation S9975, S9976
    Stem cells, cord blood derived S2142
Transportation
    Ambulance A0021-A0999
    Conventional air A0430, A0431
    Corneal tissue V2785
    EKG equipment, portable R0076
    Neonatal, emergency ambulance service A0225
    Nonemergency A0080-A0210, T2001-T2005
        Air A0140, T2007
        Ancillary
            Lodging A0180, A0200
            Meals A0190, A0210, S9977
            Out-of-state ambulance transport A0021
            Parking fees/tolls A0170
        Bus A0110
        Case worker or social worker A0160
        Mini-bus A0120
        Stretcher van T2005, T2049
        Taxi A0100
        Vehicle provided by
            Individual A0090
            Volunteer A0080
        Wheelchair van A0130, S0209
        X-ray equipment, portable R0070, R0075
Transtracheal oxygen catheter A4608
Trapeze bar E0910, E0911, E0912, E0940
Trauma response team G0390
Tray
    Insertion A4310-A4316
    Irrigation A4320
    Surgical A4550
    Wheelchair E0950
Treatment, acute care at NF G9679-G9684, G9685
Treatment planning and care coordination S0353, S0354
Treprostinil J3285
Tretinoin, topical S0117
Triamcinolone J3301-J3303
    Acetonide
        Not otherwise specified (NOS) J3301
        Preservative free J3300
    Diacetate J3302
    Hexacetonide J3303
    Inhalation solution
        Concentrated J7683
        Unit dose J7684
Triflupromazine HCl J3400
Trifocal, glass or plastic V2300-V2399

Trimethobenzamide HCl
    Injection J3250
    Oral Q0173
Trimetrexate glucuronate J3305
Trimming, routine foot care
    Corns/calluses/nails S0390
Triptorelin extended release C9016
Triptorelin pamoate J3315
Truss L8300, L8310, L8320, L8330
Tube/Tubing
    Anchoring device A5200
    Blood A4750, A4755
    Drainage extension A4331
    Gastrostomy/Jejunostomy B4087, B4088
    Irrigation A4355
    Nasogastric B4081, B4082
    Oxygen A4616
    Serum clotting time A4771
    Stomach B4083
    Suction pump, each A7002
    Urinary drainage A4331

U

Ultrafiltration monitor S9007
Ultrasonic nebulizer E0575
Ultrasound
    Abdominal w contrast C9744
    Catheter, intravascular C1753
    Gel A4559
    Guidance for placement of radiation therapy fields G6001
    Intravascular C1753
Ultraviolet light therapy system A4633, E0691-E0694
Unclassified drug J3490
Unipuncture control system, dialysis E1580
Unspecified oral dosage form Q0181
Upper extremity addition, locking elbow L6693
Upper extremity orthosis L3980-L3999
    Addition of joint L3956
Upper limb prosthesis L6000-L7499
Urea J3350
Ureteral
    Catheter C1758
    Injury G9631, G9632, G9633
Ureterostomy supplies A4450-A4554
Urethral suppository J0275
Urgent care center
    Global fee S9083
    Services S9088
Urinal
    Jug-type, female E0326
    Jug-type, male E0325
Urinary
    Catheter A4338-A4346, A4351-A4353
    Collection and retention (supplies) A4310-A4360
    Repair device without sling graft C2631
    Sphincter prosthesis C1815
    Tract implant
        Collagen L8603
        Synthetic L8606
Urine
    Sensitivity study P7001
    Tests A4250
Urofollitropin J3355
Urokinase J3364, J3365
Ustekinumab J3357, J3358
UV lens V2755

Wood
- Canes, all materials E0100
- Crutches
    - Other than wood E0114, E0116
    - Wood E0112, E0113

Wound
- Cleanser A6260
- Cover
    - Alginate dressing A6196-A6198
    - Collagen dressing A6021-A6024
    - Foam dressing A6209-A6214
        - Hydrocolloid dressing A6234-A6239
    - Hydrogel dressing A6242-A6247
    - Specialty absorptive dressing A6251-A6256
    - Wound warming device, noncontact E0231, E0232
- Dressing K0744, K0745, K0746, L3254, L3255
- Filler
    - Adhesive tissue G0168
    - Alginate dressing A6199
    - Collagen based A6010
    - Foam dressing per gram A6215
    - Hydrocolloid dressing A6240, A6241
    - Hydrogel dressing A6248
    - Not elsewhere classified (NEC) A6261, A6262
- Pouch A6154
- Suction pump K0743
- Treatment
    - Autologous platelet rich plasma G0460
    - Biologicals and skin substitutes Q4100-Q4165, S9055
    - Compression burn mask A6513
    - Electric or electromagnetic stimulation E0769, G0295, G0329
    - Gel sheet A6025
    - Packing strips A6407

WoundEx® Q4162, Q4163

Wrap, chest E0459

Wrist
- Disarticulation prosthesis L6050, L6055
- Electronic wrist rotator L7259
- Hand/finger orthosis (WHFO) E1805, E1825, L3808, L3809, L3900, L3901, L3904

Xenon (Xe) 133 A9558
X-ray equipment, portable Q0092, R0070, R0075

Yttrium-90 (Y-90) ibritumomab A9543

Z

Ziconotide J2278
Zidovudine J3485, S0104
Ziprasidone mesylate J3486
Zoledronic acid J3489

NOTES

> CMS includes parenthetical coding guidelines for several codes throughout the Tabular List, which are effective for 2018. Some of these guidelines include deleted CPT® or HCPCS codes, even though the guidelines were from the latest updates from CMS for 2018. Please check the CMS website for further updates or guideline changes.
>
> Generic and brand-name drugs have been validated prior to the date this book went to press. Please check the FDA website for the latest drug updates, including any drugs that have been discontinued.

TRANSPORTATION SERVICES INCLUDING AMBULANCE (A0021- A0999)

HCPCS Level II codes for ambulance services (A0021-A0999) must be reported with modifiers indicating pick-up origins and destinations. The modifier describing the arrangement (QM, QN) is listed first. The modifiers describing the origin and destination are listed second. Origin and destination modifiers are created by combining two alpha characters from the following list. Each alpha character, with the exception of X, represents either an origin or destination. Each pair of the alpha characters creates one modifier. The first position represents the origin and the second the destination. The modifiers most commonly used are:

D   Diagnostic or therapeutic site other than P or H when these are used as origin codes

E   Residential, domiciliary, custodial facility (other than 1819 facility)

G   Hospital-based dialysis facility

H   Hospital

I   Site of transfer (e.g., airport or helicopter pad) between modes of ambulance transport

J   Free standing ESRD facility

N   Skilled nursing facility (SNF)

P   Physician's office

R   Residence

S   Scene of accident or acute event

X   Intermediate stop at physician's office on way to hospital (destination code only)

AMBULANCE AND OTHER TRANSPORT SERVICES AND SUPPLIES (A0021-A0999)

A0021 Ambulance service, outside state per mile, transport (Medicaid only)   E1
BETOS: O1A   Ambulance
Service not separately priced by Part B

A0080 Non-emergency transportation, per mile - vehicle provided by volunteer (individual or organization), with no vested interest   E1
BETOS: O1A   Ambulance
Service not separately priced by Part B

A0090 Non-emergency transportation, per mile - vehicle provided by individual (family member, self, neighbor) with vested interest   E1
BETOS: O1A   Ambulance
Service not separately priced by Part B

A0100 Non-emergency transportation; taxi   E1
BETOS: O1A   Ambulance
Service not separately priced by Part B

A0110 Non-emergency transportation and bus, intra- or inter-state carrier   E1
BETOS: O1A   Ambulance
Service not separately priced by Part B

A0120 Non-emergency transportation: mini-bus, mountain area transports, or other transportation systems   E1
BETOS: O1A   Ambulance
Service not separately priced by Part B

A0130 Non-emergency transportation: wheelchair van   E1
BETOS: O1A   Ambulance
Service not separately priced by Part B

A0140 Non-emergency transportation and air travel (private or commercial) intra- or inter-state   E1
BETOS: O1A   Ambulance
Service not separately priced by Part B

A0160 Non-emergency transportation: per mile - case worker or social worker   E1
BETOS: O1A   Ambulance
Service not separately priced by Part B

A0170 Transportation ancillary: parking fees, tolls, other   E1
BETOS: O1A   Ambulance
Service not separately priced by Part B

A0180 Non-emergency transportation: ancillary: lodging-recipient   E1
BETOS: O1A   Ambulance
Service not separately priced by Part B

A0190 Non-emergency transportation: ancillary: meals-recipient   E1
BETOS: O1A   Ambulance
Service not separately priced by Part B

A0200 Non-emergency transportation: ancillary: lodging escort   E1
BETOS: O1A   Ambulance
Service not separately priced by Part B

A0210 Non-emergency transportation: ancillary: meals-escort   E1
BETOS: O1A   Ambulance
Service not separately priced by Part B

A0225 Ambulance service, neonatal transport, base rate, emergency transport, one-way   E1
BETOS: O1A   Ambulance
Service not separately priced by Part B
Pub: 100-4, Chap. 1, 10.1.4.1

A0380 BLS mileage (per mile)   E1
BETOS: O1A   Ambulance

Service not separately priced by Part B
Pub: 100-4, Chap. 1, 10.1.4.1; 100-4, Chap. 15, 20.2; 100-4, Chap. 15, 30.2

I A0382 BLS routine disposable supplies   E1
BETOS: O1A   Ambulance
Service not separately priced by Part B
Pub: 100-2, Chap. 10, 30.1.1

I A0384 BLS specialized service disposable supplies; defibrillation (used by ALS ambulances and BLS ambulances in jurisdictions where defibrillation is permitted in BLS ambulances)   E1
BETOS: O1A   Ambulance
Service not separately priced by Part B

I A0390 ALS mileage (per mile)   E1
BETOS: O1A   Ambulance
Service not separately priced by Part B
Pub: 100-4, Chap. 15, 20.2; 100-4, Chap. 15, 30.2

I A0392 ALS specialized service disposable supplies; defibrillation (to be used only in jurisdictions where defibrillation cannot be performed in BLS ambulances)   E1
BETOS: O1A   Ambulance
Service not separately priced by Part B
Pub: 100-2, Chap. 10, 30.1.1

I A0394 ALS specialized service disposable supplies; IV drug therapy   E1
BETOS: O1A   Ambulance
Service not separately priced by Part B

I A0396 ALS specialized service disposable supplies; esophageal intubation   E1
BETOS: O1A   Ambulance
Service not separately priced by Part B

I A0398 ALS routine disposable supplies   E1
BETOS: O1A   Ambulance
Service not separately priced by Part B

Waiting Time Units for Ambulance Services	
Units	Total Time
1	1/2 to 1 hour
2	1 to 1-1/2 hours
3	1-1/2 to 2 hours
4	2 to 2-1/2 hours
5	2-1/2 to 3 hours
6	3 to 3-1/2 hours
7	3-1/2 to 4 hours
8	4 to 4-1/2 hours
9	4-1/2 to 5 hours
10	5 to 5-1/2 hours

I A0420 Ambulance waiting time (ALS or BLS), one half (1/2) hour increments   E1
BETOS: O1A   Ambulance
Service not separately priced by Part B

I A0422 Ambulance (ALS or BLS) oxygen and oxygen supplies, life sustaining situation   E1
BETOS: O1A   Ambulance
Service not separately priced by Part B

I A0424 Extra ambulance attendant, ground (ALS or BLS) or air (fixed or rotary winged); (requires medical review)   E1
BETOS: O1A   Ambulance
Service not separately priced by Part B
Pub: 100-4, Chap. 15, 30.2.1

C A0425 Ground mileage, per statute mile   A
BETOS: O1A   Ambulance
Reasonable charge
Coding Clinic: 2012, Q4

C A0426 Ambulance service, advanced life support, non-emergency transport, level 1 (ALS 1)   A
BETOS: O1A   Ambulance
Reasonable charge
Coding Clinic: 2012, Q4
Pub: 100-2, Chap. 10, 20; 100-4, Chap. 1, 10.1.4.1; 100-4, Chap. 15, 30.2; 100-4, Chap. 15, 30.2.1

C A0427 Ambulance service, advanced life support, emergency transport, level 1 (ALS 1-emergency)   A
BETOS: O1A   Ambulance
Reasonable charge
Coding Clinic: 2012, Q4
Pub: 100-2, Chap. 10, 20; 100-4, Chap. 1, 10.1.4.1; 100-4, Chap. 15, 30.2.1

C A0428 Ambulance service, basic life support, non-emergency transport, (BLS)   A
BETOS: O1A   Ambulance
Reasonable charge
Coding Clinic: 2012, Q4
Pub: 100-2, Chap. 10, 20; 100-4, Chap. 1, 10.1.4.1; 100-4, Chap. 15, 20.6; 100-4, Chap. 15, 30.2.1

C A0429 Ambulance service, basic life support, emergency transport (BLS-emergency)   A
BETOS: O1A   Ambulance
Reasonable charge
Coding Clinic: 2012, Q4
Pub: 100-2, Chap. 10, 20; 100-4, Chap. 1, 10.1.4.1; 100-4, Chap. 15, 30.2.1

C A0430 Ambulance service, conventional air services, transport, one-way (fixed wing)   A
BETOS: O1A   Ambulance
Reasonable charge
Coding Clinic: 2012, Q4
Pub: 100-2, Chap. 10, 20; 100-4, Chap. 1, 10.1.4.1; 100-4, Chap. 15, 20.3; 100-4, Chap. 15, 30.2.1

▲ Revised code   ● New code   **C** Carrier judgment   **D** Special coverage instructions apply
I Not payable by Medicare   **M** Non-covered by Medicare   **S** Non-covered by Medicare statute   AHA Coding Clinic®

C **A0431** Ambulance service, conventional air
services, transport, one-way (rotary wing)   A
BETOS: O1A   Ambulance
Reasonable charge
Coding Clinic: 2012, Q4
Pub: 100-2, Chap. 10, 20; 100-4, Chap. 1,
10.1.4.1; 100-4, Chap. 15, 30.2.1

C **A0432** Paramedic intercept (PI), rural area,
transport furnished by a volunteer
ambulance company which is prohibited by
state law from billing third party payers   A
BETOS: O1A   Ambulance
Reasonable charge
Coding Clinic: 2012, Q4
Pub: 100-2, Chap. 10, 20; 100-2, Chap. 10,
30.1.1; 100-4, Chap. 15, 30.2.1

C **A0433** Advanced life support, level 2 (ALS 2)   A
BETOS: O1A   Ambulance
Reasonable charge
Coding Clinic: 2012, Q4
Pub: 100-2, Chap. 10, 20; 100-4, Chap. 15,
30.2.1

C **A0434** Specialty care transport (SCT)   A
BETOS: O1A   Ambulance
Reasonable charge
Coding Clinic: 2012, Q4
Pub: 100-2, Chap. 10, 20; 100-4, Chap. 15,
30.2.1

C **A0435** Fixed wing air mileage, per statute mile   A
BETOS: O1A   Ambulance
Reasonable charge
Coding Clinic: 2012, Q4
Pub: 100-2, Chap. 10, 20; 100-4, Chap. 15,
20.2; 100-4, Chap. 15, 20.3; 100-4, Chap. 15,
30.2; 100-4, Chap. 15, 30.2.1

C **A0436** Rotary wing air mileage, per statute mile   A
BETOS: O1A   Ambulance
Reasonable charge
Coding Clinic: 2012, Q4
Pub: 100-2, Chap. 10, 20; 100-4, Chap. 15,
20.2; 100-4, Chap. 15, 30.2.1

M **A0888** Noncovered ambulance mileage, per mile
(e.g., for miles traveled beyond closest
appropriate facility)   E1
BETOS: O1A   Ambulance
Service not separately priced by Part B
Pub: 100-2, Chap. 10, 20; 100-4, Chap. 15,
20.2; 100-4, Chap. 15, 30.1.2; 100-4, Chap. 15,
30.2.4

I **A0998** Ambulance response and treatment, no
transport   E1
BETOS: O1A   Ambulance
Service not separately priced by Part B

D **A0999** Unlisted ambulance service   A
BETOS: O1A   Ambulance
Other carrier priced
Coding Clinic: 2009, Q2
Pub: 100-2, Chap. 10, 20

♂ Male only   ♀ Female only   **Ⓐ** Age   A2 - Z3 = ASC Payment indicator   A - Y = APC Status indicator
ASC = ASC-approved procedure   **DME** Paid under the DME fee schedule   **MIPS** MIPS code

NOTES

MEDICAL AND SURGICAL SUPPLIES (A4206-A8004)

INJECTION AND INFUSION SUPPLIES (A4206-A4232)

C A4206 Syringe with needle, sterile, 1 cc or less, each   N
BETOS: D1A   Medical/surgical supplies
Service not separately priced by Part B

C A4207 Syringe with needle, sterile 2 cc, each   N
BETOS: D1A   Medical/surgical supplies
Service not separately priced by Part B

C A4208 Syringe with needle, sterile 3 cc, each   N
BETOS: D1A   Medical/surgical supplies
Service not separately priced by Part B

C A4209 Syringe with needle, sterile 5 cc or greater, each   N
BETOS: D1A   Medical/surgical supplies
Service not separately priced by Part B

M A4210 Needle-free injection device, each   E1
BETOS: D1A   Medical/surgical supplies
Service not separately priced by Part B

D A4211 Supplies for self-administered injections   N
BETOS: D1A   Medical/surgical supplies
Service not separately priced by Part B

C A4212 Non-coring needle or stylet with or without catheter   N
BETOS: D1A   Medical/surgical supplies
Other carrier priced

C A4213 Syringe, sterile, 20 cc or greater, each   N
BETOS: D1A   Medical/surgical supplies
Service not separately priced by Part B

C A4215 Needle, sterile, any size, each   N
BETOS: D1A   Medical/surgical supplies
Service not separately priced by Part B

D A4216 Sterile water, saline and/or dextrose, diluent/flush, 10 ml   N1 **DME** ASC N
BETOS: D1F   Prosthetic/orthotic devices

D A4217 Sterile water/saline, 500 ml   N1 **DME** ASC N
BETOS: D1F   Prosthetic/orthotic devices
DME Modifier: AU

D A4218 Sterile saline or water, metered dose dispenser, 10 ml   N1 ASC N
BETOS: O1E   Other drugs

D A4220 Refill kit for implantable infusion pump   N1 ASC N
BETOS: D1A   Medical/surgical supplies
Other carrier priced

C A4221 Supplies for maintenance of non-insulin drug infusion catheter, per week (list drugs separately)   **DME** N
BETOS: D1E   Other DME

C A4222 Infusion supplies for external drug infusion pump, per cassette or bag (list drugs separately)   **DME** N
BETOS: D1E   Other DME

C A4223 Infusion supplies not used with external infusion pump, per cassette or bag (list drugs separately)   N
BETOS: D1A   Medical/surgical supplies
Service not separately priced by Part B

C A4224 Supplies for maintenance of insulin infusion catheter, per week   **DME** N
BETOS: D1E   Other DME

D A4225 Supplies for external insulin infusion pump, syringe type cartridge, sterile, each   **DME** N
BETOS: D1E   Other DME

D A4230 Infusion set for external insulin pump, non needle cannula type   N
BETOS: D1E   Other DME

Insulin pump

D A4231 Infusion set for external insulin pump, needle type   N
BETOS: D1E   Other DME

I A4232 Syringe with needle for external insulin pump, sterile, 3 cc   E1
BETOS: D1E   Other DME
Service not separately priced by Part B

REPLACEMENT BATTERIES (A4233-A4236)

C A4233 Replacement battery, alkaline (other than J cell), for use with medically necessary home blood glucose monitor owned by patient, each   **DME** E1
BETOS: D1E   Other DME
DME Modifier: NU
Pub: 100-4, Chap. 23, 60.3

C A4234 Replacement battery, alkaline, J cell, for use with medically necessary home blood glucose monitor owned by patient, each   **DME** E1
BETOS: D1E   Other DME
DME Modifier: NU

C **A4235** Replacement battery, lithium, for use with medically necessary home blood glucose monitor owned by patient, each **DME** E1
BETOS: D1E   Other DME
DME Modifier: NU

C **A4236** Replacement battery, silver oxide, for use with medically necessary home blood glucose monitor owned by patient, each **DME** E1
BETOS: D1E   Other DME
DME Modifier: NU

OTHER SUPPLIES INCLUDING DIABETES SUPPLIES AND CONTRACEPTIVES (A4244-A4290)

C **A4244** Alcohol or peroxide, per pint N1 ASC N
BETOS: D1A   Medical/surgical supplies
Service not separately priced by Part B

C **A4245** Alcohol wipes, per box N1 ASC N
BETOS: D1A   Medical/surgical supplies
Service not separately priced by Part B

C **A4246** Betadine or pHisoHex solution, per pint N1 ASC N
BETOS: D1A   Medical/surgical supplies
Service not separately priced by Part B

C **A4247** Betadine or iodine swabs/wipes, per box N1 ASC N
BETOS: D1A   Medical/surgical supplies
Service not separately priced by Part B

C **A4248** Chlorhexidine containing antiseptic, 1 ml N1 ASC N
BETOS: P9B   Dialysis services (non-Medicare fee schedule)
Service not separately priced by Part B

M **A4250** Urine test or reagent strips or tablets (100 tablets or strips) E1
BETOS: T1E   Lab tests - glucose
Service not separately priced by Part B
Pub: 100-2, Chap. 15, 110

S **A4252** Blood ketone test or reagent strip, each E1
BETOS: D1E   Other DME
Service not separately priced by Part B
Statute: 1861(n)

D **A4253** Blood glucose test or reagent strips for home blood glucose monitor, per 50 strips **DME** N
BETOS: D1E   Other DME
DME Modifier: NU
Pub: 100-4, Chap. 23, 60.3

D **A4255** Platforms for home blood glucose monitor, 50 per box **DME** N
BETOS: D1E   Other DME

D **A4256** Normal, low and high calibrator solution / chips **DME** N
BETOS: D1E   Other DME
Pub: 100-4, Chap. 23, 60.3

C **A4257** Replacement lens shield cartridge for use with laser skin piercing device, each **DME** E1
BETOS: D1E   Other DME
Coding Clinic: 2002, Q1

D **A4258** Spring-powered device for lancet, each **DME** N
BETOS: D1E   Other DME
Pub: 100-4, Chap. 23, 60.3

D **A4259** Lancets, per box of 100 **DME** N
BETOS: D1E   Other DME

S **A4261** Cervical cap for contraceptive use ♀ E1
BETOS: Z2   Undefined codes
Service not separately priced by Part B
Statute: 1862a1

D **A4262** Temporary, absorbable lacrimal duct implant, each N1 ASC N
BETOS: D1A   Medical/surgical supplies
Service not separately priced by Part B

D **A4263** Permanent, long term, non-dissolvable lacrimal duct implant, each N1 ASC N
BETOS: Y1   Other - Medicare fee schedule
Price established using national RVUs

I **A4264** Permanent implantable contraceptive intratubal occlusion device(s) and delivery system ♀ E1
BETOS: Z2   Undefined codes
Service not separately priced by Part B

D **A4265** Paraffin, per pound **DME** N
BETOS: D1E   Other DME

I **A4266** Diaphragm for contraceptive use ♀ E1
BETOS: Z2   Undefined codes
Service not separately priced by Part B

I **A4267** Contraceptive supply, condom, male, each ♂ E1
BETOS: Z2   Undefined codes
Service not separately priced by Part B

I **A4268** Contraceptive supply, condom, female, each ♀ E1
BETOS: Z2   Undefined codes
Service not separately priced by Part B

I **A4269** Contraceptive supply, spermicide (e.g., foam, gel), each ♀ E1
BETOS: Z2   Undefined codes
Service not separately priced by Part B

C **A4270** Disposable endoscope sheath, each N1 ASC N
BETOS: P8D   Endoscopy - colonoscopy
Service not separately priced by Part B

C **A4280** Adhesive skin support attachment for use with external breast prosthesis, each ♀ **DME** N
BETOS: D1F   Prosthetic/orthotic devices

C **A4281** Tubing for breast pump, replacement ♀ E1
BETOS: Z2   Undefined codes
Service not separately priced by Part B

▲ Revised code   ● New code   **C** Carrier judgment   **D** Special coverage instructions apply
I Not payable by Medicare   **M** Non-covered by Medicare   **S** Non-covered by Medicare statute   AHA Coding Clinic®

C **A4282** Adapter for breast pump, replacement ♀ E1
BETOS: Z2 Undefined codes
Service not separately priced by Part B

C **A4283** Cap for breast pump bottle, replacement ♀ E1
BETOS: Z2 Undefined codes
Service not separately priced by Part B

C **A4284** Breast shield and splash protector for use with breast pump, replacement ♀ E1
BETOS: Z2 Undefined codes
Service not separately priced by Part B

C **A4285** Polycarbonate bottle for use with breast pump, replacement ♀ E1
BETOS: Z2 Undefined codes
Service not separately priced by Part B

C **A4286** Locking ring for breast pump, replacement ♀ E1
BETOS: Z2 Undefined codes
Service not separately priced by Part B

C **A4290** Sacral nerve stimulation test lead, each N
BETOS: Z2 Undefined codes
Service not separately priced by Part B
Coding Clinic: 2002, Q1
Pub: 100-4, Chap. 32, 40.1

ACCESS CATHETERS AND DRUG DELIVERY SYSTEMS (A4300-A4306)

D **A4300** Implantable access catheter, (e.g., venous, arterial, epidural subarachnoid, or peritoneal, etc.) external access N1 ASC N
BETOS: Y1 Other - Medicare fee schedule
Price established using national RVUs

C **A4301** Implantable access total catheter, port/reservoir (e.g., venous, arterial, epidural, subarachnoid, peritoneal, etc.) N1 ASC N
BETOS: D1A Medical/surgical supplies
Service not separately priced by Part B

C **A4305** Disposable drug delivery system, flow rate of 50 ml or greater per hour N1 ASC N
BETOS: D1A Medical/surgical supplies
Service not separately priced by Part B

C **A4306** Disposable drug delivery system, flow rate of less than 50 ml per hour N1 ASC N
BETOS: D1A Medical/surgical supplies
Service not separately priced by Part B

INCONTINENCE DEVICES AND SUPPLIES (A4310-A4360), SEE ALSO INCONTINENCE DEVICES AND SUPPLIES (A5102-A5200)

D **A4310** Insertion tray without drainage bag and without catheter (accessories only) DME N
BETOS: D1F Prosthetic/orthotic devices

D **A4311** Insertion tray without drainage bag with indwelling catheter, Foley-type, two-way latex with coating (Teflon, silicone, silicone elastomer or hydrophilic, etc.) DME N
BETOS: D1F Prosthetic/orthotic devices

D **A4312** Insertion tray without drainage bag with indwelling catheter, Foley-type, two-way, all silicone DME N
BETOS: D1F Prosthetic/orthotic devices

D **A4313** Insertion tray without drainage bag with indwelling catheter, Foley-type, three-way, for continuous irrigation DME N
BETOS: D1F Prosthetic/orthotic devices

D **A4314** Insertion tray with drainage bag with indwelling catheter, Foley-type, two-way latex with coating (Teflon, silicone, silicone elastomer or hydrophilic, etc.) DME N
BETOS: D1F Prosthetic/orthotic devices

D **A4315** Insertion tray with drainage bag with indwelling catheter, Foley-type, two-way, all silicone DME N
BETOS: D1F Prosthetic/orthotic devices

D **A4316** Insertion tray with drainage bag with indwelling catheter, Foley-type, three-way, for continuous irrigation DME N
BETOS: D1F Prosthetic/orthotic devices

D **A4320** Irrigation tray with bulb or piston syringe, any purpose DME N
BETOS: D1A Medical/surgical supplies

D **A4321** Therapeutic agent for urinary catheter irrigation DME N
BETOS: D1F Prosthetic/orthotic devices

D **A4322** Irrigation syringe, bulb or piston, each DME N
BETOS: D1F Prosthetic/orthotic devices

D **A4326** Male external catheter with integral collection chamber, any type, each ♂ DME N
BETOS: D1F Prosthetic/orthotic devices

D **A4327** Female external urinary collection device; meatal cup, each ♀ DME N
BETOS: D1F Prosthetic/orthotic devices

D **A4328** Female external urinary collection device; pouch, each ♀ DME N
BETOS: D1F Prosthetic/orthotic devices

D **A4330** Perianal fecal collection pouch with adhesive, each DME N
BETOS: D1F Prosthetic/orthotic devices

D **A4331** Extension drainage tubing, any type, any length, with connector/adaptor, for use with urinary leg bag or urostomy pouch, each DME N
BETOS: D1F Prosthetic/orthotic devices

D **A4332** Lubricant, individual sterile packet, each DME N
BETOS: D1F Prosthetic/orthotic devices

D **A4333** Urinary catheter anchoring device, adhesive skin attachment, each DME N
BETOS: D1F Prosthetic/orthotic devices

D **A4334** Urinary catheter anchoring device, leg strap, each DME N
BETOS: D1F Prosthetic/orthotic devices

♂ Male only   ♀ Female only   🅐 Age   A2 - Z3 = ASC Payment indicator   A - Y = APC Status indicator
ASC = ASC-approved procedure   DME Paid under the DME fee schedule   MIPS MIPS code

CPT® is a registered trademark of the American Medical Association. All rights reserved.

105

MEDICAL AND SURGICAL SUPPLIES (A4206-A8004)

A4282 - A4334

D **A4335** Incontinence supply; miscellaneous   N
BETOS: D1F   Prosthetic/orthotic devices

D **A4336** Incontinence supply, urethral insert, any type, each   DME   N
BETOS: D1F   Prosthetic/orthotic devices

D **A4337** Incontinence supply, rectal insert, any type, each   N
BETOS: D1F   Prosthetic/orthotic devices

D **A4338** Indwelling catheter; Foley-type, two-way latex with coating (Teflon, silicone, silicone elastomer, or hydrophilic, etc.), each   DME   N
BETOS: D1F   Prosthetic/orthotic devices

D **A4340** Indwelling catheter; specialty type, (e.g., Coude, mushroom, wing, etc.), each   DME   N
BETOS: D1F   Prosthetic/orthotic devices

D **A4344** Indwelling catheter, Foley-type, two-way, all silicone, each   DME   N
BETOS: D1F   Prosthetic/orthotic devices

D **A4346** Indwelling catheter; Foley-type, three-way for continuous irrigation, each   DME   N
BETOS: D1F   Prosthetic/orthotic devices

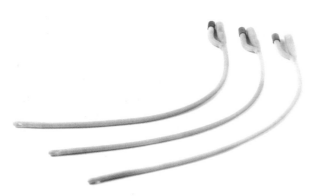

Foley catheter

D **A4349** Male external catheter, with or without adhesive, disposable, each   ♂ DME   N
BETOS: D1A   Medical/surgical supplies

D **A4351** Intermittent urinary catheter; straight tip, with or without coating (Teflon, silicone, silicone elastomer, or hydrophilic, etc.), each   DME   N
BETOS: D1F   Prosthetic/orthotic devices

D **A4352** Intermittent urinary catheter; Coude (curved) tip, with or without coating (Teflon, silicone, silicone elastomeric, or hydrophilic, etc.), each   DME   N
BETOS: D1F   Prosthetic/orthotic devices

D **A4353** Intermittent urinary catheter, with insertion supplies   DME   N
BETOS: D1F   Prosthetic/orthotic devices

D **A4354** Insertion tray with drainage bag but without catheter   DME   N
BETOS: D1F   Prosthetic/orthotic devices

D **A4355** Irrigation tubing set for continuous bladder irrigation through a three-way indwelling Foley catheter, each   DME   N
BETOS: D1F   Prosthetic/orthotic devices

D **A4356** External urethral clamp or compression device (not to be used for catheter clamp), each   DME   N
BETOS: D1F   Prosthetic/orthotic devices

D **A4357** Bedside drainage bag, day or night, with or without anti-reflux device, with or without tube, each   DME   N
BETOS: D1F   Prosthetic/orthotic devices

D **A4358** Urinary drainage bag, leg or abdomen, vinyl, with or without tube, with straps, each   DME   N
BETOS: D1F   Prosthetic/orthotic devices

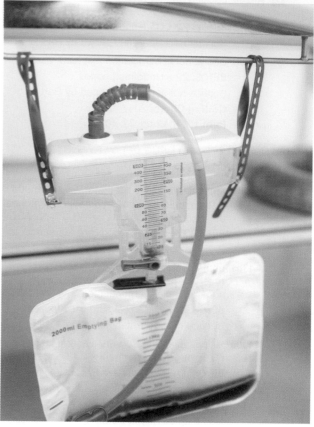

Urinary drainage bag

D **A4360** Disposable external urethral clamp or compression device, with pad and/or pouch, each   DME   N
BETOS: D1F   Prosthetic/orthotic devices

OSTOMY POUCHES AND SUPPLIES (A4361-A4435), SEE ALSO OSTOMY POUCHES AND SUPPLIES (A5051-A5093)

D **A4361** Ostomy faceplate, each   DME   N
BETOS: D1F   Prosthetic/orthotic devices

D **A4362** Skin barrier; solid, 4 x 4 or equivalent; each   DME   N
BETOS: D1F   Prosthetic/orthotic devices

▲ Revised code   ● New code   **C** Carrier judgment   **D** Special coverage instructions apply
I Not payable by Medicare   **M** Non-covered by Medicare   **S** Non-covered by Medicare statute   AHA Coding Clinic®

D **A4363** Ostomy clamp, any type, replacement only, each DME E1
BETOS: D1F Prosthetic/orthotic devices

D **A4364** Adhesive, liquid or equal, any type, per oz. DME N
BETOS: D1F Prosthetic/orthotic devices

C **A4366** Ostomy vent, any type, each DME N
BETOS: D1F Prosthetic/orthotic devices

D **A4367** Ostomy belt, each DME N
BETOS: D1F Prosthetic/orthotic devices

C **A4368** Ostomy filter, any type, each DME N
BETOS: D1F Prosthetic/orthotic devices

D **A4369** Ostomy skin barrier, liquid (spray, brush, etc.), per oz. DME N
BETOS: D1F Prosthetic/orthotic devices

D **A4371** Ostomy skin barrier, powder, per oz. DME N
BETOS: D1F Prosthetic/orthotic devices

D **A4372** Ostomy skin barrier, solid 4 x 4 or equivalent, standard wear, with built-in convexity, each DME N
BETOS: D1F Prosthetic/orthotic devices

D **A4373** Ostomy skin barrier, with flange (solid, flexible or accordion), with built-in convexity, any size, each DME N
BETOS: D1F Prosthetic/orthotic devices

D **A4375** Ostomy pouch, drainable, with faceplate attached, plastic, each DME N
BETOS: D1F Prosthetic/orthotic devices

D **A4376** Ostomy pouch, drainable, with faceplate attached, rubber, each DME N
BETOS: D1F Prosthetic/orthotic devices

D **A4377** Ostomy pouch, drainable, for use on faceplate, plastic, each DME N
BETOS: D1F Prosthetic/orthotic devices

D **A4378** Ostomy pouch, drainable, for use on faceplate, rubber, each DME N
BETOS: D1F Prosthetic/orthotic devices

D **A4379** Ostomy pouch, urinary, with faceplate attached, plastic, each DME N
BETOS: D1F Prosthetic/orthotic devices

D **A4380** Ostomy pouch, urinary, with faceplate attached, rubber, each DME N
BETOS: D1F Prosthetic/orthotic devices

D **A4381** Ostomy pouch, urinary, for use on faceplate, plastic, each DME N
BETOS: D1F Prosthetic/orthotic devices

D **A4382** Ostomy pouch, urinary, for use on faceplate, heavy plastic, each DME N
BETOS: D1F Prosthetic/orthotic devices

D **A4383** Ostomy pouch, urinary, for use on faceplate, rubber, each DME N
BETOS: D1F Prosthetic/orthotic devices

D **A4384** Ostomy faceplate equivalent, silicone ring, each DME N
BETOS: D1F Prosthetic/orthotic devices

D **A4385** Ostomy skin barrier, solid 4 x 4 or equivalent, extended wear, without built-in convexity, each DME N
BETOS: D1F Prosthetic/orthotic devices

D **A4387** Ostomy pouch, closed, with barrier attached, with built-in convexity (1 piece), each DME N
BETOS: D1F Prosthetic/orthotic devices

D **A4388** Ostomy pouch, drainable, with extended wear barrier attached, (1 piece), each DME N
BETOS: D1F Prosthetic/orthotic devices

D **A4389** Ostomy pouch, drainable, with barrier attached, with built-in convexity (1 piece), each DME N
BETOS: D1F Prosthetic/orthotic devices

D **A4390** Ostomy pouch, drainable, with extended wear barrier attached, with built-in convexity (1 piece), each DME N
BETOS: D1F Prosthetic/orthotic devices

D **A4391** Ostomy pouch, urinary, with extended wear barrier attached (1 piece), each DME N
BETOS: D1F Prosthetic/orthotic devices

D **A4392** Ostomy pouch, urinary, with standard wear barrier attached, with built-in convexity (1 piece), each DME N
BETOS: D1F Prosthetic/orthotic devices

D **A4393** Ostomy pouch, urinary, with extended wear barrier attached, with built-in convexity (1 piece), each DME N
BETOS: D1F Prosthetic/orthotic devices

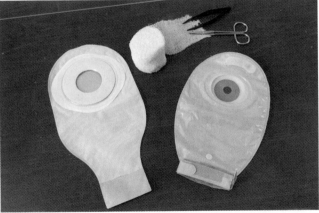

Ostomy pouch

D **A4394** Ostomy deodorant, with or without lubricant, for use in ostomy pouch, per fluid ounce DME N
BETOS: D1F Prosthetic/orthotic devices

D **A4395** Ostomy deodorant for use in ostomy pouch, solid, per tablet DME N
BETOS: D1F Prosthetic/orthotic devices

♂ Male only   ♀ Female only   Ⓐ Age   A2 - Z3 = ASC Payment indicator   A - Y = APC Status indicator
ASC = ASC-approved procedure   DME Paid under the DME fee schedule   MIPS MIPS code

D **A4396** Ostomy belt with peristomal hernia support `DME` N
BETOS: D1F   Prosthetic/orthotic devices

D **A4397** Irrigation supply; sleeve, each `DME` N
BETOS: D1F   Prosthetic/orthotic devices

D **A4398** Ostomy irrigation supply; bag, each `DME` N
BETOS: D1F   Prosthetic/orthotic devices

D **A4399** Ostomy irrigation supply; cone/catheter, with or without brush `DME` N
BETOS: D1F   Prosthetic/orthotic devices

D **A4400** Ostomy irrigation set `DME` N
BETOS: D1F   Prosthetic/orthotic devices

D **A4402** Lubricant, per ounce `DME` N
BETOS: D1F   Prosthetic/orthotic devices

D **A4404** Ostomy ring, each `DME` N
BETOS: D1F   Prosthetic/orthotic devices

D **A4405** Ostomy skin barrier, non-pectin based, paste, per ounce `DME` N
BETOS: D1F   Prosthetic/orthotic devices

D **A4406** Ostomy skin barrier, pectin-based, paste, per ounce `DME` N
BETOS: D1F   Prosthetic/orthotic devices

D **A4407** Ostomy skin barrier, with flange (solid, flexible, or accordion), extended wear, with built-in convexity, 4 x 4 inches or smaller, each `DME` N
BETOS: D1F   Prosthetic/orthotic devices

D **A4408** Ostomy skin barrier, with flange (solid, flexible or accordion), extended wear, with built-in convexity, larger than 4 x 4 inches, each `DME` N
BETOS: D1F   Prosthetic/orthotic devices

D **A4409** Ostomy skin barrier, with flange (solid, flexible or accordion), extended wear, without built-in convexity, 4 x 4 inches or smaller, each `DME` N
BETOS: D1F   Prosthetic/orthotic devices

D **A4410** Ostomy skin barrier, with flange (solid, flexible or accordion), extended wear, without built-in convexity, larger than 4 x 4 inches, each `DME` N
BETOS: D1F   Prosthetic/orthotic devices

D **A4411** Ostomy skin barrier, solid 4 x 4 or equivalent, extended wear, with built-in convexity, each `DME` N
BETOS: D1F   Prosthetic/orthotic devices

D **A4412** Ostomy pouch, drainable, high output, for use on a barrier with flange (2 piece system), without filter, each `DME` N
BETOS: D1F   Prosthetic/orthotic devices

D **A4413** Ostomy pouch, drainable, high output, for use on a barrier with flange (2 piece system), with filter, each `DME` N
BETOS: D1F   Prosthetic/orthotic devices

D **A4414** Ostomy skin barrier, with flange (solid, flexible or accordion), without built-in convexity, 4 x 4 inches or smaller, each `DME` N
BETOS: D1F   Prosthetic/orthotic devices

D **A4415** Ostomy skin barrier, with flange (solid, flexible or accordion), without built-in convexity, larger than 4 x 4 inches, each `DME` N
BETOS: D1F   Prosthetic/orthotic devices

C **A4416** Ostomy pouch, closed, with barrier attached, with filter (1 piece), each `DME` N
BETOS: D1F   Prosthetic/orthotic devices

C **A4417** Ostomy pouch, closed, with barrier attached, with built-in convexity, with filter (1 piece), each `DME` N
BETOS: D1F   Prosthetic/orthotic devices

C **A4418** Ostomy pouch, closed; without barrier attached, with filter (1 piece), each `DME` N
BETOS: D1F   Prosthetic/orthotic devices

C **A4419** Ostomy pouch, closed; for use on barrier with non-locking flange, with filter (2 piece), each `DME` N
BETOS: D1F   Prosthetic/orthotic devices

C **A4420** Ostomy pouch, closed; for use on barrier with locking flange (2 piece), each `DME` N
BETOS: D1F   Prosthetic/orthotic devices

C **A4421** Ostomy supply; miscellaneous N
BETOS: D1F   Prosthetic/orthotic devices

D **A4422** Ostomy absorbent material (sheet/pad/crystal packet) for use in ostomy pouch to thicken liquid stomal output, each `DME` N
BETOS: D1F   Prosthetic/orthotic devices

C **A4423** Ostomy pouch, closed; for use on barrier with locking flange, with filter (2 piece), each `DME` N
BETOS: D1F   Prosthetic/orthotic devices

C **A4424** Ostomy pouch, drainable, with barrier attached, with filter (1 piece), each `DME` N
BETOS: D1F   Prosthetic/orthotic devices

C **A4425** Ostomy pouch, drainable; for use on barrier with non-locking flange, with filter (2 piece system), each `DME` N
BETOS: D1F   Prosthetic/orthotic devices

C **A4426** Ostomy pouch, drainable; for use on barrier with locking flange (2 piece system), each `DME` N
BETOS: D1F   Prosthetic/orthotic devices

C **A4427** Ostomy pouch, drainable; for use on barrier with locking flange, with filter (2 piece system), each `DME` N
BETOS: D1F   Prosthetic/orthotic devices

C **A4428** Ostomy pouch, urinary, with extended wear barrier attached, with faucet-type tap with valve (1 piece), each `DME` N
BETOS: D1F   Prosthetic/orthotic devices

C **A4429** Ostomy pouch, urinary, with barrier attached, with built-in convexity, with faucet-type tap with valve (1 piece), each   **DME** N

  BETOS: D1F   Prosthetic/orthotic devices

C **A4430** Ostomy pouch, urinary, with extended wear barrier attached, with built-in convexity, with faucet-type tap with valve (1 piece), each   **DME** N

  BETOS: D1F   Prosthetic/orthotic devices

C **A4431** Ostomy pouch, urinary; with barrier attached, with faucet-type tap with valve (1 piece), each   **DME** N

  BETOS: D1F   Prosthetic/orthotic devices

C **A4432** Ostomy pouch, urinary; for use on barrier with non-locking flange, with faucet-type tap with valve (2 piece), each   **DME** N

  BETOS: D1F   Prosthetic/orthotic devices

C **A4433** Ostomy pouch, urinary; for use on barrier with locking flange (2 piece), each   **DME** N

  BETOS: D1F   Prosthetic/orthotic devices

C **A4434** Ostomy pouch, urinary; for use on barrier with locking flange, with faucet-type tap with valve (2 piece), each   **DME** N

  BETOS: D1F   Prosthetic/orthotic devices

C **A4435** Ostomy pouch, drainable, high output, with extended wear barrier (one-piece system), with or without filter, each   **DME** N

  BETOS: D1F   Prosthetic/orthotic devices

VARIOUS MEDICAL SUPPLIES INCLUDING TAPES AND SURGICAL DRESSINGS (A4450-A4608)

D **A4450** Tape, non-waterproof, per 18 square inches   **DME** N

  BETOS: D1F   Prosthetic/orthotic devices

  DME Modifier: AU,AV,AW

D **A4452** Tape, waterproof, per 18 square inches   **DME** N

  BETOS: D1F   Prosthetic/orthotic devices

  DME Modifier: AU,AV,AW

D **A4455** Adhesive remover or solvent (for tape, cement or other adhesive), per ounce   **DME** N

  BETOS: D1F   Prosthetic/orthotic devices

D **A4456** Adhesive remover, wipes, any type, each   **DME** N

  BETOS: D1F   Prosthetic/orthotic devices

C **A4458** Enema bag with tubing, reusable   N

  BETOS: Z2   Undefined codes

  Service not separately priced by Part B

C **A4459** Manual pump-operated enema system, includes balloon, catheter and all accessories, reusable, any type   N

  BETOS: Z2   Undefined codes

  Service not separately priced by Part B

C **A4461** Surgical dressing holder, non-reusable, each   **DME** N

  BETOS: D1A   Medical/surgical supplies

C **A4463** Surgical dressing holder, reusable, each   **DME** N

  BETOS: D1A   Medical/surgical supplies

C **A4465** Non-elastic binder for extremity   N

  BETOS: D1A   Medical/surgical supplies

  Service not separately priced by Part B

M **A4467** Belt, strap, sleeve, garment, or covering, any type   E1

  BETOS: Z2   Undefined codes

  Service not separately priced by Part B

D **A4470** Gravlee jet washer   N

  BETOS: D1A   Medical/surgical supplies

  Service not separately priced by Part B

D **A4480** Vabra aspirator   N

  BETOS: D1A   Medical/surgical supplies

  Service not separately priced by Part B

D **A4481** Tracheostoma filter, any type, any size, each   **DME** N

  BETOS: D1F   Prosthetic/orthotic devices

D **A4483** Moisture exchanger, disposable, for use with invasive mechanical ventilation   **DME** N

  BETOS: D1F   Prosthetic/orthotic devices

M **A4490** Surgical stockings above knee length, each   E1

  BETOS: D1A   Medical/surgical supplies

  Service not separately priced by Part B

  Pub: 100-2, Chap. 15, 110

M **A4495** Surgical stockings thigh length, each   E1

  BETOS: D1A   Medical/surgical supplies

  Service not separately priced by Part B

  Pub: 100-2, Chap. 15, 110

M **A4500** Surgical stockings below knee length, each   E1

  BETOS: D1A   Medical/surgical supplies

  Service not separately priced by Part B

  Pub: 100-2, Chap. 15, 110

M **A4510** Surgical stockings full length, each   E1

  BETOS: D1A   Medical/surgical supplies

  Service not separately priced by Part B

  Pub: 100-2, Chap. 15, 110

M **A4520** Incontinence garment, any type, (e.g., brief, diaper), each   E1

  BETOS: D1A   Medical/surgical supplies

  Service not separately priced by Part B

D **A4550** Surgical trays   B

  BETOS: Y1   Other - Medicare fee schedule

  Price established using national RVUs

M **A4553** Non-disposable underpads, all sizes   E1

  BETOS: D1A   Medical/surgical supplies

  Service not separately priced by Part B

M **A4554** Disposable underpads, all sizes   E1

  BETOS: D1A   Medical/surgical supplies

  Service not separately priced by Part B

I **A4555** Electrode/transducer for use with electrical stimulation device used for cancer treatment, replacement only   E1
    BETOS: D1E   Other DME
    Service not separately priced by Part B

C **A4556** Electrodes, (e.g., apnea monitor), per pair   DME N
    BETOS: D1E   Other DME

C **A4557** Lead wires, (e.g., apnea monitor), per pair   DME N
    BETOS: D1E   Other DME

C **A4558** Conductive gel or paste, for use with electrical device (e.g., TENS, NMES), per oz.   DME N
    BETOS: D1E   Other DME

C **A4559** Coupling gel or paste, for use with ultrasound device, per oz.   DME N
    BETOS: D1E   Other DME

C **A4561** Pessary, rubber, any type   ♀ DME N
    BETOS: D1F   Prosthetic/orthotic devices

Pessary

C **A4562** Pessary, non rubber, any type   ♀ DME N
    BETOS: D1F   Prosthetic/orthotic devices

C **A4565** Slings   DME N
    BETOS: D1A   Medical/surgical supplies

I **A4566** Shoulder sling or vest design, abduction restrainer, with or without swathe control, prefabricated, includes fitting and adjustment   E1
    BETOS: Z2   Undefined codes
    Service not separately priced by Part B

I **A4570** Splint   E1
    BETOS: D1A   Medical/surgical supplies
    Reasonable charge

C **A4575** Topical hyperbaric oxygen chamber, disposable   A
    BETOS: D1A   Medical/surgical supplies
    Service not separately priced by Part B

I **A4580** Cast supplies (e.g., plaster)   E1
    BETOS: D1A   Medical/surgical supplies
    Service not separately priced by Part B

I **A4590** Special casting material (e.g., fiberglass)   E1
    BETOS: D1A   Medical/surgical supplies
    Service not separately priced by Part B

D **A4595** Electrical stimulator supplies, 2 lead, per month, (e.g., TENS, NMES)   DME N
    BETOS: D1E   Other DME

C **A4600** Sleeve for intermittent limb compression device, replacement only, each   E1
    BETOS: D1E   Other DME

C **A4601** Lithium ion battery, rechargeable, for non-prosthetic use, replacement   E1
    BETOS: D1E   Other DME

C **A4602** Replacement battery for external infusion pump owned by patient, lithium, 1.5 volt, each   DME N
    BETOS: D1E   Other DME
    DME Modifier: NU

C **A4604** Tubing with integrated heating element for use with positive airway pressure device   DME N
    BETOS: D1E   Other DME
    DME Modifier: NU
    Pub: 100-4, Chap. 23, 60.3; 100-4, Chap. 36, 50.14

C **A4605** Tracheal suction catheter, closed system, each   DME N
    BETOS: D1E   Other DME
    DME Modifier: NU

C **A4606** Oxygen probe for use with oximeter device, replacement   N
    BETOS: D1E   Other DME
    Service not separately priced by Part B

C **A4608** Transtracheal oxygen catheter, each   DME N
    BETOS: D1C   Oxygen and supplies
    Service not separately priced by Part B
    Pub: 100-4, Chap. 23, 60.3

RESPIRATORY SUPPLIES AND EQUIPMENT (A4611-A4629)

S **A4611** Battery, heavy duty; replacement for patient owned ventilator   E1
    BETOS: D1E   Other DME
    Service not separately priced by Part B
    Statute: 1834a3A

S **A4612** Battery cables; replacement for patient-owned ventilator   E1
    BETOS: D1E   Other DME
    Service not separately priced by Part B
    Statute: 1834a3A

S **A4613** Battery charger; replacement for patient-owned ventilator   E1
    BETOS: D1E   Other DME
    Service not separately priced by Part B
    Statute: 1834a3A

▲ Revised code   ● New code   **C** Carrier judgment   **D** Special coverage instructions apply
I Not payable by Medicare   **M** Non-covered by Medicare   **S** Non-covered by Medicare statute   AHA Coding Clinic®

C **A4614** Peak expiratory flow rate meter, hand held DME N
BETOS: Z2 Undefined codes

D **A4615** Cannula, nasal DME N
BETOS: D1C Oxygen and supplies
Service not separately priced by Part B
Pub: 100-4, Chap. 20, 100.2.2; 100-4, Chap. 23, 60.3

Nasal cannula

D **A4616** Tubing (oxygen), per foot DME N
BETOS: D1C Oxygen and supplies
Service not separately priced by Part B
Pub: 100-4, Chap. 20, 100.2.2

D **A4617** Mouth piece DME N
BETOS: D1C Oxygen and supplies
Service not separately priced by Part B
Pub: 100-4, Chap. 20, 100.2.2

D **A4618** Breathing circuits DME N
BETOS: D1E Other DME
DME Modifier: NU,RR,UE
Pub: 100-4, Chap. 20, 100.2.2

D **A4619** Face tent DME N
BETOS: D1E Other DME
DME Modifier: NU
Pub: 100-4, Chap. 20, 100.2.2

D **A4620** Variable concentration mask DME N
BETOS: D1C Oxygen and supplies
Service not separately priced by Part B
Pub: 100-4, Chap. 20, 100.2.2; 100-4, Chap. 23, 60.3

D **A4623** Tracheostomy, inner cannula DME N
BETOS: D1F Prosthetic/orthotic devices

C **A4624** Tracheal suction catheter, any type other than closed system, each DME N
BETOS: D1E Other DME
DME Modifier: NU

D **A4625** Tracheostomy care kit for new tracheostomy DME N
BETOS: D1F Prosthetic/orthotic devices

D **A4626** Tracheostomy cleaning brush, each DME N
BETOS: D1F Prosthetic/orthotic devices

M **A4627** Spacer, bag or reservoir, with or without mask, for use with metered dose inhaler E1
BETOS: D1A Medical/surgical supplies
Service not separately priced by Part B
Pub: 100-2, Chap. 15, 110

C **A4628** Oropharyngeal suction catheter, each DME N
BETOS: D1E Other DME
DME Modifier: NU

D **A4629** Tracheostomy care kit for established tracheostomy DME N
BETOS: D1F Prosthetic/orthotic devices

REPLACEMENT PARTS (A4630-A4640)

D **A4630** Replacement batteries, medically necessary, transcutaneous electrical stimulator, owned by patient DME E1
BETOS: D1E Other DME
DME Modifier: NU

C **A4633** Replacement bulb/lamp for ultraviolet light therapy system, each DME E1
BETOS: D1E Other DME
DME Modifier: NU

C **A4634** Replacement bulb for therapeutic light box, tabletop model N
BETOS: D1E Other DME
Service not separately priced by Part B

D **A4635** Underarm pad, crutch, replacement, each DME E1
BETOS: D1E Other DME
DME Modifier: NU,RR,UE

D **A4636** Replacement, handgrip, cane, crutch, or walker, each DME E1
BETOS: D1E Other DME
DME Modifier: NU,RR,UE
Pub: 100-4, Chap. 23, 60.3; 100-4, Chap. 36, 50.15

D **A4637** Replacement, tip, cane, crutch, walker, each. DME E1
BETOS: D1E Other DME
DME Modifier: NU,RR,UE

C **A4638** Replacement battery for patient-owned ear pulse generator, each DME E1
BETOS: D1E Other DME
DME Modifier: NU,RR,UE

C **A4639** Replacement pad for infrared heating pad system, each DME E1
BETOS: D1E Other DME
DME Modifier: RR

D **A4640** Replacement pad for use with medically necessary alternating pressure pad owned by patient DME E1
BETOS: D1E Other DME
DME Modifier: NU,RR,UE

♂ Male only   ♀ Female only   Ⓐ Age   A2 - Z3 = ASC Payment indicator   A - Y = APC Status indicator
ASC = ASC-approved procedure   DME Paid under the DME fee schedule   MIPS MIPS code

CPT® is a registered trademark of the American Medical Association. All rights reserved.

111

DIAGNOSTIC RADIOPHARMACEUTICALS (A4641-A4642),
SEE ALSO DIAGNOSTIC AND THERAPEUTIC
RADIOPHARMACEUTICALS (A9500-A9700)

C **A4641** Radiopharmaceutical, diagnostic, not
otherwise classified   N1 ASC N
  BETOS: I1E   Standard imaging - nuclear
  medicine
  Coding Clinic: 2005, Q4
  Pub: 100-4, Chap. 13, 60.3; 100-4, Chap. 13,
  60.3.1; 100-4, Chap. 13, 60.3.2

C **A4642** Indium In-111 satumomab pendetide,
diagnostic, per study dose, up to
6 millicuries   N1 ASC N
  BETOS: I1E   Standard imaging - nuclear
  medicine
  Coding Clinic: 2002, Q2; 2005, Q4

OTHER SUPPLIES (A4648-A4652)

C **A4648** Tissue marker, implantable, any type,
each   N1 ASC N
  BETOS: I1E   Standard imaging - nuclear
  medicine
  Other carrier priced
  Coding Clinic: 2013, Q3

C **A4649** Surgical supply; miscellaneous   N
  BETOS: D1A   Medical/surgical supplies

C **A4650** Implantable radiation dosimeter,
each   N1 ASC N
  BETOS: I1E   Standard imaging - nuclear
  medicine
  Other carrier priced

D **A4651** Calibrated microcapillary tube, each   N
  BETOS: P9B   Dialysis services
  (non-Medicare fee schedule)
  Service not separately priced by Part B
  Coding Clinic: 2002, Q1

D **A4652** Microcapillary tube sealant   N
  BETOS: P9B   Dialysis services
  (non-Medicare fee schedule)
  Service not separately priced by Part B
  Coding Clinic: 2002, Q1

DIALYSIS EQUIPMENT AND SUPPLIES (A4653-A4932)

C **A4653** Peritoneal dialysis catheter anchoring
device, belt, each   N
  BETOS: P9B   Dialysis services
  (non-Medicare fee schedule)
  Service not separately priced by Part B

D **A4657** Syringe, with or without needle, each   N
  BETOS: P9B   Dialysis services
  (non-Medicare fee schedule)
  Service not separately priced by Part B
  Coding Clinic: 2002, Q1
  Pub: 100-4, Chap. 8, 60.4.6.3; 100-4, Chap. 8,
  60.7; 100-4, Chap. 13, 60.7.1

D **A4660** Sphygmomanometer/blood pressure
apparatus with cuff and stethoscope   N
  BETOS: P9B   Dialysis services
  (non-Medicare fee schedule)
  Service not separately priced by Part B

D **A4663** Blood pressure cuff only   N
  BETOS: P9B   Dialysis services
  (non-Medicare fee schedule)
  Service not separately priced by Part B

M **A4670** Automatic blood pressure monitor   E1
  BETOS: P9B   Dialysis services
  (non-Medicare fee schedule)
  Service not separately priced by Part B

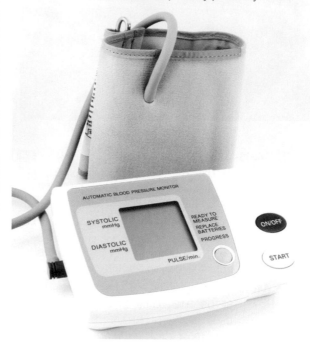

Blood pressure cuff

D **A4671** Disposable cycler set used with cycler
dialysis machine, each   B
  BETOS: P9B   Dialysis services
  (non-Medicare fee schedule)
  Service not separately priced by Part B

D **A4672** Drainage extension line, sterile, for dialysis,
each   B
  BETOS: P9B   Dialysis services
  (non-Medicare fee schedule)
  Service not separately priced by Part B

D **A4673** Extension line with easy lock connectors,
used with dialysis   B
  BETOS: P9B   Dialysis services
  (non-Medicare fee schedule)
  Service not separately priced by Part B

D **A4674** Chemicals/antiseptics solution used to clean/
sterilize dialysis equipment, per 8 oz.   B
  BETOS: P9B   Dialysis services
  (non-Medicare fee schedule)
  Service not separately priced by Part B

▲ Revised code   ● New code   **C** Carrier judgment   **D** Special coverage instructions apply
I Not payable by Medicare   **M** Non-covered by Medicare   **S** Non-covered by Medicare statute   AHA Coding Clinic®

CPT® is a registered trademark of the American Medical Association. All rights reserved.

D A4680 Activated carbon filter for hemodialysis, each   N
     BETOS: P9B   Dialysis services (non-Medicare fee schedule)
     Service not separately priced by Part B

D A4690 Dialyzer (artificial kidneys), all types, all sizes, for hemodialysis, each   N
     BETOS: P9B   Dialysis services (non-Medicare fee schedule)
     Service not separately priced by Part B

D A4706 Bicarbonate concentrate, solution, for hemodialysis, per gallon   N
     BETOS: P9B   Dialysis services (non-Medicare fee schedule)
     Service not separately priced by Part B
     Coding Clinic: 2002, Q1

D A4707 Bicarbonate concentrate, powder, for hemodialysis, per packet   N
     BETOS: P9B   Dialysis services (non-Medicare fee schedule)
     Service not separately priced by Part B
     Coding Clinic: 2002, Q1

D A4708 Acetate concentrate solution, for hemodialysis, per gallon   N
     BETOS: P9B   Dialysis services (non-Medicare fee schedule)
     Service not separately priced by Part B
     Coding Clinic: 2002, Q1

D A4709 Acid concentrate, solution, for hemodialysis, per gallon   N
     BETOS: P9B   Dialysis services (non-Medicare fee schedule)
     Service not separately priced by Part B
     Coding Clinic: 2002, Q1

D A4714 Treated water (deionized, distilled, or reverse osmosis) for peritoneal dialysis, per gallon   N
     BETOS: P9B   Dialysis services (non-Medicare fee schedule)
     Service not separately priced by Part B

D A4719 "Y set" tubing for peritoneal dialysis   N
     BETOS: P9B   Dialysis services (non-Medicare fee schedule)
     Service not separately priced by Part B
     Coding Clinic: 2002, Q1

D A4720 Dialysate solution, any concentration of dextrose, fluid volume greater than 249 cc, but less than or equal to 999 cc, for peritoneal dialysis   N
     BETOS: P9B   Dialysis services (non-Medicare fee schedule)
     Service not separately priced by Part B
     Coding Clinic: 2002, Q1

D A4721 Dialysate solution, any concentration of dextrose, fluid volume greater than 999 cc but less than or equal to 1999 cc, for peritoneal dialysis   N

     BETOS: P9B   Dialysis services (non-Medicare fee schedule)
     Service not separately priced by Part B
     Coding Clinic: 2002, Q1

D A4722 Dialysate solution, any concentration of dextrose, fluid volume greater than 1999 cc but less than or equal to 2999 cc, for peritoneal dialysis   N
     BETOS: P9B   Dialysis services (non-Medicare fee schedule)
     Service not separately priced by Part B
     Coding Clinic: 2002, Q1

D A4723 Dialysate solution, any concentration of dextrose, fluid volume greater than 2999 cc but less than or equal to 3999 cc, for peritoneal dialysis   N
     BETOS: P9B   Dialysis services (non-Medicare fee schedule)
     Service not separately priced by Part B
     Coding Clinic: 2002, Q1

D A4724 Dialysate solution, any concentration of dextrose, fluid volume greater than 3999 cc but less than or equal to 4999 cc, for peritoneal dialysis   N
     BETOS: P9B   Dialysis services (non-Medicare fee schedule)
     Service not separately priced by Part B
     Coding Clinic: 2002, Q1

D A4725 Dialysate solution, any concentration of dextrose, fluid volume greater than 4999 cc but less than or equal to 5999 cc, for peritoneal dialysis   N
     BETOS: P9B   Dialysis services (non-Medicare fee schedule)
     Service not separately priced by Part B
     Coding Clinic: 2002, Q1

D A4726 Dialysate solution, any concentration of dextrose, fluid volume greater than 5999 cc, for peritoneal dialysis   N
     BETOS: P9B   Dialysis services (non-Medicare fee schedule)
     Service not separately priced by Part B
     Coding Clinic: 2002, Q1

C A4728 Dialysate solution, non-dextrose containing, 500 ml   B
     BETOS: P9B   Dialysis services (non-Medicare fee schedule)
     Service not separately priced by Part B

D A4730 Fistula cannulation set for hemodialysis, each   N
     BETOS: P9B   Dialysis services (non-Medicare fee schedule)
     Service not separately priced by Part B

D A4736 Topical anesthetic, for dialysis, per gram   N
     BETOS: P9B   Dialysis services (non-Medicare fee schedule)
     Service not separately priced by Part B
     Coding Clinic: 2002, Q1

♂ Male only   ♀ Female only   Ⓐ Age   A2 - Z3 = ASC Payment indicator   A - Y = APC Status indicator
ASC = ASC-approved procedure   **DME** Paid under the DME fee schedule   **MIPS** MIPS code

D **A4737** Injectable anesthetic, for dialysis, per 10 ml N
    BETOS: P9B   Dialysis services
    (non-Medicare fee schedule)
    Service not separately priced by Part B
    Coding Clinic: 2002, Q1

D **A4740** Shunt accessory, for hemodialysis, any type,
    each   N
    BETOS: P9B   Dialysis services
    (non-Medicare fee schedule)
    Service not separately priced by Part B

D **A4750** Blood tubing, arterial or venous, for
    hemodialysis, each   N
    BETOS: P9B   Dialysis services
    (non-Medicare fee schedule)
    Service not separately priced by Part B

D **A4755** Blood tubing, arterial and venous combined,
    for hemodialysis, each   N
    BETOS: P9B   Dialysis services
    (non-Medicare fee schedule)
    Service not separately priced by Part B

D **A4760** Dialysate solution test kit, for peritoneal
    dialysis, any type, each   N
    BETOS: P9B   Dialysis services
    (non-Medicare fee schedule)
    Service not separately priced by Part B

D **A4765** Dialysate concentrate, powder, additive for
    peritoneal dialysis, per packet   N
    BETOS: P9B   Dialysis services
    (non-Medicare fee schedule)
    Service not separately priced by Part B

D **A4766** Dialysate concentrate, solution, additive for
    peritoneal dialysis, per 10 ml   N
    BETOS: P9B   Dialysis services
    (non-Medicare fee schedule)
    Service not separately priced by Part B
    Coding Clinic: 2002, Q1

D **A4770** Blood collection tube, vacuum, for dialysis,
    per 50   N
    BETOS: P9B   Dialysis services
    (non-Medicare fee schedule)
    Service not separately priced by Part B

D **A4771** Serum clotting time tube, for dialysis,
    per 50   N
    BETOS: P9B   Dialysis services
    (non-Medicare fee schedule)
    Service not separately priced by Part B

D **A4772** Blood glucose test strips, for dialysis,
    per 50   N
    BETOS: P9B   Dialysis services
    (non-Medicare fee schedule)
    Service not separately priced by Part B

D **A4773** Occult blood test strips, for dialysis, per 50 N
    BETOS: P9B   Dialysis services
    (non-Medicare fee schedule)
    Service not separately priced by Part B

D **A4774** Ammonia test strips, for dialysis, per 50   N
    BETOS: P9B   Dialysis services
    (non-Medicare fee schedule)
    Service not separately priced by Part B

D **A4802** Protamine sulfate, for hemodialysis,
    per 50 mg   N
    BETOS: P9B   Dialysis services
    (non-Medicare fee schedule)
    Service not separately priced by Part B
    Coding Clinic: 2002, Q1

D **A4860** Disposable catheter tips for peritoneal
    dialysis, per 10   N
    BETOS: P9B   Dialysis services
    (non-Medicare fee schedule)
    Service not separately priced by Part B

D **A4870** Plumbing and/or electrical work for home
    hemodialysis equipment   N
    BETOS: P9B   Dialysis services
    (non-Medicare fee schedule)
    Service not separately priced by Part B

D **A4890** Contracts, repair and maintenance, for
    hemodialysis equipment   N
    BETOS: P9B   Dialysis services
    (non-Medicare fee schedule)
    Service not separately priced by Part B

D **A4911** Drain bag/bottle, for dialysis, each   N
    BETOS: P9B   Dialysis services
    (non-Medicare fee schedule)
    Service not separately priced by Part B
    Coding Clinic: 2002, Q1

D **A4913** Miscellaneous dialysis supplies, not
    otherwise specified   N
    BETOS: P9B   Dialysis services
    (non-Medicare fee schedule)
    Service not separately priced by Part B

D **A4918** Venous pressure clamp, for hemodialysis,
    each   N
    BETOS: P9B   Dialysis services
    (non-Medicare fee schedule)
    Service not separately priced by Part B

D **A4927** Gloves, non-sterile, per 100   N
    BETOS: P9B   Dialysis services
    (non-Medicare fee schedule)
    Service not separately priced by Part B

D **A4928** Surgical mask, per 20   N
    BETOS: P9B   Dialysis services
    (non-Medicare fee schedule)
    Service not separately priced by Part B
    Coding Clinic: 2002, Q1

D **A4929** Tourniquet for dialysis, each   N
    BETOS: P9B   Dialysis services
    (non-Medicare fee schedule)
    Service not separately priced by Part B
    Coding Clinic: 2002, Q1

▲ Revised code   ● New code   **C** Carrier judgment   **D** Special coverage instructions apply
I Not payable by Medicare   **M** Non-covered by Medicare   **S** Non-covered by Medicare statute   AHA Coding Clinic®

D **A4930** Gloves, sterile, per pair   N
BETOS: P9B   Dialysis services
(non-Medicare fee schedule)
Service not separately priced by Part B

C **A4931** Oral thermometer, reusable, any type, each   N
BETOS: P9B   Dialysis services
(non-Medicare fee schedule)
Service not separately priced by Part B

C **A4932** Rectal thermometer, reusable, any type,
each   N
BETOS: Z2   Undefined codes
Service not separately priced by Part B

OSTOMY POUCHES AND SUPPLIES (A5051-A5093), SEE
ALSO OSTOMY POUCHES AND SUPPLIES (A4361-A4435)

D **A5051** Ostomy pouch, closed; with barrier attached
(1 piece), each   DME N
BETOS: D1F   Prosthetic/orthotic devices

D **A5052** Ostomy pouch, closed; without barrier
attached (1 piece), each   DME N
BETOS: D1F   Prosthetic/orthotic devices

D **A5053** Ostomy pouch, closed; for use on faceplate,
each   DME N
BETOS: D1F   Prosthetic/orthotic devices

D **A5054** Ostomy pouch, closed; for use on barrier
with flange (2 piece), each   DME N
BETOS: D1F   Prosthetic/orthotic devices

D **A5055** Stoma cap   DME N
BETOS: D1F   Prosthetic/orthotic devices

D **A5056** Ostomy pouch, drainable, with extended
wear barrier attached, with filter, (1 piece),
each   DME N
BETOS: D1F   Prosthetic/orthotic devices

D **A5057** Ostomy pouch, drainable, with extended
wear barrier attached, with built in convexity,
with filter, (1 piece), each   DME N
BETOS: D1F   Prosthetic/orthotic devices

C **A5061** Ostomy pouch, drainable; with barrier
attached, (1 piece), each   DME N
BETOS: D1F   Prosthetic/orthotic devices

D **A5062** Ostomy pouch, drainable; without barrier
attached (1 piece), each   DME N
BETOS: D1F   Prosthetic/orthotic devices

D **A5063** Ostomy pouch, drainable; for use on barrier
with flange (2 piece system), each   DME N
BETOS: D1F   Prosthetic/orthotic devices

D **A5071** Ostomy pouch, urinary; with barrier attached
(1 piece), each   DME N
BETOS: D1F   Prosthetic/orthotic devices

D **A5072** Ostomy pouch, urinary; without barrier
attached (1 piece), each   DME N
BETOS: D1F   Prosthetic/orthotic devices

D **A5073** Ostomy pouch, urinary; for use on barrier
with flange (2 piece), each   DME N
BETOS: D1F   Prosthetic/orthotic devices

D **A5081** Stoma plug or seal, any type   DME N
BETOS: D1F   Prosthetic/orthotic devices

D **A5082** Continent device; catheter for continent
stoma   DME N
BETOS: D1F   Prosthetic/orthotic devices

C **A5083** Continent device, stoma absorptive cover for
continent stoma   DME N
BETOS: D1F   Prosthetic/orthotic devices

D **A5093** Ostomy accessory; convex insert   DME N
BETOS: D1F   Prosthetic/orthotic devices

INCONTINENCE DEVICES AND SUPPLIES (A5102-A5200),
SEE ALSO INCONTINENCE DEVICES AND SUPPLIES
(A4310-A4360)

D **A5102** Bedside drainage bottle with or without
tubing, rigid or expandable, each   DME N
BETOS: D1F   Prosthetic/orthotic devices

D **A5105** Urinary suspensory with leg bag, with or
without tube, each   DME N
BETOS: D1F   Prosthetic/orthotic devices

D **A5112** Urinary drainage bag, leg or abdomen, latex,
with or without tube, with straps, each   DME N
BETOS: D1F   Prosthetic/orthotic devices

D **A5113** Leg strap; latex, replacement only,
per set   DME E1
BETOS: D1F   Prosthetic/orthotic devices

D **A5114** Leg strap; foam or fabric, replacement only,
per set   DME E1
BETOS: D1F   Prosthetic/orthotic devices

D **A5120** Skin barrier, wipes or swabs, each   DME N
BETOS: D1F   Prosthetic/orthotic devices
DME Modifier: AU,AV

D **A5121** Skin barrier; solid, 6 x 6 or equivalent,
each   DME N
BETOS: D1F   Prosthetic/orthotic devices

D **A5122** Skin barrier; solid, 8 x 8 or equivalent,
each   DME N
BETOS: D1F   Prosthetic/orthotic devices

D **A5126** Adhesive or non-adhesive; disk or
foam pad   DME N
BETOS: D1F   Prosthetic/orthotic devices

D **A5131** Appliance cleaner, incontinence and ostomy
appliances, per 16 oz.   DME N
BETOS: D1F   Prosthetic/orthotic devices

D **A5200** Percutaneous catheter/tube anchoring
device, adhesive skin attachment   DME N
BETOS: D1F   Prosthetic/orthotic devices

DIABETIC FOOTWEAR (A5500-A5513)

D **A5500** For diabetics only, fitting (including follow-
up), custom preparation and supply of
off-the-shelf depth-inlay shoe manufactured
to accommodate multi-density insert(s), per
shoe   DME Y

BETOS: D1F   Prosthetic/orthotic devices
Pub: 100-2, Chap. 15, 140

D A5501 For diabetics only, fitting (including follow-up), custom preparation and supply of shoe molded from cast(s) of patient's foot (custom molded shoe), per shoe   DME Y
BETOS: D1F   Prosthetic/orthotic devices
Pub: 100-2, Chap. 15, 140

D A5503 For diabetics only, modification (including fitting) of off-the-shelf depth-inlay shoe or custom-molded shoe with roller or rigid rocker bottom, per shoe   DME Y
BETOS: D1F   Prosthetic/orthotic devices
Pub: 100-2, Chap. 15, 140

D A5504 For diabetics only, modification (including fitting) of off-the-shelf depth-inlay shoe or custom-molded shoe with wedge(s), per shoe   DME Y
BETOS: D1F   Prosthetic/orthotic devices
Pub: 100-2, Chap. 15, 140

D A5505 For diabetics only, modification (including fitting) of off-the-shelf depth-inlay shoe or custom-molded shoe with metatarsal bar, per shoe   DME Y
BETOS: D1F   Prosthetic/orthotic devices
Pub: 100-2, Chap. 15, 140

D A5506 For diabetics only, modification (including fitting) of off-the-shelf depth-inlay shoe or custom-molded shoe with off-set heel(s), per shoe   DME Y
BETOS: D1F   Prosthetic/orthotic devices
Pub: 100-2, Chap. 15, 140

D A5507 For diabetics only, not otherwise specified modification (including fitting) of off-the-shelf depth-inlay shoe or custom-molded shoe, per shoe   DME Y
BETOS: D1F   Prosthetic/orthotic devices
Pub: 100-2, Chap. 15, 140

D A5508 For diabetics only, deluxe feature of off-the-shelf depth-inlay shoe or custom-molded shoe, per shoe   Y
BETOS: D1F   Prosthetic/orthotic devices
Pub: 100-2, Chap. 15, 140

D A5510 For diabetics only, direct formed, compression molded to patient's foot without external heat source, multiple-density insert(s) prefabricated, per shoe   N
BETOS: D1F   Prosthetic/orthotic devices
Coding Clinic: 2002, Q1
Pub: 100-2, Chap. 15, 140

C A5512 For diabetics only, multiple density insert, direct formed, molded to foot after external heat source of 230 degrees Fahrenheit or higher, total contact with patient's foot, including arch, base layer minimum of 1/4 inch material of shore a 35 durometer or 3/16 inch material of shore a 40 durometer (or higher), prefabricated, each   DME Y
BETOS: D1F   Prosthetic/orthotic devices

C A5513 For diabetics only, multiple density insert, custom molded from model of patient's foot, total contact with patient's foot, including arch, base layer minimum of 3/16 inch material of shore a 35 durometer (or higher), includes arch filler and other shaping material, custom fabricated, each   DME Y
BETOS: D1F   Prosthetic/orthotic devices

MISCELLANEOUS DRESSING AND WOUND SUPPLIES (A6000-A6208)

M A6000 Non-contact wound warming wound cover for use with the non-contact wound warming device and warming card   E1
BETOS: D1E   Other DME
Service not separately priced by Part B
Coding Clinic: 2002, Q1

D A6010 Collagen based wound filler, dry form, sterile, per gram of collagen   DME N
BETOS: D1A   Medical/surgical supplies
Coding Clinic: 2002, Q1

D A6011 Collagen based wound filler, gel/paste, per gram of collagen   DME N
BETOS: D1A   Medical/surgical supplies

D A6021 Collagen dressing, sterile, size 16 sq. in. or less, each   DME N
BETOS: D1A   Medical/surgical supplies

D A6022 Collagen dressing, sterile, size more than 16 sq. in. but less than or equal to 48 sq. in., each   DME N
BETOS: D1A   Medical/surgical supplies

D A6023 Collagen dressing, sterile, size more than 48 sq. in., each   DME N
BETOS: D1A   Medical/surgical supplies

D A6024 Collagen dressing wound filler, sterile, per 6 inches   DME N
BETOS: D1A   Medical/surgical supplies

C A6025 Gel sheet for dermal or epidermal application, (e.g., silicone, hydrogel, other), each   N
BETOS: D1A   Medical/surgical supplies
Service not separately priced by Part B

D A6154 Wound pouch, each   DME N
BETOS: D1A   Medical/surgical supplies

D A6196 Alginate or other fiber gelling dressing, wound cover, sterile, pad size 16 sq. in. or less, each dressing   DME N
BETOS: D1A   Medical/surgical supplies

D A6197 Alginate or other fiber gelling dressing, wound cover, sterile, pad size more than 16 sq. in. but less than or equal to 48 sq. in., each dressing   DME N
BETOS: D1A   Medical/surgical supplies

▲ Revised code   ● New code   C Carrier judgment   D Special coverage instructions apply
I Not payable by Medicare   M Non-covered by Medicare   S Non-covered by Medicare statute   AHA Coding Clinic®

116   *CPT® is a registered trademark of the American Medical Association. All rights reserved.*

D **A6198** Alginate or other fiber gelling dressing, wound cover, sterile, pad size more than 48 sq. in., each dressing   N
BETOS: D1A   Medical/surgical supplies

D **A6199** Alginate or other fiber gelling dressing, wound filler, sterile, per 6 inches   DME N
BETOS: D1A   Medical/surgical supplies

D **A6203** Composite dressing, sterile, pad size 16 sq. in. or less, with any size adhesive border, each dressing   DME N
BETOS: D1A   Medical/surgical supplies

D **A6204** Composite dressing, sterile, pad size more than 16 sq. in. but less than or equal to 48 sq. in., with any size adhesive border, each dressing   DME N
BETOS: D1A   Medical/surgical supplies

D **A6205** Composite dressing, sterile, pad size more than 48 sq. in., with any size adhesive border, each dressing   N
BETOS: D1A   Medical/surgical supplies

D **A6206** Contact layer, sterile, 16 sq. in. or less, each dressing   N
BETOS: D1A   Medical/surgical supplies

D **A6207** Contact layer, sterile, more than 16 sq. in. but less than or equal to 48 sq. in., each dressing   DME N
BETOS: D1A   Medical/surgical supplies

D **A6208** Contact layer, sterile, more than 48 sq. in., each dressing   N
BETOS: D1A   Medical/surgical supplies

FOAM DRESSINGS (A6209-A6215)

D **A6209** Foam dressing, wound cover, sterile, pad size 16 sq. in. or less, without adhesive border, each dressing   DME N
BETOS: D1A   Medical/surgical supplies

D **A6210** Foam dressing, wound cover, sterile, pad size more than 16 sq. in. but less than or equal to 48 sq. in., without adhesive border, each dressing   DME N
BETOS: D1A   Medical/surgical supplies

D **A6211** Foam dressing, wound cover, sterile, pad size more than 48 sq. in., without adhesive border, each dressing   DME N
BETOS: D1A   Medical/surgical supplies

D **A6212** Foam dressing, wound cover, sterile, pad size 16 sq. in. or less, with any size adhesive border, each dressing   DME N
BETOS: D1A   Medical/surgical supplies

D **A6213** Foam dressing, wound cover, sterile, pad size more than 16 sq. in. but less than or equal to 48 sq. in., with any size adhesive border, each dressing   N
BETOS: D1A   Medical/surgical supplies

D **A6214** Foam dressing, wound cover, sterile, pad size more than 48 sq. in., with any size adhesive border, each dressing   DME N
BETOS: D1A   Medical/surgical supplies

D **A6215** Foam dressing, wound filler, sterile, per gram   N
BETOS: D1A   Medical/surgical supplies

GAUZE DRESSINGS (A6216-A6233)

D **A6216** Gauze, non-impregnated, non-sterile, pad size 16 sq. in. or less, without adhesive border, each dressing   DME N
BETOS: D1A   Medical/surgical supplies

D **A6217** Gauze, non-impregnated, non-sterile, pad size more than 16 sq. in. but less than or equal to 48 sq. in., without adhesive border, each dressing   DME N
BETOS: D1A   Medical/surgical supplies

D **A6218** Gauze, non-impregnated, non-sterile, pad size more than 48 sq. in., without adhesive border, each dressing   N
BETOS: D1A   Medical/surgical supplies

D **A6219** Gauze, non-impregnated, sterile, pad size 16 sq. in. or less, with any size adhesive border, each dressing   DME N
BETOS: D1A   Medical/surgical supplies

D **A6220** Gauze, non-impregnated, sterile, pad size more than 16 sq. in. but less than or equal to 48 sq. in., with any size adhesive border, each dressing   DME N
BETOS: D1A   Medical/surgical supplies

D **A6221** Gauze, non-impregnated, sterile, pad size more than 48 sq. in., with any size adhesive border, each dressing   N
BETOS: D1A   Medical/surgical supplies

D **A6222** Gauze, impregnated with other than water, normal saline, or hydrogel, sterile, pad size 16 sq. in. or less, without adhesive border, each dressing   DME N
BETOS: D1A   Medical/surgical supplies

D **A6223** Gauze, impregnated with other than water, normal saline, or hydrogel, sterile, pad size more than 16 sq. in., but less than or equal to 48 sq. in., without adhesive border, each dressing   DME N
BETOS: D1A   Medical/surgical supplies

D **A6224** Gauze, impregnated with other than water, normal saline, or hydrogel, sterile, pad size more than 48 sq. in., without adhesive border, each dressing   DME N
BETOS: D1A   Medical/surgical supplies

D **A6228** Gauze, impregnated, water or normal saline, sterile, pad size 16 sq. in. or less, without adhesive border, each dressing   N
BETOS: D1A   Medical/surgical supplies

♂ Male only   ♀ Female only   **Ⓐ** Age   A2 - Z3 = ASC Payment indicator   A - Y = APC Status indicator
ASC = ASC-approved procedure   DME Paid under the DME fee schedule   MIPS MIPS code

D A6229 Gauze, impregnated, water or normal saline, sterile, pad size more than 16 sq. in. but less than or equal to 48 sq. in., without adhesive border, each dressing   DME N

     BETOS: D1A   Medical/surgical supplies

D A6230 Gauze, impregnated, water or normal saline, sterile, pad size more than 48 sq. in., without adhesive border, each dressing   N

     BETOS: D1A   Medical/surgical supplies

D A6231 Gauze, impregnated, hydrogel, for direct wound contact, sterile, pad size 16 sq. in. or less, each dressing   DME N

     BETOS: D1A   Medical/surgical supplies

D A6232 Gauze, impregnated, hydrogel, for direct wound contact, sterile, pad size greater than 16 sq. in., but less than or equal to 48 sq. in., each dressing   DME N

     BETOS: D1A   Medical/surgical supplies

D A6233 Gauze, impregnated, hydrogel, for direct wound contact, sterile, pad size more than 48 sq. in., each dressing   DME N

     BETOS: D1A   Medical/surgical supplies

HYDROCOLLOID DRESSINGS (A6234-A6241)

D A6234 Hydrocolloid dressing, wound cover, sterile, pad size 16 sq. in. or less, without adhesive border, each dressing   DME N

     BETOS: D1A   Medical/surgical supplies

D A6235 Hydrocolloid dressing, wound cover, sterile, pad size more than 16 sq. in. but less than or equal to 48 sq. in., without adhesive border, each dressing   DME N

     BETOS: D1A   Medical/surgical supplies

D A6236 Hydrocolloid dressing, wound cover, sterile, pad size more than 48 sq. in., without adhesive border, each dressing   DME N

     BETOS: D1A   Medical/surgical supplies

D A6237 Hydrocolloid dressing, wound cover, sterile, pad size 16 sq. in. or less, with any size adhesive border, each dressing   DME N

     BETOS: D1A   Medical/surgical supplies

D A6238 Hydrocolloid dressing, wound cover, sterile, pad size more than 16 sq. in. but less than or equal to 48 sq. in., with any size adhesive border, each dressing   DME N

     BETOS: D1A   Medical/surgical supplies

D A6239 Hydrocolloid dressing, wound cover, sterile, pad size more than 48 sq. in., with any size adhesive border, each dressing   N

     BETOS: D1A   Medical/surgical supplies

D A6240 Hydrocolloid dressing, wound filler, paste, sterile, per ounce   DME N

     BETOS: D1A   Medical/surgical supplies

D A6241 Hydrocolloid dressing, wound filler, dry form, sterile, per gram   DME N

     BETOS: D1A   Medical/surgical supplies

HYDROGEL DRESSINGS (A6242-A6248)

D A6242 Hydrogel dressing, wound cover, sterile, pad size 16 sq. in. or less, without adhesive border, each dressing   DME N

     BETOS: D1A   Medical/surgical supplies

D A6243 Hydrogel dressing, wound cover, sterile, pad size more than 16 sq. in. but less than or equal to 48 sq. in., without adhesive border, each dressing   DME N

     BETOS: D1A   Medical/surgical supplies

D A6244 Hydrogel dressing, wound cover, sterile, pad size more than 48 sq. in., without adhesive border, each dressing   DME N

     BETOS: D1A   Medical/surgical supplies

D A6245 Hydrogel dressing, wound cover, sterile, pad size 16 sq. in. or less, with any size adhesive border, each dressing   DME N

     BETOS: D1A   Medical/surgical supplies

D A6246 Hydrogel dressing, wound cover, sterile, pad size more than 16 sq. in. but less than or equal to 48 sq. in., with any size adhesive border, each dressing   DME N

     BETOS: D1A   Medical/surgical supplies

D A6247 Hydrogel dressing, wound cover, sterile, pad size more than 48 sq. in., with any size adhesive border, each dressing   DME N

     BETOS: D1A   Medical/surgical supplies

D A6248 Hydrogel dressing, wound filler, gel, per fluid ounce   DME N

     BETOS: D1A   Medical/surgical supplies

OTHER DRESSINGS, COVERINGS, AND WOUND TREATMENT SUPPLIES (A6250-A6412)

D A6250 Skin sealants, protectants, moisturizers, ointments, any type, any size   N

     BETOS: D1A   Medical/surgical supplies

     Service not separately priced by Part B

D A6251 Specialty absorptive dressing, wound cover, sterile, pad size 16 sq. in. or less, without adhesive border, each dressing   DME N

     BETOS: D1A   Medical/surgical supplies

D A6252 Specialty absorptive dressing, wound cover, sterile, pad size more than 16 sq. in. but less than or equal to 48 sq. in., without adhesive border, each dressing   DME N

     BETOS: D1A   Medical/surgical supplies

D A6253 Specialty absorptive dressing, wound cover, sterile, pad size more than 48 sq. in., without adhesive border, each dressing   DME N

     BETOS: D1A   Medical/surgical supplies

D A6254 Specialty absorptive dressing, wound cover, sterile, pad size 16 sq. in. or less, with any size adhesive border, each dressing   DME N

     BETOS: D1A   Medical/surgical supplies

▲ Revised code   ● New code   **C** Carrier judgment   **D** Special coverage instructions apply

I Not payable by Medicare   **M** Non-covered by Medicare   **S** Non-covered by Medicare statute   AHA Coding Clinic®

D A6255 Specialty absorptive dressing, wound cover, sterile, pad size more than 16 sq. in. but less than or equal to 48 sq. in., with any size adhesive border, each dressing   DME N
BETOS: D1A Medical/surgical supplies

D A6256 Specialty absorptive dressing, wound cover, sterile, pad size more than 48 sq. in., with any size adhesive border, each dressing   N
BETOS: D1A Medical/surgical supplies

D A6257 Transparent film, sterile, 16 sq. in. or less, each dressing   DME N
BETOS: D1A Medical/surgical supplies

D A6258 Transparent film, sterile, more than 16 sq. in. but less than or equal to 48 sq. in., each dressing   DME N
BETOS: D1A Medical/surgical supplies

D A6259 Transparent film, sterile, more than 48 sq. in., each dressing   DME N
BETOS: D1A Medical/surgical supplies

D A6260 Wound cleansers, any type, any size   N
BETOS: D1A Medical/surgical supplies
Service not separately priced by Part B

D A6261 Wound filler, gel/paste, per fluid ounce, not otherwise specified   N
BETOS: D1A Medical/surgical supplies

D A6262 Wound filler, dry form, per gram, not otherwise specified   N
BETOS: D1A Medical/surgical supplies

D A6266 Gauze, impregnated, other than water, normal saline, or zinc paste, sterile, any width, per linear yard   DME N
BETOS: D1A Medical/surgical supplies

D A6402 Gauze, non-impregnated, sterile, pad size 16 sq. in. or less, without adhesive border, each dressing   DME N
BETOS: D1A Medical/surgical supplies

D A6403 Gauze, non-impregnated, sterile, pad size more than 16 sq. in. less than or equal to 48 sq. in., without adhesive border, each dressing   DME N
BETOS: D1A Medical/surgical supplies

D A6404 Gauze, non-impregnated, sterile, pad size more than 48 sq. in., without adhesive border, each dressing   N
BETOS: D1A Medical/surgical supplies

C A6407 Packing strips, non-impregnated, sterile, up to 2 inches in width, per linear yard   DME N
BETOS: D1A Medical/surgical supplies

D A6410 Eye pad, sterile, each   DME N
BETOS: D1A Medical/surgical supplies

D A6411 Eye pad, non-sterile, each   DME N
BETOS: D1A Medical/surgical supplies

C A6412 Eye patch, occlusive, each   N
BETOS: Z2 Undefined codes
Service not separately priced by Part B

BANDAGES (A6413-A6457)

S A6413 Adhesive bandage, first-aid type, any size, each   E1
BETOS: D1A Medical/surgical supplies
Service not separately priced by Part B
Statute: 1861(s)(5)

C A6441 Padding bandage, non-elastic, non-woven/non-knitted, width greater than or equal to three inches and less than five inches, per yard   DME N
BETOS: D1A Medical/surgical supplies

C A6442 Conforming bandage, non-elastic, knitted/woven, non-sterile, width less than three inches, per yard   DME N
BETOS: D1A Medical/surgical supplies

C A6443 Conforming bandage, non-elastic, knitted/woven, non-sterile, width greater than or equal to three inches and less than five inches, per yard   DME N
BETOS: D1A Medical/surgical supplies

C A6444 Conforming bandage, non-elastic, knitted/woven, non-sterile, width greater than or equal to 5 inches, per yard   DME N
BETOS: D1A Medical/surgical supplies

C A6445 Conforming bandage, non-elastic, knitted/woven, sterile, width less than three inches, per yard   DME N
BETOS: D1A Medical/surgical supplies

C A6446 Conforming bandage, non-elastic, knitted/woven, sterile, width greater than or equal to three inches and less than five inches, per yard   DME N
BETOS: D1A Medical/surgical supplies

C A6447 Conforming bandage, non-elastic, knitted/woven, sterile, width greater than or equal to five inches, per yard   DME N
BETOS: D1A Medical/surgical supplies

C A6448 Light compression bandage, elastic, knitted woven, width less than three inches, per yard   DME N
BETOS: D1A Medical/surgical supplies

C A6449 Light compression bandage, elastic, knitted/woven, width greater than or equal to three inches and less than five inches, per yard   DME N
BETOS: D1A Medical/surgical supplies

C A6450 Light compression bandage, elastic, knitted/woven, width greater than or equal to five inches, per yard   DME N
BETOS: D1A Medical/surgical supplies

C A6451 Moderate compression bandage, elastic, knitted/woven, load resistance of 1.25 to 1.34 foot pounds at 50% maximum stretch, width greater than or equal to three inches and less than five inches, per yard   DME N
BETOS: D1A Medical/surgical supplies

Elastic ACE compression bandage

C **A6452** High compression bandage, elastic, knitted/woven, load resistance greater than or equal to 1.35 foot pounds at 50% maximum stretch, width greater than or equal to three inches and less than five inches, per yard DME N

    BETOS: D1A Medical/surgical supplies

C **A6453** Self-adherent bandage, elastic, non-knitted/non-woven, width less than three inches, per yard DME N

    BETOS: D1A Medical/surgical supplies

C **A6454** Self-adherent bandage, elastic, non-knitted/non-woven, width greater than or equal to three inches and less than five inches, per yard DME N

    BETOS: D1A Medical/surgical supplies

C **A6455** Self-adherent bandage, elastic, non-knitted/non-woven, width greater than or equal to five inches, per yard DME N

    BETOS: D1A Medical/surgical supplies

C **A6456** Zinc paste impregnated bandage, non-elastic, knitted/woven, width greater than or equal to three inches and less than five inches, per yard DME N

    BETOS: D1A Medical/surgical supplies

C **A6457** Tubular dressing with or without elastic, any width, per linear yard DME N

    BETOS: D1A Medical/surgical supplies

COMPRESSION GARMENTS AND STOCKINGS (A6501-A6550)

D **A6501** Compression burn garment, bodysuit (head to foot), custom fabricated DME N

    BETOS: D1A Medical/surgical supplies

D **A6502** Compression burn garment, chin strap, custom fabricated DME N

    BETOS: D1A Medical/surgical supplies

D **A6503** Compression burn garment, facial hood, custom fabricated DME N

    BETOS: D1A Medical/surgical supplies

D **A6504** Compression burn garment, glove to wrist, custom fabricated DME N

    BETOS: D1A Medical/surgical supplies

D **A6505** Compression burn garment, glove to elbow, custom fabricated DME N

    BETOS: D1A Medical/surgical supplies

D **A6506** Compression burn garment, glove to axilla, custom fabricated DME N

    BETOS: D1A Medical/surgical supplies

D **A6507** Compression burn garment, foot to knee length, custom fabricated DME N

    BETOS: D1A Medical/surgical supplies

D **A6508** Compression burn garment, foot to thigh length, custom fabricated DME N

    BETOS: D1A Medical/surgical supplies

D **A6509** Compression burn garment, upper trunk to waist including arm openings (vest), custom fabricated DME N

    BETOS: D1A Medical/surgical supplies

D **A6510** Compression burn garment, trunk, including arms down to leg openings (leotard), custom fabricated DME N

    BETOS: D1A Medical/surgical supplies

D **A6511** Compression burn garment, lower trunk including leg openings (panty), custom fabricated DME N

    BETOS: D1A Medical/surgical supplies

D **A6512** Compression burn garment, not otherwise classified N

    BETOS: D1A Medical/surgical supplies

C **A6513** Compression burn mask, face and/or neck, plastic or equal, custom fabricated DME B

    BETOS: D1A Medical/surgical supplies

    Service not separately priced by Part B

M **A6530** Gradient compression stocking, below knee, 18-30 mmHg, each E1

    BETOS: D1A Medical/surgical supplies

    Service not separately priced by Part B

D **A6531** Gradient compression stocking, below knee, 30-40 mmHg, each DME N

    BETOS: D1A Medical/surgical supplies

    DME Modifier: AW

D **A6532** Gradient compression stocking, below knee, 40-50 mmHg, each DME N

    BETOS: D1A Medical/surgical supplies

    DME Modifier: AW

M **A6533** Gradient compression stocking, thigh length, 18-30 mmHg, each E1

    BETOS: D1A Medical/surgical supplies

    Service not separately priced by Part B

M **A6534** Gradient compression stocking, thigh length, 30-40 mmHg, each E1

    BETOS: D1A Medical/surgical supplies

    Service not separately priced by Part B

M **A6535** Gradient compression stocking, thigh length, 40-50 mmHg, each E1

    BETOS: D1A Medical/surgical supplies

    Service not separately priced by Part B

▲ Revised code   ● New code   C Carrier judgment   D Special coverage instructions apply

I Not payable by Medicare   M Non-covered by Medicare   S Non-covered by Medicare statute   AHA Coding Clinic®

M A6536 Gradient compression stocking, full length/chap style, 18-30 mmHg, each   E1
BETOS: D1A   Medical/surgical supplies
Service not separately priced by Part B

M A6537 Gradient compression stocking, full length/chap style, 30-40 mmHg, each   E1
BETOS: D1A   Medical/surgical supplies
Service not separately priced by Part B

M A6538 Gradient compression stocking, full length/chap style, 40-50 mmHg, each   E1
BETOS: D1A   Medical/surgical supplies
Service not separately priced by Part B

M A6539 Gradient compression stocking, waist length, 18-30 mmHg, each   E1
BETOS: D1A   Medical/surgical supplies
Service not separately priced by Part B

M A6540 Gradient compression stocking, waist length, 30-40 mmHg, each   E1
BETOS: D1A   Medical/surgical supplies
Service not separately priced by Part B

M A6541 Gradient compression stocking, waist length, 40-50 mmHg, each   E1
BETOS: D1A   Medical/surgical supplies
Service not separately priced by Part B

M A6544 Gradient compression stocking, garter belt   E1
BETOS: D1A   Medical/surgical supplies
Service not separately priced by Part B

D A6545 Gradient compression wrap, non-elastic, below knee, 30-50 mmHg, each   DME N
BETOS: D1A   Medical/surgical supplies
DME Modifier: AW
Coding Clinic: 2008, Q4

M A6549 Gradient compression stocking/sleeve, not otherwise specified   E1
BETOS: D1A   Medical/surgical supplies
Service not separately priced by Part B

C A6550 Wound care set, for negative pressure wound therapy electrical pump, includes all supplies and accessories   DME N
BETOS: D1E   Other DME
Pub: 100-4, Chap. 23, 60.3

BREATHING AIDS (A7000-A7048)

C A7000 Canister, disposable, used with suction pump, each   DME Y
BETOS: D1E   Other DME
DME Modifier: NU
Pub: 100-4, Chap. 23, 60.3

C A7001 Canister, non-disposable, used with suction pump, each   DME Y
BETOS: D1E   Other DME
DME Modifier: NU

C A7002 Tubing, used with suction pump, each   DME Y
BETOS: D1E   Other DME
DME Modifier: NU

C A7003 Administration set, with small volume nonfiltered pneumatic nebulizer, disposable   DME Y
BETOS: D1E   Other DME
DME Modifier: NU

C A7004 Small volume nonfiltered pneumatic nebulizer, disposable   DME Y
BETOS: D1E   Other DME
DME Modifier: NU

C A7005 Administration set, with small volume nonfiltered pneumatic nebulizer, non-disposable   DME Y
BETOS: D1E   Other DME
DME Modifier: NU

C A7006 Administration set, with small volume filtered pneumatic nebulizer   DME Y
BETOS: D1E   Other DME
DME Modifier: NU

C A7007 Large volume nebulizer, disposable, unfilled, used with aerosol compressor   DME Y
BETOS: D1E   Other DME
DME Modifier: NU

C A7008 Large volume nebulizer, disposable, prefilled, used with aerosol compressor   DME Y
BETOS: D1E   Other DME
DME Modifier: NU

C A7009 Reservoir bottle, non-disposable, used with large volume ultrasonic nebulizer   DME Y
BETOS: D1E   Other DME
DME Modifier: NU

C A7010 Corrugated tubing, disposable, used with large volume nebulizer, 100 feet   DME Y
BETOS: D1E   Other DME
DME Modifier: NU

C A7012 Water collection device, used with large volume nebulizer   DME Y
BETOS: D1E   Other DME
DME Modifier: NU

C A7013 Filter, disposable, used with aerosol compressor or ultrasonic generator   DME Y
BETOS: D1E   Other DME
DME Modifier: NU

C A7014 Filter, nondisposable, used with aerosol compressor or ultrasonic generator   DME Y
BETOS: D1E   Other DME
DME Modifier: NU

C A7015 Aerosol mask, used with DME nebulizer   DME Y
BETOS: D1E   Other DME
DME Modifier: NU

C A7016 Dome and mouthpiece, used with small volume ultrasonic nebulizer   DME Y
BETOS: D1E   Other DME
DME Modifier: NU

D **A7017** Nebulizer, durable, glass or autoclavable plastic, bottle type, not used with oxygen   `DME` Y
  BETOS: D1E   Other DME
  DME Modifier: NU,RR,UE

C **A7018** Water, distilled, used with large volume nebulizer, 1000 ml   `DME` Y
  BETOS: D1E   Other DME

C **A7020** Interface for cough stimulating device, includes all components, replacement only   `DME` Y
  BETOS: D1E   Other DME
  DME Modifier: NU

C **A7025** High frequency chest wall oscillation system vest, replacement for use with patient owned equipment, each   `DME` N
  BETOS: D1E   Other DME
  DME Modifier: RR

C **A7026** High frequency chest wall oscillation system hose, replacement for use with patient owned equipment, each   `DME` Y
  BETOS: D1E   Other DME
  DME Modifier: NU

C **A7027** Combination oral/nasal mask, used with continuous positive airway pressure device, each   `DME` Y
  BETOS: D1E   Other DME
  DME Modifier: NU

C **A7028** Oral cushion for combination oral/nasal mask, replacement only, each   `DME` Y
  BETOS: D1E   Other DME
  DME Modifier: NU

C **A7029** Nasal pillows for combination oral/nasal mask, replacement only, pair   `DME` Y
  BETOS: D1E   Other DME
  DME Modifier: NU

C **A7030** Full face mask used with positive airway pressure device, each   `DME` Y
  BETOS: D1E   Other DME
  DME Modifier: NU
  Pub: 100-4, Chap. 23, 60.3; 100-4, Chap. 36, 50.14

C **A7031** Face mask interface, replacement for full face mask, each   `DME` Y
  BETOS: D1E   Other DME
  DME Modifier: NU

C **A7032** Cushion for use on nasal mask interface, replacement only, each   `DME` Y
  BETOS: D1E   Other DME
  DME Modifier: NU

C **A7033** Pillow for use on nasal cannula type interface, replacement only, pair   `DME` Y
  BETOS: D1E   Other DME
  DME Modifier: NU

C **A7034** Nasal interface (mask or cannula type) used with positive airway pressure device, with or without head strap   `DME` Y
  BETOS: D1E   Other DME
  DME Modifier: NU

C **A7035** Headgear used with positive airway pressure device   `DME` Y
  BETOS: D1E   Other DME
  DME Modifier: NU

C **A7036** Chinstrap used with positive airway pressure device   `DME` Y
  BETOS: D1E   Other DME
  DME Modifier: NU

C **A7037** Tubing used with positive airway pressure device   `DME` Y
  BETOS: D1E   Other DME
  DME Modifier: NU

C **A7038** Filter, disposable, used with positive airway pressure device   `DME` Y
  BETOS: D1E   Other DME
  DME Modifier: NU

C **A7039** Filter, non disposable, used with positive airway pressure device   `DME` Y
  BETOS: D1E   Other DME
  DME Modifier: NU

C **A7040** One-way chest drain valve   `DME` N
  BETOS: D1F   Prosthetic/orthotic devices

C **A7041** Water seal drainage container and tubing for use with implanted chest tube   `DME` N
  BETOS: D1F   Prosthetic/orthotic devices

C **A7044** Oral interface used with positive airway pressure device, each   `DME` Y
  BETOS: D1E   Other DME
  DME Modifier: NU

D **A7045** Exhalation port with or without swivel used with accessories for positive airway devices, replacement only   `DME` Y
  BETOS: D1E   Other DME
  DME Modifier: NU,RR,UE

D **A7046** Water chamber for humidifier, used with positive airway pressure device, replacement, each   `DME` Y
  BETOS: D1E   Other DME
  DME Modifier: NU

C **A7047** Oral interface used with respiratory suction pump, each   `DME` N
  BETOS: D1E   Other DME
  DME Modifier: NU

C **A7048** Vacuum drainage collection unit and tubing kit, including all supplies needed for collection unit change, for use with implanted catheter, each   `DME` N
  BETOS: D1F   Prosthetic/orthotic devices

▲ Revised code   ● New code   **C** Carrier judgment   **D** Special coverage instructions apply
I Not payable by Medicare   **M** Non-covered by Medicare   **S** Non-covered by Medicare statute   AHA Coding Clinic®

TRACHEOSTOMY SUPPLIES (A7501-A7527)

D A7501 Tracheostoma valve, including diaphragm, each   DME N
BETOS: D1F   Prosthetic/orthotic devices

D A7502 Replacement diaphragm/faceplate for tracheostoma valve, each   DME N
BETOS: D1F   Prosthetic/orthotic devices

D A7503 Filter holder or filter cap, reusable, for use in a tracheostoma heat and moisture exchange system, each   DME N
BETOS: D1F   Prosthetic/orthotic devices

D A7504 Filter for use in a tracheostoma heat and moisture exchange system, each   DME N
BETOS: D1F   Prosthetic/orthotic devices

D A7505 Housing, reusable without adhesive, for use in a heat and moisture exchange system and/or with a tracheostoma valve, each   DME N
BETOS: D1F   Prosthetic/orthotic devices

D A7506 Adhesive disc for use in a heat and moisture exchange system and/or with tracheostoma valve, any type each   DME N
BETOS: D1F   Prosthetic/orthotic devices

D A7507 Filter holder and integrated filter without adhesive, for use in a tracheostoma heat and moisture exchange system, each   DME N
BETOS: D1F   Prosthetic/orthotic devices

D A7508 Housing and integrated adhesive, for use in a tracheostoma heat and moisture exchange system and/or with a tracheostoma valve, each   DME N
BETOS: D1F   Prosthetic/orthotic devices

D A7509 Filter holder and integrated filter housing, and adhesive, for use as a tracheostoma heat and moisture exchange system, each   DME N
BETOS: D1F   Prosthetic/orthotic devices

C A7520 Tracheostomy/laryngectomy tube, non-cuffed, polyvinylchloride (PVC), silicone or equal, each   DME N
BETOS: D1F   Prosthetic/orthotic devices
Pub: 100-2, Chap. 1, 40

C A7521 Tracheostomy/laryngectomy tube, cuffed, polyvinylchloride (PVC), silicone or equal, each   DME N
BETOS: D1F   Prosthetic/orthotic devices
Pub: 100-2, Chap. 1, 40

C A7522 Tracheostomy/laryngectomy tube, stainless steel or equal (sterilizable and reusable), each   DME N
BETOS: D1F   Prosthetic/orthotic devices
Pub: 100-2, Chap. 1, 40

C A7523 Tracheostomy shower protector, each   N
BETOS: D1F   Prosthetic/orthotic devices

C A7524 Tracheostoma stent/stud/button, each   DME N
BETOS: D1F   Prosthetic/orthotic devices

C A7525 Tracheostomy mask, each   DME N
BETOS: D1F   Prosthetic/orthotic devices

C A7526 Tracheostomy tube collar/holder, each   DME N
BETOS: D1F   Prosthetic/orthotic devices

C A7527 Tracheostomy/laryngectomy tube plug/stop, each   DME N
BETOS: D1A   Medical/surgical supplies

HELMETS (A8000-A8004)

C A8000 Helmet, protective, soft, prefabricated, includes all components and accessories   DME Y
BETOS: D1E   Other DME
DME Modifier: NU,RR,UE

Helmet

C A8001 Helmet, protective, hard, prefabricated, includes all components and accessories   DME Y
BETOS: D1E   Other DME
DME Modifier: NU,RR,UE

C A8002 Helmet, protective, soft, custom fabricated, includes all components and accessories   DME Y
BETOS: D1E   Other DME
DME Modifier: NU,RR,UE

C A8003 Helmet, protective, hard, custom fabricated, includes all components and accessories   DME Y
BETOS: D1E   Other DME
DME Modifier: NU,RR,UE

C A8004 Soft interface for helmet, replacement only   DME Y
BETOS: D1E   Other DME
DME Modifier: NU,RR,UE

NOTES

ADMINISTRATIVE, MISCELLANEOUS AND INVESTIGATIONAL (A9150-A9999)

MISCELLANEOUS SUPPLIES AND EQUIPMENT (A9150-A9300)

D A9150 Non-prescription drugs   B
BETOS: O1E   Other drugs
Other carrier priced

I A9152 Single vitamin/mineral/trace element, oral, per dose, not otherwise specified   E1
BETOS: Z2   Undefined codes
Service not separately priced by Part B

I A9153 Multiple vitamins, with or without minerals and trace elements, oral, per dose, not otherwise specified   E1
BETOS: Z2   Undefined codes
Service not separately priced by Part B

C A9155 Artificial saliva, 30 ml   B
BETOS: Z2   Undefined codes
Other carrier priced

I A9180 Pediculosis (lice infestation) treatment, topical, for administration by patient/caretaker   E1
BETOS: Z2   Undefined codes
Service not separately priced by Part B

M A9270 Non-covered item or service   E1
BETOS: Z2   Undefined codes
Service not separately priced by Part B
Pub: 100-4, Chap. 11, 100.1

S A9272 Wound suction, disposable, includes dressing, all accessories and components, any type, each   E1
BETOS: D1A   Medical/surgical supplies
Service not separately priced by Part B
Statute: 1861(n)

M A9273 Hot water bottle, ice cap or collar, heat and/or cold wrap, any type   E1
BETOS: Z2   Undefined codes
Service not separately priced by Part B

S A9274 External ambulatory insulin delivery system, disposable, each, includes all supplies and accessories   E1
BETOS: D1A   Medical/surgical supplies
Service not separately priced by Part B
Statute: 1861(n)

M A9275 Home glucose disposable monitor, includes test strips   E1
BETOS: T1E   Lab tests - glucose
Service not separately priced by Part B

S A9276 Sensor; invasive (e.g., subcutaneous), disposable, for use with interstitial continuous glucose monitoring system, one unit = 1 day supply   E1
BETOS: D1E   Other DME
Service not separately priced by Part B
Statute: 1861(n)

S A9277 Transmitter; external, for use with interstitial continuous glucose monitoring system   E1
BETOS: D1E   Other DME
Service not separately priced by Part B
Statute: 1861(n)

S A9278 Receiver (monitor); external, for use with interstitial continuous glucose monitoring system   E1
BETOS: D1E   Other DME
Service not separately priced by Part B
Statute: 1861(n)

S A9279 Monitoring feature/device, stand-alone or integrated, any type, includes all accessories, components and electronics, not otherwise classified   E1
BETOS: T2D   Other tests - other
Service not separately priced by Part B
Statute: 1861(n)

S A9280 Alert or alarm device, not otherwise classified   E1
BETOS: Z2   Undefined codes
Service not separately priced by Part B
Statute: 1861

S A9281 Reaching/grabbing device, any type, any length, each   E1
BETOS: D1E   Other DME
Service not separately priced by Part B
Statute: 1862SSA

S A9282 Wig, any type, each   E1
BETOS: Z2   Undefined codes
Service not separately priced by Part B
Statute: 1861SSA

S A9283 Foot pressure off loading/supportive device, any type, each   E1
BETOS: D1E   Other DME
Service not separately priced by Part B
Statute: 1862a(i)13

D A9284 Spirometer, non-electronic, includes all accessories   N
BETOS: Z2   Undefined codes
Service not separately priced by Part B
Coding Clinic: 2008, Q4

C A9285 Inversion/eversion correction device   A
BETOS: Z2   Undefined codes
Service not separately priced by Part B

S A9286 Hygienic item or device, disposable or non-disposable, any type, each   E1
BETOS: D1A   Medical/surgical supplies
Service not separately priced by Part B
Statute: 1834

M A9300 Exercise equipment   E1
BETOS: Z2   Undefined codes
Service not separately priced by Part B

ADMINISTRATIVE, MISCELLANEOUS AND INVESTIGATIONAL (A9150-A9999)   **A9500 - A9526**

DIAGNOSTIC AND THERAPEUTIC RADIOPHARMACEUTICALS (A9500-A9700), SEE ALSO DIAGNOSTIC RADIOPHARMACEUTICALS (A4641-A4642)

C A9500 Technetium Tc-99m sestamibi, diagnostic, per study dose   N1 ASC N
BETOS: I1E   Standard imaging - nuclear medicine
Other carrier priced
Coding Clinic: 2005, Q4; 2006, Q2

C A9501 Technetium Tc-99m teboroxime, diagnostic, per study dose   N1 ASC N
BETOS: I1E   Standard imaging - nuclear medicine
Other carrier priced
Coding Clinic: 2008, Q1

C A9502 Technetium Tc-99m tetrofosmin, diagnostic, per study dose   N1 ASC N
BETOS: I1E   Standard imaging - nuclear medicine
Other carrier priced
Coding Clinic: 2005, Q4; 2006, Q2

C A9503 Technetium Tc-99m medronate, diagnostic, per study dose, up to 30 millicuries N1 ASC N
BETOS: I1E   Standard imaging - nuclear medicine
Other carrier priced
Coding Clinic: 2002, Q2; 2004, Q3; 2005, Q4

C A9504 Technetium Tc-99m apcitide, diagnostic, per study dose, up to 20 millicuries   N1 ASC N
BETOS: I1E   Standard imaging - nuclear medicine
Other carrier priced
Coding Clinic: 2001, Q4; 2002, Q2

C A9505 Thallium Tl-201 thallous chloride, diagnostic, per millicurie   N1 ASC N
BETOS: I1E   Standard imaging - nuclear medicine
Other carrier priced
Coding Clinic: 2002, Q2; 2004, Q3; 2005, Q4

C A9507 Indium In-111 capromab pendetide, diagnostic, per study dose, up to 10 millicuries   N1 ASC N
BETOS: I1E   Standard imaging - nuclear medicine
Other carrier priced
Coding Clinic: 2005, Q4

C A9508 Iodine I-131 iobenguane sulfate, diagnostic, per 0.5 millicurie   N1 ASC N
BETOS: I1E   Standard imaging - nuclear medicine
Coding Clinic: 2002, Q2; 2005, Q4

C A9509 Iodine I-123 sodium iodide, diagnostic, per millicurie   N1 ASC N
BETOS: I1E   Standard imaging - nuclear medicine

Other carrier priced
Coding Clinic: 2008, Q1

C A9510 Technetium Tc-99m disofenin, diagnostic, per study dose, up to 15 millicuries   N1 ASC N
BETOS: I1E   Standard imaging - nuclear medicine
Coding Clinic: 2005, Q4

C A9512 Technetium Tc-99m pertechnetate, diagnostic, per millicurie   N1 ASC N
BETOS: I1E   Standard imaging - nuclear medicine
Other carrier priced
Coding Clinic: 2005, Q4

C A9515 Choline c-11, diagnostic, per study dose up to 20 millicuries   K2 ASC G
BETOS: I1E   Standard imaging - nuclear medicine
Other carrier priced
Drugs: CHOLINE C 11
Coding Clinic: 2005, Q4

C A9516 Iodine I-123 sodium iodide, diagnostic, per 100 microcuries, up to 999 microcuries   N1 ASC N
BETOS: I1E   Standard imaging - nuclear medicine
Other carrier priced
Coding Clinic: 2005, Q4

C A9517 Iodine I-131 sodium iodide capsule(s), therapeutic, per millicurie   K
BETOS: I1E   Standard imaging - nuclear medicine
Other carrier priced
Coding Clinic: 2005, Q4; 2008, Q3

C A9520 Technetium Tc-99m, tilmanocept, diagnostic, up to 0.5 millicuries   N1 ASC N
BETOS: I1E   Standard imaging - nuclear medicine
Other carrier priced
Coding Clinic: 2013, Q4

C A9521 Technetium Tc-99m exametazime, diagnostic, per study dose, up to 25 millicuries   N1 ASC N
BETOS: I1E   Standard imaging - nuclear medicine
Other carrier priced
Coding Clinic: 2005, Q4

C A9524 Iodine I-131 iodinated serum albumin, diagnostic, per 5 microcuries   N1 ASC N
BETOS: I1E   Standard imaging - nuclear medicine
Other carrier priced
Coding Clinic: 2005, Q4

C A9526 Nitrogen N-13 ammonia, diagnostic, per study dose, up to 40 millicuries   N1 ASC N
BETOS: I1E   Standard imaging - nuclear medicine
Coding Clinic: 2005, Q4

▲ Revised code   ● New code   **C** Carrier judgment   **D** Special coverage instructions apply
I Not payable by Medicare   **M** Non-covered by Medicare   **S** Non-covered by Medicare statute   AHA Coding Clinic®

     CPT® is a registered trademark of the American Medical Association. All rights reserved.

Pub: 100-4, Chap. 13, 60.3; 100-4, Chap. 13, 60.3.1; 100-4, Chap. 13, 60.3.2

C **A9527** Iodine I-125, sodium iodide solution, therapeutic, per millicurie   H2 ASC U
BETOS: I1E   Standard imaging - nuclear medicine
Other carrier priced
Coding Clinic: 2007, Q2

C **A9528** Iodine I-131 sodium iodide capsule(s), diagnostic, per millicurie   N1 ASC N
BETOS: I1E   Standard imaging - nuclear medicine
Other carrier priced
Coding Clinic: 2005, Q4

C **A9529** Iodine I-131 sodium iodide solution, diagnostic, per millicurie   N1 ASC N
BETOS: I1E   Standard imaging - nuclear medicine
Other carrier priced
Coding Clinic: 2005, Q4

C **A9530** Iodine I-131 sodium iodide solution, therapeutic, per millicurie   K
BETOS: I1E   Standard imaging - nuclear medicine
Other carrier priced
Coding Clinic: 2005, Q4

C **A9531** Iodine I-131 sodium iodide, diagnostic, per microcurie (up to 100 microcuries) N1 ASC N
BETOS: I1E   Standard imaging - nuclear medicine
Other carrier priced
Coding Clinic: 2005, Q4

C **A9532** Iodine I-125 serum albumin, diagnostic, per 5 microcuries   N1 ASC N
BETOS: I1E   Standard imaging - nuclear medicine
Other carrier priced
Coding Clinic: 2005, Q4

C **A9536** Technetium Tc-99m depreotide, diagnostic, per study dose, up to 35 millicuries N1 ASC N
BETOS: I1E   Standard imaging - nuclear medicine
Other carrier priced
Coding Clinic: 2005, Q4

C **A9537** Technetium Tc-99m mebrofenin, diagnostic, per study dose, up to 15 millicuries N1 ASC N
BETOS: I1E   Standard imaging - nuclear medicine
Other carrier priced
Coding Clinic: 2005, Q4

C **A9538** Technetium Tc-99m pyrophosphate, diagnostic, per study dose, up to 25 millicuries   N1 ASC N
BETOS: I1E   Standard imaging - nuclear medicine
Other carrier priced
Coding Clinic: 2005, Q4

C **A9539** Technetium Tc-99m pentetate, diagnostic, per study dose, up to 25 millicuries N1 ASC N
BETOS: I1E   Standard imaging - nuclear medicine
Other carrier priced
Coding Clinic: 2005, Q4

C **A9540** Technetium Tc-99m macroaggregated albumin, diagnostic, per study dose, up to 10 millicuries   N1 ASC N
BETOS: I1E   Standard imaging - nuclear medicine
Other carrier priced
Coding Clinic: 2005, Q4

C **A9541** Technetium Tc-99m sulfur colloid, diagnostic, per study dose, up to 20 millicuries N1 ASC N
BETOS: I1E   Standard imaging - nuclear medicine
Other carrier priced
Coding Clinic: 2005, Q4

C **A9542** Indium In-111 ibritumomab tiuxetan, diagnostic, per study dose, up to 5 millicuries   N1 ASC N
BETOS: I1E   Standard imaging - nuclear medicine
Coding Clinic: 2005, Q4

C **A9543** Yttrium Y-90 ibritumomab tiuxetan, therapeutic, per treatment dose, up to 40 millicuries   K
BETOS: I1E   Standard imaging - nuclear medicine
Drugs: ZEVALIN Y-90
Coding Clinic: 2005, Q4

C **A9546** Cobalt Co-57/58, cyanocobalamin, diagnostic, per study dose, up to 1 microcurie   N1 ASC N
BETOS: I1E   Standard imaging - nuclear medicine
Coding Clinic: 2005, Q4

C **A9547** Indium In-111 oxyquinoline, diagnostic, per 0.5 millicurie   N1 ASC N
BETOS: I1E   Standard imaging - nuclear medicine
Coding Clinic: 2005, Q4

C **A9548** Indium In-111 pentetate, diagnostic, per 0.5 millicurie   N1 ASC N
BETOS: I1E   Standard imaging - nuclear medicine
Coding Clinic: 2005, Q4

C **A9550** Technetium Tc-99m sodium gluceptate, diagnostic, per study dose, up to 25 millicurie   N1 ASC N
BETOS: I1E   Standard imaging - nuclear medicine
Coding Clinic: 2005, Q4

♂ Male only   ♀ Female only   Ⓐ Age   A2 - Z3 = ASC Payment indicator   A - Y = APC Status indicator
ASC = ASC-approved procedure   DME Paid under the DME fee schedule   MIPS MIPS code

C **A9551** Technetium Tc-99m succimer, diagnostic, per study dose, up to 10 millicuries   N1 ASC N
   BETOS: I1E   Standard imaging - nuclear medicine
   Coding Clinic: 2005, Q4

C **A9552** Fluorodeoxyglucose F-18 FDG, diagnostic, per study dose, up to 45 millicuries N1 ASC N
   BETOS: I1E   Standard imaging - nuclear medicine
   Coding Clinic: 2005, Q4; 2008, Q3
   Pub: 100-3, Chap. 1, Part-4, 220.6.17; 100-4, Chap. 13, 60.3.2

C **A9553** Chromium Cr-51 sodium chromate, diagnostic, per study dose, up to 250 microcuries   N1 ASC N
   BETOS: I1E   Standard imaging - nuclear medicine
   Coding Clinic: 2005, Q4

C **A9554** Iodine I-125 sodium iothalamate, diagnostic, per study dose, up to 10 microcuries   N1 ASC N
   BETOS: I1E   Standard imaging - nuclear medicine
   Coding Clinic: 2005, Q4

C **A9555** Rubidium Rb-82, diagnostic, per study dose, up to 60 millicuries   N1 ASC N
   BETOS: I1E   Standard imaging - nuclear medicine
   Value not established
   Coding Clinic: 2005, Q4
   Pub: 100-3, Chap. 1, Part-4, 220.6.1; 100-4, Chap. 13, 60.3.2

C **A9556** Gallium Ga-67 citrate, diagnostic, per millicurie   N1 ASC N
   BETOS: I1E   Standard imaging - nuclear medicine
   Other carrier priced
   Coding Clinic: 2005, Q4

C **A9557** Technetium Tc-99m bicisate, diagnostic, per study dose, up to 25 millicuries   N1 ASC N
   BETOS: I1E   Standard imaging - nuclear medicine
   Other carrier priced
   Coding Clinic: 2005, Q4

C **A9558** Xenon Xe-133 gas, diagnostic, per 10 millicuries   N1 ASC N
   BETOS: I1E   Standard imaging - nuclear medicine
   Other carrier priced
   Coding Clinic: 2005, Q4

C **A9559** Cobalt Co-57 cyanocobalamin, oral, diagnostic, per study dose, up to 1 microcurie   N1 ASC N
   BETOS: I1E   Standard imaging - nuclear medicine
   Other carrier priced
   Coding Clinic: 2005, Q4

C **A9560** Technetium Tc-99m labeled red blood cells, diagnostic, per study dose, up to 30 millicuries   N1 ASC N
   BETOS: I1E   Standard imaging - nuclear medicine
   Other carrier priced
   Coding Clinic: 2005, Q4; 2008, Q3

C **A9561** Technetium Tc-99m oxidronate, diagnostic, per study dose, up to 30 millicuries N1 ASC N
   BETOS: I1E   Standard imaging - nuclear medicine
   Other carrier priced
   Coding Clinic: 2005, Q4

C **A9562** Technetium Tc-99m mertiatide, diagnostic, per study dose, up to 15 millicuries N1 ASC N
   BETOS: I1E   Standard imaging - nuclear medicine
   Other carrier priced
   Coding Clinic: 2005, Q4

C **A9563** Sodium phosphate P-32, therapeutic, per millicurie   K
   BETOS: I1E   Standard imaging - nuclear medicine
   Other carrier priced
   Coding Clinic: 2005, Q4

C **A9564** Chromic phosphate P-32 suspension, therapeutic, per millicurie   K
   BETOS: I1E   Standard imaging - nuclear medicine
   Other carrier priced
   Coding Clinic: 2005, Q4

C **A9566** Technetium Tc-99m fanolesomab, diagnostic, per study dose, up to 25 millicuries N1 ASC N
   BETOS: I1E   Standard imaging - nuclear medicine
   Other carrier priced
   Coding Clinic: 2005, Q4

C **A9567** Technetium Tc-99m pentetate, diagnostic, aerosol, per study dose, up to 75 millicuries   N1 ASC N
   BETOS: I1E   Standard imaging - nuclear medicine
   Other carrier priced
   Coding Clinic: 2005, Q4

C **A9568** Technetium Tc-99m arcitumomab, diagnostic, per study dose, up to 45 millicuries N1 ASC N
   BETOS: I1E   Standard imaging - nuclear medicine

C **A9569** Technetium Tc-99m exametazime labeled autologous white blood cells, diagnostic, per study dose   N1 ASC N
   BETOS: I1E   Standard imaging - nuclear medicine
   Other carrier priced
   Coding Clinic: 2008, Q1

▲ Revised code   ● New code   **C** Carrier judgment   **D** Special coverage instructions apply
I Not payable by Medicare   **M** Non-covered by Medicare   **S** Non-covered by Medicare statute   AHA Coding Clinic®

C **A9570** Indium In-111 labeled autologous white blood cells, diagnostic, per study dose   N1 ASC N
BETOS: I1E   Standard imaging - nuclear medicine
Other carrier priced
Coding Clinic: 2008, Q1

C **A9571** Indium In-111 labeled autologous platelets, diagnostic, per study dose   N1 ASC N
BETOS: I1E   Standard imaging - nuclear medicine
Other carrier priced
Coding Clinic: 2008, Q1

C **A9572** Indium In-111 pentetreotide, diagnostic, per study dose, up to 6 millicuries   N1 ASC N
BETOS: I1E   Standard imaging - nuclear medicine
Other carrier priced
Coding Clinic: 2008, Q1

C **A9575** Injection, gadoterate meglumine, 0.1 ml   N1 ASC N
BETOS: I1E   Standard imaging - nuclear medicine
Other carrier priced
Drugs: DOTAREM
Coding Clinic: 2014, Q1

C **A9576** Injection, gadoteridol, (ProHance multipack), per ml   N1 ASC N
BETOS: I1E   Standard imaging - nuclear medicine
Drugs: PROHANCE MULTIPACK
Coding Clinic: 2008, Q1

C **A9577** Injection, gadobenate dimeglumine (MultiHance), per ml   N1 ASC N
BETOS: I1E   Standard imaging - nuclear medicine
Drugs: MULTIHANCE, MULTIHANCE 5X15 ML SYRINGE
Coding Clinic: 2008, Q1

C **A9578** Injection, gadobenate dimeglumine (MultiHance multipack), per ml   N1 ASC N
BETOS: I1E   Standard imaging - nuclear medicine
Drugs: MULTIHANCE MULTIPACK
Coding Clinic: 2008, Q1

C **A9579** Injection, gadolinium-based magnetic resonance contrast agent, not otherwise specified (NOS), per ml   N1 ASC N
BETOS: I1E   Standard imaging - nuclear medicine
Drugs: MAGNEVIST 46.9%, NOVAPLUS® OMNISCAN, OMNISCAN, OPTIMARK, PROHANCE, PROHANCE PREFILLED SYRINGES
Coding Clinic: 2008, Q1

C **A9580** Sodium fluoride F-18, diagnostic, per study dose, up to 30 millicuries   N1 ASC N
BETOS: I1E   Standard imaging - nuclear medicine

Other carrier priced
Coding Clinic: 2008, Q4; 2009, Q1
Pub: 100-3, Chap. 1, Part-4, 220.6.19; 100-4, Chap. 13, 60.3.2

C **A9581** Injection, gadoxetate disodium, 1 ml   N1 ASC N
BETOS: I2D   Advanced imaging - MRI/MRA: other
Drugs: EOVIST, GADOXETATE DISODIUM

C **A9582** Iodine I-123 iobenguane, diagnostic, per study dose, up to 15 millicuries   N1 ASC N
BETOS: I1E   Standard imaging - nuclear medicine

C **A9583** Injection, gadofosveset trisodium, 1 ml   N1 ASC N
BETOS: I1E   Standard imaging - nuclear medicine

C **A9584** Iodine 1-123 ioflupane, diagnostic, per study dose, up to 5 millicuries   N1 ASC N
BETOS: I1E   Standard imaging - nuclear medicine
Other carrier priced

C **A9585** Injection, gadobutrol, 0.1 ml   N1 ASC N
BETOS: I1E   Standard imaging - nuclear medicine
Other carrier priced
Drugs: GADAVIST
Coding Clinic: 2012, Q 1

D **A9586** Florbetapir F18, diagnostic, per study dose, up to 10 millicuries   K2 ASC G
BETOS: I1E   Standard imaging - nuclear medicine
Service not separately priced by Part B
Coding Clinic: 2014, Q1; 2014, Q3

C **A9587** Gallium ga-68, dotatate, diagnostic, 0.1 millicurie   K2 ASC G
BETOS: I1E   Standard imaging - nuclear medicine
Other carrier priced
Drugs: NETSPOT
Coding Clinic: 2017, Q1

C **A9588** Fluciclovine f-18, diagnostic, 1 millicurie   K2 ASC G
BETOS: I1E   Standard imaging - nuclear medicine
Other carrier priced
Drugs: AXUMIN
Coding Clinic: 2017, Q1

C **A9597** Positron emission tomography radiopharmaceutical, diagnostic, for tumor identification, not otherwise classified   N1 ASC N
BETOS: I1E   Standard imaging - nuclear medicine
Other carrier priced
Coding Clinic: 2017, Q1

C **A9598** Positron emission tomography radiopharmaceutical, diagnostic, for non-tumor identification, not otherwise classified N1 ASC N

BETOS: I1E   Standard imaging - nuclear medicine
Other carrier priced
Coding Clinic: 2017, Q1

C **A9600** Strontium Sr-89 chloride, therapeutic, per millicurie K

BETOS: I1E   Standard imaging - nuclear medicine
Other carrier priced
Drugs: METASTRON
Coding Clinic: 2002, Q2; 2005, Q4

C **A9604** Samarium Sm-153 lexidronam, therapeutic, per treatment dose, up to 150 millicuries K

BETOS: I1E   Standard imaging - nuclear medicine
Other carrier priced
Drugs: QUADRAMET

C **A9606** Radium Ra-223 dichloride, therapeutic, per microcurie K

BETOS: I1E   Standard imaging - nuclear medicine
Other carrier priced
Drugs: XOFIGO
Coding Clinic: 2014, Q4

D **A9698** Non-radioactive contrast imaging material, not otherwise classified, per study N1 ASC N

BETOS: I1E   Standard imaging - nuclear medicine
Coding Clinic: 2017, Q1

C **A9699** Radiopharmaceutical, therapeutic, not otherwise classified N

BETOS: I1E   Standard imaging - nuclear medicine
Other carrier priced
Coding Clinic: 2005, Q4

D **A9700** Supply of injectable contrast material for use in echocardiography, per study N1 ASC N

BETOS: I1E   Standard imaging - nuclear medicine
Other carrier priced
Coding Clinic: 2017, Q1

MISCELLANEOUS DME SUPPLIES AND SERVICES (A9900-A9999)

C **A9900** Miscellaneous DME supply, accessory, and/or service component of another HCPCS code Y

BETOS: D1E   Other DME

C **A9901** DME delivery, set up, and/or dispensing service component of another HCPCS code A

BETOS: D1E   Other DME

C **A9999** Miscellaneous DME supply or accessory, not otherwise specified Y

BETOS: D1F   Prosthetic/orthotic devices

▲ Revised code   ● New code   **C** Carrier judgment   **D** Special coverage instructions apply
I Not payable by Medicare   **M** Non-covered by Medicare   **S** Non-covered by Medicare statute   AHA Coding Clinic®

NOTES

NOTES

ENTERAL AND PARENTERAL THERAPY (B4034-B9999)

ENTERAL FEEDING SUPPLIES AND EQUIPMENT (B4034-B4088)

D B4034 Enteral feeding supply kit; syringe fed, per day, includes but not limited to feeding/flushing syringe, administration set tubing, dressings, tape   Y
BETOS: O1C   Enteral and parenteral
Pub: 100-4, Chap. 23, 60.3

D B4035 Enteral feeding supply kit; pump fed, per day, includes but not limited to feeding/flushing syringe, administration set tubing, dressings, tape   Y
BETOS: O1C   Enteral and parenteral

D B4036 Enteral feeding supply kit; gravity fed, per day, includes but not limited to feeding/flushing syringe, administration set tubing, dressings, tape   Y
BETOS: O1C   Enteral and parenteral

D B4081 Nasogastric tubing with stylet   Y
BETOS: O1C   Enteral and parenteral
Pub: 100-4, Chap. 23, 60.3

D B4082 Nasogastric tubing without stylet   Y
BETOS: O1C   Enteral and parenteral

D B4083 Stomach tube - Levine type   Y
BETOS: O1C   Enteral and parenteral

C B4087 Gastrostomy/jejunostomy tube, standard, any material, any type, each   A
BETOS: O1C   Enteral and parenteral

C B4088 Gastrostomy/jejunostomy tube, low-profile, any material, any type, each   A
BETOS: O1C   Enteral and parenteral

ENTERAL FORMULAS AND ADDITIVES (B4100-B4162)

M B4100 Food thickener, administered orally, per ounce   E1
BETOS: Z2   Undefined codes
Service not separately priced by Part B

D B4102 Enteral formula, for adults, used to replace fluids and electrolytes (e.g., clear liquids), 500 ml = 1 unit   Ⓐ Y
BETOS: O1C   Enteral and parenteral

D B4103 Enteral formula, for pediatrics, used to replace fluids and electrolytes (e.g., clear liquids), 500 ml = 1 unit   Ⓐ Y
BETOS: O1C   Enteral and parenteral

D B4104 Additive for enteral formula (e.g., fiber)   E1
BETOS: O1C   Enteral and parenteral
Service not separately priced by Part B

D B4149 Enteral formula, manufactured blenderized natural foods with intact nutrients, includes proteins, fats, carbohydrates, vitamins and minerals, may include fiber, administered through an enteral feeding tube, 100 calories = 1 unit   Y
BETOS: O1C   Enteral and parenteral
Pub: 100-4, Chap. 23, 60.3

D B4150 Enteral formula, nutritionally complete with intact nutrients, includes proteins, fats, carbohydrates, vitamins and minerals, may include fiber, administered through an enteral feeding tube, 100 calories = 1 unit   Y
BETOS: O1C   Enteral and parenteral

D B4152 Enteral formula, nutritionally complete, calorically dense (equal to or greater than 1.5 kcal/ml) with intact nutrients, includes proteins, fats, carbohydrates, vitamins and minerals, may include fiber, administered through an enteral feeding tube, 100 calories = 1 unit   Y
BETOS: O1C   Enteral and parenteral

D B4153 Enteral formula, nutritionally complete, hydrolyzed proteins (amino acids and peptide chain), includes fats, carbohydrates, vitamins and minerals, may include fiber, administered through an enteral feeding tube, 100 calories = 1 unit   Y
BETOS: O1C   Enteral and parenteral

D B4154 Enteral formula, nutritionally complete, for special metabolic needs, excludes inherited disease of metabolism, includes altered composition of proteins, fats, carbohydrates, vitamins and/or minerals, may include fiber, administered through an enteral feeding tube, 100 calories = 1 unit   Y
BETOS: O1C   Enteral and parenteral

D B4155 Enteral formula, nutritionally incomplete/modular nutrients, includes specific nutrients, carbohydrates (e.g., glucose polymers), proteins/amino acids (e.g., glutamine, arginine), fat (e.g., medium chain triglycerides) or combination, administered through an enteral feeding tube, 100 calories = 1 unit   Y
BETOS: O1C   Enteral and parenteral

D B4157 Enteral formula, nutritionally complete, for special metabolic needs for inherited disease of metabolism, includes proteins, fats, carbohydrates, vitamins and minerals, may include fiber, administered through an enteral feeding tube, 100 calories = 1 unit   Y
BETOS: O1C   Enteral and parenteral

D B4158 Enteral formula, for pediatrics, nutritionally complete with intact nutrients, includes proteins, fats, carbohydrates, vitamins and minerals, may include fiber and/or iron, administered through an enteral feeding tube, 100 calories = 1 unit   Ⓐ Y
BETOS: O1C   Enteral and parenteral

♂ Male only   ♀ Female only   Ⓐ Age   A2 - Z3 = ASC Payment indicator   A - Y = APC Status indicator
ASC = ASC-approved procedure   **DME** Paid under the DME fee schedule   **MIPS** MIPS code

D B4159 Enteral formula, for pediatrics, nutritionally complete soy based with intact nutrients, includes proteins, fats, carbohydrates, vitamins and minerals, may include fiber and/or iron, administered through an enteral feeding tube, 100 calories = 1 unit   (A) Y

BETOS: O1C   Enteral and parenteral

D B4160 Enteral formula, for pediatrics, nutritionally complete calorically dense (equal to or greater than 0.7 kcal/ml) with intact nutrients, includes proteins, fats, carbohydrates, vitamins and minerals, may include fiber, administered through an enteral feeding tube, 100 calories = 1 unit   (A) Y

BETOS: O1C   Enteral and parenteral

D B4161 Enteral formula, for pediatrics, hydrolyzed/ amino acids and peptide chain proteins, includes fats, carbohydrates, vitamins and minerals, may include fiber, administered through an enteral feeding tube, 100 calories = 1 unit   (A) Y

BETOS: O1C   Enteral and parenteral

D B4162 Enteral formula, for pediatrics, special metabolic needs for inherited disease of metabolism, includes proteins, fats, carbohydrates, vitamins and minerals, may include fiber, administered through an enteral feeding tube, 100 calories = 1 unit   (A) Y

BETOS: O1C   Enteral and parenteral

PARENTERAL SOLUTIONS AND SUPPLIES (B4164-B5200)

D B4164 Parenteral nutrition solution: carbohydrates (dextrose), 50% or less (500 ml = 1 unit) - home mix   Y

BETOS: O1C   Enteral and parenteral

D B4168 Parenteral nutrition solution; amino acid, 3.5%, (500 ml = 1 unit) - home mix   Y

BETOS: O1C   Enteral and parenteral

D B4172 Parenteral nutrition solution; amino acid, 5.5% through 7%, (500 ml = 1 unit) - home mix   Y

BETOS: O1C   Enteral and parenteral

D B4176 Parenteral nutrition solution; amino acid, 7% through 8.5%, (500 ml = 1 unit) - home mix   Y

BETOS: O1C   Enteral and parenteral

D B4178 Parenteral nutrition solution: amino acid, greater than 8.5% (500 ml = 1 unit) - home mix   Y

BETOS: O1C   Enteral and parenteral

D B4180 Parenteral nutrition solution; carbohydrates (dextrose), greater than 50% (500 ml = 1 unit) - home mix   Y

BETOS: O1C   Enteral and parenteral

D B4185 Parenteral nutrition solution, per 10 grams lipids   B

BETOS: O1C   Enteral and parenteral

D B4189 Parenteral nutrition solution; compounded amino acid and carbohydrates with electrolytes, trace elements, and vitamins, including preparation, any strength, 10 to 51 grams of protein - premix   Y

BETOS: O1C   Enteral and parenteral

D B4193 Parenteral nutrition solution; compounded amino acid and carbohydrates with electrolytes, trace elements, and vitamins, including preparation, any strength, 52 to 73 grams of protein - premix   Y

BETOS: O1C   Enteral and parenteral

D B4197 Parenteral nutrition solution; compounded amino acid and carbohydrates with electrolytes, trace elements and vitamins, including preparation, any strength, 74 to 100 grams of protein - premix   Y

BETOS: O1C   Enteral and parenteral

D B4199 Parenteral nutrition solution; compounded amino acid and carbohydrates with electrolytes, trace elements and vitamins, including preparation, any strength, over 100 grams of protein - premix   Y

BETOS: O1C   Enteral and parenteral

D B4216 Parenteral nutrition; additives (vitamins, trace elements, heparin, electrolytes), home mix, per day   Y

BETOS: O1C   Enteral and parenteral

D B4220 Parenteral nutrition supply kit; premix, per day   Y

BETOS: O1C   Enteral and parenteral

D B4222 Parenteral nutrition supply kit; home mix, per day   Y

BETOS: O1C   Enteral and parenteral

D B4224 Parenteral nutrition administration kit, per day   Y

BETOS: O1C   Enteral and parenteral

D B5000 Parenteral nutrition solution compounded amino acid and carbohydrates with electrolytes, trace elements, and vitamins, including preparation, any strength, renal-Amirosyn RF, NephrAmine, RenAmine-premix   Y

BETOS: O1C   Enteral and parenteral

D B5100 Parenteral nutrition solution compounded amino acid and carbohydrates with electrolytes, trace elements, and vitamins, including preparation, any strength, hepatic, HepAtamine-premix   Y

BETOS: O1C   Enteral and parenteral

D B5200 Parenteral nutrition solution compounded amino acid and carbohydrates with electrolytes, trace elements, and vitamins, including preparation, any strength, stress-branch chain amino acids-freamine-hbc-premix   Y

BETOS: O1C   Enteral and parenteral

▲ Revised code   ● New code   **C** Carrier judgment   **D** Special coverage instructions apply
I Not payable by Medicare   **M** Non-covered by Medicare   **S** Non-covered by Medicare statute   AHA Coding Clinic®

NUTRITION INFUSION PUMPS AND SUPPLIES NOT
OTHERWISE CLASSIFIED (NOC) (B9002-B9999)

　D　**B9002** Enteral nutrition infusion pump, any type　　Y
　　　　　BETOS: O1C　Enteral and parenteral

　D　**B9004** Parenteral nutrition infusion pump, portable Y
　　　　　BETOS: O1C　Enteral and parenteral

　D　**B9006** Parenteral nutrition infusion pump,
　　　　　stationary　　　　　　　　　　　　　　　　　Y
　　　　　BETOS: O1C　Enteral and parenteral

　D　**B9998** NOC for enteral supplies　　　　　　　　Y
　　　　　BETOS: O1C　Enteral and parenteral
　　　　　Other carrier priced

　D　**B9999** NOC for parenteral supplies　　　　　　Y
　　　　　BETOS: O1C　Enteral and parenteral
　　　　　Other carrier priced
　　　　　Coding Clinic: 2009, Q2

♂ Male only　　♀ Female only　　Ⓐ Age　　A2 - Z3 = ASC Payment indicator　　A - Y = APC Status indicator

ASC = ASC-approved procedure　　**DME** Paid under the DME fee schedule　　**MIPS** MIPS code

NOTES

OUTPATIENT PPS (C1713-C9899)

ASSORTED DEVICES AND SUPPLIES (C1713-C1715)

D **C1713** Anchor/screw for opposing bone-to-bone or soft tissue-to-bone (implantable)   N1 ASC N
BETOS: D1A   Medical/surgical supplies
Statute: 1833(T)
Coding Clinic: 2010, Q1

D **C1714** Catheter, transluminal atherectomy, directional   N1 ASC N
BETOS: D1A   Medical/surgical supplies
Statute: 1833(T)
Coding Clinic: 2001, Q1; 2002, Q3; 2003, Q4; 2004, Q4

D **C1715** Brachytherapy needle   N1 ASC N
BETOS: D1A   Medical/surgical supplies
Statute: 1833(T)
Coding Clinic: 2001, Q1; 2002, Q3

BRACHYTHERAPY SOURCES (C1716-C1719), SEE ALSO BRACHYTHERAPY SOURCES (C2616), (C2634-C2699)

D **C1716** Brachytherapy source, non-stranded, gold-198, per source   H2 ASC U
BETOS: I4B   Imaging/procedure - other
Statute: 1833(T)
Coding Clinic: 2001, Q1; 2002, Q3; 2004, Q2; 2004, Q4; 2007, Q2

D **C1717** Brachytherapy source, non-stranded, high dose rate iridium-192, per source   H2 ASC U
BETOS: I4B   Imaging/procedure - other
Statute: 1833(T)
Coding Clinic: 2001, Q1; 2002, Q3; 2004, Q2; 2004, Q4; 2007, Q2

D **C1719** Brachytherapy source, non-stranded, non-high dose rate iridium-192, per source   H2 ASC U
BETOS: I4B   Imaging/procedure - other
Statute: 1833(T)
Coding Clinic: 2001, Q1; 2002, Q3; 2004, Q2; 2004, Q4; 2007, Q2

CARDIOVERTER-DEFIBRILLATORS (C1721-C1722)

D **C1721** Cardioverter-defibrillator, dual chamber (implantable)   N1 ASC N
BETOS: D1A   Medical/surgical supplies
Statute: 1833(T)
Coding Clinic: 2001, Q1; 2002, Q3; 2004, Q4; 2006, Q4
Pub: 100-4, Chap. 14, 40.8

D **C1722** Cardioverter-defibrillator, single chamber (implantable)   N1 ASC N
BETOS: D1A   Medical/surgical supplies
Statute: 1833(T)
Coding Clinic: 2017, Q2

CATHETERS FOR MULTIPLE APPLICATIONS (C1724-C1759)

D **C1724** Catheter, transluminal atherectomy, rotational   N1 ASC N
BETOS: D1A   Medical/surgical supplies
Statute: 1833(T)
Coding Clinic: 2001, Q1; 2002, Q3; 2003, Q4; 2004, Q4

D **C1725** Catheter, transluminal angioplasty, non-laser (may include guidance, infusion/perfusion capability)   N1 ASC N
BETOS: D1A   Medical/surgical supplies
Statute: 1833(T)
Coding Clinic: 2001, Q1; 2002, Q3; 2003, Q4; 2004, Q4

D **C1726** Catheter, balloon dilatation, non-vascular   N1 ASC N
BETOS: D1A   Medical/surgical supplies
Statute: 1833(T)
Coding Clinic: 2001, Q1; 2002, Q3

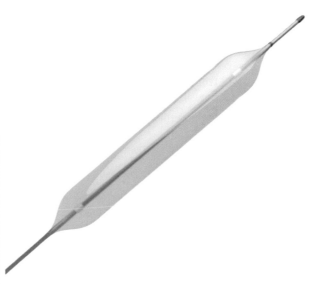

Balloon angioplasty

D **C1727** Catheter, balloon tissue dissector, non-vascular (insertable)   N1 ASC N
BETOS: D1A   Medical/surgical supplies
Statute: 1833(T)
Coding Clinic: 2001, Q1; 2002, Q3

D **C1728** Catheter, brachytherapy seed administration   N1 ASC N
BETOS: D1A   Medical/surgical supplies
Statute: 1833(T)
Coding Clinic: 2001, Q1; 2002, Q3

D **C1729** Catheter, drainage   N1 ASC N
BETOS: D1A   Medical/surgical supplies
Statute: 1833(T)
Coding Clinic: 2001, Q1; 2002, Q3

D **C1730** Catheter, electrophysiology, diagnostic, other than 3D mapping (19 or fewer electrodes)   N1 ASC N

BETOS: D1A   Medical/surgical supplies
Statute: 1833(T)
Coding Clinic: 2001, Q1; 2001, Q3; 2002, Q3; 2004, Q4

D **C1731** Catheter, electrophysiology, diagnostic, other than 3D mapping (20 or more electrodes)   N1 ASC N
BETOS: D1A   Medical/surgical supplies
Statute: 1833(T)
Coding Clinic: 2001, Q1; 2002, Q3; 2004, Q4

D **C1732** Catheter, electrophysiology, diagnostic/ ablation, 3D or vector mapping   N1 ASC N
BETOS: D1A   Medical/surgical supplies
Statute: 1833(T)
Coding Clinic: 2001, Q1; 2001, Q3; 2002, Q3; 2004, Q4

D **C1733** Catheter, electrophysiology, diagnostic/ ablation, other than 3D or vector mapping, other than cool-tip   N1 ASC N
BETOS: D1A   Medical/surgical supplies
Statute: 1833(T)
Coding Clinic: 2001, Q1; 2001, Q3; 2002, Q3; 2004, Q4

D **C1749** Endoscope, retrograde imaging/illumination colonoscope device (implantable)   N1 ASC N
BETOS: D1A   Medical/surgical supplies
Statute: 1833(t)

D **C1750** Catheter, hemodialysis/peritoneal, long-term   N1 ASC N
BETOS: D1A   Medical/surgical supplies
Statute: 1833(T)
Coding Clinic: 2012, Q4

D **C1751** Catheter, infusion, inserted peripherally, centrally or midline (other than hemodialysis)   N1 ASC N
BETOS: D1A   Medical/surgical supplies
Statute: 1833(T)
Coding Clinic: 2014, Q3

D **C1752** Catheter, hemodialysis/peritoneal, short-term   N1 ASC N
BETOS: D1A   Medical/surgical supplies
Statute: 1833(T)
Coding Clinic: 2001, Q1; 2002, Q3; 2003, Q4

D **C1753** Catheter, intravascular ultrasound   N1 ASC N
BETOS: D1A   Medical/surgical supplies
Statute: 1833(T)
Coding Clinic: 2001, Q1; 2002, Q3; 2003, Q4

D **C1754** Catheter, intradiscal   N1 ASC N
BETOS: D1A   Medical/surgical supplies
Statute: 1833(T)
Coding Clinic: 2001, Q1; 2002, Q3; 2003, Q4

D **C1755** Catheter, intraspinal   N1 ASC N
BETOS: D1A   Medical/surgical supplies
Statute: 1833(T)
Coding Clinic: 2001, Q1; 2002, Q3; 2003, Q4

D **C1756** Catheter, pacing, transesophageal N1 ASC N
BETOS: D1A   Medical/surgical supplies
Statute: 1833(T)
Coding Clinic: 2001, Q1; 2002, Q3; 2003, Q4

D **C1757** Catheter, thrombectomy/ embolectomy   N1 ASC N
BETOS: D1A   Medical/surgical supplies
Statute: 1833(T)
Coding Clinic: 2001, Q1; 2002, Q3; 2003, Q4

D **C1758** Catheter, ureteral   N1 ASC N
BETOS: D1A   Medical/surgical supplies
Statute: 1833(T)
Coding Clinic: 2001, Q1; 2002, Q3; 2003, Q4

D **C1759** Catheter, intracardiac echocardiography   N1 ASC N
BETOS: D1A   Medical/surgical supplies
Statute: 1833(T)
Coding Clinic: 2001, Q1; 2001, Q3; 2002, Q3; 2003, Q4

ASSORTED DEVICES, IMPLANTS, AND SYSTEMS (C1760-C2615)

D **C1760** Closure device, vascular (implantable/ insertable)   N1 ASC N
BETOS: D1A   Medical/surgical supplies
Statute: 1833(T)
Coding Clinic: 2001, Q1; 2002, Q3; 2003, Q4

D **C1762** Connective tissue, human (includes fascia lata)   N1 ASC N
BETOS: D1A   Medical/surgical supplies
Statute: 1833(T)
Coding Clinic: 2010, Q1

D **C1763** Connective tissue, non-human (includes synthetic)   N1 ASC N
BETOS: D1A   Medical/surgical supplies
Statute: 1833(T)
Coding Clinic: 2010, Q1; 2010, Q4

D **C1764** Event recorder, cardiac (implantable)   N1 ASC N
BETOS: D1A   Medical/surgical supplies
Statute: 1833(T)
Coding Clinic: 2001, Q1; 2002, Q3; 2003, Q4
Pub: 100-4, Chap. 14, 40.8

D **C1765** Adhesion barrier   N1 ASC N
BETOS: D1A   Medical/surgical supplies
Statute: 1833(T)

D **C1766** Introducer/sheath, guiding, intracardiac electrophysiological, steerable, other than peel-away   N1 ASC N
BETOS: D1A   Medical/surgical supplies
Statute: 1833(T)
Coding Clinic: 2001, Q3; 2002, Q3; 2004, Q4

D **C1767** Generator, neurostimulator (implantable), non-rechargeable   N1 ASC N
BETOS: D1A   Medical/surgical supplies
Statute: 1833(T)

▲ Revised code   ● New code   **C** Carrier judgment   **D** Special coverage instructions apply
I Not payable by Medicare   **M** Non-covered by Medicare   **S** Non-covered by Medicare statute   AHA Coding Clinic®

Coding Clinic: 2001, Q1; 2002, Q1; 2002, Q3; 2003, Q4; 2004, Q4; 2006, Q1; 2006, Q4; 2007, Q1

Pub: 100-4, Chap. 14, 40.8; 100-4, Chap. 32, 40.1

D C1768 Graft, vascular   N1 ASC N
BETOS: D1A   Medical/surgical supplies
Statute: 1833(T)
Coding Clinic: 2001, Q1; 2002, Q3; 2003, Q4

D C1769 Guide wire   N1 ASC N
BETOS: D1A   Medical/surgical supplies
Statute: 1833(T)
Coding Clinic: 2014, Q3

D C1770 Imaging coil, magnetic resonance (insertable)   N1 ASC N
BETOS: D1A   Medical/surgical supplies
Statute: 1833(T)
Coding Clinic: 2001, Q1; 2002, Q3; 2003, Q4

D C1771 Repair device, urinary, incontinence, with sling graft   N1 ASC N
BETOS: D1A   Medical/surgical supplies
Statute: 1833(T)
Coding Clinic: 2001, Q1; 2001, Q3; 2002, Q3; 2003, Q4; 2008, Q3
Pub: 100-4, Chap. 14, 40.8

D C1772 Infusion pump, programmable (implantable)   N1 ASC N
BETOS: D1A   Medical/surgical supplies
Statute: 1833(T)
Coding Clinic: 2001, Q1; 2002, Q3; 2004, Q4

D C1773 Retrieval device, insertable (used to retrieve fractured medical devices)   N1 ASC N
BETOS: D1A   Medical/surgical supplies
Statute: 1833(T)
Coding Clinic: 2001, Q1; 2002, Q3; 2003, Q4

D C1776 Joint device (implantable)   N1 ASC N
BETOS: D1A   Medical/surgical supplies
Statute: 1833(T)
Coding Clinic: 2010, Q3
Pub: 100-4, Chap. 14, 40.8

D C1777 Lead, cardioverter-defibrillator, endocardial single coil (implantable)   N1 ASC N
BETOS: D1A   Medical/surgical supplies
Statute: 1833(T)
Coding Clinic: 2017, Q2

D C1778 Lead, neurostimulator (implantable) N1 ASC N
BETOS: D1A   Medical/surgical supplies
Statute: 1833(T)
Coding Clinic: 2011, Q4
Pub: 100-4, Chap. 14, 40.8; 100-4, Chap. 32, 40.1

D C1779 Lead, pacemaker, transvenous VDD single pass   N1 ASC N
BETOS: D1A   Medical/surgical supplies
Statute: 1833(T)
Coding Clinic: 2001, Q1; 2002, Q3; 2004, Q4; 2006, Q4

D C1780 Lens, intraocular (new technology) N1 ASC N
BETOS: D1A   Medical/surgical supplies
Statute: 1833(T)
Coding Clinic: 2001, Q1; 2002, Q3

D C1781 Mesh (implantable)   N1 ASC N
BETOS: D1A   Medical/surgical supplies
Statute: 1833(T)
Coding Clinic: 2010, Q1; 2012, Q 2

D C1782 Morcellator   N1 ASC N
BETOS: D1A   Medical/surgical supplies
Statute: 1833(T)
Coding Clinic: 2001, Q1; 2002, Q3

D C1783 Ocular implant, aqueous drainage assist device   N1 ASC N
BETOS: D1A   Medical/surgical supplies
Statute: 1833(T)
Coding Clinic: 2017, Q1

D C1784 Ocular device, intraoperative, detached retina   N1 ASC N
BETOS: D1A   Medical/surgical supplies
Statute: 1833(T)
Coding Clinic: 2001, Q1; 2002, Q3

D C1785 Pacemaker, dual chamber, rate-responsive (implantable)   N1 ASC N
BETOS: D1A   Medical/surgical supplies
Statute: 1833(T)
Coding Clinic: 2001, Q1; 2002, Q3; 2003, Q4; 2006, Q4
Pub: 100-4, Chap. 14, 40.8

D C1786 Pacemaker, single chamber, rate-responsive (implantable)   N1 ASC N
BETOS: D1A   Medical/surgical supplies
Statute: 1833(T)
Coding Clinic: 2001, Q1; 2002, Q3; 2003, Q4; 2004, Q4; 2006, Q4
Pub: 100-2, Chap. 1, 40

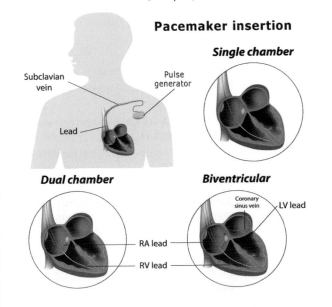

Pacemaker insertion

Single chamber

Dual chamber   *Biventricular*

D C1787 Patient programmer, neurostimulator   N1 ASC N
BETOS: D1A   Medical/surgical supplies
Statute: 1833(T)
Coding Clinic: 2001, Q1; 2002, Q3; 2003, Q4

D C1788 Port, indwelling (implantable)   N1 ASC N
BETOS: D1A   Medical/surgical supplies
Statute: 1833(T)
Coding Clinic: 2014, Q3

D C1789 Prosthesis, breast (implantable)   N1 ♀ ASC N
BETOS: D1A   Medical/surgical supplies
Statute: 1833(T)
Coding Clinic: 2001, Q1; 2002, Q3; 2003, Q4

D C1813 Prosthesis, penile, inflatable   N1 ♂ ASC N
BETOS: D1A   Medical/surgical supplies
Statute: 1833(T)
Coding Clinic: 2001, Q1; 2002, Q3; 2003, Q4
Pub: 100-4, Chap. 14, 40.8

D C1814 Retinal tamponade device, silicone oil   N1 ASC N
BETOS: D1A   Medical/surgical supplies
Statute: 1833t
Coding Clinic: 2006, Q2

D C1815 Prosthesis, urinary sphincter (implantable)   N1 ASC N
BETOS: D1A   Medical/surgical supplies
Statute: 1833(T)
Coding Clinic: 2001, Q1; 2002, Q3; 2003, Q4
Pub: 100-4, Chap. 14, 40.8

D C1816 Receiver and/or transmitter, neurostimulator (implantable)   N1 ASC N
BETOS: D1A   Medical/surgical supplies
Statute: 1833(T)
Coding Clinic: 2001, Q1; 2002, Q3; 2003, Q4

D C1817 Septal defect implant system, intracardiac   N1 ASC N
BETOS: D1A   Medical/surgical supplies
Statute: 1833(T)
Coding Clinic: 2001, Q1; 2002, Q3; 2003, Q4

D C1818 Integrated keratoprosthesis   N1 ASC N
BETOS: D1A   Medical/surgical supplies
Statute: 1833T

D C1819 Surgical tissue localization and excision device (implantable)   N1 ASC N
BETOS: D1A   Medical/surgical supplies
Statute: 1833T
Coding Clinic: 2004, Q1

D C1820 Generator, neurostimulator (implantable), with rechargeable battery and charging system   N1 ASC N
BETOS: D1A   Medical/surgical supplies
Statute: 1833(T)
Coding Clinic: 2016, Q1; 2016, Q2
Pub: 100-4, Chap. 14, 40.8

D C1821 Interspinous process distraction device (implantable)   N1 ASC N
BETOS: D1A   Medical/surgical supplies
Statute: 1833(T)
Coding Clinic: 2007, Q1; 2009, Q2

D C1822 Generator, neurostimulator (implantable), high frequency, with rechargeable battery and charging system   J7 ASC H
BETOS: D1A   Medical/surgical supplies
Statute: 1833(T)
Coding Clinic: 2016, Q1; 2016, Q2

D C1830 Powered bone marrow biopsy needle   N1 ASC N
BETOS: D1A   Medical/surgical supplies
Statute: 1833(t)
Coding Clinic: 2011, Q4

D C1840 Lens, intraocular (telescopic)   N1 ASC N
BETOS: D1A   Medical/surgical supplies
Statute: 1833(t)
Coding Clinic: 2011, Q4; 2012, Q 1; 2012, Q3

D C1841 Retinal prosthesis, includes all internal and external components   J7 ASC N
BETOS: D1E   Other DME
Statute: 1833(t)
Coding Clinic: 2017, Q1

D C1842 Retinal prosthesis, includes all internal and external components; add-on to C1841   J7 ASC E1
BETOS: D1E   Other DME
Statute: 1833(t)
Coding Clinic: 2017, Q1

D C1874 Stent, coated/covered, with delivery system   N1 ASC N
BETOS: D1A   Medical/surgical supplies
Statute: 1833(T)
Coding Clinic: 2001, Q1; 2001, Q3; 2002, Q3; 2003, Q4; 2004, Q3; 2004, Q4

D C1875 Stent, coated/covered, without delivery system   N1 ASC N
BETOS: D1A   Medical/surgical supplies
Statute: 1833(T)
Coding Clinic: 2001, Q1; 2002, Q3; 2003, Q4; 2004, Q4

D C1876 Stent, non-coated/non-covered, with delivery system   N1 ASC N
BETOS: D1A   Medical/surgical supplies
Statute: 1833(T)
Coding Clinic: 2001, Q1; 2001, Q3; 2002, Q3; 2003, Q4; 2004, Q4

D C1877 Stent, non-coated/non-covered, without delivery system   N1 ASC N
BETOS: D1A   Medical/surgical supplies
Statute: 1833(T)
Coding Clinic: 2001, Q1; 2001, Q3; 2002, Q3; 2003, Q4; 2004, Q4

D C1878 Material for vocal cord medialization, synthetic (implantable)   N1 ASC N

▲ Revised code   ● New code   **C** Carrier judgment   **D** Special coverage instructions apply
I Not payable by Medicare   **M** Non-covered by Medicare   **S** Non-covered by Medicare statute   AHA Coding Clinic®

BETOS: D1A   Medical/surgical supplies
Statute: 1833(T)
Coding Clinic: 2001, Q1; 2002, Q3

D C1880 Vena cava filter   N1 ASC N
BETOS: D1A   Medical/surgical supplies
Statute: 1833(T)
Coding Clinic: 2001, Q1; 2002, Q3; 2003, Q4

D C1881 Dialysis access system
(implantable)   N1 ASC N
BETOS: D1A   Medical/surgical supplies
Statute: 1833(T)
Coding Clinic: 2001, Q1; 2002, Q3; 2003, Q4
Pub: 100-4, Chap. 14, 40.8

D C1882 Cardioverter-defibrillator, other than single or
dual chamber (implantable)   N1 ASC N
BETOS: D1A   Medical/surgical supplies
Statute: 1833(T)
Coding Clinic: 2012, Q 2

D C1883 Adapter/extension, pacing lead or
neurostimulator lead (implantable) N1 ASC N
BETOS: D1A   Medical/surgical supplies
Statute: 1833(T)
Coding Clinic: 2001, Q1; 2002, Q1; 2002,
Q3; 2007, Q1
Pub: 100-4, Chap. 32, 40.1

D C1884 Embolization protective system   N1 ASC N
BETOS: D1A   Medical/surgical supplies
Statute: 1833T
Coding Clinic: 2014, Q3

D C1885 Catheter, transluminal angioplasty,
laser   N1 ASC N
BETOS: D1A   Medical/surgical supplies
Statute: 1833(T)
Coding Clinic: 2016, Q1

D C1886 Catheter, extravascular tissue ablation, any
modality (insertable)   N1 ASC N
BETOS: D1A   Medical/surgical supplies
Statute: 1833(t)

D C1887 Catheter, guiding (may include infusion/
perfusion capability)   N1 ASC N
BETOS: D1A   Medical/surgical supplies
Statute: 1833(T)
Coding Clinic: 2001, Q1; 2001, Q3; 2002,
Q3; 2004, Q4

D C1888 Catheter, ablation, non-cardiac,
endovascular (implantable)   N1 ASC N
BETOS: D1A   Medical/surgical supplies
Statute: 1833(T)

D C1889 Implantable/insertable device for device
intensive procedure, not otherwise
classified   N1 ASC N
BETOS: D1A   Medical/surgical supplies
Statute: 1833(T)

D C1891 Infusion pump, non-programmable,
permanent (implantable)   N1 ASC N
BETOS: D1A   Medical/surgical supplies

Statute: 1833(T)
Coding Clinic: 2001, Q1; 2002, Q3; 2003,
Q4; 2004, Q4
Pub: 100-4, Chap. 14, 40.8

D C1892 Introducer/sheath, guiding, intracardiac
electrophysiological, fixed-curve,
peel-away   N1 ASC N
BETOS: D1A   Medical/surgical supplies
Statute: 1833(T)
Coding Clinic: 2001, Q1; 2002, Q3; 2004, Q4

D C1893 Introducer/sheath, guiding, intracardiac
electrophysiological, fixed-curve, other than
peel-away   N1 ASC N
BETOS: D1A   Medical/surgical supplies
Statute: 1833(T)
Coding Clinic: 2001, Q1; 2001, Q3; 2002,
Q3; 2004, Q4

D C1894 Introducer/sheath, other than guiding, other
than intracardiac electrophysiological,
non-laser   N1 ASC N
BETOS: D1A   Medical/surgical supplies
Statute: 1833(T)
Coding Clinic: 2001, Q1; 2002, Q3

D C1895 Lead, cardioverter-defibrillator, endocardial
dual coil (implantable)   N1 ASC N
BETOS: D1A   Medical/surgical supplies
Statute: 1833(T)
Coding Clinic: 2001, Q1; 2002, Q3; 2004,
Q4; 2006, Q2; 2006, Q4

D C1896 Lead, cardioverter-defibrillator, other
than endocardial single or dual coil
(implantable)   N1 ASC N
BETOS: D1A   Medical/surgical supplies
Statute: 1833(T)
Coding Clinic: 2001, Q1; 2002, Q3; 2004,
Q4; 2006, Q2; 2006, Q4

D C1897 Lead, neurostimulator test kit
(implantable)   N1 ASC N
BETOS: D1A   Medical/surgical supplies
Statute: 1833(T)
Coding Clinic: 2001, Q1; 2002, Q1; 2002,
Q3; 2006, Q4; 2007, Q1
Pub: 100-4, Chap. 14, 40.8; 100-4, Chap. 32,
40.1

D C1898 Lead, pacemaker, other than transvenous
VDD single pass   N1 ASC N
BETOS: D1A   Medical/surgical supplies
Statute: 1833(T)
Coding Clinic: 2001, Q1; 2001, Q3; 2002,
Q3; 2006, Q4

D C1899 Lead, pacemaker/cardioverter-defibrillator
combination (implantable)   N1 ASC N
BETOS: D1A   Medical/surgical supplies
Statute: 1833(T)
Coding Clinic: 2001, Q1; 2002, Q3; 2004,
Q4; 2006, Q4

♂ Male only   ♀ Female only   **A** Age   A2 - Z3 = ASC Payment indicator   A - Y = APC Status indicator
ASC = ASC-approved procedure   **DME** Paid under the DME fee schedule   **MIPS** MIPS code

C1900 - C2628 (side margin)

OUTPATIENT PPS (C1713-C9899) (side margin)

D **C1900** Lead, left ventricular coronary venous system N1 ASC N
BETOS: D1A   Medical/surgical supplies
Statute: 1833(T)
Coding Clinic: 2004, Q4; 2006, Q4
Pub: 100-4, Chap. 14, 40.8

D **C2613** Lung biopsy plug with delivery system J7 ASC H
BETOS: D1A   Medical/surgical supplies
Statute: 1833(t)

D **C2614** Probe, percutaneous lumbar discectomy N1 ASC N
BETOS: D1A   Medical/surgical supplies
Statute: 1833(T)

D **C2615** Sealant, pulmonary, liquid N1 ASC N
BETOS: D1A   Medical/surgical supplies
Statute: 1833(T)
Coding Clinic: 2001, Q1; 2002, Q3; 2003, Q4

BRACHYTHERAPY SOURCES (C2616), SEE ALSO
BRACHYTHERAPY SOURCES (C1716-C1719);
BRACHYTHERAPY SOURCES (C2634-C2699)

D **C2616** Brachytherapy source, non-stranded, yttrium-90, per source H2 ASC U
BETOS: I4B   Imaging/procedure - other
Statute: 1833(T)
Coding Clinic: 2002, Q3; 2003, Q3; 2004, Q2; 2004, Q4; 2007, Q2

ASSORTED CARDIOVASCULAR AND GENITOURINARY
DEVICES (C2617-C2631)

D **C2617** Stent, non-coronary, temporary, without delivery system N1 ASC N
BETOS: D1A   Medical/surgical supplies
Statute: 1833(T)
Coding Clinic: 2001, Q1; 2002, Q3; 2003, Q4; 2004, Q4

D **C2618** Probe/needle, cryoablation N1 ASC N
BETOS: D1A   Medical/surgical supplies
Statute: 1833(T)
Coding Clinic: 2001, Q1; 2002, Q3; 2003, Q4; 2004, Q4

D **C2619** Pacemaker, dual chamber, non rate-responsive (implantable) N1 ASC N
BETOS: D1A   Medical/surgical supplies
Statute: 1833(T)
Coding Clinic: 2001, Q1; 2001, Q3; 2002, Q3; 2006, Q4
Pub: 100-4, Chap. 14, 40.8

D **C2620** Pacemaker, single chamber, non rate-responsive (implantable) N1 ASC N
BETOS: D1A   Medical/surgical supplies
Statute: 1833(T)
Coding Clinic: 2001, Q1; 2002, Q3; 2003, Q4; 2004, Q4; 2006, Q4

Pacemaker

D **C2621** Pacemaker, other than single or dual chamber (implantable) N1 ASC N
BETOS: D1A   Medical/surgical supplies
Statute: 1833(T)
Coding Clinic: 2001, Q1; 2002, Q3; 2003, Q4; 2006, Q4

D **C2622** Prosthesis, penile, non-inflatable N1 ♂ ASC N
BETOS: D1A   Medical/surgical supplies
Statute: 1833(T)
Coding Clinic: 2001, Q1; 2002, Q3; 2003, Q4

D **C2623** Catheter, transluminal angioplasty, drug-coated, non-laser J7 ASC H
BETOS: D1A   Medical/surgical supplies
Statute: 1833(t)

D **C2624** Implantable wireless pulmonary artery pressure sensor with delivery catheter, including all system components N1 ASC N
BETOS: D1A   Medical/surgical supplies
Statute: 1833(t)

D **C2625** Stent, non-coronary, temporary, with delivery system N1 ASC N
BETOS: D1A   Medical/surgical supplies
Statute: 1833(T)
Coding Clinic: 2001, Q1; 2002, Q3; 2003, Q4; 2004, Q4

D **C2626** Infusion pump, non-programmable, temporary (implantable) N1 ASC N
BETOS: D1A   Medical/surgical supplies
Statute: 1833(T)
Coding Clinic: 2001, Q1; 2002, Q3; 2004, Q4
Pub: 100-4, Chap. 14, 40.8

D **C2627** Catheter, suprapubic/cystoscopic N1 ASC N
BETOS: D1A   Medical/surgical supplies
Statute: 1833(T)
Coding Clinic: 2001, Q1; 2002, Q3; 2003, Q4

D **C2628** Catheter, occlusion N1 ASC N
BETOS: D1A   Medical/surgical supplies
Statute: 1833(T)
Coding Clinic: 2001, Q1; 2002, Q3; 2003, Q4; 2004, Q4

D **C2629** Introducer/sheath, other than guiding, other than intracardiac electrophysiological, laser N1 ASC N
BETOS: D1A Medical/surgical supplies
Statute: 1833(T)
Coding Clinic: 2001, Q1; 2002, Q3

D **C2630** Catheter, electrophysiology, diagnostic/ ablation, other than 3D or vector mapping, cool-tip N1 ASC N
BETOS: D1A Medical/surgical supplies
Statute: 1833(T)
Coding Clinic: 2001, Q1; 2002, Q3; 2009, Q2

D **C2631** Repair device, urinary, incontinence, without sling graft N1 ASC N
BETOS: D1A Medical/surgical supplies
Statute: 1833(T)
Coding Clinic: 2001, Q1; 2002, Q3; 2003, Q4
Pub: 100-4, Chap. 14, 40.8

BRACHYTHERAPY SOURCES (C2634-C2699), SEE ALSO
BRACHYTHERAPY SOURCES (C1716-C1719), (C2616)

D **C2634** Brachytherapy source, non-stranded, high activity, Iodine-125, greater than 1.01 mCi (NIST), per source H2 ASC U
BETOS: I4B Imaging/procedure - other
Statute: 1833(T)
Coding Clinic: 2004, Q4; 2005, Q2; 2007, Q2; 2009, Q2

D **C2635** Brachytherapy source, non-stranded, high activity, Palladium-103, greater than 2.2 mCi (NIST), per source H2 ASC U
BETOS: I4B Imaging/procedure - other
Statute: 1833(T)
Coding Clinic: 2004, Q4; 2005, Q2; 2007, Q2

D **C2636** Brachytherapy linear source, non-stranded, Palladium-103, per 1 mm H2 ASC U
BETOS: I4B Imaging/procedure - other
Statute: 1833(T)
Coding Clinic: 2004, Q4; 2007, Q2

D **C2637** Brachytherapy source, non-stranded, Ytterbium-169, per source B
BETOS: I4B Imaging/procedure - other
Statute: 1833(T)
Coding Clinic: 2005, Q3; 2007, Q2

D **C2638** Brachytherapy source, stranded, Iodine-125, per source H2 ASC U
BETOS: I4B Imaging/procedure - other
Statute: 1833(t)(2)
Coding Clinic: 2007, Q2

D **C2639** Brachytherapy source, non-stranded, Iodine-125, per source H2 ASC U
BETOS: I4B Imaging/procedure - other
Statute: 1833(t)(2)
Coding Clinic: 2007, Q2

D **C2640** Brachytherapy source, stranded, Palladium-103, per source H2 ASC U

BETOS: I4B Imaging/procedure - other
Statute: 1833(t)(2)
Coding Clinic: 2007, Q2

D **C2641** Brachytherapy source, non-stranded, Palladium-103, per source H2 ASC U
BETOS: I4B Imaging/procedure - other
Statute: 1833(t)(2)
Coding Clinic: 2007, Q2

D **C2642** Brachytherapy source, stranded, Cesium-131, per source H2 ASC U
BETOS: I4B Imaging/procedure - other
Statute: 1833(t)(2)
Coding Clinic: 2007, Q2

D **C2643** Brachytherapy source, non-stranded, Cesium-131, per source H2 ASC U
BETOS: I4B Imaging/procedure - other
Statute: 1833(t)(2)
Coding Clinic: 2007, Q2

D **C2644** Brachytherapy source, Cesium-131 chloride solution, per millicurie E2
BETOS: I4B Imaging/procedure - other
Statute: 1833(t)

D **C2645** Brachytherapy planar source, Palladium-103, per square millimeter H2 ASC U
BETOS: I4B Imaging/procedure - other
Statute: 1833(T)

D **C2698** Brachytherapy source, stranded, not otherwise specified, per source H2 ASC U
BETOS: I4B Imaging/procedure - other
Statute: 1833(t)(2)
Coding Clinic: 2007, Q2; 2007, Q3

D **C2699** Brachytherapy source, non-stranded, not otherwise specified, per source H2 ASC U
BETOS: I4B Imaging/procedure - other
Statute: 1833(t)(2)
Coding Clinic: 2007, Q2; 2007, Q3; 2009, Q2

SKIN SUBSTITUTE GRAFT APPLICATION (C5271-C5278)

D **C5271** Application of low cost skin substitute graft to trunk, arms, legs, total wound surface area up to 100 sq cm; first 25 sq cm or less wound surface area T
BETOS: P5A Ambulatory procedures - skin
Statute: 1833(t)
Coding Clinic: 2013, Q4

D **C5272** Application of low cost skin substitute graft to trunk, arms, legs, total wound surface area up to 100 sq cm; each additional 25 sq cm wound surface area, or part thereof (list separately in addition to code for primary procedure) N
BETOS: P5A Ambulatory procedures - skin
Statute: 1833(t)
Coding Clinic: 2013, Q4

D C5273 Application of low cost skin substitute graft to trunk, arms, legs, total wound surface area greater than or equal to 100 sq cm; first 100 sq cm wound surface area, or 1% of body area of infants and children Ⓐ T
BETOS: P5A Ambulatory procedures - skin
Statute: 1833(t)
Coding Clinic: 2013, Q4

D C5274 Application of low cost skin substitute graft to trunk, arms, legs, total wound surface area greater than or equal to 100 sq cm; each additional 100 sq cm wound surface area, or part thereof, or each additional 1% of body area of infants and children, or part thereof (list separately in addition to code for primary procedure) Ⓐ N
BETOS: P5A Ambulatory procedures - skin
Statute: 1833(t)
Coding Clinic: 2013, Q4

D C5275 Application of low cost skin substitute graft to face, scalp, eyelids, mouth, neck, ears, orbits, genitalia, hands, feet, and/or multiple digits, total wound surface area up to 100 sq cm; first 25 sq cm or less wound surface area T
BETOS: P5A Ambulatory procedures - skin
Statute: 1833(t)
Coding Clinic: 2013, Q4

D C5276 Application of low cost skin substitute graft to face, scalp, eyelids, mouth, neck, ears, orbits, genitalia, hands, feet, and/or multiple digits, total wound surface area up to 100 sq cm; each additional 25 sq cm wound surface area, or part thereof (list separately in addition to code for primary procedure) N
BETOS: P5A Ambulatory procedures - skin
Statute: 1833(t)
Coding Clinic: 2013, Q4

D C5277 Application of low cost skin substitute graft to face, scalp, eyelids, mouth, neck, ears, orbits, genitalia, hands, feet, and/or multiple digits, total wound surface area greater than or equal to 100 sq cm; first 100 sq cm wound surface area, or 1% of body area of infants and children Ⓐ T
BETOS: P5A Ambulatory procedures - skin
Statute: 1833(t)
Coding Clinic: 2013, Q4

D C5278 Application of low cost skin substitute graft to face, scalp, eyelids, mouth, neck, ears, orbits, genitalia, hands, feet, and/or multiple digits, total wound surface area greater than or equal to 100 sq cm; each additional 100 sq cm wound surface area, or part thereof, or each additional 1% of body area of infants and children, or part thereof (list separately in addition to code for primary procedure) Ⓐ N
BETOS: P5A Ambulatory procedures - skin
Statute: 1833(t)
Coding Clinic: 2013, Q4

MAGNETIC RESONANCE ANGIOGRAPHY, TRUNK AND LOWER EXTREMITIES (C8900-C8920)

D C8900 Magnetic resonance angiography with contrast, abdomen Z2 ASC Q3
BETOS: I2D Advanced imaging - MRI/MRA: other
Statute: 1833(t)(2)
Coding Clinic: 2009, Q2
Pub: 100-4, Chap. 13, 40.1.2

D C8901 Magnetic resonance angiography without contrast, abdomen Z2 ASC Q3
BETOS: I2D Advanced imaging - MRI/MRA: other
Statute: 1833(t)(2)
Pub: 100-4, Chap. 13, 40.1.2

D C8902 Magnetic resonance angiography without contrast followed by with contrast, abdomen Z2 ASC Q3
BETOS: I2D Advanced imaging - MRI/MRA: other
Statute: 1833(t)(2)
Pub: 100-4, Chap. 13, 40.1.2

D C8903 Magnetic resonance imaging with contrast, breast; unilateral Z2 ASC Q3
BETOS: I2D Advanced imaging - MRI/MRA: other
Statute: 1833(t)(2)

D C8904 Magnetic resonance imaging without contrast, breast; unilateral Z2 ASC Q3
BETOS: I2D Advanced imaging - MRI/MRA: other
Statute: 1833(t)(2)

D C8905 Magnetic resonance imaging without contrast followed by with contrast, breast; unilateral Z2 ASC Q3
BETOS: I2D Advanced imaging - MRI/MRA: other
Statute: 1833(t)(2)

D C8906 Magnetic resonance imaging with contrast, breast; bilateral Z2 ASC Q3
BETOS: I2D Advanced imaging - MRI/MRA: other
Statute: 1833(t)(2)

D C8907 Magnetic resonance imaging without contrast, breast; bilateral Z2 ASC Q3
BETOS: I2D Advanced imaging - MRI/MRA: other
Statute: 1833(t)(2)

D C8908 Magnetic resonance imaging without contrast followed by with contrast, breast; bilateral Z2 ASC Q3
BETOS: I2D Advanced imaging - MRI/MRA: other
Statute: 1833(t)(2)

▲ Revised code ● New code C Carrier judgment D Special coverage instructions apply
I Not payable by Medicare M Non-covered by Medicare S Non-covered by Medicare statute AHA Coding Clinic®

144 CPT® is a registered trademark of the American Medical Association. All rights reserved.

D **C8909** Magnetic resonance angiography with contrast, chest (excluding myocardium) Z2 ASC Q3
BETOS: I2D Advanced imaging - MRI/MRA: other
Statute: 1833(t)(2)
Pub: 100-4, Chap. 13, 40.1.2

D **C8910** Magnetic resonance angiography without contrast, chest (excluding myocardium) Z2 ASC Q3
BETOS: I2D Advanced imaging - MRI/MRA: other
Statute: 1833(t)(2)
Pub: 100-4, Chap. 13, 40.1.2

D **C8911** Magnetic resonance angiography without contrast followed by with contrast, chest (excluding myocardium) Z2 ASC Q3
BETOS: I2D Advanced imaging - MRI/MRA: other
Statute: 1833(t)(2)
Pub: 100-4, Chap. 13, 40.1.2

D **C8912** Magnetic resonance angiography with contrast, lower extremity Z2 ASC Q3
BETOS: I2D Advanced imaging - MRI/MRA: other
Statute: 1833(t)(2)
Pub: 100-4, Chap. 13, 40.1.2

D **C8913** Magnetic resonance angiography without contrast, lower extremity Z2 ASC Q3
BETOS: I2D Advanced imaging - MRI/MRA: other
Statute: 1833(t)(2)
Pub: 100-4, Chap. 13, 40.1.2

D **C8914** Magnetic resonance angiography without contrast followed by with contrast, lower extremity Z2 ASC Q3
BETOS: I2D Advanced imaging - MRI/MRA: other
Statute: 1833(t)(2)
Pub: 100-4, Chap. 13, 40.1.2

D **C8918** Magnetic resonance angiography with contrast, pelvis Z2 ASC Q3
BETOS: I2D Advanced imaging - MRI/MRA: other
Statute: 430BIPA
Pub: 100-4, Chap. 13, 40.1.2

D **C8919** Magnetic resonance angiography without contrast, pelvis Z2 ASC Q3
BETOS: I2D Advanced imaging - MRI/MRA: other
Statute: 430BIPA
Pub: 100-4, Chap. 13, 40.1.2

D **C8920** Magnetic resonance angiography without contrast followed by with contrast, pelvis Z2 ASC Q3
BETOS: I2D Advanced imaging - MRI/MRA: other

Statute: 430BIPA
Coding Clinic: 2009, Q2
Pub: 100-4, Chap. 13, 40.1.2

TRANSESOPHAGEAL/TRANSTHORACIC ECHOCARDIOGRAPHY (C8921-C8930)

D **C8921** Transthoracic echocardiography with contrast, or without contrast followed by with contrast, for congenital cardiac anomalies; complete S
BETOS: I3C Echography/ultrasonography - heart
Statute: 1833(t)(2)
Coding Clinic: 2012, Q3
Pub: 100-4, Chap. 4, 200.7.2

D **C8922** Transthoracic echocardiography with contrast, or without contrast followed by with contrast, for congenital cardiac anomalies; follow-up or limited study S
BETOS: I3C Echography/ultrasonography - heart
Statute: 1833(t)(2)
Coding Clinic: 2007, Q4; 2008, Q2

D **C8923** Transthoracic echocardiography with contrast, or without contrast followed by with contrast, real-time with image documentation (2D), includes M-mode recording, when performed, complete, without spectral or color doppler echocardiography S
BETOS: I3C Echography/ultrasonography - heart
Statute: 1833(t)(2)
Coding Clinic: 2007, Q4; 2008, Q2

D **C8924** Transthoracic echocardiography with contrast, or without contrast followed by with contrast, real-time with image documentation (2D), includes M-mode recording, when performed, follow-up or limited study S
BETOS: I3C Echography/ultrasonography - heart
Statute: 1833(t)(2)
Coding Clinic: 2007, Q4; 2008, Q2

D **C8925** Transesophageal echocardiography (TEE) with contrast, or without contrast followed by with contrast, real time with image documentation (2D) (with or without M-mode recording); including probe placement, image acquisition, interpretation and report S
BETOS: I3C Echography/ultrasonography - heart
Statute: 1833(t)(2)
Coding Clinic: 2007, Q4; 2008, Q2

D **C8926** Transesophageal echocardiography (TEE) with contrast, or without contrast followed by with contrast, for congenital cardiac anomalies; including probe placement, image acquisition, interpretation and report   S
BETOS: I3C   Echography/ultrasonography - heart
Statute: 1833(t)(2)
Coding Clinic: 2007, Q4; 2008, Q2

D **C8927** Transesophageal echocardiography (TEE) with contrast, or without contrast followed by with contrast, for monitoring purposes, including probe placement, real time 2-dimensional image acquisition and interpretation leading to ongoing (continuous) assessment of (dynamically changing) cardiac pumping function and to therapeutic measures on an immediate time basis   S
BETOS: I3C   Echography/ultrasonography - heart
Statute: 1833(t)(2)
Coding Clinic: 2007, Q4; 2008, Q2

D **C8928** Transthoracic echocardiography with contrast, or without contrast followed by with contrast, real-time with image documentation (2D), includes M-mode recording, when performed, during rest and cardiovascular stress test using treadmill, bicycle exercise and/or pharmacologically induced stress, with interpretation and report   S
BETOS: I3C   Echography/ultrasonography - heart
Statute: 1833(t)(2)
Coding Clinic: 2007, Q4; 2008, Q2

D **C8929** Transthoracic echocardiography with contrast, or without contrast followed by with contrast, real-time with image documentation (2D), includes M-mode recording, when performed, complete, with spectral doppler echocardiography, and with color flow doppler echocardiography   S
BETOS: I3C   Echography/ultrasonography - heart
Statute: 1833(t)(2)
Coding Clinic: 2008, Q4

D **C8930** Transthoracic echocardiography, with contrast, or without contrast followed by with contrast, real-time with image documentation (2D), includes M-mode recording, when performed, during rest and cardiovascular stress test using treadmill, bicycle exercise and/or pharmacologically induced stress, with interpretation and report; including performance of continuous electrocardiographic monitoring, with physician supervision   S
BETOS: I3C   Echography/ultrasonography - heart
Statute: 1833(t)(2)
Coding Clinic: 2012, Q3

MAGNETIC RESONANCE ANGIOGRAPHY, SPINE AND UPPER EXTREMITIES (C8931-C8936)

D **C8931** Magnetic resonance angiography with contrast, spinal canal and contents   Z2 ASC Q3
BETOS: I2D   Advanced imaging - MRI/MRA: other
Statute: 1833(t)

D **C8932** Magnetic resonance angiography without contrast, spinal canal and contents   Z2 ASC Q3
BETOS: I2D   Advanced imaging - MRI/MRA: other
Statute: 1833(t)

D **C8933** Magnetic resonance angiography without contrast followed by with contrast, spinal canal and contents   Z2 ASC Q3
BETOS: I2D   Advanced imaging - MRI/MRA: other
Statute: 1833(t)

D **C8934** Magnetic resonance angiography with contrast, upper extremity   Z2 ASC Q3
BETOS: I2D   Advanced imaging - MRI/MRA: other
Statute: 1833(t)

D **C8935** Magnetic resonance angiography without contrast, upper extremity   Z2 ASC Q3
BETOS: I2D   Advanced imaging - MRI/MRA: other
Statute: 1833(t)

D **C8936** Magnetic resonance angiography without contrast followed by with contrast, upper extremity   Z2 ASC Q3
BETOS: I2D   Advanced imaging - MRI/MRA: other
Statute: 1833(t)

MISCELLANEOUS DRUGS, BIOLOGICALS, AND SUPPLIES (C8957-C9497)

D **C8957** Intravenous infusion for therapy/diagnosis; initiation of prolonged infusion (more than 8 hours), requiring use of portable or implantable pump   S
BETOS: P6D   Minor procedures - other (non-Medicare fee schedule)
Value not established Statute: 1833(t)
Coding Clinic: 2005, Q4; 2006, Q4; 2008, Q3
Pub: 100-4, Chap. 4, 230.2

● **D** **C9014** Injection, Cerliponase alfa, 1 mg
BETOS: O1E   Other drugs
Statute: 1833(t)

● **D** **C9015** Injection, c-1 esterase inhibitor (human), Haegarda®, 10 units
BETOS: O1E   Other drugs
Statute: 1833(t)

▲ Revised code   ● New code   **C** Carrier judgment   **D** Special coverage instructions apply
I Not payable by Medicare   **M** Non-covered by Medicare   **S** Non-covered by Medicare statute   AHA Coding Clinic®

146   CPT® is a registered trademark of the American Medical Association. All rights reserved.

- D **C9016** Injection, Triptorelin extended release, 3.75 mg
  BETOS: O1E   Other drugs
  Statute: 1833(t)

- D **C9024** Injection, Liposomal, 1 mg Daunorubicin and 2.27 mg Cytarabine
  BETOS: O1D   Chemotherapy
  Statute: 1833(t)

- D **C9028** Injection, Inotuzumab ozogamicin, 0.1 mg
  BETOS: O1D   Chemotherapy
  Statute: 1833(t)

- D **C9029** Injection, Guselkumab, 1 mg
  BETOS: O1E   Other drugs
  Statute: 1833(t)

D **C9113** Injection, Pantoprazole sodium, per vial   N1 ASC N
  BETOS: O1E   Other drugs
  Statute: 1833(T)
  Coding Clinic: 2002, Q1

D **C9132** Prothrombin complex concentrate (human), kcentra, per IU of Factor IX activity   K2 ASC K
  BETOS: O1E   Other drugs
  Statute: 1833(t)
  Drugs: KCENTRA

D **C9248** Injection, Clevidipine butyrate, 1 mg   K2 ASC K
  BETOS: O1E   Other drugs
  Statute: 1833(t)
  Drugs: CLEVIPREX
  Coding Clinic: 2008, Q4; 2009, Q1

D **C9250** Human plasma fibrin sealant, vapor-heated, solvent-detergent (Artiss), 2ml   K2 ASC K
  BETOS: O1E   Other drugs
  Statute: 621MMA
  Drugs: ARTISS
  Coding Clinic: 2009, Q3

D **C9254** Injection, Lacosamide, 1 mg   N1 ASC N
  BETOS: O1E   Other drugs
  Statute: 621MMA

D **C9257** Injection, Bevacizumab, 0.25 mg   K2 ASC K
  BETOS: O1E   Other drugs
  Statute: 1833(t)
  Drugs: AVASTIN
  Coding Clinic: 2013, Q3

D **C9275** Injection, Hexaminolevulinate hydrochloride, 100 mg, per study dose   N1 ASC N
  BETOS: O1E   Other drugs
  Statute: 1833(t)
  Coding Clinic: 2011, Q1

D **C9285** Lidocaine 70 mg/Tetracaine 70 mg, per patch   N1 ASC N
  BETOS: O1E   Other drugs
  Statute: 1833(t)

D **C9290** Injection, Bupivacaine liposome, 1 mg   N1 ASC N
  BETOS: O1E   Other drugs

Statute: 1833(t)
  Coding Clinic: 2012, Q 2

D **C9293** Injection, Glucarpidase, 10 units   K2 ASC K
  BETOS: O1E   Other drugs
  Statute: 1833(t)
  Drugs: VORAXAZE

D **C9352** Microporous collagen implantable tube (NeuraGen Nerve Guide), per centimeter length   N1 ASC N
  BETOS: D1A   Medical/surgical supplies
  Statute: 621MMA
  Coding Clinic: 2008, Q1

D **C9353** Microporous collagen implantable slit tube (NeuraWrap Nerve Protector), per centimeter length   N1 ASC N
  BETOS: D1A   Medical/surgical supplies
  Statute: 621MMA
  Coding Clinic: 2008, Q1

D **C9354** Acellular pericardial tissue matrix of non-human origin (Veritas), per square centimeter   N1 ASC N
  BETOS: D1A   Medical/surgical supplies
  Statute: 621MMA
  Coding Clinic: 2008, Q1

D **C9355** Collagen nerve cuff (NeuroMatrix), per 0.5 centimeter length   N1 ASC N
  BETOS: D1A   Medical/surgical supplies
  Statute: 621MMA
  Coding Clinic: 2008, Q1

D **C9356** Tendon, porous matrix of cross-linked collagen and glycosaminoglycan matrix (TenoGlide Tendon Protector Sheet), per square centimeter   N1 ASC N
  BETOS: D1A   Medical/surgical supplies
  Statute: 621MMA
  Coding Clinic: 2008, Q3

D **C9358** Dermal substitute, native, non-denatured collagen, fetal bovine origin (SurgiMend Collagen Matrix), per 0.5 square centimeters   N1 ASC N
  BETOS: D1A   Medical/surgical supplies
  Statute: 621MMA
  Coding Clinic: 2012, Q 2

D **C9359** Porous purified collagen matrix bone void filler (Integra Mozaik Osteoconductive Scaffold Putty, Integra Os Osteoconductive Scaffold Putty), per 0.5 cc   N1 ASC N
  BETOS: D1A   Medical/surgical supplies
  Statute: 1833(T)
  Coding Clinic: 2009, Q3

D **C9360** Dermal substitute, native, non-denatured collagen, neonatal bovine origin (SurgiMend Collagen Matrix), per 0.5 square centimeters   N1 ASC N
  BETOS: D1A   Medical/surgical supplies
  Statute: 621MMA
  Coding Clinic: 2012, Q 2

♂ Male only   ♀ Female only   Ⓐ Age   A2 - Z3 = ASC Payment indicator   A - Y = APC Status indicator
ASC = ASC-approved procedure   DME Paid under the DME fee schedule   MIPS MIPS code

D **C9361** Collagen matrix nerve wrap (NeuroMend Collagen Nerve Wrap), per 0.5 centimeter length   N1 ASC N
    BETOS: D1A   Medical/surgical supplies
    Statute: 621MMA
    Coding Clinic: 2009, Q3

D **C9362** Porous purified collagen matrix bone void filler (Integra Mozaik Osteoconductive Scaffold Strip), per 0.5 cc   N1 ASC N
    BETOS: D1A   Medical/surgical supplies
    Statute: 621MMA
    Coding Clinic: 2010, Q1

D **C9363** Skin substitute, Integra Meshed Bilayer Wound Matrix, per square centimeter   N1 ASC N
    BETOS: D1A   Medical/surgical supplies
    Statute: 621MMA
    Coding Clinic: 2010, Q1; 2012, Q 2

D **C9364** Porcine implant, Permacol, per square centimeter   N1 ASC N
    BETOS: D1A   Medical/surgical supplies
    Statute: 621MMA
    Coding Clinic: 2009, Q3

D **C9399** Unclassified drugs or biologicals   K7 ASC A
    BETOS: O1E   Other drugs
    Statute: 621MMA
    Coding Clinic: 2010, Q3; 2011, Q4; 2013, Q1; 2014, Q2; 2014, Q4; 2016, Q4; 2017, Q1
    Pub: 100-4, Chap. 17, 90.3

D **C9447** Injection, Phenylephrine and Ketorolac, 4 ml vial   K2 ASC G
    BETOS: O1E   Other drugs
    Statute: 1833(t)
    Drugs: OMIDRIA (PHENYLEPHRINE + KETOROLAC IRRIGATION)
    Coding Clinic: 2014, Q4

D **C9460** Injection, Cangrelor, 1 mg   K2 ASC G
    BETOS: O1E   Other drugs
    Statute: 1833(t)
    Drugs: KENGREAL
    Coding Clinic: 2016, Q1

D **C9482** Injection, Sotalol hydrochloride, 1 mg   K2 ASC G
    BETOS: O1E   Other drugs
    Statute: 1833(t)
    Drugs: SOTALOL
    Coding Clinic: 2016, Q4

● **D** **C9488** Injection, Conivaptan hydrochloride, 1 mg   K2 ASC G
    BETOS: O1E   Other drugs
    Statute: 1833(t)
    Drugs: VAPRISOL

● **D** **C9492** Injection, Durvalumab, 10 mg   K2 ASC G
    BETOS: O1D   Chemotherapy
    Statute: 1833(t)
    Drugs: IMFINZI
    Coding Clinic: 2017, Q3

● **D** **C9493** Injection, Edaravone, 1 mg   K2 ASC G
    BETOS: O1E   Other drugs
    Statute: 1833(t)
    Drugs: RADICAVA
    Coding Clinic: 2017, Q3

D **C9497** Loxapine, inhalation powder, 10 mg   K2 ASC K
    BETOS: O1E   Other drugs
    Statute: 1833(t)
    Drugs: ADASUVE
    Coding Clinic: 2014, Q1

PERCUTANEOUS TRANSCATHETER/TRANSLUMINAL CORONARY PROCEDURES (C9600-C9608)

D **C9600** Percutaneous transcatheter placement of drug-eluting intracoronary stent(s), with coronary angioplasty when performed; single major coronary artery or branch   J1
    BETOS: P2F   Major procedure, cardiovascular-other
    Statute: 1833(t)
    Coding Clinic: 2012, Q4

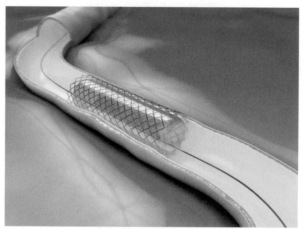

Coronary angioplasty

D **C9601** Percutaneous transcatheter placement of drug-eluting intracoronary stent(s), with coronary angioplasty when performed; each additional branch of a major coronary artery (list separately in addition to code for primary procedure)   N
    BETOS: P2F   Major procedure, cardiovascular-other
    Statute: 1833(t)
    Coding Clinic: 2012, Q4

D **C9602** Percutaneous transluminal coronary atherectomy, with drug-eluting intracoronary stent, with coronary angioplasty when performed; single major coronary artery or branch   J1
    BETOS: P2F   Major procedure, cardiovascular-other
    Statute: 1833(t)
    Coding Clinic: 2012, Q4

▲ Revised code   ● New code   **C** Carrier judgment   **D** Special coverage instructions apply
I Not payable by Medicare   **M** Non-covered by Medicare   **S** Non-covered by Medicare statute   AHA Coding Clinic®

Build-up of cholesterol partially blocking blood flow through the artery.

Stent with balloon inserted into partially blocked artery.

Balloon inflated to expand stent.

Balloon removed from expanded stent.

Stent angioplasty

D C9603 Percutaneous transluminal coronary atherectomy, with drug-eluting intracoronary stent, with coronary angioplasty when performed; each additional branch of a major coronary artery (list separately in addition to code for primary procedure) N
BETOS: P2F Major procedure, cardiovascular-other
Statute: 1833(t)
Coding Clinic: 2012, Q4

D C9604 Percutaneous transluminal revascularization of or through coronary artery bypass graft (internal mammary, free arterial, venous), any combination of drug-eluting intracoronary stent, atherectomy and angioplasty, including distal protection when performed; single vessel J1
BETOS: P2F Major procedure, cardiovascular-other
Statute: 1833(t)
Coding Clinic: 2012, Q4

D C9605 Percutaneous transluminal revascularization of or through coronary artery bypass graft (internal mammary, free arterial, venous), any combination of drug-eluting intracoronary stent, atherectomy and angioplasty, including distal protection when performed; each additional branch subtended by the bypass graft (list separately in addition to code for primary procedure) N

BETOS: P2F Major procedure, cardiovascular-other
Statute: 1833(t)
Coding Clinic: 2012, Q4

D C9606 Percutaneous transluminal revascularization of acute total/subtotal occlusion during acute myocardial infarction, coronary artery or coronary artery bypass graft, any combination of drug-eluting intracoronary stent, atherectomy and angioplasty, including aspiration thrombectomy when performed, single vessel J1
BETOS: P2F Major procedure, cardiovascular-other
Statute: 1833(t)
Coding Clinic: 2012, Q4

D C9607 Percutaneous transluminal revascularization of chronic total occlusion, coronary artery, coronary artery branch, or coronary artery bypass graft, any combination of drug-eluting intracoronary stent, atherectomy and angioplasty; single vessel J1
BETOS: P2F Major procedure, cardiovascular-other
Statute: 1833(t)

D C9608 Percutaneous transluminal revascularization of chronic total occlusion, coronary artery, coronary artery branch, or coronary artery bypass graft, any combination of drug-eluting intracoronary stent, atherectomy and angioplasty; each additional coronary artery, coronary artery branch, or bypass graft (list separately in addition to code for primary procedure) N
BETOS: P2F Major procedure, cardiovascular-other
Statute: 1833(t)

OTHER THERAPEUTIC SERVICES AND SUPPLIES (C9725-C9899)

D C9725 Placement of endorectal intracavitary applicator for high intensity brachytherapy T
BETOS: P7A Oncology - radiation therapy
Statute: 1833(T)
Coding Clinic: 2005, Q3

D C9726 Placement and removal (if performed) of applicator into breast for intraoperative radiation therapy, add-on to primary breast procedure N
BETOS: P7A Oncology - radiation therapy
Statute: 1833(T)
Coding Clinic: 2006, Q1; 2007, Q2

D C9727 Insertion of implants into the soft palate; minimum of three implants T
BETOS: P6D Minor procedures - other (non-Medicare fee schedule)
Statute: 1833(T)

♂ Male only   ♀ Female only   🅐 Age   A2 - Z3 = ASC Payment indicator   A - Y = APC Status indicator
ASC = ASC-approved procedure   **DME** Paid under the DME fee schedule   **MIPS** MIPS code

D **C9728** Placement of interstitial device(s) for radiation therapy/surgery guidance (e.g., fiducial markers, dosimeter), for other than the following sites (any approach): abdomen, pelvis, prostate, retroperitoneum, thorax, single or multiple   S
BETOS: P5E   Ambulatory procedures - other
Statute: 1833(T)
Coding Clinic: 2007, Q2

D **C9733** Non-ophthalmic fluorescent vascular angiography   N1 ASC Q2
BETOS: I4B   Imaging/procedure - other
Statute: 1833(t)

D **C9734** Focused ultrasound ablation/therapeutic intervention, other than uterine leiomyomata, with magnetic resonance (MR) guidance   J1
BETOS: P5E   Ambulatory procedures - other
Statute: 1833(t)
Coding Clinic: 2013, Q3

● **D** **C9738** Adjunctive blue light cystoscopy with fluorescent imaging agent (list separately in addition to code for primary procedure)
BETOS: I1F   Standard imaging - other
Statute: 1833(t)

D **C9739** Cystourethroscopy, with insertion of transprostatic implant; 1 to 3 implants   ♂ J1
BETOS: P5E   Ambulatory procedures - other
Statute: 1833(t)
Coding Clinic: 2014, Q2

D **C9740** Cystourethroscopy, with insertion of transprostatic implant; 4 or more implants   ♂ J1
BETOS: P5E   Ambulatory procedures - other
Statute: 1833(t)
Coding Clinic: 2014, Q2

D **C9741** Right heart catheterization with implantation of wireless pressure sensor in the pulmonary artery, including any type of measurement, angiography, imaging supervision, interpretation, and report   J1
BETOS: P6D   Minor procedures - other (non-Medicare fee schedule)
Statute: 1833(t)
Coding Clinic: 2014, Q3

D **C9744** Ultrasound, abdominal, with contrast   Z2 ASC S
BETOS: I3B   Echography/ultrasonography - abdomen/pelvis
Statute: 1833(t)
Coding Clinic: 2016, Q4

● **D** **C9745** Nasal endoscopy, surgical; balloon dilation of eustachian tube   J1
BETOS: P8I   Endoscopy - other
Statute: 1833(t)
Coding Clinic: 2017, Q2; 2017, Q3

● **D** **C9746** Transperineal implantation of permanent adjustable balloon continence device, with cystourethroscopy, when performed and/or fluoroscopy, when performed   J1
BETOS: P6C   Minor procedures - other (Medicare fee schedule)
Statute: 1833(t)
Coding Clinic: 2017, Q2; 2017, Q3

● **D** **C9747** Ablation of prostate, transrectal, high intensity focused ultrasound (HIFU), including imaging guidance   ♂ J1
BETOS: P6C   Minor procedures - other (Medicare fee schedule)
Statute: 1833(t)
Coding Clinic: 2017, Q2; 2017, Q3

● **D** **C9748** Transurethral destruction of prostate tissue; by radiofrequency water vapor (steam) thermal therapy   ♂
BETOS: P5E   Ambulatory procedures - other
Statute: 1833(t)

D **C9898** Radiolabeled product provided during a hospital inpatient stay   N
BETOS: Z2   Undefined codes
Service not separately priced by Part B

D **C9899** Implanted prosthetic device, payable only for inpatients who do not have inpatient coverage   A
BETOS: Z2   Undefined codes
Statute: 1833(t)
Coding Clinic: 2008, Q4

▲ Revised code   ● New code   **C** Carrier judgment   **D** Special coverage instructions apply
I Not payable by Medicare   **M** Non-covered by Medicare   **S** Non-covered by Medicare statute   AHA Coding Clinic®

NOTES

NOTES

DURABLE MEDICAL EQUIPMENT (E0100-E8002)

WALKING AIDS AND ATTACHMENTS (E0100-E0159)

D **E0100** Cane, includes canes of all materials, adjustable or fixed, with tip   DME Y
   BETOS: D1E   Other DME
   DME Modifier: NU,RR,UE
   Coding Clinic: 2009, Q2

D **E0105** Cane, quad or three prong, includes canes of all materials, adjustable or fixed, with tips   DME Y
   BETOS: D1E   Other DME
   DME Modifier: NU,RR,UE

D **E0110** Crutches, forearm, includes crutches of various materials, adjustable or fixed, pair, complete with tips and handgrips   DME Y
   BETOS: D1E   Other DME
   DME Modifier: NU,RR,UE

D **E0111** Crutch forearm, includes crutches of various materials, adjustable or fixed, each, with tip and handgrips   DME Y
   BETOS: D1E   Other DME
   DME Modifier: NU,RR,UE

D **E0112** Crutches underarm, wood, adjustable or fixed, pair, with pads, tips and handgrips   DME Y
   BETOS: D1E   Other DME
   DME Modifier: NU,RR,UE

D **E0113** Crutch underarm, wood, adjustable or fixed, each, with pad, tip and handgrip   DME Y
   BETOS: D1E   Other DME
   DME Modifier: NU,RR,UE

D **E0114** Crutches underarm, other than wood, adjustable or fixed, pair, with pads, tips and handgrips   DME Y
   BETOS: D1E   Other DME
   DME Modifier: NU,RR,UE
   Coding Clinic: 2002, Q2

D **E0116** Crutch, underarm, other than wood, adjustable or fixed, with pad, tip, handgrip, with or without shock absorber, each   DME Y
   BETOS: D1E   Other DME
   DME Modifier: NU,RR,UE

D **E0117** Crutch, underarm, articulating, spring assisted, each   DME Y
   BETOS: D1E   Other DME
   DME Modifier: RR

C **E0118** Crutch substitute, lower leg platform, with or without wheels, each   E1
   BETOS: D1E   Other DME

D **E0130** Walker, rigid (pickup), adjustable or fixed height   DME Y
   BETOS: D1E   Other DME

DME Modifier: NU,RR,UE
   Pub: 100-4, Chap. 23, 60.3; 100-4, Chap. 36, 50.15

D **E0135** Walker, folding (pickup), adjustable or fixed height   DME Y
   BETOS: D1E   Other DME
   DME Modifier: NU,RR,UE
   Pub: 100-4, Chap. 36, 50.15

D **E0140** Walker, with trunk support, adjustable or fixed height, any type   DME Y
   BETOS: D1E   Other DME
   DME Modifier: RR
   Pub: 100-4, Chap. 36, 50.15

D **E0141** Walker, rigid, wheeled, adjustable or fixed height   DME Y
   BETOS: D1E   Other DME
   DME Modifier: NU,RR,UE

D **E0143** Walker, folding, wheeled, adjustable or fixed height   DME Y
   BETOS: D1E   Other DME
   DME Modifier: NU,RR,UE
   Pub: 100-4, Chap. 36, 50.15

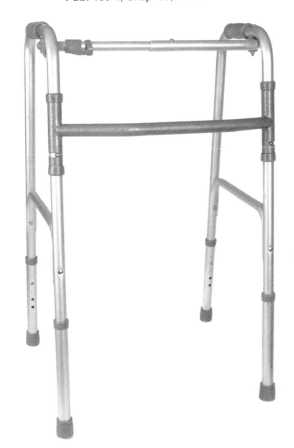

Walker

D **E0144** Walker, enclosed, four sided framed, rigid or folding, wheeled with posterior seat   DME Y
   BETOS: D1E   Other DME
   DME Modifier: RR

D **E0147** Walker, heavy duty, multiple braking system, variable wheel resistance `DME` Y
BETOS: D1E   Other DME
DME Modifier: NU,RR,UE
Pub: 100-4, Chap. 36, 50.15

C **E0148** Walker, heavy duty, without wheels, rigid or folding, any type, each `DME` Y
BETOS: D1E   Other DME
DME Modifier: NU,RR,UE

C **E0149** Walker, heavy duty, wheeled, rigid or folding, any type `DME` Y
BETOS: D1E   Other DME
DME Modifier: RR

C **E0153** Platform attachment, forearm crutch, each `DME` Y
BETOS: D1E   Other DME
DME Modifier: NU,RR,UE

C **E0154** Platform attachment, walker, each `DME` Y
BETOS: D1E   Other DME
DME Modifier: NU,RR,UE
Pub: 100-4, Chap. 23, 60.3; 100-4, Chap. 36, 50.14; 100-4, Chap. 36, 50.15

C **E0155** Wheel attachment, rigid pick-up walker, per pair `DME` Y
BETOS: D1E   Other DME
DME Modifier: NU,RR,UE

C **E0156** Seat attachment, walker `DME` Y
BETOS: D1E   Other DME
DME Modifier: NU,RR,UE
Pub: 100-4, Chap. 36, 50.14

C **E0157** Crutch attachment, walker, each `DME` Y
BETOS: D1E   Other DME
DME Modifier: NU,RR,UE

C **E0158** Leg extensions for walker, per set of four (4) `DME` Y
BETOS: D1E   Other DME
DME Modifier: NU,RR,UE

C **E0159** Brake attachment for wheeled walker, replacement, each `DME` Y
BETOS: D1E   Other DME
DME Modifier: NU,RR,UE

SITZ BATH/EQUIPMENT (E0160-E0162)

D **E0160** Sitz type bath or equipment, portable, used with or without commode `DME` Y
BETOS: D1E   Other DME
DME Modifier: NU,RR,UE

D **E0161** Sitz type bath or equipment, portable, used with or without commode, with faucet attachment/s `DME` Y
BETOS: D1E   Other DME
DME Modifier: NU,RR,UE
Coding Clinic: 2009, Q2

D **E0162** Sitz bath chair `DME` Y
BETOS: D1E   Other DME
DME Modifier: NU,RR,UE

COMMODE CHAIR AND SUPPLIES (E0163-E0175)

D **E0163** Commode chair, mobile or stationary, with fixed arms `DME` Y
BETOS: D1E   Other DME
DME Modifier: NU,RR,UE

D **E0165** Commode chair, mobile or stationary, with detachable arms `DME` Y
BETOS: D1E   Other DME
DME Modifier: RR

D **E0167** Pail or pan for use with commode chair, replacement only `DME` Y
BETOS: D1E   Other DME
DME Modifier: NU,RR,UE

C **E0168** Commode chair, extra wide and/or heavy duty, stationary or mobile, with or without arms, any type, each `DME` Y
BETOS: D1E   Other DME
DME Modifier: NU,RR,UE

C **E0170** Commode chair with integrated seat lift mechanism, electric, any type `DME` Y
BETOS: D1E   Other DME
DME Modifier: RR

C **E0171** Commode chair with integrated seat lift mechanism, non-electric, any type `DME` Y
BETOS: D1E   Other DME
DME Modifier: RR

S **E0172** Seat lift mechanism placed over or on top of toilet, any type E1
BETOS: D1E   Other DME
Service not separately priced by Part B
Statute: 1861SSA

C **E0175** Footrest, for use with commode chair, each `DME` Y
BETOS: D1E   Other DME
DME Modifier: NU,RR,UE

PRESSURE MATTRESSES, PADS, AND OTHER SUPPLIES (E0181-E0199)

D **E0181** Powered pressure reducing mattress overlay/pad, alternating, with pump, includes heavy duty `DME` Y
BETOS: D1E   Other DME
DME Modifier: RR

D **E0182** Pump for alternating pressure pad, for replacement only `DME` Y
BETOS: D1E   Other DME
DME Modifier: RR

D **E0184** Dry pressure mattress `DME` Y
BETOS: D1E   Other DME
DME Modifier: NU,RR,UE

▲ Revised code   ● New code   C Carrier judgment   D Special coverage instructions apply
I Not payable by Medicare   M Non-covered by Medicare   S Non-covered by Medicare statute   AHA Coding Clinic®

D E0185 Gel or gel-like pressure pad for mattress, standard mattress length and width **DME** Y
BETOS: D1E Other DME
DME Modifier: NU,RR,UE

D E0186 Air pressure mattress **DME** Y
BETOS: D1E Other DME
DME Modifier: RR

D E0187 Water pressure mattress **DME** Y
BETOS: D1E Other DME
DME Modifier: RR

D E0188 Synthetic sheepskin pad **DME** Y
BETOS: D1E Other DME
DME Modifier: NU,RR,UE

D E0189 Lambswool sheepskin pad, any size **DME** Y
BETOS: D1E Other DME
DME Modifier: NU,RR,UE

D E0190 Positioning cushion/pillow/wedge, any shape or size, includes all components and accessories E1
BETOS: D1E Other DME
Service not separately priced by Part B

C E0191 Heel or elbow protector, each **DME** Y
BETOS: D1E Other DME
DME Modifier: NU,RR,UE

C E0193 Powered air flotation bed (low air loss therapy) **DME** Y
BETOS: D1E Other DME
DME Modifier: RR
Pub: 100-4, Chap. 23, 60.3

D E0194 Air fluidized bed **DME** Y
BETOS: D1E Other DME
DME Modifier: RR

D E0196 Gel pressure mattress **DME** Y
BETOS: D1E Other DME
DME Modifier: RR

D E0197 Air pressure pad for mattress, standard mattress length and width **DME** Y
BETOS: D1E Other DME
DME Modifier: RR

D E0198 Water pressure pad for mattress, standard mattress length and width **DME** Y
BETOS: D1E Other DME
DME Modifier: RR

D E0199 Dry pressure pad for mattress, standard mattress length and width **DME** Y
BETOS: D1E Other DME
DME Modifier: NU,RR,UE

HEAT, COLD, AND LIGHT THERAPIES (E0200-E0239), SEE ALSO ULTRAVIOLET LIGHT THERAPY SYSTEMS (E0691-E0694)

D E0200 Heat lamp, without stand (table model), includes bulb, or infrared element **DME** Y
BETOS: D1E Other DME
DME Modifier: NU,RR,UE

C E0202 Phototherapy (bilirubin) light with photometer **DME** Y
BETOS: D1E Other DME
DME Modifier: RR

M E0203 Therapeutic lightbox, minimum 10,000 lux, table top model E1
BETOS: D1E Other DME
Service not separately priced by Part B

D E0205 Heat lamp, with stand, includes bulb, or infrared element **DME** Y
BETOS: D1E Other DME
DME Modifier: NU,RR,UE

D E0210 Electric heat pad, standard **DME** Y
BETOS: D1E Other DME
DME Modifier: NU,RR,UE

D E0215 Electric heat pad, moist **DME** Y
BETOS: D1E Other DME
DME Modifier: NU,RR,UE

D E0217 Water circulating heat pad with pump **DME** Y
BETOS: D1E Other DME
DME Modifier: NU,RR,UE

D E0218 Water circulating cold pad with pump Y
BETOS: D1E Other DME

C E0221 Infrared heating pad system Y
BETOS: D1E Other DME
Service not separately priced by Part B
Coding Clinic: 2002, Q1

D E0225 Hydrocollator unit, includes pads **DME** Y
BETOS: D1E Other DME
DME Modifier: NU,RR,UE
Pub: 100-2, Chap. 15, 230

M E0231 Non-contact wound warming device (temperature control unit, AC adapter and power cord) for use with warming card and wound cover E1
BETOS: D1E Other DME
Service not separately priced by Part B
Coding Clinic: 2002, Q1

M E0232 Warming card for use with the non contact wound warming device and non contact wound warming wound cover E1
BETOS: D1E Other DME
Service not separately priced by Part B
Coding Clinic: 2002, Q1

D E0235 Paraffin bath unit, portable (see medical supply code A4265 for paraffin) **DME** Y
BETOS: D1E   Other DME
DME Modifier: RR
Pub: 100-2, Chap. 15, 230

D E0236 Pump for water circulating pad **DME** Y
BETOS: D1E   Other DME
DME Modifier: RR

D E0239 Hydrocollator unit, portable **DME** Y
BETOS: D1E   Other DME
DME Modifier: NU,RR,UE
Pub: 100-2, Chap. 15, 230

BATHING SUPPLIES (E0240-E0249)

M E0240 Bath/shower chair, with or without wheels, any size E1
BETOS: D1E   Other DME
Service not separately priced by Part B

M E0241 Bath tub wall rail, each E1
BETOS: D1E   Other DME
Service not separately priced by Part B

M E0242 Bath tub rail, floor base E1
BETOS: D1E   Other DME
Service not separately priced by Part B

M E0243 Toilet rail, each E1
BETOS: D1E   Other DME
Service not separately priced by Part B

M E0244 Raised toilet seat E1
BETOS: D1E   Other DME
Service not separately priced by Part B

M E0245 Tub stool or bench E1
BETOS: D1E   Other DME
Service not separately priced by Part B

C E0246 Transfer tub rail attachment E1
BETOS: D1E   Other DME
Service not separately priced by Part B

D E0247 Transfer bench for tub or toilet with or without commode opening E1
BETOS: D1E   Other DME
Service not separately priced by Part B

D E0248 Transfer bench, heavy duty, for tub or toilet with or without commode opening E1
BETOS: D1E   Other DME
Service not separately priced by Part B

D E0249 Pad for water circulating heat unit, for replacement only **DME** Y
BETOS: D1E   Other DME
DME Modifier: NU,RR,UE

HOSPITAL BEDS AND ASSOCIATED SUPPLIES (E0250-E0373)

D E0250 Hospital bed, fixed height, with any type side rails, with mattress **DME** Y
BETOS: D1B   Hospital beds

DME Modifier: RR
Pub: 100-4, Chap. 23, 60.3

D E0251 Hospital bed, fixed height, with any type side rails, without mattress **DME** Y
BETOS: D1B   Hospital beds
DME Modifier: RR

D E0255 Hospital bed, variable height, hi-lo, with any type side rails, with mattress **DME** Y
BETOS: D1B   Hospital beds
DME Modifier: RR

D E0256 Hospital bed, variable height, hi-lo, with any type side rails, without mattress **DME** Y
BETOS: D1B   Hospital beds
DME Modifier: RR

D E0260 Hospital bed, semi-electric (head and foot adjustment), with any type side rails, with mattress **DME** Y
BETOS: D1B   Hospital beds
DME Modifier: RR

D E0261 Hospital bed, semi-electric (head and foot adjustment), with any type side rails, without mattress **DME** Y
BETOS: D1B   Hospital beds
DME Modifier: RR

D E0265 Hospital bed, total electric (head, foot and height adjustments), with any type side rails, with mattress **DME** Y
BETOS: D1B   Hospital beds
DME Modifier: RR

D E0266 Hospital bed, total electric (head, foot and height adjustments), with any type side rails, without mattress **DME** Y
BETOS: D1B   Hospital beds
DME Modifier: RR

M E0270 Hospital bed, institutional type includes: oscillating, circulating and stryker frame, with mattress E1
BETOS: D1B   Hospital beds
Service not separately priced by Part B

D E0271 Mattress, innerspring **DME** Y
BETOS: D1B   Hospital beds
DME Modifier: NU,RR,UE
Pub: 100-4, Chap. 23, 60.3; 100-4, Chap. 36, 50.14

D E0272 Mattress, foam rubber **DME** Y
BETOS: D1B   Hospital beds
DME Modifier: NU,RR,UE

M E0273 Bed board E1
BETOS: D1B   Hospital beds
Service not separately priced by Part B

M E0274 Over-bed table E1
BETOS: D1B   Hospital beds
Service not separately priced by Part B

▲ Revised code   ● New code   **C** Carrier judgment   **D** Special coverage instructions apply
I Not payable by Medicare   **M** Non-covered by Medicare   **S** Non-covered by Medicare statute   AHA Coding Clinic®

D E0275 Bed pan, standard, metal or plastic   `DME` Y
   BETOS: D1E   Other DME
   DME Modifier: NU,RR,UE

D E0276 Bed pan, fracture, metal or plastic   `DME` Y
   BETOS: D1E   Other DME
   DME Modifier: NU,RR,UE

D E0277 Powered pressure-reducing air
   mattress   `DME` Y
   BETOS: D1E   Other DME
   DME Modifier: RR
   Pub: 100-4, Chap. 23, 60.3

C E0280 Bed cradle, any type   `DME` Y
   BETOS: D1B   Hospital beds
   DME Modifier: NU,RR,UE
   Pub: 100-4, Chap. 36, 50.14

D E0290 Hospital bed, fixed height, without side rails,
   with mattress   `DME` Y
   BETOS: D1B   Hospital beds
   DME Modifier: RR

D E0291 Hospital bed, fixed height, without side rails,
   without mattress   `DME` Y
   BETOS: D1B   Hospital beds
   DME Modifier: RR

D E0292 Hospital bed, variable height, hi-lo, without
   side rails, with mattress   `DME` Y
   BETOS: D1B   Hospital beds
   DME Modifier: RR

D E0293 Hospital bed, variable height, hi-lo, without
   side rails, without mattress   `DME` Y
   BETOS: D1B   Hospital beds
   DME Modifier: RR

D E0294 Hospital bed, semi-electric (head and foot
   adjustment), without side rails, with
   mattress   `DME` Y
   BETOS: D1B   Hospital beds
   DME Modifier: RR

D E0295 Hospital bed, semi-electric (head and foot
   adjustment), without side rails, without
   mattress   `DME` Y
   BETOS: D1B   Hospital beds
   DME Modifier: RR

D E0296 Hospital bed, total electric (head, foot and
   height adjustments), without side rails, with
   mattress   `DME` Y
   BETOS: D1B   Hospital beds
   DME Modifier: RR

D E0297 Hospital bed, total electric (head, foot and
   height adjustments), without side rails,
   without mattress   `DME` Y
   BETOS: D1B   Hospital beds
   DME Modifier: RR

C E0300 Pediatric crib, hospital grade, fully enclosed,
   with or without top enclosure   `DME` Ⓐ Y

   BETOS: D1B   Hospital beds
   DME Modifier: RR

D E0301 Hospital bed, heavy duty, extra wide, with
   weight capacity greater than 350 pounds, but
   less than or equal to 600 pounds, with any
   type side rails, without mattress   `DME` Y
   BETOS: D1B   Hospital beds
   DME Modifier: RR

D E0302 Hospital bed, extra heavy duty, extra wide,
   with weight capacity greater than 600
   pounds, with any type side rails, without
   mattress   `DME` Y
   BETOS: D1B   Hospital beds
   DME Modifier: RR

D E0303 Hospital bed, heavy duty, extra wide, with
   weight capacity greater than 350 pounds, but
   less than or equal to 600 pounds, with any
   type side rails, with mattress   `DME` Y
   BETOS: D1B   Hospital beds
   DME Modifier: RR

D E0304 Hospital bed, extra heavy duty, extra
   wide, with weight capacity greater than
   600 pounds, with any type side rails, with
   mattress   `DME` Y
   BETOS: D1B   Hospital beds
   DME Modifier: RR

D E0305 Bed side rails, half length   `DME` Y
   BETOS: D1B   Hospital beds
   DME Modifier: RR

D E0310 Bed side rails, full length   `DME` Y
   BETOS: D1B   Hospital beds
   DME Modifier: NU,RR,UE
   Pub: 100-4, Chap. 36, 50.14

M E0315 Bed accessory: board, table, or support
   device, any type   E1
   BETOS: D1B   Hospital beds
   Service not separately priced by Part B

C E0316 Safety enclosure frame/canopy for use with
   hospital bed, any type   `DME` Y
   BETOS: D1B   Hospital beds
   DME Modifier: RR
   Coding Clinic: 2002, Q1
   Pub: 100-4, Chap. 23, 60.3

D E0325 Urinal; male, jug-type, any material ♂ `DME` Y
   BETOS: D1E   Other DME
   DME Modifier: NU,RR,UE

D E0326 Urinal; female, jug-type, any material ♀ `DME` Y
   BETOS: D1E   Other DME
   DME Modifier: NU,RR,UE

C E0328 Hospital bed, pediatric, manual, 360 degree
   side enclosures, top of headboard, footboard
   and side rails up to 24 inches above the
   spring, includes mattress   Ⓐ Y
   BETOS: D1B   Hospital beds

C **E0329** Hospital bed, pediatric, electric or semi-electric, 360 degree side enclosures, top of headboard, footboard and side rails up to 24 inches above the spring, includes mattress   Ⓐ Y

    BETOS: D1B   Hospital beds

C **E0350** Control unit for electronic bowel irrigation/evacuation system   E1

    BETOS: Z2   Undefined codes
    Other carrier priced

C **E0352** Disposable pack (water reservoir bag, speculum, valving mechanism and collection bag/box) for use with the electronic bowel irrigation/evacuation system   E1

    BETOS: Z2   Undefined codes
    Other carrier priced

C **E0370** Air pressure elevator for heel   E1

    BETOS: D1E   Other DME
    Service not separately priced by Part B

C **E0371** Nonpowered advanced pressure reducing overlay for mattress, standard mattress length and width   DME Y

    BETOS: D1E   Other DME
    DME Modifier: RR
    Pub: 100-4, Chap. 23, 60.3

C **E0372** Powered air overlay for mattress, standard mattress length and width   DME Y

    BETOS: D1E   Other DME
    DME Modifier: RR

C **E0373** Nonpowered advanced pressure reducing mattress   DME Y

    BETOS: D1E   Other DME
    DME Modifier: RR

OXYGEN DELIVERY SYSTEMS AND RELATED SUPPLIES (E0424-E0487)

D **E0424** Stationary compressed gaseous oxygen system, rental; includes container, contents, regulator, flowmeter, humidifier, nebulizer, cannula or mask, and tubing   DME Y

    BETOS: D1C   Oxygen and supplies
    DME Modifier: RR

D **E0425** Stationary compressed gas system, purchase; includes regulator, flowmeter, humidifier, nebulizer, cannula or mask, and tubing   E1

    BETOS: D1C   Oxygen and supplies
    Service not separately priced by Part B

D **E0430** Portable gaseous oxygen system, purchase; includes regulator, flowmeter, humidifier, cannula or mask, and tubing   E1

    BETOS: D1C   Oxygen and supplies
    Service not separately priced by Part B

D **E0431** Portable gaseous oxygen system, rental; includes portable container, regulator, flowmeter, humidifier, cannula or mask, and tubing   DME Y

    BETOS: D1C   Oxygen and supplies
    DME Modifier: RR

C **E0433** Portable liquid oxygen system, rental; home liquefier used to fill portable liquid oxygen containers, includes portable containers, regulator, flowmeter, humidifier, cannula or mask and tubing, with or without supply reservoir and contents gauge   DME Y

    BETOS: D1C   Oxygen and supplies
    DME Modifier: RR

D **E0434** Portable liquid oxygen system, rental; includes portable container, supply reservoir, humidifier, flowmeter, refill adaptor, contents gauge, cannula or mask, and tubing   DME Y

    BETOS: D1C   Oxygen and supplies
    DME Modifier: RR

D **E0435** Portable liquid oxygen system, purchase; includes portable container, supply reservoir, flowmeter, humidifier, contents gauge, cannula or mask, tubing and refill adaptor   E1

    BETOS: D1C   Oxygen and supplies
    Service not separately priced by Part B

D **E0439** Stationary liquid oxygen system, rental; includes container, contents, regulator, flowmeter, humidifier, nebulizer, cannula or mask, & tubing   DME Y

    BETOS: D1C   Oxygen and supplies
    DME Modifier: RR

D **E0440** Stationary liquid oxygen system, purchase; includes use of reservoir, contents indicator, regulator, flowmeter, humidifier, nebulizer, cannula or mask, and tubing   E1

    BETOS: D1C   Oxygen and supplies
    Service not separately priced by Part B

D **E0441** Stationary oxygen contents, gaseous, 1 month's supply = 1 unit   DME Y

    BETOS: D1C   Oxygen and supplies

D **E0442** Stationary oxygen contents, liquid, 1 month's supply = 1 unit   DME Y

    BETOS: D1C   Oxygen and supplies

D **E0443** Portable oxygen contents, gaseous, 1 month's supply = 1 unit   DME Y

    BETOS: D1C   Oxygen and supplies

D **E0444** Portable oxygen contents, liquid, 1 month's supply = 1 unit   DME Y

    BETOS: D1C   Oxygen and supplies

C **E0445** Oximeter device for measuring blood oxygen levels non-invasively   N

    BETOS: Z2   Undefined codes
    Service not separately priced by Part B

▲ Revised code   ● New code   **C** Carrier judgment   **D** Special coverage instructions apply
I Not payable by Medicare   **M** Non-covered by Medicare   **S** Non-covered by Medicare statute   AHA Coding Clinic®

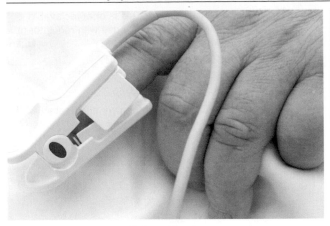

Pulse oximeter

C E0446 Topical oxygen delivery system, not otherwise specified, includes all supplies and accessories   A
BETOS: D1E   Other DME
Service not separately priced by Part B

D E0455 Oxygen tent, excluding croup or pediatric tents   Y
BETOS: D1C   Oxygen and supplies

I E0457 Chest shell (cuirass)   E1
BETOS: D1E   Other DME
Service not separately priced by Part B

I E0459 Chest wrap   E1
BETOS: D1E   Other DME
Service not separately priced by Part B

C E0462 Rocking bed with or without side rails   DME Y
BETOS: D1B   Hospital beds
DME Modifier: RR

D E0465 Home ventilator, any type, used with invasive interface, (e.g., tracheostomy tube)   DME Y
BETOS: D1E   Other DME
DME Modifier: RR

D E0466 Home ventilator, any type, used with non-invasive interface, (e.g., mask, chest shell)   DME Y
BETOS: D1E   Other DME
DME Modifier: RR

D E0470 Respiratory assist device, bi-level pressure capability, without backup rate feature, used with noninvasive interface, e.g., nasal or facial mask (intermittent assist device with continuous positive airway pressure device)   DME Y
BETOS: D1E   Other DME
DME Modifier: RR
Pub: 100-4, Chap. 23, 60.3

D E0471 Respiratory assist device, bi-level pressure capability, with back-up rate feature, used with noninvasive interface, e.g., nasal or facial mask (intermittent assist device with continuous positive airway pressure device)   DME Y
BETOS: D1E   Other DME
DME Modifier: RR

D E0472 Respiratory assist device, bi-level pressure capability, with backup rate feature, used with invasive interface, e.g., tracheostomy tube (intermittent assist device with continuous positive airway pressure device)   DME Y
BETOS: D1E   Other DME
DME Modifier: RR

D E0480 Percussor, electric or pneumatic, home model   DME Y
BETOS: D1E   Other DME
DME Modifier: RR

M E0481 Intrapulmonary percussive ventilation system and related accessories   E1
BETOS: D1E   Other DME
Service not separately priced by Part B
Coding Clinic: 2002, Q1

C E0482 Cough stimulating device, alternating positive and negative airway pressure   DME Y
BETOS: D1E   Other DME
DME Modifier: RR
Coding Clinic: 2002, Q1

C E0483 High frequency chest wall oscillation air-pulse generator system, (includes hoses and vest), each   DME Y
BETOS: D1E   Other DME
DME Modifier: RR

C E0484 Oscillatory positive expiratory pressure device, non-electric, any type, each   DME Y
BETOS: D1E   Other DME
DME Modifier: NU,RR,UE

C E0485 Oral device/appliance used to reduce upper airway collapsibility, adjustable or non-adjustable, prefabricated, includes fitting and adjustment   DME Y
BETOS: D1E   Other DME
DME Modifier: NU,RR,UE

C E0486 Oral device/appliance used to reduce upper airway collapsibility, adjustable or non-adjustable, custom fabricated, includes fitting and adjustment   DME Y
BETOS: D1E   Other DME
DME Modifier: NU,RR,UE

D E0487 Spirometer, electronic, includes all accessories   N
BETOS: Z2   Undefined codes
Service not separately priced by Part B
Coding Clinic: 2008, Q4

INTERMITTENT POSITIVE PRESSURE BREATHING DEVICES (E0500), SEE ALSO BREATHING AIDS (A7000-A7048); OTHER BREATHING AIDS (E0605, E0606); ASSISTED BREATHING SUPPLIES (S8096-S8210)

D **E0500** IPPB machine, all types, with built-in nebulization; manual or automatic valves; internal or external power source **DME** Y
BETOS: D1E   Other DME
DME Modifier: RR

HUMIDIFIERS AND NEBULIZERS WITH RELATED EQUIPMENT (E0550-E0601)

D **E0550** Humidifier, durable for extensive supplemental humidification during IPPB treatments or oxygen delivery **DME** Y
BETOS: D1E   Other DME
DME Modifier: RR

D **E0555** Humidifier, durable, glass or autoclavable plastic bottle type, for use with regulator or flowmeter Y
BETOS: D1C   Oxygen and supplies

D **E0560** Humidifier, durable for supplemental humidification during IPPB treatment or oxygen delivery **DME** Y
BETOS: D1E   Other DME
DME Modifier: NU,RR,UE
Pub: 100-4, Chap. 23, 60.3

C **E0561** Humidifier, non-heated, used with positive airway pressure device **DME** Y
BETOS: D1E   Other DME
DME Modifier: NU,RR,UE
Pub: 100-3, Chap. 1, Part-4, 240.4; 100-4, Chap. 36, 50.14

C **E0562** Humidifier, heated, used with positive airway pressure device **DME** Y
BETOS: D1E   Other DME
DME Modifier: NU,RR,UE

C **E0565** Compressor, air power source for equipment which is not self-contained or cylinder driven **DME** Y
BETOS: D1E   Other DME
DME Modifier: RR

D **E0570** Nebulizer, with compressor **DME** Y
BETOS: D1E   Other DME
DME Modifier: RR

C **E0572** Aerosol compressor, adjustable pressure, light duty for intermittent use **DME** Y
BETOS: D1E   Other DME
DME Modifier: RR

C **E0574** Ultrasonic/electronic aerosol generator with small volume nebulizer **DME** Y
BETOS: D1E   Other DME
DME Modifier: RR

D **E0575** Nebulizer, ultrasonic, large volume **DME** Y
BETOS: D1E   Other DME
DME Modifier: RR

D **E0580** Nebulizer, durable, glass or autoclavable plastic, bottle type, for use with regulator or flowmeter **DME** Y
BETOS: D1E   Other DME
DME Modifier: NU,RR,UE
Pub: 100-4, Chap. 23, 60.3

D **E0585** Nebulizer, with compressor and heater **DME** Y
BETOS: D1E   Other DME
DME Modifier: RR

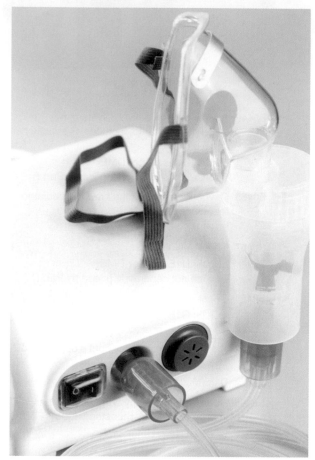

Nebulizer

D **E0600** Respiratory suction pump, home model, portable or stationary, electric **DME** Y
BETOS: D1E   Other DME
DME Modifier: RR

D **E0601** Continuous positive airway pressure (CPAP) device **DME** Y
BETOS: D1E   Other DME
DME Modifier: RR
Pub: 100-3, Chap. 1, Part-4, 240.4; 100-4, Chap. 23, 60.3

BREAST PUMPS (E0602-E0604)

C **E0602** Breast pump, manual, any type ♀ **DME** Y
BETOS: D1E   Other DME
DME Modifier: NU,RR,UE

▲ Revised code   ● New code   **C** Carrier judgment   **D** Special coverage instructions apply
I Not payable by Medicare   **M** Non-covered by Medicare   **S** Non-covered by Medicare statute   AHA Coding Clinic®

C **E0603** Breast pump, electric (AC and/or DC), any type ♀ N
BETOS: Z2 Undefined codes
Service not separately priced by Part B
Coding Clinic: 2002, Q1

C **E0604** Breast pump, hospital grade, electric (AC and /or DC), any type ♀ A
BETOS: Z2 Undefined codes
Service not separately priced by Part B
Coding Clinic: 2002, Q1

OTHER BREATHING AIDS (E0605, E0606), SEE ALSO BREATHING AIDS (A7000-A7048); INTERMITTENT POSITIVE PRESSURE BREATHING DEVICES (E0500); ASSISTED BREATHING SUPPLIES (S8096-S8210)

D **E0605** Vaporizer, room type `DME` Y
BETOS: D1E Other DME
DME Modifier: NU,RR,UE

D **E0606** Postural drainage board `DME` Y
BETOS: D1E Other DME
DME Modifier: RR

MONITORING EQUIPMENT (E0607-E0620)

D **E0607** Home blood glucose monitor `DME` Y
BETOS: D1E Other DME
DME Modifier: NU,RR,UE

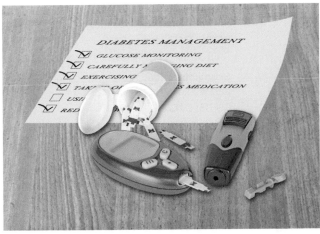

Glucose monitor

D **E0610** Pacemaker monitor, self-contained, (checks battery depletion, includes audible and visible check systems) `DME` Y
BETOS: D1E Other DME
DME Modifier: NU,RR,UE

D **E0615** Pacemaker monitor, self contained, checks battery depletion and other pacemaker components, includes digital/visible check systems `DME` Y
BETOS: D1E Other DME
DME Modifier: NU,RR,UE

C **E0616** Implantable cardiac event recorder with memory, activator and programmer N
BETOS: D1E Other DME
Service not separately priced by Part B

C **E0617** External defibrillator with integrated electrocardiogram analysis `DME` Y
BETOS: D1E Other DME
DME Modifier: RR

C **E0618** Apnea monitor, without recording feature `DME` Y
BETOS: D1E Other DME
Service not separately priced by Part B
DME Modifier: RR

C **E0619** Apnea monitor, with recording feature `DME` Y
BETOS: D1E Other DME
Service not separately priced by Part B
DME Modifier: RR

C **E0620** Skin piercing device for collection of capillary blood, laser, each `DME` Y
BETOS: D1E Other DME
DME Modifier: RR
Coding Clinic: 2002, Q1

PATIENT LIFTS AND SUPPORT SYSTEMS (E0621-E0642)

D **E0621** Sling or seat, patient lift, canvas or nylon `DME` Y
BETOS: D1E Other DME
DME Modifier: NU,RR,UE

M **E0625** Patient lift, bathroom or toilet, not otherwise classified E1
BETOS: D1E Other DME
Service not separately priced by Part B

D **E0627** Seat lift mechanism, electric, any type `DME` Y
BETOS: D1E Other DME
DME Modifier: NU,RR,UE

D **E0629** Seat lift mechanism, non-electric, any type `DME` Y
BETOS: D1E Other DME
DME Modifier: NU,RR,UE

D **E0630** Patient lift, hydraulic or mechanical, includes any seat, sling, strap(s) or pad(s) `DME` Y
BETOS: D1E Other DME
DME Modifier: RR

D **E0635** Patient lift, electric with seat or sling `DME` Y
BETOS: D1E Other DME
DME Modifier: RR

C **E0636** Multipositional patient support system, with integrated lift, patient accessible controls `DME` Y
BETOS: D1E Other DME
DME Modifier: RR

M **E0637** Combination sit to stand frame/table system, any size including pediatric, with seat lift feature, with or without wheels E1
BETOS: D1E Other DME
Service not separately priced by Part B

M **E0638** Standing frame/table system, one position (e.g., upright, supine or prone stander), any size including pediatric, with or without wheels E1
BETOS: D1E Other DME
Service not separately priced by Part B

C **E0639** Patient lift, moveable from room to room with disassembly and reassembly, includes all components/accessories DME E1
BETOS: Y2 Other - non-Medicare fee schedule
Service not separately priced by Part B
DME Modifier: RR

C **E0640** Patient lift, fixed system, includes all components/accessories DME E1
BETOS: Y2 Other - non-Medicare fee schedule
Service not separately priced by Part B
DME Modifier: RR

M **E0641** Standing frame/table system, multi-position (e.g., three-way stander), any size including pediatric, with or without wheels E1
BETOS: D1E Other DME
Service not separately priced by Part B

M **E0642** Standing frame/table system, mobile (dynamic stander), any size including pediatric E1
BETOS: D1E Other DME
Service not separately priced by Part B

PNEUMATIC COMPRESSORS AND APPLIANCES (E0650-E0676)

D **E0650** Pneumatic compressor, non-segmental home model DME Y
BETOS: D1E Other DME
DME Modifier: NU,RR,UE

D **E0651** Pneumatic compressor, segmental home model without calibrated gradient pressure DME Y
BETOS: D1E Other DME
DME Modifier: NU,RR,UE

D **E0652** Pneumatic compressor, segmental home model with calibrated gradient pressure DME Y
BETOS: D1E Other DME
DME Modifier: NU,RR,UE

D **E0655** Non-segmental pneumatic appliance for use with pneumatic compressor, half arm DME Y
BETOS: D1E Other DME
DME Modifier: NU,RR,UE

D **E0656** Segmental pneumatic appliance for use with pneumatic compressor, trunk DME Y
BETOS: D1E Other DME
DME Modifier: RR
Coding Clinic: 2008, Q4

D **E0657** Segmental pneumatic appliance for use with pneumatic compressor, chest DME Y
BETOS: D1E Other DME
DME Modifier: RR
Coding Clinic: 2008, Q4

D **E0660** Non-segmental pneumatic appliance for use with pneumatic compressor, full leg DME Y
BETOS: D1E Other DME
DME Modifier: NU,RR,UE

D **E0665** Non-segmental pneumatic appliance for use with pneumatic compressor, full arm DME Y
BETOS: D1E Other DME
DME Modifier: NU,RR,UE

D **E0666** Non-segmental pneumatic appliance for use with pneumatic compressor, half leg DME Y
BETOS: D1E Other DME
DME Modifier: NU,RR,UE

D **E0667** Segmental pneumatic appliance for use with pneumatic compressor, full leg DME Y
BETOS: D1E Other DME
DME Modifier: NU,RR,UE

D **E0668** Segmental pneumatic appliance for use with pneumatic compressor, full arm DME Y
BETOS: D1E Other DME
DME Modifier: NU,RR,UE

D **E0669** Segmental pneumatic appliance for use with pneumatic compressor, half leg DME Y
BETOS: D1E Other DME
DME Modifier: NU,RR,UE

D **E0670** Segmental pneumatic appliance for use with pneumatic compressor, integrated, 2 full legs and trunk DME Y
BETOS: D1E Other DME
DME Modifier: NU,RR,UE

D **E0671** Segmental gradient pressure pneumatic appliance, full leg DME Y
BETOS: D1E Other DME
DME Modifier: NU,RR,UE

D **E0672** Segmental gradient pressure pneumatic appliance, full arm DME Y
BETOS: D1E Other DME
DME Modifier: NU,RR,UE

D **E0673** Segmental gradient pressure pneumatic appliance, half leg DME Y
BETOS: D1E Other DME
DME Modifier: NU,RR,UE

C **E0675** Pneumatic compression device, high pressure, rapid inflation/deflation cycle, for arterial insufficiency (unilateral or bilateral system) `DME` Y
BETOS: D1E   Other DME
DME Modifier: RR

C **E0676** Intermittent limb compression device (includes all accessories), not otherwise specified Y
BETOS: D1E   Other DME
Service not separately priced by Part B

ULTRAVIOLET LIGHT THERAPY SYSTEMS (E0691-E0694), SEE ALSO HEAT, COLD, AND LIGHT THERAPIES (E0200-E0239)

C **E0691** Ultraviolet light therapy system, includes bulbs/lamps, timer and eye protection; treatment area 2 square feet or less `DME` Y
BETOS: D1E   Other DME
DME Modifier: NU,RR,UE

C **E0692** Ultraviolet light therapy system panel, includes bulbs/lamps, timer and eye protection, 4 foot panel `DME` Y
BETOS: D1E   Other DME
DME Modifier: NU,RR,UE

C **E0693** Ultraviolet light therapy system panel, includes bulbs/lamps, timer and eye protection, 6 foot panel `DME` Y
BETOS: D1E   Other DME
DME Modifier: NU,RR,UE

C **E0694** Ultraviolet multidirectional light therapy system in 6 foot cabinet, includes bulbs/lamps, timer and eye protection `DME` Y
BETOS: D1E   Other DME
DME Modifier: NU,RR,UE

SAFETY DEVICES (E0700-E0710)

C **E0700** Safety equipment, device or accessory, any type E1
BETOS: D1E   Other DME
Service not separately priced by Part B

D **E0705** Transfer device, any type, each `DME` B
BETOS: D1E   Other DME
DME Modifier: NU,RR,UE

C **E0710** Restraints, any type (body, chest, wrist or ankle) E1
BETOS: Z2   Undefined codes
Other carrier priced

STIMULATION DEVICES (E0720-E0770)

D **E0720** Transcutaneous electrical nerve stimulation (TENS) device, two lead, localized stimulation `DME` Y
BETOS: D1E   Other DME
DME Modifier: NU

D **E0730** Transcutaneous electrical nerve stimulation (TENS) device, four or more leads, for multiple nerve stimulation `DME` Y
BETOS: D1E   Other DME
DME Modifier: NU
Pub: 100-3, Chap. 1, 10.2; 100-3, Chap. 1, Part 2, 160.7.1; 100-3, Chap. 1, Part 2, 160.27; 100-4, Chap. 20, 30.1.2

D **E0731** Form fitting conductive garment for delivery of TENS or NMES (with conductive fibers separated from the patient's skin by layers of fabric) `DME` Y
BETOS: D1E   Other DME
DME Modifier: NU
Pub: 100-3, Chap. 1, 10.2; 100-3, Chap. 1, Part 2, 160.13

D **E0740** Non-implanted pelvic floor electrical stimulator, complete system `DME` Y
BETOS: D1E   Other DME
DME Modifier: RR

C **E0744** Neuromuscular stimulator for scoliosis `DME` Y
BETOS: D1E   Other DME
DME Modifier: RR

D **E0745** Neuromuscular stimulator, electronic shock unit `DME` Y
BETOS: D1E   Other DME
DME Modifier: RR

D **E0746** Electromyography (EMG), biofeedback device N
BETOS: D1E   Other DME
Reasonable charge

D **E0747** Osteogenesis stimulator, electrical, non-invasive, other than spinal applications `DME` Y
BETOS: D1E   Other DME
DME Modifier: NU,RR,UE

D **E0748** Osteogenesis stimulator, electrical, non-invasive, spinal applications `DME` Y
BETOS: D1E   Other DME
DME Modifier: NU,RR,UE

D **E0749** Osteogenesis stimulator, electrical, surgically implanted `DME` N
BETOS: D1E   Other DME
DME Modifier: RR

C **E0755** Electronic salivary reflex stimulator (intra-oral/non-invasive) E1
BETOS: Z2   Undefined codes
Reasonable charge

C **E0760** Osteogenesis stimulator, low intensity ultrasound, non-invasive `DME` Y
BETOS: D1E   Other DME
DME Modifier: NU,RR,UE
Pub: 100-4, Chap. 32, 110.5

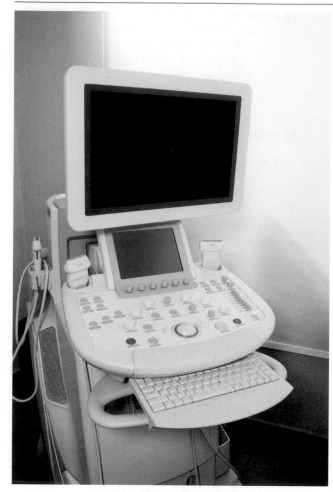

Ultrasound diagnostic equipment

D E0761 Non-thermal pulsed high frequency radiowaves, high peak power electromagnetic energy treatment device   E1
BETOS: D1E   Other DME
Service not separately priced by Part B

C E0762 Transcutaneous electrical joint stimulation device system, includes all accessories   DME B
BETOS: D1E   Other DME
DME Modifier: RR

D E0764 Functional neuromuscular stimulation, transcutaneous stimulation of sequential muscle groups of ambulation with computer control, used for walking by spinal cord injured, entire system, after completion of training program   DME Y
BETOS: D1F   Prosthetic/orthotic devices
DME Modifier: RR

C E0765 FDA-approved nerve stimulator, with replaceable batteries, for treatment of nausea and vomiting   DME Y
BETOS: D1E   Other DME
DME Modifier: NU,RR,UE

C E0766 Electrical stimulation device used for cancer treatment, includes all accessories, any type   Y
BETOS: D1E   Other DME

D E0769 Electrical stimulation or electromagnetic wound treatment device, not otherwise classified   B
BETOS: Y2   Other - non-Medicare fee schedule
Service not separately priced by Part B
Pub: 100-4, Chap. 32, 11.1

D E0770 Functional electrical stimulator, transcutaneous stimulation of nerve and/or muscle groups, any type, complete system, not otherwise specified   Y
BETOS: D1E   Other DME
Coding Clinic: 2008, Q4

INFUSION PUMPS AND SUPPLIES (E0776-E0791)

C E0776 IV pole   DME Y
BETOS: D1E   Other DME
DME Modifier: NU,RR,UE
Pub: 100-4, Chap. 23, 60.3

C E0779 Ambulatory infusion pump, mechanical, reusable, for infusion 8 hours or greater   DME Y
BETOS: D1E   Other DME
DME Modifier: RR

C E0780 Ambulatory infusion pump, mechanical, reusable, for infusion less than 8 hours   DME Y
BETOS: D1E   Other DME
DME Modifier: NU

D E0781 Ambulatory infusion pump, single or multiple channels, electric or battery operated, with administrative equipment, worn by patient   DME Y
BETOS: D1E   Other DME
DME Modifier: RR

D E0782 Infusion pump, implantable, non-programmable (includes all components, e.g., pump, catheter, connectors, etc.)   DME N
BETOS: D1E   Other DME
DME Modifier: NU,RR,UE

D E0783 Infusion pump system, implantable, programmable (includes all components, e.g., pump, catheter, connectors, etc.)   DME N
BETOS: D1E   Other DME
DME Modifier: NU,RR,UE

D E0784 External ambulatory infusion pump, insulin   DME Y
BETOS: D1E   Other DME
DME Modifier: RR

D E0785 Implantable intraspinal (epidural/intrathecal) catheter used with implantable infusion pump, replacement   DME N

▲ Revised code   ● New code   **C** Carrier judgment   **D** Special coverage instructions apply
I Not payable by Medicare   **M** Non-covered by Medicare   **S** Non-covered by Medicare statute   AHA Coding Clinic®

BETOS: D1E　Other DME

DME Modifier: KF

D E0786　Implantable programmable infusion pump, replacement (excludes implantable intraspinal catheter)　**DME** N

BETOS: D1E　Other DME

DME Modifier: NU,RR,UE

D E0791　Parenteral infusion pump, stationary, single or multi-channel　**DME** Y

BETOS: D1E　Other DME

DME Modifier: RR

TRACTION AND OTHER ORTHOPEDIC DEVICES
(E0830-E0948)

D E0830　Ambulatory traction device, all types, each　N

BETOS: D1E　Other DME

Service not separately priced by Part B

D E0840　Traction frame, attached to headboard, cervical traction　**DME** Y

BETOS: D1E　Other DME

DME Modifier: NU,RR,UE

C E0849　Traction equipment, cervical, free-standing stand/frame, pneumatic, applying traction force to other than mandible　**DME** Y

BETOS: D1E　Other DME

DME Modifier: RR

D E0850　Traction stand, free standing, cervical traction　**DME** Y

BETOS: D1E　Other DME

DME Modifier: NU,RR,UE

C E0855　Cervical traction equipment not requiring additional stand or frame　**DME** Y

BETOS: D1E　Other DME

DME Modifier: RR

C E0856　Cervical traction device, with inflatable air bladder(s)　**DME** Y

BETOS: D1E　Other DME

DME Modifier: RR

D E0860　Traction equipment, overdoor, cervical　**DME** Y

BETOS: D1E　Other DME

DME Modifier: NU,RR,UE

D E0870　Traction frame, attached to footboard, extremity traction, (e.g., Buck's)　**DME** Y

BETOS: D1E　Other DME

DME Modifier: NU,RR,UE

D E0880　Traction stand, free standing, extremity traction, (e.g., Buck's)　**DME** Y

BETOS: D1E　Other DME

DME Modifier: NU,RR,UE

D E0890　Traction frame, attached to footboard, pelvic traction　**DME** Y

BETOS: D1E　Other DME

DME Modifier: NU,RR,UE

D E0900　Traction stand, free standing, pelvic traction, (e.g., Buck's)　**DME** Y

BETOS: D1E　Other DME

DME Modifier: NU,RR,UE

D E0910　Trapeze bars, also known as Patient Helper, attached to bed, with grab bar　**DME** Y

BETOS: D1E　Other DME

DME Modifier: RR

Pub: 100-4, Chap. 23, 60.3

D E0911　Trapeze bar, heavy duty, for patient weight capacity greater than 250 pounds, attached to bed, with grab bar　**DME** Y

BETOS: D1B　Hospital beds

DME Modifier: RR

D E0912　Trapeze bar, heavy duty, for patient weight capacity greater than 250 pounds, free standing, complete with grab bar　**DME** Y

BETOS: D1B　Hospital beds

DME Modifier: RR

D E0920　Fracture frame, attached to bed, includes weights　**DME** Y

BETOS: D1E　Other DME

DME Modifier: RR

D E0930　Fracture frame, free standing, includes weights　**DME** Y

BETOS: D1E　Other DME

DME Modifier: RR

D E0935　Continuous passive motion exercise device for use on knee only　**DME** Y

BETOS: D1E　Other DME

DME Modifier: RR

M E0936　Continuous passive motion exercise device for use other than knee　E1

BETOS: D1E　Other DME

Service not separately priced by Part B

D E0940　Trapeze bar, free standing, complete with grab bar　**DME** Y

BETOS: D1B　Hospital beds

DME Modifier: RR

Pub: 100-4, Chap. 23, 60.3

D E0941　Gravity assisted traction device, any type　**DME** Y

BETOS: D1E　Other DME

DME Modifier: RR

C E0942　Cervical head harness/halter　**DME** Y

BETOS: D1E　Other DME

DME Modifier: NU,RR,UE

C E0944　Pelvic belt/harness/boot　**DME** Y

BETOS: D1E　Other DME

DME Modifier: NU,RR,UE

C E0945　Extremity belt/harness　**DME** Y

BETOS: D1E　Other DME

DME Modifier: NU,RR,UE

♂ Male only　　♀ Female only　　**A** Age　　A2 - Z3 = ASC Payment indicator　　A - Y = APC Status indicator

ASC = ASC-approved procedure　　**DME** Paid under the DME fee schedule　　**MIPS** MIPS code

E0946 - E0974 (side tab)

DURABLE MEDICAL EQUIPMENT (E0100-E8002) (side tab)

D **E0946** Fracture, frame, dual with cross bars, attached to bed, (e.g., Balken, 4 poster) **DME** Y
  BETOS: D1E   Other DME
  DME Modifier: RR

D **E0947** Fracture frame, attachments for complex pelvic traction **DME** Y
  BETOS: D1E   Other DME
  DME Modifier: NU,RR,UE

D **E0948** Fracture frame, attachments for complex cervical traction **DME** Y
  BETOS: D1E   Other DME
  DME Modifier: NU,RR,UE

WHEELCHAIR ACCESSORIES (E0950-E1036)

D **E0950** Wheelchair accessory, tray, each **DME** Y
  BETOS: D1D   Wheelchairs
  DME Modifier: NU,RR,UE
  Pub: 100-4, Chap. 23, 60.3

C **E0951** Heel loop/holder, any type, with or without ankle strap, each **DME** Y
  BETOS: D1D   Wheelchairs
  Service not separately priced by Part B
  DME Modifier: NU,RR,UE

D **E0952** Toe loop/holder, any type, each **DME** Y
  BETOS: D1D   Wheelchairs
  Service not separately priced by Part B
  DME Modifier: NU,RR,UE

● **C** **E0953** Wheelchair accessory, lateral thigh or knee support, any type including fixed mounting hardware, each
  BETOS: D1D   Wheelchairs

● **C** **E0954** Wheelchair accessory, foot box, any type, includes attachment and mounting hardware, each foot
  BETOS: D1D   Wheelchairs

C **E0955** Wheelchair accessory, headrest, cushioned, any type, including fixed mounting hardware, each **DME** Y
  BETOS: D1D   Wheelchairs
  DME Modifier: RR

C **E0956** Wheelchair accessory, lateral trunk or hip support, any type, including fixed mounting hardware, each **DME** Y
  BETOS: D1D   Wheelchairs
  DME Modifier: NU,RR,UE

C **E0957** Wheelchair accessory, medial thigh support, any type, including fixed mounting hardware, each **DME** Y
  BETOS: D1D   Wheelchairs
  DME Modifier: NU,RR,UE

D **E0958** Manual wheelchair accessory, one-arm drive attachment, each **DME** Y
  BETOS: D1D   Wheelchairs

Service not separately priced by Part B
  DME Modifier: RR

C **E0959** Manual wheelchair accessory, adapter for amputee, each **DME** B
  BETOS: D1D   Wheelchairs
  Service not separately priced by Part B
  DME Modifier: NU,RR,UE

C **E0960** Wheelchair accessory, shoulder harness/ straps or chest strap, including any type mounting hardware **DME** Y
  BETOS: D1D   Wheelchairs
  DME Modifier: NU,RR,UE
  Pub: 100-4, Chap. 23, 60.3

C **E0961** Manual wheelchair accessory, wheel lock brake extension (handle), each **DME** B
  BETOS: D1D   Wheelchairs
  Service not separately priced by Part B
  DME Modifier: NU,RR,UE

C **E0966** Manual wheelchair accessory, headrest extension, each **DME** B
  BETOS: D1D   Wheelchairs
  Service not separately priced by Part B
  DME Modifier: NU,RR,UE

D **E0967** Manual wheelchair accessory, hand rim with projections, any type, replacement only, each **DME** Y
  BETOS: D1D   Wheelchairs
  DME Modifier: NU,RR,UE

D **E0968** Commode seat, wheelchair **DME** Y
  BETOS: D1D   Wheelchairs
  DME Modifier: RR

D **E0969** Narrowing device, wheelchair **DME** Y
  BETOS: D1D   Wheelchairs
  DME Modifier: NU,RR,UE

I **E0970** No. 2 footplates, except for elevating leg rest E1
  BETOS: D1D   Wheelchairs
  Service not separately priced by Part B

C **E0971** Manual wheelchair accessory, anti-tipping device, each **DME** B
  BETOS: D1D   Wheelchairs
  Service not separately priced by Part B
  DME Modifier: NU,RR,UE

D **E0973** Wheelchair accessory, adjustable height, detachable armrest, complete assembly, each **DME** B
  BETOS: D1D   Wheelchairs
  Service not separately priced by Part B
  DME Modifier: NU,RR,UE
  Pub: 100-4, Chap. 23, 60.3

D **E0974** Manual wheelchair accessory, anti-rollback device, each **DME** B
  BETOS: D1D   Wheelchairs
  Service not separately priced by Part B
  DME Modifier: NU,RR,UE

▲ Revised code   ● New code   **C** Carrier judgment   **D** Special coverage instructions apply
I Not payable by Medicare   **M** Non-covered by Medicare   **S** Non-covered by Medicare statute   AHA Coding Clinic®

C **E0978** Wheelchair accessory, positioning belt/safety belt/pelvic strap, each `DME` B
BETOS: D1D Wheelchairs
DME Modifier: NU,RR,UE
Pub: 100-4, Chap. 23, 60.3

C **E0980** Safety vest, wheelchair `DME` Y
BETOS: D1D Wheelchairs
DME Modifier: NU,RR,UE

C **E0981** Wheelchair accessory, seat upholstery, replacement only, each `DME` Y
BETOS: D1D Wheelchairs
DME Modifier: NU,RR,UE
Pub: 100-4, Chap. 23, 60.3

C **E0982** Wheelchair accessory, back upholstery, replacement only, each `DME` Y
BETOS: D1D Wheelchairs
DME Modifier: NU,RR,UE

C **E0983** Manual wheelchair accessory, power add-on to convert manual wheelchair to motorized wheelchair, joystick control `DME` Y
BETOS: D1D Wheelchairs
DME Modifier: RR

C **E0984** Manual wheelchair accessory, power add-on to convert manual wheelchair to motorized wheelchair, tiller control `DME` Y
BETOS: D1D Wheelchairs
DME Modifier: RR

C **E0985** Wheelchair accessory, seat lift mechanism `DME` Y
BETOS: D1D Wheelchairs
DME Modifier: RR

C **E0986** Manual wheelchair accessory, push-rim activated power assist system `DME` Y
BETOS: D1D Wheelchairs
DME Modifier: RR

C **E0988** Manual wheelchair accessory, lever-activated, wheel drive, pair `DME` Y
BETOS: D1D Wheelchairs
DME Modifier: RR

C **E0990** Wheelchair accessory, elevating leg rest, complete assembly, each `DME` B
BETOS: D1D Wheelchairs
Service not separately priced by Part B
DME Modifier: NU,RR,UE
Pub: 100-4, Chap. 23, 60.3

C **E0992** Manual wheelchair accessory, solid seat insert `DME` B
BETOS: D1D Wheelchairs
DME Modifier: NU,RR,UE

D **E0994** Arm rest, each `DME` Y
BETOS: D1D Wheelchairs
DME Modifier: NU,RR,UE

C **E0995** Wheelchair accessory, calf rest/pad, replacement only, each `DME` B
BETOS: D1D Wheelchairs
Service not separately priced by Part B
DME Modifier: NU,RR,UE
Pub: 100-4, Chap. 23, 60.3

C **E1002** Wheelchair accessory, power seating system, tilt only `DME` Y
BETOS: D1D Wheelchairs
DME Modifier: RR
Pub: 100-4, Chap. 23, 60.3

C **E1003** Wheelchair accessory, power seating system, recline only, without shear reduction `DME` Y
BETOS: D1D Wheelchairs
DME Modifier: RR

C **E1004** Wheelchair accessory, power seating system, recline only, with mechanical shear reduction `DME` Y
BETOS: D1D Wheelchairs
DME Modifier: RR

C **E1005** Wheelchair accessory, power seatng system, recline only, with power shear reduction `DME` Y
BETOS: D1D Wheelchairs
DME Modifier: RR

C **E1006** Wheelchair accessory, power seating system, combination tilt and recline, without shear reduction `DME` Y
BETOS: D1D Wheelchairs
DME Modifier: RR

C **E1007** Wheelchair accessory, power seating system, combination tilt and recline, with mechanical shear reduction `DME` Y
BETOS: D1D Wheelchairs
DME Modifier: RR

C **E1008** Wheelchair accessory, power seating system, combination tilt and recline, with power shear reduction `DME` Y
BETOS: D1D Wheelchairs
DME Modifier: RR

C **E1009** Wheelchair accessory, addition to power seating system, mechanically linked leg elevation system, including pushrod and leg rest, each `DME` Y
BETOS: D1D Wheelchairs
DME Modifier: NU,RR,UE

C **E1010** Wheelchair accessory, addition to power seating system, power leg elevation system, including leg rest, pair `DME` Y
BETOS: D1D Wheelchairs
DME Modifier: RR

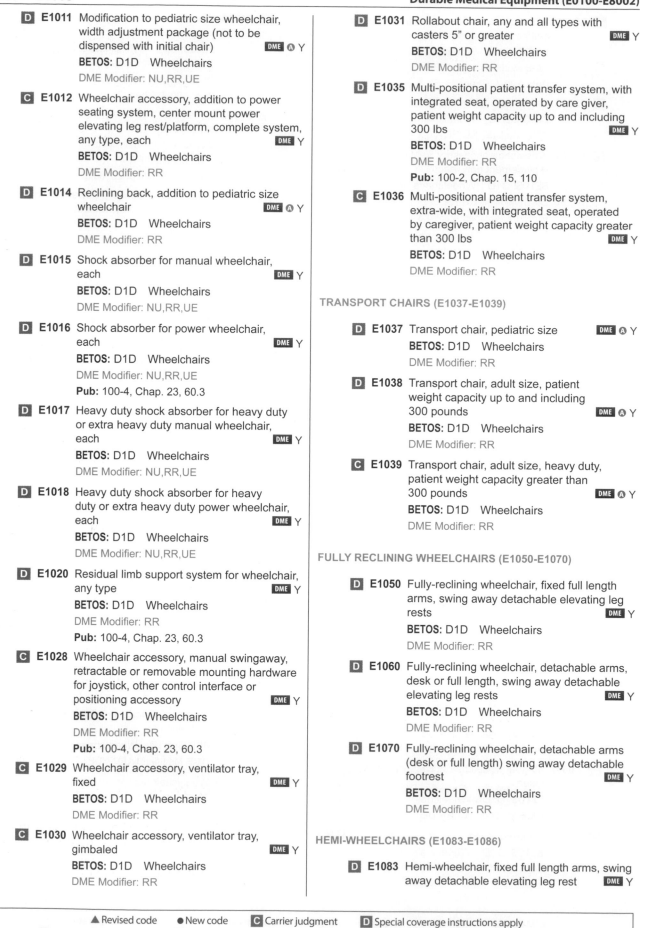

D **E1011** Modification to pediatric size wheelchair, width adjustment package (not to be dispensed with initial chair) DME Ⓐ Y

BETOS: D1D   Wheelchairs

DME Modifier: NU,RR,UE

C **E1012** Wheelchair accessory, addition to power seating system, center mount power elevating leg rest/platform, complete system, any type, each DME Y

BETOS: D1D   Wheelchairs

DME Modifier: RR

D **E1014** Reclining back, addition to pediatric size wheelchair DME Ⓐ Y

BETOS: D1D   Wheelchairs

DME Modifier: RR

D **E1015** Shock absorber for manual wheelchair, each DME Y

BETOS: D1D   Wheelchairs

DME Modifier: NU,RR,UE

D **E1016** Shock absorber for power wheelchair, each DME Y

BETOS: D1D   Wheelchairs

DME Modifier: NU,RR,UE

Pub: 100-4, Chap. 23, 60.3

D **E1017** Heavy duty shock absorber for heavy duty or extra heavy duty manual wheelchair, each DME Y

BETOS: D1D   Wheelchairs

DME Modifier: NU,RR,UE

D **E1018** Heavy duty shock absorber for heavy duty or extra heavy duty power wheelchair, each DME Y

BETOS: D1D   Wheelchairs

DME Modifier: NU,RR,UE

D **E1020** Residual limb support system for wheelchair, any type DME Y

BETOS: D1D   Wheelchairs

DME Modifier: RR

Pub: 100-4, Chap. 23, 60.3

C **E1028** Wheelchair accessory, manual swingaway, retractable or removable mounting hardware for joystick, other control interface or positioning accessory DME Y

BETOS: D1D   Wheelchairs

DME Modifier: RR

Pub: 100-4, Chap. 23, 60.3

C **E1029** Wheelchair accessory, ventilator tray, fixed DME Y

BETOS: D1D   Wheelchairs

DME Modifier: RR

C **E1030** Wheelchair accessory, ventilator tray, gimbaled DME Y

BETOS: D1D   Wheelchairs

DME Modifier: RR

D **E1031** Rollabout chair, any and all types with casters 5" or greater DME Y

BETOS: D1D   Wheelchairs

DME Modifier: RR

D **E1035** Multi-positional patient transfer system, with integrated seat, operated by care giver, patient weight capacity up to and including 300 lbs DME Y

BETOS: D1D   Wheelchairs

DME Modifier: RR

Pub: 100-2, Chap. 15, 110

C **E1036** Multi-positional patient transfer system, extra-wide, with integrated seat, operated by caregiver, patient weight capacity greater than 300 lbs DME Y

BETOS: D1D   Wheelchairs

DME Modifier: RR

TRANSPORT CHAIRS (E1037-E1039)

D **E1037** Transport chair, pediatric size DME Ⓐ Y

BETOS: D1D   Wheelchairs

DME Modifier: RR

D **E1038** Transport chair, adult size, patient weight capacity up to and including 300 pounds DME Ⓐ Y

BETOS: D1D   Wheelchairs

DME Modifier: RR

C **E1039** Transport chair, adult size, heavy duty, patient weight capacity greater than 300 pounds DME Ⓐ Y

BETOS: D1D   Wheelchairs

DME Modifier: RR

FULLY RECLINING WHEELCHAIRS (E1050-E1070)

D **E1050** Fully-reclining wheelchair, fixed full length arms, swing away detachable elevating leg rests DME Y

BETOS: D1D   Wheelchairs

DME Modifier: RR

D **E1060** Fully-reclining wheelchair, detachable arms, desk or full length, swing away detachable elevating leg rests DME Y

BETOS: D1D   Wheelchairs

DME Modifier: RR

D **E1070** Fully-reclining wheelchair, detachable arms (desk or full length) swing away detachable footrest DME Y

BETOS: D1D   Wheelchairs

DME Modifier: RR

HEMI-WHEELCHAIRS (E1083-E1086)

D **E1083** Hemi-wheelchair, fixed full length arms, swing away detachable elevating leg rest DME Y

▲ Revised code   ● New code   **C** Carrier judgment   **D** Special coverage instructions apply

I Not payable by Medicare   **M** Non-covered by Medicare   **S** Non-covered by Medicare statute   AHA Coding Clinic®

BETOS: D1D   Wheelchairs

DME Modifier: RR

D **E1084** Hemi-wheelchair, detachable arms desk or full length arms, swing away detachable elevating leg rests   DME Y

BETOS: D1D   Wheelchairs

DME Modifier: RR

I **E1085** Hemi-wheelchair, fixed full length arms, swing away detachable footrests   E1

BETOS: D1D   Wheelchairs

Service not separately priced by Part B

I **E1086** Hemi-wheelchair detachable arms desk or full length, swing away detachable footrests   E1

BETOS: D1D   Wheelchairs

Service not separately priced by Part B

LIGHTWEIGHT, HIGH-STRENGTH WHEELCHAIRS (E1087-E1090)

D **E1087** High strength lightweight wheelchair, fixed full length arms, swing away detachable elevating leg rests   DME Y

BETOS: D1D   Wheelchairs

DME Modifier: RR

D **E1088** High strength lightweight wheelchair, detachable arms desk or full length, swing away detachable elevating leg rests   DME Y

BETOS: D1D   Wheelchairs

DME Modifier: RR

I **E1089** High strength lightweight wheelchair, fixed length arms, swing away detachable footrests   E1

BETOS: D1D   Wheelchairs

Service not separately priced by Part B

I **E1090** High strength lightweight wheelchair, detachable arms desk or full length, swing away detachable footrests   E1

BETOS: D1D   Wheelchairs

Service not separately priced by Part B

HEAVY DUTY, WIDE WHEELCHAIRS (E1092, E1093)

D **E1092** Wide heavy duty wheel chair, detachable arms (desk or full length), swing away detachable elevating leg rests   DME Y

BETOS: D1D   Wheelchairs

DME Modifier: RR

D **E1093** Wide heavy duty wheelchair, detachable arms desk or full length arms, swing away detachable footrests   DME Y

BETOS: D1D   Wheelchairs

DME Modifier: RR

SEMI-RECLINING WHEELCHAIRS (E1100, E1110)

D **E1100** Semi-reclining wheelchair, fixed full length arms, swing away detachable elevating leg rests   DME Y

BETOS: D1D   Wheelchairs

DME Modifier: RR

D **E1110** Semi-reclining wheelchair, detachable arms (desk or full length) elevating leg rests   DME Y

BETOS: D1D   Wheelchairs

DME Modifier: RR

STANDARD WHEELCHAIRS (E1130-E1161)

I **E1130** Standard wheelchair, fixed full length arms, fixed or swing away detachable footrests   E1

BETOS: D1D   Wheelchairs

Service not separately priced by Part B

I **E1140** Wheelchair, detachable arms, desk or full length, swing away detachable footrests   E1

BETOS: D1D   Wheelchairs

Service not separately priced by Part B

D **E1150** Wheelchair, detachable arms, desk or full length swing away detachable elevating leg rests   DME Y

BETOS: D1D   Wheelchairs

DME Modifier: RR

D **E1160** Wheelchair, fixed full length arms, swing away detachable elevating leg rests   DME Y

BETOS: D1D   Wheelchairs

DME Modifier: RR

C **E1161** Manual adult size wheelchair, includes tilt in space   DME Ⓐ Y

BETOS: D1D   Wheelchairs

DME Modifier: RR

AMPUTEE WHEELCHAIRS (E1170-E1200)

D **E1170** Amputee wheelchair, fixed full length arms, swing away detachable elevating leg rests   DME Y

BETOS: D1D   Wheelchairs

DME Modifier: RR

D **E1171** Amputee wheelchair, fixed full length arms, without footrests or leg rest   DME Y

BETOS: D1D   Wheelchairs

DME Modifier: RR

D **E1172** Amputee wheelchair, detachable arms (desk or full length) without footrests or leg rest   DME Y

BETOS: D1D   Wheelchairs

DME Modifier: RR

D **E1180** Amputee wheelchair, detachable arms (desk or full length) swing away detachable footrests   DME Y

BETOS: D1D   Wheelchairs

DME Modifier: RR

D **E1190** Amputee wheelchair, detachable arms (desk or full length) swing away detachable elevating leg rests `DME` Y
  BETOS: D1D   Wheelchairs
  DME Modifier: RR

D **E1195** Heavy duty wheelchair, fixed full length arms, swing away detachable elevating leg rests `DME` Y
  BETOS: D1D   Wheelchairs
  DME Modifier: RR

D **E1200** Amputee wheelchair, fixed full length arms, swing away detachable footrest `DME` Y
  BETOS: D1D   Wheelchairs
  DME Modifier: RR

OTHER WHEELCHAIRS AND ACCESSORIES (E1220-E1228)

D **E1220** Wheelchair; specially sized or constructed, (indicate brand name, model number, if any) and justification Y
  BETOS: D1D   Wheelchairs

D **E1221** Wheelchair with fixed arm, footrests `DME` Y
  BETOS: D1D   Wheelchairs
  DME Modifier: RR

D **E1222** Wheelchair with fixed arm, elevating leg rests `DME` Y
  BETOS: D1D   Wheelchairs
  DME Modifier: RR

D **E1223** Wheelchair with detachable arms, footrests `DME` Y
  BETOS: D1D   Wheelchairs
  DME Modifier: RR

D **E1224** Wheelchair with detachable arms, elevating leg rests `DME` Y
  BETOS: D1D   Wheelchairs
  DME Modifier: RR

D **E1225** Wheelchair accessory, manual semi-reclining back, (recline greater than 15 degrees, but less than 80 degrees), each `DME` Y
  BETOS: D1D   Wheelchairs
  DME Modifier: RR

D **E1226** Wheelchair accessory, manual fully reclining back, (recline greater than 80 degrees), each `DME` B
  BETOS: D1D   Wheelchairs
  Service not separately priced by Part B
  DME Modifier: NU,RR,UE

D **E1227** Special height arms for wheelchair `DME` Y
  BETOS: D1D   Wheelchairs
  DME Modifier: NU,RR,UE

D **E1228** Special back height for wheelchair `DME` Y
  BETOS: D1D   Wheelchairs
  DME Modifier: RR

PEDIATRIC WHEELCHAIRS (E1229-E1239)

C **E1229** Wheelchair, pediatric size, not otherwise specified Ⓐ Y
  BETOS: D1D   Wheelchairs

D **E1230** Power operated vehicle (three or four wheel nonhighway) specify brand name and model number `DME` Y
  BETOS: D1D   Wheelchairs
  DME Modifier: NU,RR,UE

D **E1231** Wheelchair, pediatric size, tilt-in-space, rigid, adjustable, with seating system `DME` Ⓐ Y
  BETOS: D1D   Wheelchairs
  DME Modifier: NU,RR,UE

D **E1232** Wheelchair, pediatric size, tilt-in-space, folding, adjustable, with seating system `DME` Ⓐ Y
  BETOS: D1D   Wheelchairs
  DME Modifier: RR

D **E1233** Wheelchair, pediatric size, tilt-in-space, rigid, adjustable, without seating system `DME` Ⓐ Y
  BETOS: D1D   Wheelchairs
  DME Modifier: RR

D **E1234** Wheelchair, pediatric size, tilt-in-space, folding, adjustable, without seating system `DME` Ⓐ Y
  BETOS: D1D   Wheelchairs
  DME Modifier: RR

D **E1235** Wheelchair, pediatric size, rigid, adjustable, with seating system `DME` Ⓐ Y
  BETOS: D1D   Wheelchairs
  DME Modifier: RR

D **E1236** Wheelchair, pediatric size, folding, adjustable, with seating system `DME` Ⓐ Y
  BETOS: D1D   Wheelchairs
  DME Modifier: RR

D **E1237** Wheelchair, pediatric size, rigid, adjustable, without seating system `DME` Ⓐ Y
  BETOS: D1D   Wheelchairs
  DME Modifier: RR

D **E1238** Wheelchair, pediatric size, folding, adjustable, without seating system `DME` Ⓐ Y
  BETOS: D1D   Wheelchairs
  DME Modifier: RR

C **E1239** Power wheelchair, pediatric size, not otherwise specified Ⓐ Y
  BETOS: D1D   Wheelchairs
  Coding Clinic: 2006, Q1

LIGHTWEIGHT WHEELCHAIRS (E1240-E1270)

D **E1240** Lightweight wheelchair, detachable arms, (desk or full length) swing away detachable, elevating leg rest `DME` Y
  BETOS: D1D   Wheelchairs
  DME Modifier: RR

I **E1250** Lightweight wheelchair, fixed full length arms, swing away detachable footrest   E1
    BETOS: D1D   Wheelchairs
    Service not separately priced by Part B

I **E1260** Lightweight wheelchair, detachable arms (desk or full length) swing away detachable footrest   E1
    BETOS: D1D   Wheelchairs
    Service not separately priced by Part B

D **E1270** Lightweight wheelchair, fixed full length arms, swing away detachable elevating leg rests   DME Y
    BETOS: D1D   Wheelchairs
    DME Modifier: RR

HEAVY DUTY AND SPECIAL WHEELCHAIRS (E1280-E1298)

D **E1280** Heavy duty wheelchair, detachable arms (desk or full length) elevating leg rests   DME Y
    BETOS: D1D   Wheelchairs
    DME Modifier: RR

I **E1285** Heavy duty wheelchair, fixed full length arms, swing away detachable footrest   E1
    BETOS: D1D   Wheelchairs
    Service not separately priced by Part B

I **E1290** Heavy duty wheelchair, detachable arms (desk or full length) swing away detachable footrest   E1
    BETOS: D1D   Wheelchairs
    Service not separately priced by Part B

D **E1295** Heavy duty wheelchair, fixed full length arms, elevating leg rest   DME Y
    BETOS: D1D   Wheelchairs
    DME Modifier: RR

D **E1296** Special wheelchair seat height from floor   DME Y
    BETOS: D1D   Wheelchairs
    DME Modifier: NU,RR,UE

D **E1297** Special wheelchair seat depth, by upholstery   DME Y
    BETOS: D1D   Wheelchairs
    DME Modifier: NU,RR,UE

D **E1298** Special wheelchair seat depth and/or width, by construction   DME Y
    BETOS: D1D   Wheelchairs
    DME Modifier: NU,RR,UE

WHIRLPOOL BATHS (E1300, E1310)

M **E1300** Whirlpool, portable (overtub-type)   E1
    BETOS: D1E   Other DME
    Service not separately priced by Part B

D **E1310** Whirlpool, non-portable (built-in type)   DME Y
    BETOS: D1E   Other DME
    DME Modifier: NU,RR,UE

ACCESSORIES FOR OXYGEN DELIVERY DEVICES (E1352-E1406)

C **E1352** Oxygen accessory, flow regulator capable of positive inspiratory pressure   Y
    BETOS: D1C   Oxygen and supplies
    Service not separately priced by Part B

D **E1353** Regulator   DME Y
    BETOS: D1C   Oxygen and supplies
    Service not separately priced by Part B
    Pub: 100-4, Chap. 23, 60.3

C **E1354** Oxygen accessory, wheeled cart for portable cylinder or portable concentrator, any type, replacement only, each   Y
    BETOS: D1C   Oxygen and supplies
    Service not separately priced by Part B
    Coding Clinic: 2008, Q4

D **E1355** Stand/rack   DME Y
    BETOS: D1C   Oxygen and supplies
    Service not separately priced by Part B
    Pub: 100-4, Chap. 23, 60.3

C **E1356** Oxygen accessory, battery pack/cartridge for portable concentrator, any type, replacement only, each   Y
    BETOS: D1C   Oxygen and supplies
    Service not separately priced by Part B
    Coding Clinic: 2008, Q4

C **E1357** Oxygen accessory, battery charger for portable concentrator, any type, replacement only, each   Y
    BETOS: D1C   Oxygen and supplies
    Service not separately priced by Part B
    Coding Clinic: 2008, Q4

D **E1358** Oxygen accessory, DC power adapter for portable concentrator, any type, replacement only, each   Y
    BETOS: D1C   Oxygen and supplies
    Service not separately priced by Part B
    Coding Clinic: 2008, Q4

D **E1372** Immersion external heater for nebulizer   DME Y
    BETOS: D1E   Other DME
    DME Modifier: NU,RR,UE

D **E1390** Oxygen concentrator, single delivery port, capable of delivering 85 percent or greater oxygen concentration at the prescribed flow rate   DME Y
    BETOS: D1C   Oxygen and supplies
    DME Modifier: RR

D **E1391** Oxygen concentrator, dual delivery port, capable of delivering 85 percent or greater oxygen concentration at the prescribed flow rate, each   DME Y
    BETOS: D1C   Oxygen and supplies
    DME Modifier: RR

D **E1392** Portable oxygen concentrator, rental   DME Y
    BETOS: D1C   Oxygen and supplies
    DME Modifier: RR

♂ Male only   ♀ Female only   **A** Age   A2 - Z3 = ASC Payment indicator   A - Y = APC Status indicator
ASC = ASC-approved procedure   DME Paid under the DME fee schedule   MIPS MIPS code

C **E1399** Durable medical equipment, miscellaneous   Y
  BETOS: D1E   Other DME
  Pub: 100-4, Chap. 32, 110.5

D **E1405** Oxygen and water vapor enriching system with heated delivery   **DME** Y
  BETOS: D1C   Oxygen and supplies
  DME Modifier: RR

D **E1406** Oxygen and water vapor enriching system without heated delivery   **DME** Y
  BETOS: D1C   Oxygen and supplies
  DME Modifier: RR

DIALYSIS SYSTEMS AND ACCESSORIES (E1500-E1699)

D **E1500** Centrifuge, for dialysis   A
  BETOS: P9B   Dialysis services (non-Medicare fee schedule)
  Service not separately priced by Part B
  Coding Clinic: 2002, Q1

D **E1510** Kidney, dialysate delivery system kidney machine, pump recirculating, air removal system, flowrate meter, power off, heater and temperature control with alarm, IV poles, pressure gauge, concentrate container   A
  BETOS: P9B   Dialysis services (non-Medicare fee schedule)
  Service not separately priced by Part B

D **E1520** Heparin infusion pump for hemodialysis   A
  BETOS: P9B   Dialysis services (non-Medicare fee schedule)
  Service not separately priced by Part B

D **E1530** Air bubble detector for hemodialysis, each, replacement   A
  BETOS: P9B   Dialysis services (non-Medicare fee schedule)
  Service not separately priced by Part B

D **E1540** Pressure alarm for hemodialysis, each, replacement   A
  BETOS: P9B   Dialysis services (non-Medicare fee schedule)
  Service not separately priced by Part B

D **E1550** Bath conductivity meter for hemodialysis, each   A
  BETOS: P9B   Dialysis services (non-Medicare fee schedule)
  Service not separately priced by Part B

D **E1560** Blood leak detector for hemodialysis, each, replacement   A
  BETOS: P9B   Dialysis services (non-Medicare fee schedule)
  Service not separately priced by Part B

D **E1570** Adjustable chair, for ESRD patients   A
  BETOS: P9B   Dialysis services (non-Medicare fee schedule)
  Service not separately priced by Part B

D **E1575** Transducer protectors/fluid barriers, for hemodialysis, any size, per 10   A
  BETOS: P9B   Dialysis services (non-Medicare fee schedule)
  Service not separately priced by Part B

D **E1580** Unipuncture control system for hemodialysis   A
  BETOS: P9B   Dialysis services (non-Medicare fee schedule)
  Service not separately priced by Part B

D **E1590** Hemodialysis machine   A
  BETOS: P9B   Dialysis services (non-Medicare fee schedule)
  Service not separately priced by Part B

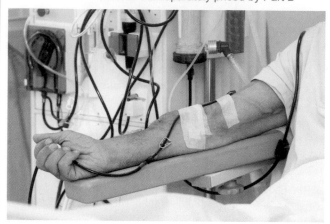

Dialysis medical device

D **E1592** Automatic intermittent peritoneal dialysis system   A
  BETOS: P9B   Dialysis services (non-Medicare fee schedule)
  Service not separately priced by Part B

D **E1594** Cycler dialysis machine for peritoneal dialysis   A
  BETOS: P9B   Dialysis services (non-Medicare fee schedule)
  Service not separately priced by Part B

D **E1600** Delivery and/or installation charges for hemodialysis equipment   A
  BETOS: P9B   Dialysis services (non-Medicare fee schedule)
  Service not separately priced by Part B

D **E1610** Reverse osmosis water purification system, for hemodialysis   A
  BETOS: P9B   Dialysis services (non-Medicare fee schedule)
  Service not separately priced by Part B

D **E1615** Deionizer water purification system, for hemodialysis   A
  BETOS: P9B   Dialysis services (non-Medicare fee schedule)
  Service not separately priced by Part B

▲ Revised code   ● New code   **C** Carrier judgment   **D** Special coverage instructions apply
I Not payable by Medicare   **M** Non-covered by Medicare   **S** Non-covered by Medicare statute   AHA Coding Clinic®

D **E1620** Blood pump for hemodialysis, replacement　A
　　BETOS: P9B　Dialysis services
　　(non-Medicare fee schedule)
　　Service not separately priced by Part B

D **E1625** Water softening system, for hemodialysis　A
　　BETOS: P9B　Dialysis services
　　(non-Medicare fee schedule)
　　Service not separately priced by Part B

C **E1630** Reciprocating peritoneal dialysis system　A
　　BETOS: P9B　Dialysis services
　　(non-Medicare fee schedule)
　　Service not separately priced by Part B

D **E1632** Wearable artificial kidney, each　A
　　BETOS: P9B　Dialysis services
　　(non-Medicare fee schedule)
　　Service not separately priced by Part B

D **E1634** Peritoneal dialysis clamps, each　B
　　BETOS: P9B　Dialysis services
　　(non-Medicare fee schedule)
　　Service not separately priced by Part B

D **E1635** Compact (portable) travel hemodialyzer
　　system　A
　　BETOS: P9B　Dialysis services
　　(non-Medicare fee schedule)
　　Service not separately priced by Part B

D **E1636** Sorbent cartridges, for hemodialysis, per 10　A
　　BETOS: P9B　Dialysis services
　　(non-Medicare fee schedule)
　　Service not separately priced by Part B

D **E1637** Hemostats, each　A
　　BETOS: P9B　Dialysis services
　　(non-Medicare fee schedule)
　　Service not separately priced by Part B
　　Coding Clinic: 2002, Q1

D **E1639** Scale, each　A
　　BETOS: P9B　Dialysis services
　　(non-Medicare fee schedule)
　　Service not separately priced by Part B
　　Coding Clinic: 2002, Q1

D **E1699** Dialysis equipment, not otherwise specified　A
　　BETOS: P9B　Dialysis services
　　(non-Medicare fee schedule)
　　Service not separately priced by Part B

JAW MOTION REHABILITATION SYSTEMS (E1700-E1702)

C **E1700** Jaw motion rehabilitation system　DME　Y
　　BETOS: D1E　Other DME
　　DME Modifier: RR

C **E1701** Replacement cushions for jaw motion
　　rehabilitation system, pkg. of 6　DME　Y
　　BETOS: D1E　Other DME

C **E1702** Replacement measuring scales for jaw motion
　　rehabilitation system, pkg. of 200　DME　Y
　　BETOS: D1E　Other DME

**EXTENSION/FLEXION REHABILITATION DEVICES
(E1800-E1841)**

C **E1800** Dynamic adjustable elbow extension/flexion
　　device, includes soft interface material　DME　Y
　　BETOS: D1E　Other DME
　　DME Modifier: RR

C **E1801** Static progressive stretch elbow device,
　　extension and/or flexion, with or without
　　range of motion adjustment, includes all
　　components and accessories　DME　Y
　　BETOS: D1E　Other DME
　　DME Modifier: RR
　　Coding Clinic: 2002, Q1

C **E1802** Dynamic adjustable forearm pronation/
　　supination device, includes soft interface
　　material　DME　Y
　　BETOS: D1E　Other DME
　　DME Modifier: RR

C **E1805** Dynamic adjustable wrist extension / flexion
　　device, includes soft interface material　DME　Y
　　BETOS: D1E　Other DME
　　DME Modifier: RR

C **E1806** Static progressive stretch wrist device,
　　flexion and/or extension, with or without
　　range of motion adjustment, includes all
　　components and accessories　DME　Y
　　BETOS: D1E　Other DME
　　DME Modifier: RR
　　Coding Clinic: 2002, Q1

C **E1810** Dynamic adjustable knee extension / flexion
　　device, includes soft interface material　DME　Y
　　BETOS: D1E　Other DME
　　DME Modifier: RR

C **E1811** Static progressive stretch knee device,
　　extension and/or flexion, with or without
　　range of motion adjustment, includes all
　　components and accessories　DME　Y
　　BETOS: D1E　Other DME
　　DME Modifier: RR
　　Coding Clinic: 2002, Q1

C **E1812** Dynamic knee, extension/flexion device with
　　active resistance control　DME　Y
　　BETOS: D1E　Other DME
　　DME Modifier: RR

C **E1815** Dynamic adjustable ankle extension/flexion
　　device, includes soft interface material　DME　Y
　　BETOS: D1E　Other DME
　　DME Modifier: RR

C **E1816** Static progressive stretch ankle device,
　　flexion and/or extension, with or without
　　range of motion adjustment, includes all
　　components and accessories　DME　Y
　　BETOS: D1E　Other DME
　　DME Modifier: RR
　　Coding Clinic: 2002, Q1

♂ Male only　　♀ Female only　　**A** Age　　A2 - Z3 = ASC Payment indicator　　A - Y = APC Status indicator
ASC = ASC-approved procedure　　**DME** Paid under the DME fee schedule　　**MIPS** MIPS code

C E1818 Static progressive stretch forearm pronation/ supination device, with or without range of motion adjustment, includes all components and accessories **DME** Y
BETOS: D1E   Other DME
DME Modifier: RR
Coding Clinic: 2002, Q1

C E1820 Replacement soft interface material, dynamic adjustable extension/flexion device **DME** Y
BETOS: D1E   Other DME
DME Modifier: NU,RR,UE

C E1821 Replacement soft interface material/cuffs for bi-directional static progressive stretch device **DME** Y
BETOS: D1E   Other DME
DME Modifier: NU,RR,UE
Coding Clinic: 2002, Q1

C E1825 Dynamic adjustable finger extension/flexion device, includes soft interface material **DME** Y
BETOS: D1E   Other DME
DME Modifier: RR

C E1830 Dynamic adjustable toe extension/flexion device, includes soft interface material **DME** Y
BETOS: D1E   Other DME
DME Modifier: RR

C E1831 Static progressive stretch toe device, extension and/or flexion, with or without range of motion adjustment, includes all components and accessories **DME** Y
BETOS: D1E   Other DME
DME Modifier: RR

C E1840 Dynamic adjustable shoulder flexion / abduction / rotation device, includes soft interface material **DME** Y
BETOS: D1E   Other DME
DME Modifier: RR
Coding Clinic: 2002, Q1

C E1841 Static progressive stretch shoulder device, with or without range of motion adjustment, includes all components and accessories **DME** Y
BETOS: D1E   Other DME
DME Modifier: RR

COMMUNICATION BOARDS (E1902)

C E1902 Communication board, non-electronic augmentative or alternative communication device Y
BETOS: Z2   Undefined codes
Service not separately priced by Part B
Coding Clinic: 2002, Q1

MISCELLANEOUS PUMPS AND MONITORS (E2000-E2120)

C E2000 Gastric suction pump, home model, portable or stationary, electric **DME** Y
BETOS: D1E   Other DME
DME Modifier: RR
Coding Clinic: 2002, Q1

D E2100 Blood glucose monitor with integrated voice synthesizer **DME** Y
BETOS: D1E   Other DME
DME Modifier: NU,RR,UE
Coding Clinic: 2002, Q1

D E2101 Blood glucose monitor with integrated lancing/blood sample **DME** Y
BETOS: D1E   Other DME
DME Modifier: NU,RR,UE
Coding Clinic: 2002, Q1

C E2120 Pulse generator system for tympanic treatment of inner ear endolymphatic fluid **DME** Y
BETOS: D1E   Other DME
DME Modifier: RR

MANUAL WHEELCHAIR ACCESSORIES (E2201-E2295)

C E2201 Manual wheelchair accessory, nonstandard seat frame, width greater than or equal to 20 inches and less than 24 inches **DME** Y
BETOS: D1D   Wheelchairs
DME Modifier: NU,RR,UE

C E2202 Manual wheelchair accessory, nonstandard seat frame width, 24-27 inches **DME** Y
BETOS: D1D   Wheelchairs
DME Modifier: NU,RR,UE

C E2203 Manual wheelchair accessory, nonstandard seat frame depth, 20 to less than 22 inches **DME** Y
BETOS: D1D   Wheelchairs
DME Modifier: NU,RR,UE

C E2204 Manual wheelchair accessory, nonstandard seat frame depth, 22 to 25 inches **DME** Y
BETOS: D1D   Wheelchairs
DME Modifier: NU,RR,UE

C E2205 Manual wheelchair accessory, handrim without projections (includes ergonomic or contoured), any type, replacement only, each **DME** Y
BETOS: D1D   Wheelchairs
DME Modifier: NU,RR,UE

C E2206 Manual wheelchair accessory, wheel lock assembly, complete, replacement only, each **DME** Y
BETOS: D1D   Wheelchairs
DME Modifier: NU,RR,UE

C **E2207** Wheelchair accessory, crutch and cane holder, each `DME` Y
  BETOS: D1D   Wheelchairs
  DME Modifier: NU,RR,UE

C **E2208** Wheelchair accessory, cylinder tank carrier, each `DME` Y
  BETOS: D1D   Wheelchairs
  DME Modifier: NU,RR,UE
  Pub: 100-4, Chap. 23, 60.3

C **E2209** Accessory, arm trough, with or without hand support, each `DME` Y
  BETOS: D1D   Wheelchairs
  DME Modifier: NU,RR,UE

C **E2210** Wheelchair accessory, bearings, any type, replacement only, each `DME` Y
  BETOS: D1D   Wheelchairs
  DME Modifier: NU,RR,UE

C **E2211** Manual wheelchair accessory, pneumatic propulsion tire, any size, each `DME` Y
  BETOS: D1D   Wheelchairs
  DME Modifier: NU,RR,UE

C **E2212** Manual wheelchair accessory, tube for pneumatic propulsion tire, any size, each `DME` Y
  BETOS: D1D   Wheelchairs
  DME Modifier: NU,RR,UE

C **E2213** Manual wheelchair accessory, insert for pneumatic propulsion tire (removable), any type, any size, each `DME` Y
  BETOS: D1D   Wheelchairs
  DME Modifier: NU,RR,UE

C **E2214** Manual wheelchair accessory, pneumatic caster tire, any size, each `DME` Y
  BETOS: D1D   Wheelchairs
  DME Modifier: NU,RR,UE

C **E2215** Manual wheelchair accessory, tube for pneumatic caster tire, any size, each `DME` Y
  BETOS: D1D   Wheelchairs
  DME Modifier: NU,RR,UE

C **E2216** Manual wheelchair accessory, foam filled propulsion tire, any size, each `DME` Y
  BETOS: D1D   Wheelchairs
  DME Modifier: NU,RR,UE

C **E2217** Manual wheelchair accessory, foam filled caster tire, any size, each `DME` Y
  BETOS: D1D   Wheelchairs
  DME Modifier: NU,RR,UE

C **E2218** Manual wheelchair accessory, foam propulsion tire, any size, each `DME` Y
  BETOS: D1D   Wheelchairs
  DME Modifier: NU,RR,UE

C **E2219** Manual wheelchair accessory, foam caster tire, any size, each `DME` Y

BETOS: D1D   Wheelchairs
  DME Modifier: NU,RR,UE

C **E2220** Manual wheelchair accessory, solid (rubber/plastic) propulsion tire, any size, replacement only, each `DME` Y
  BETOS: D1D   Wheelchairs
  DME Modifier: NU,RR,UE

C **E2221** Manual wheelchair accessory, solid (rubber/plastic) caster tire (removable), any size, replacement only, each `DME` Y
  BETOS: D1D   Wheelchairs
  DME Modifier: NU,RR,UE

C **E2222** Manual wheelchair accessory, solid (rubber/plastic) caster tire with integrated wheel, any size, replacement only, each `DME` Y
  BETOS: D1D   Wheelchairs
  DME Modifier: NU,RR,UE

C **E2224** Manual wheelchair accessory, propulsion wheel excludes tire, any size, replacement only, each `DME` Y
  BETOS: D1D   Wheelchairs
  DME Modifier: NU,RR,UE

C **E2225** Manual wheelchair accessory, caster wheel excludes tire, any size, replacement only, each `DME` Y
  BETOS: D1D   Wheelchairs
  DME Modifier: NU,RR,UE

C **E2226** Manual wheelchair accessory, caster fork, any size, replacement only, each `DME` Y
  BETOS: D1D   Wheelchairs
  DME Modifier: NU,RR,UE

C **E2227** Manual wheelchair accessory, gear reduction drive wheel, each `DME` Y
  BETOS: D1D   Wheelchairs
  DME Modifier: RR

C **E2228** Manual wheelchair accessory, wheel braking system and lock, complete, each `DME` Y
  BETOS: D1D   Wheelchairs
  DME Modifier: RR

C **E2230** Manual wheelchair accessory, manual standing system Y
  BETOS: D1D   Wheelchairs
  Service not separately priced by Part B
  Coding Clinic: 2008, Q4

C **E2231** Manual wheelchair accessory, solid seat support base (replaces sling seat), includes any type mounting hardware `DME` Y
  BETOS: D1D   Wheelchairs
  DME Modifier: NU,RR,UE
  Coding Clinic: 2008, Q4

C **E2291** Back, planar, for pediatric size wheelchair including fixed attaching hardware Ⓐ Y
  BETOS: D1D   Wheelchairs

C **E2292** Seat, planar, for pediatric size wheelchair including fixed attaching hardware　Ⓐ Y
　　　BETOS: D1D　Wheelchairs

C **E2293** Back, contoured, for pediatric size wheelchair including fixed attaching hardware　Ⓐ Y
　　　BETOS: D1D　Wheelchairs

C **E2294** Seat, contoured, for pediatric size wheelchair including fixed attaching hardware　Ⓐ Y
　　　BETOS: D1D　Wheelchairs

C **E2295** Manual wheelchair accessory, for pediatric size wheelchair, dynamic seating frame, allows coordinated movement of multiple positioning features　Ⓐ Y
　　　BETOS: D1D　Wheelchairs
　　　Coding Clinic: 2008, Q4

POWER WHEELCHAIR ACCESSORIES (E2300-E2397)

C **E2300** Wheelchair accessory, power seat elevation system, any type　Y
　　　BETOS: D1D　Wheelchairs

C **E2301** Wheelchair accessory, power standing system, any type　Y
　　　BETOS: D1D　Wheelchairs
　　　Service not separately priced by Part B

C **E2310** Power wheelchair accessory, electronic connection between wheelchair controller and one power seating system motor, including all related electronics, indicator feature, mechanical function selection switch, and fixed mounting hardware　DME Y
　　　BETOS: D1D　Wheelchairs
　　　DME Modifier: RR
　　　Pub: 100-4, Chap. 23, 60.3

C **E2311** Power wheelchair accessory, electronic connection between wheelchair controller and two or more power seating system motors, including all related electronics, indicator feature, mechanical function selection switch, and fixed mounting hardware　DME Y
　　　BETOS: D1D　Wheelchairs
　　　DME Modifier: RR

C **E2312** Power wheelchair accessory, hand or chin control interface, mini-proportional remote joystick, proportional, including fixed mounting hardware　DME Y
　　　BETOS: D1D　Wheelchairs
　　　DME Modifier: RR

C **E2313** Power wheelchair accessory, harness for upgrade to expandable controller, including all fasteners, connectors and mounting hardware, each　DME Y
　　　BETOS: D1D　Wheelchairs
　　　DME Modifier: RR

C **E2321** Power wheelchair accessory, hand control interface, remote joystick, nonproportional, including all related electronics, mechanical stop switch, and fixed mounting hardware　DME Y
　　　BETOS: D1D　Wheelchairs
　　　DME Modifier: RR
　　　Pub: 100-4, Chap. 23, 60.3

C **E2322** Power wheelchair accessory, hand control interface, multiple mechanical switches, nonproportional, including all related electronics, mechanical stop switch, and fixed mounting hardware　DME Y
　　　BETOS: D1D　Wheelchairs
　　　DME Modifier: RR

C **E2323** Power wheelchair accessory, specialty joystick handle for hand control interface, prefabricated　DME Y
　　　BETOS: D1D　Wheelchairs
　　　DME Modifier: NU,RR,UE

C **E2324** Power wheelchair accessory, chin cup for chin control interface　DME Y
　　　BETOS: D1D　Wheelchairs
　　　DME Modifier: NU,RR,UE

C **E2325** Power wheelchair accessory, sip and puff interface, nonproportional, including all related electronics, mechanical stop switch, and manual swingaway mounting hardware　DME Y
　　　BETOS: D1D　Wheelchairs
　　　DME Modifier: RR

C **E2326** Power wheelchair accessory, breath tube kit for sip and puff interface　DME Y
　　　BETOS: D1D　Wheelchairs
　　　DME Modifier: RR

C **E2327** Power wheelchair accessory, head control interface, mechanical, proportional, including all related electronics, mechanical direction change switch, and fixed mounting hardware　DME Y
　　　BETOS: D1D　Wheelchairs
　　　DME Modifier: RR

C **E2328** Power wheelchair accessory, head control or extremity control interface, electronic, proportional, including all related electronics and fixed mounting hardware　DME Y
　　　BETOS: D1D　Wheelchairs
　　　DME Modifier: RR

C **E2329** Power wheelchair accessory, head control interface, contact switch mechanism, nonproportional, including all related electronics, mechanical stop switch, mechanical direction change switch, head array, and fixed mounting hardware　DME Y
　　　BETOS: D1D　Wheelchairs
　　　DME Modifier: RR

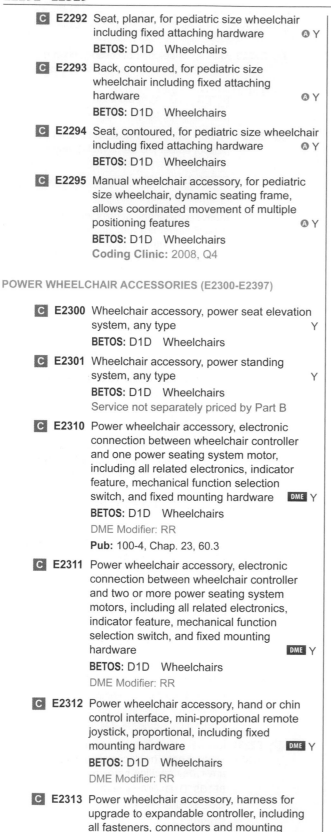

▲ Revised code　● New code　C Carrier judgment　D Special coverage instructions apply
I Not payable by Medicare　M Non-covered by Medicare　S Non-covered by Medicare statute　AHA Coding Clinic®

C E2330 Power wheelchair accessory, head control interface, proximity switch mechanism, nonproportional, including all related electronics, mechanical stop switch, mechanical direction change switch, head array, and fixed mounting hardware DME Y
BETOS: D1D   Wheelchairs
DME Modifier: RR

C E2331 Power wheelchair accessory, attendant control, proportional, including all related electronics and fixed mounting hardware Y
BETOS: D1D   Wheelchairs

C E2340 Power wheelchair accessory, nonstandard seat frame width, 20-23 inches DME Y
BETOS: D1D   Wheelchairs
DME Modifier: NU,RR,UE

C E2341 Power wheelchair accessory, nonstandard seat frame width, 24-27 inches DME Y
BETOS: D1D   Wheelchairs
DME Modifier: NU,RR,UE

C E2342 Power wheelchair accessory, nonstandard seat frame depth, 20 or 21 inches DME Y
BETOS: D1D   Wheelchairs
DME Modifier: NU,RR,UE

C E2343 Power wheelchair accessory, nonstandard seat frame depth, 22-25 inches DME Y
BETOS: D1D   Wheelchairs
DME Modifier: NU,RR,UE

C E2351 Power wheelchair accessory, electronic interface to operate speech generating device using power wheelchair control interface DME Y
BETOS: D1D   Wheelchairs
DME Modifier: NU,RR,UE
Pub: 100-4, Chap. 23, 60.3

C E2358 Power wheelchair accessory, group 34 non-sealed lead acid battery, each Y
BETOS: D1D   Wheelchairs

C E2359 Power wheelchair accessory, group 34 sealed lead acid battery, each (e.g., gel cell, absorbed glassmat) DME Y
BETOS: D1D   Wheelchairs
DME Modifier: NU,RR,UE

C E2360 Power wheelchair accessory, 22 NF non-sealed lead acid battery, each DME Y
BETOS: D1D   Wheelchairs
DME Modifier: NU,RR,UE

C E2361 Power wheelchair accessory, 22 NF sealed lead acid battery, each, (e.g., gel cell, absorbed glassmat) DME Y
BETOS: D1D   Wheelchairs
DME Modifier: NU,RR,UE
Pub: 100-4, Chap. 23, 60.3

C E2362 Power wheelchair accessory, group 24 non-sealed lead acid battery, each DME Y
BETOS: D1D   Wheelchairs
DME Modifier: NU,RR,UE

C E2363 Power wheelchair accessory, group 24 sealed lead acid battery, each (e.g., gel cell, absorbed glassmat) DME Y
BETOS: D1D   Wheelchairs
DME Modifier: NU,RR,UE
Pub: 100-4, Chap. 23, 60.3

C E2364 Power wheelchair accessory, U-1 non-sealed lead acid battery, each DME Y
BETOS: D1D   Wheelchairs
DME Modifier: NU,RR,UE

C E2365 Power wheelchair accessory, U-1 sealed lead acid battery, each (e.g., gel cell, absorbed glassmat) DME Y
BETOS: D1D   Wheelchairs
DME Modifier: NU,RR,UE
Pub: 100-4, Chap. 23, 60.3

C E2366 Power wheelchair accessory, battery charger, single mode, for use with only one battery type, sealed or non-sealed, each DME Y
BETOS: D1D   Wheelchairs
DME Modifier: NU,RR,UE

C E2367 Power wheelchair accessory, battery charger, dual mode, for use with either battery type, sealed or non-sealed, each DME Y
BETOS: D1D   Wheelchairs
DME Modifier: NU,RR,UE

C E2368 Power wheelchair component, drive wheel motor, replacement only DME Y
BETOS: D1D   Wheelchairs
DME Modifier: RR

C E2369 Power wheelchair component, drive wheel gear box, replacement only DME Y
BETOS: D1D   Wheelchairs
DME Modifier: RR

C E2370 Power wheelchair component, integrated drive wheel motor and gear box combination, replacement only DME Y
BETOS: D1D   Wheelchairs
DME Modifier: RR

C E2371 Power wheelchair accessory, group 27 sealed lead acid battery, (e.g., gel cell, absorbed glassmat), each DME Y
BETOS: D1D   Wheelchairs
DME Modifier: NU,RR,UE

C E2372 Power wheelchair accessory, group 27 non-sealed lead acid battery, each DME Y
BETOS: D1D   Wheelchairs
DME Modifier: NU,RR,UE

E2373 - E2396

DURABLE MEDICAL EQUIPMENT (E0100-E8002)

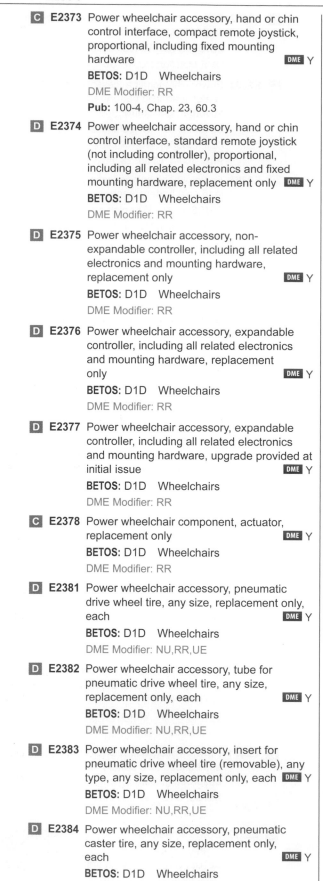

C **E2373** Power wheelchair accessory, hand or chin control interface, compact remote joystick, proportional, including fixed mounting hardware ▪ DME ▪ Y

　　BETOS: D1D　Wheelchairs

　　DME Modifier: RR

　　Pub: 100-4, Chap. 23, 60.3

D **E2374** Power wheelchair accessory, hand or chin control interface, standard remote joystick (not including controller), proportional, including all related electronics and fixed mounting hardware, replacement only ▪ DME ▪ Y

　　BETOS: D1D　Wheelchairs

　　DME Modifier: RR

D **E2375** Power wheelchair accessory, non-expandable controller, including all related electronics and mounting hardware, replacement only ▪ DME ▪ Y

　　BETOS: D1D　Wheelchairs

　　DME Modifier: RR

D **E2376** Power wheelchair accessory, expandable controller, including all related electronics and mounting hardware, replacement only ▪ DME ▪ Y

　　BETOS: D1D　Wheelchairs

　　DME Modifier: RR

D **E2377** Power wheelchair accessory, expandable controller, including all related electronics and mounting hardware, upgrade provided at initial issue ▪ DME ▪ Y

　　BETOS: D1D　Wheelchairs

　　DME Modifier: RR

C **E2378** Power wheelchair component, actuator, replacement only ▪ DME ▪ Y

　　BETOS: D1D　Wheelchairs

　　DME Modifier: RR

D **E2381** Power wheelchair accessory, pneumatic drive wheel tire, any size, replacement only, each ▪ DME ▪ Y

　　BETOS: D1D　Wheelchairs

　　DME Modifier: NU,RR,UE

D **E2382** Power wheelchair accessory, tube for pneumatic drive wheel tire, any size, replacement only, each ▪ DME ▪ Y

　　BETOS: D1D　Wheelchairs

　　DME Modifier: NU,RR,UE

D **E2383** Power wheelchair accessory, insert for pneumatic drive wheel tire (removable), any type, any size, replacement only, each ▪ DME ▪ Y

　　BETOS: D1D　Wheelchairs

　　DME Modifier: NU,RR,UE

D **E2384** Power wheelchair accessory, pneumatic caster tire, any size, replacement only, each ▪ DME ▪ Y

　　BETOS: D1D　Wheelchairs

　　DME Modifier: NU,RR,UE

D **E2385** Power wheelchair accessory, tube for pneumatic caster tire, any size, replacement only, each ▪ DME ▪ Y

　　BETOS: D1D　Wheelchairs

　　DME Modifier: NU,RR,UE

D **E2386** Power wheelchair accessory, foam filled drive wheel tire, any size, replacement only, each ▪ DME ▪ Y

　　BETOS: D1D　Wheelchairs

　　DME Modifier: NU,RR,UE

D **E2387** Power wheelchair accessory, foam filled caster tire, any size, replacement only, each ▪ DME ▪ Y

　　BETOS: D1D　Wheelchairs

　　DME Modifier: NU,RR,UE

D **E2388** Power wheelchair accessory, foam drive wheel tire, any size, replacement only, each ▪ DME ▪ Y

　　BETOS: D1D　Wheelchairs

　　DME Modifier: NU,RR,UE

D **E2389** Power wheelchair accessory, foam caster tire, any size, replacement only, each ▪ DME ▪ Y

　　BETOS: D1D　Wheelchairs

　　DME Modifier: NU,RR,UE

D **E2390** Power wheelchair accessory, solid (rubber/plastic) drive wheel tire, any size, replacement only, each ▪ DME ▪ Y

　　BETOS: D1D　Wheelchairs

　　DME Modifier: NU,RR,UE

D **E2391** Power wheelchair accessory, solid (rubber/plastic) caster tire (removable), any size, replacement only, each ▪ DME ▪ Y

　　BETOS: D1D　Wheelchairs

　　DME Modifier: NU,RR,UE

D **E2392** Power wheelchair accessory, solid (rubber/plastic) caster tire with integrated wheel, any size, replacement only, each ▪ DME ▪ Y

　　BETOS: D1D　Wheelchairs

　　DME Modifier: NU,RR,UE

D **E2394** Power wheelchair accessory, drive wheel excludes tire, any size, replacement only, each ▪ DME ▪ Y

　　BETOS: D1D　Wheelchairs

　　DME Modifier: NU,RR,UE

D **E2395** Power wheelchair accessory, caster wheel excludes tire, any size, replacement only, each ▪ DME ▪ Y

　　BETOS: D1D　Wheelchairs

　　DME Modifier: NU,RR,UE

D **E2396** Power wheelchair accessory, caster fork, any size, replacement only, each ▪ DME ▪ Y

　　BETOS: D1D　Wheelchairs

　　DME Modifier: NU,RR,UE

▲ Revised code　● New code　**C** Carrier judgment　**D** Special coverage instructions apply
I Not payable by Medicare　**M** Non-covered by Medicare　**S** Non-covered by Medicare statute　AHA Coding Clinic®

C **E2397** Power wheelchair accessory, lithium-based battery, each DME Y
BETOS: D1D Wheelchairs
DME Modifier: NU,RR,UE

WOUND THERAPY PUMPS (E2402)

C **E2402** Negative pressure wound therapy electrical pump, stationary or portable DME Y
BETOS: D1E Other DME
DME Modifier: RR
Pub: 100-4, Chap. 23, 60.3

SPEECH GENERATING DEVICES, SOFTWARE, AND ACCESSORIES (E2500-E2599)

D **E2500** Speech generating device, digitized speech, using pre-recorded messages, less than or equal to 8 minutes recording time DME Y
BETOS: D1E Other DME
DME Modifier: NU,RR,UE

D **E2502** Speech generating device, digitized speech, using pre-recorded messages, greater than 8 minutes but less than or equal to 20 minutes recording time DME Y
BETOS: D1E Other DME
DME Modifier: NU,RR,UE

D **E2504** Speech generating device, digitized speech, using pre-recorded messages, greater than 20 minutes but less than or equal to 40 minutes recording time DME Y
BETOS: D1E Other DME
DME Modifier: NU,RR,UE

D **E2506** Speech generating device, digitized speech, using pre-recorded messages, greater than 40 minutes recording time DME Y
BETOS: D1E Other DME
DME Modifier: NU,RR,UE

D **E2508** Speech generating device, synthesized speech, requiring message formulation by spelling and access by physical contact with the device DME Y
BETOS: D1E Other DME
DME Modifier: NU,RR,UE

D **E2510** Speech generating device, synthesized speech, permitting multiple methods of message formulation and multiple methods of device access DME Y
BETOS: D1E Other DME
DME Modifier: NU,RR,UE

D **E2511** Speech generating software program, for personal computer or personal digital assistant DME Y
BETOS: D1E Other DME
DME Modifier: NU,RR,UE

D **E2512** Accessory for speech generating device, mounting system DME Y
BETOS: D1E Other DME
DME Modifier: NU,RR,UE

D **E2599** Accessory for speech generating device, not otherwise classified Y
BETOS: D1E Other DME

WHEELCHAIR SEAT AND BACK CUSHIONS (E2601-E2625)

C **E2601** General use wheelchair seat cushion, width less than 22 inches, any depth DME Y
BETOS: D1D Wheelchairs
DME Modifier: NU,RR,UE
Pub: 100-4, Chap. 23, 60.3

C **E2602** General use wheelchair seat cushion, width 22 inches or greater, any depth DME Y
BETOS: D1D Wheelchairs
DME Modifier: NU,RR,UE

C **E2603** Skin protection wheelchair seat cushion, width less than 22 inches, any depth DME Y
BETOS: D1D Wheelchairs
DME Modifier: NU,RR,UE

C **E2604** Skin protection wheelchair seat cushion, width 22 inches or greater, any depth DME Y
BETOS: D1D Wheelchairs
DME Modifier: NU,RR,UE

C **E2605** Positioning wheelchair seat cushion, width less than 22 inches, any depth DME Y
BETOS: D1D Wheelchairs
DME Modifier: NU,RR,UE

C **E2606** Positioning wheelchair seat cushion, width 22 inches or greater, any depth DME Y
BETOS: D1D Wheelchairs
DME Modifier: NU,RR,UE

C **E2607** Skin protection and positioning wheelchair seat cushion, width less than 22 inches, any depth DME Y
BETOS: D1D Wheelchairs
DME Modifier: NU,RR,UE

C **E2608** Skin protection and positioning wheelchair seat cushion, width 22 inches or greater, any depth DME Y
BETOS: D1D Wheelchairs
DME Modifier: NU,RR,UE

C **E2609** Custom fabricated wheelchair seat cushion, any size Y
BETOS: D1D Wheelchairs

C **E2610** Wheelchair seat cushion, powered B
BETOS: D1D Wheelchairs

C **E2611** General use wheelchair back cushion, width less than 22 inches, any height, including any type mounting hardware DME Y

♂ Male only   ♀ Female only   Ⓐ Age   A2 - Z3 = ASC Payment indicator   A - Y = APC Status indicator
ASC = ASC-approved procedure   DME Paid under the DME fee schedule   MIPS MIPS code

BETOS: D1D   Wheelchairs

DME Modifier: NU,RR,UE

Pub: 100-4, Chap. 23, 60.3

C **E2612** General use wheelchair back cushion, width 22 inches or greater, any height, including any type mounting hardware DME Y

BETOS: D1D   Wheelchairs

DME Modifier: NU,RR,UE

C **E2613** Positioning wheelchair back cushion, posterior, width less than 22 inches, any height, including any type mounting hardware DME Y

BETOS: D1D   Wheelchairs

DME Modifier: NU,RR,UE

C **E2614** Positioning wheelchair back cushion, posterior, width 22 inches or greater, any height, including any type mounting hardware DME Y

BETOS: D1D   Wheelchairs

DME Modifier: NU,RR,UE

C **E2615** Positioning wheelchair back cushion, posterior-lateral, width less than 22 inches, any height, including any type mounting hardware DME Y

BETOS: D1D   Wheelchairs

DME Modifier: NU,RR,UE

C **E2616** Positioning wheelchair back cushion, posterior-lateral, width 22 inches or greater, any height, including any type mounting hardware DME Y

BETOS: D1D   Wheelchairs

DME Modifier: NU,RR,UE

C **E2617** Custom fabricated wheelchair back cushion, any size, including any type mounting hardware Y

BETOS: D1D   Wheelchairs

C **E2619** Replacement cover for wheelchair seat cushion or back cushion, each DME Y

BETOS: D1D   Wheelchairs

DME Modifier: NU,RR,UE

Pub: 100-4, Chap. 23, 60.3

C **E2620** Positioning wheelchair back cushion, planar back with lateral supports, width less than 22 inches, any height, including any type mounting hardware DME Y

BETOS: D1D   Wheelchairs

DME Modifier: NU,RR,UE

C **E2621** Positioning wheelchair back cushion, planar back with lateral supports, width 22 inches or greater, any height, including any type mounting hardware DME Y

BETOS: D1D   Wheelchairs

DME Modifier: NU,RR,UE

C **E2622** Skin protection wheelchair seat cushion, adjustable, width less than 22 inches, any depth DME Y

BETOS: D1D   Wheelchairs

DME Modifier: NU,RR,UE

C **E2623** Skin protection wheelchair seat cushion, adjustable, width 22 inches or greater, any depth DME Y

BETOS: D1D   Wheelchairs

DME Modifier: NU,RR,UE

C **E2624** Skin protection and positioning wheelchair seat cushion, adjustable, width less than 22 inches, any depth DME Y

BETOS: D1D   Wheelchairs

DME Modifier: NU,RR,UE

C **E2625** Skin protection and positioning wheelchair seat cushion, adjustable, width 22 inches or greater, any depth DME Y

BETOS: D1D   Wheelchairs

DME Modifier: NU,RR,UE

WHEELCHAIR MOBILE ARM SUPPORTS (E2626-E2633)

C **E2626** Wheelchair accessory, shoulder elbow, mobile arm support attached to wheelchair, balanced, adjustable DME Y

BETOS: D1D   Wheelchairs

DME Modifier: NU,RR,UE

C **E2627** Wheelchair accessory, shoulder elbow, mobile arm support attached to wheelchair, balanced, adjustable rancho type DME Y

BETOS: D1D   Wheelchairs

DME Modifier: NU,RR,UE

C **E2628** Wheelchair accessory, shoulder elbow, mobile arm support attached to wheelchair, balanced, reclining DME Y

BETOS: D1D   Wheelchairs

DME Modifier: NU,RR,UE

C **E2629** Wheelchair accessory, shoulder elbow, mobile arm support attached to wheelchair, balanced, friction arm support (friction dampening to proximal and distal joints) DME Y

BETOS: D1D   Wheelchairs

DME Modifier: NU,RR,UE

C **E2630** Wheelchair accessory, shoulder elbow, mobile arm support, monosuspension arm and hand support, overhead elbow forearm hand sling support, yoke type suspension support DME Y

BETOS: D1D   Wheelchairs

DME Modifier: NU,RR,UE

C **E2631** Wheelchair accessory, addition to mobile arm support, elevating proximal arm DME Y

BETOS: D1D   Wheelchairs

DME Modifier: NU,RR,UE

C **E2632** Wheelchair accessory, addition to mobile arm support, offset or lateral rocker arm with elastic balance control   DME Y

       BETOS: D1D   Wheelchairs

       DME Modifier: NU,RR,UE

C **E2633** Wheelchair accessory, addition to mobile arm support, supinator   DME Y

       BETOS: D1D   Wheelchairs

       DME Modifier: NU,RR,UE

PEDIATRIC GAIT TRAINERS (E8000-E8002)

I **E8000** Gait trainer, pediatric size, posterior support, includes all accessories and components   Ⓐ E1

       BETOS: Z2   Undefined codes

       Service not separately priced by Part B

I **E8001** Gait trainer, pediatric size, upright support, includes all accessories and components   Ⓐ E1

       BETOS: Z2   Undefined codes

       Service not separately priced by Part B

I **E8002** Gait trainer, pediatric size, anterior support, includes all accessories and components   Ⓐ E1

       BETOS: Z2   Undefined codes

       Service not separately priced by Part B

♂ Male only   ♀ Female only   Ⓐ Age   A2 - Z3 = ASC Payment indicator   A - Y = APC Status indicator

ASC = ASC-approved procedure   DME Paid under the DME fee schedule   MIPS MIPS code

NOTES

PROCEDURES / PROFESSIONAL SERVICES (G0008-G9977)

VACCINE ADMINISTRATION (G0008-G0010)

C **G0008** Administration of influenza virus vaccine   S
  BETOS: O1G   Influenza immunization
  Coding Clinic: 2016, Q4
  Pub: 100-2, Chap. 12, 40.11; 100-4, Chap. 18, 10.2.1; 100-4, Chap. 18, 10.2.2.1; 100-4, Chap. 18, 10.2.5.2; 100-4, Chap. 18, 10.3.1.1; 100-4, Chap. 18, 10.4.1; 100-4, Chap. 18, 10.4.2; 100-4, Chap. 18, 10.4.3

C **G0009** Administration of pneumococcal vaccine   S
  BETOS: O1G   Influenza immunization
  Coding Clinic: 2016, Q4
  Pub: 100-4, Chap. 18, 10.2.2.1

C **G0010** Administration of hepatitis B vaccine   S
  BETOS: O1G   Influenza immunization
  Coding Clinic: 2016, Q4
  Pub: 100-4, Chap. 18, 10.2.2.1

ANALYSIS OF SEMEN SPECIMEN (G0027)

C **G0027** Semen analysis; presence and/or motility of sperm excluding huhner   ♂ Q4
  BETOS: T1H   Lab tests - other (non-Medicare fee schedule)
  Price subject to national limitation amount

SCREENING EXAMINATIONS AND DISEASE MANAGEMENT TRAINING (G0101-G0124)

D **G0101** Cervical or vaginal cancer screening; pelvic and clinical breast examination   ♀ S MIPS
  BETOS: M1A   Office visits - new
  Coding Clinic: 2001, Q3; 2002, Q4; 2008, Q3
  Price established using national RVUs

D **G0102** Prostate cancer screening; digital rectal examination   ♂ N MIPS
  BETOS: Y1   Other - Medicare fee schedule
  Price established using national RVUs

D **G0103** Prostate cancer screening; prostate specific antigen test (PSA)   ♂ A
  BETOS: T1H   Lab tests - other (non-Medicare fee schedule)
  Price subject to national limitation amount

D **G0104** Colorectal cancer screening; flexible sigmoidoscopy   T MIPS
  BETOS: P8C   Endoscopy - sigmoidoscopy
  Coding Clinic: 2011, 2011
  Pub: 100-4, Chap. 18, 60.1; 100-4, Chap. 18, 60.2; 100-4, Chap. 18, 60.6
  Price established using national RVUs

D **G0105** Colorectal cancer screening; colonoscopy on individual at high risk   T MIPS
  BETOS: P8D   Endoscopy - colonoscopy
  Coding Clinic: 2009, Q2

Pub: 100-4, Chap. 18, 60.1; 100-4, Chap. 18, 60.2; 100-4, Chap. 18, 60.6
  Price established using national RVUs

D **G0106** Colorectal cancer screening; alternative to G0104, screening sigmoidoscopy, barium enema   S MIPS
  BETOS: I1D   Standard imaging - contrast gastrointestinal
  Coding Clinic: 2011, 2011
  Pub: 100-4, Chap. 18, 60.1; 100-4, Chap. 18, 60.2; 100-4, Chap. 18, 60.6
  Price established using national RVUs

C **G0108** Diabetes outpatient self-management training services, individual, per 30 minutes   A MIPS
  BETOS: Y1   Other - Medicare fee schedule
  Pub: 100-2, Chap. 15, 270; 100-2, Chap. 15, 270.4.3; 100-2, Chap. 15, 300; 100-2, Chap. 15, 300.2; 100-2, Chap. 15, 300.3; 100-2, Chap. 15, 300.4; 100-4, Chap. 4, 300.6; 100-4, Chap. 9, 181; 100-4, Chap. 12, 190.3; 100-4, Chap. 12, 190.7; 100-4, Chap. 18, 120.1
  Price established using national RVUs

C **G0109** Diabetes outpatient self-management training services, group session (2 or more), per 30 minutes   A
  BETOS: Y1   Other - Medicare fee schedule
  Pub: 100-2, Chap. 15, 300.2; 100-4, Chap. 4, 300.6; 100-4, Chap. 9, 181
  Price established using national RVUs

C **G0117** Glaucoma screening for high risk patients furnished by an optometrist or ophthalmologist   S MIPS
  BETOS: T2D   Other tests - other
  Coding Clinic: 2001, Q3; 2002, Q1
  Pub: 100-2, Chap. 15, 280.1
  Price established using national RVUs

C **G0118** Glaucoma screening for high risk patient furnished under the direct supervision of an optometrist or ophthalmologist   S MIPS
  BETOS: T2D   Other tests - other
  Coding Clinic: 2001, Q3; 2002, Q1
  Pub: 100-2, Chap. 15, 280.1
  Price established using national RVUs

D **G0120** Colorectal cancer screening; alternative to G0105, screening colonoscopy, barium enema.   S MIPS
  BETOS: I1D   Standard imaging - contrast gastrointestinal
  Pub: 100-4, Chap. 18, 60.1; 100-4, Chap. 18, 60.2; 100-4, Chap. 18, 60.6
  Price established using national RVUs

D **G0121** Colorectal cancer screening; colonoscopy on individual not meeting criteria for high risk   T MIPS
  BETOS: I1D   Standard imaging - contrast gastrointestinal
  Coding Clinic: 2001, Q3

♂ Male only   ♀ Female only   Ⓐ Age   A2 - Z3 = ASC Payment indicator   A - Y = APC Status indicator
ASC = ASC-approved procedure   DME Paid under the DME fee schedule   MIPS MIPS code

Pub: 100-4, Chap. 18, 60.1; 100-4, Chap. 18, 60.2; 100-4, Chap. 18, 60.6
Price established using national RVUs

M G0122 Colorectal cancer screening; barium enema   E1 MIPS
BETOS: I1D   Standard imaging - contrast gastrointestinal
Service not separately priced by Part B
Pub: 100-4, Chap. 18, 60.2; 100-4, Chap. 18, 60.6

D G0123 Screening cytopathology, cervical or vaginal (any reporting system), collected in preservative fluid, automated thin layer preparation, screening by cytotechnologist under physician supervision   ♀ A
BETOS: T1H   Lab tests - other (non-Medicare fee schedule)
Price subject to national limitation amount

D G0124 Screening cytopathology, cervical or vaginal (any reporting system), collected in preservative fluid, automated thin layer preparation, requiring interpretation by physician   ♀ B
BETOS: T1H   Lab tests - other (non-Medicare fee schedule)
Price established using national RVUs

MISCELLANEOUS DIAGNOSTIC AND THERAPEUTIC SERVICES (G0127-G0372)

D G0127 Trimming of dystrophic nails, any number Q1
BETOS: P5A   Ambulatory procedures - skin
Pub: 100-2, Chap. 15, 290
Price established using national RVUs

D G0128 Direct (face-to-face with patient) skilled nursing services of a registered nurse provided in a comprehensive outpatient rehabilitation facility, each 10 minutes beyond the first 5 minutes   B
BETOS: Y2   Other - non-Medicare fee schedule
Value not established
Statute: 1833(a)
Pub: 100-2, Chap. 12, 30.1; 100-2, Chap. 12, 40.8; 100-4, Chap. 5, 20.4

C G0129 Occupational therapy services requiring the skills of a qualified occupational therapist, furnished as a component of a partial hospitalization treatment program, per session (45 minutes or more)   P
BETOS: Y1   Other - Medicare fee schedule
Service not separately priced by Part B
Coding Clinic: 2012, Q4

D G0130 Single energy X-ray absorptiometry (SEXA) bone density study, one or more sites; appendicular skeleton (peripheral) (e.g., radius, wrist, heel)   Z3 ASC S
BETOS: I4B   Imaging/procedure - other
Price established using national RVUs

C G0141 Screening cytopathology smears, cervical or vaginal, performed by automated system, with manual rescreening, requiring interpretation by physician   ♀ B
BETOS: T1H   Lab tests - other (non-Medicare fee schedule)
Price established using national RVUs

C G0143 Screening cytopathology, cervical or vaginal (any reporting system), collected in preservative fluid, automated thin layer preparation, with manual screening and rescreening by cytotechnologist under physician supervision   ♀ A
BETOS: T1H   Lab tests - other (non-Medicare fee schedule)
Price subject to national limitation amount

C G0144 Screening cytopathology, cervical or vaginal (any reporting system), collected in preservative fluid, automated thin layer preparation, with screening by automated system, under physician supervision   ♀ A
BETOS: T1H   Lab tests - other (non-Medicare fee schedule)
Price subject to national limitation amount

C G0145 Screening cytopathology, cervical or vaginal (any reporting system), collected in preservative fluid, automated thin layer preparation, with screening by automated system and manual rescreening under physician supervision   ♀ A
BETOS: T1H   Lab tests - other (non-Medicare fee schedule)
Price subject to national limitation amount

C G0147 Screening cytopathology smears, cervical or vaginal, performed by automated system under physician supervision   ♀ A
BETOS: T1H   Lab tests - other (non-Medicare fee schedule)
Price subject to national limitation amount

C G0148 Screening cytopathology smears, cervical or vaginal, performed by automated system with manual rescreening   ♀ A
BETOS: T1H   Lab tests - other (non-Medicare fee schedule)
Price subject to national limitation amount

C G0151 Services performed by a qualified physical therapist in the home health or hospice setting, each 15 minutes   B
BETOS: Y2   Other - non-Medicare fee schedule
Service not separately priced by Part B

C G0152 Services performed by a qualified occupational therapist in the home health or hospice setting, each 15 minutes   B
BETOS: Y2   Other - non-Medicare fee schedule
Service not separately priced by Part B

▲ Revised code   ● New code   C Carrier judgment   D Special coverage instructions apply
I Not payable by Medicare   M Non-covered by Medicare   S Non-covered by Medicare statute   AHA Coding Clinic®

C **G0153** Services performed by a qualified speech-language pathologist in the home health or hospice setting, each 15 minutes   B

> **BETOS:** Y2   Other - non-Medicare fee schedule
> Service not separately priced by Part B

C **G0155** Services of clinical social worker in home health or hospice settings, each 15 minutes B

> **BETOS:** Y2   Other - non-Medicare fee schedule
> Service not separately priced by Part B

C **G0156** Services of home health/hospice aide in home health or hospice settings, each 15 minutes   B

> **BETOS:** Y2   Other - non-Medicare fee schedule
> Service not separately priced by Part B

C **G0157** Services performed by a qualified physical therapist assistant in the home health or hospice setting, each 15 minutes   B

> **BETOS:** Y2   Other - non-Medicare fee schedule
> Service not separately priced by Part B

C **G0158** Services performed by a qualified occupational therapist assistant in the home health or hospice setting, each 15 minutes   B

> **BETOS:** Y2   Other - non-Medicare fee schedule
> Service not separately priced by Part B

C **G0159** Services performed by a qualified physical therapist, in the home health setting, in the establishment or delivery of a safe and effective physical therapy maintenance program, each 15 minutes   B

> **BETOS:** Y2   Other - non-Medicare fee schedule
> Service not separately priced by Part B

C **G0160** Services performed by a qualified occupational therapist, in the home health setting, in the establishment or delivery of a safe and effective occupational therapy maintenance program, each 15 minutes   B

> **BETOS:** Y2   Other - non-Medicare fee schedule
> Service not separately priced by Part B
> **Pub:** 100-4, Chap. 10, 40.2

C **G0161** Services performed by a qualified speech-language pathologist, in the home health setting, in the establishment or delivery of a safe and effective speech-language pathology maintenance program, each 15 minutes   B

> **BETOS:** Y2   Other - non-Medicare fee schedule
> Service not separately priced by Part B

C **G0162** Skilled services by a registered nurse (RN) for management and evaluation of the plan of care; each 15 minutes (the patient's underlying condition or complication requires an RN to ensure that essential non-skilled care achieves its purpose in the home health or hospice setting)   B

> **BETOS:** Y2   Other - non-Medicare fee schedule
> Service not separately priced by Part B

D **G0166** External counterpulsation, per treatment session   Q1

> **BETOS:** P6C   Minor procedures - other (Medicare fee schedule)
> **Pub:** 100-4, Chap. 32, 130; 100-4, Chap. 32, 130.1
> Price established using national RVUs

C **G0168** Wound closure utilizing tissue adhesive(s) only   B MIPS

> **BETOS:** P6C   Minor procedures - other (Medicare fee schedule)
> Service not separately priced by Part B
> **Coding Clinic:** 2001, Q3; 2001, Q4; 2005, Q1

C **G0175** Scheduled interdisciplinary team conference (minimum of three exclusive of patient care nursing staff) with patient present   V

> **BETOS:** M6   Consultations
> Service not separately priced by Part B
> **Coding Clinic:** 2001, Q3; 2006, Q4

D **G0176** Activity therapy, such as music, dance, art or play therapies not for recreation, related to the care and treatment of patient's disabling mental health problems, per session (45 minutes or more)   P

> **BETOS:** Y2   Other - non-Medicare fee schedule
> Service not separately priced by Part B
> **Coding Clinic:** 2012, Q4

D **G0177** Training and educational services related to the care and treatment of patient's disabling mental health problems per session (45 minutes or more)   N

> **BETOS:** Y2   Other - non-Medicare fee schedule
> Service not separately priced by Part B
> **Coding Clinic:** 2012, Q4
> **Pub:** 100-1, Chap. 3, 30

C **G0179** Physician re-certification for Medicare-covered home health services under a home health plan of care (patient not present), including contacts with home health agency and review of reports of patient status required by physicians to affirm the initial implementation of the plan of care that meets patient's needs, per re-certification period   M

> **BETOS:** Y1   Other - Medicare fee schedule
> **Pub:** 100-4, Chap. 11, 40.1.3.1; 100-4, Chap. 12, 180; 100-4, Chap. 12, 180.1
> Price established using national RVUs

♂ Male only   ♀ Female only   🅐 Age   A2 - Z3 = ASC Payment indicator   A - Y = APC Status indicator
ASC = ASC-approved procedure   **DME** Paid under the DME fee schedule   **MIPS** MIPS code

C **G0180** Physician certification for Medicare-covered home health services under a home health plan of care (patient not present), including contacts with home health agency and review of reports of patient status required by physicians to affirm the initial implementation of the plan of care that meets patient's needs, per certification period M

BETOS: Y1 Other - Medicare fee schedule
Pub: 100-4, Chap. 11, 40.1.3.1; 100-4, Chap. 12, 180; 100-4, Chap. 12, 180.1
Price established using national RVUs

C **G0181** Physician supervision of a patient receiving Medicare-covered services provided by a participating home health agency (patient not present) requiring complex and multidisciplinary care modalities involving regular physician development and/or revision of care plans, review of subsequent reports of patient status, review of laboratory and other studies, communication (including telephone calls) with other health care professionals involved in the patient's care, integration of new information into the medical treatment plan and/or adjustment of medical therapy, within a calendar month, 30 minutes or more M

BETOS: Y1 Other - Medicare fee schedule
Pub: 100-4, Chap. 11, 40.1.3.1; 100-4, Chap. 12, 180; 100-4, Chap. 12, 180.1
Price established using national RVUs

C **G0182** Physician supervision of a patient under a Medicare-approved hospice (patient not present) requiring complex and multidisciplinary care modalities involving regular physician development and/or revision of care plans, review of subsequent reports of patient status, review of laboratory and other studies, communication (including telephone calls) with other health care professionals involved in the patient's care, integration of new information into the medical treatment plan and/or adjustment of medical therapy, within a calendar month, 30 minutes or more M

BETOS: Y1 Other - Medicare fee schedule
Pub: 100-4, Chap. 11, 40.1.3.1; 100-4, Chap. 12, 180; 100-4, Chap. 12, 180.1
Price established using national RVUs

C **G0186** Destruction of localized lesion of choroid (for example, choroidal neovascularization); photocoagulation, feeder vessel technique (one or more sessions) T

BETOS: P4D Eye procedure - treatment of retinal lesions
Service not separately priced by Part B

M **G0219** PET imaging whole body; melanoma for non-covered indications E1

BETOS: I4B Imaging/procedure - other
Service not separately priced by Part B

Coding Clinic: 2001, Q2; 2002, Q1; 2007, Q1
Pub: 100-3, Chap. 1, Part-4, 220.6.17

M **G0235** PET imaging, any site, not otherwise specified E1

BETOS: T2D Other tests - other
Service not separately priced by Part B
Coding Clinic: 2007, Q1
Pub: 100-3, Chap. 1, Part-4, 220.6.17; 100-4, Chap. 13, 60

C **G0237** Therapeutic procedures to increase strength or endurance of respiratory muscles, face to face, one on one, each 15 minutes (includes monitoring) S

BETOS: P6C Minor procedures - other (Medicare fee schedule)
Coding Clinic: 2002, Q1
Pub: 100-2, Chap. 12, 30.1; 100-2, Chap. 12, 40.5
Price established using national RVUs

C **G0238** Therapeutic procedures to improve respiratory function, other than described by G0237, one on one, face to face, per 15 minutes (includes monitoring) S

BETOS: P6C Minor procedures - other (Medicare fee schedule)
Coding Clinic: 2002, Q1
Pub: 100-2, Chap. 12, 40.5
Price established using national RVUs

C **G0239** Therapeutic procedures to improve respiratory function or increase strength or endurance of respiratory muscles, two or more individuals (includes monitoring) S

BETOS: P6C Minor procedures - other (Medicare fee schedule)
Coding Clinic: 2002, Q1
Pub: 100-2, Chap. 12, 40.5
Price established using national RVUs

D **G0245** Initial physician evaluation and management of a diabetic patient with diabetic sensory neuropathy resulting in a loss of protective sensation (LOPS) which must include: (1) the diagnosis of LOPS, (2) a patient history, (3) a physical examination that consists of at least the following elements: (a) visual inspection of the forefoot, hindfoot and toe web spaces, (b) evaluation of a protective sensation, (c) evaluation of foot structure and biomechanics, (d) evaluation of vascular status and skin integrity, and (e) evaluation and recommendation of footwear and (4) patient education V MIPS

BETOS: M1A Office visits - new
Coding Clinic: 2002, Q3; 2002, Q4
Pub: 100-4, Chap. 32, 80.2; 100-4, Chap. 32, 80.8
Price established using national RVUs

D **G0246** Follow-up physician evaluation and management of a diabetic patient with diabetic sensory neuropathy resulting in

---

▲ Revised code   ● New code   C Carrier judgment   D Special coverage instructions apply
I Not payable by Medicare   M Non-covered by Medicare   S Non-covered by Medicare statute   AHA Coding Clinic®

a loss of protective sensation (LOPS) to include at least the following: (1) a patient history, (2) a physical examination that includes: (a) visual inspection of the forefoot, hindfoot and toe web spaces, (b) evaluation of protective sensation, (c) evaluation of foot structure and biomechanics, (d) evaluation of vascular status and skin integrity, and (e) evaluation and recommendation of footwear, and (3) patient education   V MIPS

BETOS: M1B   Office visits - established
Coding Clinic: 2002, Q4
Pub: 100-4, Chap. 32, 80.2; 100-4, Chap. 32, 80.8
Price established using national RVUs

D G0247 Routine foot care by a physician of a diabetic patient with diabetic sensory neuropathy resulting in a loss of protective sensation (LOPS) to include, the local care of superficial wounds (i.e. superficial to muscle and fascia) and at least the following if present: (1) local care of superficial wounds, (2) debridement of corns and calluses, and (3) trimming and debridement of nails Q1 MIPS

BETOS: M1B   Office visits - established
Coding Clinic: 2002, Q4
Pub: 100-4, Chap. 32, 80.8
Price established using national RVUs

D G0248 Demonstration, prior to initiation of home INR monitoring, for patient with either mechanical heart valve(s), chronic atrial fibrillation, or venous thromboembolism who meets Medicare coverage criteria, under the direction of a physician; includes: face-to-face demonstration of use and care of the INR monitor, obtaining at least one blood sample, provision of instructions for reporting home INR test results, and documentation of patient's ability to perform testing and report results   V

BETOS: M1A   Office visits - new
Coding Clinic: 2002, Q4
Pub: 100-3, Chap. 1, Part 3, 190.11; 100-4, Chap. 32, 60.4.1
Price established using national RVUs

D G0249 Provision of test materials and equipment for home INR monitoring of patient with either mechanical heart valve(s), chronic atrial fibrillation, or venous thromboembolism who meets Medicare coverage criteria; includes: provision of materials for use in the home and reporting of test results to physician; testing not occurring more frequently than once a week; testing materials, billing units of service include 4 tests   V

BETOS: Y1   Other - Medicare fee schedule
Coding Clinic: 2002, Q4
Price established using national RVUs

D G0250 Physician review, interpretation, and patient management of home INR testing for patient with either mechanical heart valve(s), chronic atrial fibrillation, or venous thromboembolism who meets Medicare coverage criteria; testing not occurring more frequently than once a week; billing units of service include 4 tests   M

BETOS: M1B   Office visits - established
Coding Clinic: 2002, Q3; 2002, Q4
Price established using national RVUs

M G0252 PET imaging, full and partial-ring PET scanners only, for initial diagnosis of breast cancer and/or surgical planning for breast cancer (e.g., initial staging of axillary lymph nodes)   E1

BETOS: I2D   Advanced imaging - MRI/MRA: other
Service not separately priced by Part B
Coding Clinic: 2002, Q4; 2006, Q1; 2007, Q1
Pub: 100-4, Chap. 13, 60

M G0255 Current perception threshold/sensory nerve conduction test, (SNCT) per limb, any nerve E1

BETOS: T2D   Other tests - other
Service not separately priced by Part B
Coding Clinic: 2002, Q4

D G0257 Unscheduled or emergency dialysis treatment for an ESRD patient in a hospital outpatient department that is not certified as an ESRD facility   S

BETOS: P6D   Minor procedures - other (non-Medicare fee schedule)
Service not separately priced by Part B
Coding Clinic: 2014, Q3
Pub: 100-4, Chap. 4, 200.2; 100-4, Chap. 8, 60.4.7

D G0259 Injection procedure for sacroiliac joint; arthrography   N

BETOS: O1E   Other drugs
Service not separately priced by Part B
Coding Clinic: 2002, Q4

D G0260 Injection procedure for sacroiliac joint; provision of anesthetic, steroid and/or other therapeutic agent, with or without arthrography   T

BETOS: O1E   Other drugs
Service not separately priced by Part B
Coding Clinic: 2002, Q4

C G0268 Removal of impacted cerumen (one or both ears) by physician on same date of service as audiologic function testing   N

BETOS: P6C   Minor procedures - other (Medicare fee schedule)
Coding Clinic: 2016, Q2
Price established using national RVUs

D G0269 Placement of occlusive device into either a venous or arterial access site, post surgical or interventional procedure (e.g., angioseal plug, vascular plug)   N
BETOS: P6D   Minor procedures - other (non-Medicare fee schedule)
Service not separately priced by Part B
Coding Clinic: 2010, Q4; 2012, Q4

C G0270 Medical nutrition therapy; reassessment and subsequent intervention(s) following second referral in same year for change in diagnosis, medical condition or treatment regimen (including additional hours needed for renal disease), individual, face to face with the patient, each 15 minutes   A MIPS
BETOS: M5D   Specialist - other
Pub: 100-2, Chap. 15, 270; 100-2, Chap. 15, 270.2; 100-4, Chap. 9, 182; 100-4, Chap. 12, 190.3; 100-4, Chap. 12, 190.7
Price established using national RVUs

C G0271 Medical nutrition therapy, reassessment and subsequent intervention(s) following second referral in same year for change in diagnosis, medical condition, or treatment regimen (including additional hours needed for renal disease), group (2 or more individuals), each 30 minutes   A MIPS
BETOS: M5D   Specialist - other
Pub: 100-4, Chap. 9, 182
Price established using national RVUs

D G0276 Blinded procedure for lumbar stenosis, percutaneous image-guided lumbar decompression (PILD) or placebo-control, performed in an approved coverage with evidence development (CED) clinical trial   J1
BETOS: P6D   Minor procedures - other (non-Medicare fee schedule)
Price established by carriers

D G0277 Hyperbaric oxygen under pressure, full body chamber, per 30 minute interval   S
BETOS: P5E   Ambulatory procedures - other
Price established by carriers

C G0278 Iliac and/or femoral artery angiography, non-selective, bilateral or ipsilateral to catheter insertion, performed at the same time as cardiac catheterization and/or coronary angiography, includes positioning or placement of the catheter in the distal aorta or ipsilateral femoral or iliac artery, injection of dye, production of permanent images, and radiologic supervision and interpretation (list separately in addition to primary procedure)   N MIPS
BETOS: I4A   Imaging/procedure - heart including cardiac catheterization
Coding Clinic: 2006, Q4
Price established using national RVUs

C G0279 Diagnostic digital breast tomosynthesis, unilateral or bilateral (list separately in addition to G0204 or G0206)   A
BETOS: I1C   Standard imaging - breast
Price established by carriers

C G0281 Electrical stimulation, (unattended), to one or more areas, for chronic Stage III and Stage IV pressure ulcers, arterial ulcers, diabetic ulcers, and venous stasis ulcers not demonstrating measurable signs of healing after 30 days of conventional care, as part of a therapy plan of care   A
BETOS: P5E   Ambulatory procedures - other
Coding Clinic: 2003, Q1; 2003, Q2
Pub: 100-4, Chap. 32, 11.1
Price established using national RVUs

M G0282 Electrical stimulation, (unattended), to one or more areas, for wound care other than described in G0281   E1
BETOS: P5E   Ambulatory procedures - other
Service not separately priced by Part B
Coding Clinic: 2003, Q1; 2003, Q2
Pub: 100-4, Chap. 32, 11.1

C G0283 Electrical stimulation (unattended), to one or more areas for indication(s) other than wound care, as part of a therapy plan of care   A
BETOS: P5E   Ambulatory procedures - other
Coding Clinic: 2003, Q1; 2003, Q2; 2009, Q2
Price established using national RVUs

C G0288 Reconstruction, computed tomographic angiography of aorta for surgical planning for vascular surgery   N
BETOS: I2B   Advanced imaging - CAT/CT/CTA: other
Price established using national RVUs

C G0289 Arthroscopy, knee, surgical, for removal of loose body, foreign body, debridement/shaving of articular cartilage (chondroplasty) at the time of other surgical knee arthroscopy in a different compartment of the same knee   N
BETOS: P8A   Endoscopy - arthroscopy
Coding Clinic: 2011, 2011; 2011, Q2
Price established using national RVUs

D G0293 Noncovered surgical procedure(s) using conscious sedation, regional, general or spinal anesthesia in a Medicare qualifying clinical trial, per day   Q1
BETOS: Y2   Other - non-Medicare fee schedule
Service not separately priced by Part B
Coding Clinic: 2002, Q4

D G0294 Noncovered procedure(s) using either no anesthesia or local anesthesia only, in a Medicare qualifying clinical trial, per day   Q1
BETOS: Y2   Other - non-Medicare fee schedule
Service not separately priced by Part B
Coding Clinic: 2002, Q4

▲ Revised code   ● New code   **C** Carrier judgment   **D** Special coverage instructions apply
I Not payable by Medicare   **M** Non-covered by Medicare   **S** Non-covered by Medicare statute   AHA Coding Clinic®

M **G0295** Electromagnetic therapy, to one or more areas, for wound care other than described in G0329 or for other uses   E1
BETOS: I2B   Advanced imaging - CAT/CT/CTA: other
Service not separately priced by Part B
Coding Clinic: 2003, Q1

C **G0296** Counseling visit to discuss need for lung cancer screening using low dose CT scan (LDCT) (service is for eligibility determination and shared decision making)   S
BETOS: M6   Consultations
Price established by carriers
Coding Clinic: 2005, Q2

C **G0297** Low dose CT scan (LDCT) for lung cancer screening   S MIPS
BETOS: I2B   Advanced imaging - CAT/CT/CTA: other
Price established by carriers
Coding Clinic: 2003, Q4; 2006, Q2; 2008, Q2

C **G0299** Direct skilled nursing services of a registered nurse (RN) in the home health or hospice setting, each 15 minutes   B
BETOS: M5D   Specialist - other
Service not separately priced by Part B
Coding Clinic: 2003, Q4; 2006, Q2; 2008, Q2

C **G0300** Direct skilled nursing services of a licensed practical nurse (LPN) in the home health or hospice setting, each 15 minutes   B
BETOS: M5D   Specialist - other
Service not separately priced by Part B
Coding Clinic: 2003, Q4; 2007, Q1; 2008, Q2

C **G0302** Pre-operative pulmonary surgery services for preparation for LVRS, complete course of services, to include a minimum of 16 days of services   S
BETOS: T2D   Other tests - other
Service not separately priced by Part B

C **G0303** Pre-operative pulmonary surgery services for preparation for LVRS, 10 to 15 days of services   S
BETOS: T2D   Other tests - other
Service not separately priced by Part B

C **G0304** Pre-operative pulmonary surgery services for preparation for LVRS, 1 to 9 days of services   S
BETOS: T2D   Other tests - other
Service not separately priced by Part B

C **G0305** Post-discharge pulmonary surgery services after LVRS, minimum of 6 days of services S
BETOS: T2D   Other tests - other
Service not separately priced by Part B

C **G0306** Complete CBC, automated (HgB, HCT, RBC, WBC, without platelet count) and automated WBC differential count   Q4
BETOS: T1D   Lab tests - blood counts
Price subject to national limitation amount

C **G0307** Complete (CBC), automated (HgB, HCT, RBC, WBC; without platelet count)   Q4
BETOS: T1D   Lab tests - blood counts
Price subject to national limitation amount

D **G0328** Colorectal cancer screening; fecal occult blood test, immunoassay, 1-3 simultaneous A
BETOS: T1H   Lab tests - other (non-Medicare fee schedule)
Price subject to national limitation amount
Coding Clinic: 2012, Q 2

C **G0329** Electromagnetic therapy, to one or more areas for chronic Stage III and Stage IV pressure ulcers, arterial ulcers, diabetic ulcers and venous stasis ulcers not demonstrating measurable signs of healing after 30 days of conventional care as part of a therapy plan of care   A
BETOS: I2B   Advanced imaging - CAT/CT/CTA: other
Service not separately priced by Part B
Pub: 100-4, Chap. 32, 11.2

D **G0333** Pharmacy dispensing fee for inhalation drug(s); initial 30-day supply as a beneficiary   M
BETOS: D1E   Other DME

C **G0337** Hospice evaluation and counseling services, pre-election   B
BETOS: M5D   Specialist - other
Pub: 100-4, Chap. 11, 10.1
Price established using national RVUs

C **G0339** Image-guided robotic linear accelerator-based stereotactic radiosurgery, complete course of therapy in one session or first session of fractionated treatment   B
BETOS: P5E   Ambulatory procedures - other
Price established by carriers
Coding Clinic: 2004, Q1
Pub: 100-4, Chap. 4, 200.3.4

C **G0340** Image-guided robotic linear accelerator-based stereotactic radiosurgery, delivery including collimator changes and custom plugging, fractionated treatment, all lesions, per session, second through fifth sessions, maximum five sessions per course of treatment   B
BETOS: P5E   Ambulatory procedures - other
Price established by carriers
Coding Clinic: 2004, Q1
Pub: 100-4, Chap. 4, 200.3.4

D **G0341** Percutaneous islet cell transplant, includes portal vein catheterization and infusion   C
BETOS: P1G   Major procedure - other
Price established by carriers

D **G0342** Laparoscopy for islet cell transplant, includes portal vein catheterization and infusion   C
BETOS: P1G   Major procedure - other
Price established by carriers

D **G0343** Laparotomy for islet cell transplant, includes portal vein catheterization and infusion   C

BETOS: P1G   Major procedure - other
Price established by carriers

C **G0365** Vessel mapping of vessels for hemodialysis access (services for preoperative vessel mapping prior to creation of hemodialysis access using an autogenous hemodialysis conduit, including arterial inflow and venous outflow)   S

BETOS: P9A   Dialysis services (Medicare fee schedule)
Price established using national RVUs

D **G0372** Physician service required to establish and document the need for a power mobility device   M

BETOS: M5D   Specialist - other
Price established by carriers
Pub: 100-4, Chap. 12, 30.6.15.4

HOSPITAL OBSERVATION AND EMERGENCY SERVICES (G0378-G0384)

D **G0378** Hospital observation service, per hour   N

BETOS: M2A   Hospital visit - initial
Service not separately priced by Part B
Coding Clinic: 2005, Q4; 2006, Q3; 2007, Q1
Pub: 100-2, Chap. 6, 20.6; 100-4, Chap. 1, 50.3.2; 100-4, Chap. 4, 290.1; 100-4, Chap. 4, 290.2.2; 100-4, Chap. 4, 290.4.1; 100-4, Chap. 4, 290.4.2; 100-4, Chap. 4, 290.4.3; 100-4, Chap. 4, 290.5.1; 100-4, Chap. 4, 290.5.2

D **G0379** Direct admission of patient for hospital observation care   J2

BETOS: M2A   Hospital visit - initial
Service not separately priced by Part B
Coding Clinic: 2005, Q4; 2007, Q1
Pub: 100-2, Chap. 6, 20.6; 100-4, Chap. 4, 290.4.1; 100-4, Chap. 4, 290.4.2; 100-4, Chap. 4, 290.4.3; 100-4, Chap. 4, 290.5.1; 100-4, Chap. 4, 290.5.2

C **G0380** Level 1 hospital emergency department visit provided in a type B emergency department; (the ED must meet at least one of the following requirements: (1) it is licensed by the state in which it is located under applicable state law as an emergency room or emergency department; (2) it is held out to the public (by name, posted signs, advertising, or other means) as a place that provides care for emergency medical conditions on an urgent basis without requiring a previously scheduled appointment; or (3) during the calendar year immediately preceding the calendar year in which a determination under 42 CFR 489.24 is being made, based on a representative sample of patient visits that occurred during that calendar year, it provides at least one-third of all of its outpatient visits for the treatment of emergency medical conditions on an urgent basis without requiring a previously scheduled appointment)   J2

BETOS: M3   Emergency room visit
Service not separately priced by Part B
Coding Clinic: 2013, Q4
Pub: 100-4, Chap. 4, 160

C **G0381** Level 2 hospital emergency department visit provided in a type B emergency department; (the ED must meet at least one of the following requirements: (1) it is licensed by the state in which it is located under applicable state law as an emergency room or emergency department; (2) it is held out to the public (by name, posted signs, advertising, or other means) as a place that provides care for emergency medical conditions on an urgent basis without requiring a previously scheduled appointment; or (3) during the calendar year immediately preceding the calendar year in which a determination under 42 CFR 489.24 is being made, based on a representative sample of patient visits that occurred during that calendar year, it provides at least one-third of all of its outpatient visits for the treatment of emergency medical conditions on an urgent basis without requiring a previously scheduled appointment)   J2

BETOS: M3   Emergency room visit
Service not separately priced by Part B
Coding Clinic: 2013, Q4
Pub: 100-4, Chap. 4, 160

C **G0382** Level 3 hospital emergency department visit provided in a type B emergency department; (the ED must meet at least one of the following requirements: (1) it is licensed by the state in which it is located under applicable state law as an emergency room or emergency department; (2) it is held out to the public (by name, posted signs, advertising, or other means) as a place that provides care for emergency medical conditions on an urgent basis without requiring a previously scheduled appointment; or (3) during the calendar year immediately preceding the calendar year in which a determination under 42 CFR 489.24 is being made, based on a representative sample of patient visits that occurred during that calendar year, it provides at least one-third of all of its outpatient visits for the treatment of emergency medical conditions on an urgent basis without requiring a previously scheduled appointment)   J2

BETOS: M3   Emergency room visit
Service not separately priced by Part B
Coding Clinic: 2013, Q4
Pub: 100-4, Chap. 4, 160

C **G0383** Level 4 hospital emergency department visit provided in a type B emergency department; (the ED must meet at least one of the following requirements: (1) it is licensed by the state in which it is located under applicable state law as an emergency room or emergency department; (2) it is held out to the public (by name, posted signs, advertising, or other means) as a place that provides care for emergency medical conditions on an urgent basis without requiring a previously scheduled appointment; or (3) during the calendar year immediately preceding the calendar year in which a determination under 42 CFR 489.24 is being made, based on a representative sample of patient visits that occurred during that calendar year, it provides at least one-third of all of its outpatient visits for the treatment of emergency medical conditions on an urgent basis without requiring a previously scheduled appointment)   J2
BETOS: M3   Emergency room visit
Service not separately priced by Part B
Coding Clinic: 2013, Q4
Pub: 100-4, Chap. 4, 160

C **G0384** Level 5 hospital emergency department visit provided in a type B emergency department; (the ED must meet at least one of the following requirements: (1) it is licensed by the state in which it is located under applicable state law as an emergency room or emergency department; (2) it is held out to the public (by name, posted signs, advertising, or other means) as a place that provides care for emergency medical conditions on an urgent basis without requiring a previously scheduled appointment; or (3) during the calendar year immediately preceding the calendar year in which a determination under 42 CFR 489.24 is being made, based on a representative sample of patient visits that occurred during that calendar year, it provides at least one-third of all of its outpatient visits for the treatment of emergency medical conditions on an urgent basis without requiring a previously scheduled appointment)   J2
BETOS: M3   Emergency room visit
Service not separately priced by Part B
Coding Clinic: 2013, Q4
Pub: 100-4, Chap. 4, 160; 100-4, Chap. 4, 290.5.1

OTHER EMERGENCY SERVICES (G0390)

D **G0390** Trauma response team associated with hospital critical care service   S
BETOS: M5D   Specialist - other
Service not separately priced by Part B
Coding Clinic: 2006, Q4; 2007, Q2
Pub: 100-4, Chap. 4, 160.1

ALCOHOL AND SUBSTANCE ABUSE ASSESSMENTS (G0396, G0397)

C **G0396** Alcohol and/or substance (other than tobacco) abuse structured assessment (e.g., audit, dast), and brief intervention 15 to 30 minutes   S MIPS
BETOS: M5D   Specialist - other
Coding Clinic: 2007, Q4
Pub: 100-2, Chap. 15, 270; 100-2, Chap. 15, 270.2; 100-4, Chap. 4, 200.6; 100-4, Chap. 12, 190.3; 100-4, Chap. 12, 190.7
Price established using national RVUs

C **G0397** Alcohol and/or substance (other than tobacco) abuse structured assessment (e.g., audit, dast), and intervention, greater than 30 minutes   S MIPS
BETOS: M5D   Specialist - other
Pub: 100-4, Chap. 4, 200.6
Price established using national RVUs

SLEEP STUDIES, IN HOME (G0398-G0400)

C **G0398** Home sleep study test (HST) with type II portable monitor, unattended; minimum of 7 channels: EEG, EOG, EMG, ECG/heart rate, airflow, respiratory effort and oxygen saturation   S
BETOS: T2D   Other tests - other
Price established by carriers
Coding Clinic: 2008, Q3
Pub: 100-3, Chap. 1, Part-4, 240.4

C **G0399** Home sleep test (HST) with type III portable monitor, unattended; minimum of 4 channels: 2 respiratory movement/airflow, 1 ECG/heart rate and 1 oxygen saturation   S
BETOS: T2D   Other tests - other
Price established by carriers
Coding Clinic: 2008, Q3

C **G0400** Home sleep test (HST) with type IV portable monitor, unattended; minimum of 3 channels   S
BETOS: T2D   Other tests - other
Price established by carriers
Coding Clinic: 2008, Q3

INITIAL SERVICES FOR MEDICARE ENROLLMENT (G0402-G0405)

C **G0402** Initial preventive physical examination; face-to-face visit, services limited to new beneficiary during the first 12 months of Medicare enrollment   V MIPS
BETOS: M1A   Office visits - new
Coding Clinic: 2008, Q4; 2009, Q4
Pub: 100-4, Chap. 9, 150; 100-4, Chap. 12, 80.1; 100-4, Chap. 12, 100.1.1; 100-4, Chap. 18, 80; 100-4, Chap. 18, 80.1; 100-4, Chap. 18, 80.2; 100-4, Chap. 18, 80.3.3; 100-4, Chap. 18, 80.4; 100-4, Chap. 18, 140.6
Price established using national RVUs

♂ Male only   ♀ Female only   🅐 Age   A2 - Z3 = ASC Payment indicator   A - Y = APC Status indicator
ASC = ASC-approved procedure   **DME** Paid under the DME fee schedule   **MIPS** MIPS code

C **G0403** Electrocardiogram, routine ECG with 12 leads; performed as a screening for the initial preventive physical examination with interpretation and report   M

BETOS: T2C   Other tests - EKG monitoring

Coding Clinic: 2008, Q4

Price established using national RVUs

C **G0404** Electrocardiogram, routine ECG with 12 leads; tracing only, without interpretation and report, performed as a screening for the initial preventive physical examination   S

BETOS: T2C   Other tests - EKG monitoring

Coding Clinic: 2008, Q4

Pub: 100-4, Chap. 18, 80.3.3

Price established using national RVUs

C **G0405** Electrocardiogram, routine ECG with 12 leads; interpretation and report only, performed as a screening for the initial preventive physical examination   B

BETOS: T2C   Other tests - EKG monitoring

Coding Clinic: 2008, Q4

Price established using national RVUs

FOLLOW-UP TELEHEALTH CONSULTATIONS (G0406-G0408), SEE ALSO INITIAL TELEHEALTH CONSULTATIONS (G0425-G0427)

C **G0406** Follow-up inpatient consultation, limited, physicians typically spend 15 minutes communicating with the patient via telehealth   B MIPS

BETOS: M6   Consultations

Price established by carriers

Coding Clinic: 2008, Q4

Pub: 100-2, Chap. 15, 270; 100-2, Chap. 15, 270.2; 100-4, Chap. 12, 190.3; 100-4, Chap. 12, 190.3.1; 100-4, Chap. 12, 190.3.3; 100-4, Chap. 12, 190.7

C **G0407** Follow-up inpatient consultation, intermediate, physicians typically spend 25 minutes communicating with the patient via telehealth   B MIPS

BETOS: M6   Consultations

Coding Clinic: 2008, Q4

Price established using national RVUs

C **G0408** Follow-up inpatient consultation, complex, physicians typically spend 35 minutes communicating with the patient via telehealth   B MIPS

BETOS: M6   Consultations

Coding Clinic: 2008, Q4

Price established using national RVUs

PSYCHOLOGICAL SERVICES (G0409-G0411)

C **G0409** Social work and psychological services, directly relating to and/or furthering the patient's rehabilitation goals, each 15 minutes, face-to-face; individual (services

provided by a CORF-qualified social worker or psychologist in a CORF)   B

BETOS: M5D   Specialist - other

Price established by carriers

Coding Clinic: 2008, Q4

Pub: 100-2, Chap. 12, 30.1; 100-4, Chap. 5, 100.4; 100-4, Chap. 5, 100.11

C **G0410** Group psychotherapy other than of a multiple-family group, in a partial hospitalization setting, approximately 45 to 50 minutes   P

BETOS: P6D   Minor procedures - other (non-Medicare fee schedule)

Price established by carriers

Coding Clinic: 2012, Q4

C **G0411** Interactive group psychotherapy, in a partial hospitalization setting, approximately 45 to 50 minutes   P

BETOS: P6D   Minor procedures - other (non-Medicare fee schedule)

Price established by carriers

Coding Clinic: 2012, Q4

FRACTURE TREATMENT (G0412-G0415)

C **G0412** Open treatment of iliac spine(s), tuberosity avulsion, or iliac wing fracture(s), unilateral or bilateral for pelvic bone fracture patterns which do not disrupt the pelvic ring includes internal fixation, when performed   C

BETOS: P3D   Major procedure, orthopedic - other

Price established by carriers

Coding Clinic: 2008, Q4

C **G0413** Percutaneous skeletal fixation of posterior pelvic bone fracture and/or dislocation, for fracture patterns which disrupt the pelvic ring, unilateral or bilateral, (includes ilium, sacroiliac joint and/or sacrum)   J1

BETOS: P3D   Major procedure, orthopedic - other

Price established by carriers

Coding Clinic: 2008, Q4

C **G0414** Open treatment of anterior pelvic bone fracture and/or dislocation for fracture patterns which disrupt the pelvic ring, unilateral or bilateral, includes internal fixation when performed (includes pubic symphysis and/or superior/inferior rami)   C

BETOS: P3D   Major procedure, orthopedic - other

Price established by carriers

Coding Clinic: 2008, Q4

C **G0415** Open treatment of posterior pelvic bone fracture and/or dislocation, for fracture patterns which disrupt the pelvic ring, unilateral or bilateral, includes internal fixation, when performed (includes ilium, sacroiliac joint and/or sacrum)   C

▲ Revised code   ● New code   C Carrier judgment   D Special coverage instructions apply

I Not payable by Medicare   M Non-covered by Medicare   S Non-covered by Medicare statute   AHA Coding Clinic®

BETOS: P3D   Major procedure, orthopedic - other
Price established by carriers
Coding Clinic: 2008, Q4

GROSS AND MICROSCOPIC EXAMINATIONS, PROSTATE BIOPSY (G0416)

C **G0416** Surgical pathology, gross and microscopic examinations, for prostate needle biopsy, any method   ♂ Q2
BETOS: T1G   Lab tests - other (Medicare fee schedule)
Price established by carriers
Coding Clinic: 2008, Q4

FACE-TO-FACE EDUCATIONAL SERVICES (G0420, G0421)

C **G0420** Face-to-face educational services related to the care of chronic kidney disease; individual, per session, per one hour   A
BETOS: M1B   Office visits - established
Pub: 100-2, Chap. 15, 270; 100-2, Chap. 15, 270.2; 100-2, Chap. 15, 310; 100-2, Chap. 15, 310.1; 100-2, Chap. 15, 310.2; 100-2, Chap. 15, 310.3; 100-2, Chap. 15, 310.4; 100-2, Chap. 15, 310.5; 100-4, Chap. 12, 190.3; 100-4, Chap. 12, 190.7
Price established using national RVUs

C **G0421** Face-to-face educational services related to the care of chronic kidney disease; group, per session, per one hour   A
BETOS: M1B   Office visits - established
Price established using national RVUs

CARDIAC AND PULMONARY REHABILITATION SERVICES (G0422-G0424)

C **G0422** Intensive cardiac rehabilitation; with or without continuous ECG monitoring with exercise, per session   S
BETOS: M5D   Specialist - other
Pub: 100-2, Chap. 15, 232; 100-4, Chap. 32, 140.2.2.1; 100-4, Chap. 32, 140.3; 100-4, Chap. 32, 140.3.1
Price established using national RVUs

C **G0423** Intensive cardiac rehabilitation; with or without continuous ECG monitoring; without exercise, per session   S
BETOS: M5D   Specialist - other
Pub: 100-4, Chap. 32, 140.3.1
Price established using national RVUs

C **G0424** Pulmonary rehabilitation, including exercise (includes monitoring), one hour, per session, up to two sessions per day   S
BETOS: M5D   Specialist - other
Pub: 100-2, Chap. 15, 231; 100-4, Chap. 32, 140.4; 100-4, Chap. 32, 140.4.1
Price established using national RVUs

INITIAL TELEHEALTH CONSULTATIONS (G0425-G0427), SEE ALSO FOLLOW-UP TELEHEALTH CONSULTATIONS (G0406-G0408)

C **G0425** Telehealth consultation, emergency department or initial inpatient, typically 30 minutes communicating with the patient via telehealth   B
BETOS: M6   Consultations
Price established by carriers
Pub: 100-2, Chap. 15, 270; 100-2, Chap. 15, 270.2; 100-4, Chap. 12, 190.3; 100-4, Chap. 12, 190.3.1; 100-4, Chap. 12, 190.3.2; 100-4, Chap. 12, 190.7

C **G0426** Telehealth consultation, emergency department or initial inpatient, typically 50 minutes communicating with the patient via telehealth   B
BETOS: M6   Consultations
Price established by carriers

C **G0427** Telehealth consultation, emergency department or initial inpatient, typically 70 minutes or more communicating with the patient via telehealth   B
BETOS: M6   Consultations
Price established by carriers

FILLER PROCEDURES (G0428, G0429)

M **G0428** Collagen meniscus implant procedure for filling meniscal defects (e.g., CMI, collagen scaffold, Menaflex)   E1
BETOS: P1G   Major procedure - other
Service not separately priced by Part B
Pub: 100-3, Chap. 1, Part 2, 150.12

C **G0429** Dermal filler injection(s) for the treatment of facial lipodystrophy syndrome (LDS) (e.g., as a result of highly active antiretroviral therapy)   T
BETOS: P6A   Minor procedures - skin
Price established by carriers
Coding Clinic: 2010, Q3
Pub: 100-3, Chap. 1, Part-4, 250.5; 100-4, Chap. 32, 260.1; 100-4, Chap. 32, 260.2.1; 100-4, Chap. 32, 260.2.2

LABORATORY SCREENING TESTS (G0432-G0435)

C **G0432** Infectious agent antibody detection by enzyme immunoassay (EIA) technique, HIV-1 and/or HIV-2, screening   A
BETOS: T1H   Lab tests - other (non-Medicare fee schedule)
Price subject to national limitation amount
Coding Clinic: 2010, Q1
Pub: 100-3, Chap. 1, Part 3, 190.14; 100-3, Chap. 1, Part-4, 210.7; 100-4, Chap. 18, 130, 130.1; 100-4, Chap. 18, 130, 130.4

C **G0433** Infectious agent antibody detection by enzyme-linked immunosorbent assay (ELISA) technique, HIV-1 and/or HIV-2, screening   A

♂ Male only   ♀ Female only   **A** Age   A2 - Z3 = ASC Payment indicator   A - Y = APC Status indicator
ASC = ASC-approved procedure   **DME** Paid under the DME fee schedule   **MIPS** MIPS code

BETOS: T1H   Lab tests - other (non-Medicare fee schedule)

Price subject to national limitation amount

Coding Clinic: 2010, Q1

Pub: 100-3, Chap. 1, Part-4, 210.7; 100-4, Chap. 16, 70.8; 100-4, Chap. 18, 130, 130.1; 100-4, Chap. 18, 130, 130.4

C G0435 Infectious agent antibody detection by rapid antibody test, HIV-1 and/or HIV-2, screening   A

BETOS: T1H   Lab tests - other (non-Medicare fee schedule)

Price subject to national limitation amount

Coding Clinic: 2010, Q1

Pub: 100-3, Chap. 1, Part-4, 210.7; 100-4, Chap. 18, 130, 130.1; 100-4, Chap. 18, 130, 130.4

COUNSELING, SCREENING, AND PREVENTION SERVICES (G0438-G0451)

C G0438 Annual wellness visit; includes a personalized prevention plan of service (PPPS), initial visit   A MIPS

BETOS: M5D   Specialist - other

Price established by carriers

Pub: 100-2, Chap. 15, 280.5; 100-4, Chap. 12, 100.1.1; 100-4, Chap. 18, 140; 100-4, Chap. 18, 140.1; 100-4, Chap. 18, 140.5; 100-4, Chap. 18, 140.6

C G0439 Annual wellness visit, includes a personalized prevention plan of service (PPPS), subsequent visit   A MIPS

BETOS: M5D   Specialist - other

Price established by carriers

Pub: 100-2, Chap. 15, 280.5; 100-4, Chap. 18, 140; 100-4, Chap. 18, 140.1; 100-4, Chap. 18, 140.5

C G0442 Annual alcohol misuse screening, 15 minutes   S MIPS

BETOS: Y1   Other - Medicare fee schedule

Price established by carriers

Coding Clinic: 2012, Q 1

Pub: 100-2, Chap. 15, 270; 100-2, Chap. 15, 270.2; 100-3, Chap. 1, Part-4, 210.8; 100-4, Chap. 12, 190.3; 100-4, Chap. 12, 190.7; 100-4, Chap. 18, 180; 100-4, Chap. 18, 180.1; 100-4, Chap. 18, 180.2; 100-4, Chap. 18, 180.3; 100-4, Chap. 18, 180.4; 100-4, Chap. 18, 180.5

C G0443 Brief face-to-face behavioral counseling for alcohol misuse, 15 minutes   S MIPS

BETOS: Y1   Other - Medicare fee schedule

Price established by carriers

Coding Clinic: 2012, Q 1

Pub: 100-4, Chap. 18, 180; 100-4, Chap. 18, 180.1; 100-4, Chap. 18, 180.2; 100-4, Chap. 18, 180.3; 100-4, Chap. 18, 180.4; 100-4, Chap. 18, 180.5

C G0444 Annual depression screening, 15 minutes   S MIPS

BETOS: Y1   Other - Medicare fee schedule

Price established by carriers

Pub: 100-4, Chap. 18, 190; 100-4, Chap. 18, 190.1; 100-4, Chap. 18, 190.2; 100-4, Chap. 18, 190.3

C G0445 High intensity behavioral counseling to prevent sexually transmitted infection; face-to-face, individual, includes: education, skills training and guidance on how to change sexual behavior; performed semi-annually, 30 minutes   S MIPS

BETOS: Y1   Other - Medicare fee schedule

Price established by carriers

Pub: 100-3, Chap. 1, Part-4, 210.10; 100-4, Chap. 18, 170.1; 100-4, Chap. 18, 170.2; 100-4, Chap. 18, 170.3; 100-4, Chap. 18, 170.4; 100-4, Chap. 18, 170.4.1; 100-4, Chap. 18, 170.5

C G0446 Annual, face-to-face intensive behavioral therapy for cardiovascular disease, individual, 15 minutes   S MIPS

BETOS: Y1   Other - Medicare fee schedule

Price established by carriers

Coding Clinic: 2012, Q 2

Pub: 100-3, Chap. 1, Part-4, 210.11; 100-4, Chap. 18, 160; 100-4, Chap. 18, 160.1; 100-4, Chap. 18, 160.2.1; 100-4, Chap. 18, 160.2.2; 100-4, Chap. 18, 160.3; 100-4, Chap. 18, 160.4; 100-4, Chap. 18, 160.5

C G0447 Face-to-face behavioral counseling for obesity, 15 minutes   S MIPS

BETOS: Y1   Other - Medicare fee schedule

Price established by carriers

Coding Clinic: 2012, Q 1

Pub: 100-3, Chap. 1, Part-4, 210.12; 100-4, Chap. 18, 200; 100-4, Chap. 18, 200.1; 100-4, Chap. 18, 200.2; 100-4, Chap. 18, 200.3; 100-4, Chap. 18, 200.4; 100-4, Chap. 18, 200.5

C G0448 Insertion or replacement of a permanent pacing cardioverter-defibrillator system with transvenous lead(s), single or dual chamber with insertion of pacing electrode, cardiac venous system, for left ventricular pacing   B

BETOS: Y1   Other - Medicare fee schedule

Price established by carriers

C G0451 Development testing, with interpretation and report, per standardized instrument form   Q3

BETOS: M5D   Specialist - other

Price established by carriers

Pub: 100-1, Chap. 3, 30

MISCELLANEOUS SERVICES (G0452-G0463)

C G0452 Molecular pathology procedure; physician interpretation and report   B

BETOS: T2D   Other tests - other

Price established by carriers

C G0453 Continuous intraoperative neurophysiology monitoring, from outside the operating room (remote or nearby), per patient, (attention directed exclusively to one patient) each 15 minutes (list in addition to primary procedure)   N

▲ Revised code   ● New code   C Carrier judgment   D Special coverage instructions apply
I Not payable by Medicare   M Non-covered by Medicare   S Non-covered by Medicare statute   AHA Coding Clinic®

BETOS: T2D   Other tests - other
Price established by carriers

C G0454 Physician documentation of face-to-face visit for durable medical equipment determination performed by nurse practitioner, physician assistant or clinical nurse specialist   B

BETOS: M5D   Specialist - other
Price established by carriers

C G0455 Preparation with instillation of fecal microbiota by any method, including assessment of donor specimen   Q1

BETOS: T2D   Other tests - other
Price established by carriers
Coding Clinic: 2013, Q3

C G0458 Low dose rate (LDR) prostate brachytherapy services, composite rate   ♂ B

BETOS: P7A   Oncology - radiation therapy
Service not separately priced by Part B

C G0459 Inpatient telehealth pharmacologic management, including prescription, use, and review of medication with no more than minimal medical psychotherapy   B

BETOS: M5D   Specialist - other
Price established by carriers
Pub: 100-2, Chap. 15, 270; 100-2, Chap. 15, 270.2; 100-4, Chap. 12, 190.3; 100-4, Chap. 12, 190.7

C G0460 Autologous platelet rich plasma for chronic wounds/ulcers, including phlebotomy, centrifugation, and all other preparatory procedures, administration and dressings, per treatment   T

BETOS: P5E   Ambulatory procedures - other
Price established by carriers
Pub: 100-3, Chap. 1, Part-4, 270.3; 100-4, Chap. 32, 11.3.1; 100-4, Chap. 32, 11.3.2; 100-4, Chap. 32, 11.3.3; 100-4, Chap. 32, 11.3.4; 100-4, Chap. 32, 11.3.5; 100-4, Chap. 32, 11.3.6

C G0463 Hospital outpatient clinic visit for assessment and management of a patient   J2

BETOS: M1B   Office visits - established
Service not separately priced by Part B
Coding Clinic: 2013, Q4; 2014, Q4

FEDERALLY QUALIFIED HEALTH CENTER (FQHC) VISITS (G0466-G0470)

C G0466 Federally qualified health center (FQHC) visit, new patient; a medically-necessary, face-to-face encounter (one-on-one) between a new patient and a FQHC practitioner during which time one or more FQHC services are rendered and includes a typical bundle of medicare-covered services that would be furnished per diem to a patient receiving a FQHC visit   A

BETOS: M1A   Office visits - new
Price established by carriers

C G0467 Federally qualified health center (FQHC) visit, established patient; a medically-necessary, face-to-face encounter (one-on-one) between an established patient and a FQHC practitioner during which time one or more FQHC services are rendered and includes a typical bundle of medicare-covered services that would be furnished per diem to a patient receiving a FQHC visit   A

BETOS: M1B   Office visits - established
Price established by carriers

C G0468 Federally qualified health center (FQHC) visit, IPPE or AWV; a FQHC visit that includes an initial preventive physical examination (IPPE) or annual wellness visit (AWV) and includes a typical bundle of medicare-covered services that would be furnished per diem to a patient receiving an IPPE or AWV   A

BETOS: M1B   Office visits - established
Price established by carriers

C G0469 Federally qualified health center (FQHC) visit, mental health, new patient; a medically-necessary, face-to-face mental health encounter (one-on-one) between a new patient and a FQHC practitioner during which time one or more FQHC services are rendered and includes a typical bundle of medicare-covered services that would be furnished per diem to a patient receiving a mental health visit   A

BETOS: M1A   Office visits - new
Price established by carriers

C G0470 Federally qualified health center (FQHC) visit, mental health, established patient; a medically-necessary, face-to-face mental health encounter (one-on-one) between an established patient and a FQHC practitioner during which time one or more FQHC services are rendered and includes a typical bundle of medicare-covered services that would be furnished per diem to a patient receiving a mental health visit   A

BETOS: M1B   Office visits - established
Price established by carriers

OTHER SERVICES (G0471-G0659)

C G0471 Collection of venous blood by venipuncture or urine sample by catheterization from an individual in a skilled nursing facility (SNF) or by a laboratory on behalf of a home health agency (HHA)   A

BETOS: Z2   Undefined codes
Price subject to national limitation amount

D G0472 Hepatitis C antibody screening, for individual at high risk and other covered indication(s) A

BETOS: P5E   Ambulatory procedures - other
Price established by carriers
Statute: 1861SSA

♂ Male only   ♀ Female only   **A** Age   A2 - Z3 = ASC Payment indicator   A - Y = APC Status indicator
ASC = ASC-approved procedure   **DME** Paid under the DME fee schedule   **MIPS** MIPS code

G0473 - G0491

PROCEDURES / PROFESSIONAL SERVICES (G0008-G9977)

C **G0473** Face-to-face behavioral counseling for obesity, group (2-10), 30 minutes   S

  BETOS: M1B   Office visits - established
  Price established by carriers

C **G0475** HIV antigen/antibody, combination assay, screening   A

  BETOS: T2D   Other tests - other
  Price established by carriers

C **G0476** Infectious agent detection by nucleic acid (DNA or RNA); human papillomavirus (HPV), high-risk types (e.g., 16, 18, 31, 33, 35, 39, 45, 51, 52, 56, 58, 59, 68) for cervical cancer screening, must be performed in addition to pap test   A

  BETOS: T2D   Other tests - other
  Price established by carriers

C **G0480** Drug test(s), definitive, utilizing (1) drug identification methods able to identify individual drugs and distinguish between structural isomers (but not necessarily stereoisomers), including, but not limited to GC/MS (any type, single or tandem) and LC/MS (any type, single or tandem and excluding immunoassays (e.g., IA, EIA, ELISA, EMIT, FPIA) and enzymatic methods (e.g., alcohol dehydrogenase)), (2) stable isotope or other universally recognized internal standards in all samples (e.g., to control for matrix effects, interferences and variations in signal strength), and (3) method or drug-specific calibration and matrix-matched quality control material (e.g., to control for instrument variations and mass spectral drift); qualitative or quantitative, all sources, includes specimen validity testing, per day; 1-7 drug class(es), including metabolite(s) if performed   Q4

  BETOS: T1H   Lab tests - other (non-Medicare fee schedule)
  Price subject to national limitation amount

C **G0481** Drug test(s), definitive, utilizing (1) drug identification methods able to identify individual drugs and distinguish between structural isomers (but not necessarily stereoisomers), including, but not limited to GC/MS (any type, single or tandem) and LC/MS (any type, single or tandem and excluding immunoassays (e.g., IA, EIA, ELISA, EMIT, FPIA) and enzymatic methods (e.g., alcohol dehydrogenase)), (2) stable isotope or other universally recognized internal standards in all samples (e.g., to control for matrix effects, interferences and variations in signal strength), and (3) method or drug-specific calibration and matrix-matched quality control material (e.g., to control for instrument variations and mass spectral drift); qualitative or quantitative, all sources, includes specimen validity testing, per day; 8-14 drug class(es), including metabolite(s) if performed   Q4

  BETOS: T1H   Lab tests - other (non-Medicare fee schedule)
  Price subject to national limitation amount

C **G0482** Drug test(s), definitive, utilizing (1) drug identification methods able to identify individual drugs and distinguish between structural isomers (but not necessarily stereoisomers), including, but not limited to GC/MS (any type, single or tandem) and LC/MS (any type, single or tandem and excluding immunoassays (e.g., IA, EIA, ELISA, EMIT, FPIA) and enzymatic methods (e.g., alcohol dehydrogenase)), (2) stable isotope or other universally recognized internal standards in all samples (e.g., to control for matrix effects, interferences and variations in signal strength), and (3) method or drug-specific calibration and matrix-matched quality control material (e.g., to control for instrument variations and mass spectral drift); qualitative or quantitative, all sources, includes specimen validity testing, per day; 15-21 drug class(es), including metabolite(s) if performed   Q4

  BETOS: T1H   Lab tests - other (non-Medicare fee schedule)
  Price subject to national limitation amount

C **G0483** Drug test(s), definitive, utilizing (1) drug identification methods able to identify individual drugs and distinguish between structural isomers (but not necessarily stereoisomers), including, but not limited to GC/MS (any type, single or tandem) and LC/MS (any type, single or tandem and excluding immunoassays (e.g., IA, EIA, ELISA, EMIT, FPIA) and enzymatic methods (e.g., alcohol dehydrogenase)), (2) stable isotope or other universally recognized internal standards in all samples (e.g., to control for matrix effects, interferences and variations in signal strength), and (3) method or drug-specific calibration and matrix-matched quality control material (e.g., to control for instrument variations and mass spectral drift); qualitative or quantitative, all sources, includes specimen validity testing, per day; 22 or more drug class(es), including metabolite(s) if performed   Q4

  BETOS: T1H   Lab tests - other (non-Medicare fee schedule)
  Price subject to national limitation amount

C **G0490** Face-to-face home health nursing visit by a rural health clinic (RHC) or federally qualified health center (FQHC) in an area with a shortage of home health agencies; (services limited to RN or LPN only)   A

  BETOS: M4A   Home visit
  Price established by carriers

C **G0491** Dialysis procedure at a medicare certified ESRD facility for acute kidney injury without ESRD   B

BETOS: P9A Dialysis services (Medicare fee schedule)
Price established by carriers

G0492 Dialysis procedure with single evaluation by a physician or other qualified health care professional for acute kidney injury without ESRD   B
BETOS: P9A Dialysis services (Medicare fee schedule)
Price established by carriers

G0493 Skilled services of a registered nurse (RN) for the observation and assessment of the patient's condition, each 15 minutes (the change in the patient's condition requires skilled nursing personnel to identify and evaluate the patient's need for possible modification of treatment in the home health or hospice setting)   B
BETOS: Y2 Other - non-Medicare fee schedule
Service not separately priced by Part B

G0494 Skilled services of a licensed practical nurse (LPN) for the observation and assessment of the patient's condition, each 15 minutes (the change in the patient's condition requires skilled nursing personnel to identify and evaluate the patient's need for possible modification of treatment in the home health or hospice setting)   B
BETOS: Y2 Other - non-Medicare fee schedule
Service not separately priced by Part B

G0495 Skilled services of a registered nurse (RN), in the training and/or education of a patient or family member, in the home health or hospice setting, each 15 minutes   B
BETOS: Y2 Other - non-Medicare fee schedule
Service not separately priced by Part B

G0496 Skilled services of a licensed practical nurse (LPN), in the training and/or education of a patient or family member, in the home health or hospice setting, each 15 minutes   B
BETOS: Y2 Other - non-Medicare fee schedule
Service not separately priced by Part B

G0498 Chemotherapy administration, intravenous infusion technique; initiation of infusion in the office/clinic setting using office/clinic pump/supplies, with continuation of the infusion in the community setting (e.g., home, domiciliary, rest home or assisted living) using a portable pump provided by the office/clinic, includes follow-up office/clinic visit at the conclusion of the infusion   S
BETOS: P7B Oncology - other
Price established by carriers
Coding Clinic: 2017, Q2

G0499 Hepatitis B screening in non-pregnant, high risk individual includes hepatitis B surface antigen (HBSAG) followed by a neutralizing confirmatory test for initially reactive results, and antibodies to HBSAG (anti-HBs) and Hepatitis B core antigen (anti-HBc)   A
BETOS: T1H Lab tests - other (non-Medicare fee schedule)
Price established by carriers

G0500 Moderate sedation services provided by the same physician or other qualified health care professional performing a gastrointestinal endoscopic service that sedation supports, requiring the presence of an independent trained observer to assist in the monitoring of the patient's level of consciousness and physiological status; initial 15 minutes of intra-service time; patient age 5 years or older (additional time may be reported with 99153, as appropriate)   N
BETOS: P0 Anesthesia
Price established by carriers

G0501 Resource-intensive services for patients for whom the use of specialized mobility-assistive technology (such as adjustable height chairs or tables, patient lift, and adjustable padded leg supports) is medically necessary and used during the provision of an office/outpatient, evaluation and management visit (list separately in addition to primary service)   N
BETOS: M5D Specialist - other
Price established by carriers

G0506 Comprehensive assessment of and care planning for patients requiring chronic care management services (list separately in addition to primary monthly care management service)   N
BETOS: M5D Specialist - other
Price established by carriers

G0508 Telehealth consultation, critical care, initial, physicians typically spend 60 minutes communicating with the patient and providers via telehealth   B
BETOS: M5D Specialist - other
Price established by carriers

G0509 Telehealth consultation, critical care, subsequent, physicians typically spend 50 minutes communicating with the patient and providers via telehealth   B
BETOS: M5D Specialist - other
Price established by carriers

● **D G0511** Rural health clinic or federally qualified health center (RHC or FQHC) only, general care management, 20 minutes or more of clinical staff time for chronic care management services or behavioral health integration services directed by an RHC or FQHC practitioner (physician, NP, PA, or CNM), per calendar month

---

♂ Male only   ♀ Female only   🅐 Age   A2 - Z3 = ASC Payment indicator   A - Y = APC Status indicator
ASC = ASC-approved procedure   **DME** Paid under the DME fee schedule   **MIPS** MIPS code

BETOS: M5D Specialist - other
Price established by carriers

● **D** **G0512** Rural health clinic or federally qualified health center (RHC or FQHC) only, psychiatric collaborative care model (psychiatric COCM), 60 minutes or more of clinical staff time for psychiatric COCM services directed by an RHC or FQHC practitioner (physician, NP, PA, or CNM) and including services furnished by a behavioral health care manager and consultation with a psychiatric consultant, per calendar month
BETOS: M5D Specialist - other
Price established by carriers

● **C** **G0513** Prolonged preventive service(s) (beyond the typical service time of the primary procedure), in the office or other outpatient setting requiring direct patient contact beyond the usual service; first 30 minutes (list separately in addition to code for preventive service)
BETOS: M5D Specialist - other
Price established by carriers

● **C** **G0514** Prolonged preventive service(s) (beyond the typical service time of the primary procedure), in the office or other outpatient setting requiring direct patient contact beyond the usual service; each additional 30 minutes (list separately in addition to code G0513 for additional 30 minutes of preventive service)
BETOS: M5D Specialist - other
Price established by carriers

● **C** **G0515** Development of cognitive skills to improve attention, memory, problem solving (includes compensatory training), direct (one-on-one) patient contact, each 15 minutes
BETOS: M5D Specialist - other
Price established using national RVUs

● **C** **G0516** Insertion of non-biodegradable drug delivery implants, 4 or more (services for subdermal rod implant)
BETOS: P6C Minor procedures - other (Medicare fee schedule)
Price established by carriers

● **C** **G0517** Removal of non-biodegradable drug delivery implants, 4 or more (services for subdermal implants)
BETOS: P6C Minor procedures - other (Medicare fee schedule)
Price established by carriers

● **C** **G0518** Removal with reinsertion, non-biodegradable drug delivery implants, 4 or more (services for subdermal implants)
BETOS: P6C Minor procedures - other (Medicare fee schedule)
Price established by carriers

C **G0659** Drug test(s), definitive, utilizing drug identification methods able to identify individual drugs and distinguish between structural isomers (but not necessarily stereoisomers), including but not limited to GC/MS (any type, single or tandem) and LC/MS (any type, single or tandem), excluding immunoassays (e.g., IA, EIA, ELISA, EMIT, FPIA) and enzymatic methods (e.g., alcohol dehydrogenase), performed without method or drug-specific calibration, without matrix-matched quality control material, or without use of stable isotope or other universally recognized internal standard(s) for each drug, drug metabolite or drug class per specimen; qualitative or quantitative, all sources, includes specimen validity testing, per day, any number of drug classes   Q4
BETOS: T1H Lab tests - other (non-Medicare fee schedule)
Price subject to national limitation amount

QUALITY MEASURES FOR CATARACT SURGERY (G0913-G0918)

C **G0913** Improvement in visual function achieved within 90 days following cataract surgery   M
BETOS: M5D Specialist - other
Service not separately priced by Part B

C **G0914** Patient care survey was not completed by patient   M
BETOS: M5D Specialist - other
Service not separately priced by Part B

C **G0915** Improvement in visual function not achieved within 90 days following cataract surgery   M
BETOS: M5D Specialist - other
Service not separately priced by Part B

C **G0916** Satisfaction with care achieved within 90 days following cataract surgery   M
BETOS: M5D Specialist - other
Service not separately priced by Part B

C **G0917** Patient satisfaction survey was not completed by patient   M
BETOS: M5D Specialist - other
Service not separately priced by Part B

C **G0918** Satisfaction with care not achieved within 90 days following cataract surgery   M
BETOS: M5D Specialist - other
Service not separately priced by Part B

RADIATION THERAPY SERVICES (G6001-G6017)

D **G6001** Ultrasonic guidance for placement of radiation therapy fields   B
BETOS: I3F Echography/ultrasonography - other
Price established by carriers

C **G6002** Stereoscopic X-ray guidance for localization of target volume for the delivery of radiation therapy   B
BETOS: I4B   Imaging/procedure - other
Price established by carriers

C **G6003** Radiation treatment delivery, single treatment area, single port or parallel opposed ports, simple blocks or no blocks: up to 5 MeV   B
BETOS: P7A   Oncology - radiation therapy
Price established by carriers

C **G6004** Radiation treatment delivery, single treatment area, single port or parallel opposed ports, simple blocks or no blocks: 6-10 MeV   B
BETOS: P7A   Oncology - radiation therapy
Price established by carriers

C **G6005** Radiation treatment delivery, single treatment area, single port or parallel opposed ports, simple blocks or no blocks: 11-19 MeV   B
BETOS: P7A   Oncology - radiation therapy
Price established by carriers

C **G6006** Radiation treatment delivery, single treatment area, single port or parallel opposed ports, simple blocks or no blocks: 20 MeV or greater   B
BETOS: P7A   Oncology - radiation therapy
Price established by carriers

C **G6007** Radiation treatment delivery, 2 separate treatment areas, 3 or more ports on a single treatment area, use of multiple blocks: up to 5 MeV   B
BETOS: P7A   Oncology - radiation therapy
Price established by carriers

C **G6008** Radiation treatment delivery, 2 separate treatment areas, 3 or more ports on a single treatment area, use of multiple blocks: 6-10 MeV   B
BETOS: P7A   Oncology - radiation therapy
Price established by carriers

C **G6009** Radiation treatment delivery, 2 separate treatment areas, 3 or more ports on a single treatment area, use of multiple blocks: 11-19 MeV   B
BETOS: P7A   Oncology - radiation therapy
Price established by carriers

C **G6010** Radiation treatment delivery, 2 separate treatment areas, 3 or more ports on a single treatment area, use of multiple blocks: 20 MeV or greater   B
BETOS: P7A   Oncology - radiation therapy
Price established by carriers

C **G6011** Radiation treatment delivery, 3 or more separate treatment areas, custom blocking, tangential ports, wedges, rotational beam, compensators, electron beam; up to 5 MeV B
BETOS: P7A   Oncology - radiation therapy
Price established by carriers

C **G6012** Radiation treatment delivery, 3 or more separate treatment areas, custom blocking, tangential ports, wedges, rotational beam, compensators, electron beam; 6-10 MeV   B
BETOS: P7A   Oncology - radiation therapy
Price established by carriers

C **G6013** Radiation treatment delivery, 3 or more separate treatment areas, custom blocking, tangential ports, wedges, rotational beam, compensators, electron beam; 11-19 MeV   B
BETOS: P7A   Oncology - radiation therapy
Price established by carriers

C **G6014** Radiation treatment delivery, 3 or more separate treatment areas, custom blocking, tangential ports, wedges, rotational beam, compensators, electron beam; 20 MeV or greater   B
BETOS: P7A   Oncology - radiation therapy
Price established by carriers

C **G6015** Intensity modulated treatment delivery, single or multiple fields/arcs, via narrow spatially and temporally modulated beams, binary, dynamic MLC, per treatment session   B
BETOS: P7A   Oncology - radiation therapy
Price established by carriers

C **G6016** Compensator-based beam modulation treatment delivery of inverse planned treatment using 3 or more high resolution (milled or cast) compensator, convergent beam modulated fields, per treatment session   B
BETOS: P7A   Oncology - radiation therapy
Price established by carriers

C **G6017** Intra-fraction localization and tracking of target or patient motion during delivery of radiation therapy (e.g., 3D positional tracking, gating, 3D surface tracking), each fraction of treatment   B
BETOS: P6C   Minor procedures - other (Medicare fee schedule)
Price established by carriers

ADDITIONAL QUALITY MEASURES (G8395-G8635)

C **G8395** Left ventricular ejection fraction (LVEF) >= 40% or documentation as normal or mildly depressed left ventricular systolic function   M
BETOS: M5D   Specialist - other
Service not separately priced by Part B

C **G8396** Left ventricular ejection fraction (LVEF) not performed or documented   M
BETOS: M5D   Specialist - other
Service not separately priced by Part B

C **G8397** Dilated macular or fundus exam performed, including documentation of the presence or absence of macular edema and level of severity of retinopathy   M MIPS
BETOS: M5D   Specialist - other
Service not separately priced by Part B

♂ Male only   ♀ Female only   🅐 Age   A2 - Z3 = ASC Payment indicator   A - Y = APC Status indicator
ASC = ASC-approved procedure   **DME** Paid under the DME fee schedule   **MIPS** MIPS code

C **G8398** Dilated macular or fundus exam not performed M [MIPS]
BETOS: M5D   Specialist - other
Service not separately priced by Part B

C **G8399** Patient with documented results of a central dual-energy X-ray absorptiometry (DXA) ever being performed M [MIPS]
BETOS: M5D   Specialist - other
Service not separately priced by Part B

C **G8400** Patient with central dual-energy X-ray absorptiometry (DXA) results not documented, reason not given M [MIPS]
BETOS: M5D   Specialist - other
Service not separately priced by Part B

C **G8404** Lower extremity neurological exam performed and documented M
BETOS: M5D   Specialist - other
Service not separately priced by Part B

C **G8405** Lower extremity neurological exam not performed M
BETOS: M5D   Specialist - other
Service not separately priced by Part B

C **G8410** Footwear evaluation performed and documented M
BETOS: M5D   Specialist - other
Service not separately priced by Part B

C **G8415** Footwear evaluation was not performed M
BETOS: M5D   Specialist - other
Service not separately priced by Part B

C **G8416** Clinician documented that patient was not an eligible candidate for footwear evaluation measure M
BETOS: M5D   Specialist - other
Service not separately priced by Part B

C **G8417** BMI is documented above normal parameters and a follow-up plan is documented M [MIPS]
BETOS: M5D   Specialist - other
Service not separately priced by Part B

C **G8418** BMI is documented below normal parameters and a follow-up plan is documented M [MIPS]
BETOS: M5D   Specialist - other
Service not separately priced by Part B

C **G8419** BMI documented outside normal parameters, no follow-up plan documented, no reason given M [MIPS]
BETOS: M5D   Specialist - other
Service not separately priced by Part B

C **G8420** BMI is documented within normal parameters and no follow-up plan is required M [MIPS]
BETOS: M5D   Specialist - other
Service not separately priced by Part B

C **G8421** BMI not documented and no reason is given M [MIPS]

BETOS: M5D   Specialist - other
Service not separately priced by Part B

C **G8422** BMI not documented, documentation the patient is not eligible for BMI calculation M [MIPS]
BETOS: M5D   Specialist - other
Service not separately priced by Part B

C **G8427** Eligible clinician attests to documenting in the medical record they obtained, updated, or reviewed the patient's current medications M [MIPS]
BETOS: M5D   Specialist - other
Service not separately priced by Part B

C **G8428** Current list of medications not documented as obtained, updated, or reviewed by the eligible clinician, reason not given M [MIPS]
BETOS: M5D   Specialist - other
Service not separately priced by Part B

C **G8430** Eligible clinician attests to documenting in the medical record the patient is not eligible for a current list of medications being obtained, updated, or reviewed by the eligible clinician M [MIPS]
BETOS: M5D   Specialist - other
Service not separately priced by Part B

C **G8431** Screening for depression is documented as being positive and a follow-up plan is documented M [MIPS]
BETOS: M5D   Specialist - other
Service not separately priced by Part B

C **G8432** Depression screening not documented, reason not given M [MIPS]
BETOS: M5D   Specialist - other
Service not separately priced by Part B

C **G8433** Screening for depression not completed, documented reason M [MIPS]
BETOS: M5D   Specialist - other
Service not separately priced by Part B

▲ C **G8442** Pain assessment not documented as being performed, documentation the patient is not eligible for a pain assessment using a standardized tool at the time of the encounter M [MIPS]
BETOS: M5D   Specialist - other
Service not separately priced by Part B

C **G8450** Beta-blocker therapy prescribed M
BETOS: M5D   Specialist - other
Service not separately priced by Part B

C **G8451** Beta-blocker therapy for LVEF < 40% not prescribed for reasons documented by the clinician (e.g., low blood pressure, fluid overload, asthma, patients recently treated with an intravenous positive inotropic agent, allergy, intolerance, other medical reasons, patient declined, other patient reasons, or other reasons attributable to the healthcare system) M

▲ Revised code   ● New code   C Carrier judgment   D Special coverage instructions apply
I Not payable by Medicare   M Non-covered by Medicare   S Non-covered by Medicare statute   AHA Coding Clinic®

BETOS: M5D   Specialist - other
Service not separately priced by Part B

C **G8452** Beta-blocker therapy not prescribed   M
BETOS: M5D   Specialist - other
Service not separately priced by Part B

C **G8465** High or very high risk of recurrence of
prostate cancer   ♂ M
BETOS: M5D   Specialist - other
Service not separately priced by Part B

C **G8473** Angiotensin converting enzyme (ACE)
inhibitor or angiotensin receptor blocker
(ARB) therapy prescribed   M
BETOS: M5D   Specialist - other
Service not separately priced by Part B

C **G8474** Angiotensin converting enzyme (ACE)
inhibitor or angiotensin receptor blocker
(ARB) therapy not prescribed for reasons
documented by the clinician (e.g., allergy,
intolerance, pregnancy, renal failure due
to ACE inhibitor, diseases of the aortic or
mitral valve, other medical reasons) or (e.g.,
patient declined, other patient reasons) or
(e.g., lack of drug availability, other reasons
attributable to the health care system)   M
BETOS: M5D   Specialist - other
Service not separately priced by Part B

C **G8475** Angiotensin converting enzyme (ACE) inhibitor
or angiotensin receptor blocker (ARB) therapy
not prescribed, reason not given   M
BETOS: M5D   Specialist - other
Service not separately priced by Part B

C **G8476** Most recent blood pressure has a systolic
measurement of < 140 mmHg and a diastolic
measurement of < 90 mmHg   M
BETOS: M5D   Specialist - other
Service not separately priced by Part B

C **G8477** Most recent blood pressure has a systolic
measurement of >=140 mmHg and/or a
diastolic measurement of >=90 mmHg   M
BETOS: M5D   Specialist - other
Service not separately priced by Part B

C **G8478** Blood pressure measurement not performed
or documented, reason not given   M
BETOS: M5D   Specialist - other
Service not separately priced by Part B

C **G8482** Influenza immunization administered or
previously received   M MIPS
BETOS: M5D   Specialist - other
Service not separately priced by Part B

C **G8483** Influenza immunization was not administered
for reasons documented by clinician (e.g.,
patient allergy or other medical reasons,
patient declined or other patient reasons,
vaccine not available or other system
reasons)   M MIPS
BETOS: M5D   Specialist - other
Service not separately priced by Part B

C **G8484** Influenza immunization was not
administered, reason not given   M MIPS
BETOS: M5D   Specialist - other
Service not separately priced by Part B

C **G8506** Patient receiving angiotensin converting
enzyme (ACE) inhibitor or angiotensin
receptor blocker (ARB) therapy   M
BETOS: M5D   Specialist - other
Service not separately priced by Part B
Coding Clinic: 2008, Q4

C **G8509** Pain assessment documented as positive
using a standardized tool, follow-up plan not
documented, reason not given   M MIPS
BETOS: M5D   Specialist - other
Service not separately priced by Part B
Coding Clinic: 2008, Q4

C **G8510** Screening for depression is documented
as negative, a follow-up plan is not
required   M MIPS
BETOS: M5D   Specialist - other
Service not separately priced by Part B
Coding Clinic: 2008, Q4

C **G8511** Screening for depression documented as
positive, follow-up plan not documented,
reason not given   M MIPS
BETOS: M5D   Specialist - other
Service not separately priced by Part B
Coding Clinic: 2008, Q4

▲ C **G8535** Elder maltreatment screen not documented;
documentation that patient is not eligible for
the elder maltreatment screen at the time of
the encounter   Ⓐ M MIPS
BETOS: M5D   Specialist - other
Service not separately priced by Part B
Coding Clinic: 2008, Q4

C **G8536** No documentation of an elder maltreatment
screen, reason not given   Ⓐ M MIPS
BETOS: M5D   Specialist - other
Service not separately priced by Part B
Coding Clinic: 2008, Q4

C **G8539** Functional outcome assessment
documented as positive using a standardized
tool and a care plan based on identified
deficiencies on the date of functional
outcome assessment, is documented   M MIPS
BETOS: M5D   Specialist - other
Service not separately priced by Part B
Coding Clinic: 2008, Q4

▲ C **G8540** Functional outcome assessment not
documented as being performed,
documentation the patient is not eligible
for a functional outcome assessment
using a standardized tool at the time of the
encounter   M MIPS
BETOS: M5D   Specialist - other
Service not separately priced by Part B
Coding Clinic: 2008, Q4

C **G8541** Functional outcome assessment using a standardized tool not documented, reason not given M [MIPS]

BETOS: M5D   Specialist - other

Service not separately priced by Part B

Coding Clinic: 2008, Q4

C **G8542** Functional outcome assessment using a standardized tool is documented; no functional deficiencies identified, care plan not required M [MIPS]

BETOS: M5D   Specialist - other

Service not separately priced by Part B

Coding Clinic: 2008, Q4

C **G8543** Documentation of a positive functional outcome assessment using a standardized tool; care plan not documented, reason not given M [MIPS]

BETOS: M5D   Specialist - other

Service not separately priced by Part B

Coding Clinic: 2008, Q4

C **G8559** Patient referred to a physician (preferably a physician with training in disorders of the ear) for an otologic evaluation M

BETOS: M5D   Specialist - other

Service not separately priced by Part B

C **G8560** Patient has a history of active drainage from the ear within the previous 90 days M

BETOS: M5D   Specialist - other

Service not separately priced by Part B

C **G8561** Patient is not eligible for the referral for otologic evaluation for patients with a history of active drainage measure M

BETOS: M5D   Specialist - other

Service not separately priced by Part B

C **G8562** Patient does not have a history of active drainage from the ear within the previous 90 days M

BETOS: M5D   Specialist - other

Service not separately priced by Part B

C **G8563** Patient not referred to a physician (preferably a physician with training in disorders of the ear) for an otologic evaluation, reason not given M

BETOS: M5D   Specialist - other

Service not separately priced by Part B

C **G8564** Patient was referred to a physician (preferably a physician with training in disorders of the ear) for an otologic evaluation, reason not specified) M

BETOS: M5D   Specialist - other

Service not separately priced by Part B

C **G8565** Verification and documentation of sudden or rapidly progressive hearing loss M

BETOS: M5D   Specialist - other

Service not separately priced by Part B

C **G8566** Patient is not eligible for the "referral for otologic evaluation for sudden or rapidly progressive hearing loss" measure M

BETOS: M5D   Specialist - other

Service not separately priced by Part B

C **G8567** Patient does not have verification and documentation of sudden or rapidly progressive hearing loss M

BETOS: M5D   Specialist - other

Service not separately priced by Part B

C **G8568** Patient was not referred to a physician (preferably a physician with training in disorders of the ear) for an otologic evaluation, reason not given M

BETOS: M5D   Specialist - other

Service not separately priced by Part B

C **G8569** Prolonged postoperative intubation (> 24 hrs) required M

BETOS: M5D   Specialist - other

Service not separately priced by Part B

C **G8570** Prolonged postoperative intubation (> 24 hrs) not required M

BETOS: M5D   Specialist - other

Service not separately priced by Part B

C **G8571** Development of deep sternal wound infection/mediastinitis within 30 days postoperatively M

BETOS: M5D   Specialist - other

Service not separately priced by Part B

C **G8572** No deep sternal wound infection/mediastinitis M

BETOS: M5D   Specialist - other

Service not separately priced by Part B

C **G8573** Stroke following isolated CABG surgery M

BETOS: M5D   Specialist - other

Service not separately priced by Part B

C **G8574** No stroke following isolated CABG surgery M

BETOS: M5D   Specialist - other

Service not separately priced by Part B

C **G8575** Developed postoperative renal failure or required dialysis M

BETOS: M5D   Specialist - other

Service not separately priced by Part B

C **G8576** No postoperative renal failure/dialysis not required M

BETOS: M5D   Specialist - other

Service not separately priced by Part B

C **G8577** Re-exploration required due to mediastinal bleeding with or without tamponade, graft occlusion, valve dysfunction or other cardiac reason M

BETOS: M5D   Specialist - other

Service not separately priced by Part B

▲ Revised code   ● New code   **C** Carrier judgment   **D** Special coverage instructions apply

I Not payable by Medicare   **M** Non-covered by Medicare   **S** Non-covered by Medicare statute   AHA Coding Clinic®

C **G8578** Re-exploration not required due to mediastinal bleeding with or without tamponade, graft occlusion, valve dysfunction or other cardiac reason   M
BETOS: M5D   Specialist - other
Service not separately priced by Part B

C **G8598** Aspirin or another antiplatelet therapy used   M MIPS
BETOS: M5D   Specialist - other
Service not separately priced by Part B

C **G8599** Aspirin or another antiplatelet therapy not used, reason not given   M MIPS
BETOS: M5D   Specialist - other
Service not separately priced by Part B

C **G8600** IV tPA initiated within three hours (<= 180 minutes) of time last known well   M
BETOS: M5D   Specialist - other
Service not separately priced by Part B

C **G8601** IV tPA not initiated within three hours (<= 180 minutes) of time last known well for reasons documented by clinician   M
BETOS: M5D   Specialist - other
Service not separately priced by Part B

C **G8602** IV tPA not initiated within three hours (<= 180 minutes) of time last known well, reason not given   M
BETOS: M5D   Specialist - other
Service not separately priced by Part B

C **G8627** Surgical procedure performed within 30 days following cataract surgery for major complications (e.g., retained nuclear fragments, endophthalmitis, dislocated or wrong power IOL, retinal detachment, or wound dehiscence)   M
BETOS: M5D   Specialist - other
Service not separately priced by Part B

C **G8628** Surgical procedure not performed within 30 days following cataract surgery for major complications (e.g., retained nuclear fragments, endophthalmitis, dislocated or wrong power IOL, retinal detachment, or wound dehiscence)   M
BETOS: M5D   Specialist - other
Service not separately priced by Part B

C **G8633** Pharmacologic therapy (other than minerals/vitamins) for osteoporosis prescribed   M MIPS
BETOS: M5B   Specialist - psychiatry
Service not separately priced by Part B

C **G8635** Pharmacologic therapy for osteoporosis was not prescribed, reason not given   M MIPS
BETOS: M5B   Specialist - psychiatry
Service not separately priced by Part B

QUALITY MEASURES RELATED FOR RISK-ADJUSTED FUNCTIONAL STATUS SCORING (G8647-G8674)

C **G8647** Risk-adjusted functional status change residual score for the knee successfully calculated and the score was equal to zero (0) or greater than zero (>0)   M
BETOS: M5B   Specialist - psychiatry
Service not separately priced by Part B

C **G8648** Risk-adjusted functional status change residual score for the knee successfully calculated and the score was less than zero (<0)   M
BETOS: M5B   Specialist - psychiatry
Service not separately priced by Part B

C **G8649** Risk-adjusted functional status change residual scores for the knee not measured because the patient did not complete FOTO's status survey near discharge, not appropriate   M
BETOS: M5B   Specialist - psychiatry
Service not separately priced by Part B

C **G8650** Risk-adjusted functional status change residual scores for the knee not measured because the patient did not complete FOTO's functional intake on admission and/or follow-up status survey near discharge, reason not given   M
BETOS: M5B   Specialist - psychiatry
Service not separately priced by Part B

C **G8651** Risk-adjusted functional status change residual score for the hip successfully calculated and the score was equal to zero (0) or greater than zero (>0)   M
BETOS: M5B   Specialist - psychiatry
Service not separately priced by Part B

C **G8652** Risk-adjusted functional status change residual score for the hip successfully calculated and the score was less than zero (<0)   M
BETOS: M5B   Specialist - psychiatry
Service not separately priced by Part B

C **G8653** Risk-adjusted functional status change residual scores for the hip not measured because the patient did not complete follow-up status survey near discharge, patient not appropriate   M
BETOS: M5B   Specialist - psychiatry
Service not separately priced by Part B

C **G8654** Risk-adjusted functional status change residual scores for the hip not measured because the patient did not complete FOTO's functional intake on admission and/or follow-up status survey near discharge, reason not given   M
BETOS: M5B   Specialist - psychiatry
Service not separately priced by Part B

♂ Male only   ♀ Female only   🅐 Age   A2 - Z3 = ASC Payment indicator   A - Y = APC Status indicator
ASC = ASC-approved procedure   **DME** Paid under the DME fee schedule   **MIPS** MIPS code

G8655 Risk-adjusted functional status change residual score for the foot or ankle successfully calculated and the score was equal to zero (0) or greater than zero (> 0) M
BETOS: M5B Specialist - psychiatry
Service not separately priced by Part B

G8656 Risk-adjusted functional status change residual score for the foot or ankle successfully calculated and the score was less than zero (< 0) M
BETOS: M5B Specialist - psychiatry
Service not separately priced by Part B

G8657 Risk-adjusted functional status change residual scores for the foot or ankle not measured because the patient did not complete FOTO's status survey near discharge, patient not appropriate M
BETOS: M5B Specialist - psychiatry
Service not separately priced by Part B

G8658 Risk-adjusted functional status change residual scores for the foot or ankle not measured because the patient did not complete FOTO's functional intake on admission and/or follow-up status survey near discharge, reason not given M
BETOS: M5B Specialist - psychiatry
Service not separately priced by Part B

G8659 Risk-adjusted functional status change residual score for the lumbar impairment successfully calculated and the score was equal to zero (0) or greater than zero (> 0) M
BETOS: M5B Specialist - psychiatry
Service not separately priced by Part B

G8660 Risk-adjusted functional status change residual score for the lumbar impairment successfully calculated and the score was less than zero (< 0) M
BETOS: M5B Specialist - psychiatry
Service not separately priced by Part B

G8661 Risk-adjusted functional status change residual scores for the lumbar impairment not measured because the patient did not complete FOTO's status survey near discharge, patient not appropriate M
BETOS: M5B Specialist - psychiatry
Service not separately priced by Part B

G8662 Risk-adjusted functional status change residual scores for the lumbar impairment not measured because the patient did not complete FOTO's functional intake on admission and/or follow-up status survey near discharge, reason not given M
BETOS: M5B Specialist - psychiatry
Service not separately priced by Part B

G8663 Risk-adjusted functional status change residual score for the shoulder successfully calculated and the score was equal to zero (0) or greater than zero (>0) M

BETOS: M5B Specialist - psychiatry
Service not separately priced by Part B

G8664 Risk-adjusted functional status change residual score for the shoulder successfully calculated and the score was less than zero (<0) M
BETOS: M5B Specialist - psychiatry
Service not separately priced by Part B

G8665 Risk-adjusted functional status change residual scores for the shoulder not measured because the patient did not complete FOTO's functional status survey near discharge, patient not appropriate M
BETOS: M5B Specialist - psychiatry
Service not separately priced by Part B

G8666 Risk-adjusted functional status change residual scores for the shoulder not measured because the patient did not complete FOTO's functional intake on admission and/or follow-up status survey near discharge, reason not given M
BETOS: M5B Specialist - psychiatry
Service not separately priced by Part B

G8667 Risk-adjusted functional status change residual score for the elbow, wrist or hand successfully calculated and the score was equal to zero (0) or greater than zero (>0) M
BETOS: M5B Specialist - psychiatry
Service not separately priced by Part B

G8668 Risk-adjusted functional status change residual score for the elbow, wrist or hand successfully calculated and the score was less than zero (<0) M
BETOS: M5B Specialist - psychiatry
Service not separately priced by Part B

G8669 Risk-adjusted functional status change residual scores for the elbow, wrist or hand not measured because the patient did not complete FOTO's functional follow-up status survey near discharge, patient not appropriate M
BETOS: M5B Specialist - psychiatry
Service not separately priced by Part B

G8670 Risk-adjusted functional status change residual scores for the elbow, wrist or hand not measured because the patient did not complete FOTO's functional intake on admission and/or follow-up status survey near discharge, reason not given M
BETOS: M5B Specialist - psychiatry
Service not separately priced by Part B

G8671 Risk-adjusted functional status change residual score for the neck, cranium, mandible, thoracic spine, ribs, or other general orthopaedic impairment successfully calculated and the score was equal to zero (0) or greater than zero (> 0) M
BETOS: M5B Specialist - psychiatry
Service not separately priced by Part B

▲ Revised code ● New code C Carrier judgment D Special coverage instructions apply
I Not payable by Medicare M Non-covered by Medicare S Non-covered by Medicare statute AHA Coding Clinic®

G8672 Risk-adjusted functional status change residual score for the neck, cranium, mandible, thoracic spine, ribs, or other general orthopaedic impairment successfully calculated and the score was less than zero (< 0)　　M
BETOS: M5B　Specialist - psychiatry
Service not separately priced by Part B

G8673 Risk-adjusted functional status change residual scores for the neck, cranium, mandible, thoracic spine, ribs, or other general orthopaedic impairment not measured because the patient did not complete FOTO's functional follow-up status survey near discharge, patient not appropriate　　M
BETOS: M5B　Specialist - psychiatry
Service not separately priced by Part B

G8674 Risk-adjusted functional status change residual scores for the neck, cranium, mandible, thoracic spine, ribs, or other general orthopaedic impairment not measured because the patient did not complete FOTO's functional intake on admission and/or follow-up status survey near discharge, reason not given　　M
BETOS: M5B　Specialist - psychiatry
Service not separately priced by Part B

MORE QUALITY MEASURES (G8694-G8976)

G8694 Left ventricular ejection fraction (LVEF) < 40%　　M
BETOS: M5B　Specialist - psychiatry
Service not separately priced by Part B

G8708 Patient not prescribed or dispensed antibiotic　　M
BETOS: M5B　Specialist - psychiatry
Service not separately priced by Part B

G8709 Patient prescribed or dispensed antibiotic for documented medical reason(s) (e.g., intestinal infection, pertussis, bacterial infection, lyme disease, otitis media, acute sinusitis, acute pharyngitis, acute tonsillitis, chronic sinusitis, infection of the pharynx/larynx/tonsils/adenoids, prostatitis, cellulitis, mastoiditis, or bone infections, acute lymphadenitis, impetigo, skin staph infections, pneumonia/gonococcal infections, venereal disease (syphilis, chlamydia, inflammatory diseases (female reproductive organs)), infections of the kidney, cystitis or UTI, and acne)　　M
BETOS: M5B　Specialist - psychiatry
Service not separately priced by Part B

G8710 Patient prescribed or dispensed antibiotic　　M
BETOS: M5B　Specialist - psychiatry
Service not separately priced by Part B

G8711 Prescribed or dispensed antibiotic　　M
BETOS: M5B　Specialist - psychiatry
Service not separately priced by Part B

G8712 Antibiotic not prescribed or dispensed　　M
BETOS: M5B　Specialist - psychiatry
Service not separately priced by Part B

G8721 pT category (primary tumor), pN category (regional lymph nodes), and histologic grade were documented in pathology report　M MIPS
BETOS: M5B　Specialist - psychiatry
Service not separately priced by Part B

G8722 Documentation of medical reason(s) for not including the pT category, the pN category or the histologic grade in the pathology report (e.g., re-excision without residual tumor; non-carcinomasanal canal)　M MIPS
BETOS: M5B　Specialist - psychiatry
Service not separately priced by Part B

G8723 Specimen site is other than anatomic location of primary tumor　M MIPS
BETOS: M5B　Specialist - psychiatry
Service not separately priced by Part B

G8724 pT category, pN category and histologic grade were not documented in the pathology report, reason not given　M MIPS
BETOS: M5B　Specialist - psychiatry
Service not separately priced by Part B

G8730 Pain assessment documented as positive using a standardized tool and a follow-up plan is documented　M MIPS
BETOS: M5B　Specialist - psychiatry
Service not separately priced by Part B

G8731 Pain assessment using a standardized tool is documented as negative, no follow-up plan required　M MIPS
BETOS: M5B　Specialist - psychiatry
Service not separately priced by Part B

G8732 No documentation of pain assessment, reason not given　M MIPS
BETOS: M5B　Specialist - psychiatry
Service not separately priced by Part B

G8733 Elder maltreatment screen documented as positive and a follow-up plan is documented　Ⓐ M MIPS
BETOS: M5B　Specialist - psychiatry
Service not separately priced by Part B

G8734 Elder maltreatment screen documented as negative, no follow-up required　Ⓐ M MIPS
BETOS: M5B　Specialist - psychiatry
Service not separately priced by Part B

G8735 Elder maltreatment screen documented as positive, follow-up plan not documented, reason not given　Ⓐ M MIPS
BETOS: M5B　Specialist - psychiatry
Service not separately priced by Part B

C **G8749** Absence of signs of melanoma (cough, dyspnea, tenderness, localized neurologic signs such as weakness, jaundice or any other sign suggesting systemic spread) or absence of symptoms of melanoma (pain, paresthesia, or any other symptom suggesting the possibility of systemic spread of melanoma)　　M
BETOS: M5B　Specialist - psychiatry
Service not separately priced by Part B

C **G8752** Most recent systolic blood pressure < 140 mmHg　　M MIPS
BETOS: M5B　Specialist - psychiatry
Service not separately priced by Part B

C **G8753** Most recent systolic blood pressure >= 140 mmHg　　M MIPS
BETOS: M5B　Specialist - psychiatry
Service not separately priced by Part B

C **G8754** Most recent diastolic blood pressure < 90 mmHg　　M MIPS
BETOS: M5B　Specialist - psychiatry
Service not separately priced by Part B

C **G8755** Most recent diastolic blood pressure >= 90 mmHg　　M MIPS
BETOS: M5B　Specialist - psychiatry
Service not separately priced by Part B

C **G8756** No documentation of blood pressure measurement, reason not given　M MIPS
BETOS: M5B　Specialist - psychiatry
Service not separately priced by Part B

C **G8783** Normal blood pressure reading documented, follow-up not required　　M MIPS
BETOS: M5B　Specialist - psychiatry
Service not separately priced by Part B

C **G8785** Blood pressure reading not documented, reason not given　　M MIPS
BETOS: M5B　Specialist - psychiatry
Service not separately priced by Part B

C **G8797** Specimen site other than anatomic location of esophagus　　M MIPS
BETOS: M5B　Specialist - psychiatry
Service not separately priced by Part B

C **G8798** Specimen site other than anatomic location of prostate　　M MIPS
BETOS: M5B　Specialist - psychiatry
Service not separately priced by Part B

C **G8806** Performance of trans-abdominal or trans-vaginal ultrasound　♀ M MIPS
BETOS: M5B　Specialist - psychiatry
Service not separately priced by Part B

C **G8807** Trans-abdominal or trans-vaginal ultrasound not performed for reasons documented by clinician (e.g., patient has visited the ED multiple times within 72 hours, patient has a documented intrauterine pregnancy [IUP])　♀ M MIPS

BETOS: M5B　Specialist - psychiatry
Service not separately priced by Part B

▲ **C** **G8808** Trans-abdominal or trans-vaginal ultrasound not performed, reason not given　♀ M MIPS
BETOS: M5B　Specialist - psychiatry
Service not separately priced by Part B

C **G8809** Rh-immunoglobulin (RhoGAM) ordered　♀ M MIPS
BETOS: M5B　Specialist - psychiatry
Service not separately priced by Part B

C **G8810** Rh-immunoglobulin (RhoGAM) not ordered for reasons documented by clinician (e.g., patient had prior documented receipt of RhoGAM within 12 weeks, patient refusal)　♀ M MIPS
BETOS: M5B　Specialist - psychiatry
Service not separately priced by Part B

C **G8811** Documentation Rh-immunoglobulin (RhoGAM) was not ordered, reason not given　♀ M MIPS
BETOS: M5B　Specialist - psychiatry
Service not separately priced by Part B

C **G8815** Documented reason in the medical records for why the statin therapy was not prescribed (i.e., lower extremity bypass was for a patient with non-artherosclerotic disease)　M
BETOS: M5B　Specialist - psychiatry
Service not separately priced by Part B

C **G8816** Statin medication prescribed at discharge　M
BETOS: M5B　Specialist - psychiatry
Service not separately priced by Part B

C **G8817** Statin therapy not prescribed at discharge, reason not given　M
BETOS: M5B　Specialist - psychiatry
Service not separately priced by Part B

C **G8818** Patient discharge to home no later than post-operative day #7　M
BETOS: M5B　Specialist - psychiatry
Service not separately priced by Part B

C **G8825** Patient not discharged to home by post-operative day #7　M
BETOS: M5B　Specialist - psychiatry
Service not separately priced by Part B

C **G8826** Patient discharge to home no later than post-operative day #2 following EVAR　M
BETOS: M5B　Specialist - psychiatry
Service not separately priced by Part B

C **G8833** Patient not discharged to home by post-operative day #2 following EVAR　M
BETOS: M5B　Specialist - psychiatry
Service not separately priced by Part B

C **G8834** Patient discharged to home no later than post-operative day #2 following CEA　M
BETOS: M5B　Specialist - psychiatry
Service not separately priced by Part B

C **G8838** Patient not discharged to home by post-operative day #2 following CEA   M

BETOS: M5B   Specialist - psychiatry

Service not separately priced by Part B

C **G8839** Sleep apnea symptoms assessed, including presence or absence of snoring and daytime sleepiness   M

BETOS: M5B   Specialist - psychiatry

Service not separately priced by Part B

C **G8840** Documentation of reason(s) for not documenting an assessment of sleep symptoms (e.g., patient didn't have initial daytime sleepiness, patient visited between initial testing and initiation of therapy)   M

BETOS: M5B   Specialist - psychiatry

Service not separately priced by Part B

C **G8841** Sleep apnea symptoms not assessed, reason not given   M

BETOS: M5B   Specialist - psychiatry

Service not separately priced by Part B

C **G8842** Apnea hypopnea index (AHI) or respiratory disturbance index (RDI) measured at the time of initial diagnosis   M

BETOS: M5B   Specialist - psychiatry

Service not separately priced by Part B

C **G8843** Documentation of reason(s) for not measuring an apnea hypopnea index (AHI) or a respiratory disturbance index (RDI) at the time of initial diagnosis (e.g., psychiatric disease, dementia, patient declined, financial, insurance coverage, test ordered but not yet completed)   M

BETOS: M5B   Specialist - psychiatry

Service not separately priced by Part B

C **G8844** Apnea hypopnea index (AHI) or respiratory disturbance index (RDI) not measured at the time of initial diagnosis, reason not given   M

BETOS: M5B   Specialist - psychiatry

Service not separately priced by Part B

C **G8845** Positive airway pressure therapy prescribed   M

BETOS: M5B   Specialist - psychiatry

Service not separately priced by Part B

C **G8846** Moderate or severe obstructive sleep apnea (apnea hypopnea index (AHI) or respiratory disturbance index (RDI) of 15 or greater)   M

BETOS: M5B   Specialist - psychiatry

Service not separately priced by Part B

C **G8849** Documentation of reason(s) for not prescribing positive airway pressure therapy (e.g., patient unable to tolerate, alternative therapies use, patient declined, financial, insurance coverage)   M

BETOS: M5B   Specialist - psychiatry

Service not separately priced by Part B

C **G8850** Positive airway pressure therapy not prescribed, reason not given   M

BETOS: M5B   Specialist - psychiatry

Service not separately priced by Part B

C **G8851** Objective measurement of adherence to positive airway pressure therapy, documented   M

BETOS: M5B   Specialist - psychiatry

Service not separately priced by Part B

C **G8852** Positive airway pressure therapy prescribed   M

BETOS: M5B   Specialist - psychiatry

Service not separately priced by Part B

C **G8854** Documentation of reason(s) for not objectively measuring adherence to positive airway pressure therapy (e.g., patient didn't bring data from continuous positive airway pressure [CPAP], therapy not yet initiated, not available on machine)   M

BETOS: M5B   Specialist - psychiatry

Service not separately priced by Part B

C **G8855** Objective measurement of adherence to positive airway pressure therapy not performed, reason not given   M

BETOS: M5B   Specialist - psychiatry

Service not separately priced by Part B

C **G8856** Referral to a physician for an otologic evaluation performed   M MIPS

BETOS: M5B   Specialist - psychiatry

Service not separately priced by Part B

C **G8857** Patient is not eligible for the referral for otologic evaluation measure (e.g., patients who are already under the care of a physician for acute or chronic dizziness)   M MIPS

BETOS: M5B   Specialist - psychiatry

Service not separately priced by Part B

C **G8858** Referral to a physician for an otologic evaluation not performed, reason not given   M MIPS

BETOS: M5B   Specialist - psychiatry

Service not separately priced by Part B

C **G8861** Within the past 2 years, central dual-energy X-ray absorptiometry (DXA) ordered and documented, review of systems and medication history or pharmacologic therapy (other than minerals/vitamins) for osteoporosis prescribed   M

BETOS: M5B   Specialist - psychiatry

Service not separately priced by Part B

C **G8863** Patients not assessed for risk of bone loss, reason not given   M

BETOS: M5B   Specialist - psychiatry

Service not separately priced by Part B

C **G8864** Pneumococcal vaccine administered or previously received   M

BETOS: M5B   Specialist - psychiatry

Service not separately priced by Part B

♂ Male only   ♀ Female only   **A** Age   A2 - Z3 = ASC Payment indicator   A - Y = APC Status indicator

ASC = ASC-approved procedure   **DME** Paid under the DME fee schedule   **MIPS** MIPS code

C **G8865** Documentation of medical reason(s) for not administering or previously receiving pneumococcal vaccine (e.g., patient allergic reaction, potential adverse drug reaction)   M

BETOS: M5B   Specialist - psychiatry
Service not separately priced by Part B

C **G8866** Documentation of patient reason(s) for not administering or previously receiving pneumococcal vaccine (e.g., patient refusal)   M

BETOS: M5B   Specialist - psychiatry
Service not separately priced by Part B

C **G8867** Pneumococcal vaccine not administered or previously received, reason not given   M

BETOS: M5B   Specialist - psychiatry
Service not separately priced by Part B

▲ C **G8869** Patient has documented immunity to hepatitis B and initiating anti-TNF therapy   M

BETOS: M5B   Specialist - psychiatry
Service not separately priced by Part B

C **G8872** Excised tissue evaluated by imaging intraoperatively to confirm successful inclusion of targeted lesion   M

BETOS: M5B   Specialist - psychiatry
Service not separately priced by Part B

C **G8873** Patients with needle localization specimens which are not amenable to intraoperative imaging such as MRI needle wire localization, or targets which are tentatively identified on mammogram or ultrasound which do not contain a biopsy marker but which can be verified on intraoperative inspection or pathology (e.g., needle biopsy site where the biopsy marker is remote from the actual biopsy site)   M

BETOS: M5B   Specialist - psychiatry
Service not separately priced by Part B

C **G8874** Excised tissue not evaluated by imaging intraoperatively to confirm successful inclusion of targeted lesion   M

BETOS: M5B   Specialist - psychiatry
Service not separately priced by Part B

C **G8875** Clinician diagnosed breast cancer preoperatively by a minimally invasive biopsy method   M

BETOS: M5B   Specialist - psychiatry
Service not separately priced by Part B

C **G8876** Documentation of reason(s) for not performing minimally invasive biopsy to diagnose breast cancer preoperatively (e.g., lesion too close to skin, implant, chest wall, etc., lesion could not be adequately visualized for needle biopsy, patient condition prevents needle biopsy [weight, breast thickness, etc.], duct excision without imaging abnormality, prophylactic mastectomy, reduction mammoplasty, excisional biopsy performed by another physician)   M

BETOS: M5B   Specialist - psychiatry
Service not separately priced by Part B

C **G8877** Clinician did not attempt to achieve the diagnosis of breast cancer preoperatively by a minimally invasive biopsy method, reason not given   M

BETOS: M5B   Specialist - psychiatry
Service not separately priced by Part B

C **G8878** Sentinel lymph node biopsy procedure performed   M

BETOS: M5B   Specialist - psychiatry
Service not separately priced by Part B

▲ C **G8880** Documentation of reason(s) sentinel lymph node biopsy not performed (e.g., reasons could include but not limited to; non-invasive cancer, incidental discovery of breast cancer on prophylactic mastectomy, incidental discovery of breast cancer on reduction mammoplasty, pre-operative biopsy proven lymph node (IN) metastases, inflammatory carcinoma, stage 3 locally advanced cancer, recurrent invasive breast cancer, clinically node positive after neoadjuvant systemic therapy, patient refusal after informed consent)   ♀ M

BETOS: M5B   Specialist - psychiatry
Service not separately priced by Part B

C **G8881** Stage of breast cancer is greater than T1N0M0 or T2N0M0   M

BETOS: M5B   Specialist - psychiatry
Service not separately priced by Part B

C **G8882** Sentinel lymph node biopsy procedure not performed, reason not given   M

BETOS: M5B   Specialist - psychiatry
Service not separately priced by Part B

C **G8883** Biopsy results reviewed, communicated, tracked and documented   M

BETOS: M5B   Specialist - psychiatry
Service not separately priced by Part B

C **G8884** Clinician documented reason that patient's biopsy results were not reviewed   M

BETOS: M5B   Specialist - psychiatry
Service not separately priced by Part B

C **G8885** Biopsy results not reviewed, communicated, tracked or documented   M

BETOS: M5B   Specialist - psychiatry
Service not separately priced by Part B

C **G8907** Patient documented not to have experienced any of the following events: a burn prior to discharge; a fall within the facility; wrong site/side/patient/procedure/implant event; or a hospital transfer or hospital admission upon discharge from the facility   M

BETOS: M5B   Specialist - psychiatry
Service not separately priced by Part B

C G8908 Patient documented to have received a burn prior to discharge   M
BETOS: M5B   Specialist - psychiatry
Service not separately priced by Part B

C G8909 Patient documented not to have received a burn prior to discharge   M
BETOS: M5B   Specialist - psychiatry
Service not separately priced by Part B

C G8910 Patient documented to have experienced a fall within ASC   M
BETOS: M5B   Specialist - psychiatry
Service not separately priced by Part B

C G8911 Patient documented not to have experienced a fall within ambulatory surgical center   M
BETOS: M5B   Specialist - psychiatry
Service not separately priced by Part B

C G8912 Patient documented to have experienced a wrong site, wrong side, wrong patient, wrong procedure or wrong implant event   M
BETOS: M5B   Specialist - psychiatry
Service not separately priced by Part B

C G8913 Patient documented not to have experienced a wrong site, wrong side, wrong patient, wrong procedure or wrong implant event   M
BETOS: M5B   Specialist - psychiatry
Service not separately priced by Part B

C G8914 Patient documented to have experienced a hospital transfer or hospital admission upon discharge from ASC   M
BETOS: M5B   Specialist - psychiatry
Service not separately priced by Part B

C G8915 Patient documented not to have experienced a hospital transfer or hospital admission upon discharge from ASC   M
BETOS: M5B   Specialist - psychiatry
Service not separately priced by Part B

C G8916 Patient with preoperative order for IV antibiotic surgical site infection (SSI) prophylaxis, antibiotic initiated on time   M
BETOS: M5B   Specialist - psychiatry
Service not separately priced by Part B

C G8917 Patient with preoperative order for IV antibiotic surgical site infection (SSI) prophylaxis, antibiotic not initiated on time   M
BETOS: M5B   Specialist - psychiatry
Service not separately priced by Part B

C G8918 Patient without preoperative order for IV antibiotic surgical site infection (SSI) prophylaxis   M
BETOS: M5B   Specialist - psychiatry
Service not separately priced by Part B

C G8923 Left ventricular ejection fraction (LVEF) < 40% or documentation of moderately or severely depressed left ventricular systolic function   M
BETOS: M5B   Specialist - psychiatry
Service not separately priced by Part B

C G8924 Spirometry test results demonstrate FEV1/FVC < 70%, fev < 60% predicted and patient has COPD symptoms (e.g., dyspnea, cough/sputum, wheezing)   M MIPS
BETOS: M5B   Specialist - psychiatry
Service not separately priced by Part B

C G8925 Spirometry test results demonstrate fev1 >= 60% FEV1/FVC >= 70%, predicted or patient does not have COPD symptoms   M MIPS
BETOS: M5B   Specialist - psychiatry
Service not separately priced by Part B

C G8926 Spirometry test not performed or documented, reason not given   M MIPS
BETOS: M5B   Specialist - psychiatry
Service not separately priced by Part B

C G8934 Left ventricular ejection fraction (LVEF) <40% or documentation of moderately or severely depressed left ventricular systolic function   M
BETOS: M5B   Specialist - psychiatry
Service not separately priced by Part B

C G8935 Clinician prescribed angiotensin converting enzyme (ACE) inhibitor or angiotensin receptor blocker (ARB) therapy   M
BETOS: M5B   Specialist - psychiatry
Service not separately priced by Part B

C G8936 Clinician documented that patient was not an eligible candidate for angiotensin converting enzyme (ACE) inhibitor or angiotensin receptor blocker (ARB) therapy (e.g., allergy, intolerance, pregnancy, renal failure due to ACE inhibitor, diseases of the aortic or mitral valve, other medical reasons) or (e.g., patient declined, other patient reasons) or (e.g., lack of drug availability, other reasons attributable to the health care system)   M
BETOS: M5B   Specialist - psychiatry
Service not separately priced by Part B

C G8937 Clinician did not prescribe angiotensin converting enzyme (ACE) inhibitor or angiotensin receptor blocker (ARB) therapy, reason not given   M
BETOS: M5B   Specialist - psychiatry
Service not separately priced by Part B

C G8938 BMI is documented as being outside of normal limits, follow-up plan is not documented, documentation the patient is not eligible   M MIPS
BETOS: M5B   Specialist - psychiatry
Service not separately priced by Part B

▲ **C G8939** Pain assessment documented as positive, follow-up plan not documented, documentation the patient is not eligible at the time of the encounter   M MIPS
BETOS: M5B   Specialist - psychiatry
Service not separately priced by Part B

▲ C **G8941** Elder maltreatment screen documented as positive, follow-up plan not documented, documentation the patient is not eligible for follow-up plan at the time of the encounter　　　　　　　Ⓐ M MIPS
BETOS: M5B　Specialist - psychiatry
Service not separately priced by Part B

C **G8942** Functional outcomes assessment using a standardized tool is documented within the previous 30 days and care plan, based on identified deficiencies on the date of the functional outcome assessment, is documented　　　　　　　　　　M MIPS
BETOS: M5B　Specialist - psychiatry
Service not separately priced by Part B

C **G8944** AJCC melanoma cancer Stage 0 through IIC melanoma　　　　　　　　　　　　M
BETOS: M5B　Specialist - psychiatry
Service not separately priced by Part B

C **G8946** Minimally invasive biopsy method attempted but not diagnostic of breast cancer (e.g., high risk lesion of breast such as atypical ductal hyperplasia, lobular neoplasia, atypical lobular hyperplasia, lobular carcinoma in situ, atypical columnar hyperplasia, flat epithelial atypia, radial scar, complex sclerosing lesion, papillary lesion, or any lesion with spindle cells)　　　　　　　　　　　　　M
BETOS: M5B　Specialist - psychiatry
Service not separately priced by Part B

C **G8950** Pre-hypertensive or hypertensive blood pressure reading documented, and the indicated follow-up is documented　M MIPS
BETOS: M5B　Specialist - psychiatry
Service not separately priced by Part B

C **G8952** Pre-hypertensive or hypertensive blood pressure reading documented, indicated follow-up not documented, reason not given　　　　　　　　　　　　M MIPS
BETOS: M5B　Specialist - psychiatry
Service not separately priced by Part B

C **G8955** Most recent assessment of adequacy of volume management documented　　　M
BETOS: M5B　Specialist - psychiatry
Service not separately priced by Part B

C **G8956** Patient receiving maintenance hemodialysis in an outpatient dialysis facility　　M
BETOS: M5B　Specialist - psychiatry
Service not separately priced by Part B

C **G8958** Assessment of adequacy of volume management not documented, reason not given　　　　　　　　　　　　　M
BETOS: M5B　Specialist - psychiatry
Service not separately priced by Part B

C **G8959** Clinician treating major depressive disorder communicates to clinician treating comorbid condition　　　　　　　　　　　　M

BETOS: M5B　Specialist - psychiatry
Service not separately priced by Part B

C **G8960** Clinician treating major depressive disorder did not communicate to clinician treating comorbid condition, reason not given　　M
BETOS: M5B　Specialist - psychiatry
Service not separately priced by Part B

C **G8961** Cardiac stress imaging test primarily performed on low-risk surgery patient for preoperative evaluation within 30 days preceding this surgery　　　　　　M
BETOS: M5B　Specialist - psychiatry
Service not separately priced by Part B

C **G8962** Cardiac stress imaging test performed on patient for any reason including those who did not have low risk surgery or test that was performed more than 30 days preceding low risk surgery　　　　　　　　　M
BETOS: M5B　Specialist - psychiatry
Service not separately priced by Part B

C **G8963** Cardiac stress imaging performed primarily for monitoring of asymptomatic patient who had PCI within 2 years　　　　　M
BETOS: M5B　Specialist - psychiatry
Service not separately priced by Part B

C **G8964** Cardiac stress imaging test performed primarily for any other reason than monitoring of asymptomatic patient who had PCI within 2 years (e.g., symptomatic patient, patient greater than 2 years since PCI, initial evaluation, etc)　　　　M
BETOS: M5B　Specialist - psychiatry
Service not separately priced by Part B

C **G8965** Cardiac stress imaging test primarily performed on low CHD risk patient for initial detection and risk assessment　　M
BETOS: M5B　Specialist - psychiatry
Service not separately priced by Part B

C **G8966** Cardiac stress imaging test performed on symptomatic or higher than low CHD risk patient or for any reason other than initial detection and risk assessment　　M
BETOS: M5B　Specialist - psychiatry
Service not separately priced by Part B

▲ C **G8967** Warfarin or another FDA-approved oral anticoagulant is prescribed　　　M MIPS
BETOS: M5B　Specialist - psychiatry
Service not separately priced by Part B

▲ C **G8968** Documentation of medical reason(s) for not prescribing warfarin or another FDA-approved anticoagulant (e.g., atrial appendage device in place)　　M MIPS
BETOS: M5B　Specialist - psychiatry
Service not separately priced by Part B

▲ Revised code　　● New code　　C Carrier judgment　　D Special coverage instructions apply
I Not payable by Medicare　　M Non-covered by Medicare　　S Non-covered by Medicare statute　　AHA Coding Clinic®

▲ C **G8969** Documentation of patient reason(s) for not prescribing warfarin or another FDA-approved oral anticoagulant that is FDA-approved for the prevention of thromboembolism (e.g., patient choice of having atrial appendage device placed)　　　　　　　　　　　M MIPS
BETOS: M5B　Specialist - psychiatry
Service not separately priced by Part B

C **G8970** No risk factors or one moderate risk factor for thromboembolism　　　　　M MIPS
BETOS: M5B　Specialist - psychiatry
Service not separately priced by Part B

C **G8973** Most recent hemoglobin (HgB) level < 10 g/dl　　　　　　　　　　　　M
BETOS: M5B　Specialist - psychiatry
Service not separately priced by Part B

C **G8974** Hemoglobin level measurement not documented, reason not given　　　　M
BETOS: M5B　Specialist - psychiatry
Service not separately priced by Part B

C **G8975** Documentation of medical reason(s) for patient having a hemoglobin level < 10 g/dl (e.g., patients who have non-renal etiologies of anemia [e.g., sickle cell anemia or other hemoglobinopathies, hypersplenism, primary bone marrow disease, anemia related to chemotherapy for diagnosis of malignancy, postoperative bleeding, active bloodstream or peritoneal infection], other medical reasons)　　　　　　　　　M
BETOS: M5B　Specialist - psychiatry
Service not separately priced by Part B

C **G8976** Most recent hemoglobin (HgB) level >= 10 g/dl　　　　　　　　　　　M
BETOS: M5B　Specialist - psychiatry
Service not separately priced by Part B

FUNCTIONAL LIMITATION REPORTING (G8978-G8999)

C **G8978** Mobility: walking & moving around functional limitation, current status, at therapy episode outset and at reporting intervals　　　　　　　　　E1
BETOS: M5D　Specialist - other
Service not separately priced by Part B

C **G8979** Mobility: walking & moving around functional limitation, projected goal status, at therapy episode outset, at reporting intervals, and at discharge or to end reporting　　　　　E1
BETOS: M5D　Specialist - other
Service not separately priced by Part B

C **G8980** Mobility: walking & moving around functional limitation, discharge status, at discharge from therapy or to end reporting　　　　　E1
BETOS: M5D　Specialist - other
Service not separately priced by Part B

C **G8981** Changing & maintaining body position functional limitation, current status, at therapy episode outset and at reporting intervals　　　　　　　　　E1
BETOS: M5D　Specialist - other
Service not separately priced by Part B

C **G8982** Changing & maintaining body position functional limitation, projected goal status, at therapy episode outset, at reporting intervals, and at discharge or to end reporting　　　E1
BETOS: M5D　Specialist - other
Service not separately priced by Part B

C **G8983** Changing & maintaining body position functional limitation, discharge status, at discharge from therapy or to end reporting E1
BETOS: M5D　Specialist - other
Service not separately priced by Part B

C **G8984** Carrying, moving & handling objects functional limitation, current status, at therapy episode outset and at reporting intervals　　　　　　　　　E1
BETOS: M5D　Specialist - other
Service not separately priced by Part B

C **G8985** Carrying, moving and handling objects, projected goal status, at therapy episode outset, at reporting intervals, and at discharge or to end reporting　　　E1
BETOS: M5D　Specialist - other
Service not separately priced by Part B

C **G8986** Carrying, moving & handling objects functional limitation, discharge status, at discharge from therapy or to end reporting E1
BETOS: M5D　Specialist - other
Service not separately priced by Part B

C **G8987** Self-care functional limitation, current status, at therapy episode outset and at reporting intervals　　　　　　　　　E1
BETOS: M5D　Specialist - other
Service not separately priced by Part B

C **G8988** Self-care functional limitation, projected goal status, at therapy episode outset, at reporting intervals, and at discharge or to end reporting　　　　　　　　E1
BETOS: M5D　Specialist - other
Service not separately priced by Part B

C **G8989** Self-care functional limitation, discharge status, at discharge from therapy or to end reporting　　　　　　　　　E1
BETOS: M5D　Specialist - other
Service not separately priced by Part B

C **G8990** Other physical or occupational therapy primary functional limitation, current status, at therapy episode outset and at reporting intervals　　　　　　　　　E1
BETOS: M5D　Specialist - other
Service not separately priced by Part B

♂ Male only　　♀ Female only　　Ⓐ Age　　A2 - Z3 = ASC Payment indicator　　A - Y = APC Status indicator
ASC = ASC-approved procedure　　DME Paid under the DME fee schedule　　MIPS MIPS code

C **G8991** Other physical or occupational therapy primary functional limitation, projected goal status, at therapy episode outset, at reporting intervals, and at discharge or to end reporting   E1

BETOS: M5D   Specialist - other

Service not separately priced by Part B

C **G8992** Other physical or occupational therapy primary functional limitation, discharge status, at discharge from therapy or to end reporting   E1

BETOS: M5D   Specialist - other

Service not separately priced by Part B

C **G8993** Other physical or occupational therapy subsequent functional limitation, current status, at therapy episode outset and at reporting intervals   E1

BETOS: M5D   Specialist - other

Service not separately priced by Part B

C **G8994** Other physical or occupational therapy subsequent functional limitation, projected goal status, at therapy episode outset, at reporting intervals, and at discharge or to end reporting   E1

BETOS: M5D   Specialist - other

Service not separately priced by Part B

C **G8995** Other physical or occupational therapy subsequent functional limitation, discharge status, at discharge from therapy or to end reporting   E1

BETOS: M5D   Specialist - other

Service not separately priced by Part B

C **G8996** Swallowing functional limitation, current status at therapy episode outset and at reporting intervals   E1

BETOS: M5D   Specialist - other

Service not separately priced by Part B

Pub: 100-4, Chap. 5, 10.6

C **G8997** Swallowing functional limitation, projected goal status, at therapy episode outset, at reporting intervals, and at discharge or to end reporting   E1

BETOS: M5D   Specialist - other

Service not separately priced by Part B

C **G8998** Swallowing functional limitation, discharge status, at discharge from therapy or to end reporting   E1

BETOS: M5D   Specialist - other

Service not separately priced by Part B

C **G8999** Motor speech functional limitation, current status at therapy episode outset and at reporting intervals   E1

BETOS: M5D   Specialist - other

Service not separately priced by Part B

MCCD (MEDICARE COORDINATED CARE DEMONSTRATION) SERVICES (G9001-G9012)

D **G9001** Coordinated care fee, initial rate   B

BETOS: Y2   Other - non-Medicare fee schedule

Service not separately priced by Part B

D **G9002** Coordinated care fee, maintenance rate   B

BETOS: Y2   Other - non-Medicare fee schedule

Service not separately priced by Part B

D **G9003** Coordinated care fee, risk adjusted high, initial   B

BETOS: Y2   Other - non-Medicare fee schedule

Service not separately priced by Part B

D **G9004** Coordinated care fee, risk adjusted low, initial   B

BETOS: Y2   Other - non-Medicare fee schedule

Service not separately priced by Part B

D **G9005** Coordinated care fee, risk adjusted maintenance   B

BETOS: Y2   Other - non-Medicare fee schedule

Service not separately priced by Part B

D **G9006** Coordinated care fee, home monitoring   B

BETOS: Y2   Other - non-Medicare fee schedule

Service not separately priced by Part B

D **G9007** Coordinated care fee, scheduled team conference   B

BETOS: Y2   Other - non-Medicare fee schedule

Service not separately priced by Part B

D **G9008** Coordinated care fee, physician coordinated care oversight services   B

BETOS: Y2   Other - non-Medicare fee schedule

Service not separately priced by Part B

D **G9009** Coordinated care fee, risk adjusted maintenance, level 3   B

BETOS: Y2   Other - non-Medicare fee schedule

Service not separately priced by Part B

D **G9010** Coordinated care fee, risk adjusted maintenance, level 4   B

BETOS: Y2   Other - non-Medicare fee schedule

Service not separately priced by Part B

D **G9011** Coordinated care fee, risk adjusted maintenance, level 5   B

BETOS: Y2   Other - non-Medicare fee schedule

Service not separately priced by Part B

▲ Revised code   ● New code   C Carrier judgment   D Special coverage instructions apply

I Not payable by Medicare   M Non-covered by Medicare   S Non-covered by Medicare statute   AHA Coding Clinic®

D **G9012** Other specified case management service not elsewhere classified   B
BETOS: Y2   Other - non-Medicare fee schedule
Service not separately priced by Part B

MEDICARE DEMONSTRATION PROJECTS (G9013-G9140)

M **G9013** ESRD demo basic bundle level I   E1
BETOS: Y2   Other - non-Medicare fee schedule
Service not separately priced by Part B

M **G9014** ESRD demo expanded bundle including venous access and related services   E1
BETOS: Y2   Other - non-Medicare fee schedule
Service not separately priced by Part B

M **G9016** Smoking cessation counseling, individual, in the absence of or in addition to any other evaluation and management service, per session (6-10 minutes) [demo project code only]   E1
BETOS: Y2   Other - non-Medicare fee schedule
Service not separately priced by Part B
Pub: 100-3, Chap. 1, Part 4, 210.4

C **G9017** Amantadine hydrochloride, oral, per 100 mg (for use in a Medicare-approved demonstration project)   A
BETOS: O1E   Other drugs
Price established by carriers

C **G9018** Zanamivir, inhalation powder, administered through inhaler, per 10 mg (for use in a Medicare-approved demonstration project)   A
BETOS: O1E   Other drugs
Price established by carriers

C **G9019** Oseltamivir phosphate, oral, per 75 mg (for use in a Medicare-approved demonstration project)   A
BETOS: O1E   Other drugs
Price established by carriers

C **G9020** Rimantadine hydrochloride, oral, per 100 mg (for use in a Medicare-approved demonstration project)   A
BETOS: O1E   Other drugs
Price established by carriers

C **G9033** Amantadine hydrochloride, oral brand, per 100 mg (for use in a Medicare-approved demonstration project)   A
BETOS: O1E   Other drugs
Price established by carriers

C **G9034** Zanamivir, inhalation powder, administered through inhaler, brand, per 10 mg (for use in a Medicare-approved demonstration project)   A
BETOS: O1E   Other drugs
Service not separately priced by Part B

C **G9035** Oseltamivir phosphate, oral, brand, per 75 mg (for use in a Medicare-approved demonstration project)   A
BETOS: O1E   Other drugs
Service not separately priced by Part B

C **G9036** Rimantadine hydrochloride, oral, brand, per 100 mg (for use in a Medicare-approved demonstration project)   A
BETOS: O1E   Other drugs
Service not separately priced by Part B

I **G9050** Oncology; primary focus of visit; work-up, evaluation, or staging at the time of cancer diagnosis or recurrence (for use in a Medicare-approved demonstration project) E1
BETOS: P7B   Oncology - other
Service not separately priced by Part B

I **G9051** Oncology; primary focus of visit; treatment decision-making after disease is staged or restaged, discussion of treatment options, supervising/coordinating active cancer directed therapy or managing consequences of cancer directed therapy (for use in a Medicare-approved demonstration project) E1
BETOS: P7B   Oncology - other
Service not separately priced by Part B

I **G9052** Oncology; primary focus of visit; surveillance for disease recurrence for patient who has completed definitive cancer-directed therapy and currently lacks evidence of recurrent disease; cancer directed therapy might be considered in the future (for use in a Medicare-approved demonstration project) E1
BETOS: P7B   Oncology - other
Service not separately priced by Part B

I **G9053** Oncology; primary focus of visit; expectant management of patient with evidence of cancer for whom no cancer directed therapy is being administered or arranged at present; cancer directed therapy might be considered in the future (for use in a Medicare-approved demonstration project) E1
BETOS: P7B   Oncology - other
Service not separately priced by Part B

I **G9054** Oncology; primary focus of visit; supervising, coordinating or managing care of patient with terminal cancer or for whom other medical illness prevents further cancer treatment; includes symptom management, end-of-life care planning, management of palliative therapies (for use in a Medicare-approved demonstration project) E1
BETOS: P7B   Oncology - other
Service not separately priced by Part B

I **G9055** Oncology; primary focus of visit; other, unspecified service not otherwise listed (for use in a Medicare-approved demonstration project) E1
BETOS: P7B   Oncology - other
Service not separately priced by Part B

♂ Male only   ♀ Female only   **A** Age   A2 - Z3 = ASC Payment indicator   A - Y = APC Status indicator
ASC = ASC-approved procedure   **DME** Paid under the DME fee schedule   **MIPS** MIPS code

I **G9056** Oncology; practice guidelines; management adheres to guidelines (for use in a Medicare-approved demonstration project)   E1
BETOS: P7B   Oncology - other
Service not separately priced by Part B

I **G9057** Oncology; practice guidelines; management differs from guidelines as a result of patient enrollment in an institutional review board approved clinical trial (for use in a Medicare-approved demonstration project)   E1
BETOS: P7B   Oncology - other
Service not separately priced by Part B

I **G9058** Oncology; practice guidelines; management differs from guidelines because the treating physician disagrees with guideline recommendations (for use in a Medicare-approved demonstration project)   E1
BETOS: P7B   Oncology - other
Service not separately priced by Part B

I **G9059** Oncology; practice guidelines; management differs from guidelines because the patient, after being offered treatment consistent with guidelines, has opted for alternative treatment or management, including no treatment (for use in a Medicare-approved demonstration project)   E1
BETOS: P7B   Oncology - other
Service not separately priced by Part B

I **G9060** Oncology; practice guidelines; management differs from guidelines for reason(s) associated with patient comorbid illness or performance status not factored into guidelines (for use in a Medicare-approved demonstration project)   E1
BETOS: P7B   Oncology - other
Service not separately priced by Part B

I **G9061** Oncology; practice guidelines; patient's condition not addressed by available guidelines (for use in a Medicare-approved demonstration project)   E1
BETOS: P7B   Oncology - other
Service not separately priced by Part B

I **G9062** Oncology; practice guidelines; management differs from guidelines for other reason(s) not listed (for use in a Medicare-approved demonstration project)   E1
BETOS: P7B   Oncology - other
Service not separately priced by Part B

C **G9063** Oncology; disease status; limited to non-small cell lung cancer; extent of disease initially established as Stage I (prior to neo-adjuvant therapy, if any) with no evidence of disease progression, recurrence, or metastases (for use in a Medicare-approved demonstration project)   M
BETOS: P7B   Oncology - other
Service not separately priced by Part B

C **G9064** Oncology; disease status; limited to non-small cell lung cancer; extent of disease initially established as Stage II (prior to neo-adjuvant therapy, if any) with no evidence of disease progression, recurrence, or metastases (for use in a Medicare-approved demonstration project)   M
BETOS: P7B   Oncology - other
Service not separately priced by Part B

C **G9065** Oncology; disease status; limited to non-small cell lung cancer; extent of disease initially established as Stage III A (prior to neo-adjuvant therapy, if any) with no evidence of disease progression, recurrence, or metastases (for use in a Medicare-approved demonstration project)   M
BETOS: P7B   Oncology - other
Service not separately priced by Part B

C **G9066** Oncology; disease status; limited to non-small cell lung cancer; Stage III B- IV at diagnosis, metastatic, locally recurrent, or progressive (for use in a Medicare-approved demonstration project)   M
BETOS: P7B   Oncology - other
Service not separately priced by Part B

C **G9067** Oncology; disease status; limited to non-small cell lung cancer; extent of disease unknown, staging in progress, or not listed (for use in a Medicare-approved demonstration project)   M
BETOS: P7B   Oncology - other
Service not separately priced by Part B

C **G9068** Oncology; disease status; limited to small cell and combined small cell/non-small cell; extent of disease initially established as limited with no evidence of disease progression, recurrence, or metastases (for use in a Medicare-approved demonstration project)   M
BETOS: P7B   Oncology - other
Service not separately priced by Part B

C **G9069** Oncology; disease status; small cell lung cancer, limited to small cell and combined small cell/non-small cell; extensive Stage at diagnosis, metastatic, locally recurrent, or progressive (for use in a Medicare-approved demonstration project)   M
BETOS: P7B   Oncology - other
Service not separately priced by Part B

C **G9070** Oncology; disease status; small cell lung cancer, limited to small cell and combined small cell/non-small; extent of disease unknown, staging in progress, or not listed (for use in a Medicare-approved demonstration project)   M
BETOS: P7B   Oncology - other
Service not separately priced by Part B

▲ Revised code   ● New code   **C** Carrier judgment   **D** Special coverage instructions apply
I Not payable by Medicare   **M** Non-covered by Medicare   **S** Non-covered by Medicare statute   AHA Coding Clinic®

C **G9071** Oncology; disease status; invasive female breast cancer (does not include ductal carcinoma in situ); adenocarcinoma as predominant cell type; Stage I or Stage IIA-IIB; or T3, N1, M0; and ER and/or pr positive; with no evidence of disease progression, recurrence, or metastases (for use in a Medicare-approved demonstration project)　　♀ M

    BETOS: P7B　Oncology - other

    Service not separately priced by Part B

C **G9072** Oncology; disease status; invasive female breast cancer (does not include ductal carcinoma in situ); adenocarcinoma as predominant cell type; Stage I, or Stage IIA-IIB; or T3, N1, M0; and ER and PR negative; with no evidence of disease progression, recurrence, or metastases (for use in a Medicare-approved demonstration project)　　♀ M

    BETOS: P7B　Oncology - other

    Service not separately priced by Part B

C **G9073** Oncology; disease status; invasive female breast cancer (does not include ductal carcinoma in situ); adenocarcinoma as predominant cell type; Stage IIIA-IIIB; and not T3, N1, M0; and ER and/or PR positive; with no evidence of disease progression, recurrence, or metastases (for use in a Medicare-approved demonstration project)　　♀ M

    BETOS: P7B　Oncology - other

    Service not separately priced by Part B

C **G9074** Oncology; disease status; invasive female breast cancer (does not include ductal carcinoma in situ); adenocarcinoma as predominant cell type; Stage IIIA-IIIB; and not T3, N1, M0; and ER and PR negative; with no evidence of disease progression, recurrence, or metastases (for use in a Medicare-approved demonstration project)　　♀ M

    BETOS: P7B　Oncology - other

    Service not separately priced by Part B

C **G9075** Oncology; disease status; invasive female breast cancer (does not include ductal carcinoma in situ); adenocarcinoma as predominant cell type; M1 at diagnosis, metastatic, locally recurrent, or progressive (for use in a Medicare-approved demonstration project)　　♀ M

    BETOS: P7B　Oncology - other

    Service not separately priced by Part B

C **G9077** Oncology; disease status; prostate cancer, limited to adenocarcinoma as predominant cell type; T1-T2C and gleason 2-7 and PSA < or equal to 20 at diagnosis with no evidence of disease progression, recurrence, or metastases (for use in a Medicare-approved demonstration project)　　♂ M

    BETOS: P7B　Oncology - other

    Service not separately priced by Part B

C **G9078** Oncology; disease status; prostate cancer, limited to adenocarcinoma as predominant cell type; T2 or T3A Gleason 8-10 or PSA > 20 at diagnosis with no evidence of disease progression, recurrence, or metastases (for use in a Medicare-approved demonstration project)　　♂ M

    BETOS: P7B　Oncology - other

    Service not separately priced by Part B

C **G9079** Oncology; disease status; prostate cancer, limited to adenocarcinoma as predominant cell type; T3B-T4, any N; any T, N1 at diagnosis with no evidence of disease progression, recurrence, or metastases (for use in a Medicare-approved demonstration project)　　♂ M

    BETOS: P7B　Oncology - other

    Service not separately priced by Part B

C **G9080** Oncology; disease status; prostate cancer, limited to adenocarcinoma; after initial treatment with rising PSA or failure of PSA decline (for use in a Medicare-approved demonstration project)　　♂ M

    BETOS: P7B　Oncology - other

    Service not separately priced by Part B

C **G9083** Oncology; disease status; prostate cancer, limited to adenocarcinoma; extent of disease unknown, staging in progress, or not listed (for use in a Medicare-approved demonstration project)　　♂ M

    BETOS: P7B　Oncology - other

    Service not separately priced by Part B

C **G9084** Oncology; disease status; colon cancer, limited to invasive cancer, adenocarcinoma as predominant cell type; extent of disease initially established as T1-3, N0, M0 with no evidence of disease progression, recurrence, or metastases (for use in a Medicare-approved demonstration project)　　M

    BETOS: P7B　Oncology - other

    Service not separately priced by Part B

C **G9085** Oncology; disease status; colon cancer, limited to invasive cancer, adenocarcinoma as predominant cell type; extent of disease initially established as T4, N0, M0 with no evidence of disease progression, recurrence, or metastases (for use in a Medicare-approved demonstration project)　　M

    BETOS: P7B　Oncology - other

    Service not separately priced by Part B

C **G9086** Oncology; disease status; colon cancer, limited to invasive cancer, adenocarcinoma as predominant cell type; extent of disease initially established as T1-4, N1-2, M0 with no evidence of disease progression, recurrence, or metastases (for use in a Medicare-approved demonstration project) M

    BETOS: P7B　Oncology - other

    Service not separately priced by Part B

♂ Male only　　♀ Female only　　🅐 Age　　A2 - Z3 = ASC Payment indicator　　A - Y = APC Status indicator

ASC = ASC-approved procedure　　**DME** Paid under the DME fee schedule　　**MIPS** MIPS code

C **G9087** Oncology; disease status; colon cancer, limited to invasive cancer, adenocarcinoma as predominant cell type; M1 at diagnosis, metastatic, locally recurrent, or progressive with current clinical, radiologic, or biochemical evidence of disease (for use in a Medicare-approved demonstration project) M
BETOS: P7B   Oncology - other
Service not separately priced by Part B

C **G9088** Oncology; disease status; colon cancer, limited to invasive cancer, adenocarcinoma as predominant cell type; M1 at diagnosis, metastatic, locally recurrent, or progressive without current clinical, radiologic, or biochemical evidence of disease (for use in a Medicare-approved demonstration project) M
BETOS: P7B   Oncology - other
Service not separately priced by Part B

C **G9089** Oncology; disease status; colon cancer, limited to invasive cancer, adenocarcinoma as predominant cell type; extent of disease unknown, staging in progress, or not listed (for use in a Medicare-approved demonstration project)   M
BETOS: P7B   Oncology - other
Service not separately priced by Part B

C **G9090** Oncology; disease status; rectal cancer, limited to invasive cancer, adenocarcinoma as predominant cell type; extent of disease initially established as T1-2, N0, M0 (prior to neo-adjuvant therapy, if any) with no evidence of disease progression, recurrence, or metastases (for use in a Medicare-approved demonstration project)   M
BETOS: P7B   Oncology - other
Service not separately priced by Part B

C **G9091** Oncology; disease status; rectal cancer, limited to invasive cancer, adenocarcinoma as predominant cell type; extent of disease initially established as T3, N0, M0 (prior to neo-adjuvant therapy, if any) with no evidence of disease progression, recurrence, or metastases (for use in a Medicare-approved demonstration project)   M
BETOS: P7B   Oncology - other
Service not separately priced by Part B

C **G9092** Oncology; disease status; rectal cancer, limited to invasive cancer, adenocarcinoma as predominant cell type; extent of disease initially established as T1-3, N1-2, M0 (prior to neo-adjuvant therapy, if any) with no evidence of disease progression, recurrence or metastases (for use in a Medicare-approved demonstration project)   M
BETOS: P7B   Oncology - other
Service not separately priced by Part B

C **G9093** Oncology; disease status; rectal cancer, limited to invasive cancer, adenocarcinoma as predominant cell type; extent of disease

initially established as T4, any N, M0 (prior to neo-adjuvant therapy, if any) with no evidence of disease progression, recurrence, or metastases (for use in a Medicare-approved demonstration project)   M
BETOS: P7B   Oncology - other
Service not separately priced by Part B

C **G9094** Oncology; disease status; rectal cancer, limited to invasive cancer, adenocarcinoma as predominant cell type; M1 at diagnosis, metastatic, locally recurrent, or progressive (for use in a Medicare-approved demonstration project)   M
BETOS: P7B   Oncology - other
Service not separately priced by Part B

C **G9095** Oncology; disease status; rectal cancer, limited to invasive cancer, adenocarcinoma as predominant cell type; extent of disease unknown, staging in progress, or not listed (for use in a Medicare-approved demonstration project)   M
BETOS: P7B   Oncology - other
Service not separately priced by Part B

C **G9096** Oncology; disease status; esophageal cancer, limited to adenocarcinoma or squamous cell carcinoma as predominant cell type; extent of disease initially established as T1-T3, N0-N1 or NX (prior to neo-adjuvant therapy, if any) with no evidence of disease progression, recurrence, or metastases (for use in a Medicare-approved demonstration project)   M
BETOS: P7B   Oncology - other
Service not separately priced by Part B

C **G9097** Oncology; disease status; esophageal cancer, limited to adenocarcinoma or squamous cell carcinoma as predominant cell type; extent of disease initially established as T4, any N, M0 (prior to neo-adjuvant therapy, if any) with no evidence of disease progression, recurrence, or metastases (for use in a Medicare-approved demonstration project)   M
BETOS: P7B   Oncology - other
Service not separately priced by Part B

C **G9098** Oncology; disease status; esophageal cancer, limited to adenocarcinoma or squamous cell carcinoma as predominant cell type; M1 at diagnosis, metastatic, locally recurrent, or progressive (for use in a Medicare-approved demonstration project) M
BETOS: P7B   Oncology - other
Service not separately priced by Part B

C **G9099** Oncology; disease status; esophageal cancer, limited to adenocarcinoma or squamous cell carcinoma as predominant cell type; extent of disease unknown, staging in progress, or not listed (for use in a Medicare-approved demonstration project) M
BETOS: P7B   Oncology - other
Service not separately priced by Part B

▲ Revised code   ● New code   **C** Carrier judgment   **D** Special coverage instructions apply
I Not payable by Medicare   **M** Non-covered by Medicare   **S** Non-covered by Medicare statute   AHA Coding Clinic®

C **G9100** Oncology; disease status; gastric cancer, limited to adenocarcinoma as predominant cell type; post R0 resection (with or without neoadjuvant therapy) with no evidence of disease recurrence, progression, or metastases (for use in a Medicare-approved demonstration project) M

BETOS: P7B   Oncology - other
Service not separately priced by Part B

C **G9101** Oncology; disease status; gastric cancer, limited to adenocarcinoma as predominant cell type; post R1 or R2 resection (with or without neoadjuvant therapy) with no evidence of disease progression, or metastases (for use in a Medicare-approved demonstration project) M

BETOS: P7B   Oncology - other
Service not separately priced by Part B

C **G9102** Oncology; disease status; gastric cancer, limited to adenocarcinoma as predominant cell type; clinical or pathologic M0, unresectable with no evidence of disease progression, or metastases (for use in a Medicare-approved demonstration project) M

BETOS: P7B   Oncology - other
Service not separately priced by Part B

C **G9103** Oncology; disease status; gastric cancer, limited to adenocarcinoma as predominant cell type; clinical or pathologic M1 at diagnosis, metastatic, locally recurrent, or progressive (for use in a Medicare-approved demonstration project) M

BETOS: P7B   Oncology - other
Service not separately priced by Part B

C **G9104** Oncology; disease status; gastric cancer, limited to adenocarcinoma as predominant cell type; extent of disease unknown, staging in progress, or not listed (for use in a Medicare-approved demonstration project) M

BETOS: P7B   Oncology - other
Service not separately priced by Part B

C **G9105** Oncology; disease status; pancreatic cancer, limited to adenocarcinoma as predominant cell type; post R0 resection without evidence of disease progression, recurrence, or metastases (for use in a Medicare-approved demonstration project) M

BETOS: P7B   Oncology - other
Service not separately priced by Part B

C **G9106** Oncology; disease status; pancreatic cancer, limited to adenocarcinoma; post R1 or R2 resection with no evidence of disease progression, or metastases (for use in a Medicare-approved demonstration project) M

BETOS: P7B   Oncology - other
Service not separately priced by Part B

C **G9107** Oncology; disease status; pancreatic cancer, limited to adenocarcinoma; unresectable at diagnosis, M1 at diagnosis, metastatic, locally recurrent, or progressive (for use in a Medicare-approved demonstration project) M

BETOS: P7B   Oncology - other
Service not separately priced by Part B

C **G9108** Oncology; disease status; pancreatic cancer, limited to adenocarcinoma; extent of disease unknown, staging in progress, or not listed (for use in a Medicare-approved demonstration project) M

BETOS: P7B   Oncology - other
Service not separately priced by Part B

C **G9109** Oncology; disease status; head and neck cancer, limited to cancers of oral cavity, pharynx and larynx with squamous cell as predominant cell type; extent of disease initially established as T1-T2 and N0, M0 (prior to neo-adjuvant therapy, if any) with no evidence of disease progression, recurrence, or metastases (for use in a Medicare-approved demonstration project) M

BETOS: P7B   Oncology - other
Service not separately priced by Part B

C **G9110** Oncology; disease status; head and neck cancer, limited to cancers of oral cavity, pharynx and larynx with squamous cell as predominant cell type; extent of disease initially established as T3-4 and/or N1-3, M0 (prior to neo-adjuvant therapy, if any) with no evidence of disease progression, recurrence, or metastases (for use in a Medicare-approved demonstration project) M

BETOS: P7B   Oncology - other
Service not separately priced by Part B

C **G9111** Oncology; disease status; head and neck cancer, limited to cancers of oral cavity, pharynx and larynx with squamous cell as predominant cell type; M1 at diagnosis, metastatic, locally recurrent, or progressive (for use in a Medicare-approved demonstration project) M

BETOS: P7B   Oncology - other
Service not separately priced by Part B

C **G9112** Oncology; disease status; head and neck cancer, limited to cancers of oral cavity, pharynx and larynx with squamous cell as predominant cell type; extent of disease unknown, staging in progress, or not listed (for use in a Medicare-approved demonstration project) M

BETOS: P7B   Oncology - other
Service not separately priced by Part B

C **G9113** Oncology; disease status; ovarian cancer, limited to epithelial cancer; pathologic Stage IA-B (Grade 1) without evidence of disease progression, recurrence, or metastases (for use in a Medicare-approved demonstration project) ♀ M

BETOS: P7B   Oncology - other
Service not separately priced by Part B

C **G9114** Oncology; disease status; ovarian cancer, limited to epithelial cancer; pathologic Stage IA-B (Grade 2-3); or Stage IC (all grades); or Stage II; without evidence of disease progression, recurrence, or metastases (for use in a Medicare-approved demonstration project) ♀ M
BETOS: P7B   Oncology - other
Service not separately priced by Part B

C **G9115** Oncology; disease status; ovarian cancer, limited to epithelial cancer; pathologic Stage III-IV; without evidence of progression, recurrence, or metastases (for use in a Medicare-approved demonstration project) ♀ M
BETOS: P7B   Oncology - other
Service not separately priced by Part B

C **G9116** Oncology; disease status; ovarian cancer, limited to epithelial cancer; evidence of disease progression, or recurrence, and/or platinum resistance (for use in a Medicare-approved demonstration project) ♀ M
BETOS: P7B   Oncology - other
Service not separately priced by Part B

C **G9117** Oncology; disease status; ovarian cancer, limited to epithelial cancer; extent of disease unknown, staging in progress, or not listed (for use in a Medicare-approved demonstration project) ♀ M
BETOS: P7B   Oncology - other
Service not separately priced by Part B

C **G9123** Oncology; disease status; chronic myelogenous leukemia, limited to Philadelphia chromosome positive and/or BCR-ABL positive; chronic phase not in hematologic, cytogenetic, or molecular remission (for use in a Medicare-approved demonstration project) M
BETOS: P7B   Oncology - other
Service not separately priced by Part B

C **G9124** Oncology; disease status; chronic myelogenous leukemia, limited to Philadelphia chromosome positive and/or BCR-ABL positive; accelerated phase not in hematologic cytogenetic, or molecular remission (for use in a Medicare-approved demonstration project) M
BETOS: P7B   Oncology - other
Service not separately priced by Part B

C **G9125** Oncology; disease status; chronic myelogenous leukemia, limited to Philadelphia chromosome positive and/or BCR-ABL positive; blast phase not in hematologic, cytogenetic, or molecular remission (for use in a Medicare-approved demonstration project) M
BETOS: P7B   Oncology - other
Service not separately priced by Part B

C **G9126** Oncology; disease status; chronic myelogenous leukemia, limited to Philadelphia chromosome positive and/or BCR-ABL positive; in hematologic, cytogenetic, or molecular remission (for use in a Medicare-approved demonstration project) M
BETOS: P7B   Oncology - other
Service not separately priced by Part B

C **G9128** Oncology; disease status; limited to multiple myeloma, systemic disease; smoldering, Stage I (for use in a Medicare-approved demonstration project) M
BETOS: P7B   Oncology - other
Service not separately priced by Part B

C **G9129** Oncology; disease status; limited to multiple myeloma, systemic disease; Stage II or higher (for use in a Medicare-approved demonstration project) M
BETOS: P7B   Oncology - other
Service not separately priced by Part B

C **G9130** Oncology; disease status; limited to multiple myeloma, systemic disease; extent of disease unknown, staging in progress, or not listed (for use in a Medicare-approved demonstration project) M
BETOS: P7B   Oncology - other
Service not separately priced by Part B

C **G9131** Oncology; disease status; invasive female breast cancer (does not include ductal carcinoma in situ); adenocarcinoma as predominant cell type; extent of disease unknown, staging in progress, or not listed (for use in a Medicare-approved demonstration project) ♀ M
BETOS: P7B   Oncology - other
Service not separately priced by Part B

C **G9132** Oncology; disease status; prostate cancer, limited to adenocarcinoma; hormone-refractory/androgen-independent (e.g., rising PSA on anti-androgen therapy or post-orchiectomy); clinical metastases (for use in a Medicare-approved demonstration project) ♂ M
BETOS: P7B   Oncology - other
Service not separately priced by Part B

C **G9133** Oncology; disease status; prostate cancer, limited to adenocarcinoma; hormone-responsive; clinical metastases or M1 at diagnosis (for use in a Medicare-approved demonstration project) ♂ M
BETOS: P7B   Oncology - other
Service not separately priced by Part B

C **G9134** Oncology; disease status; non-Hodgkin's lymphoma, any cellular classification; Stage I, II at diagnosis, not relapsed, not refractory (for use in a Medicare-approved demonstration project) M

▲ Revised code   ● New code   C Carrier judgment   D Special coverage instructions apply
I Not payable by Medicare   M Non-covered by Medicare   S Non-covered by Medicare statute   AHA Coding Clinic®

BETOS: P7B Oncology - other
Service not separately priced by Part B

C **G9135** Oncology; disease status; non-Hodgkin's lymphoma, any cellular classification; Stage III, IV, not relapsed, not refractory (for use in a Medicare-approved demonstration project) M

BETOS: P7B Oncology - other
Service not separately priced by Part B

C **G9136** Oncology; disease status; non-Hodgkin's lymphoma, transformed from original cellular diagnosis to a second cellular classification (for use in a Medicare-approved demonstration project) M

BETOS: P7B Oncology - other
Service not separately priced by Part B

C **G9137** Oncology; disease status; non-Hodgkin's lymphoma, any cellular classification; relapsed/refractory (for use in a Medicare-approved demonstration project) M

BETOS: P7B Oncology - other
Service not separately priced by Part B

C **G9138** Oncology; disease status; non-Hodgkin's lymphoma, any cellular classification; diagnostic evaluation, stage not determined, evaluation of possible relapse or non-response to therapy, or not listed (for use in a Medicare-approved demonstration project) M

BETOS: P7B Oncology - other
Service not separately priced by Part B

C **G9139** Oncology; disease status; chronic myelogenous leukemia, limited to Philadelphia chromosome positive and/or BCR-ABL positive; extent of disease unknown, staging in progress, not listed (for use in a Medicare-approved demonstration project) M

BETOS: P7B Oncology - other
Service not separately priced by Part B

C **G9140** Frontier extended stay clinic demonstration; for a patient stay in a clinic approved for the CMS demonstration project; the following measures should be present: the stay must be equal to or greater than 4 hours; weather or other conditions must prevent transfer or the case falls into a category of monitoring and observation cases that are permitted by the rules of the demonstration; there is a maximum frontier extended stay clinic (FESC) visit of 48 hours, except in the case when weather or other conditions prevent transfer; payment is made on each period up to 4 hours, after the first 4 hours A

BETOS: Z2 Undefined codes
Service not separately priced by Part B

WARFARIN RESPONSIVENESS TESTING (G9143)

C **G9143** Warfarin responsiveness testing by genetic technique using any method, any number of specimen(s) N

BETOS: M5D Specialist - other
Price established by carriers
Coding Clinic: 2010, Q1
Pub: 100-3, Chap. 1, Part 2, 90.1; 100-4, Chap. 32, 250.1; 100-4, Chap. 32, 250.2

OUTPATIENT INTRAVENOUS INSULIN TREATMENT (G9147)

M **G9147** Outpatient intravenous insulin treatment (OIVIT) either pulsatile or continuous, by any means, guided by the results of measurements for: respiratory quotient; and/or, urine urea nitrogen (UUN); and/or, arterial, venous or capillary glucose; and/or potassium concentration E1

BETOS: P5E Ambulatory procedures - other
Service not separately priced by Part B
Coding Clinic: 2010, Q1
Pub: 100-3, Chap. 1, Part 1, 40.7; 100-4, Chap. 4, 320.1; 100-4, Chap. 4, 320.2

PRIMARY CARE QUALITY MEASURES (G9148-G9153)

C **G9148** National Committee for Quality Assurance - Level 1 medical home M

BETOS: Z2 Undefined codes
Service not separately priced by Part B

C **G9149** National Committee for Quality Assurance - Level 2 medical home M

BETOS: Z2 Undefined codes
Service not separately priced by Part B

C **G9150** National Committee for Quality Assurance - Level 3 medical home M

BETOS: Z2 Undefined codes
Service not separately priced by Part B

C **G9151** MAPCP Demonstration - state provided services M

BETOS: Z2 Undefined codes
Service not separately priced by Part B

C **G9152** MAPCP Demonstration - Community Health Teams M

BETOS: Z2 Undefined codes
Service not separately priced by Part B

C **G9153** MAPCP Demonstration - Physician Incentive Pool M

BETOS: Z2 Undefined codes
Service not separately priced by Part B

PROVIDER ASSESSMENT FOR WHEELCHAIR (G9156)

C **G9156** Evaluation for wheelchair requiring face to face visit with physician M

BETOS: Z2 Undefined codes
Service not separately priced by Part B

♂ Male only	♀ Female only	Ⓐ Age	A2 - Z3 = ASC Payment indicator	A - Y = APC Status indicator
	ASC = ASC-approved procedure	**DME** Paid under the DME fee schedule	**MIPS** MIPS code	

DIAGNOSTIC CARDIAC DOPPLER ULTRASOUND (G9157)

C **G9157** Transesophageal doppler measurement of cardiac output (including probe placement, image acquisition, and interpretation per course of treatment) for monitoring purposes B
BETOS: T2C   Other tests - EKG monitoring
Service not separately priced by Part B
Pub: 100-4, Chap. 32, 310; 100-4, Chap. 32, 310.2

FUNCTIONAL LIMITATION REPORTING (G9158-G9186)

C **G9158** Motor speech functional limitation, discharge status, at discharge from therapy or to end reporting E1
BETOS: M5D   Specialist - other
Service not separately priced by Part B
Pub: 100-4, Chap. 5, 10.6

C **G9159** Spoken language comprehension functional limitation, current status at therapy episode outset and at reporting intervals E1
BETOS: M5D   Specialist - other
Service not separately priced by Part B

C **G9160** Spoken language comprehension functional limitation, projected goal status at therapy episode outset, at reporting intervals, and at discharge or to end reporting E1
BETOS: M5D   Specialist - other
Service not separately priced by Part B

C **G9161** Spoken language comprehension functional limitation, discharge status, at discharge from therapy or to end reporting E1
BETOS: M5D   Specialist - other
Service not separately priced by Part B

C **G9162** Spoken language expression functional limitation, current status at therapy episode outset and at reporting intervals E1
BETOS: M5D   Specialist - other
Service not separately priced by Part B

C **G9163** Spoken language expression functional limitation, projected goal status at therapy episode outset, at reporting intervals, and at discharge or to end reporting E1
BETOS: M5D   Specialist - other
Service not separately priced by Part B

C **G9164** Spoken language expression functional limitation, discharge status at discharge from therapy or to end reporting E1
BETOS: M5D   Specialist - other
Service not separately priced by Part B

C **G9165** Attention functional limitation, current status at therapy episode outset and at reporting intervals E1
BETOS: M5D   Specialist - other
Service not separately priced by Part B

C **G9166** Attention functional limitation, projected goal status at therapy episode outset, at reporting intervals, and at discharge or to end reporting E1
BETOS: M5D   Specialist - other
Service not separately priced by Part B

C **G9167** Attention functional limitation, discharge status at discharge from therapy or to end reporting E1
BETOS: M5D   Specialist - other
Service not separately priced by Part B

C **G9168** Memory functional limitation, current status at therapy episode outset and at reporting intervals E1
BETOS: M5D   Specialist - other
Service not separately priced by Part B

C **G9169** Memory functional limitation, projected goal status at therapy episode outset, at reporting intervals, and at discharge or to end reporting E1
BETOS: M5D   Specialist - other
Service not separately priced by Part B

C **G9170** Memory functional limitation, discharge status at discharge from therapy or to end reporting E1
BETOS: M5D   Specialist - other
Service not separately priced by Part B

C **G9171** Voice functional limitation, current status at therapy episode outset and at reporting intervals E1
BETOS: M5D   Specialist - other
Service not separately priced by Part B

C **G9172** Voice functional limitation, projected goal status at therapy episode outset, at reporting intervals, and at discharge or to end reporting E1
BETOS: M5D   Specialist - other
Service not separately priced by Part B

C **G9173** Voice functional limitation, discharge status at discharge from therapy or to end reporting E1
BETOS: M5D   Specialist - other
Service not separately priced by Part B

C **G9174** Other speech language pathology functional limitation, current status at therapy episode outset and at reporting intervals E1
BETOS: M5D   Specialist - other
Service not separately priced by Part B

C **G9175** Other speech language pathology functional limitation, projected goal status at therapy episode outset, at reporting intervals, and at discharge or to end reporting E1
BETOS: M5D   Specialist - other
Service not separately priced by Part B

C **G9176** Other speech language pathology functional limitation, discharge status at discharge from therapy or to end reporting E1
BETOS: M5D   Specialist - other
Service not separately priced by Part B

▲ Revised code   ● New code   **C** Carrier judgment   **D** Special coverage instructions apply
I Not payable by Medicare   **M** Non-covered by Medicare   **S** Non-covered by Medicare statute   AHA Coding Clinic®

C **G9186** Motor speech functional limitation, projected goal status at therapy episode outset, at reporting intervals, and at discharge or to end reporting   E1

    BETOS: M5D   Specialist - other
    Service not separately priced by Part B
    Pub: 100-4, Chap. 5, 10.6

BUNDLED PAYMENT CARE (G9187)

C **G9187** Bundled payments for care improvement initiative home visit for patient assessment performed by a qualified health care professional for individuals not considered homebound including, but not limited to, assessment of safety, falls, clinical status, fluid status, medication reconciliation/management, patient compliance with orders/plan of care, performance of activities of daily living, appropriateness of care setting; (for use only in the Medicare-approved bundled payments for care improvement initiative); may not be billed for a 30-day period covered by a transitional care management code   E1

    BETOS: M5D   Specialist - other
    Price established by carriers

ADDITIONAL ASSORTED QUALITY MEASURES (G9188-G9977)

C **G9188** Beta-blocker therapy not prescribed, reason not given   M

    BETOS: M5B   Specialist - psychiatry
    Service not separately priced by Part B

C **G9189** Beta-blocker therapy prescribed or currently being taken   M

    BETOS: M5B   Specialist - psychiatry
    Service not separately priced by Part B

C **G9190** Documentation of medical reason(s) for not prescribing beta-blocker therapy (e.g., allergy, intolerance, other medical reasons)   M

    BETOS: M5B   Specialist - psychiatry
    Service not separately priced by Part B

C **G9191** Documentation of patient reason(s) for not prescribing beta-blocker therapy (e.g., patient declined, other patient reasons)   M

    BETOS: M5B   Specialist - psychiatry
    Service not separately priced by Part B

C **G9192** Documentation of system reason(s) for not prescribing beta-blocker therapy (e.g., other reasons attributable to the health care system)   M

    BETOS: M5B   Specialist - psychiatry
    Service not separately priced by Part B

C **G9196** Documentation of medical reason(s) for not ordering a first or second generation cephalosporin for antimicrobial prophylaxis (e.g., patients enrolled in clinical trials, patients with documented infection prior to surgical procedure of interest, patients who were receiving antibiotics more than 24 hours prior to surgery [except colon surgery patients taking oral prophylactic antibiotics], patients who were receiving antibiotics within 24 hours prior to arrival [except colon surgery patients taking oral prophylactic antibiotics], other medical reason(s))   M MIPS

    BETOS: M5B   Specialist - psychiatry
    Service not separately priced by Part B

C **G9197** Documentation of order for first or second generation cephalosporin for antimicrobial prophylaxis   M MIPS

    BETOS: M5B   Specialist - psychiatry
    Service not separately priced by Part B

C **G9198** Order for first or second generation cephalosporin for antimicrobial prophylaxis was not documented, reason not given   M MIPS

    BETOS: M5B   Specialist - psychiatry
    Service not separately priced by Part B

C **G9212** DSM-IVTM criteria for major depressive disorder documented at the initial evaluation   M

    BETOS: M5B   Specialist - psychiatry
    Service not separately priced by Part B

C **G9213** DSM-IV-TR criteria for major depressive disorder not documented at the initial evaluation, reason not otherwise specified   M

    BETOS: M5B   Specialist - psychiatry
    Service not separately priced by Part B

C **G9223** Pneumocystis jiroveci pneumonia prophylaxis prescribed within 3 months of low CD4+ cell count below 500 cells/mm3 or a CD4 percentage below 15%   M

    BETOS: M5B   Specialist - psychiatry
    Service not separately priced by Part B

C **G9225** Foot exam was not performed, reason not given   M

    BETOS: M5B   Specialist - psychiatry
    Service not separately priced by Part B

C **G9226** Foot examination performed (includes examination through visual inspection, sensory exam with 10-g monofilament plus testing any one of the following: vibration using 128-Hz tuning fork, pinprick sensation, ankle reflexes, or vibration perception threshold, and pulse exam; report when all of the 3 components are completed)   M

    BETOS: M5B   Specialist - psychiatry
    Service not separately priced by Part B

▲ **C** **G9227** Functional outcome assessment documented, care plan not documented, documentation the patient is not eligible for a care plan at the time of the encounter   M MIPS

    BETOS: M5B   Specialist - psychiatry
    Service not separately priced by Part B

♂ Male only   ♀ Female only   **A** Age   A2 - Z3 = ASC Payment indicator   A - Y = APC Status indicator
ASC = ASC-approved procedure   **DME** Paid under the DME fee schedule   **MIPS** MIPS code

G9228 Chlamydia, gonorrhea and syphilis screening results documented (report when results are present for all of the 3 screenings) M

BETOS: M5B   Specialist - psychiatry
Service not separately priced by Part B

G9229 Chlamydia, gonorrhea, and syphilis screening results not documented (patient refusal is the only allowed exception) M

BETOS: M5B   Specialist - psychiatry
Service not separately priced by Part B

G9230 Chlamydia, gonorrhea, and syphilis not screened, reason not given M

BETOS: M5B   Specialist - psychiatry
Service not separately priced by Part B

G9231 Documentation of end stage renal disease (ESRD), dialysis, renal transplant before or during the measurement period or pregnancy during the measurement period M MIPS

BETOS: M5B   Specialist - psychiatry
Service not separately priced by Part B

G9232 Clinician treating major depressive disorder did not communicate to clinician treating comorbid condition for specified patient reason (e.g., patient is unable to communicate the diagnosis of a comorbid condition; the patient is unwilling to communicate the diagnosis of a comorbid condition; or the patient is unaware of the comorbid condition, or any other specified patient reason) M

BETOS: M5B   Specialist - psychiatry
Service not separately priced by Part B

G9239 Documentation of reasons for patient initiaiting maintenance hemodialysis with a catheter as the mode of vascular access (e.g., patient has a maturing AVF/AVG, time-limited trial of hemodialysis, other medical reasons, patient declined AVF/AVG, other patient reasons, patient followed by reporting nephrologist for fewer than 90 days, other system reasons) M

BETOS: M5B   Specialist - psychiatry
Service not separately priced by Part B

G9240 Patient whose mode of vascular access is a catheter at the time maintenance hemodialysis is initiated M

BETOS: M5B   Specialist - psychiatry
Service not separately priced by Part B

G9241 Patient whose mode of vascular access is not a catheter at the time maintenance hemodialysis is initiated M

BETOS: M5B   Specialist - psychiatry
Service not separately priced by Part B

G9242 Documentation of viral load equal to or greater than 200 copies/ml or viral load not performed M

BETOS: M5B   Specialist - psychiatry
Service not separately priced by Part B

G9243 Documentation of viral load less than 200 copies/ml M

BETOS: M5B   Specialist - psychiatry
Service not separately priced by Part B

G9246 Patient did not have at least one medical visit in each 6 month period of the 24 month measurement period, with a minimum of 60 days between medical visits M

BETOS: M5B   Specialist - psychiatry
Service not separately priced by Part B

G9247 Patient had at least one medical visit in each 6 month period of the 24 month measurement period, with a minimum of 60 days between medical visits M

BETOS: M5B   Specialist - psychiatry
Service not separately priced by Part B

G9250 Documentation of patient pain brought to a comfortable level within 48 hours from initial assessment M

BETOS: M5B   Specialist - psychiatry
Service not separately priced by Part B

G9251 Documentation of patient with pain not brought to a comfortable level within 48 hours from initial assessment M

BETOS: M5B   Specialist - psychiatry
Service not separately priced by Part B

G9254 Documentation of patient discharged to home later than post-operative day 2 following CAS M

BETOS: M5B   Specialist - psychiatry
Service not separately priced by Part B

G9255 Documentation of patient discharged to home no later than post operative day 2 following CAS M

BETOS: M5B   Specialist - psychiatry
Service not separately priced by Part B

G9256 Documentation of patient death following CAS M

BETOS: M5B   Specialist - psychiatry
Service not separately priced by Part B

G9257 Documentation of patient stroke following CAS M

BETOS: M5B   Specialist - psychiatry
Service not separately priced by Part B

G9258 Documentation of patient stroke following CEA M

BETOS: M5B   Specialist - psychiatry
Service not separately priced by Part B

G9259 Documentation of patient survival and absence of stroke following CAS M

BETOS: M5B   Specialist - psychiatry
Service not separately priced by Part B

G9260 Documentation of patient death following CEA M

BETOS: M5B   Specialist - psychiatry
Service not separately priced by Part B

C G9261 Documentation of patient survival and absence of stroke following CEA M
BETOS: M5B Specialist - psychiatry
Service not separately priced by Part B

C G9262 Documentation of patient death in the hospital following endovascular AAA repair M
BETOS: M5B Specialist - psychiatry
Service not separately priced by Part B

▲ **C G9263** Documentation of patient discharged alive following endovascular AAA repair M
BETOS: M5B Specialist - psychiatry
Service not separately priced by Part B

C G9264 Documentation of patient receiving maintenance hemodialysis for greater than or equal to 90 days with a catheter for documented reasons (e.g., other medical reasons, patient declined AVF/AVG, other patient reasons) M
BETOS: M5B Specialist - psychiatry
Service not separately priced by Part B

C G9265 Patient receiving maintenance hemodialysis for greater than or equal to 90 days with a catheter as the mode of vascular access M
BETOS: M5B Specialist - psychiatry
Service not separately priced by Part B

C G9266 Patient receiving maintenance hemodialysis for greater than or equal to 90 days without a catheter as the mode of vascular access M
BETOS: M5B Specialist - psychiatry
Service not separately priced by Part B

C G9267 Documentation of patient with one or more complications or mortality within 30 days M
BETOS: M5B Specialist - psychiatry
Service not separately priced by Part B

C G9268 Documentation of patient with one or more complications within 90 days M
BETOS: M5B Specialist - psychiatry
Service not separately priced by Part B

C G9269 Documentation of patient without one or more complications and without mortality within 30 days M
BETOS: M5B Specialist - psychiatry
Service not separately priced by Part B

C G9270 Documentation of patient without one or more complications within 90 days M
BETOS: M5B Specialist - psychiatry
Service not separately priced by Part B

C G9273 Blood pressure has a systolic value of < 140 and a diastolic value of < 90 M
BETOS: M5B Specialist - psychiatry
Service not separately priced by Part B

C G9274 Blood pressure has a systolic value of =140 and a diastolic value of = 90 or systolic value < 140 and diastolic value = 90 or systolic value = 140 and diastolic value < 90 M
BETOS: M5B Specialist - psychiatry
Service not separately priced by Part B

C G9275 Documentation that patient is a current non-tobacco user M
BETOS: M5B Specialist - psychiatry
Service not separately priced by Part B

C G9276 Documentation that patient is a current tobacco user M
BETOS: M5B Specialist - psychiatry
Service not separately priced by Part B

C G9277 Documentation that the patient is on daily aspirin or anti-platelet or has documentation of a valid contraindication or exception to aspirin/anti-platelet; contraindications/exceptions include anti-coagulant use, allergy to aspirin or anti-platelets, history of gastrointestinal bleed and bleeding disorder; additionally, the following exceptions documented by the physician as a reason for not taking daily aspirin or anti-platelet are acceptable (use of non-steroidal anti-inflammatory agents, documented risk for drug interaction, uncontrolled hypertension defined as >180 systolic or >110 diastolic or gastroesophageal reflux) M
BETOS: M5B Specialist - psychiatry
Service not separately priced by Part B

C G9278 Documentation that the patient is not on daily aspirin or anti-platelet regimen M
BETOS: M5B Specialist - psychiatry
Service not separately priced by Part B

C G9279 Pneumococcal screening performed and documentation of vaccination received prior to discharge M
BETOS: M5B Specialist - psychiatry
Service not separately priced by Part B

C G9280 Pneumococcal vaccination not administered prior to discharge, reason not specified M
BETOS: M5B Specialist - psychiatry
Service not separately priced by Part B

C G9281 Screening performed and documentation that vaccination not indicated/patient refusal M
BETOS: M5B Specialist - psychiatry
Service not separately priced by Part B

C G9282 Documentation of medical reason(s) for not reporting the histological type or NSCLC-NOS classification with an explanation (e.g., biopsy taken for other purposes in a patient with a history of non-small cell lung cancer or other documented medical reasons) M
BETOS: M5B Specialist - psychiatry
Service not separately priced by Part B

C G9283 Non-small cell lung cancer biopsy and cytology specimen report documents classification into specific histologic type or classified as NSCLC-NOS with an explanation M
BETOS: M5B Specialist - psychiatry
Service not separately priced by Part B

♂ Male only ♀ Female only 🄰 Age A2 - Z3 = ASC Payment indicator A - Y = APC Status indicator

ASC = ASC-approved procedure **DME** Paid under the DME fee schedule **MIPS** MIPS code

C **G9284** Non-small cell lung cancer biopsy and cytology specimen report does not document classification into specific histologic type or classified as NSCLC-NOS with an explanation   M

BETOS: M5B   Specialist - psychiatry
Service not separately priced by Part B

C **G9285** Specimen site other than anatomic location of lung or is not classified as non-small cell lung cancer   M

BETOS: M5B   Specialist - psychiatry
Service not separately priced by Part B

C **G9286** Antibiotic regimen prescribed within 10 days after onset of symptoms   M

BETOS: M5B   Specialist - psychiatry
Service not separately priced by Part B

C **G9287** Antibiotic regimen not prescribed within 10 days after onset of symptoms   M

BETOS: M5B   Specialist - psychiatry
Service not separately priced by Part B

C **G9288** Documentation of medical reason(s) for not reporting the histological type or NSCLC-NOS classification with an explanation (e.g., a solitary fibrous tumor in a person with a history of non-small cell carcinoma or other documented medical reasons)   M

BETOS: M5B   Specialist - psychiatry
Service not separately priced by Part B

C **G9289** Non-small cell lung cancer biopsy and cytology specimen report documents classification into specific histologic type or classified as NSCLC-NOS with an explanation   M

BETOS: M5B   Specialist - psychiatry
Service not separately priced by Part B

C **G9290** Non-small cell lung cancer biopsy and cytology specimen report does not document classification into specific histologic type or classified as NSCLC-NOS with an explanation   M

BETOS: M5B   Specialist - psychiatry
Service not separately priced by Part B

C **G9291** Specimen site other than anatomic location of lung, is not classified as non-small cell lung cancer or classified as NSCLC-NOS   M

BETOS: M5B   Specialist - psychiatry
Service not separately priced by Part B

C **G9292** Documentation of medical reason(s) for not reporting pt category and a statement on thickness and ulceration and for PT1, mitotic rate (e.g., negative skin biopsies in a patient with a history of melanoma or other documented medical reasons)   M

BETOS: M5B   Specialist - psychiatry
Service not separately priced by Part B

C **G9293** Pathology report does not include the pt category and a statement on thickness and ulceration and for PT1, mitotic rate   M

BETOS: M5B   Specialist - psychiatry
Service not separately priced by Part B

C **G9294** Pathology report includes the pt category and a statement on thickness and ulceration and for PT1, mitotic rate   M

BETOS: M5B   Specialist - psychiatry
Service not separately priced by Part B

C **G9295** Specimen site other than anatomic cutaneous location   M

BETOS: M5B   Specialist - psychiatry
Service not separately priced by Part B

C **G9296** Patients with documented shared decision-making including discussion of conservative (non-surgical) therapy (e.g., nsaids, analgesics, weight loss, exercise, injections) prior to the procedure   M

BETOS: M5B   Specialist - psychiatry
Service not separately priced by Part B

C **G9297** Shared decision-making including discussion of conservative (non-surgical) therapy (e.g., nsaids, analgesics, weight loss, exercise, injections) prior to the procedure, not documented, reason not given   M

BETOS: M5B   Specialist - psychiatry
Service not separately priced by Part B

C **G9298** Patients who are evaluated for venous thromboembolic and cardiovascular risk factors within 30 days prior to the procedure (e.g., history of DVT, PE, MI, arrhythmia and stroke)   M

BETOS: M5B   Specialist - psychiatry
Service not separately priced by Part B

C **G9299** Patients who are not evaluated for venous thromboembolic and cardiovascular risk factors within 30 days prior to the procedure including (e.g., history of DVT, PE, MI, arrhythmia and stroke, reason not given)   M

BETOS: M5B   Specialist - psychiatry
Service not separately priced by Part B

C **G9300** Documentation of medical reason(s) for not completely infusing the prophylactic antibiotic prior to the inflation of the proximal tourniquet (e.g., a tourniquet was not used) M

BETOS: M5B   Specialist - psychiatry
Service not separately priced by Part B

C **G9301** Patients who had the prophylactic antibiotic completely infused prior to the inflation of the proximal tourniquet   M

BETOS: M5B   Specialist - psychiatry
Service not separately priced by Part B

C **G9302** Prophylactic antibiotic not completely infused prior to the inflation of the proximal tourniquet, reason not given   M

BETOS: M5B   Specialist - psychiatry
Service not separately priced by Part B

▲ Revised code   ● New code   C Carrier judgment   D Special coverage instructions apply

I Not payable by Medicare   M Non-covered by Medicare   S Non-covered by Medicare statute   AHA Coding Clinic®

C G9303 Operative report does not identify the prosthetic implant specifications including the prosthetic implant manufacturer, the brand name of the prosthetic implant and the size of each prosthetic implant, reason not given   M
BETOS: M5B   Specialist - psychiatry
Service not separately priced by Part B

C G9304 Operative report identifies the prosthetic implant specifications including the prosthetic implant manufacturer, the brand name of the prosthetic implant and the size of each prosthetic implant   M
BETOS: M5B   Specialist - psychiatry
Service not separately priced by Part B

C G9305 Intervention for presence of leak of endoluminal contents through an anastomosis not required   M
BETOS: M5B   Specialist - psychiatry
Service not separately priced by Part B

C G9306 Intervention for presence of leak of endoluminal contents through an anastomosis required   M
BETOS: M5B   Specialist - psychiatry
Service not separately priced by Part B

C G9307 No return to the operating room for a surgical procedure, for complications of the principal operative procedure, within 30 days of the principal operative procedure   M
BETOS: M5B   Specialist - psychiatry
Service not separately priced by Part B

C G9308 Unplanned return to the operating room for a surgical procedure, for complications of the principal operative procedure, within 30 days of the principal operative procedure   M
BETOS: M5B   Specialist - psychiatry
Service not separately priced by Part B

C G9309 No unplanned hospital readmission within 30 days of principal procedure   M
BETOS: M5B   Specialist - psychiatry
Service not separately priced by Part B

C G9310 Unplanned hospital readmission within 30 days of principal procedure   M
BETOS: M5B   Specialist - psychiatry
Service not separately priced by Part B

C G9311 No surgical site infection   M
BETOS: M5B   Specialist - psychiatry
Service not separately priced by Part B

C G9312 Surgical site infection   M
BETOS: M5B   Specialist - psychiatry
Service not separately priced by Part B

▲ C G9313 Amoxicillin, with or without clavulanate, not prescribed as first line antibiotic at the time of diagnosis for documented reason   M
BETOS: M5B   Specialist - psychiatry
Service not separately priced by Part B

C G9314 Amoxicillin, with or without clavulanate, not prescribed as first line antibiotic at the time of diagnosis, reason not given   M
BETOS: M5B   Specialist - psychiatry
Service not separately priced by Part B

C G9315 Documentation amoxicillin, with or without clavulanate, prescribed as a first line antibiotic at the time of diagnosis   M
BETOS: M5B   Specialist - psychiatry
Service not separately priced by Part B

C G9316 Documentation of patient-specific risk assessment with a risk calculator based on multi-institutional clinical data, the specific risk calculator used, and communication of risk assessment from risk calculator with the patient or family   M
BETOS: M5B   Specialist - psychiatry
Service not separately priced by Part B

C G9317 Documentation of patient-specific risk assessment with a risk calculator based on multi-institutional clinical data, the specific risk calculator used, and communication of risk assessment from risk calculator with the patient or family not completed   M
BETOS: M5B   Specialist - psychiatry
Service not separately priced by Part B

C G9318 Imaging study named according to standardized nomenclature   M
BETOS: M5B   Specialist - psychiatry
Service not separately priced by Part B

C G9319 Imaging study not named according to standardized nomenclature, reason not given   M
BETOS: M5B   Specialist - psychiatry
Service not separately priced by Part B

C G9321 Count of previous CT (any type of CT) and cardiac nuclear medicine (myocardial perfusion) studies documented in the 12-month period prior to the current study   M
BETOS: M5B   Specialist - psychiatry
Service not separately priced by Part B

C G9322 Count of previous CT and cardiac nuclear medicine (myocardial perfusion) studies not documented in the 12-month period prior to the current study, reason not given   M
BETOS: M5B   Specialist - psychiatry
Service not separately priced by Part B

C G9326 CT studies performed not reported to a radiation dose index registry that is capable of collecting at a minimum all necessary data elements, reason not given   M
BETOS: M5B   Specialist - psychiatry
Service not separately priced by Part B

C G9327 CT studies performed reported to a radiation dose index registry that is capable of collecting at a minimum all necessary data elements   M

♂ Male only   ♀ Female only   Ⓐ Age   A2 - Z3 = ASC Payment indicator   A - Y = APC Status indicator
ASC = ASC-approved procedure   **DME** Paid under the DME fee schedule   **MIPS** MIPS code

BETOS: M5B Specialist - psychiatry
Service not separately priced by Part B

C G9329 Dicom format image data available to non-affiliated external healthcare facilities or entities on a secure, media free, reciprocally searchable basis with patient authorization for at least a 12-month period after the study not documented in final report, reason not given M
BETOS: M5B Specialist - psychiatry
Service not separately priced by Part B

C G9340 Final report documented that dicom format image data available to non-affiliated external healthcare facilities or entities on a secure, media free, reciprocally searchable basis with patient authorization for at least a 12-month period after the study M
BETOS: M5B Specialist - psychiatry
Service not separately priced by Part B

C G9341 Search conducted for prior patient CT studies completed at non-affiliated external healthcare facilities or entities within the past 12-months and are available through a secure, authorized, media-free, shared archive prior to an imaging study being performed M
BETOS: M5B Specialist - psychiatry
Service not separately priced by Part B

C G9342 Search not conducted prior to an imaging study being performed for prior patient CT studies completed at non-affiliated external healthcare facilities or entities within the past 12-months and are available through a secure, authorized, media-free, shared archive, reason not given M
BETOS: M5B Specialist - psychiatry
Service not separately priced by Part B

C G9344 Due to system reasons search not conducted for dicom format images for prior patient CT imaging studies completed at non-affiliated external healthcare facilities or entities within the past 12 months that are available through a secure, authorized, media-free, shared archive (e.g., non-affiliated external healthcare facilities or entities does not have archival abilities through a shared archival system) M
BETOS: M5B Specialist - psychiatry
Service not separately priced by Part B

C G9345 Follow-up recommendations documented according to recommended guidelines for incidentally detected pulmonary nodules (e.g., follow-up CT imaging studies needed or that no follow-up is needed) based at a minimum on nodule size and patient risk factors M
BETOS: M5B Specialist - psychiatry
Service not separately priced by Part B

C G9347 Follow-up recommendations not documented according to recommended guidelines for incidentally detected pulmonary nodules, reason not given M
BETOS: M5B Specialist - psychiatry
Service not separately priced by Part B

▲ C G9348 CT scan of the paranasal sinuses ordered at the time of diagnosis for documented reasons M
BETOS: M5B Specialist - psychiatry
Service not separately priced by Part B

C G9349 Documentation of a CT scan of the paranasal sinuses ordered at the time of diagnosis or received within 28 days after date of diagnosis M
BETOS: M5B Specialist - psychiatry
Service not separately priced by Part B

C G9350 CT scan of the paranasal sinuses not ordered at the time of diagnosis or received within 28 days after date of diagnosis M
BETOS: M5B Specialist - psychiatry
Service not separately priced by Part B

C G9351 More than one CT scan of the paranasal sinuses ordered or received within 90 days after diagnosis M
BETOS: M5B Specialist - psychiatry
Service not separately priced by Part B

C G9352 More than one CT scan of the paranasal sinuses ordered or received within 90 days after the date of diagnosis, reason not given M
BETOS: M5B Specialist - psychiatry
Service not separately priced by Part B

C G9353 More than one CT scan of the paranasal sinuses ordered or received within 90 days after the date of diagnosis for documented reasons (e.g., patients with complications, second CT obtained prior to surgery, other medical reasons) M
BETOS: M5B Specialist - psychiatry
Service not separately priced by Part B

C G9354 One CT scan or no CT scan of the paranasal sinuses ordered within 90 days after the date of diagnosis M
BETOS: M5B Specialist - psychiatry
Service not separately priced by Part B

C G9355 Elective delivery or early induction not performed ♀ M
BETOS: M5B Specialist - psychiatry
Service not separately priced by Part B

C G9356 Elective delivery or early induction performed ♀ M
BETOS: M5B Specialist - psychiatry
Service not separately priced by Part B

C G9357 Post-partum screenings, evaluations and education performed ♀ M
BETOS: M5B Specialist - psychiatry
Service not separately priced by Part B

▲ Revised code ● New code **C** Carrier judgment **D** Special coverage instructions apply
I Not payable by Medicare **M** Non-covered by Medicare **S** Non-covered by Medicare statute AHA Coding Clinic®

C G9358 Post-partum screenings, evaluations and education not performed ♀ M
BETOS: M5B Specialist - psychiatry
Service not separately priced by Part B

C G9359 Documentation of negative or managed positive TB screen with further evidence that TB is not active within one year of patient visit M
BETOS: M5B Specialist - psychiatry
Service not separately priced by Part B

C G9360 No documentation of negative or managed positive TB screen M
BETOS: M5B Specialist - psychiatry
Service not separately priced by Part B

C G9361 Medical indication for induction [documentation of reason(s) for elective delivery (C-section) or early induction (e.g., hemorrhage and placental complications, hypertension, preeclampsia and eclampsia, rupture of membranes-premature or prolonged, maternal conditions complicating pregnancy/delivery, fetal conditions complicating pregnancy/delivery, late pregnancy, prior uterine surgery, or participation in clinical trial)] M
BETOS: Z2 Undefined codes
Service not separately priced by Part B

C G9364 Sinusitis caused by, or presumed to be caused by, bacterial infection M
BETOS: Z2 Undefined codes
Service not separately priced by Part B

C G9365 One high-risk medication ordered M
BETOS: Z2 Undefined codes
Service not separately priced by Part B

C G9366 One high-risk medication not ordered M
BETOS: Z2 Undefined codes
Service not separately priced by Part B

C G9367 At least two different high-risk medications ordered M
BETOS: Z2 Undefined codes
Service not separately priced by Part B

C G9368 At least two different high-risk medications not ordered M
BETOS: Z2 Undefined codes
Service not separately priced by Part B

C G9380 Patient offered assistance with end of life issues during the measurement period M
BETOS: Z2 Undefined codes
Service not separately priced by Part B

C G9382 Patient not offered assistance with end of life issues during the measurement period M
BETOS: Z2 Undefined codes
Service not separately priced by Part B

C G9383 Patient received screening for HCV infection within the 12 month reporting period M
BETOS: Z2 Undefined codes
Service not separately priced by Part B

C G9384 Documentation of medical reason(s) for not receiving annual screening for HCV infection (e.g., decompensated cirrhosis indicating advanced disease [i.e., ascites, esophageal variceal bleeding, hepatic encephalopathy], hepatocellular carcinoma, waitlist for organ transplant, limited life expectancy, other medical reasons) M
BETOS: Z2 Undefined codes
Service not separately priced by Part B

C G9385 Documentation of patient reason(s) for not receiving annual screening for HCV infection (e.g., patient declined, other patient reasons) M
BETOS: Z2 Undefined codes
Service not separately priced by Part B

C G9386 Screening for HCV infection not received within the 12 month reporting period, reason not given M
BETOS: Z2 Undefined codes
Service not separately priced by Part B

C G9389 Unplanned rupture of the posterior capsule requiring vitrectomy during cataract surgery M
BETOS: Z2 Undefined codes
Service not separately priced by Part B

C G9390 No unplanned rupture of the posterior capsule requiring vitrectomy during cataract surgery M
BETOS: Z2 Undefined codes
Service not separately priced by Part B

C G9393 Patient with an initial PHQ-9 score greater than nine who achieves remission at twelve months as demonstrated by a twelve month (+/- 30 days) PHQ-9 score of less than five M
BETOS: Z2 Undefined codes
Service not separately priced by Part B

C G9394 Patient who had a diagnosis of bipolar disorder or personality disorder, death, permanent nursing home resident or receiving hospice or palliative care any time during the measurement or assessment period M
BETOS: Z2 Undefined codes
Service not separately priced by Part B

C G9395 Patient with an initial PHQ-9 score greater than nine who did not achieve remission at twelve months as demonstrated by a twelve month (+/- 30 days) PHQ-9 score greater than or equal to five M
BETOS: Z2 Undefined codes
Service not separately priced by Part B

C G9396 Patient with an initial PHQ-9 score greater than nine who was not assessed for remission at twelve months (+/- 30 days) M
BETOS: Z2 Undefined codes
Service not separately priced by Part B

♂ Male only ♀ Female only **A** Age A2 - Z3 = ASC Payment indicator A - Y = APC Status indicator
ASC = ASC-approved procedure **DME** Paid under the DME fee schedule **MIPS** MIPS code

C **G9399** Documentation in the patient record of a discussion between the physician/clinician and the patient that includes all of the following: treatment choices appropriate to genotype, risks and benefits, evidence of effectiveness, and patient preferences toward the outcome of the treatment M
BETOS: Z2 Undefined codes
Service not separately priced by Part B

C **G9400** Documentation of medical or patient reason(s) for not discussing treatment options; medical reasons: patient is not a candidate for treatment due to advanced physical or mental health comorbidity (including active substance use); currently receiving antiviral treatment; successful antiviral treatment (with sustained virologic response) prior to reporting period; other documented medical reasons; patient reasons: patient unable or unwilling to participate in the discussion or other patient reasons M
BETOS: Z2 Undefined codes
Service not separately priced by Part B

C **G9401** No documentation of a discussion in the patient record of a discussion between the physician or other qualified healthcare professional and the patient that includes all of the following: treatment choices appropriate to genotype, risks and benefits, evidence of effectiveness, and patient preferences toward treatment M
BETOS: Z2 Undefined codes
Service not separately priced by Part B

C **G9402** Patient received follow-up on the date of discharge or within 30 days after discharge M
BETOS: Z2 Undefined codes
Service not separately priced by Part B

C **G9403** Clinician documented reason patient was not able to complete 30 day follow-up from acute inpatient setting discharge (e.g., patient death prior to follow-up visit, patient non-compliant for visit follow-up) M
BETOS: Z2 Undefined codes
Service not separately priced by Part B

C **G9404** Patient did not receive follow-up on the date of discharge or within 30 days after discharge M
BETOS: Z2 Undefined codes
Service not separately priced by Part B

C **G9405** Patient received follow-up within 7 days from discharge M
BETOS: Z2 Undefined codes
Service not separately priced by Part B

C **G9406** Clinician documented reason patient was not able to complete 7 day follow-up from acute inpatient setting discharge (i.e patient death prior to follow-up visit, patient non-compliance for visit follow-up) M

BETOS: Z2 Undefined codes
Service not separately priced by Part B

C **G9407** Patient did not receive follow-up on or within 7 days after discharge M
BETOS: Z2 Undefined codes
Service not separately priced by Part B

C **G9408** Patients with cardiac tamponade and/or pericardiocentesis occurring within 30 days M
BETOS: Z2 Undefined codes
Service not separately priced by Part B

C **G9409** Patients without cardiac tamponade and/or pericardiocentesis occurring within 30 days M
BETOS: Z2 Undefined codes
Service not separately priced by Part B

C **G9410** Patient admitted within 180 days, status post CIED implantation, replacement, or revision with an infection requiring device removal or surgical revision M
BETOS: Z2 Undefined codes
Service not separately priced by Part B

C **G9411** Patient not admitted within 180 days, status post CIED implantation, replacement, or revision with an infection requiring device removal or surgical revision M
BETOS: Z2 Undefined codes
Service not separately priced by Part B

C **G9412** Patient admitted within 180 days, status post CIED implantation, replacement, or revision with an infection requiring device removal or surgical revision M
BETOS: Z2 Undefined codes
Service not separately priced by Part B

C **G9413** Patient not admitted within 180 days, status post CIED implantation, replacement, or revision with an infection requiring device removal or surgical revision M
BETOS: Z2 Undefined codes
Service not separately priced by Part B

C **G9414** Patient had one dose of meningococcal vaccine on or between the patient's 11th and 13th birthdays M
BETOS: Z2 Undefined codes
Service not separately priced by Part B

C **G9415** Patient did not have one dose of meningococcal vaccine on or between the patient's 11th and 13th birthdays M
BETOS: Z2 Undefined codes
Service not separately priced by Part B

C **G9416** Patient had one tetanus, diphtheria toxoids and acellular pertussis vaccine (TDAP) on or between the patient's 10th and 13th birthdays M
BETOS: Z2 Undefined codes
Service not separately priced by Part B

C **G9417** Patient did not have one tetanus, diphtheria toxoids and acellular pertussis vaccine (TDAP) on or between the patient's 10th and 13th birthdays   M

   BETOS: Z2   Undefined codes
   Service not separately priced by Part B

C **G9418** Primary non-small cell lung cancer biopsy and cytology specimen report documents classification into specific histologic type or classified as NSCLC-NOS with an explanation   M MIPS

   BETOS: Z2   Undefined codes
   Service not separately priced by Part B

C **G9419** Documentation of medical reason(s) for not including the histological type or NSCLC-NOS classification with an explanation (e.g., biopsy taken for other purposes in a patient with a history of primary non-small cell lung cancer or other documented medical reasons)   M MIPS

   BETOS: Z2   Undefined codes
   Service not separately priced by Part B

C **G9420** Specimen site other than anatomic location of lung or is not classified as primary non-small cell lung cancer   M MIPS

   BETOS: Z2   Undefined codes
   Service not separately priced by Part B

C **G9421** Primary non-small cell lung cancer biopsy and cytology specimen report does not document classification into specific histologic type or classified as NSCLC-NOS with an explanation   M MIPS

   BETOS: Z2   Undefined codes
   Service not separately priced by Part B

C **G9422** Primary lung carcinoma resection report documents pT category, pN category and for non-small cell lung cancer, histologic type (squamous cell carcinoma, adenocarcinoma and not NSCLC-NOS)   M MIPS

   BETOS: Z2   Undefined codes
   Service not separately priced by Part B

C **G9423** Documentation of medical reason for not including pT category, pn category and histologic type [for patient with appropriate exclusion criteria (e.g., metastatic disease, benign tumors, malignant tumors other than carcinomas, inadequate surgical specimens)]   M MIPS

   BETOS: Z2   Undefined codes
   Service not separately priced by Part B

C **G9424** Specimen site other than anatomic location of lung, or classified as NSCLC-NOS   M MIPS

   BETOS: Z2   Undefined codes
   Service not separately priced by Part B

C **G9425** Primary lung carcinoma resection report does not document pt category, pn category and for non-small cell lung cancer, histologic type (squamous cell carcinoma, adenocarcinoma)   M MIPS

   BETOS: Z2   Undefined codes
   Service not separately priced by Part B

C **G9426** Improvement in median time from ED arrival to initial ED oral or parenteral pain medication administration performed for ED admitted patients   M

   BETOS: Z2   Undefined codes
   Service not separately priced by Part B

C **G9427** Improvement in median time from ED arrival to initial ED oral or parenteral pain medication administration not performed for ED admitted patients   M

   BETOS: Z2   Undefined codes
   Service not separately priced by Part B

C **G9428** Pathology report includes the Pt category and a statement on thickness and ulceration and for pT1, mitotic rate   M MIPS

   BETOS: Z2   Undefined codes
   Service not separately priced by Part B

C **G9429** Documentation of medical reason(s) for not including Pt category and a statement on thickness and ulceration and for pT1, mitotic rate (e.g., negative skin biopsies in a patient with a history of melanoma or other documented medical reasons)   M MIPS

   BETOS: Z2   Undefined codes
   Service not separately priced by Part B

C **G9430** Specimen site other than anatomic cutaneous location   M MIPS

   BETOS: Z2   Undefined codes
   Service not separately priced by Part B

C **G9431** Pathology report does not include the Pt category and a statement on thickness and ulceration and for pT1, mitotic rate   M MIPS

   BETOS: Z2   Undefined codes
   Service not separately priced by Part B

C **G9432** Asthma well-controlled based on the ACT, C-ACT, ACQ, or ATAQ score and results documented   M

   BETOS: Z2   Undefined codes
   Service not separately priced by Part B

C **G9434** Asthma not well-controlled based on the ACT, C-ACT, ACQ, or ATAQ score, or specified asthma control tool not used, reason not given   M

   BETOS: Z2   Undefined codes
   Service not separately priced by Part B

C **G9448** Patients who were born in the years 1945-1965   M

   BETOS: Z2   Undefined codes
   Service not separately priced by Part B

C **G9449** History of receiving blood transfusions prior to 1992   M

   BETOS: Z2   Undefined codes
   Service not separately priced by Part B

♂ Male only   ♀ Female only   **A** Age   A2 - Z3 = ASC Payment indicator   A - Y = APC Status indicator
ASC = ASC-approved procedure   **DME** Paid under the DME fee schedule   **MIPS** MIPS code

C **G9450** History of injection drug use   M
   BETOS: Z2   Undefined codes
   Service not separately priced by Part B

C **G9451** Patient received one-time screening for HCV infection   M
   BETOS: Z2   Undefined codes
   Service not separately priced by Part B

C **G9452** Documentation of medical reason(s) for not receiving one-time screening for HCV infection (e.g., decompensated cirrhosis indicating advanced disease [ie, ascites, esophageal variceal bleeding, hepatic encephalopathy], hepatocellular carcinoma, waitlist for organ transplant, limited life expectancy, other medical reasons)   M
   BETOS: Z2   Undefined codes
   Service not separately priced by Part B

C **G9453** Documentation of patient reason(s) for not receiving one-time screening for HCV infection (e.g., patient declined, other patient reasons)   M
   BETOS: Z2   Undefined codes
   Service not separately priced by Part B

C **G9454** One-time screening for HCV infection not received within 12 month reporting period and no documentation of prior screening for HCV infection, reason not given   M
   BETOS: Z2   Undefined codes
   Service not separately priced by Part B

C **G9455** Patient underwent abdominal imaging with ultrasound, contrast enhanced CT or contrast MRI for HCC   M
   BETOS: Z2   Undefined codes
   Service not separately priced by Part B

C **G9456** Documentation of medical or patient reason(s) for not ordering or performing screening for HCC. medical reason: comorbid medical conditions with expected survival < 5 years, hepatic decompensation and not a candidate for liver transplantation, or other medical reasons; patient reasons: patient declined or other patient reasons (e.g., cost of tests, time related to accessing testing equipment)   M
   BETOS: Z2   Undefined codes
   Service not separately priced by Part B

C **G9457** Patient did not undergo abdominal imaging and did not have a documented reason for not undergoing abdominal imaging in the reporting period   M
   BETOS: Z2   Undefined codes
   Service not separately priced by Part B

C **G9458** Patient documented as tobacco user and received tobacco cessation intervention (must include at least one of the following: advice given to quit smoking or tobacco use, counseling on the benefits of quitting smoking or tobacco use, assistance with or referral to external smoking or tobacco cessation support programs, or current enrollment in smoking or tobacco use cessation program) if identified as a tobacco user   M
   BETOS: Z2   Undefined codes
   Service not separately priced by Part B

C **G9459** Currently a tobacco non-user   M
   BETOS: Z2   Undefined codes
   Service not separately priced by Part B

C **G9460** Tobacco assessment or tobacco cessation intervention not performed, reason not given   M
   BETOS: Z2   Undefined codes
   Service not separately priced by Part B

C **G9468** Patient not receiving corticosteroids greater than or equal to 10 mg/day of prednisone equivalents for 60 or greater consecutive days or a single prescription equating to 600 mg prednisone or greater for all fills   M
   BETOS: Z2   Undefined codes
   Service not separately priced by Part B

C **G9469** Patients who have received or are receiving corticosteroids greater than or equal to 10 mg/day of prednisone equivalents for 60 or greater consecutive days or a single prescription equating to 600 mg prednisone or greater for all fills   M
   BETOS: Z2   Undefined codes
   Service not separately priced by Part B

C **G9470** Patients not receiving corticosteroids greater than or equal to 10 mg/day of prednisone equivalents for 60 or greater consecutive days or a single prescription equating to 600 mg prednisone or greater for all fills   M
   BETOS: Z2   Undefined codes
   Service not separately priced by Part B

C **G9471** Within the past 2 years, central dual-energy X-ray absorptiometry (DXA) not ordered or documented   M
   BETOS: Z2   Undefined codes
   Service not separately priced by Part B

C **G9472** Within the past 2 years, central dual-energy X-ray absorptiometry (DXA) not ordered and documented, no review of systems and no medication history or pharmacologic therapy (other than minerals/vitamins) for osteoporosis prescribed   M
   BETOS: Z2   Undefined codes
   Service not separately priced by Part B

C **G9473** Services performed by chaplain in the hospice setting, each 15 minutes   B
   BETOS: M5D   Specialist - other
   Service not separately priced by Part B

C **G9474** Services performed by dietary counselor in the hospice setting, each 15 minutes   B
   BETOS: M5D   Specialist - other
   Service not separately priced by Part B

C **G9475** Services performed by other counselor in the hospice setting, each 15 minutes   B
BETOS: M5D   Specialist - other
Service not separately priced by Part B

C **G9476** Services performed by volunteer in the hospice setting, each 15 minutes   B
BETOS: M5D   Specialist - other
Service not separately priced by Part B

C **G9477** Services performed by care coordinator in the hospice setting, each 15 minutes   B
BETOS: M5D   Specialist - other
Service not separately priced by Part B

C **G9478** Services performed by other qualified therapist in the hospice setting, each 15 minutes   B
BETOS: M5D   Specialist - other
Service not separately priced by Part B

C **G9479** Services performed by qualified pharmacist in the hospice setting, each 15 minutes   B
BETOS: M5D   Specialist - other
Service not separately priced by Part B

C **G9480** Admission to medicare care choice model program (MCCM)   B
BETOS: M5D   Specialist - other
Service not separately priced by Part B

C **G9481** Remote in-home visit for the evaluation and management of a new patient for use only in the medicare-approved comprehensive care for joint replacement model, which requires these 3 key components: a problem focused history; a problem focused examination; and straightforward medical decision making, furnished in real time using interactive audio and video technology. counseling and coordination of care with other physicians, other qualified health care professionals or agencies are provided consistent with the nature of the problem(s) and the needs of the patient or the family or both. usually, the presenting problem(s) are self limited or minor. typically, 10 minutes are spent with the patient or family or both via real time, audio and video intercommunications technology   B
BETOS: Z2   Undefined codes
Service not separately priced by Part B
Coding Clinic: 2016, Q1

C **G9482** Remote in-home visit for the evaluation and management of a new patient for use only in the medicare-approved comprehensive care for joint replacement model, which requires these 3 key components: an expanded problem focused history; an expanded problem focused examination; straightforward medical decision making, furnished in real time using interactive audio and video technology. counseling and coordination of care with other physicians, other qualified health care professionals or agencies are

provided consistent with the nature of the problem(s) and the needs of the patient or the family or both. usually, the presenting problem(s) are of low to moderate severity. typically, 20 minutes are spent with the patient or family or both via real time, audio and video intercommunications technology   B
BETOS: Z2   Undefined codes
Service not separately priced by Part B
Coding Clinic: 2016, Q1

C **G9483** Remote in-home visit for the evaluation and management of a new patient for use only in the medicare-approved comprehensive care for joint replacement model, which requires these 3 key components: a detailed history; a detailed examination; medical decision making of low complexity, furnished in real time using interactive audio and video technology. counseling and coordination of care with other physicians, other qualified health care professionals or agencies are provided consistent with the nature of the problem(s) and the needs of the patient or the family or both. usually, the presenting problem(s) are of moderate severity. typically, 30 minutes are spent with the patient or family or both via real time, audio and video intercommunications technology   B
BETOS: Z2   Undefined codes
Service not separately priced by Part B
Coding Clinic: 2016, Q1

C **G9484** Remote in-home visit for the evaluation and management of a new patient for use only in the medicare-approved comprehensive care for joint replacement model, which requires these 3 key components: a comprehensive history; a comprehensive examination; medical decision making of moderate complexity, furnished in real time using interactive audio and video technology. counseling and coordination of care with other physicians, other qualified health care professionals or agencies are provided consistent with the nature of the problem(s) and the needs of the patient or the family or both. usually, the presenting problem(s) are of moderate to high severity. typically, 45 minutes are spent with the patient or family or both via real time, audio and video intercommunications technology   B
BETOS: Z2   Undefined codes
Service not separately priced by Part B
Coding Clinic: 2016, Q1

C **G9485** Remote in-home visit for the evaluation and management of a new patient for use only in the medicare-approved comprehensive care for joint replacement model, which requires these 3 key components: a comprehensive history; a comprehensive examination; medical decision making of high complexity, furnished in real time using interactive audio and video technology. counseling and coordination of care with other physicians, other qualified health care professionals or agencies are provided consistent with the nature of the problem(s) and the needs of the patient or the family or both. usually, the presenting problem(s) are of moderate to high severity. typically, 60 minutes are spent with the patient or family or both via real time, audio and video intercommunications technology   B

BETOS: Z2 Undefined codes

Service not separately priced by Part B

Coding Clinic: 2016, Q1

C **G9486** Remote in-home visit for the evaluation and management of an established patient for use only in the medicare-approved comprehensive care for joint replacement model, which requires at least 2 of the following 3 key components: a problem focused history; a problem focused examination; straightforward medical decision making, furnished in real time using interactive audio and video technology. counseling and coordination of care with other physicians, other qualified health care professionals or agencies are provided consistent with the nature of the problem(s) and the needs of the patient or the family or both. usually, the presenting problem(s) are self limited or minor. typically, 10 minutes are spent with the patient or family or both via real time, audio and video intercommunications technology   B

BETOS: Z2 Undefined codes

Service not separately priced by Part B

Coding Clinic: 2016, Q1

C **G9487** Remote in-home visit for the evaluation and management of an established patient for use only in the medicare-approved comprehensive care for joint replacement model, which requires at least 2 of the following 3 key components: an expanded problem focused history; an expanded problem focused examination; medical decision making of low complexity, furnished in real time using interactive audio and video technology. counseling and coordination of care with other physicians, other qualified health care professionals or agencies are provided consistent with the nature of the problem(s) and the needs of the patient or the family or both. usually, the presenting problem(s) are of low to moderate severity. typically, 15 minutes are spent with the patient or family or both via real time, audio and video intercommunications technology B

BETOS: Z2 Undefined codes

Service not separately priced by Part B

Coding Clinic: 2016, Q1

C **G9488** Remote in-home visit for the evaluation and management of an established patient for use only in the medicare-approved comprehensive care for joint replacement

model, which requires at least 2 of the following 3 key components: a detailed history; a detailed examination; medical decision making of moderate complexity, furnished in real time using interactive audio and video technology. counseling and coordination of care with other physicians, other qualified health care professionals or agencies are provided consistent with the nature of the problem(s) and the needs of the patient or the family or both. usually, the presenting problem(s) are of moderate to high severity. typically, 25 minutes are spent with the patient or family or both via real time, audio and video intercommunications technology   B

BETOS: Z2 Undefined codes

Service not separately priced by Part B

Coding Clinic: 2016, Q1

C **G9489** Remote in-home visit for the evaluation and management of an established patient for use only in the medicare-approved comprehensive care for joint replacement model, which requires at least 2 of the following 3 key components: a comprehensive history; a comprehensive examination; medical decision making of high complexity, furnished in real time using interactive audio and video technology. counseling and coordination of care with other physicians, other qualified health care professionals or agencies are provided consistent with the nature of the problem(s) and the needs of the patient or the family or both. usually, the presenting problem(s) are of moderate to high severity. typically, 40 minutes are spent with the patient or family or both via real time, audio and video intercommunications technology   B

BETOS: Z2 Undefined codes

Service not separately priced by Part B

Coding Clinic: 2016, Q1

C **G9490** Comprehensive care for joint replacement model, home visit for patient assessment performed by clinical staff for an individual not considered homebound, including, but not necessarily limited to patient assessment of clinical status, safety/fall prevention, functional status/ambulation, medication reconciliation/management, compliance with orders/plan of care, performance of activities of daily living, and ensuring beneficiary connections to community and other services. (for use only in the medicare-approved CJR model); may not be billed for a 30 day period covered by a transitional care management code   B

BETOS: Z2 Undefined codes

Service not separately priced by Part B

Coding Clinic: 2016, Q1

G **G9497** Received instruction from the anesthesiologist or proxy prior to the day of surgery to abstain from smoking on the day of surgery   M
BETOS: Z2   Undefined codes
Service not separately priced by Part B

G **G9498** Antibiotic regimen prescribed   M
BETOS: Z2   Undefined codes
Service not separately priced by Part B

G **G9500** Radiation exposure indices, or exposure time and number of fluorographic images in final report for procedures using fluoroscopy, documented   M MIPS
BETOS: Z2   Undefined codes
Service not separately priced by Part B

G **G9501** Radiation exposure indices, or exposure time and number of fluorographic images not documented in final report for procedure using fluoroscopy, reason not given   M MIPS
BETOS: Z2   Undefined codes
Service not separately priced by Part B

G **G9502** Documentation of medical reason for not performing foot exam (i.e., patients who have had either a bilateral amputation above or below the knee, or both a left and right amputation above or below the knee before or during the measurement period)   M
BETOS: Z2   Undefined codes
Service not separately priced by Part B

G **G9503** Patient taking tamsulosin hydrochloride   M
BETOS: Z2   Undefined codes
Service not separately priced by Part B

▲ **G** **G9504** Documented reason for not assessing hepatitis B virus (HBV) status (e.g., patient not initiating anti-TNF therapy, patient declined) prior to initiating anti-TNF therapy   M
BETOS: Z2   Undefined codes
Service not separately priced by Part B

G **G9505** Antibiotic regimen prescribed within 10 days after onset of symptoms for documented medical reason   M
BETOS: Z2   Undefined codes
Service not separately priced by Part B

G **G9506** Biologic immune response modifier prescribed   M
BETOS: Z2   Undefined codes
Service not separately priced by Part B

G **G9507** Documentation that the patient is on a statin medication or has documentation of a valid contraindication or exception to statin medications; contraindications/exceptions that can be defined by diagnosis codes include pregnancy during the measurement period, active liver disease, rhabdomyolysis, end stage renal disease on dialysis and heart failure; provider documented contraindications/exceptions include breastfeeding during the measurement period, woman of child-bearing age not actively taking birth control, allergy to statin, drug interaction (HIV protease inhibitors, nefazodone, cyclosporine, gemfibrozil, and danazol) and intolerance (with supporting documentation of trying a statin at least once within the last 5 years or diagnosis codes for myostitis or toxic myopathy related to drugs)   M
BETOS: Z2   Undefined codes
Service not separately priced by Part B

G **G9508** Documentation that the patient is not on a statin medication   M
BETOS: Z2   Undefined codes
Service not separately priced by Part B

G **G9509** Remission at twelve months as demonstrated by a twelve month (+/-30 days) PHQ-9 score of less than 5   M
BETOS: Z2   Undefined codes
Service not separately priced by Part B

G **G9510** Remission at twelve months not demonstrated by a twelve month (+/-30 days) PHQ-9 score of less than five; either PHQ-9 score was not assessed or is greater than or equal to 5   M
BETOS: Z2   Undefined codes
Service not separately priced by Part B

G **G9511** Index date PHQ-9 score greater than 9 documented during the twelve month denominator identification period   M
BETOS: Z2   Undefined codes
Service not separately priced by Part B

G **G9512** Individual had a PDC of 0.8 or greater   M
BETOS: Z2   Undefined codes
Service not separately priced by Part B

G **G9513** Individual did not have a PDC of 0.8 or greater   M
BETOS: Z2   Undefined codes
Service not separately priced by Part B

G **G9514** Patient required a return to the operating room within 90 days of surgery   M
BETOS: Z2   Undefined codes
Service not separately priced by Part B

G **G9515** Patient did not require a return to the operating room within 90 days of surgery   M
BETOS: Z2   Undefined codes
Service not separately priced by Part B

G **G9516** Patient achieved an improvement in visual acuity, from their preoperative level, within 90 days of surgery   M
BETOS: Z2   Undefined codes
Service not separately priced by Part B

G **G9517** Patient did not achieve an improvement in visual acuity, from their preoperative level, within 90 days of surgery, reason not given M
BETOS: Z2   Undefined codes
Service not separately priced by Part B

C G9518 Documentation of active injection drug use M
  BETOS: Z2 Undefined codes
  Service not separately priced by Part B

C G9519 Patient achieves final refraction (spherical equivalent) +/- 0.5 diopters of their planned refraction within 90 days of surgery M
  BETOS: Z2 Undefined codes
  Service not separately priced by Part B

C G9520 Patient does not achieve final refraction (spherical equivalent) +/- 0.5 diopters of their planned refraction within 90 days of surgery M
  BETOS: Z2 Undefined codes
  Service not separately priced by Part B

C G9521 Total number of emergency department visits and inpatient hospitalizations less than two in the past 12 months M
  BETOS: Z2 Undefined codes
  Service not separately priced by Part B

C G9522 Total number of emergency department visits and inpatient hospitalizations equal to or greater than two in the past 12 months or patient not screened, reason not given M
  BETOS: Z2 Undefined codes
  Service not separately priced by Part B

C G9523 Patient discontinued from hemodialysis or peritoneal dialysis M
  BETOS: Z2 Undefined codes
  Service not separately priced by Part B

C G9524 Patient was referred to hospice care M
  BETOS: Z2 Undefined codes
  Service not separately priced by Part B

C G9525 Documentation of patient reason(s) for not referring to hospice care (e.g., patient declined, other patient reasons) M
  BETOS: Z2 Undefined codes
  Service not separately priced by Part B

C G9526 Patient was not referred to hospice care, reason not given M
  BETOS: Z2 Undefined codes
  Service not separately priced by Part B

C G9529 Patient with minor blunt head trauma had an appropriate indication(s) for a head CT M MIPS
  BETOS: Z2 Undefined codes
  Service not separately priced by Part B

C G9530 Patient presented within 24 hours of a minor blunt head trauma with a GCS score of 15 and had a head CT ordered for trauma by an emergency care provider M MIPS
  BETOS: Z2 Undefined codes
  Service not separately priced by Part B

C G9531 Patient has documentation of ventricular shunt, brain tumor, multisystem trauma, pregnancy, or is currently taking an antiplatelet medication including: ASA/ dipyridamole, clopidogrel, prasugrel, ticlopidine, ticagrelor or cilstazol) M MIPS
  BETOS: Z2 Undefined codes
  Service not separately priced by Part B

C G9532 Patient's head injury occurred greater than 24 hours before presentation to the emergency department, or has a GCS score less than 15 or does not have a GCS score documented, or had a head CT for trauma ordered by someone other than an emergency care provider, or was ordered for a reason other than trauma M MIPS
  BETOS: Z2 Undefined codes
  Service not separately priced by Part B

C G9533 Patient with minor blunt head trauma did not have an appropriate indication(s) for a head CT M MIPS
  BETOS: Z2 Undefined codes
  Service not separately priced by Part B

C G9534 Advanced brain imaging (CTA, CT, MRA or MRI) was not ordered M MIPS
  BETOS: Z2 Undefined codes
  Service not separately priced by Part B

C G9535 Patients with a normal neurological examination M MIPS
  BETOS: Z2 Undefined codes
  Service not separately priced by Part B

C G9536 Documentation of medical reason(s) for ordering an advanced brain imaging study (i.e., patient has an abnormal neurological examination; patient has the coexistence of seizures, or both; recent onset of severe headache; change in the type of headache; signs of increased intracranial pressure (e.g., papilledema, absent venous pulsations on funduscopic examination, altered mental status, focal neurologic deficits, signs of meningeal irritation); HIV-positive patients with a new type of headache; immunocompromised patient with unexplained headache symptoms; patient on coagulopathy/anti-coagulation or anti-platelet therapy; very young patients with unexplained headache symptoms) M MIPS
  BETOS: Z2 Undefined codes
  Service not separately priced by Part B

C G9537 Documentation of system reason(s) for ordering an advanced brain imaging study (i.e., needed as part of a clinical trial; other clinician ordered the study) M MIPS
  BETOS: Z2 Undefined codes
  Service not separately priced by Part B

C G9538 Advanced brain imaging (CTA, CT, MRA or MRI) was ordered M MIPS
  BETOS: Z2 Undefined codes
  Service not separately priced by Part B

C G9539 Intent for potential removal at time of placement   M
    BETOS: Z2   Undefined codes
    Service not separately priced by Part B

C G9540 Patient alive 3 months post procedure   M
    BETOS: Z2   Undefined codes
    Service not separately priced by Part B

C G9541 Filter removed within 3 months of placement   M
    BETOS: Z2   Undefined codes
    Service not separately priced by Part B

C G9542 Documented re-assessment for the appropriateness of filter removal within 3 months of placement   M
    BETOS: Z2   Undefined codes
    Service not separately priced by Part B

C G9543 Documentation of at least two attempts to reach the patient to arrange a clinical re-assessment for the appropriateness of filter removal within 3 months of placement   M
    BETOS: Z2   Undefined codes
    Service not separately priced by Part B

C G9544 Patients that do not have the filter removed, documented re-assessment for the appropriateness of filter removal, or documentation of at least two attempts to reach the patient to arrange a clinical re-assessment for the appropriateness of filter removal within 3 months of placement   M
    BETOS: Z2   Undefined codes
    Service not separately priced by Part B

C G9547 Incidental finding: liver lesion <= 0.5 cm, cystic kidney lesion < 1.0 cm or adrenal lesion <= 1.0 cm   M MIPS
    BETOS: Z2   Undefined codes
    Service not separately priced by Part B

C G9548 Final reports for abdominal imaging studies with follow-up imaging recommended   M MIPS
    BETOS: Z2   Undefined codes
    Service not separately priced by Part B

C G9549 Documentation of medical reason(s) that follow-up imaging is indicated (e.g., patient has a known malignancy that can metastasize, other medical reason(s) such as fever in an immunocompromised patient)   M MIPS
    BETOS: Z2   Undefined codes
    Service not separately priced by Part B

C G9550 Final reports for abdominal imaging studies with follow-up imaging not recommended   M MIPS
    BETOS: Z2   Undefined codes
    Service not separately priced by Part B

C G9551 Final reports for abdominal imaging studies without an incidentally found lesion noted: liver lesion <= 0.5 cm, cystic kidney lesion < 1.0 cm or adrenal lesion <= 1.0 cm noted or no lesion found   M MIPS
    BETOS: Z2   Undefined codes
    Service not separately priced by Part B

C G9552 Incidental thyroid nodule < 1.0 cm noted in report   M MIPS
    BETOS: Z2   Undefined codes
    Service not separately priced by Part B

C G9553 Prior thyroid disease diagnosis   M
    BETOS: Z2   Undefined codes
    Service not separately priced by Part B

C G9554 Final reports for CT, CTA, MRI or MRA of the chest or neck or ultrasound of the neck with follow-up imaging recommended   M MIPS
    BETOS: Z2   Undefined codes
    Service not separately priced by Part B

C G9555 Documentation of medical reason(s) for recommending follow-up imaging (e.g., patient has multiple endocrine neoplasia, patient has cervical lymphadenopathy, other medical reason(s))   M MIPS
    BETOS: Z2   Undefined codes
    Service not separately priced by Part B

C G9556 Final reports for CT, CTA, MRI or MRA of the chest or neck or ultrasound of the neck with follow-up imaging not recommended   M MIPS
    BETOS: Z2   Undefined codes
    Service not separately priced by Part B

C G9557 Final reports for CT, CTA, MRI or MRA studies of the chest or neck or ultrasound of the neck without an incidentally found thyroid nodule < 1.0 cm noted or no nodule found   M MIPS
    BETOS: Z2   Undefined codes
    Service not separately priced by Part B

C G9558 Patient treated with a beta-lactam antibiotic as definitive therapy   M MIPS
    BETOS: Z2   Undefined codes
    Service not separately priced by Part B

C G9559 Documentation of medical reason(s) for not prescribing a beta-lactam antibiotic (e.g., allergy, intolerance to beta -lactam antibiotics)   M MIPS
    BETOS: Z2   Undefined codes
    Service not separately priced by Part B

C G9560 Patient not treated with a beta-lactam antibiotic as definitive therapy, reason not given   M MIPS
    BETOS: Z2   Undefined codes
    Service not separately priced by Part B

C G9561 Patients prescribed opiates for longer than six weeks   M
    BETOS: Z2   Undefined codes
    Service not separately priced by Part B

♂ Male only   ♀ Female only   **A** Age   A2 - Z3 = ASC Payment indicator   A - Y = APC Status indicator
ASC = ASC-approved procedure   **DME** Paid under the DME fee schedule   MIPS MIPS code

C **G9562** Patients who had a follow-up evaluation conducted at least every three months during opioid therapy   M
BETOS: Z2   Undefined codes
Service not separately priced by Part B

C **G9563** Patients who did not have a follow-up evaluation conducted at least every three months during opioid therapy   M
BETOS: Z2   Undefined codes
Service not separately priced by Part B

C **G9573** Remission at six months as demonstrated by a six month (+/-30 days) PHQ-9 score of less than five   M
BETOS: Z2   Undefined codes
Service not separately priced by Part B

C **G9574** Remission at six months not demonstrated by a six month (+/-30 days) PHQ-9 score of less than five; either PHQ-9 score was not assessed or is greater than or equal to five M
BETOS: Z2   Undefined codes
Service not separately priced by Part B

C **G9577** Patients prescribed opiates for longer than six weeks   M
BETOS: Z2   Undefined codes
Service not separately priced by Part B

C **G9578** Documentation of signed opioid treatment agreement at least once during opioid therapy   M
BETOS: Z2   Undefined codes
Service not separately priced by Part B

C **G9579** No documentation of signed an opioid treatment agreement at least once during opioid therapy   M
BETOS: Z2   Undefined codes
Service not separately priced by Part B

C **G9580** Door to puncture time of less than 2 hours M
BETOS: Z2   Undefined codes
Service not separately priced by Part B

C **G9582** Door to puncture time of greater than 2 hours, no reason given   M
BETOS: Z2   Undefined codes
Service not separately priced by Part B

C **G9583** Patients prescribed opiates for longer than six weeks   M
BETOS: Z2   Undefined codes
Service not separately priced by Part B

C **G9584** Patient evaluated for risk of misuse of opiates by using a brief validated instrument (e.g., opioid risk tool, SOAPP-R) or patient interviewed at least once during opioid therapy   M
BETOS: Z2   Undefined codes
Service not separately priced by Part B

C **G9585** Patient not evaluated for risk of misuse of opiates by using a brief validated instrument (e.g., opioid risk tool, SOAPP-R) or patient

not interviewed at least once during opioid therapy   M
BETOS: Z2   Undefined codes
Service not separately priced by Part B

C **G9593** Pediatric patient with minor blunt head trauma classified as low risk according to the pecarn prediction rules   M MIPS
BETOS: Z2   Undefined codes
Service not separately priced by Part B

C **G9594** Patient presented within 24 hours of a minor blunt head trauma with a GCS score of 15 and had a head CT ordered for trauma by an emergency care provider   M MIPS
BETOS: Z2   Undefined codes
Service not separately priced by Part B

C **G9595** Patient has documentation of ventricular shunt, brain tumor, coagulopathy, including thrombocytopenia   M MIPS
BETOS: Z2   Undefined codes
Service not separately priced by Part B

C **G9596** Pediatric patient's head injury occurred greater than 24 hours before presentation to the emergency department, or has a GCS score less than 15 or does not have a GCS score documented, or had a head CT for trauma ordered by someone other than an emergency care provider, or was ordered for a reason other than trauma   M MIPS
BETOS: Z2   Undefined codes
Service not separately priced by Part B

C **G9597** Pediatric patient with minor blunt head trauma not classified as low risk according to the pecarn prediction rules   M MIPS
BETOS: Z2   Undefined codes
Service not separately priced by Part B

C **G9598** Aortic aneurysm 5.5 - 5.9 cm maximum diameter on centerline formatted CT or minor diameter on axial formatted CT   M
BETOS: Z2   Undefined codes
Service not separately priced by Part B

C **G9599** Aortic aneurysm 6.0 cm or greater maximum diameter on centerline formatted CT or minor diameter on axial formatted CT   M
BETOS: Z2   Undefined codes
Service not separately priced by Part B

C **G9600** Symptomatic AAAs that required urgent/emergent (non-elective) repair   M
BETOS: Z2   Undefined codes
Service not separately priced by Part B

C **G9601** Patient discharge to home no later than post-operative day #7   M
BETOS: Z2   Undefined codes
Service not separately priced by Part B

C **G9602** Patient not discharged to home by post-operative day #7   M
BETOS: Z2   Undefined codes
Service not separately priced by Part B

▲ Revised code   ● New code   C Carrier judgment   D Special coverage instructions apply
I Not payable by Medicare   M Non-covered by Medicare   S Non-covered by Medicare statute   AHA Coding Clinic®

C **G9603** Patient survey score improved from baseline following treatment M
BETOS: Z2 Undefined codes
Service not separately priced by Part B

C **G9604** Patient survey results not available M
BETOS: Z2 Undefined codes
Service not separately priced by Part B

C **G9605** Patient survey score did not improve from baseline following treatment M
BETOS: Z2 Undefined codes
Service not separately priced by Part B

C **G9606** Intraoperative cystoscopy performed to evaluate for lower tract injury M MIPS
BETOS: Z2 Undefined codes
Service not separately priced by Part B

▲ C **G9607** Documented medical reasons for not performing intraoperative cystoscopy (e.g., urethral pathology precluding cystoscopy, any patient who has a congenital or acquired absence of the urethra) or in the case of patient death M MIPS
BETOS: Z2 Undefined codes
Service not separately priced by Part B

C **G9608** Intraoperative cystoscopy not performed to evaluate for lower tract injury M MIPS
BETOS: Z2 Undefined codes
Service not separately priced by Part B

C **G9609** Documentation of an order for anti-platelet agents M MIPS
BETOS: Z2 Undefined codes
Service not separately priced by Part B

C **G9610** Documentation of medical reason(s) in the patient's record for not ordering anti-platelet agents M MIPS
BETOS: Z2 Undefined codes
Service not separately priced by Part B

C **G9611** Order for anti-platelet agents was not documented in the patient's record, reason not given M MIPS
BETOS: Z2 Undefined codes
Service not separately priced by Part B

C **G9612** Photodocumentation of one or more cecal landmarks to establish a complete examination M MIPS
BETOS: Z2 Undefined codes
Service not separately priced by Part B

C **G9613** Documentation of post-surgical anatomy (e.g., right hemicolectomy, ileocecal resection, etc.) M MIPS
BETOS: Z2 Undefined codes
Service not separately priced by Part B

C **G9614** No photodocumentation of cecal landmarks to establish a complete examination M MIPS
BETOS: Z2 Undefined codes
Service not separately priced by Part B

C **G9615** Preoperative assessment documented M
BETOS: Z2 Undefined codes
Service not separately priced by Part B

C **G9616** Documentation of reason(s) for not documenting a preoperative assessment (e.g., patient with a gynecologic or other pelvic malignancy noted at the time of surgery) M
BETOS: Z2 Undefined codes
Service not separately priced by Part B

C **G9617** Preoperative assessment not documented, reason not given M
BETOS: Z2 Undefined codes
Service not separately priced by Part B

C **G9618** Documentation of screening for uterine malignancy or those that had an ultrasound and/or endometrial sampling of any kind M MIPS
BETOS: Z2 Undefined codes
Service not separately priced by Part B

C **G9620** Patient not screened for uterine malignancy, or those that have not had an ultrasound and/or endometrial sampling of any kind, reason not given M MIPS
BETOS: Z2 Undefined codes
Service not separately priced by Part B

C **G9621** Patient identified as an unhealthy alcohol user when screened for unhealthy alcohol use using a systematic screening method and received brief counseling M
BETOS: Z2 Undefined codes
Service not separately priced by Part B

C **G9622** Patient not identified as an unhealthy alcohol user when screened for unhealthy alcohol use using a systematic screening method M
BETOS: Z2 Undefined codes
Service not separately priced by Part B

C **G9623** Documentation of medical reason(s) for not screening for unhealthy alcohol use (e.g., limited life expectancy, other medical reasons) M
BETOS: Z2 Undefined codes
Service not separately priced by Part B

▲ C **G9624** Patient not screened for unhealthy alcohol use using a systematic screening method or patient did not receive brief counseling if identified as an unhealthy alcohol user, reason not given M
BETOS: Z2 Undefined codes
Service not separately priced by Part B

C **G9625** Patient sustained bladder injury at the time of surgery or discovered subsequently up to 1 month post-surgery M
BETOS: Z2 Undefined codes
Service not separately priced by Part B

♂ Male only	♀ Female only	Ⓐ Age	A2 - Z3 = ASC Payment indicator	A - Y = APC Status indicator
	ASC = ASC-approved procedure		DME Paid under the DME fee schedule	MIPS MIPS code

C **G9626** Documented medical reason for not reporting bladder injury (e.g., gynecologic or other pelvic malignancy documented, concurrent surgery involving bladder pathology, injury that occurs during urinary incontinence procedure, patient death from non-medical causes not related to surgery, patient died during procedure without evidence of bladder injury)   M

BETOS: Z2   Undefined codes
Service not separately priced by Part B

C **G9627** Patient did not sustain bladder injury at the time of surgery nor discovered subsequently up to 1 month post-surgery   M

BETOS: Z2   Undefined codes
Service not separately priced by Part B

C **G9628** Patient sustained bowel injury at the time of surgery or discovered subsequently up to 1 month post-surgery   M

BETOS: Z2   Undefined codes
Service not separately priced by Part B

C **G9629** Documented medical reasons for not reporting bowel injury (e.g., gynecologic or other pelvic malignancy documented, planned (e.g., not due to an unexpected bowel injury) resection and/or re-anastomosis of bowel, or patient death from non-medical causes not related to surgery, patient died during procedure without evidence of bowel injury)   M

BETOS: Z2   Undefined codes
Service not separately priced by Part B

C **G9630** Patient did not sustain a bowel injury at the time of surgery nor discovered subsequently up to 1 month post-surgery   M

BETOS: Z2   Undefined codes
Service not separately priced by Part B

C **G9631** Patient sustained ureter injury at the time of surgery or discovered subsequently up to 1 month post-surgery   M

BETOS: Z2   Undefined codes
Service not separately priced by Part B

C **G9632** Documented medical reasons for not reporting ureter injury (e.g., gynecologic or other pelvic malignancy documented, concurrent surgery involving bladder pathology, injury that occurs during a urinary incontinence procedure, patient death from non-medical causes not related to surgery, patient died during procedure without evidence of ureter injury)   M

BETOS: Z2   Undefined codes
Service not separately priced by Part B

C **G9633** Patient did not sustain ureter injury at the time of surgery nor discovered subsequently up to 1 month post-surgery   M

BETOS: Z2   Undefined codes
Service not separately priced by Part B

C **G9634** Health-related quality of life assessed with tool during at least two visits and quality of life score remained the same or improved   M MIPS

BETOS: Z2   Undefined codes
Service not separately priced by Part B

C **G9635** Health-related quality of life not assessed with tool for documented reason(s) (e.g., patient has a cognitive or neuropsychiatric impairment that impairs his/her ability to complete the HRQOL survey, patient has the inability to read and/or write in order to complete the HRQOL questionnaire)   M MIPS

BETOS: Z2   Undefined codes
Service not separately priced by Part B

C **G9636** Health-related quality of life not assessed with tool during at least two visits or quality of life score declined   M MIPS

BETOS: Z2   Undefined codes
Service not separately priced by Part B

▲ **C** **G9637** At least two orders for the same high-risk medication   M MIPS

BETOS: Z2   Undefined codes
Service not separately priced by Part B

▲ **C** **G9638** At least two orders for the same high-risk medications not ordered   M MIPS

BETOS: Z2   Undefined codes
Service not separately priced by Part B

C **G9639** Major amputation or open surgical bypass not required within 48 hours of the index endovascular lower extremity revascularization procedure   M MIPS

BETOS: Z2   Undefined codes
Service not separately priced by Part B

C **G9640** Documentation of planned hybrid or staged procedure   M MIPS

BETOS: Z2   Undefined codes
Service not separately priced by Part B

C **G9641** Major amputation or open surgical bypass required within 48 hours of the index endovascular lower extremity revascularization procedure   M MIPS

BETOS: Z2   Undefined codes
Service not separately priced by Part B

C **G9642** Current smokers (e.g., cigarette, cigar, pipe, e-cigarette or marijuana)   M

BETOS: Z2   Undefined codes
Service not separately priced by Part B

C **G9643** Elective surgery   M

BETOS: Z2   Undefined codes
Service not separately priced by Part B

C **G9644** Patients who abstained from smoking prior to anesthesia on the day of surgery or procedure   M

BETOS: Z2   Undefined codes
Service not separately priced by Part B

▲ Revised code   ● New code   **C** Carrier judgment   **D** Special coverage instructions apply
I Not payable by Medicare   **M** Non-covered by Medicare   **S** Non-covered by Medicare statute   AHA Coding Clinic®

C **G9645** Patients who did not abstain from smoking prior to anesthesia on the day of surgery or procedure **M**
BETOS: Z2   Undefined codes
Service not separately priced by Part B

C **G9646** Patients with 90 day MRS score of 0 to 2   **M**
BETOS: Z2   Undefined codes
Service not separately priced by Part B

C **G9647** Patients in whom MRS score could not be obtained at 90 day follow-up   **M**
BETOS: Z2   Undefined codes
Service not separately priced by Part B

C **G9648** Patients with 90 day MRS score greater than 2   **M**
BETOS: Z2   Undefined codes
Service not separately priced by Part B

C **G9649** Psoriasis assessment tool documented meeting any one of the specified benchmarks (e.g., (PGA; 6-point scale), body surface area (BSA), psoriasis area and severity index (PASI) and/or dermatology life quality index) (DLQI))   **M** MIPS
BETOS: Z2   Undefined codes
Service not separately priced by Part B

C **G9651** Psoriasis assessment tool documented not meeting any one of the specified benchmarks (e.g., (PGA; 6-point scale), body surface area (BSA), psoriasis area and severity index (PASI) and/or dermatology life quality index) (DLQI)) or psoriasis assessment tool not documented   **M** MIPS
BETOS: Z2   Undefined codes
Service not separately priced by Part B

C **G9654** Monitored anesthesia care (MAC)   **M**
BETOS: Z2   Undefined codes
Service not separately priced by Part B

C **G9655** A transfer of care protocol or handoff tool/checklist that includes the required key handoff elements is used   **M**
BETOS: Z2   Undefined codes
Service not separately priced by Part B

▲ C **G9656** Patient transferred directly from anesthetizing location to PASU or other non-ICU location   **M**
BETOS: Z2   Undefined codes
Service not separately priced by Part B

C **G9658** A transfer of care protocol or handoff tool/checklist that includes the required key handoff elements is not used   **M**
BETOS: Z2   Undefined codes
Service not separately priced by Part B

C **G9659** Patients greater than 85 years of age who did not have a history of colorectal cancer or valid medical reason for the colonoscopy, including: iron deficiency anemia, lower gastrointestinal bleeding, Crohn's disease (i.e., regional enteritis), familial adenomatous polyposis, lynch syndrome (i.e., hereditary non-polyposis colorectal cancer), inflammatory bowel disease, ulcerative colitis, abnormal finding of gastrointestinal tract, or changes in bowel habits   **M**
BETOS: Z2   Undefined codes
Service not separately priced by Part B

C **G9660** Documentation of medical reason(s) for a colonoscopy performed on a patient greater than 85 years of age (e.g., last colonoscopy incomplete, last colonoscopy had inadequate prep, iron deficiency anemia, lower gastrointestinal bleeding, Crohn's disease (i.e., regional enteritis), familial history of adenomatous polyposis, lynch syndrome (i.e., hereditary non-polyposis colorectal cancer), inflammatory bowel disease, ulcerative colitis, abnormal finding of gastrointestinal tract, or changes in bowel habits)   **M**
BETOS: Z2   Undefined codes
Service not separately priced by Part B

C **G9661** Patients greater than 85 years of age who received a routine colonoscopy for a reason other than the following: an assessment of signs/symptoms of GI tract illness, and/or the patient is considered high risk, and/or to follow-up on previously diagnosed advance lesions   M
BETOS: Z2   Undefined codes
Service not separately priced by Part B

C **G9662** Previously diagnosed or have an active diagnosis of clinical ASCVD   **M**
BETOS: Z2   Undefined codes
Service not separately priced by Part B

C **G9663** Any fasting or direct LDL-C laboratory test result = 190 mg/dl   **M**
BETOS: Z2   Undefined codes
Service not separately priced by Part B

C **G9664** Patients who are currently statin therapy users or received an order (prescription) for statin therapy   **M**
BETOS: Z2   Undefined codes
Service not separately priced by Part B

C **G9665** Patients who are not currently statin therapy users or did not receive an order (prescription) for statin therapy   **M**
BETOS: Z2   Undefined codes
Service not separately priced by Part B

C **G9666** The highest fasting or direct LDL-C laboratory test result of 70-189 mg/dl in the measurement period or two years prior to the beginning of the measurement period   **M**
BETOS: Z2   Undefined codes
Service not separately priced by Part B

C **G9674** Patients with clinical ASCVD diagnosis   **M**
BETOS: Z2   Undefined codes
Service not separately priced by Part B

♂ Male only   ♀ Female only   Ⓐ Age   A2 - Z3 = ASC Payment indicator   A - Y = APC Status indicator
ASC = ASC-approved procedure   DME Paid under the DME fee schedule   MIPS MIPS code

C G9675 Patients who have ever had a fasting or direct laboratory result of LDL-C = 190 mg/dl M

    BETOS: Z2   Undefined codes

    Service not separately priced by Part B

C G9676 Patients aged 40 to 75 years at the beginning of the measurement period with type 1 or type 2 diabetes and with an LDL-C result of 70-189 mg/dl recorded as the highest fasting or direct laboratory test result in the measurement year or during the two years prior to the beginning of the measurement period M

    BETOS: Z2   Undefined codes

    Service not separately priced by Part B

C G9678 Oncology care model (OCM) monthly enhanced oncology services (MEOS) payment for OCM enhanced services. G9678 payments may only be made to OCM practitioners for OCM beneficiaries for the furnishing of enhanced services as defined in the OCM participation agreement B

    BETOS: Z2   Undefined codes

    Service not separately priced by Part B

C G9679 This code is for onsite acute care treatment of a nursing facility resident with pneumonia; may only be billed once per day per beneficiary B

    BETOS: Z2   Undefined codes

    Service not separately priced by Part B

C G9680 This code is for onsite acute care treatment of a nursing facility resident with CHF; may only be billed once per day per beneficiary B

    BETOS: Z2   Undefined codes

    Service not separately priced by Part B

C G9681 This code is for onsite acute care treatment of a resident with COPD or asthma; may only be billed once per day per beneficiary B

    BETOS: Z2   Undefined codes

    Service not separately priced by Part B

C G9682 This code is for the onsite acute care treatment a nursing facility resident with a skin infection; may only be billed once per day per beneficiary B

    BETOS: Z2   Undefined codes

    Service not separately priced by Part B

C G9683 This code is for the onsite acute care treatment of a nursing facility resident with fluid or electrolyte disorder or dehydration (similar pattern); may only be billed once per day per beneficiary B

    BETOS: Z2   Undefined codes

    Service not separately priced by Part B

C G9684 This code is for the onsite acute care treatment of a nursing facility resident for a UTI; may only be billed once per day per beneficiary B

    BETOS: Z2   Undefined codes

    Service not separately priced by Part B

C G9685 This code is for the evaluation and management of a beneficiary's acute change in condition in a nursing facility M

    BETOS: Z2   Undefined codes

    Service not separately priced by Part B

C G9686 Onsite nursing facility conference, that is separate and distinct from an evaluation and management visit, including qualified practitioner and at least one member of the nursing facility interdisciplinary care team M

    BETOS: Z2   Undefined codes

    Service not separately priced by Part B

C G9687 Hospice services provided to patient any time during the measurement period M MIPS

    BETOS: Z2   Undefined codes

    Service not separately priced by Part B

C G9688 Patients using hospice services any time during the measurement period M MIPS

    BETOS: Z2   Undefined codes

    Service not separately priced by Part B

C G9689 Patient admitted for performance of elective carotid intervention M MIPS

    BETOS: Z2   Undefined codes

    Service not separately priced by Part B

C G9690 Patient receiving hospice services any time during the measurement period M MIPS

    BETOS: Z2   Undefined codes

    Service not separately priced by Part B

C G9691 Patient had hospice services any time during the measurement period M MIPS

    BETOS: Z2   Undefined codes

    Service not separately priced by Part B

C G9692 Hospice services received by patient any time during the measurement period M MIPS

    BETOS: Z2   Undefined codes

    Service not separately priced by Part B

C G9693 Patient use of hospice services any time during the measurement period M MIPS

    BETOS: Z2   Undefined codes

    Service not separately priced by Part B

C G9694 Hospice services utilized by patient any time during the measurement period M MIPS

    BETOS: Z2   Undefined codes

    Service not separately priced by Part B

C G9695 Long-acting inhaled bronchodilator prescribed M MIPS

    BETOS: Z2   Undefined codes

    Service not separately priced by Part B

C G9696 Documentation of medical reason(s) for not prescribing a long-acting inhaled bronchodilator M MIPS

    BETOS: Z2   Undefined codes

    Service not separately priced by Part B

C G9697 Documentation of patient reason(s) for not prescribing a long-acting inhaled bronchodilator M MIPS

▲ Revised code   ● New code   **C** Carrier judgment   **D** Special coverage instructions apply

I Not payable by Medicare   **M** Non-covered by Medicare   **S** Non-covered by Medicare statute   AHA Coding Clinic®

BETOS: Z2   Undefined codes
Service not separately priced by Part B

C   **G9698**   Documentation of system reason(s) for not prescribing a long-acting inhaled bronchodilator   M MIPS
BETOS: Z2   Undefined codes
Service not separately priced by Part B

C   **G9699**   Long-acting inhaled bronchodilator not prescribed, reason not otherwise specified   M MIPS
BETOS: Z2   Undefined codes
Service not separately priced by Part B

C   **G9700**   Patients who use hospice services any time during the measurement period   M
BETOS: Z2   Undefined codes
Service not separately priced by Part B

C   **G9701**   Children who are taking antibiotics in the 30 days prior to the date of the encounter during which the diagnosis was established   M
BETOS: Z2   Undefined codes
Service not separately priced by Part B

C   **G9702**   Patients who use hospice services any time during the measurement period   M
BETOS: Z2   Undefined codes
Service not separately priced by Part B

C   **G9703**   Children who are taking antibiotics in the 30 days prior to the diagnosis of pharyngitis   M
BETOS: Z2   Undefined codes
Service not separately priced by Part B

C   **G9704**   AJCC breast cancer stage I: T1 mic or T1a documented   M
BETOS: Z2   Undefined codes
Service not separately priced by Part B

C   **G9705**   AJCC breast cancer stage I: T1b (tumor > 0.5 cm but <= 1 cm in greatest dimension) documented   M
BETOS: Z2   Undefined codes
Service not separately priced by Part B

C   **G9706**   Low (or very low) risk of recurrence, prostate cancer   M
BETOS: Z2   Undefined codes
Service not separately priced by Part B

C   **G9707**   Patient received hospice services any time during the measurement period   M MIPS
BETOS: Z2   Undefined codes
Service not separately priced by Part B

C   **G9708**   Women who had a bilateral mastectomy or who have a history of a bilateral mastectomy or for whom there is evidence of a right and a left unilateral mastectomy   M MIPS
BETOS: Z2   Undefined codes
Service not separately priced by Part B

C   **G9709**   Hospice services used by patient any time during the measurement period   M MIPS
BETOS: Z2   Undefined codes
Service not separately priced by Part B

C   **G9710**   Patient was provided hospice services any time during the measurement period   M MIPS
BETOS: Z2   Undefined codes
Service not separately priced by Part B

C   **G9711**   Patients with a diagnosis or past history of total colectomy or colorectal cancer   M MIPS
BETOS: Z2   Undefined codes
Service not separately priced by Part B

C   **G9712**   Documentation of medical reason(s) for prescribing or dispensing antibiotic (e.g., intestinal infection, pertussis, bacterial infection, lyme disease, otitis media, acute sinusitis, acute pharyngitis, acute tonsillitis, chronic sinusitis, infection of the pharynx/larynx/tonsils/adenoids, prostatitis, cellulitis/ mastoiditis/bone infections, acute lymphadenitis, impetigo, skin staph infections, pneumonia, gonococcal infections/venereal disease (syphilis, chlamydia, inflammatory diseases [female reproductive organs]), infections of the kidney, cystitis/UTI, acne, HIV disease/ asymptomatic HIV, cystic fibrosis, disorders of the immune system, malignancy neoplasms, chronic bronchitis, emphysema, bronchiectasis, extrinsic allergic alveolitis, chronic airway obstruction, chronic obstructive asthma, pneumoconiosis and other lung disease due to external agents, other diseases of the respiratory system, and tuberculosis   M
BETOS: Z2   Undefined codes
Service not separately priced by Part B

C   **G9713**   Patients who use hospice services any time during the measurement period   M
BETOS: Z2   Undefined codes
Service not separately priced by Part B

C   **G9714**   Patient is using hospice services any time during the measurement period   M MIPS
BETOS: Z2   Undefined codes
Service not separately priced by Part B

C   **G9715**   Patients who use hospice services any time during the measurement period   M
BETOS: Z2   Undefined codes
Service not separately priced by Part B

C   **G9716**   BMI is documented as being outside of normal limits, follow-up plan is not completed for documented reason   M MIPS
BETOS: Z2   Undefined codes
Service not separately priced by Part B

C   **G9717**   Documentation stating the patient has an active diagnosis of depression or has a diagnosed bipolar disorder, therefore screening or follow-up not required   M MIPS
BETOS: Z2   Undefined codes
Service not separately priced by Part B

♂ Male only   ♀ Female only   **A** Age   A2 - Z3 = ASC Payment indicator   A - Y = APC Status indicator
ASC = ASC-approved procedure   **DME** Paid under the DME fee schedule   **MIPS** MIPS code

C G9718 Hospice services for patient provided any time during the measurement period M MIPS
BETOS: Z2 Undefined codes
Service not separately priced by Part B

C G9719 Patient is not ambulatory, bed ridden, immobile, confined to chair, wheelchair bound, dependent on helper pushing wheelchair, independent in wheelchair or minimal help in wheelchair M
BETOS: Z2 Undefined codes
Service not separately priced by Part B

C G9720 Hospice services for patient occurred any time during the measurement period M MIPS
BETOS: Z2 Undefined codes
Service not separately priced by Part B

C G9721 Patient not ambulatory, bed ridden, immobile, confined to chair, wheelchair bound, dependent on helper pushing wheelchair, independent in wheelchair or minimal help in wheelchair M
BETOS: Z2 Undefined codes
Service not separately priced by Part B

C G9722 Documented history of renal failure or baseline serum creatinine = 4.0 mg/dl; renal transplant recipients are not considered to have preoperative renal failure, unless, since transplantation the CR has been or is 4.0 or higher M
BETOS: Z2 Undefined codes
Service not separately priced by Part B

C G9723 Hospice services for patient received any time during the measurement period M MIPS
BETOS: Z2 Undefined codes
Service not separately priced by Part B

C G9724 Patients who had documentation of use of anticoagulant medications overlapping the measurement year M MIPS
BETOS: Z2 Undefined codes
Service not separately priced by Part B

C G9725 Patients who use hospice services any time during the measurement period M
BETOS: Z2 Undefined codes
Service not separately priced by Part B

C G9726 Patient refused to participate M
BETOS: Z2 Undefined codes
Service not separately priced by Part B

C G9727 Patient unable to complete the FOTO knee intake prom at admission and discharge due to blindness, illiteracy, severe mental incapacity or language incompatibility and an adequate proxy is not available M
BETOS: Z2 Undefined codes
Service not separately priced by Part B

C G9728 Patient refused to participate M
BETOS: Z2 Undefined codes
Service not separately priced by Part B

C G9729 Patient unable to complete the FOTO hip intake prom at admission and discharge due to blindness, illiteracy, severe mental incapacity or language incompatibility and an adequate proxy is not available M
BETOS: Z2 Undefined codes
Service not separately priced by Part B

C G9730 Patient refused to participate M
BETOS: Z2 Undefined codes
Service not separately priced by Part B

C G9731 Patient unable to complete the FOTO foot or ankle intake prom at admission and discharge due to blindness, illiteracy, severe mental incapacity or language incompatibility and an adequate proxy is not available M
BETOS: Z2 Undefined codes
Service not separately priced by Part B

C G9732 Patient refused to participate M
BETOS: Z2 Undefined codes
Service not separately priced by Part B

C G9733 Patient unable to complete the FOTO lumbar intake prom at admission and discharge due to blindness, illiteracy, severe mental incapacity or language incompatibility and an adequate proxy is not available M
BETOS: Z2 Undefined codes
Service not separately priced by Part B

C G9734 Patient refused to participate M
BETOS: Z2 Undefined codes
Service not separately priced by Part B

C G9735 Patient unable to complete the FOTO shoulder intake prom at admission and discharge due to blindness, illiteracy, severe mental incapacity or language incompatibility and an adequate proxy is not available M
BETOS: Z2 Undefined codes
Service not separately priced by Part B

C G9736 Patient refused to participate M
BETOS: Z2 Undefined codes
Service not separately priced by Part B

C G9737 Patient unable to complete the FOTO elbow, wrist or hand intake prom at admission and discharge due to blindness, illiteracy, severe mental incapacity or language incompatibility and an adequate proxy is not available M
BETOS: Z2 Undefined codes
Service not separately priced by Part B

C G9738 Patient refused to participate M
BETOS: Z2 Undefined codes
Service not separately priced by Part B

C G9739 Patient unable to complete the FOTO general orthopedic intake prom at admission and discharge due to blindness, illiteracy, severe mental incapacity or language incompatibility and an adequate proxy is not available M

C **G9740** Hospice services given to patient any time during the measurement period M MIPS
BETOS: Z2 Undefined codes
Service not separately priced by Part B

C **G9741** Patients who use hospice services any time during the measurement period M
BETOS: Z2 Undefined codes
Service not separately priced by Part B

C **G9742** Psychiatric symptoms assessed M
BETOS: Z2 Undefined codes
Service not separately priced by Part B

C **G9743** Psychiatric symptoms not assessed, reason not otherwise specified M
BETOS: Z2 Undefined codes
Service not separately priced by Part B

C **G9744** Patient not eligible due to active diagnosis of hypertension M MIPS
BETOS: Z2 Undefined codes
Service not separately priced by Part B

C **G9745** Documented reason for not screening or recommending a follow-up for high blood pressure M MIPS
BETOS: Z2 Undefined codes
Service not separately priced by Part B

C **G9746** Patient has mitral stenosis or prosthetic heart valves or patient has transient or reversible cause of AF (e.g., pneumonia, hyperthyroidism, pregnancy, cardiac surgery) M MIPS
BETOS: Z2 Undefined codes
Service not separately priced by Part B

C **G9747** Patient is undergoing palliative dialysis with a catheter M
BETOS: Z2 Undefined codes
Service not separately priced by Part B

C **G9748** Patient approved by a qualified transplant program and scheduled to receive a living donor kidney transplant M
BETOS: Z2 Undefined codes
Service not separately priced by Part B

C **G9749** Patient is undergoing palliative dialysis with a catheter M
BETOS: Z2 Undefined codes
Service not separately priced by Part B

C **G9750** Patient approved by a qualified transplant program and scheduled to receive a living donor kidney transplant M
BETOS: Z2 Undefined codes
Service not separately priced by Part B

C **G9751** Patient died at any time during the 24-month measurement period M
BETOS: Z2 Undefined codes
Service not separately priced by Part B

BETOS: Z2 Undefined codes
Service not separately priced by Part B

C **G9752** Emergency surgery M
BETOS: Z2 Undefined codes
Service not separately priced by Part B

C **G9753** Documentation of medical reason for not conducting a search for dicom format images for prior patient CT imaging studies completed at non-affiliated external healthcare facilities or entities within the past 12 months that are available through a secure, authorized, media-free, shared archive (e.g., trauma, acute myocardial infarction, stroke, aortic aneurysm where time is of the essence) M
BETOS: Z2 Undefined codes
Service not separately priced by Part B

C **G9754** A finding of an incidental pulmonary nodule M
BETOS: Z2 Undefined codes
Service not separately priced by Part B

C **G9755** Documentation of medical reason(s) that follow-up imaging is indicated (e.g., patient has a known malignancy that can metastasize, other medical reason(s) M
BETOS: Z2 Undefined codes
Service not separately priced by Part B

C **G9756** Surgical procedures that included the use of silicone oil M
BETOS: Z2 Undefined codes
Service not separately priced by Part B

C **G9757** Surgical procedures that included the use of silicone oil M
BETOS: Z2 Undefined codes
Service not separately priced by Part B

▲ C **G9758** Patient in hospice at any time during the measurement period M
BETOS: Z2 Undefined codes
Service not separately priced by Part B

C **G9759** History of preoperative posterior capsule rupture M
BETOS: Z2 Undefined codes
Service not separately priced by Part B

C **G9760** Patients who use hospice services any time during the measurement period M
BETOS: Z2 Undefined codes
Service not separately priced by Part B

C **G9761** Patients who use hospice services any time during the measurement period M
BETOS: Z2 Undefined codes
Service not separately priced by Part B

▲ C **G9762** Patient had at least two HPV vaccines (with at least 146 days between the two) or three HPV vaccines on or between the patient's 9th and 13th birthdays Ⓐ M
BETOS: Z2 Undefined codes
Service not separately priced by Part B

▲ C **G9763** Patient did not have at least two HPV vaccines (with at least 146 days between the two) or three HPV vaccines on or between the patient's 9th and 13th birthdays Ⓐ M

♂ Male only	♀ Female only	Ⓐ Age	A2 - Z3 = ASC Payment indicator	A - Y = APC Status indicator
	ASC = ASC-approved procedure		DME Paid under the DME fee schedule	MIPS MIPS code

BETOS: Z2   Undefined codes
Service not separately priced by Part B

▲ **C G9764** Patient has been treated with an oral systemic or biologic medication for psoriasis vulgaris   M MIPS

BETOS: Z2   Undefined codes
Service not separately priced by Part B

▲ **C G9765** Documentation that the patient declined therapy change or alternative therapies were unavailable, has documented contraindications, or has not been treated with an oral systemic or biologic for at least six consecutive months (e.g., experienced adverse effects or lack of efficacy with all other therapy options) in order to achieve better disease control as measured by PGA, BSA, PASI, or DLQI   M MIPS

BETOS: Z2   Undefined codes
Service not separately priced by Part B

C G9766 Patients who are transferred from one institution to another with a known diagnosis of CVA for endovascular stroke treatment   M

BETOS: Z2   Undefined codes
Service not separately priced by Part B

C G9767 Hospitalized patients with newly diagnosed CVA considered for endovascular stroke treatment   M

BETOS: Z2   Undefined codes
Service not separately priced by Part B

C G9768 Patients who utilize hospice services any time during the measurement period   M MIPS

BETOS: Z2   Undefined codes
Service not separately priced by Part B

C G9769 Patient had a bone mineral density test in the past two years or received osteoporosis medication or therapy in the past 12 months   M MIPS

BETOS: Z2   Undefined codes
Service not separately priced by Part B

C G9770 Peripheral nerve block (PNB)   M

BETOS: Z2   Undefined codes
Service not separately priced by Part B

C G9771 At least 1 body temperature measurement equal to or greater than 35.5 degrees celsius (or 95.9 degrees fahrenheit) achieved within the 30 minutes immediately before or the 15 minutes immediately after anesthesia end time   M

BETOS: Z2   Undefined codes
Service not separately priced by Part B

C G9772 Documentation of one of the following medical reason(s) for not achieving at least 1 body temperature measurement equal to or greater than 35.5 degrees celsius (or 95.9 degrees fahrenheit) achieved within the 30 minutes immediately before or the 15 minutes immediately after anesthesia end

time (e.g., emergency cases, intentional hypothermia, etc.)   M

BETOS: Z2   Undefined codes
Service not separately priced by Part B

C G9773 At least 1 body temperature measurement equal to or greater than 35.5 degrees celsius (or 95.9 degrees fahrenheit) not achieved within the 30 minutes immediately before or the 15 minutes immediately after anesthesia end time   M

BETOS: Z2   Undefined codes
Service not separately priced by Part B

C G9774 Patients who have had a hysterectomy   M MIPS

BETOS: Z2   Undefined codes
Service not separately priced by Part B

C G9775 Patient received at least 2 prophylactic pharmacologic anti-emetic agents of different classes preoperatively and/or intraoperatively   M

BETOS: Z2   Undefined codes
Service not separately priced by Part B

C G9776 Documentation of medical reason for not receiving at least 2 prophylactic pharmacologic anti-emetic agents of different classes preoperatively and/or intraoperatively (e.g., intolerance or other medical reason)   M

BETOS: Z2   Undefined codes
Service not separately priced by Part B

C G9777 Patient did not receive at least 2 prophylactic pharmacologic anti-emetic agents of different classes preoperatively and/or intraoperatively   M

BETOS: Z2   Undefined codes
Service not separately priced by Part B

C G9778 Patients who have a diagnosis of pregnancy   M

BETOS: Z2   Undefined codes
Service not separately priced by Part B

C G9779 Patients who are breastfeeding   M

BETOS: Z2   Undefined codes
Service not separately priced by Part B

C G9780 Patients who have a diagnosis of rhabdomyolysis   M

BETOS: Z2   Undefined codes
Service not separately priced by Part B

C G9781 Documentation of medical reason(s) for not currently being a statin therapy user or receive an order (prescription) for statin therapy (e.g., patient with adverse effect, allergy or intolerance to statin medication therapy, patients who are receiving palliative care, patients with active liver disease or hepatic disease or insufficiency, and patients with end stage renal disease (ESRD))   M

BETOS: Z2   Undefined codes
Service not separately priced by Part B

C **G9782** History of or active diagnosis of familial or pure hypercholesterolemia M
BETOS: Z2 Undefined codes
Service not separately priced by Part B

C **G9783** Documentation of patients with diabetes who have a most recent fasting or direct LDL-C laboratory test result < 70 mg/dl and are not taking statin therapy M
BETOS: Z2 Undefined codes
Service not separately priced by Part B

C **G9784** Pathologists/dermatopathologists providing a second opinion on a biopsy M MIPS
BETOS: Z2 Undefined codes
Service not separately priced by Part B

▲ C **G9785** Pathology report diagnosing cutaneous basal cell carcinoma or squamous cell carcinoma (to include in situ disease) sent from the pathologist/dermatopathologist to the biopsying clinician for review within 7 days from the time when the tissue specimen was received by the pathologist M MIPS
BETOS: Z2 Undefined codes
Service not separately priced by Part B

▲ C **G9786** Pathology report diagnosing cutaneous basal cell carcinoma or squamous cell carcinoma (to include in situ disease) was not sent from the pathologist/dermatopathologist to the biopsying clinician for review within 7 days from the time when the tissue specimen was received by the pathologist M MIPS
BETOS: Z2 Undefined codes
Service not separately priced by Part B

C **G9787** Patient alive as of the last day of the measurement year M
BETOS: Z2 Undefined codes
Service not separately priced by Part B

C **G9788** Most recent BP is less than or equal to 140/90 mmHg M
BETOS: Z2 Undefined codes
Service not separately priced by Part B

C **G9789** Blood pressure recorded during inpatient stays, emergency room visits, urgent care visits, and patient self-reported BP's (home and health fair BP results) M
BETOS: Z2 Undefined codes
Service not separately priced by Part B

C **G9790** Most recent BP is greater than 140/90 mmHg, or blood pressure not documented M
BETOS: Z2 Undefined codes
Service not separately priced by Part B

C **G9791** Most recent tobacco status is tobacco free M
BETOS: Z2 Undefined codes
Service not separately priced by Part B

C **G9792** Most recent tobacco status is not tobacco free M
BETOS: Z2 Undefined codes
Service not separately priced by Part B

C **G9793** Patient is currently on a daily aspirin or other antiplatelet M
BETOS: Z2 Undefined codes
Service not separately priced by Part B

▲ C **G9794** Documentation of medical reason(s) for not on a daily aspirin or other antiplatelet (e.g., history of gastrointestinal bleed, intra-cranial bleed, idiopathic thrombocytopenic purpura (ITP), gastric bypass or documentation of active anticoagulant use during the measurement period) M
BETOS: Z2 Undefined codes
Service not separately priced by Part B

C **G9795** Patient is not currently on a daily aspirin or other antiplatelet M
BETOS: Z2 Undefined codes
Service not separately priced by Part B

C **G9796** Patient is currently on a statin therapy M
BETOS: Z2 Undefined codes
Service not separately priced by Part B

C **G9797** Patient is not on a statin therapy M
BETOS: Z2 Undefined codes
Service not separately priced by Part B

C **G9798** Discharge(s) for AMI between July 1 of the year prior measurement year to June 30 of the measurement period M
BETOS: Z2 Undefined codes
Service not separately priced by Part B

C **G9799** Patients with a medication dispensing event indicator of a history of asthma any time during the patient's history through the end of the measure period M
BETOS: Z2 Undefined codes
Service not separately priced by Part B

C **G9800** Patients who are identified as having an intolerance or allergy to beta-blocker therapy M
BETOS: Z2 Undefined codes
Service not separately priced by Part B

C **G9801** Hospitalizations in which the patient was transferred directly to a non-acute care facility for any diagnosis M
BETOS: Z2 Undefined codes
Service not separately priced by Part B

C **G9802** Patients who use hospice services any time during the measurement period M
BETOS: Z2 Undefined codes
Service not separately priced by Part B

C **G9803** Patient prescribed a 180-day course of treatment with beta-blockers post discharge for AMI M
BETOS: Z2 Undefined codes
Service not separately priced by Part B

C **G9804** Patient was not prescribed a 180-day course of treatment with beta-blockers post discharge for AMI M

♂ Male only ♀ Female only 🅐 Age A2 - Z3 = ASC Payment indicator A - Y = APC Status indicator
ASC = ASC-approved procedure DME Paid under the DME fee schedule MIPS MIPS code

CPT® is a registered trademark of the American Medical Association. All rights reserved.

PROCEDURES / PROFESSIONAL SERVICES (G0008-G9977)

245

BETOS: Z2   Undefined codes
Service not separately priced by Part B

C G9805 Patients who use hospice services any time during the measurement period   M
BETOS: Z2   Undefined codes
Service not separately priced by Part B

C G9806 Patients who received cervical cytology or an HPV test   M
BETOS: Z2   Undefined codes
Service not separately priced by Part B

C G9807 Patients who did not receive cervical cytology or an HPV test   M
BETOS: Z2   Undefined codes
Service not separately priced by Part B

C G9808 Any patients who had no asthma controller medications dispensed during the measurement year   M
BETOS: Z2   Undefined codes
Service not separately priced by Part B

C G9809 Patients who use hospice services any time during the measurement period   M
BETOS: Z2   Undefined codes
Service not separately priced by Part B

C G9810 Patient achieved a PDC of at least 75% for their asthma controller medication   M
BETOS: Z2   Undefined codes
Service not separately priced by Part B

C G9811 Patient did not achieve a PDC of at least 75% for their asthma controller medication   M
BETOS: Z2   Undefined codes
Service not separately priced by Part B

C G9812 Patient died including all deaths occurring during the hospitalization in which the operation was performed, even if after 30 days, and those deaths occurring after discharge from the hospital, but within 30 days of the procedure   M
BETOS: Z2   Undefined codes
Service not separately priced by Part B

C G9813 Patient did not die within 30 days of the procedure or during the index hospitalization   M
BETOS: Z2   Undefined codes
Service not separately priced by Part B

▲ C G9814 Death occurring during the index acute care hospitalization   M
BETOS: Z2   Undefined codes
Service not separately priced by Part B

▲ C G9815 Death did not occur during the index acute care hospitalization   M
BETOS: Z2   Undefined codes
Service not separately priced by Part B

▲ C G9816 Death occurring after discharge from the hospital but within 30 days post procedure   M
BETOS: Z2   Undefined codes
Service not separately priced by Part B

▲ C G9817 Death did not occur after discharge from the hospital within 30 days post procedure   M
BETOS: Z2   Undefined codes
Service not separately priced by Part B

C G9818 Documentation of sexual activity   M
BETOS: Z2   Undefined codes
Service not separately priced by Part B

C G9819 Patients who use hospice services any time during the measurement period   M
BETOS: Z2   Undefined codes
Service not separately priced by Part B

C G9820 Documentation of a chlamydia screening test with proper follow-up   M
BETOS: Z2   Undefined codes
Service not separately priced by Part B

C G9821 No documentation of a chlamydia screening test with proper follow-up   M
BETOS: Z2   Undefined codes
Service not separately priced by Part B

C G9822 Women who had an endometrial ablation procedure during the year prior to the index date (exclusive of the index date)   M
BETOS: Z2   Undefined codes
Service not separately priced by Part B

C G9823 Endometrial sampling or hysteroscopy with biopsy and results documented   M
BETOS: Z2   Undefined codes
Service not separately priced by Part B

C G9824 Endometrial sampling or hysteroscopy with biopsy and results not documented   M
BETOS: Z2   Undefined codes
Service not separately priced by Part B

C G9825 HER2/neu negative or undocumented/unknown   M
BETOS: Z2   Undefined codes
Service not separately priced by Part B

C G9826 Patient transferred to practice after initiation of chemotherapy   M
BETOS: Z2   Undefined codes
Service not separately priced by Part B

C G9827 HER2-targeted therapies not administered during the initial course of treatment   M
BETOS: Z2   Undefined codes
Service not separately priced by Part B

C G9828 HER2-targeted therapies administered during the initial course of treatment   M
BETOS: Z2   Undefined codes
Service not separately priced by Part B

C G9829 Breast adjuvant chemotherapy administered   M
BETOS: Z2   Undefined codes
Service not separately priced by Part B

C G9830 HER2/neu positive   M
BETOS: Z2   Undefined codes
Service not separately priced by Part B

▲ Revised code   ● New code   C Carrier judgment   D Special coverage instructions apply
I Not payable by Medicare   M Non-covered by Medicare   S Non-covered by Medicare statute   AHA Coding Clinic®

C **G9831** AJCC stage at breast cancer diagnosis = II or III　　M
　　　BETOS: Z2　Undefined codes
　　　Service not separately priced by Part B

C **G9832** AJCC stage at breast cancer diagnosis = I (Ia or Ib) and t-stage at breast cancer diagnosis does not equal = t1, t1a, t1b　　M
　　　BETOS: Z2　Undefined codes
　　　Service not separately priced by Part B

C **G9833** Patient transfer to practice after initiation of chemotherapy　　M
　　　BETOS: Z2　Undefined codes
　　　Service not separately priced by Part B

C **G9834** Patient has metastatic disease at diagnosis　M
　　　BETOS: Z2　Undefined codes
　　　Service not separately priced by Part B

C **G9835** Trastuzumab administered within 12 months of diagnosis　　M
　　　BETOS: Z2　Undefined codes
　　　Service not separately priced by Part B

C **G9836** Reason for not administering trastuzumab documented (e.g. patient declined, patient died, patient transferred, contraindication or other clinical exclusion, neoadjuvant chemotherapy or radiation not complete)　M
　　　BETOS: Z2　Undefined codes
　　　Service not separately priced by Part B

C **G9837** Trastuzumab not administered within 12 months of diagnosis　　M
　　　BETOS: Z2　Undefined codes
　　　Service not separately priced by Part B

C **G9838** Patient has metastatic disease at diagnosis　M
　　　BETOS: Z2　Undefined codes
　　　Service not separately priced by Part B

C **G9839** Anti-EGFR monoclonal antibody therapy　M
　　　BETOS: Z2　Undefined codes
　　　Service not separately priced by Part B

▲ C **G9840** RAS (KRAS and NRAS) gene mutation testing performed before initiation of anti-EGFR MoAb　　M
　　　BETOS: Z2　Undefined codes
　　　Service not separately priced by Part B

▲ C **G9841** RAS (KRAS and NRAS) gene mutation testing not performed before initiation of anti-EGFR MoAb　　M
　　　BETOS: Z2　Undefined codes
　　　Service not separately priced by Part B

C **G9842** Patient has metastatic disease at diagnosis　M
　　　BETOS: Z2　Undefined codes
　　　Service not separately priced by Part B

▲ C **G9843** RAS (KRAS and NRAS) gene mutation　M
　　　BETOS: Z2　Undefined codes
　　　Service not separately priced by Part B

C **G9844** Patient did not receive Anti-EGFR monoclonal antibody therapy　　M
　　　BETOS: Z2　Undefined codes
　　　Service not separately priced by Part B

C **G9845** Patient received Anti-EGFR monoclonal antibody therapy　　M
　　　BETOS: Z2　Undefined codes
　　　Service not separately priced by Part B

C **G9846** Patients who died from cancer　　M
　　　BETOS: Z2　Undefined codes
　　　Service not separately priced by Part B

C **G9847** Patient received chemotherapy in the last 14 days of life　　M
　　　BETOS: Z2　Undefined codes
　　　Service not separately priced by Part B

C **G9848** Patient did not receive chemotherapy in the last 14 days of life　　M
　　　BETOS: Z2　Undefined codes
　　　Service not separately priced by Part B

C **G9849** Patients who died from cancer　　M
　　　BETOS: Z2　Undefined codes
　　　Service not separately priced by Part B

C **G9850** Patient had more than one emergency department visit in the last 30 days of life　M
　　　BETOS: Z2　Undefined codes
　　　Service not separately priced by Part B

C **G9851** Patient had one or less emergency department visits in the last 30 days of life　M
　　　BETOS: Z2　Undefined codes
　　　Service not separately priced by Part B

C **G9852** Patients who died from cancer　　M
　　　BETOS: Z2　Undefined codes
　　　Service not separately priced by Part B

C **G9853** Patient admitted to the ICU in the last 30 days of life　　M
　　　BETOS: Z2　Undefined codes
　　　Service not separately priced by Part B

C **G9854** Patient was not admitted to the ICU in the last 30 days of life　　M
　　　BETOS: Z2　Undefined codes
　　　Service not separately priced by Part B

C **G9855** Patients who died from cancer　　M
　　　BETOS: Z2　Undefined codes
　　　Service not separately priced by Part B

C **G9856** Patient was not admitted to hospice　　M
　　　BETOS: Z2　Undefined codes
　　　Service not separately priced by Part B

C **G9857** Patient admitted to hospice　　M
　　　BETOS: Z2　Undefined codes
　　　Service not separately priced by Part B

C **G9858** Patient enrolled in hospice　　M
　　　BETOS: Z2　Undefined codes
　　　Service not separately priced by Part B

C **G9859** Patients who died from cancer　　M
　　　BETOS: Z2　Undefined codes
　　　Service not separately priced by Part B

♂ Male only　　♀ Female only　　Ⓐ Age　　A2 - Z3 = ASC Payment indicator　　A - Y = APC Status indicator
ASC = ASC-approved procedure　　**DME** Paid under the DME fee schedule　　**MIPS** MIPS code

© **G9860** Patient spent less than three days in hospice care   M

     BETOS: Z2   Undefined codes
     Service not separately priced by Part B

© **G9861** Patient spent greater than or equal to three days in hospice care   M

     BETOS: Z2   Undefined codes
     Service not separately priced by Part B

© **G9862** Documentation of medical reason(s) for not recommending at least a 10 year follow-up interval (e.g., inadequate prep, familial or personal history of colonic polyps, patient had no adenoma and age is = 66 years old, or life expectancy < 10 years old, other medical reasons)   M

     BETOS: Z2   Undefined codes
     Service not separately priced by Part B

● © **G9890** Dilated macular exam performed, including documentation of the presence or absence of macular thickening or geographic atrophy or hemorrhage and the level of macular degeneration severity

     BETOS: Z2   Undefined codes
     Service not separately priced by Part B

● © **G9891** Documentation of medical reason(s) for not performing a dilated macular examination

     BETOS: Z2   Undefined codes
     Service not separately priced by Part B

● © **G9892** Documentation of patient reason(s) for not performing a dilated macular examination

     BETOS: Z2   Undefined codes
     Service not separately priced by Part B

● © **G9893** Dilated macular exam was not performed, reason not otherwise specified

     BETOS: Z2   Undefined codes
     Service not separately priced by Part B

● © **G9894** Androgen deprivation therapy prescribed/administered in combination with external beam radiotherapy to the prostate   ♂

     BETOS: Z2   Undefined codes
     Service not separately priced by Part B

● © **G9895** Documentation of medical reason(s) for not prescribing/administering androgen deprivation therapy in combination with external beam radiotherapy to the prostate (e.g., salvage therapy)   ♂

     BETOS: Z2   Undefined codes
     Service not separately priced by Part B

● © **G9896** Documentation of patient reason(s) for not prescribing/administering androgen deprivation therapy in combination with external beam radiotherapy to the prostate   ♂

     BETOS: Z2   Undefined codes
     Service not separately priced by Part B

● © **G9897** Patients who were not prescribed/administered androgen deprivation therapy in combination with external beam

radiotherapy to the prostate, reason not given   ♂

     BETOS: Z2   Undefined codes
     Service not separately priced by Part B

● © **G9898** Patient age 65 or older in institutional special needs plans (SNP) or residing in long-term care with POS code 32, 33, 34, 54, or 56 any time during the measurement period   Ⓐ

     BETOS: Z2   Undefined codes
     Service not separately priced by Part B

● © **G9899** Screening, diagnostic, film, digital or digital breast tomosynthesis (3D) mammography results documented and reviewed   ♀

     BETOS: Z2   Undefined codes
     Service not separately priced by Part B

● © **G9900** Screening, diagnostic, film, digital or digital breast tomosynthesis (3D) mammography results were not documented and reviewed, reason not otherwise specified   ♀

     BETOS: Z2   Undefined codes
     Service not separately priced by Part B

● © **G9901** Patient age 65 or older in institutional special needs plans (SNP) or residing in long-term care with POS code 32, 33, 34, 54, or 56 any time during the measurement period   Ⓐ

     BETOS: Z2   Undefined codes
     Service not separately priced by Part B

● © **G9902** Patient screened for tobacco use and identified as a tobacco user

     BETOS: Z2   Undefined codes
     Service not separately priced by Part B

● © **G9903** Patient screened for tobacco use and identified as a tobacco non-user

     BETOS: Z2   Undefined codes
     Service not separately priced by Part B

● © **G9904** Documentation of medical reason(s) for not screening for tobacco use (e.g., limited life expectancy, other medical reason)

     BETOS: Z2   Undefined codes
     Service not separately priced by Part B

● © **G9905** Patient not screened for tobacco use, reason not given

     BETOS: Z2   Undefined codes
     Service not separately priced by Part B

● © **G9906** Patient identified as a tobacco user received tobacco cessation intervention (counseling and/or pharmacotherapy)

     BETOS: Z2   Undefined codes
     Service not separately priced by Part B

● © **G9907** Documentation of medical reason(s) for not providing tobacco cessation intervention (e.g., limited life expectancy, other medical reason)

     BETOS: Z2   Undefined codes
     Service not separately priced by Part B

▲ Revised code   ● New code   © Carrier judgment   Ⓓ Special coverage instructions apply

Ⓘ Not payable by Medicare   Ⓜ Non-covered by Medicare   Ⓢ Non-covered by Medicare statute   AHA Coding Clinic®

- **C** **G9908** Patient identified as tobacco user did not receive tobacco cessation intervention (counseling and/or pharmacotherapy), reason not given
  BETOS: Z2 Undefined codes
  Service not separately priced by Part B

- **C** **G9909** Documentation of medical reason(s) for not providing tobacco cessation intervention if identified as a tobacco user (e.g., limited life expectancy, other medical reason)
  BETOS: Z2 Undefined codes
  Service not separately priced by Part B

- **C** **G9910** Patients age 65 or older in institutional special needs plans (SNP) or residing in long-term care with POS code 32, 33, 34, 54 or 56 anytime during the measurement period Ⓐ
  BETOS: Z2 Undefined codes
  Service not separately priced by Part B

- **C** **G9911** Clinically node negative (t1n0m0 or t2n0m0) invasive breast cancer before or after neoadjuvant systemic therapy ♀
  BETOS: Z2 Undefined codes
  Service not separately priced by Part B

- **C** **G9912** Hepatitis B virus (HBV) status assessed and results interpreted prior to initiating anti-TNF (tumor necrosis factor) therapy
  BETOS: Z2 Undefined codes
  Service not separately priced by Part B

- **C** **G9913** Hepatitis B virus (HBV) status not assessed and results interpreted prior to initiating anti-TNF (tumor necrosis factor) therapy, reason not given
  BETOS: Z2 Undefined codes
  Service not separately priced by Part B

- **C** **G9914** Patient receiving an anti-TNF agent
  BETOS: Z2 Undefined codes
  Service not separately priced by Part B

- **C** **G9915** No record of HBV results documented
  BETOS: Z2 Undefined codes
  Service not separately priced by Part B

- **C** **G9916** Functional status performed once in the last 12 months
  BETOS: Z2 Undefined codes
  Service not separately priced by Part B

- **C** **G9917** Documentation of medical reason(s) for not performing functional status (e.g., patient is severely impaired and caregiver knowledge is limited, other medical reason)
  BETOS: Z2 Undefined codes
  Service not separately priced by Part B

- **C** **G9918** Functional status not performed, reason not otherwise specified
  BETOS: Z2 Undefined codes
  Service not separately priced by Part B

- **C** **G9919** Screening performed and positive and provision of recommendations
  BETOS: Z2 Undefined codes
  Service not separately priced by Part B

- **C** **G9920** Screening performed and negative
  BETOS: Z2 Undefined codes
  Service not separately priced by Part B

- **C** **G9921** No screening performed, partial screening performed or positive screen without recommendations and reason is not given or otherwise specified
  BETOS: Z2 Undefined codes
  Service not separately priced by Part B

- **C** **G9922** Safety concerns screen provided and if positive then documented mitigation recommendations
  BETOS: Z2 Undefined codes
  Service not separately priced by Part B

- **C** **G9923** Safety concerns screen provided and negative
  BETOS: Z2 Undefined codes
  Service not separately priced by Part B

- **C** **G9924** Documentation of medical reason(s) for not providing safety concerns screen or for not providing recommendations, orders or referrals for positive screen (e.g., patient in palliative care, other medical reason)
  BETOS: Z2 Undefined codes
  Service not separately priced by Part B

- **C** **G9925** Safety concerns screening not provided, reason not otherwise specified
  BETOS: Z2 Undefined codes
  Service not separately priced by Part B

- **C** **G9926** Safety concerns screening positive screen is without provision of mitigation recommendations, including but not limited to referral to other resources
  BETOS: Z2 Undefined codes
  Service not separately priced by Part B

- **C** **G9927** Documentation of system reason(s) for not prescribing warfarin or another FDA-approved anticoagulation due to patient being currently enrolled in a clinical trial related to AF/atrial flutter treatment
  BETOS: Z2 Undefined codes
  Service not separately priced by Part B

- **C** **G9928** Warfarin or another FDA-approved anticoagulant not prescribed, reason not given
  BETOS: Z2 Undefined codes
  Service not separately priced by Part B

- **C** **G9929** Patient with transient or reversible cause of AF (e.g., pneumonia, hyperthyroidism, pregnancy, cardiac surgery) ♀
  BETOS: Z2 Undefined codes
  Service not separately priced by Part B

- **C** **G9930** Patients who are receiving comfort care only
  BETOS: Z2 Undefined codes
  Service not separately priced by Part B

♂ Male only ♀ Female only Ⓐ Age A2 - Z3 = ASC Payment indicator A - Y = APC Status indicator
ASC = ASC-approved procedure **DME** Paid under the DME fee schedule **MIPS** MIPS code

G9931 Documentation of CHA2DS2-VASC risk score of 0 or 1

BETOS: Z2   Undefined codes
Service not separately priced by Part B

G9932 Documentation of patient reason(s) for not having records of negative or managed positive TB screen (e.g., patient does not return for mantoux (PPD) skin test evaluation)

BETOS: Z2   Undefined codes
Service not separately priced by Part B

G9933 Adenoma(s) or colorectal cancer detected during screening colonoscopy

BETOS: Z2   Undefined codes
Service not separately priced by Part B

G9934 Documentation that neoplasm detected is only diagnosed as traditional serrated adenoma, sessile serrated polyp, or sessile serrated adenoma

BETOS: Z2   Undefined codes
Service not separately priced by Part B

G9935 Adenoma(s) or colorectal cancer not detected during screening colonoscopy

BETOS: Z2   Undefined codes
Service not separately priced by Part B

G9936 Surveillance colonoscopy - personal history of colonic polyps, colon cancer, or other malignant neoplasm of rectum, rectosigmoid junction, and anus

BETOS: Z2   Undefined codes
Service not separately priced by Part B

G9937 Diagnostic colonoscopy

BETOS: Z2   Undefined codes
Service not separately priced by Part B

G9938 Patients age 65 or older in institutional special needs plans (SNP) or residing in long-term care with POS code 32, 33, 34, 54, or 56 any time during the measurement period   Ⓐ

BETOS: Z2   Undefined codes
Service not separately priced by Part B

G9939 Pathologists/dermatopathologists is the same clinician who performed the biopsy

BETOS: Z2   Undefined codes
Service not separately priced by Part B

G9940 Documentation of medical reason(s) for not on a statin (e.g., pregnancy, in vitro fertilization, clomiphene Rx, ESRD, cirrhosis, muscular pain and disease during the measurement period or prior year)   ♀

BETOS: Z2   Undefined codes
Service not separately priced by Part B

G9941 Back pain was measured by the visual analog scale (VAS) within three months preoperatively and at three months (6 - 20 weeks) postoperatively

BETOS: Z2   Undefined codes
Service not separately priced by Part B

G9942 Patient had any additional spine procedures performed on the same date as the lumbar discectomy/laminotomy

BETOS: Z2   Undefined codes
Service not separately priced by Part B

G9943 Back pain was not measured by the visual analog scale (VAS) within three months preoperatively and at three months (6 - 20 weeks) postoperatively

BETOS: Z2   Undefined codes
Service not separately priced by Part B

G9944 Back pain was measured by the visual analog scale (VAS) within three months preoperatively and at one year (9 to 15 months) postoperatively

BETOS: Z2   Undefined codes
Service not separately priced by Part B

G9945 Patient had cancer, fracture or infection related to the lumbar spine or patient had idiopathic or congenital scoliosis

BETOS: Z2   Undefined codes
Service not separately priced by Part B

G9946 Back pain was not measured by the visual analog scale (VAS) within three months preoperatively and at one year (9 to 15 months) postoperatively

BETOS: Z2   Undefined codes
Service not separately priced by Part B

G9947 Leg pain was measured by the visual analog scale (VAS) within three months preoperatively and at three months (6 to 20 weeks) postoperatively

BETOS: Z2   Undefined codes
Service not separately priced by Part B

G9948 Patient had any additional spine procedures performed on the same date as the lumbar discectomy/laminotomy

BETOS: Z2   Undefined codes
Service not separately priced by Part B

G9949 Leg pain was not measured by the visual analog scale (VAS) within three months preoperatively and at three months (6 to 20 weeks) postoperatively

BETOS: Z2   Undefined codes
Service not separately priced by Part B

G9954 Patient exhibits 2 or more risk factors for post-operative vomiting

BETOS: Z2   Undefined codes
Service not separately priced by Part B

G9955 Cases in which an inhalational anesthetic is used only for induction

BETOS: Z2   Undefined codes
Service not separately priced by Part B

▲ Revised code   ● New code   C Carrier judgment   D Special coverage instructions apply

I Not payable by Medicare   M Non-covered by Medicare   S Non-covered by Medicare statute   AHA Coding Clinic®

- C G9956 Patient received combination therapy consisting of at least two prophylactic pharmacologic anti-emetic agents of different classes preoperatively and/or intraoperatively
  BETOS: Z2   Undefined codes
  Service not separately priced by Part B

- C G9957 Documentation of medical reason for not receiving combination therapy consisting of at least two prophylactic pharmacologic anti-emetic agents of different classes preoperatively and/or intraoperatively (e.g., intolerance or other medical reason)
  BETOS: Z2   Undefined codes
  Service not separately priced by Part B

- C G9958 Patient did not receive combination therapy consisting of at least two prophylactic pharmacologic anti-emetic agents of different classes preoperatively and/or intraoperatively
  BETOS: Z2   Undefined codes
  Service not separately priced by Part B

- C G9959 Systemic antimicrobials not prescribed
  BETOS: Z2   Undefined codes
  Service not separately priced by Part B

- C G9960 Documentation of medical reason(s) for prescribing systemic antimicrobials
  BETOS: Z2   Undefined codes
  Service not separately priced by Part B

- C G9961 Systemic antimicrobials prescribed
  BETOS: Z2   Undefined codes
  Service not separately priced by Part B

- C G9962 Embolization endpoints are documented separately for each embolized vessel and ovarian artery angiography or embolization performed in the presence of variant uterine artery anatomy ♀
  BETOS: Z2   Undefined codes
  Service not separately priced by Part B

- C G9963 Embolization endpoints are not documented separately for each embolized vessel or ovarian artery angiography or embolization not performed in the presence of variant uterine artery anatomy ♀
  BETOS: Z2   Undefined codes
  Service not separately priced by Part B

- C G9964 Patient received at least one well-child visit with a PCP during the performance period Ⓐ
  BETOS: Z2   Undefined codes
  Service not separately priced by Part B

- C G9965 Patient did not receive at least one well-child visit with a PCP during the performance period Ⓐ
  BETOS: Z2   Undefined codes
  Service not separately priced by Part B

- C G9966 Children who were screened for risk of developmental, behavioral and social delays using a standardized tool with interpretation and report Ⓐ
  BETOS: Z2   Undefined codes
  Service not separately priced by Part B

- C G9967 Children who were not screened for risk of developmental, behavioral and social delays using a standardized tool with interpretation and report Ⓐ
  BETOS: Z2   Undefined codes
  Service not separately priced by Part B

- C G9968 Patient was referred to another provider or specialist during the performance period
  BETOS: Z2   Undefined codes
  Service not separately priced by Part B

- C G9969 Provider who referred the patient to another provider received a report from the provider to whom the patient was referred
  BETOS: Z2   Undefined codes
  Service not separately priced by Part B

- C G9970 Provider who referred the patient to another provider did not receive a report from the provider to whom the patient was referred
  BETOS: Z2   Undefined codes
  Service not separately priced by Part B

- C G9974 Dilated macular exam performed, including documentation of the presence or absence of macular thickening or geographic atrophy or hemorrhage and the level of macular degeneration severity
  BETOS: Z2   Undefined codes
  Service not separately priced by Part B

- C G9975 Documentation of medical reason(s) for not performing a dilated macular examination
  BETOS: Z2   Undefined codes
  Service not separately priced by Part B

- C G9976 Documentation of patient reason(s) for not performing a dilated macular examination
  BETOS: Z2   Undefined codes
  Service not separately priced by Part B

- C G9977 Dilated macular exam was not performed, reason not otherwise specified
  BETOS: Z2   Undefined codes
  Service not separately priced by Part B

♂ Male only   ♀ Female only   Ⓐ Age   A2 - Z3 = ASC Payment indicator   A - Y = APC Status indicator
ASC = ASC-approved procedure   DME Paid under the DME fee schedule   MIPS MIPS code

NOTES

ALCOHOL AND DRUG ABUSE TREATMENT (H0001-H2037)

DRUG, ALCOHOL, AND BEHAVIORAL HEALTH SERVICES (H0001-H0030)

▯ **H0001** Alcohol and/or drug assessment
BETOS: Z2 Undefined codes
Service not separately priced by Part B
Coding Clinic: 2009, Q2

▯ **H0002** Behavioral health screening to determine eligibility for admission to treatment program
BETOS: Z2 Undefined codes
Service not separately priced by Part B

▯ **H0003** Alcohol and/or drug screening; laboratory analysis of specimens for presence of alcohol and/or drugs
BETOS: Z2 Undefined codes
Service not separately priced by Part B

▯ **H0004** Behavioral health counseling and therapy, per 15 minutes
BETOS: Z2 Undefined codes
Service not separately priced by Part B

▯ **H0005** Alcohol and/or drug services; group counseling by a clinician
BETOS: Z2 Undefined codes
Service not separately priced by Part B

▯ **H0006** Alcohol and/or drug services; case management
BETOS: Z2 Undefined codes
Service not separately priced by Part B

▯ **H0007** Alcohol and/or drug services; crisis intervention (outpatient)
BETOS: Z2 Undefined codes
Service not separately priced by Part B

▯ **H0008** Alcohol and/or drug services; sub-acute detoxification (hospital inpatient)
BETOS: Z2 Undefined codes
Service not separately priced by Part B

▯ **H0009** Alcohol and/or drug services; acute detoxification (hospital inpatient)
BETOS: Z2 Undefined codes
Service not separately priced by Part B

▯ **H0010** Alcohol and/or drug services; sub-acute detoxification (residential addiction program inpatient)
BETOS: Z2 Undefined codes
Service not separately priced by Part B

▯ **H0011** Alcohol and/or drug services; acute detoxification (residential addiction program inpatient)
BETOS: Z2 Undefined codes
Service not separately priced by Part B

▯ **H0012** Alcohol and/or drug services; sub-acute detoxification (residential addiction program outpatient)

BETOS: Z2 Undefined codes
Service not separately priced by Part B

▯ **H0013** Alcohol and/or drug services; acute detoxification (residential addiction program outpatient)
BETOS: Z2 Undefined codes
Service not separately priced by Part B

▯ **H0014** Alcohol and/or drug services; ambulatory detoxification
BETOS: Z2 Undefined codes
Service not separately priced by Part B

▯ **H0015** Alcohol and/or drug services; intensive outpatient (treatment program that operates at least 3 hours/day and at least 3 days/week and is based on an individualized treatment plan), including assessment, counseling; crisis intervention, and activity therapies or education
BETOS: Z2 Undefined codes
Service not separately priced by Part B

▯ **H0016** Alcohol and/or drug services; medical/somatic (medical intervention in ambulatory setting)
BETOS: Z2 Undefined codes
Service not separately priced by Part B

▯ **H0017** Behavioral health; residential (hospital residential treatment program), without room and board, per diem
BETOS: Z2 Undefined codes
Service not separately priced by Part B

▯ **H0018** Behavioral health; short-term residential (non-hospital residential treatment program), without room and board, per diem
BETOS: Z2 Undefined codes
Service not separately priced by Part B

▯ **H0019** Behavioral health; long-term residential (non-medical, non-acute care in a residential treatment program where stay is typically longer than 30 days), without room and board, per diem
BETOS: Z2 Undefined codes
Service not separately priced by Part B

▯ **H0020** Alcohol and/or drug services; methadone administration and/or service (provision of the drug by a licensed program)
BETOS: Z2 Undefined codes
Service not separately priced by Part B

▯ **H0021** Alcohol and/or drug training service (for staff and personnel not employed by providers)
BETOS: Z2 Undefined codes
Service not separately priced by Part B

▯ **H0022** Alcohol and/or drug intervention service (planned facilitation)
BETOS: Z2 Undefined codes
Service not separately priced by Part B

♂ Male only   ♀ Female only   Ⓐ Age   A2 - Z3 = ASC Payment indicator   A - Y = APC Status indicator
ASC = ASC-approved procedure   **DME** Paid under the DME fee schedule   **MIPS** MIPS code

ALCOHOL AND DRUG ABUSE TREATMENT (H0001-H2037)

H0023 - H0045

I **H0023** Behavioral health outreach service (planned approach to reach a targeted population)
BETOS: Z2   Undefined codes
Service not separately priced by Part B

I **H0024** Behavioral health prevention information dissemination service (one-way direct or non-direct contact with service audiences to affect knowledge and attitude)
BETOS: Z2   Undefined codes
Service not separately priced by Part B

I **H0025** Behavioral health prevention education service (delivery of services with target population to affect knowledge, attitude and/or behavior)
BETOS: Z2   Undefined codes
Service not separately priced by Part B

I **H0026** Alcohol and/or drug prevention process service, community-based (delivery of services to develop skills of impactors)
BETOS: Z2   Undefined codes
Service not separately priced by Part B

I **H0027** Alcohol and/or drug prevention environmental service (broad range of external activities geared toward modifying systems in order to mainstream prevention through policy and law)
BETOS: Z2   Undefined codes
Service not separately priced by Part B

I **H0028** Alcohol and/or drug prevention problem identification and referral service (e.g., student assistance and employee assistance programs), does not include assessment
BETOS: Z2   Undefined codes
Service not separately priced by Part B

I **H0029** Alcohol and/or drug prevention alternatives service (services for populations that exclude alcohol and other drug use e.g., alcohol free social events)
BETOS: Z2   Undefined codes
Service not separately priced by Part B

I **H0030** Behavioral health hotline service
BETOS: Z2   Undefined codes
Service not separately priced by Part B

MENTAL HEALTH PROGRAMS AND MEDICATION ADMINISTRATION TRAINING (H0031-H0040)

I **H0031** Mental health assessment, by non-physician
BETOS: Z2   Undefined codes
Service not separately priced by Part B

I **H0032** Mental health service plan development by non-physician
BETOS: Z2   Undefined codes
Service not separately priced by Part B

I **H0033** Oral medication administration, direct observation
BETOS: Z2   Undefined codes
Service not separately priced by Part B

I **H0034** Medication training and support, per 15 minutes
BETOS: Z2   Undefined codes
Service not separately priced by Part B

I **H0035** Mental health partial hospitalization, treatment, less than 24 hours
BETOS: Z2   Undefined codes
Service not separately priced by Part B

I **H0036** Community psychiatric supportive treatment, face-to-face, per 15 minutes
BETOS: Z2   Undefined codes
Service not separately priced by Part B

I **H0037** Community psychiatric supportive treatment program, per diem
BETOS: Z2   Undefined codes
Service not separately priced by Part B

I **H0038** Self-help/peer services, per 15 minutes
BETOS: Z2   Undefined codes
Service not separately priced by Part B

I **H0039** Assertive community treatment, face-to-face, per 15 minutes
BETOS: Z2   Undefined codes
Service not separately priced by Part B

I **H0040** Assertive community treatment program, per diem
BETOS: Z2   Undefined codes
Service not separately priced by Part B

FOSTER CARE (H0041, H0042)

I **H0041** Foster care, child, non-therapeutic, per diem Ⓐ
BETOS: Z2   Undefined codes
Service not separately priced by Part B

I **H0042** Foster care, child, non-therapeutic, per month Ⓐ
BETOS: Z2   Undefined codes
Service not separately priced by Part B

SUPPORTED HOUSING (H0043, H0044)

I **H0043** Supported housing, per diem
BETOS: Z2   Undefined codes
Service not separately priced by Part B

I **H0044** Supported housing, per month
BETOS: Z2   Undefined codes
Service not separately priced by Part B

MISCELLANEOUS DRUG AND ALCOHOL SERVICES (H0045-H0050)

I **H0045** Respite care services, not in the home, per diem

BETOS: Z2   Undefined codes
Service not separately priced by Part B

H0046 Mental health services, not otherwise specified
BETOS: Z2   Undefined codes
Service not separately priced by Part B

H0047 Alcohol and/or other drug abuse services, not otherwise specified
BETOS: Z2   Undefined codes
Service not separately priced by Part B

H0048 Alcohol and/or other drug testing: collection and handling only, specimens other than blood
BETOS: Z2   Undefined codes
Service not separately priced by Part B

H0049 Alcohol and/or drug screening
BETOS: Z2   Undefined codes
Service not separately priced by Part B

H0050 Alcohol and/or drug services, brief intervention, per 15 minutes
BETOS: Z2   Undefined codes
Service not separately priced by Part B

PRENATAL CARE AND FAMILY PLANNING ASSESSMENT (H1000-H1011)

H1000 Prenatal care, at-risk assessment ♀
BETOS: Z2   Undefined codes
Service not separately priced by Part B
Coding Clinic: 2002, Q1

H1001 Prenatal care, at-risk enhanced service; antepartum management ♀
BETOS: Z2   Undefined codes
Service not separately priced by Part B
Coding Clinic: 2002, Q1

H1002 Prenatal care, at risk enhanced service; care coordination ♀
BETOS: Z2   Undefined codes
Service not separately priced by Part B
Coding Clinic: 2002, Q1

H1003 Prenatal care, at-risk enhanced service; education ♀
BETOS: Z2   Undefined codes
Service not separately priced by Part B
Coding Clinic: 2002, Q1

H1004 Prenatal care, at-risk enhanced service; follow-up home visit ♀
BETOS: Z2   Undefined codes
Service not separately priced by Part B
Coding Clinic: 2002, Q1

H1005 Prenatal care, at-risk enhanced service package (includes H1001-H1004) ♀
BETOS: Z2   Undefined codes
Service not separately priced by Part B
Coding Clinic: 2002, Q1

H1010 Non-medical family planning education, per session
BETOS: Z2   Undefined codes
Service not separately priced by Part B

H1011 Family assessment by licensed behavioral health professional for state defined purposes
BETOS: Z2   Undefined codes
Service not separately priced by Part B

OTHER MENTAL HEALTH AND COMMUNITY SUPPORT SERVICES (H2000-H2037)

H2000 Comprehensive multidisciplinary evaluation
BETOS: Z2   Undefined codes
Service not separately priced by Part B

H2001 Rehabilitation program, per 1/2 day
BETOS: Z2   Undefined codes
Service not separately priced by Part B

H2010 Comprehensive medication services, per 15 minutes
BETOS: Z2   Undefined codes
Service not separately priced by Part B

H2011 Crisis intervention service, per 15 minutes
BETOS: Z2   Undefined codes
Service not separately priced by Part B

H2012 Behavioral health day treatment, per hour
BETOS: Z2   Undefined codes
Service not separately priced by Part B

H2013 Psychiatric health facility service, per diem
BETOS: Z2   Undefined codes
Service not separately priced by Part B

H2014 Skills training and development, per 15 minutes
BETOS: Z2   Undefined codes
Service not separately priced by Part B

H2015 Comprehensive community support services, per 15 minutes
BETOS: Z2   Undefined codes
Service not separately priced by Part B

H2016 Comprehensive community support services, per diem
BETOS: Z2   Undefined codes
Service not separately priced by Part B

H2017 Psychosocial rehabilitation services, per 15 minutes
BETOS: Z2   Undefined codes
Service not separately priced by Part B

H2018 Psychosocial rehabilitation services, per diem
BETOS: Z2   Undefined codes
Service not separately priced by Part B

H2019 Therapeutic behavioral services, per 15 minutes
BETOS: Z2   Undefined codes
Service not separately priced by Part B

♂ Male only   ♀ Female only   🅐 Age   A2 - Z3 = ASC Payment indicator   A - Y = APC Status indicator
ASC = ASC-approved procedure   **DME** Paid under the DME fee schedule   **MIPS** MIPS code

▌ H2020 Therapeutic behavioral services, per diem
BETOS: Z2   Undefined codes
Service not separately priced by Part B

▌ H2021 Community-based wrap-around services, per 15 minutes
BETOS: Z2   Undefined codes
Service not separately priced by Part B

▌ H2022 Community-based wrap-around services, per diem
BETOS: Z2   Undefined codes
Service not separately priced by Part B

▌ H2023 Supported employment, per 15 minutes
BETOS: Z2   Undefined codes
Service not separately priced by Part B

▌ H2024 Supported employment, per diem
BETOS: Z2   Undefined codes
Service not separately priced by Part B

▌ H2025 Ongoing support to maintain employment, per 15 minutes
BETOS: Z2   Undefined codes
Service not separately priced by Part B

▌ H2026 Ongoing support to maintain employment, per diem
BETOS: Z2   Undefined codes
Service not separately priced by Part B

▌ H2027 Psychoeducational service, per 15 minutes
BETOS: Z2   Undefined codes
Service not separately priced by Part B

▌ H2028 Sexual offender treatment service, per 15 minutes
BETOS: Z2   Undefined codes
Service not separately priced by Part B

▌ H2029 Sexual offender treatment service, per diem
BETOS: Z2   Undefined codes
Service not separately priced by Part B

▌ H2030 Mental health clubhouse services, per 15 minutes
BETOS: Z2   Undefined codes
Service not separately priced by Part B

▌ H2031 Mental health clubhouse services, per diem
BETOS: Z2   Undefined codes
Service not separately priced by Part B

▌ H2032 Activity therapy, per 15 minutes
BETOS: Z2   Undefined codes
Service not separately priced by Part B

▌ H2033 Multisystemic therapy for juveniles, per 15 minutes
BETOS: Z2   Undefined codes
Service not separately priced by Part B

▌ H2034 Alcohol and/or drug abuse halfway house services, per diem
BETOS: Z2   Undefined codes
Service not separately priced by Part B

▌ H2035 Alcohol and/or other drug treatment program, per hour
BETOS: Z2   Undefined codes
Service not separately priced by Part B

▌ H2036 Alcohol and/or other drug treatment program, per diem
BETOS: Z2   Undefined codes
Service not separately priced by Part B

▌ H2037 Developmental delay prevention activities, dependent child of client, per 15 minutes Ⓐ
BETOS: Z2   Undefined codes
Service not separately priced by Part B
Coding Clinic: 2009, Q2

▲ Revised code   ● New code   C Carrier judgment   D Special coverage instructions apply
▌ Not payable by Medicare   M Non-covered by Medicare   S Non-covered by Medicare statute   AHA Coding Clinic®

NOTES

NOTES

DRUGS ADMINISTERED OTHER THAN ORAL METHOD (J0120-J8999)

DRUGS, ADMINISTERED BY INJECTION (J0120-J7175)

D J0120 Injection, tetracycline, up to 250 mg K2 ASC K
BETOS: O1E Other drugs

C J0129 Injection, abatacept, 10 mg (code may be used for Medicare when drug administered under the direct supervision of a physician, not for use when drug is self administered) K2 ASC K
BETOS: O1E Other drugs
Drugs: ABATACEPT, ORENCIA, ORENCIA CLICKJECT
Coding Clinic: 2006, Q4

D J0130 Injection abciximab, 10 mg K2 ASC K
BETOS: O1E Other drugs
Drugs: REOPRO

C J0131 Injection, acetaminophen, 10 mg N1 ASC N
BETOS: O1E Other drugs

C J0132 Injection, acetylcysteine, 100 mg N1 ASC N
BETOS: O1E Other drugs
Drugs: ACETADOTE, ACETYLCYSTEINE, ACETYLCYSTEINE INJ, ACETYLCYSTEINE INJECTION

C J0133 Injection, acyclovir, 5 mg N1 ASC N
BETOS: O1E Other drugs
Drugs: ACYCLOVIR SODIUM

C J0135 Injection, adalimumab, 20 mg K2 ASC K
BETOS: O1E Other drugs
Coding Clinic: 2005, Q2; 2005, Q3

D J0153 Injection, adenosine, 1 mg (not to be used to report any adenosine phosphate compounds) N1 ASC N
BETOS: O1E Other drugs
Drugs: ADENOCARD, ADENOSCAN, ADENOSINE

D J0171 Injection, adrenalin, epinephrine, 0.1 mg N1 ASC N
BETOS: O1E Other drugs
Drugs: ADRENALIN, EPINEPHRINE HCL
Coding Clinic: 2011, Q1

C J0178 Injection, aflibercept, 1 mg K2 ASC K
BETOS: O1E Other drugs
Drugs: EYLEA

C J0180 Injection, agalsidase beta, 1 mg K2 ASC K
BETOS: O1E Other drugs
Drugs: FABRAZYME
Coding Clinic: 2005, Q2

D J0190 Injection, biperiden lactate, per 5 mg E2
BETOS: O1E Other drugs

D J0200 Injection, alatrofloxacin mesylate, 100 mg E2
BETOS: O1E Other drugs

C J0202 Injection, alemtuzumab, 1 mg K2 ASC K
BETOS: O1E Other drugs
Drugs: LEMTRADA
Coding Clinic: 2016, Q1

D J0205 Injection, alglucerase, per 10 units E2
BETOS: O1E Other drugs
Coding Clinic: 2005, Q2

D J0207 Injection, amifostine, 500 mg K2 ASC K
BETOS: O1D Chemotherapy
Drugs: AMIFOSTINE FOR INJECTION, ETHYOL

D J0210 Injection, methyldopate HCl, up to 250 mg N1 ASC N
BETOS: O1E Other drugs

C J0215 Injection, alefacept, 0.5 mg K2 ASC K
BETOS: O1E Other drugs

C J0220 Injection, alglucosidase alfa, 10 mg, not otherwise specified K2 ASC K
BETOS: O1E Other drugs
Coding Clinic: 2012, Q 1

C J0221 Injection, alglucosidase alfa, (Lumizyme), 10 mg K2 ASC K
BETOS: O1E Other drugs
Drugs: LUMIZYME

D J0256 Injection, alpha 1 proteinase inhibitor (human), not otherwise specified, 10 mg K2 ASC K
BETOS: O1E Other drugs
Drugs: ARALAST NP, PROLASTIN-C, ZEMAIRA
Coding Clinic: 2012, Q 1

D J0257 Injection, alpha 1 proteinase inhibitor (human), (Glassia), 10 mg K2 ASC K
BETOS: O1E Other drugs
Drugs: GLASSIA
Coding Clinic: 2012, Q 1

D J0270 Injection, alprostadil, 1.25 mcg (code may be used for Medicare when drug administered under the direct supervision of a physician, not for use when drug is self administered) B
BETOS: O1E Other drugs

D J0275 Alprostadil urethral suppository (code may be used for Medicare when drug administered under the direct supervision of a physician, not for use when drug is self administered) B
BETOS: O1E Other drugs

C J0278 Injection, amikacin sulfate, 100 mg N1 ASC N
BETOS: O1E Other drugs
Drugs: AMIKACIN SULFATE

D J0280 Injection, aminophyllin, up to 250 mg N1 ASC N
BETOS: O1E Other drugs
Drugs: AMINOPHYLLINE, NOVAPLUS AMINOPHYLLINE
Coding Clinic: 2005, Q4

♂ Male only   ♀ Female only   Ⓐ Age   A2 - Z3 = ASC Payment indicator   A - Y = APC Status indicator
ASC = ASC-approved procedure   **DME** Paid under the DME fee schedule   **MIPS** MIPS code

D **J0282** Injection, amiodarone hydrochloride, 30 mg   N1 ASC N
     BETOS: O1E   Other drugs

D **J0285** Injection, amphotericin B, 50 mg   N1 ASC N
     BETOS: O1E   Other drugs
     Drugs: AMPHOTERICIN B

D **J0287** Injection, amphotericin B lipid complex, 10 mg   K2 ASC K
     BETOS: O1E   Other drugs
     Drugs: ABELCET

D **J0288** Injection, amphotericin B cholesteryl sulfate complex, 10 mg   N1 ASC N
     BETOS: O1E   Other drugs

D **J0289** Injection, amphotericin B liposome, 10 mg   K2 ASC K
     BETOS: O1E   Other drugs
     Drugs: AMBISOME

D **J0290** Injection, ampicillin sodium, 500 mg   N1 ASC N
     BETOS: O1E   Other drugs
     Drugs: AMPICILLIN FOR INJECTION, AMPICILLIN SODIUM

D **J0295** Injection, ampicillin sodium/sulbactam sodium, per 1.5 gm   N1 ASC N
     BETOS: O1E   Other drugs
     Drugs: AMPICILLIN-SULBACTAM, UNASYN 1.5GM, UNASYN 15GM, UNASYN 3GM

D **J0300** Injection, amobarbital, up to 125 mg   K2 ASC K
     BETOS: O1E   Other drugs

D **J0330** Injection, succinylcholine chloride, up to 20 mg   N1 ASC N
     BETOS: O1E   Other drugs

C **J0348** Injection, anidulafungin, 1 mg   N1 ASC N
     BETOS: O1E   Other drugs
     Drugs: ERAXIS

D **J0350** Injection, anistreplase, per 30 units   E2
     BETOS: O1E   Other drugs

D **J0360** Injection, hydralazine HCl, up to 20 mg   N1 ASC N
     BETOS: O1E   Other drugs
     Drugs: HYDRALAZINE HCL

C **J0364** Injection, apomorphine hydrochloride, 1 mg   E2
     BETOS: O1E   Other drugs

D **J0365** Injection, aprotinin, 10,000 kiu   E2
     BETOS: O1E   Other drugs

D **J0380** Injection, metaraminol bitartrate, per 10 mg   N1 ASC N
     BETOS: O1E   Other drugs

D **J0390** Injection, chloroquine hydrochloride, up to 250 mg   N1 ASC N
     BETOS: O1E   Other drugs

D **J0395** Injection, arbutamine HCl, 1 mg   E2
     BETOS: O1E   Other drugs

C **J0400** Injection, aripiprazole, intramuscular, 0.25 mg   N1 ASC N
     BETOS: O1E   Other drugs
     Coding Clinic: 2008, Q1

C **J0401** Injection, aripiprazole, extended release, 1 mg   K2 ASC K
     BETOS: O1E   Other drugs
     Drugs: ABILIFY MAINTENA
     Coding Clinic: 2014, Q1

D **J0456** Injection, azithromycin, 500 mg   N1 ASC N
     BETOS: O1E   Other drugs
     Drugs: AZITHROMYCIN, ZITHROMAX

D **J0461** Injection, atropine sulfate, 0.01 mg N1 ASC N
     BETOS: O1E   Other drugs
     Drugs: ATROPINE SULFATE

D **J0470** Injection, dimercaprol, per 100 mg N1 ASC N
     BETOS: O1E   Other drugs
     Drugs: BAL IN OIL

D **J0475** Injection, baclofen, 10 mg   K2 ASC K
     BETOS: O1E   Other drugs
     Drugs: GABLOFEN, LIORESAL

D **J0476** Injection, baclofen, 50 mcg for intrathecal trial   K2 ASC K
     BETOS: O1E   Other drugs
     Drugs: GABLOFEN, LIORESAL

D **J0480** Injection, basiliximab, 20 mg   K2 ASC K
     BETOS: O1E   Other drugs
     Drugs: SIMULECT

C **J0485** Injection, belatacept, 1 mg   K2 ASC K
     BETOS: O1E   Other drugs
     Drugs: NULOJIX

C **J0490** Injection, belimumab, 10 mg   K2 ASC K
     BETOS: O1E   Other drugs
     Drugs: BENLYSTA

D **J0500** Injection, dicyclomine HCl, up to 20 mg   N1 ASC N
     BETOS: O1E   Other drugs
     Drugs: BENTYL

D **J0515** Injection, benztropine mesylate, per 1 mg   N1 ASC N
     BETOS: O1E   Other drugs
     Drugs: BENZTROPINE, COGENTIN

D **J0520** Injection, bethanechol chloride, myotonachol or urecholine, up to 5 mg   N1 ASC N
     BETOS: O1E   Other drugs

C **J0558** Injection, penicillin G benzathine and penicillin G procaine, 100,000 units   N1 ASC N
     BETOS: O1E   Other drugs
     Drugs: BICILLIN C-R, BICILLIN CR PEDIATRIC
     Coding Clinic: 2011, Q1

▲ Revised code   ● New code   **C** Carrier judgment   **D** Special coverage instructions apply
I Not payable by Medicare   **M** Non-covered by Medicare   **S** Non-covered by Medicare statute   AHA Coding Clinic®

D **J0561** Injection, penicillin G benzathine, 100,000 units   K2 ASC K
BETOS: O1E   Other drugs
Drugs: BICILLIN L-A
Coding Clinic: 2011, Q1

● **C** **J0565** Injection, bezlotoxumab, 10 mg
BETOS: O1E   Other drugs

C **J0570** Buprenorphine implant, 74.2 mg   K2 ASC G
BETOS: O1E   Other drugs
Drugs: PROBUPHINE SYSTEM KIT
Coding Clinic: 2011, Q1; 2017, Q1

D **J0571** Buprenorphine, oral, 1 mg   E1
BETOS: O1E   Other drugs
Service not separately priced by Part B
Coding Clinic: 2014, Q4; 2016, Q1

D **J0572** Buprenorphine/naloxone, oral, less than or equal to 3 mg buprenorphine   E1
BETOS: O1E   Other drugs
Service not separately priced by Part B
Coding Clinic: 2014, Q4; 2016, Q1

D **J0573** Buprenorphine/naloxone, oral, greater than 3 mg, but less than or equal to 6 mg buprenorphine   E1
BETOS: O1E   Other drugs
Service not separately priced by Part B
Coding Clinic: 2014, Q4; 2016, Q1

D **J0574** Buprenorphine/naloxone, oral, greater than 6 mg, but less than or equal to 10 mg buprenorphine   E1
BETOS: O1E   Other drugs
Service not separately priced by Part B
Coding Clinic: 2014, Q4; 2016, Q1

D **J0575** Buprenorphine/naloxone, oral, greater than 10 mg buprenorphine   E1
BETOS: O1E   Other drugs
Service not separately priced by Part B
Coding Clinic: 2014, Q4; 2016, Q1

C **J0583** Injection, bivalirudin, 1 mg   K2 ASC K
BETOS: O1E   Other drugs
Drugs: ANGIOMAX, BIVALIRUDIN

D **J0585** Injection, onabotulinumtoxinA, 1 unit   K2 ASC K
BETOS: O1E   Other drugs
Drugs: BOTOX, BOTOX COSMETIC

C **J0586** Injection, abobotulinumtoxinA, 5 units   K2 ASC K
BETOS: O1E   Other drugs
Drugs: DYSPORT

D **J0587** Injection, rimabotulinumtoxinbB, 100 units   K2 ASC K
BETOS: O1E   Other drugs
Drugs: MYOBLOC
Coding Clinic: 2002, Q1; 2002, Q2

C **J0588** Injection, incobotulinumtoxin A, 1 unit   K2 ASC K

BETOS: O1E   Other drugs
Drugs: XEOMIN

D **J0592** Injection, buprenorphine hydrochloride, 0.1 mg   N1 ASC N
BETOS: O1E   Other drugs
Drugs: BUPRENORPHINE HCL, BUPRENORPHINE HCL INJECTION

C **J0594** Injection, Busulfan, 1 mg   K2 ASC K
BETOS: O1E   Other drugs
Drugs: BUSULFAN

C **J0595** Injection, butorphanol tartrate, 1 mg   N1 ASC N
BETOS: O1E   Other drugs
Drugs: BUTORPHANOL TARTRATE
Coding Clinic: 2005, Q2

C **J0596** Injection, C1 esterase inhibitor (recombinant), ruconest, 10 units   K2 ASC G
BETOS: O1E   Other drugs
Drugs: RUCONEST
Coding Clinic: 2016, Q1

C **J0597** Injection, C-1 esterase inhibitor (human), Berinert, 10 units   K2 ASC K
BETOS: O1E   Other drugs
Drugs: BERINERT
Coding Clinic: 2011, Q1

C **J0598** Injection, C-1 esterase inhibitor (human), Cinryze, 10 units   K2 ASC K
BETOS: O1E   Other drugs
Drugs: CINRYZE

D **J0600** Injection, edetate calcium disodium, up to 1000 mg   K2 ASC K
BETOS: O1E   Other drugs
Drugs: CALCIUM DISODIUM VERSENATE

● **D** **J0604** Cinacalcet, oral, 1 mg, (for ESRD on dialysis)
BETOS: O1E   Other drugs

● **D** **J0606** Injection, etelcalcetide, 0.1 mg
BETOS: O1E   Other drugs

D **J0610** Injection, calcium gluconate, per 10 ml   N1 ASC N
BETOS: O1E   Other drugs
Drugs: CALCIUM GLUCONATE

D **J0620** Injection, calcium glycerophosphate and calcium lactate, per 10 ml   N1 ASC N
BETOS: O1E   Other drugs

D **J0630** Injection, calcitonin salmon, up to 400 units   K2 ASC K
BETOS: O1E   Other drugs
Drugs: MIACALCIN
Pub: 100-4, Chap. 10, 90 .1

D **J0636** Injection, calcitriol, 0.1 mcg   N1 ASC N
BETOS: O1E   Other drugs
Drugs: CALCITRIOL

♂ Male only   ♀ Female only   **Ⓐ** Age   A2 - Z3 = ASC Payment indicator   A - Y = APC Status indicator
ASC = ASC-approved procedure   **DME** Paid under the DME fee schedule   **MIPS** MIPS code

C **J0637** Injection, caspofungin acetate, 5 mg K2 ASC K
BETOS: O1E Other drugs
Drugs: CANCIDAS

C **J0638** Injection, canakinumab, 1 mg K2 ASC K
BETOS: O1E Other drugs
Drugs: ILARIS
Coding Clinic: 2011, Q1; 2011, Q4

D **J0640** Injection, leucovorin calcium, per
50 mg N1 ASC N
BETOS: O1E Other drugs
Drugs: LEUCOVORIN CALCIUM
Coding Clinic: 2009, Q1

D **J0641** Injection, levoleucovorin calcium,
0.5 mg K2 ASC K
BETOS: O1E Other drugs
Drugs: LEVOLEUCOVORIN CALCIUM
Coding Clinic: 2008, Q4; 2009, Q1

D **J0670** Injection, mepivacaine hydrochloride,
per 10 ml N1 ASC N
BETOS: O1E Other drugs
Drugs: POLOCAINE, POLOCAINE-MPF

D **J0690** Injection, cefazolin sodium, 500 mg N1 ASC N
BETOS: O1E Other drugs
Drugs: CEFAZOLIN SODIUM, CEFAZOLIN SODIUM IN DEXTROSE

C **J0692** Injection, cefepime hydrochloride,
500 mg N1 ASC N
BETOS: O1E Other drugs
Drugs: CEFEPIME , CEFEPIME HCL, CEFEPIME HCL IN DEXTROSE, MAXIPIME
Coding Clinic: 2002, Q1

D **J0694** Injection, cefoxitin sodium, 1 gm N1 ASC N
BETOS: O1E Other drugs
Drugs: CEFOXITIN SODIUM, PREMIERPRO RX CEFOXITIN SODIUM

C **J0695** Injection, ceftolozane 50 mg and tazobactam
25 mg K2 ASC G
BETOS: O1E Other drugs
Coding Clinic: 2016, Q1

D **J0696** Injection, ceftriaxone sodium, per
250 mg N1 ASC N
BETOS: O1E Other drugs
Drugs: CEFTRIAXONE, CEFTRIAXONE IN D5W, CEFTRIAXONE SODIUM

D **J0697** Injection, sterile cefuroxime sodium, per
750 mg N1 ASC N
BETOS: O1E Other drugs
Drugs: CEFUROXIME SODIUM, ZINACEF, ZINACEF (FROZEN)

D **J0698** Injection, cefotaxime sodium, per gm N1 ASC N
BETOS: O1E Other drugs

D **J0702** Injection, betamethasone acetate 3 mg
and betamethasone sodium phosphate
3 mg N1 ASC N
BETOS: O1E Other drugs
Drugs: CELESTONE SOLUSPAN

C **J0706** Injection, caffeine citrate, 5 mg N1 ASC N
BETOS: O1E Other drugs
Coding Clinic: 2002, Q1; 2002, Q2

D **J0710** Injection, cephapirin sodium, up to 1 gm E1
BETOS: O1E Other drugs

C **J0712** Injection, ceftaroline fosamil, 10 mg K2 ASC K
BETOS: O1E Other drugs
Drugs: TEFLARO

D **J0713** Injection, ceftazidime, per 500 mg N1 ASC N
BETOS: O1E Other drugs
Drugs: CEFTAZIDIME, FORTAZ, FORTAZ (ADD-V), FORTAZ (FROZEN), FORTAZ ADD-V), TAZICEF

C **J0714** Injection, ceftazidime and avibactam,
0.5 g/0.125 g K2 ASC K
BETOS: O1E Other drugs
Coding Clinic: 2016, Q1

D **J0715** Injection, ceftizoxime sodium, per
500 mg N1 ASC N
BETOS: O1E Other drugs

C **J0716** Injection, centruroides immune f(ab)2, up to
120 milligrams K2 ASC K
BETOS: O1E Other drugs

C **J0717** Injection, certolizumab pegol, 1 mg (code
may be used for Medicare when drug
administered under the direct supervision
of a physician, not for use when drug is self
administered) K2 ASC K
BETOS: O1E Other drugs
Drugs: CIMZIA
Coding Clinic: 2014, Q1

D **J0720** Injection, chloramphenicol sodium succinate,
up to 1 gm N1 ASC N
BETOS: O1E Other drugs
Drugs: CHLORAMPHENICOL SOD SUCCINATE

D **J0725** Injection, chorionic gonadotropin, per 1,000
USP units N1 ASC N
BETOS: O1E Other drugs
Drugs: CHORIONIC GONADOTROPIN, NOVAREL

D **J0735** Injection, clonidine hydrochloride,
1 mg N1 ASC N
BETOS: O1E Other drugs
Drugs: CLONIDINE HYDROCHLORIDE, CLONIDINE HYDROCHLORIDE INJECTION, DURACLON

D **J0740** Injection, cidofovir, 375 mg K2 ASC K
BETOS: O1E Other drugs
Drugs: CIDOFOVIR

D **J0743** Injection, cilastatin sodium; imipenem, per
250 mg N1 ASC N
BETOS: O1E Other drugs
Drugs: IMIPENEM AND CILASTATIN, PRIMAXIN IV

▲ Revised code ● New code **C** Carrier judgment **D** Special coverage instructions apply
I Not payable by Medicare **M** Non-covered by Medicare **S** Non-covered by Medicare statute AHA Coding Clinic®

C **J0744** Injection, ciprofloxacin for intravenous
infusion, 200 mg   N1 ASC N
BETOS: O1E   Other drugs
Drugs: CIPROFLOXACIN
Coding Clinic: 2002, Q1

D **J0745** Injection, codeine phosphate, per
30 mg   N1 ASC N
BETOS: O1E   Other drugs

D **J0770** Injection, colistimethate sodium, up to
150 mg   N1 ASC N
BETOS: O1E   Other drugs
Drugs: COLISTIMETHATE SODIUM, COLY-
MYCIN M PARENTERAL

C **J0775** Injection, collagenase, clostridium
histolyticum, 0.01 mg   K2 ASC K
BETOS: O1E   Other drugs
Drugs: XIAFLEX (COLLAGENASE
CLOSTRIDIUM HISTOLYTICUM)
Coding Clinic: 2011, Q1

D **J0780** Injection, prochlorperazine, up to
10 mg   N1 ASC N
BETOS: O1E   Other drugs
Drugs: PROCHLORPERAZINE EDISYLATE

D **J0795** Injection, corticorelin ovine triflutate,
1 microgram   K2 ASC K
BETOS: O1E   Other drugs
Drugs: ACTHREL

D **J0800** Injection, corticotropin, up to
40 units   K2 ASC K
BETOS: O1E   Other drugs
Drugs: H.P. ACTHAR

C **J0833** Injection, cosyntropin, not otherwise
specified, 0.25 mg   N1 ASC N
BETOS: O1E   Other drugs

C **J0834** Injection, cosyntropin (Cortrosyn),
0.25 mg   N1 ASC N
BETOS: O1E   Other drugs
Drugs: CORTROSYN, COSYNTROPIN,
COSYNTROPIN (CORTROSYN GENERIC),
COSYNTROPIN NOVAPLUS (CORTROSYN
GENERIC)

C **J0840** Injection, crotalidae polyvalent immune FAB
(Ovine), up to 1 gram   K2 ASC K
BETOS: O1E   Other drugs
Drugs: CROFAB POWDER FOR
SOLUTION

D **J0850** Injection, cytomegalovirus immune globulin
intravenous (human), per vial   K2 ASC K
BETOS: O1E   Other drugs
Drugs: CYTOGAM

C **J0875** Injection, dalbavancin, 5 mg   K2 ASC G
BETOS: O1E   Other drugs
Drugs: DALVANCE
Coding Clinic: 2016, Q1

C **J0878** Injection, daptomycin, 1 mg   K2 ASC K
BETOS: O1E   Other drugs

Drugs: CUBICIN, DAPTOMYCIN
Coding Clinic: 2005, Q2

D **J0881** Injection, darbepoetin alfa, 1 microgram
(non-ESRD use)   K2 ASC K
BETOS: O1E   Other drugs
Drugs: ARANESP

D **J0882** Injection, darbepoetin alfa, 1 microgram
(for ESRD on dialysis)   K2 ASC K
BETOS: O1E   Other drugs
Other carrier priced
Drugs: ARANESP
Pub: 100-4, Chap. 8, 60.4; 100-4, Chap. 8,
60.4.1; 100-4, Chap. 8, 60.4.4.1; 100-4, Chap.
8, 60.4.4.2; 100-4, Chap. 8, 60.4.5.1; 100-4,
Chap. 8, 60.4.6.3; 100-4, Chap. 8, 60.4.6.4;
100-4, Chap. 8, 60.4.6.5; 100-4, Chap. 8,
60.4.7

D **J0883** Injection, argatroban, 1 mg (for non-ESRD
use)   K2 ASC K
BETOS: O1E   Other drugs

D **J0884** Injection, argatroban, 1 mg (for ESRD on
dialysis)   N1 ASC N
BETOS: O1E   Other drugs

D **J0885** Injection, epoetin alfa, (for non-ESRD use),
1000 units   K2 ASC K
BETOS: O1E   Other drugs
Drugs: EPOGEN, PROCRIT
Coding Clinic: 2006, Q2

D **J0887** Injection, epoetin beta, 1 microgram,
(for ESRD on dialysis)   N1 ASC N
BETOS: O1E   Other drugs
Other carrier priced
Drugs: MIRCERA

D **J0888** Injection, epoetin beta, 1 microgram,
(for Non ESRD use)   N1 ASC N
BETOS: O1E   Other drugs
Other carrier priced
Drugs: MIRCERA

C **J0890** Injection, peginesatide, 0.1 mg (for ESRD on
dialysis)   E1
BETOS: O1E   Other drugs
Pub: 100-4, Chap. 8, 60.4; 100-4, Chap. 8,
60.4.1; 100-4, Chap. 8, 60.4.4.1; 100-4, Chap.
8, 60.4.4.2; 100-4, Chap. 8, 60.4.5.1; 100-4,
Chap. 8, 60.4.7

C **J0894** Injection, decitabine, 1 mg   K2 ASC K
BETOS: O1E   Other drugs
Drugs: DACOGEN, DECITABINE

D **J0895** Injection, deferoxamine mesylate,
500 mg   N1 ASC N
BETOS: O1E   Other drugs
Drugs: DEFEROXAMINE MESYLATE,
DESFERAL

C **J0897** Injection, denosumab, 1 mg   K2 ASC K
BETOS: O1E   Other drugs
Drugs: PROLIA, XGEVA
Coding Clinic: 2013, Q1; 2016, Q1

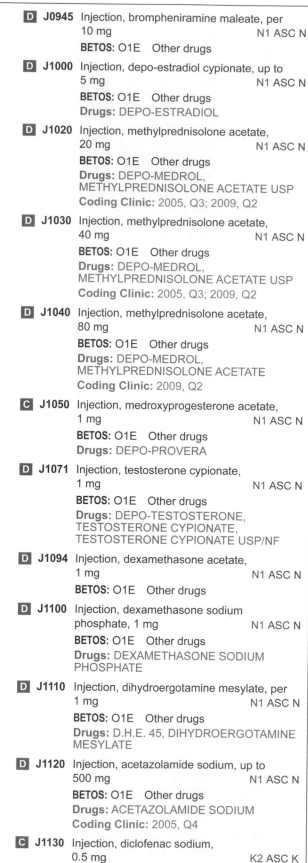

D J0945 Injection, brompheniramine maleate, per 10 mg N1 ASC N

BETOS: O1E Other drugs

D J1000 Injection, depo-estradiol cypionate, up to 5 mg N1 ASC N

BETOS: O1E Other drugs

Drugs: DEPO-ESTRADIOL

D J1020 Injection, methylprednisolone acetate, 20 mg N1 ASC N

BETOS: O1E Other drugs

Drugs: DEPO-MEDROL, METHYLPREDNISOLONE ACETATE USP

Coding Clinic: 2005, Q3; 2009, Q2

D J1030 Injection, methylprednisolone acetate, 40 mg N1 ASC N

BETOS: O1E Other drugs

Drugs: DEPO-MEDROL, METHYLPREDNISOLONE ACETATE USP

Coding Clinic: 2005, Q3; 2009, Q2

D J1040 Injection, methylprednisolone acetate, 80 mg N1 ASC N

BETOS: O1E Other drugs

Drugs: DEPO-MEDROL, METHYLPREDNISOLONE ACETATE

Coding Clinic: 2009, Q2

C J1050 Injection, medroxyprogesterone acetate, 1 mg N1 ASC N

BETOS: O1E Other drugs

Drugs: DEPO-PROVERA

D J1071 Injection, testosterone cypionate, 1 mg N1 ASC N

BETOS: O1E Other drugs

Drugs: DEPO-TESTOSTERONE, TESTOSTERONE CYPIONATE, TESTOSTERONE CYPIONATE USP/NF

D J1094 Injection, dexamethasone acetate, 1 mg N1 ASC N

BETOS: O1E Other drugs

D J1100 Injection, dexamethasone sodium phosphate, 1 mg N1 ASC N

BETOS: O1E Other drugs

Drugs: DEXAMETHASONE SODIUM PHOSPHATE

D J1110 Injection, dihydroergotamine mesylate, per 1 mg N1 ASC N

BETOS: O1E Other drugs

Drugs: D.H.E. 45, DIHYDROERGOTAMINE MESYLATE

D J1120 Injection, acetazolamide sodium, up to 500 mg N1 ASC N

BETOS: O1E Other drugs

Drugs: ACETAZOLAMIDE SODIUM

Coding Clinic: 2005, Q4

C J1130 Injection, diclofenac sodium, 0.5 mg K2 ASC K

BETOS: O1E Other drugs

Coding Clinic: 2017, Q1

D J1160 Injection, digoxin, up to 0.5 mg N1 ASC N

BETOS: O1E Other drugs

Drugs: DIGOXIN, LANOXIN, LANOXIN INJ

D J1162 Injection, digoxin immune FAB (Ovine), per vial K2 ASC K

BETOS: O1E Other drugs

Drugs: DIGIFAB

D J1165 Injection, phenytoin sodium, per 50 mg N1 ASC N

BETOS: O1E Other drugs

Drugs: PHENYTOIN, PHENYTOIN SODIUM

D J1170 Injection, hydromorphone, up to 4 mg N1 ASC N

BETOS: O1E Other drugs

Drugs: DILAUDID (PFSYR), HYDROMORPHONE, HYDROMORPHONE HCL, HYDROMORPHONE HYDROCHLORIDE

D J1180 Injection, dyphylline, up to 500 mg E2

BETOS: O1E Other drugs

D J1190 Injection, dexrazoxane hydrochloride, per 250 mg K2 ASC K

BETOS: O1E Other drugs

Drugs: DEXRAZOXANE, ZINECARD

D J1200 Injection, diphenhydramine HCl, up to 50 mg N1 ASC N

BETOS: O1E Other drugs

Drugs: BENADRYL, DIPHENHYDRAMINE HCL

Coding Clinic: 2002, Q1

D J1205 Injection, chlorothiazide sodium, per 500 mg K2 ASC K

BETOS: O1E Other drugs

Drugs: CHLOROTHIAZIDE SODIUM, DIURIL IV

D J1212 Injection, DMSO, dimethyl sulfoxide, 50%, 50 ml K2 ASC K

BETOS: O1E Other drugs

Drugs: RIMSO-50

D J1230 Injection, methadone HCl, up to 10 mg N1 ASC N

BETOS: O1E Other drugs

Drugs: METHADONE HCL

D J1240 Injection, dimenhydrinate, up to 50 mg N1 ASC N

BETOS: O1E Other drugs

Drugs: DIMENHYDRINATE

D J1245 Injection, dipyridamole, per 10 mg N1 ASC N

BETOS: O1E Other drugs

Drugs: DIPYRIDAMOLE

D J1250 Injection, Dobutamine hydrochloride, per 250 mg N1 ASC N

BETOS: O1E Other drugs

Drugs: DOBUTAMINE HCL

▲ Revised code   ● New code   **C** Carrier judgment   **D** Special coverage instructions apply

I Not payable by Medicare   **M** Non-covered by Medicare   **S** Non-covered by Medicare statute   AHA Coding Clinic®

D J1260 Injection, dolasetron mesylate, 10 mg   N1 ASC N
     BETOS: O1D   Chemotherapy

C J1265 Injection, dopamine HCl, 40 mg   N1 ASC N
     BETOS: O1E   Other drugs
     Drugs: DOPAMINE, DOPAMINE 200MG/5ML, DOPAMINE HCL 200MGIN 5% DEXTROSE LIFECARE 250ML, DOPAMINE HCL 400MGIN 5% DEXTROSE LIFECARE 250ML, DOPAMINE HCL 400MGIN 5% DEXTROSE LIFECARE 500ML, DOPAMINE HCL 800MGIN 5% DEXTROSE LIFECARE 250ML, DOPAMINE IN D5W
     Coding Clinic: 2005, Q4

C J1267 Injection, doripenem, 10 mg   N1 ASC N
     BETOS: O1E   Other drugs
     Drugs: DORIBAX
     Coding Clinic: 2008, Q4

C J1270 Injection, doxercalciferol, 1 mcg   N1 ASC N
     BETOS: O1E   Other drugs
     Drugs: DOXERCALCIFEROL, HECTOROL
     Coding Clinic: 2002, Q1

C J1290 Injection, ecallantide, 1 mg   K2 ASC K
     BETOS: O1E   Other drugs
     Drugs: KALBITOR®
     Coding Clinic: 2011, Q1

C J1300 Injection, eculizumab, 10 mg   K2 ASC K
     BETOS: O1E   Other drugs
     Drugs: SOLIRIS
     Coding Clinic: 2008, Q1

D J1320 Injection, amitriptyline HCl, up to 20 mg   N1 ASC N
     BETOS: O1E   Other drugs

C J1322 Injection, elosulfase alfa, 1 mg   K2 ASC K
     BETOS: O1E   Other drugs

C J1324 Injection, enfuvirtide, 1 mg   K2 ASC K
     BETOS: O1E   Other drugs

D J1325 Injection, epoprostenol, 0.5 mg   N1 ASC N
     BETOS: O1E   Other drugs
     Drugs: EPOPROSTENOL, EPOPROSTENOL (VELETRI), FLOLAN

D J1327 Injection, eptifibatide, 5 mg   K2 ASC K
     BETOS: O1E   Other drugs

D J1330 Injection, ergonovine maleate, up to 0.2 mg   N1 ASC N
     BETOS: O1E   Other drugs

C J1335 Injection, ertapenem sodium, 500 mg   N1 ASC N
     BETOS: O1E   Other drugs
     Drugs: INVANZ

D J1364 Injection, erythromycin lactobionate, per 500 mg   K2 ASC K
     BETOS: O1E   Other drugs
     Drugs: ERYTHROMYCIN, ERYTHROMYCIN LACTOBIONATE

D J1380 Injection, estradiol valerate, up to 10 mg   N1 ASC N
     BETOS: O1E   Other drugs
     Drugs: DELESTROGEN, ESTRADIOL VALERATE
     Coding Clinic: 2011, Q1

D J1410 Injection, estrogen conjugated, per 25 mg   K2 ASC K
     BETOS: O1E   Other drugs
     Drugs: PREMARIN

● **C** J1428 Injection, eteplirsen, 10 mg
     BETOS: O1E   Other drugs

D J1430 Injection, ethanolamine oleate, 100 mg   K2 ASC K
     BETOS: O1E   Other drugs
     Drugs: ETHANOLAMINE OLEATE

D J1435 Injection, estrone, per 1 mg   E1
     BETOS: O1E   Other drugs

D J1436 Injection, etidronate disodium, per 300 mg   N1 ASC N
     BETOS: O1E   Other drugs

D J1438 Injection, etanercept, 25 mg (code may be used for Medicare when drug administered under the direct supervision of a physician, not for use when drug is self administered)   K2 ASC K
     BETOS: O1E   Other drugs

C J1439 Injection, ferric carboxymaltose, 1 mg   K2 ASC K
     BETOS: O1E   Other drugs
     Drugs: INJECTAFER

D J1442 Injection, filgrastim (G-CSF), excludes biosimilars, 1 microgram   K2 ASC K
     BETOS: O1E   Other drugs
     Drugs: NEUPOGEN
     Coding Clinic: 2014, Q1

C J1443 Injection, ferric pyrophosphate citrate solution, 0.1 mg of iron   N1 ASC N
     BETOS: O1E   Other drugs
     Coding Clinic: 2016, Q1

D J1447 Injection, TBO-filgrastim, 1 microgram   K2 ASC K
     BETOS: O1E   Other drugs
     Drugs: GRANIX
     Coding Clinic: 2016, Q1

D J1450 Injection fluconazole, 200 mg   N1 ASC N
     BETOS: O1E   Other drugs
     Drugs: DIFLUCAN, FLUCONAZOLE IN DEXTROSE, FLUCONAZOLE IN SODIUM CHLORIDE, FLUCONAZOLE INJECTION, NOVAPLUS FLUCONAZOLE
     Pub: 100-2, Chap. 15, 50.2

D J1451 Injection, fomepizole, 15 mg   K2 ASC K
     BETOS: O1E   Other drugs

D J1452 Injection, fomivirsen sodium, intraocular, 1.65 mg   N1 ASC N

♂ Male only   ♀ Female only   Ⓐ Age   A2 - Z3 = ASC Payment indicator   A - Y = APC Status indicator
ASC = ASC-approved procedure   **DME** Paid under the DME fee schedule   **MIPS** MIPS code

BETOS: O1E   Other drugs
Pub: 100-2, Chap. 15, 50.4.2

C **J1453** Injection, fosaprepitant, 1 mg   K2 ASC K
BETOS: O1E   Other drugs
Drugs: EMEND FOR INJECTION 150MG
Coding Clinic: 2008, Q4

D **J1455** Injection, foscarnet sodium, per 1000 mg   K2 ASC K
BETOS: O1E   Other drugs

C **J1457** Injection, gallium nitrate, 1 mg   E2
BETOS: O1E   Other drugs
Coding Clinic: 2005, Q2

C **J1458** Injection, galsulfase, 1 mg   K2 ASC K
BETOS: O1E   Other drugs
Drugs: NAGLAZYME

C **J1459** Injection, immune globulin (Privigen®), intravenous, non-lyophilized (e.g., liquid), 500 mg   K2 ASC K
BETOS: O1E   Other drugs
Drugs: PRIVIGEN
Coding Clinic: 2008, Q4

D **J1460** Injection, gamma globulin, intramuscular, 1 cc   K2 ASC K
BETOS: O1E   Other drugs
Drugs: GAMASTAN S/D
Coding Clinic: 2011, Q1

● **C** **J1555** Injection, immune globulin (Cuvitru), 100 mg
BETOS: D1G   Drugs administered through DME

C **J1556** Injection, immune globulin (Bivigam®), 500 mg   K2 ASC K
BETOS: O1E   Other drugs
Drugs: BIVIGAM
Coding Clinic: 2013, Q4

C **J1557** Injection, immune globulin, (Gammaplex®), intravenous, non-lyophilized (e.g., liquid), 500 mg   K2 ASC K
BETOS: O1E   Other drugs
Drugs: GAMMAPLEX

C **J1559** Injection, immune globulin (Hizentra®), 100 mg   K2 ASC K
BETOS: O1E   Other drugs
Drugs: HIZENTRA
Coding Clinic: 2011, Q1

D **J1560** Injection, gamma globulin, intramuscular, over 10 cc   K2 ASC K
BETOS: O1E   Other drugs
Drugs: GAMASTAN S/D

D **J1561** Injection, immune globulin, (Gamunex-C®/Gammaked®), non-lyophilized (e.g., liquid), 500 mg   K2 ASC K
BETOS: O1E   Other drugs
Drugs: GAMMAKED, GAMUNEX-C
Coding Clinic: 2012, Q 1

C **J1562** Injection, immune globulin (Vivaglobin), 100 mg   E1
BETOS: O1E   Other drugs

D **J1566** Injection, immune globulin, intravenous, lyophilized (e.g., powder), not otherwise specified, 500 mg   K2 ASC K
BETOS: O1E   Other drugs
Drugs: CARIMUNE NF, GAMMAGARD S/D
Coding Clinic: 2006, Q1

C **J1568** Injection, immune globulin, (Octagam), intravenous, non-lyophilized (e.g., liquid), 500 mg   K2 ASC K
BETOS: O1E   Other drugs
Drugs: OCTAGAM
Coding Clinic: 2007, Q4; 2008, Q1

D **J1569** Injection, immune globulin, (Gammagard liquid), non-lyophilized, (e.g., liquid), 500 mg   K2 ASC K
BETOS: O1E   Other drugs
Drugs: GAMMAGARD LIQUID
Coding Clinic: 2007, Q4; 2008, Q1

D **J1570** Injection, ganciclovir sodium, 500 mg   N1 ASC N
BETOS: O1E   Other drugs
Drugs: CYTOVENE, GANCICLOVIR

D **J1571** Injection, hepatitis B immune globulin (HepaGam B), intramuscular, 0.5 ml   K2 ASC K
BETOS: O1E   Other drugs
Drugs: CBI HEPAGAM B 1 ML, CBI HEPAGAM B 5 ML, NOVA HEPAGAM B 1 ML, NOVA HEPAGAM B 5 ML
Coding Clinic: 2007, Q4; 2008, Q3; 2008, Q1

D **J1572** Injection, immune globulin, (Flebogamma/Flebogamma Dif), intravenous, non-lyophilized (e.g., liquid), 500 mg   K2 ASC K
BETOS: O1E   Other drugs
Drugs: FLEBOGAMMA 10% DIF, FLEBOGAMMA DIF
Coding Clinic: 2007, Q4; 2008, Q1

C **J1573** Injection, hepatitis B immune globulin (HepaGam B), intravenous, 0.5 ml   K2 ASC K
BETOS: O1E   Other drugs
Coding Clinic: 2008, Q3; 2008, Q1

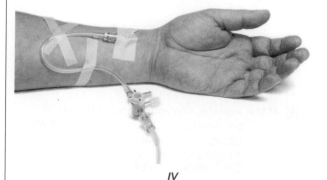
IV

▲ Revised code   ● New code   **C** Carrier judgment   **D** Special coverage instructions apply
I Not payable by Medicare   **M** Non-covered by Medicare   **S** Non-covered by Medicare statute   AHA Coding Clinic®

C J1575 Injection, immune globulin/hyaluronidase, (HYQVIA), 100 mg immuneglobulin K2 ASC K
BETOS: O1E Other drugs
Drugs: HYQVIA
Coding Clinic: 2016, Q1

D J1580 Injection, garamycin, gentamicin, up to 80 mg N1 ASC N
BETOS: O1E Other drugs
Drugs: GENTAMICIN SULFATE

D J1595 Injection, glatiramer acetate, 20 mg K2 ASC K
BETOS: O1E Other drugs

C J1599 Injection, immune globulin, intravenous, non-lyophilized (e.g., liquid), not otherwise specified, 500 mg N1 ASC N
BETOS: O1E Other drugs
Coding Clinic: 2011, Q1

D J1600 Injection, gold sodium thiomalate, up to 50 mg N1 ASC N
BETOS: O1E Other drugs
Pub: 100-4, Chap. 4, 10.4

C J1602 Injection, golimumab, 1 mg, for intravenous use K2 ASC K
BETOS: O1E Other drugs
Drugs: SIMPONI ARIA
Coding Clinic: 2014, Q1

D J1610 Injection, glucagon hydrochloride, per 1 mg K2 ASC K
BETOS: O1E Other drugs
Drugs: GLUCAGEN, GLUCAGEN DIAGNOSTIC KIT, GLUCAGEN HYPOKIT, GLUCAGEN(R) , GLUCAGON EMERGENCY, GLUCAGON HYDROCHLORIDE, GLUCAGON HYDROCHLORIDE KIT

D J1620 Injection, gonadorelin hydrochloride, per 100 mcg E2
BETOS: O1E Other drugs

D J1626 Injection, granisetron hydrochloride, 100 mcg N1 ASC N
BETOS: O1E Other drugs
Drugs: GRANISETRON HCL
Pub: 100-4, Chap. 4, 10.4

● **C** J1627 Injection, granisetron, extended-release, 0.1 mg
BETOS: O1E Other drugs

D J1630 Injection, haloperidol, up to 5 mg N1 ASC N
BETOS: O1E Other drugs
Drugs: HALDOL, HALOPERIDOL LACTATE
Pub: 100-4, Chap. 4, 10.4

D J1631 Injection, haloperidol decanoate, per 50 mg N1 ASC N
BETOS: O1E Other drugs
Drugs: HALDOL DECANOATE, HALOPERIDOL DECANOATE

D J1640 Injection, hemin, 1 mg K2 ASC K
BETOS: O1E Other drugs
Drugs: PANHEMATIN

D J1642 Injection, heparin sodium, (heparin lock flush), per 10 units N1 ASC N
BETOS: O1E Other drugs
Drugs: HEPARIN (PORCINE) LOCK FLUSH, HEPARIN LOCK FLUSH, HEPARIN SODIUM FLUSH
Coding Clinic: 2005, Q4
Pub: 100-4, Chap. 4, 10.4

D J1644 Injection, heparin sodium, per 1000 units N1 ASC N
BETOS: O1E Other drugs
Drugs: HEPARIN (PORCINE) IN D5W, HEPARIN (PORCINE) IN NACL, HEPARIN SODIUM, HEPARIN SODIUM (PORCINE), HEPARIN SODIUM IN NACL
Pub: 100-4, Chap. 4, 10.4

D J1645 Injection, dalteparin sodium, per 2500 IU N1 ASC N
BETOS: O1E Other drugs
Drugs: FRAGMIN

C J1650 Injection, enoxaparin sodium, 10 mg N1 ASC N
BETOS: O1E Other drugs
Drugs: ENOXAPARIN SODIUM, LOVENOX
Pub: 100-4, Chap. 4, 10.4

D J1652 Injection, fondaparinux sodium, 0.5 mg N1 ASC N
BETOS: O1E Other drugs
Drugs: ARIXTRA, FONDAPARINUX SODIUM

C J1655 Injection, tinzaparin sodium, 1000 IU E2
BETOS: O1E Other drugs
Coding Clinic: 2002, Q1
Pub: 100-4, Chap. 4, 10.4

D J1670 Injection, tetanus immune globulin, human, up to 250 units K2 ASC K
BETOS: O1E Other drugs
Drugs: HYPERTET S/D

D J1675 Injection, histrelin acetate, 10 micrograms B
BETOS: O1E Other drugs

D J1700 Injection, hydrocortisone acetate, up to 25 mg N1 ASC N
BETOS: O1E Other drugs
Pub: 100-4, Chap. 4, 10.4

D J1710 Injection, hydrocortisone sodium phosphate, up to 50 mg N1 ASC N
BETOS: O1E Other drugs
Pub: 100-4, Chap. 4, 10.4

D J1720 Injection, hydrocortisone sodium succinate, up to 100 mg N1 ASC N
BETOS: O1E Other drugs
Drugs: SOLU-CORTEF, SOLU-CORTEF 500MG 4ML
Pub: 100-4, Chap. 4, 10.4

● **C** J1726 Injection, hydroxyprogesterone caproate, (makena), 10 mg
BETOS: O1E Other drugs

♂ Male only   ♀ Female only   **Ⓐ** Age   A2 - Z3 = ASC Payment indicator   A - Y = APC Status indicator
ASC = ASC-approved procedure   **DME** Paid under the DME fee schedule   **MIPS** MIPS code

● C **J1729** Injection, hydroxyprogesterone caproate, not otherwise specified, 10 mg
BETOS: O1E   Other drugs

D **J1730** Injection, diazoxide, up to 300 mg   K2 ASC K
BETOS: O1E   Other drugs

C **J1740** Injection, ibandronate sodium, 1 mg   K2 ASC K
BETOS: O1E   Other drugs
Drugs: BONIVA, IBANDRONATE SODIUM
Coding Clinic: 2006, Q4

C **J1741** Injection, ibuprofen, 100 mg   N1 ASC N
BETOS: O1E   Other drugs

D **J1742** Injection, ibutilide fumarate, 1 mg   K2 ASC K
BETOS: O1E   Other drugs
Drugs: CORVERT, IBUTILIDE FUMARATE

C **J1743** Injection, idursulfase, 1 mg   K2 ASC K
BETOS: O1E   Other drugs
Drugs: ELAPRASE
Coding Clinic: 2008, Q1

C **J1744** Injection, icatibant, 1 mg   K2 ASC K
BETOS: O1E   Other drugs

D **J1745** Injection, infliximab, excludes biosimilar, 10 mg   K2 ASC K
BETOS: O1E   Other drugs
Drugs: REMICADE

D **J1750** Injection, iron dextran, 50 mg   K2 ASC K
BETOS: O1E   Other drugs
Drugs: INFED

C **J1756** Injection, iron sucrose, 1 mg   N1 ASC N
BETOS: O1E   Other drugs
Drugs: VENOFER

D **J1786** Injection, imiglucerase, 10 units   K2 ASC K
BETOS: O1E   Other drugs
Drugs: CEREZYME
Coding Clinic: 2011, Q1

D **J1790** Injection, droperidol, up to 5 mg   N1 ASC N
BETOS: O1E   Other drugs
Pub: 100-4, Chap. 4, 10.4

D **J1800** Injection, propranolol HCl, up to 1 mg   N1 ASC N
BETOS: O1E   Other drugs
Drugs: PROPRANOLOL, PROPRANOLOL HCL
Coding Clinic: 2005, Q4
Pub: 100-4, Chap. 4, 10.4

D **J1810** Injection, droperidol and fentanyl citrate, up to 2 ml ampule   E1
BETOS: O1E   Other drugs
Coding Clinic: 2002, Q2

D **J1815** Injection, insulin, per 5 units   N1 ASC N
BETOS: O1E   Other drugs
Drugs: HUMALOG, HUMALOG MIX 50/50, HUMULIN N, HUMULIN R, HUMULIN R U-500, NOVOLIN 70/30, NOVOLIN N, NOVOLIN R, NOVOLOG, NOVOLOG FLEXPEN, NOVOLOG MIX 70/30, NOVOLOG MIX 70/30 FLEXPEN, NOVOLOG PENFILL
Coding Clinic: 2005, Q4
Pub: 100-4, Chap. 4, 10.4

C **J1817** Insulin for administration through DME (i.e., insulin pump) per 50 units   N1 ASC N
BETOS: D1G   Drugs administered through DME
Drugs: HUMALOG, HUMULIN N, HUMULIN R, NOVOLIN 70/30, NOVOLIN N, NOVOLIN R, NOVOLOG, NOVOLOG FLEXPEN, NOVOLOG MIX 70/30, NOVOLOG MIX 70/30 FLEXPEN, NOVOLOG PENFILL
Coding Clinic: 2005, Q4

C **J1826** Injection, interferon beta-1a, 30 mcg   K2 ASC K
BETOS: O1E   Other drugs
Service not separately priced by Part B
Coding Clinic: 2011, Q1; 2011, Q2; 2014, Q4

D **J1830** Injection, interferon beta-1b, 0.25 mg (code may be used for Medicare when drug administered under the direct supervision of a physician, not for use when drug is self administered)   K2 ASC K
BETOS: O1E   Other drugs

C **J1833** Injection, isavuconazonium, 1 mg   K2 ASC G
BETOS: O1E   Other drugs
Coding Clinic: 2016, Q1

C **J1835** Injection, itraconazole, 50 mg   E2
BETOS: O1E   Other drugs
Coding Clinic: 2002, Q1
Pub: 100-4, Chap. 4, 10.4

D **J1840** Injection, kanamycin sulfate, up to 500 mg   N1 ASC N
BETOS: O1E   Other drugs
Pub: 100-4, Chap. 4, 10.4

D **J1850** Injection, kanamycin sulfate, up to 75 mg   N1 ASC N
BETOS: O1E   Other drugs
Pub: 100-4, Chap. 4, 10.4

D **J1885** Injection, ketorolac tromethamine, per 15 mg   N1 ASC N
BETOS: O1E   Other drugs
Drugs: KETOROLAC TROMETHAMINE
Pub: 100-4, Chap. 4, 10.4

D **J1890** Injection, cephalothin sodium, up to 1 gram   N1 ASC N
BETOS: O1E   Other drugs
Pub: 100-4, Chap. 4, 10.4

C **J1930** Injection, lanreotide, 1 mg   K2 ASC K
BETOS: O1E   Other drugs
Drugs: SOMATULINE DEPOT
Coding Clinic: 2008, Q4

▲ Revised code   ● New code   C Carrier judgment   D Special coverage instructions apply
I Not payable by Medicare   M Non-covered by Medicare   S Non-covered by Medicare statute   AHA Coding Clinic®

C J1931 Injection, laronidase, 0.1 mg   K2 ASC K
BETOS: O1E   Other drugs
Drugs: ALDURAZYME
Coding Clinic: 2005, Q1; 2005, Q2

D J1940 Injection, furosemide, up to 20 mg   N1 ASC N
BETOS: O1E   Other drugs
Drugs: FUROSEMIDE
Coding Clinic: 2005, Q4
Pub: 100-4, Chap. 4, 10.4

C J1942 Injection, aripiprazole lauroxil, 1 mg   K2 ASC G
BETOS: O1E   Other drugs
Drugs: ARISTADA

D J1945 Injection, lepirudin, 50 mg   K2 ASC K
BETOS: O1E   Other drugs

D J1950 Injection, leuprolide acetate (for depot
suspension), per 3.75 mg   K2 ASC K
BETOS: O1E   Other drugs
Drugs: LUPRON DEPOT 3-MONTH,
11.25MG , LUPRON DEPOT 3.75MG ,
LUPRON DEPOT-PED 3-MONTH, 30 MG ,
LUPRON DEPOT-PED 11.25MG, LUPRON
DEPOT-PED 3-MONTH, 11.25MG

C J1953 Injection, levetiracetam, 10 mg   N1 ASC N
BETOS: O1E   Other drugs
Drugs: LEVETIRACETAM,
LEVETIRACETAM (KEPPRA)
Coding Clinic: 2008, Q4

D J1955 Injection, levocarnitine, per 1 gm   B
BETOS: O1E   Other drugs
Drugs: CARNITOR

D J1956 Injection, levofloxacin, 250 mg   N1 ASC N
BETOS: O1E   Other drugs
Drugs: LEVAQUIN, LEVOFLOXACIN
Pub: 100-4, Chap. 4, 10.4

D J1960 Injection, levorphanol tartrate,
up to 2 mg   N1 ASC N
BETOS: O1E   Other drugs
Pub: 100-4, Chap. 4, 10.4

D J1980 Injection, hyoscyamine sulfate,
up to 0.25 mg   N1 ASC N
BETOS: O1E   Other drugs
Drugs: LEVSIN INJECTION .5MG/ML
Pub: 100-4, Chap. 4, 10.4

D J1990 Injection, chlordiazepoxide HCl, up to
100 mg   N1 ASC N
BETOS: O1E   Other drugs
Pub: 100-4, Chap. 4, 10.4

D J2001 Injection, lidocaine HCl for intravenous
infusion, 10 mg   N1 ASC N
BETOS: O1E   Other drugs
Drugs: LIDOCAINE IN D5W
Pub: 100-4, Chap. 4, 10.4

D J2010 Injection, lincomycin HCl, up to
300 mg   N1 ASC N
BETOS: O1E   Other drugs
Drugs: LINCOCIN
Pub: 100-4, Chap. 4, 10.4

C J2020 Injection, linezolid, 200 mg   N1 ASC N
BETOS: O1E   Other drugs
Drugs: LINEZOLID, ZYVOX
Coding Clinic: 2002, Q1; 2002, Q2

D J2060 Injection, lorazepam, 2 mg   N1 ASC N
BETOS: O1E   Other drugs
Drugs: ATIVAN, LORAZEPAM
Pub: 100-4, Chap. 4, 10.4

D J2150 Injection, mannitol, 25% in 50 ml N1 ASC N
BETOS: O1E   Other drugs
Drugs: MANNITOL
Pub: 100-4, Chap. 4, 10.4

C J2170 Injection, mecasermin, 1 mg   N1 ASC N
BETOS: O1E   Other drugs
Pub: 100-4, Chap. 4, 10.4

D J2175 Injection, meperidine hydrochloride, per
100 mg   N1 ASC N
BETOS: O1E   Other drugs
Drugs: DEMEROL, MEPERIDINE HCL
Pub: 100-4, Chap. 4, 10.4

D J2180 Injection, meperidine and promethazine HCl,
up to 50 mg   N1 ASC N
BETOS: O1E   Other drugs
Pub: 100-4, Chap. 4, 10.4

C J2182 Injection, mepolizumab, 1 mg   K2 ASC G
BETOS: O1E   Other drugs

C J2185 Injection, meropenem, 100 mg   N1 ASC N
BETOS: O1E   Other drugs
Drugs: MEROPENEM, MERREM
Coding Clinic: 2005, Q2
Pub: 100-4, Chap. 4, 10.4

D J2210 Injection, methylergonovine maleate, up to
0.2 mg   N1 ASC N
BETOS: O1E   Other drugs
Drugs: METHYLERGONOVINE MALEATE
Pub: 100-4, Chap. 4, 10.4

C J2212 Injection, methylnaltrexone, 0.1 mg N1 ASC N
BETOS: O1E   Other drugs

C J2248 Injection, micafungin sodium, 1 mg N1 ASC N
BETOS: O1E   Other drugs
Drugs: MICAFUNGIN SODIUM
(MYCAMINE)
Coding Clinic: 2006, Q4

D J2250 Injection, midazolam hydrochloride,
per 1 mg   N1 ASC N
BETOS: O1E   Other drugs
Drugs: MIDAZOLAM HCL
Pub: 100-4, Chap. 4, 10.4

♂ Male only   ♀ Female only   **A** Age   A2 - Z3 = ASC Payment indicator   A - Y = APC Status indicator
ASC = ASC-approved procedure   **DME** Paid under the DME fee schedule   **MIPS** MIPS code

D **J2260** Injection, milrinone lactate, 5 mg   K2 ASC K
BETOS: O1E   Other drugs
Drugs: MILRINONE IN DEXTROSE, MILRINONE LACTATE
Pub: 100-4, Chap. 4, 10.4

C **J2265** Injection, minocycline hydrochloride, 1 mg   K2 ASC K
BETOS: O1E   Other drugs

D **J2270** Injection, morphine sulfate, up to 10 mg   N1 ASC N
BETOS: O1E   Other drugs
Drugs: MORPHINE SULFATE
Coding Clinic: 2005, Q4
Pub: 100-4, Chap. 4, 10.4

D **J2274** Injection, morphine sulfate, preservative-free for epidural or intrathecal use, 10 mg   N1 ASC N
BETOS: O1E   Other drugs
Drugs: DURAMORPH, INFUMORPH 200, INFUMORPH 500, MORPHINE SULFATE

D **J2278** Injection, ziconotide, 1 microgram   K2 ASC K
BETOS: O1E   Other drugs
Drugs: PRIALT

C **J2280** Injection, moxifloxacin, 100 mg   N1 ASC N
BETOS: O1E   Other drugs
Drugs: AVELOX, MOXIFLOXACIN HCL
Coding Clinic: 2005, Q2
Pub: 100-4, Chap. 4, 10.4

D **J2300** Injection, nalbuphine hydrochloride, per 10 mg   N1 ASC N
BETOS: O1E   Other drugs
Drugs: NALBUPHINE HCL
Pub: 100-4, Chap. 4, 10.4

D **J2310** Injection, naloxone hydrochloride, per 1 mg   N1 ASC N
BETOS: O1E   Other drugs
Drugs: NALOXONE HCL

C **J2315** Injection, naltrexone, depot form, 1 mg   K2 ASC K
BETOS: O1E   Other drugs
Drugs: VIVITROL

D **J2320** Injection, nandrolone decanoate, up to 50 mg   K2 ASC K
BETOS: O1E   Other drugs
Coding Clinic: 2011, Q1

C **J2323** Injection, natalizumab, 1 mg   K2 ASC K
BETOS: O1E   Other drugs
Drugs: TYSABRI
Coding Clinic: 2008, Q1

D **J2325** Injection, nesiritide, 0.1 mg   K2 ASC K
BETOS: O1E   Other drugs

● **C** **J2326** Injection, nusinersen, 0.1 mg
BETOS: O1E   Other drugs

● **C** **J2350** Injection, ocrelizumab, 1 mg
BETOS: O1E   Other drugs

C **J2353** Injection, octreotide, depot form for intramuscular injection, 1 mg   K2 ASC K
BETOS: O1E   Other drugs
Drugs: SANDOSTATIN LAR DEPOT

C **J2354** Injection, octreotide, non-depot form for subcutaneous or intravenous injection, 25 mcg   N1 ASC N
BETOS: O1E   Other drugs
Drugs: OCTREOTIDE ACETATE, SANDOSTATIN

D **J2355** Injection, oprelvekin, 5 mg   K2 ASC K
BETOS: O1E   Other drugs
Drugs: NEUMEGA
Coding Clinic: 2005, Q2

C **J2357** Injection, omalizumab, 5 mg   K2 ASC K
BETOS: O1E   Other drugs
Drugs: XOLAIR
Coding Clinic: 2005, Q2

C **J2358** Injection, olanzapine, long-acting, 1 mg   K2 ASC K
BETOS: O1E   Other drugs
Drugs: ZYPREXA RELPREVV
Coding Clinic: 2011, Q1

D **J2360** Injection, orphenadrine citrate, up to 60 mg   N1 ASC N
BETOS: O1E   Other drugs
Drugs: ORPHENADRINE CITRATE, ORPHENADRINE CITRATE INJECTION

D **J2370** Injection, phenylephrine HCl, up to 1 ml   N1 ASC N
BETOS: O1E   Other drugs

D **J2400** Injection, chloroprocaine hydrochloride, per 30 ml   N1 ASC N
BETOS: O1E   Other drugs
Drugs: NESACAINE, NESACAINE-MPF

D **J2405** Injection, ondansetron hydrochloride, per 1 mg   N1 ASC N
BETOS: O1E   Other drugs
Drugs: ONDANSETRON HCL, ZOFRAN

D **J2407** Injection, oritavancin, 10 mg   K2 ASC G
BETOS: O1E   Other drugs
Drugs: ORBACTIV
Coding Clinic: 2016, Q1

D **J2410** Injection, oxymorphone HCl, up to 1 mg   N1 ASC N
BETOS: O1E   Other drugs
Drugs: OPANA

C **J2425** Injection, palifermin, 50 micrograms   K2 ASC K
BETOS: O1E   Other drugs
Drugs: KEPIVANCE, KEPIVANCE/ PALIFERMIN

C **J2426** Injection, paliperidone palmitate extended release, 1 mg   K2 ASC K
BETOS: O1E   Other drugs
Drugs: INVEGA SUSTENNA
Coding Clinic: 2011, Q1

▲ Revised code   ● New code   **C** Carrier judgment   **D** Special coverage instructions apply
I Not payable by Medicare   **M** Non-covered by Medicare   **S** Non-covered by Medicare statute   AHA Coding Clinic®

D J2430 Injection, pamidronate disodium,
per 30 mg　　　N1 ASC N
BETOS: O1E　Other drugs
Drugs: PAMIDRONATE DISODIUM

D J2440 Injection, papaverine HCl,
up to 60 mg　　　N1 ASC N
BETOS: O1E　Other drugs

D J2460 Injection, oxytetracycline HCl,
up to 50 mg　　　N1 ASC N
BETOS: O1E　Other drugs

C J2469 Injection, palonosetron HCl,
25 mcg　　　K2 ASC K
BETOS: O1E　Other drugs
Drugs: ALOXI
Coding Clinic: 2005, Q1; 2005, Q2

D J2501 Injection, paricalcitol, 1 mcg　　N1 ASC N
BETOS: O1E　Other drugs
Drugs: PARICALCITOL, ZEMPLAR

C J2502 Injection, pasireotide long acting,
1 mg　　　K2 ASC G
BETOS: O1E　Other drugs
Coding Clinic: 2016, Q1

C J2503 Injection, pegaptanib sodium,
0.3 mg　　　K2 ASC K
BETOS: O1E　Other drugs
Drugs: MACUGEN

D J2504 Injection, pegademase bovine,
25 IU　　　K2 ASC K
BETOS: O1E　Other drugs
Drugs: ADAGEN

C J2505 Injection, pegfilgrastim, 6 mg　　K2 ASC K
BETOS: O1E　Other drugs
Drugs: NEULASTA, NEULASTA DELIVERY KIT
Coding Clinic: 2009, Q3

C J2507 Injection, pegloticase, 1 mg　　K2 ASC K
BETOS: O1E　Other drugs
Drugs: KRYSTEXXA

D J2510 Injection, penicillin G procaine, aqueous,
up to 600,000 units　　　K2 ASC K
BETOS: O1E　Other drugs
Drugs: PENICILLIN G PROCAINE

D J2513 Injection, pentastarch, 10% solution,
100 ml　　　E2
BETOS: O1E　Other drugs

D J2515 Injection, pentobarbital sodium,
per 50 mg　　　K2 ASC K
BETOS: O1E　Other drugs
Drugs: NEMBUTAL, PENTOBARBITAL

D J2540 Injection, penicillin G potassium, up to
600,000 units　　　N1 ASC N
BETOS: O1E　Other drugs
Drugs: PENICILLIN G POT IN DEXTROSE, PENICILLIN G POTASSIUM, PFIZERPEN-G

D J2543 Injection, piperacillin sodium/tazobactam
sodium, 1 gram/0.125 grams
(1.125 grams)　　　N1 ASC N
BETOS: O1E　Other drugs
Drugs: NOVAPLUS ZOSYN, PIPERACILLIN AND TAZOBACTAM, PIPERACILLIN SODIUM-TAZOBACTAM SODIUM, PIPERACILLIN SODIUM/ TAZO, PIPERACILLIN SODIUM/ TAZO (ADD-VANTAGE), ZOSYN

D J2545 Pentamidine isethionate, inhalation
solution, FDA-approved final product, non-
compounded, administered through DME,
unit dose form, per 300 mg　　　B
BETOS: D1G　Drugs administered through DME
Drugs: NEBUPENT

C J2547 Injection, peramivir, 1 mg　　K2 ASC G
BETOS: O1E　Other drugs
Coding Clinic: 2016, Q1

D J2550 Injection, promethazine HCl,
up to 50 mg　　　N1 ASC N
BETOS: O1E　Other drugs
Drugs: PHENERGAN, PROMETHAZINE, PROMETHAZINE HCL

D J2560 Injection, phenobarbital sodium, up to
120 mg　　　N1 ASC N
BETOS: O1E　Other drugs
Drugs: PHENOBARBITAL SODIUM

C J2562 Injection, plerixafor, 1 mg　　K2 ASC K
BETOS: O1E　Other drugs
Drugs: MOZOBIL (PLERIXAFOR)

D J2590 Injection, oxytocin, up to 10 units　N1 ASC N
BETOS: O1E　Other drugs

D J2597 Injection, desmopressin acetate,
per 1 mcg　　　K2 ASC K
BETOS: O1E　Other drugs
Drugs: DDAVP, DESMOPRESSIN ACETATE

D J2650 Injection, prednisolone acetate,
up to 1 ml　　　N1 ASC N
BETOS: O1E　Other drugs

D J2670 Injection, tolazoline HCl, up to
25 mg　　　K2 ASC K
BETOS: O1E　Other drugs

D J2675 Injection, progesterone, per 50 mg　N1 ASC N
BETOS: O1E　Other drugs
Drugs: PROGESTERONE

D J2680 Injection, fluphenazine decanoate, up to
25 mg　　　N1 ASC N
BETOS: O1E　Other drugs
Drugs: FLUPHENAZINE DECANOATE

D J2690 Injection, procainamide HCl,
up to 1 gm　　　N1 ♀ ASC N
BETOS: O1E　Other drugs
Drugs: PROCAINAMIDE HCL

♂ Male only　　♀ Female only　　**A** Age　　A2 - Z3 = ASC Payment indicator　　A - Y = APC Status indicator
ASC = ASC-approved procedure　　**DME** Paid under the DME fee schedule　　**MIPS** MIPS code

D **J2700** Injection, oxacillin sodium, up to
250 mg N1 ASC N
BETOS: O1E   Other drugs
Drugs: BACTOCILL IN DEXTROSE, OXACILLIN, OXACILLIN SODIUM

C **J2704** Injection, propofol, 10 mg N1 ASC N
BETOS: O1E   Other drugs
Drugs: DIPRIVAN, PROPOFOL
Coding Clinic: 2014, Q4

D **J2710** Injection, neostigmine methylsulfate, up to
0.5 mg N1 ASC N
BETOS: O1E   Other drugs

D **J2720** Injection, protamine sulfate,
per 10 mg N1 ASC N
BETOS: O1E   Other drugs
Drugs: PROTAMINE SULFATE

C **J2724** Injection, protein C concentrate, intravenous,
human, 10 IU K2 ASC K
BETOS: O1E   Other drugs
Drugs: CEPROTIN
Coding Clinic: 2008, Q1

D **J2725** Injection, protirelin, per 250 mcg E1
BETOS: O1E   Other drugs

D **J2730** Injection, pralidoxime chloride,
up to 1 gm K2 ASC K
BETOS: O1E   Other drugs

D **J2760** Injection, phentolamine mesylate,
up to 5 mg K2 ASC K
BETOS: O1E   Other drugs

D **J2765** Injection, metoclopramide HCl,
up to 10 mg N1 ASC N
BETOS: O1E   Other drugs
Drugs: METOCLOPRAMIDE HCL

D **J2770** Injection, quinupristin/dalfopristin, 500 mg
(150/350) K2 ASC K
BETOS: O1E   Other drugs
Drugs: SYNERCID

C **J2778** Injection, ranibizumab, 0.1 mg K2 ASC K
BETOS: O1E   Other drugs
Drugs: LUCENTIS
Coding Clinic: 2008, Q1

D **J2780** Injection, ranitidine hydrochloride,
25 mg N1 ASC N
BETOS: O1E   Other drugs
Drugs: RANITIDINE, ZANTAC

C **J2783** Injection, rasburicase, 0.5 mg K2 ASC K
BETOS: O1E   Other drugs
Drugs: ELITEK
Coding Clinic: 2004, Q2; 2005, Q2

C **J2785** Injection, regadenoson, 0.1 mg N1 ASC N
BETOS: O1E   Other drugs
Drugs: REGADENOSON
Coding Clinic: 2008, Q4

C **J2786** Injection, reslizumab, 1 mg K2 ASC G
BETOS: O1E   Other drugs

D **J2788** Injection, Rho D immune globulin, human,
minidose, 50 micrograms (250 IU) N1 ASC N
BETOS: O1E   Other drugs
Drugs: HYPERRHO S/D, MICRHOGAM, MICRHOGAM UF PLUS

D **J2790** Injection, Rho D immune globulin,
human, full dose, 300 micrograms
(1500 IU) N1 ASC N
BETOS: O1E   Other drugs
Drugs: HYPERRHO S/D, RHOGAM ULTRA-FILTERED PLUS

D **J2791** Injection, Rho D immune globulin (human),
(Rhophylac), intramuscular or intravenous,
100 IU N1 ASC N
BETOS: O1E   Other drugs
Drugs: RHOPHYLAC
Coding Clinic: 2007, Q4; 2008, Q1

D **J2792** Injection, Rho D immune globulin,
intravenous, human, solvent detergent,
100 IU K2 ASC K
BETOS: O1E   Other drugs
Drugs: WINRHO SDF

D **J2793** Injection, rilonacept, 1 mg K2 ASC K
BETOS: O1E   Other drugs

C **J2794** Injection, risperidone, long acting,
0.5 mg K2 ASC K
BETOS: O1E   Other drugs
Drugs: RISPERDAL CONSTA
Coding Clinic: 2005, Q1; 2005, Q2

C **J2795** Injection, ropivacaine hydrochloride,
1 mg N1 ASC N
BETOS: O1E   Other drugs
Drugs: NAROPIN, ROPIVACAINE, ROPIVACAINE HYDROCHLORIDE

C **J2796** Injection, romiplostim,
10 micrograms K2 ASC K
BETOS: O1E   Other drugs
Drugs: NPLATE

D **J2800** Injection, methocarbamol,
up to 10 ml N1 ASC N
BETOS: O1E   Other drugs
Drugs: METHOCARBAMOL, ROBAXIN

C **J2805** Injection, sincalide, 5 micrograms N1 ASC N
BETOS: O1E   Other drugs
Drugs: SINCALIDE INJ
Coding Clinic: 2005, Q4

D **J2810** Injection, theophylline, per 40 mg N1 ASC N
BETOS: O1E   Other drugs
Drugs: THEOPHYLLINE IN D5W

D **J2820** Injection, sargramostim (GM-CSF),
50 mcg K2 ASC K
BETOS: O1E   Other drugs
Drugs: LEUKINE (LYO PWD)

▲ Revised code   ● New code   **C** Carrier judgment   **D** Special coverage instructions apply
I Not payable by Medicare   **M** Non-covered by Medicare   **S** Non-covered by Medicare statute   AHA Coding Clinic®

C **J2840**   Injection, sebelipase alfa, 1 mg   K2 ASC G
    BETOS: O1E   Other drugs

D **J2850**   Injection, secretin, synthetic, human,
    1 microgram   K2 ASC K
    BETOS: O1E   Other drugs
    Drugs: CHIRHOSTIM

C **J2860**   Injection, siltuximab, 10 mg   K2 ASC G
    BETOS: O1E   Other drugs
    Coding Clinic: 2016, Q1

D **J2910**   Injection, aurothioglucose, up to
    50 mg   N1 ASC N
    BETOS: O1E   Other drugs

D **J2916**   Injection, sodium ferric gluconate complex in
    sucrose injection, 12.5 mg   N1 ASC N
    BETOS: O1E   Other drugs
    Drugs: FERRLECIT, SODIUM FERRIC
    GLUCONATE, SODIUM FERRIC
    GLUCONATE COMPLEX IN SUCROSE

D **J2920**   Injection, methylprednisolone sodium
    succinate, up to 40 mg   N1 ASC N
    BETOS: O1E   Other drugs
    Drugs: METHYLPREDNISOLONE SODIUM
    SUCC, SOLU-MEDROL

D **J2930**   Injection, methylprednisolone sodium
    succinate, up to 125 mg   N1 ASC N
    BETOS: O1E   Other drugs
    Drugs: METHYLPREDNISOLONE SODIUM
    SUCC, SOLU-MEDROL

D **J2940**   Injection, somatrem, 1 mg   E2
    BETOS: O1E   Other drugs
    Statute: 1861s2b
    Coding Clinic: 2002, Q1; 2002, Q2

D **J2941**   Injection, somatropin, 1 mg   K2 ASC K
    BETOS: O1E   Other drugs
    Statute: 1861s2b
    Coding Clinic: 2002, Q1; 2002, Q2

D **J2950**   Injection, promazine HCl, up to
    25 mg   N1 ASC N
    BETOS: O1E   Other drugs

D **J2993**   Injection, reteplase, 18.1 mg   K2 ASC K
    BETOS: O1E   Other drugs

D **J2995**   Injection, streptokinase, per
    250,000 IU   N1 ASC N
    BETOS: O1E   Other drugs

D **J2997**   Injection, alteplase recombinant,
    1 mg   K2 ASC K
    BETOS: O1E   Other drugs
    Drugs: ACTIVASE, CATHFLO ACTIVASE

D **J3000**   Injection, streptomycin, up to 1 gm   N1 ASC N
    BETOS: O1E   Other drugs
    Drugs: STREPTOMYCIN SULFATE

D **J3010**   Injection, fentanyl Citrate, 0.1 mg   N1 ASC N
    BETOS: O1E   Other drugs
    Drugs: FENTANYL CITRATE, SUBLIMAZE

D **J3030**   Injection, sumatriptan succinate, 6 mg
    (code may be used for Medicare when drug
    administered under the direct supervision
    of a physician, not for use when drug is self
    administered)   N1 ASC N
    BETOS: O1E   Other drugs

C **J3060**   Injection, taliglucerase alfa,
    10 units   K2 ASC K
    BETOS: O1E   Other drugs
    Drugs: ELELYSO
    Coding Clinic: 2013, Q4

D **J3070**   Injection, pentazocine, 30 mg   K2 ASC K
    BETOS: O1E   Other drugs
    Drugs: TALWIN LACTATE

C **J3090**   Injection, tedizolid phosphate,
    1 mg   K2 ASC G
    BETOS: O1E   Other drugs
    Drugs: SIVEXTRO
    Coding Clinic: 2016, Q1

C **J3095**   Injection, telavancin, 10 mg   K2 ASC K
    BETOS: O1E   Other drugs
    Drugs: VIBATIV
    Coding Clinic: 2011, Q1

C **J3101**   Injection, tenecteplase, 1 mg   K2 ASC K
    BETOS: O1E   Other drugs
    Drugs: TNKASE
    Coding Clinic: 2008, Q4

D **J3105**   Injection, terbutaline sulfate, up to
    1 mg   N1 ASC N
    BETOS: O1E   Other drugs
    Drugs: TERBUTALINE, TERBUTALINE
    SULFATE

D **J3110**   Injection, teriparatide, 10 mcg   B
    BETOS: O1E   Other drugs

D **J3121**   Injection, testosterone enanthate,
    1 mg   N1 ASC N
    BETOS: O1E   Other drugs
    Drugs: TESTOSTERONE ENANTHATE

D **J3145**   Injection, testosterone undecanoate,
    1 mg   N1 ASC N
    BETOS: O1E   Other drugs

D **J3230**   Injection, chlorpromazine HCl, up to
    50 mg   N1 ASC N
    BETOS: O1E   Other drugs
    Drugs: CHLORPROMAZINE HCL

D **J3240**   Injection, thyrotropin alpha, 0.9 mg, provided
    in 1.1 mg vial   K2 ASC K
    BETOS: O1E   Other drugs
    Drugs: THYROGEN
    Coding Clinic: 2005, Q2; 2005, Q4

C **J3243**   Injection, tigecycline, 1 mg   K2 ASC K
    BETOS: O1E   Other drugs
    Drugs: TIGECYCLINE
    Coding Clinic: 2006, Q4

♂ Male only   ♀ Female only   **A** Age   A2 - Z3 = ASC Payment indicator   A - Y = APC Status indicator

ASC = ASC-approved procedure   **DME** Paid under the DME fee schedule   **MIPS** MIPS code

C J3246 Injection, tirofiban HCl, 0.25 mg   K2 ASC K
BETOS: O1E   Other drugs
Coding Clinic: 2005, Q1

D J3250 Injection, trimethobenzamide HCl, up to
200 mg   N1 ASC N
BETOS: O1E   Other drugs
Drugs: TIGAN

D J3260 Injection, tobramycin sulfate, up to
80 mg   N1 ASC N
BETOS: O1E   Other drugs
Drugs: TOBRAMYCIN INJECTION,
TOBRAMYCIN SULFATE

C J3262 Injection, tocilizumab, 1 mg   K2 ASC K
BETOS: O1E   Other drugs
Drugs: ACTEMRA
Coding Clinic: 2011, Q1

D J3265 Injection, torsemide, 10 mg/ml   N1 ASC N
BETOS: O1E   Other drugs

D J3280 Injection, thiethylperazine maleate, up to
10 mg   N1 ASC N
BETOS: O1E   Other drugs

C J3285 Injection, treprostinil, 1 mg   K2 ASC K
BETOS: O1E   Other drugs
Drugs: REMODULIN

D J3300 Injection, triamcinolone acetonide,
preservative free, 1 mg   K2 ASC K
BETOS: O1E   Other drugs
Drugs: TRIAMCINOLONE ACETONIDE,
PRESERVATIVE FREE
Coding Clinic: 2008, Q4; 2009, Q1

D J3301 Injection, triamcinolone acetonide, not
otherwise specified, 10 mg   N1 ASC N
BETOS: O1E   Other drugs
Drugs: KENALOG, KENALOG-40
Coding Clinic: 2017, Q3

D J3302 Injection, triamcinolone diacetate,
per 5 mg   N1 ASC N
BETOS: O1E   Other drugs

D J3303 Injection, triamcinolone hexacetonide, per
5 mg   N1 ASC N
BETOS: O1E   Other drugs

D J3305 Injection, trimetrexate glucuronate, per
25 mg   N1 ASC N
BETOS: O1E   Other drugs

D J3310 Injection, perphenazine, up to 5 mg   N1 ASC N
BETOS: O1E   Other drugs

D J3315 Injection, triptorelin pamoate,
3.75 mg   K2 ♂ ASC K
BETOS: O1E   Other drugs
Drugs: TRELSTAR

D J3320 Injection, spectinomycin dihydrochloride, up
to 2 gm   E1
BETOS: O1E   Other drugs

D J3350 Injection, urea, up to 40 gm   E2
BETOS: O1E   Other drugs

D J3355 Injection, urofollitropin, 75 IU   K2 ASC K
BETOS: O1E   Other drugs

C J3357 Ustekinumab, for subcutaneous injection,
1 mg   K2 ASC K
BETOS: O1E   Other drugs
Drugs: STELARA
Coding Clinic: 2011, Q1; 2016, Q4; 2017,
Q1

● **C J3358** Ustekinumab, for intravenous injection, 1 mg
BETOS: O1E   Other drugs

D J3360 Injection, diazepam, up to 5 mg   N1 ASC N
BETOS: O1E   Other drugs
Drugs: DIAZEPAM
Coding Clinic: 2007, Q2

D J3364 Injection, urokinase, 5000 IU vial   N1 ASC N
BETOS: O1E   Other drugs

D J3365 Injection, IV, urokinase,
250,000 IU vial   K2 ASC K
BETOS: O1E   Other drugs

D J3370 Injection, vancomycin HCl, 500 mg   N1 ASC N
BETOS: O1E   Other drugs
Drugs: VANCOCIN HCL, VANCOMYCIN,
VANCOMYCIN HCL, VANCOMYCIN
HYDROCHLORIDE

D J3380 Injection, vedolizumab, 1 mg   K2 ASC K
BETOS: O1E   Other drugs
Drugs: ENTYVIO
Coding Clinic: 2016, Q1

C J3385 Injection, velaglucerase alfa,
100 units   K2 ASC K
BETOS: O1E   Other drugs
Drugs: VPRIV
Coding Clinic: 2011, Q1

D J3396 Injection, verteporfin, 0.1 mg   K2 ASC K
BETOS: O1E   Other drugs
Drugs: VISUDYNE
Coding Clinic: 2005, Q1
Pub: 100-3, Chap. 1, Part 1, 80.2; 100-3, Chap.
1, Part 1, 80.2.1; 100-3, Chap. 1, Part 1, 80.3;
100-3, Chap. 1, Part 1, 80.3.1; 100-4, Chap. 32,
300; 100-4, Chap. 32, 300.1; 100-4, Chap. 32,
300.2

D J3400 Injection, triflupromazine HCl, up to 20 mg   E2
BETOS: O1E   Other drugs

D J3410 Injection, hydroxyzine HCl, up to
25 mg   N1 ASC N
BETOS: O1E   Other drugs
Drugs: HYDROXYZINE HCL

C J3411 Injection, thiamine HCl, 100 mg   N1 ASC N
BETOS: O1E   Other drugs
Drugs: THIAMINE HCL
Coding Clinic: 2005, Q2

C **J3415** Injection, pyridoxine HCl, 100 mg   N1 ASC N
BETOS: O1E   Other drugs
Drugs: PYRIDOXINE HCL
Coding Clinic: 2005, Q2

D **J3420** Injection, vitamin B-12 cyanocobalamin, up
to 1000 mcg   N1 ASC N
BETOS: O1E   Other drugs
Drugs: CYANOCOBALAMIN

D **J3430** Injection, phytonadione (vitamin K),
per 1 mg   N1 ASC N
BETOS: O1E   Other drugs
Drugs: VITAMIN K1

D **J3465** Injection, voriconazole, 10 mg   K2 ASC K
BETOS: O1E   Other drugs
Drugs: VFEND IV, VORICONAZOLE
Coding Clinic: 2005, Q2

D **J3470** Injection, hyaluronidase, up to
150 units   N1 ASC N
BETOS: O1E   Other drugs

D **J3471** Injection, hyaluronidase, ovine, preservative
free, per 1 USP unit (up to 999
USP units)   N1 ASC N
BETOS: O1E   Other drugs
Drugs: VITRASE

D **J3472** Injection, hyaluronidase, ovine, preservative
free, per 1000 USP units   N1 ASC N
BETOS: O1E   Other drugs

D **J3473** Injection, hyaluronidase, recombinant,
1 USP unit   N1 ASC N
BETOS: O1E   Other drugs
Drugs: HYLENEX

D **J3475** Injection, magnesium sulfate, per
500 mg   N1 ASC N
BETOS: O1E   Other drugs
Drugs: MAGNESIUM SULFATE,
MAGNESIUM SULFATE IN 5% DEXTROSE

D **J3480** Injection, potassium chloride,
per 2 mEq   N1 ASC N
BETOS: O1E   Other drugs
Drugs: POTASSIUM CHLORIDE,
POTASSIUM CHLORIDE/DEXTROSE,
POTASSIUM CHLORIDE/SODIUM
CHLORIDE

D **J3485** Injection, zidovudine, 10 mg   N1 ASC N
BETOS: O1E   Other drugs
Drugs: RETROVIR

C **J3486** Injection, ziprasidone mesylate,
10 mg   N1 ASC N
BETOS: O1E   Other drugs
Drugs: GEODON
Coding Clinic: 2005, Q2

C **J3489** Injection, zoledronic acid, 1 mg   N1 ASC N
BETOS: O1E   Other drugs
Drugs: RECLAST, ZOLEDRONIC ACID,
ZOMETA
Coding Clinic: 2013, Q4

D **J3490** Unclassified drugs   N1 ASC N
BETOS: O1E   Other drugs
Coding Clinic: 2010, Q3; 2012, Q4; 2013,
Q1; 2014, Q2; 2014, Q4; 2017, Q1

M **J3520** Edetate disodium, per 150 mg   E1
BETOS: O1E   Other drugs
Service not separately priced by Part B

D **J3530** Nasal vaccine inhalation   N1 ASC N
BETOS: O1E   Other drugs

M **J3535** Drug administered through a metered dose
inhaler   E1
BETOS: O1E   Other drugs
Service not separately priced by Part B

M **J3570** Laetrile, amygdalin, vitamin B17   E1
BETOS: O1E   Other drugs
Service not separately priced by Part B

C **J3590** Unclassified biologics   N1 ASC N
BETOS: O1E   Other drugs
Coding Clinic: 2012, Q4; 2016, Q4; 2017, Q1

D **J7030** Infusion, normal saline solution ,
1000 cc   N1 ASC N
BETOS: O1E   Other drugs
Drugs: SODIUM CHLORIDE, SODIUM
CHLORIDE (FDA OK'D IMPORT)

D **J7040** Infusion, normal saline solution, sterile
(500 ml = 1 unit)   N1 ASC N
BETOS: O1E   Other drugs
Drugs: SODIUM CHLORIDE, SODIUM
CHLORIDE (FDA OK'D IMPORT)

D **J7042** 5% dextrose/normal saline
(500 ml = 1 unit)   N1 ASC N
BETOS: O1E   Other drugs
Drugs: DEXTROSE-NACL

D **J7050** Infusion, normal saline solution,
250 cc   N1 ASC N
BETOS: O1E   Other drugs
Drugs: SODIUM CHLORIDE, SODIUM
CHLORIDE (FDA OK'D IMPORT)

D **J7060** 5% dextrose/water
(500 ml = 1 unit)   N1 ASC N
BETOS: O1E   Other drugs
Drugs: DEXTROSE, DEXTROSE 5%

D **J7070** Infusion, D5W, 1000 cc   N1 ASC N
BETOS: O1E   Other drugs
Drugs: DEXTROSE

D **J7100** Infusion, dextran 40, 500 ml   N1 ASC N
BETOS: O1E   Other drugs

D **J7110** Infusion, dextran 75, 500 ml   N1 ASC N
BETOS: O1E   Other drugs

D **J7120** Ringers lactate infusion, up to
1000 cc   N1 ASC N
BETOS: O1E   Other drugs
Drugs: LACTATED RINGERS

♂ Male only   ♀ Female only   🄐 Age   A2 - Z3 = ASC Payment indicator   A - Y = APC Status indicator
ASC = ASC-approved procedure   **DME** Paid under the DME fee schedule   **MIPS** MIPS code

[D] J7121 5% Dextrose in lactated ringers infusion, up to 1000 cc   **E2**
    BETOS: O1E   Other drugs
    Coding Clinic: 2016, Q1

[D] J7131 Hypertonic saline solution, 1 ml   **N1 ASC N**
    BETOS: O1E   Other drugs

[C] J7175 Injection, Factor X, (human), 1 i.u.   **K2 ASC K**
    BETOS: O1E   Other drugs
    Coding Clinic: 2017, Q1

CLOTTING FACTORS (J7178-J7211)

[C] J7178 Injection, Human fibrinogen concentrate, 1 mg   **K2 ASC K**
    BETOS: O1E   Other drugs

[D] J7179 Injection, Von Willebrand Factor (recombinant), (Vonvendi), 1 i.u. vwf:rco   **K2 ASC G**
    BETOS: O1E   Other drugs
    Coding Clinic: 2017, Q1

[C] J7180 Injection, Factor XIII (antihemophilic factor, human), 1 IU   **K2 ASC K**
    BETOS: O1E   Other drugs
    Drugs: CORIFACT
    Coding Clinic: 2012, Q 1

[C] J7181 Injection, Factor XIII a-subunit, (recombinant), per IU   **K2 ASC K**
    BETOS: O1E   Other drugs

[C] J7182 Injection, Factor VIII, (antihemophilic factor, recombinant), (Novoeight), per IU   **K2 ASC K**
    BETOS: O1E   Other drugs
    Drugs: NOVOEIGHT
    Coding Clinic: 2014, Q4

[D] J7183 Injection, Von Willebrand Factor complex (human), wilate, 1 IU VWF:RCo   **K2 ASC K**
    BETOS: O1E   Other drugs
    Drugs: WILATE

[C] J7185 Injection, Factor VIII (antihemophilic factor, recombinant) (XYNTHA), per IU   **K2 ASC K**
    BETOS: O1E   Other drugs
    Drugs: XYNTHA

[D] J7186 Injection, Antihemophilic factor VIII/Von Willebrand Factor complex (human), per Factor VIII IU   **K2 ASC K**
    BETOS: O1E   Other drugs
    Drugs: ALPHANATE /VON WILLEBRAND FACTOR COMPLEX
    Coding Clinic: 2008, Q4
    Pub: 100-4, Chap. 17, 80.4.1

[D] J7187 Injection, Von Willebrand Factor complex (Humate-P), per IU VWF:RCo   **K2 ASC K**
    BETOS: O1E   Other drugs
    Drugs: HUMATE-P LOW DILUENT
    Pub: 100-4, Chap. 17, 80.4.1

[D] J7188 Injection, Factor VIII (antihemophilic factor, recombinant), (OBIZUR), per i.u.   **K2 ASC K**

    BETOS: O1E   Other drugs
    Coding Clinic: 2016, Q1

[D] J7189 Factor VIIa (antihemophilic factor, recombinant), per 1 microgram   **K2 ASC K**
    BETOS: O1E   Other drugs
    Drugs: NOVOSEVEN RT
    Pub: 100-4, Chap. 17, 80.4.1

[D] J7190 Factor VIII (antihemophilic factor, human) per IU   **K2 ASC K**
    BETOS: O1E   Other drugs
    Drugs: ALPHANATE /VON WILLEBRAND FACTOR COMPLEX, HEMOFIL M, KOATE-DVI, MONOCLATE-P
    Pub: 100-4, Chap. 17, 80.4.1

[D] J7191 Factor VIII (antihemophilic factor (porcine)), per IU   **K2 ASC K**
    BETOS: O1E   Other drugs
    Pub: 100-4, Chap. 17, 80.4.1

[D] J7192 Factor VIII (antihemophilic factor, recombinant) per IU, not otherwise specified   **K2 ASC K**
    BETOS: O1E   Other drugs
    Drugs: ADVATE, HELIXATE FS, HELIXATE FS 3000, KOGENATE FS, KOGENATE FS 3000 BIO-SET, KOGENATE FS BIO-SET, KOGENATE FS FIXED POLY BIO-SET, RECOMBINATE
    Pub: 100-4, Chap. 17, 80.4.1

[D] J7193 Factor IX (antihemophilic factor, purified, non-recombinant) per IU   **K2 ASC K**
    BETOS: O1E   Other drugs
    Drugs: ALPHANINE®SD VF 1000 IU M2V USA, ALPHANINE®SD VF 1500 IU M2V USA, ALPHANINE®SD VF 500 IU M2V USA, MONONINE
    Coding Clinic: 2002, Q2
    Pub: 100-4, Chap. 17, 80.4.1

[D] J7194 Factor IX, complex, per IU   **K2 ASC K**
    BETOS: O1E   Other drugs
    Drugs: BEBULIN, PROFILNINE® SD FIX SD M2V(1000), PROFILNINE® SD FIX SD M2V(1500), PROFILNINE® SD FIX SD M2V(500)
    Pub: 100-4, Chap. 17, 80.4.1

[D] J7195 Injection, Factor IX (antihemophilic factor, recombinant) per IU, not otherwise specified   **K2 ASC K**
    BETOS: O1E   Other drugs
    Drugs: BENEFIX
    Coding Clinic: 2002, Q1; 2002, Q2
    Pub: 100-4, Chap. 17, 80.4.1

[C] J7196 Injection, Antithrombin recombinant, 50 IU   **K2 ASC K**
    BETOS: O1E   Other drugs
    Coding Clinic: 2011, Q1

[D] J7197 Antithrombin III (human), per IU   **K2 ASC K**
    BETOS: O1E   Other drugs
    Drugs: THROMBATE III

▲ Revised code   ● New code   **[C]** Carrier judgment   **[D]** Special coverage instructions apply
[I] Not payable by Medicare   **[M]** Non-covered by Medicare   **[S]** Non-covered by Medicare statute   AHA Coding Clinic®

D **J7198** Anti-inhibitor, per IU   K2 ASC K
    BETOS: O1E   Other drugs
    Drugs: FEIBA NF
    Pub: 100-4, Chap. 17, 80.4.1

D **J7199** Hemophilia clotting factor, not otherwise
    classified   B
    BETOS: O1E   Other drugs
    Pub: 100-4, Chap. 17, 80.4.1

D **J7200** Injection, Factor IX, (antihemophilic factor,
    recombinant), Rixubis, per IU   K2 ASC K
    BETOS: O1E   Other drugs
    Drugs: RIXUBIS

D **J7201** Injection, Factor ix, fc fusion protein,
    (recombinant), ALPROLIX, 1 i.u.   K2 ASC K
    BETOS: O1E   Other drugs
    Drugs: ALPROLIX

D **J7202** Injection, Factor ix, albumin fusion protein,
    (recombinant), IDELVION, 1 i.u.   K2 ASC G
    BETOS: O1E   Other drugs

D **J7205** Injection, Factor VIII Fc fusion protein
    (recombinant), per IU   K2 ASC K
    BETOS: O1E   Other drugs
    Drugs: ELOCTATE
    Coding Clinic: 2016, Q1

D **J7207** Injection, Factor VIII, (antihemophilic factor,
    recombinant), PEGYLATED, 1 i.u. K2 ASC G
    BETOS: O1E   Other drugs

C **J7209** Injection, Factor VIII, (antihemophilic factor,
    recombinant), (NUWIQ), 1 i.u.   K2 ASC G
    BETOS: O1E   Other drugs

● **C** **J7210** Injection, Factor VIII, (antihemophilic factor,
    recombinant), (AFSTYLA), 1 I.U.
    BETOS: O1E   Other drugs

● **C** **J7211** Injection, Factor VIII, (antihemophilic factor,
    recombinant), (KOVALTRY), 1 I.U.
    BETOS: O1E   Other drugs

CONTRACEPTIVE SYSTEMS (J7296-J7307)

● **S** **J7296** Levonorgestrel-releasing intrauterine
    contraceptive system, (Kyleena), 19.5 mg ♀
    BETOS: P6C   Minor procedures - other
    (Medicare fee schedule)
    Service not separately priced by Part B
    Statute: 1862(a)(1)

S **J7297** Levonorgestrel-releasing intrauterine
    contraceptive system (Liletta), 52 mg   E1
    BETOS: P6C   Minor procedures - other
    (Medicare fee schedule)
    Service not separately priced by Part B
    Statute: 1862(a)(1)
    Coding Clinic: 2016, Q1

S **J7298** Levonorgestrel-releasing intrauterine
    contraceptive system (Mirena), 52 mg   E1
    BETOS: P6C   Minor procedures - other
    (Medicare fee schedule)

    Service not separately priced by Part B
    Statute: 1862(a)(1)
    Coding Clinic: 2016, Q1

S **J7300** Intrauterine copper contraceptive   E1
    BETOS: P6C   Minor procedures - other
    (Medicare fee schedule)
    Service not separately priced by Part B
    Statute: 1862A1

S **J7301** Levonorgestrel-releasing intrauterine
    contraceptive system (Skyla), 13.5 mg ♀ E1
    BETOS: P6C   Minor procedures - other
    (Medicare fee schedule)
    Service not separately priced by Part B
    Statute: 1862(a)(1)
    Coding Clinic: 2014, Q4

S **J7303** Contraceptive supply, hormone containing
    vaginal ring, each   ♀ E1
    BETOS: Z2   Undefined codes
    Service not separately priced by Part B
    Statute: 1862.1

S **J7304** Contraceptive supply, hormone containing
    patch, each   ♀ E1
    BETOS: Z2   Undefined codes
    Service not separately priced by Part B
    Statute: 1862.1

I **J7306** Levonorgestrel (contraceptive) implant
    system, including implants and supplies   E1
    BETOS: P6C   Minor procedures - other
    (Medicare fee schedule)
    Service not separately priced by Part B

I **J7307** Etonogestrel (contraceptive) implant system,
    including implant and supplies   E1
    BETOS: Z2   Undefined codes
    Service not separately priced by Part B

MISCELLANEOUS DRUGS (J7308-J7345)

C **J7308** Aminolevulinic acid HCl for topical
    administration, 20%, single unit dosage form
    (354 mg)   K2 ASC K
    BETOS: O1E   Other drugs
    Drugs: LEVULAN KERASTICK
    Coding Clinic: 2002, Q1; 2005, Q2

D **J7309** Methyl aminolevulinate (MAL) for topical
    administration, 16.8%, 1 gram   K2 ASC K
    BETOS: O1E   Other drugs
    Coding Clinic: 2011, Q1

D **J7310** Ganciclovir, 4.5 mg, long-acting
    implant   K2 ASC K
    BETOS: O1E   Other drugs

C **J7311** Fluocinolone acetonide, intravitreal
    implant   K2 ASC K
    BETOS: O1E   Other drugs
    Drugs: FLUOCINOLONE ACETONIDE
    IMPLT (RETISERT)

♂ Male only   ♀ Female only   **A** Age   A2 - Z3 = ASC Payment indicator   A - Y = APC Status indicator
    ASC = ASC-approved procedure   **DME** Paid under the DME fee schedule   **MIPS** MIPS code

C **J7312** Injection, Dexamethasone, intravitreal implant, 0.1 mg   K2 ASC K
BETOS: O1E   Other drugs
Drugs: OZURDEX
Coding Clinic: 2011, Q1

C **J7313** Injection, Fluocinolone acetonide, intravitreal implant, 0.01 mg   K2 ASC G
BETOS: O1E   Other drugs
Drugs: ILUVIEN
Coding Clinic: 2016, Q1

C **J7315** Mitomycin, ophthalmic, 0.2 mg   N1 ASC N
BETOS: O1E   Other drugs
Coding Clinic: 2014, Q2; 2016, Q4

C **J7316** Injection, Ocriplasmin, 0.125 mg   K2 ASC K
BETOS: O1E   Other drugs
Drugs: JETREA
Coding Clinic: 2013, Q4

C **J7320** Hyaluronan or derivitive, Genvisc 850, for intra-articular injection, 1 mg   E2
BETOS: O1E   Other drugs
Drugs: GENVISC 850
Coding Clinic: 2006, Q1

▲ C **J7321** Hyaluronan or derivative, Hyalgan, supartz or visco-3, for intra-articular injection, per dose   K2 ASC K
BETOS: O1E   Other drugs
Drugs: HYALGAN, SUPARTZ
Coding Clinic: 2012, Q4

C **J7322** Hyaluronan or derivative, Hymovis, for intra-articular injection, 1 mg   K2 ASC G
BETOS: O1E   Other drugs
Coding Clinic: 2008, Q1

C **J7323** Hyaluronan or derivative, Euflexxa, for intra-articular injection, per dose   K2 ASC K
BETOS: O1E   Other drugs
Drugs: EUFLEXXA
Coding Clinic: 2012, Q4

C **J7324** Hyaluronan or derivative, Orthovisc, for intra-articular injection, per dose   K2 ASC K
BETOS: O1E   Other drugs
Drugs: ORTHOVISC
Coding Clinic: 2012, Q4

C **J7325** Hyaluronan or derivative, Synvisc or Synvisc-One, for intra-articular injection, 1 mg   K2 ASC K
BETOS: O1E   Other drugs
Drugs: SYNVISC, SYNVISCONE
Coding Clinic: 2012, Q4

C **J7326** Hyaluronan or derivative, Gel-One, for intra-articular injection, per dose   K2 ASC K
BETOS: O1E   Other drugs
Drugs: GEL-ONE
Coding Clinic: 2012, Q 1; 2012, Q4

C **J7327** Hyaluronan or derivative, Monovisc, for intra-articular injection, per dose   K2 ASC K
BETOS: O1E   Other drugs
Drugs: MONOVISC
Coding Clinic: 2014, Q4

C **J7328** Hyaluronan or derivative, Gel-Syn, for intra-articular injection, 0.1 mg   K2 ASC G
BETOS: O1E   Other drugs
Coding Clinic: 2016, Q1

C **J7330** Autologous cultured chondrocytes, implant B
BETOS: O1E   Other drugs
Other carrier priced
Coding Clinic: 2010, Q4

C **J7336** Capsaicin 8% patch, per square centimeter   N1 ASC N
BETOS: O1E   Other drugs
Drugs: QUTENZA

C **J7340** Carbidopa 5 mg/Levodopa 20 mg enteral suspension, 100 ml   K2 ASC K
BETOS: O1E   Other drugs
Coding Clinic: 2016, Q1

C **J7342** Instillation, Ciprofloxacin otic suspension, 6 mg   K2 ASC G
BETOS: O1E   Other drugs
Coding Clinic: 2008, Q4

● D **J7345** Aminolevulinic acid HCl for topical administration, 10% gel, 10 mg
BETOS: O1E   Other drugs
Coding Clinic: 2008, Q1

IMMUNOSUPPRESSIVE DRUGS (J7500-J7599)

D **J7500** Azathioprine, oral, 50 mg   N1 ASC N
BETOS: O1E   Other drugs
Drugs: AZASAN, AZATHIOPRINE
Pub: 100-2, Chap. 15, 50

D **J7501** Azathioprine, parenteral, 100 mg   K2 ASC K
BETOS: O1E   Other drugs

D **J7502** Cyclosporine, oral, 100 mg   N1 ASC N
BETOS: O1E   Other drugs
Other carrier priced
Drugs: CYCLOSPORINE, CYCLOSPORINE MODIFIED, GENGRAF, NEORAL, SANDIMMUNE

D **J7503** Tacrolimus, extended release, (Envarsus XR), oral, 0.25 mg   K2 ASC G
BETOS: O1E   Other drugs
Drugs: ENVARSUS XR
Coding Clinic: 2016, Q1

D **J7504** Lymphocyte immune globulin, antithymocyte globulin, equine, parenteral, 250 mg   K2 ASC K
BETOS: O1E   Other drugs
Drugs: ATGAM

D **J7505** Muromonab-CD3, parenteral, 5 mg K2 ASC K
BETOS: O1E   Other drugs

D **J7507** Tacrolimus, immediate release, oral,
1 mg   N1 ASC N
　　BETOS: O1E   Other drugs
　　Drugs: PROGRAF, TACROLIMUS,
　　TACROLIMUS, ORAL

D **J7508** Tacrolimus, extended release, (Astagraf XL),
oral, 0.1 mg   N1 ASC N
　　BETOS: O1E   Other drugs
　　Drugs: ASTAGRAF XL
　　Coding Clinic: 2014, Q1; 2016, Q1

D **J7509** Methylprednisolone oral, per 4 mg N1 ASC N
　　BETOS: O1E   Other drugs
　　Drugs: MEDROL, MEDROL
　　(PAK), METHYLPREDNISOLONE,
　　METHYLPREDNISOLONE (PAK)

D **J7510** Prednisolone oral, per 5 mg   N1 ASC N
　　BETOS: O1E   Other drugs
　　Drugs: FLO-PRED, PREDNISOLONE

C **J7511** Lymphocyte immune globulin, antithymocyte
globulin, rabbit, parenteral, 25 mg K2 ASC K
　　BETOS: O1E   Other drugs
　　Drugs: THYMOGLOBULIN
　　Coding Clinic: 2002, Q1; 2002, Q2

D **J7512** Prednisone, immediate release or delayed
release, oral, 1 mg   N1 ASC N
　　BETOS: O1E   Other drugs
　　Drugs: PREDNISONE, PREDNISONE
　　(PAK), PREDNISONE INTENSOL
　　Coding Clinic: 2016, Q1

D **J7513** Daclizumab, parenteral, 25 mg   K2 ASC K
　　BETOS: O1E   Other drugs
　　Coding Clinic: 2005, Q2

C **J7515** Cyclosporine, oral, 25 mg   N1 ASC N
　　BETOS: O1E   Other drugs
　　Drugs: CYCLOSPORINE, CYCLOSPORINE
　　MODIFIED, GENGRAF, NEORAL,
　　SANDIMMUNE

C **J7516** Cyclosporin, parenteral, 250 mg   N1 ASC N
　　BETOS: O1E   Other drugs
　　Drugs: CYCLOSPORINE, SANDIMMUNE

C **J7517** Mycophenolate mofetil, oral,
250 mg   N1 ASC N
　　BETOS: O1E   Other drugs
　　Drugs: CELLCEPT, MYCOPHENOLATE
　　MOFETIL

D **J7518** Mycophenolic acid, oral, 180 mg   N1 ASC N
　　BETOS: O1E   Other drugs
　　Drugs: MYCOPHENOLIC ACID,
　　MYCOPHENOLIC ACID DR, MYFORTIC
　　Coding Clinic: 2005, Q2

D **J7520** Sirolimus, oral, 1 mg   N1 ASC N
　　BETOS: O1E   Other drugs
　　Drugs: RAPAMUNE, SIROLIMUS

D **J7525** Tacrolimus, parenteral, 5 mg   K2 ASC K
　　BETOS: O1E   Other drugs
　　Drugs: PROGRAF

D **J7527** Everolimus, oral, 0.25 mg   N1 ASC N
　　BETOS: O1G   Influenza immunization
　　Drugs: ZORTRESS

D **J7599** Immunosuppressive drug, not otherwise
classified   N1 ASC N
　　BETOS: O1E   Other drugs

INHALATION SOLUTIONS (J7604-J7686)

C **J7604** Acetylcysteine, inhalation solution,
compounded product, administered through
DME, unit dose form, per gram   M
　　BETOS: D1G   Drugs administered through
　　DME

C **J7605** Arformoterol, inhalation solution, FDA-
approved final product, non-compounded,
administered through DME, unit dose form,
15 micrograms   M
　　BETOS: D1G   Drugs administered through
　　DME
　　Drugs: ARFORMOTEROL

C **J7606** Formoterol fumarate, inhalation solution,
FDA-approved final product, non-
compounded, administered through DME,
unit dose form, 20 micrograms   M
　　BETOS: D1G   Drugs administered through
　　DME
　　Drugs: PERFOROMIST
　　Coding Clinic: 2008, Q4

C **J7607** Levalbuterol, inhalation solution,
compounded product, administered through
DME, concentrated form, 0.5 mg   M
　　BETOS: D1G   Drugs administered through
　　DME

D **J7608** Acetylcysteine, inhalation solution, FDA-
approved final product, non-compounded,
administered through DME, unit dose form,
per gram   M
　　BETOS: D1G   Drugs administered through
　　DME
　　Drugs: ACETYLCYSTEINE

C **J7609** Albuterol, inhalation solution, compounded
product, administered through DME, unit
dose, 1 mg   M
　　BETOS: D1G   Drugs administered through
　　DME

♂ Male only   ♀ Female only   **A** Age   A2 - Z3 = ASC Payment indicator   A - Y = APC Status indicator
ASC = ASC-approved procedure   **DME** Paid under the DME fee schedule   **MIPS** MIPS code

Inhaler

C **J7610** Albuterol, inhalation solution, compounded product, administered through DME, concentrated form, 1 mg   M

BETOS: D1G   Drugs administered through DME

D **J7611** Albuterol, inhalation solution, FDA-approved final product, non-compounded, administered through DME, concentrated form, 1 mg   M

BETOS: D1G   Drugs administered through DME

Service not separately priced by Part B

Drugs: ALBUTEROL SULFATE

Coding Clinic: 2007, Q2; 2008, Q2; 2009, Q3

D **J7612** Levalbuterol, inhalation solution, FDA-approved final product, non-compounded, administered through DME, concentrated form, 0.5 mg   M

BETOS: D1G   Drugs administered through DME

Service not separately priced by Part B

Drugs: LEVALBUTEROL, LEVALBUTEROL INHALATION SOLUTION CONCENTRATED, XOPENEX

Coding Clinic: 2007, Q2; 2008, Q2; 2009, Q3

D **J7613** Albuterol, inhalation solution, FDA-approved final product, non-compounded, administered through DME, unit dose, 1 mg   M

BETOS: D1G   Drugs administered through DME

Service not separately priced by Part B

Drugs: ALBUTEROL SULFATE

Coding Clinic: 2007, Q2; 2008, Q2; 2009, Q3

D **J7614** Levalbuterol, inhalation solution, FDA-approved final product, non-compounded, administered through DME, unit dose, 0.5 mg   M

BETOS: D1G   Drugs administered through DME

Service not separately priced by Part B

Drugs: LEVALBUTEROL, XOPENEX

Coding Clinic: 2007, Q2; 2008, Q2; 2009, Q3

C **J7615** Levalbuterol, inhalation solution, compounded product, administered through DME, unit dose, 0.5 mg   M

BETOS: D1G   Drugs administered through DME

D **J7620** Albuterol, up to 2.5 mg and ipratropium bromide, up to 0.5 mg, FDA-approved final product, non-compounded, administered through DME   M

BETOS: D1G   Drugs administered through DME

Drugs: ALBUTEROL IPRATROPIUM

C **J7622** Beclomethasone, inhalation solution, compounded product, administered through DME, unit dose form, per milligram   M

BETOS: D1G   Drugs administered through DME

Coding Clinic: 2002, Q1

C **J7624** Betamethasone, inhalation solution, compounded product, administered through DME, unit dose form, per milligram   M

BETOS: D1G   Drugs administered through DME

Coding Clinic: 2002, Q1

C **J7626** Budesonide, inhalation solution, FDA-approved final product, non-compounded, administered through DME, unit dose form, up to 0.5 mg   M

BETOS: D1G   Drugs administered through DME

Drugs: BUDESONIDE, PULMICORT

Coding Clinic: 2002, Q1

C **J7627** Budesonide, inhalation solution, compounded product, administered through DME, unit dose form, up to 0.5 mg   M

BETOS: D1G   Drugs administered through DME

▲ Revised code   ● New code   **C** Carrier judgment   **D** Special coverage instructions apply

I Not payable by Medicare   **M** Non-covered by Medicare   **S** Non-covered by Medicare statute   AHA Coding Clinic®

D **J7628** Bitolterol mesylate, inhalation solution, compounded product, administered through DME, concentrated form, per milligram   M
BETOS: D1G   Drugs administered through DME

D **J7629** Bitolterol mesylate, inhalation solution, compounded product, administered through DME, unit dose form, per milligram   M
BETOS: D1G   Drugs administered through DME

D **J7631** Cromolyn sodium, inhalation solution, FDA-approved final product, non-compounded, administered through DME, unit dose form, per 10 milligrams   M
BETOS: D1G   Drugs administered through DME
Drugs: CROMOLYN SODIUM

C **J7632** Cromolyn sodium, inhalation solution, compounded product, administered through DME, unit dose form, per 10 milligrams   M
BETOS: D1G   Drugs administered through DME

C **J7633** Budesonide, inhalation solution, FDA-approved final product, non-compounded, administered through DME, concentrated form, per 0.25 milligram   M
BETOS: D1G   Drugs administered through DME

C **J7634** Budesonide, inhalation solution, compounded product, administered through DME, concentrated form, per 0.25 milligram   M
BETOS: D1G   Drugs administered through DME

D **J7635** Atropine, inhalation solution, compounded product, administered through DME, concentrated form, per milligram   M
BETOS: D1G   Drugs administered through DME

D **J7636** Atropine, inhalation solution, compounded product, administered through DME, unit dose form, per milligram   M
BETOS: D1G   Drugs administered through DME

D **J7637** Dexamethasone, inhalation solution, compounded product, administered through DME, concentrated form, per milligram   M
BETOS: D1G   Drugs administered through DME

D **J7638** Dexamethasone, inhalation solution, compounded product, administered through DME, unit dose form, per milligram   M
BETOS: D1G   Drugs administered through DME

D **J7639** Dornase alfa, inhalation solution, FDA-approved final product, non-compounded, administered through DME, unit dose form, per milligram   M
BETOS: D1G   Drugs administered through DME
Drugs: PULMOZYME

C **J7640** Formoterol, inhalation solution, compounded product, administered through DME, unit dose form, 12 micrograms   E1
BETOS: D1G   Drugs administered through DME
Service not separately priced by Part B
Coding Clinic: 2006, Q1

C **J7641** Flunisolide, inhalation solution, compounded product, administered through DME, unit dose, per milligram   M
BETOS: D1G   Drugs administered through DME
Coding Clinic: 2002, Q1

D **J7642** Glycopyrrolate, inhalation solution, compounded product, administered through DME, concentrated form, per milligram   M
BETOS: D1G   Drugs administered through DME

D **J7643** Glycopyrrolate, inhalation solution, compounded product, administered through DME, unit dose form, per milligram   M
BETOS: D1G   Drugs administered through DME

D **J7644** Ipratropium bromide, inhalation solution, FDA-approved final product, non-compounded, administered through DME, unit dose form, per milligram   M
BETOS: D1G   Drugs administered through DME
Drugs: IPRATROPIUM BROMIDE

C **J7645** Ipratropium bromide, inhalation solution, compounded product, administered through DME, unit dose form, per milligram   M
BETOS: D1G   Drugs administered through DME

C **J7647** Isoetharine HCl, inhalation solution, compounded product, administered through DME, concentrated form, per milligram   M
BETOS: D1G   Drugs administered through DME

D **J7648** Isoetharine HCl, inhalation solution, FDA-approved final product, non-compounded, administered through DME, concentrated form, per milligram   M
BETOS: D1G   Drugs administered through DME

D **J7649** Isoetharine HCl, inhalation solution, FDA-approved final product, non-compounded, administered through DME, unit dose form, per milligram   M
BETOS: D1G   Drugs administered through DME

C **J7650** Isoetharine HCl, inhalation solution, compounded product, administered through DME, unit dose form, per milligram M

    BETOS: D1G   Drugs administered through DME

C **J7657** Isoproterenol HCl, inhalation solution, compounded product, administered through DME, concentrated form, per milligram M

    BETOS: D1G   Drugs administered through DME

D **J7658** Isoproterenol HCl, inhalation solution, FDA-approved final product, non-compounded, administered through DME, concentrated form, per milligram M

    BETOS: D1G   Drugs administered through DME

D **J7659** Isoproterenol HCl, inhalation solution, FDA-approved final product, non-compounded, administered through DME, unit dose form, per milligram M

    BETOS: D1G   Drugs administered through DME

C **J7660** Isoproterenol HCl, inhalation solution, compounded product, administered through DME, unit dose form, per milligram M

    BETOS: D1G   Drugs administered through DME

C **J7665** Mannitol, administered through an inhaler, 5 mg N1 ASC N

    BETOS: O1E   Other drugs

C **J7667** Metaproterenol sulfate, inhalation solution, compounded product, concentrated form, per 10 milligrams M

    BETOS: D1G   Drugs administered through DME

D **J7668** Metaproterenol sulfate, inhalation solution, FDA-approved final product, non-compounded, administered through DME, concentrated form, per 10 milligrams M

    BETOS: D1G   Drugs administered through DME

D **J7669** Metaproterenol sulfate, inhalation solution, FDA-approved final product, non-compounded, administered through DME, unit dose form, per 10 milligrams M

    BETOS: D1G   Drugs administered through DME

C **J7670** Metaproterenol sulfate, inhalation solution, compounded product, administered through DME, unit dose form, per 10 milligrams M

    BETOS: D1G   Drugs administered through DME

C **J7674** Methacholine chloride administered as inhalation solution through a nebulizer, per 1 mg N1 ASC N

    BETOS: O1E   Other drugs

Drugs: PROVOCHOLINE
Coding Clinic: 2005, Q2

C **J7676** Pentamidine isethionate, inhalation solution, compounded product, administered through DME, unit dose form, per 300 mg M

    BETOS: D1G   Drugs administered through DME

D **J7680** Terbutaline sulfate, inhalation solution, compounded product, administered through DME, concentrated form, per milligram M

    BETOS: D1G   Drugs administered through DME

D **J7681** Terbutaline sulfate, inhalation solution, compounded product, administered through DME, unit dose form, per milligram M

    BETOS: D1G   Drugs administered through DME

D **J7682** Tobramycin, inhalation solution, FDA-approved final product, non-compounded, unit dose form, administered through DME, per 300 milligrams M

    BETOS: D1G   Drugs administered through DME

    Drugs: BETHKIS, KITABIS PAK, TOBI, TOBRAMYCIN INHALATION

D **J7683** Triamcinolone, inhalation solution, compounded product, administered through DME, concentrated form, per milligram M

    BETOS: D1G   Drugs administered through DME

D **J7684** Triamcinolone, inhalation solution, compounded product, administered through DME, unit dose form, per milligram M

    BETOS: D1G   Drugs administered through DME

C **J7685** Tobramycin, inhalation solution, compounded product, administered through DME, unit dose form, per 300 milligrams M

    BETOS: D1G   Drugs administered through DME

C **J7686** Treprostinil, inhalation solution, FDA-approved final product, non-compounded, administered through DME, unit dose form, 1.74 mg M

    BETOS: D1G   Drugs administered through DME

    Drugs: TYVASO, TYVASO (REFILL KIT), TYVASO (STARTER KIT)

DRUGS, NOT OTHERWISE CLASSIFIED (J7699-J8499)

D **J7699** Noc drugs, inhalation solution administered through DME M

    BETOS: D1G   Drugs administered through DME

▲ Revised code   ● New code   C Carrier judgment   D Special coverage instructions apply
I Not payable by Medicare   M Non-covered by Medicare   S Non-covered by Medicare statute   AHA Coding Clinic®

D **J7799** Noc drugs, other than inhalation drugs, administered through DME   N1 ASC N
BETOS: D1G   Drugs administered through DME

D **J7999** Compounded drug, not otherwise classified   N1 ASC N
BETOS: O1E   Other drugs
Coding Clinic: 2016, Q1; 2016, Q4; 2017, Q1

D **J8498** Antiemetic drug, rectal/suppository, not otherwise specified   B
BETOS: O1D   Chemotherapy
Statute: 1861s2T

M **J8499** Prescription drug, oral, non chemotherapeutic, NOS   E1
BETOS: O1E   Other drugs
Service not separately priced by Part B

CHEMOTHERAPY DRUGS, ORAL ADMINISTRATION (J8501-J8999), SEE ALSO CHEMOTHERAPY DRUGS, ADMINISTERED BY INJECTION (J9000-J9999)

D **J8501** Aprepitant, oral, 5 mg   K2 ASC K
BETOS: O1E   Other drugs
Drugs: APREPITANT, APREPITANT (BI FOLD), APREPITANT (TRI-FOLD), EMEND, EMEND BI-PACK, EMEND TRI-FOLD
Coding Clinic: 2005, Q3

D **J8510** Busulfan; oral, 2 mg   K2 ASC K
BETOS: O1D   Chemotherapy
Drugs: MYLERAN

M **J8515** Cabergoline, oral, 0.25 mg   E1
BETOS: O1E   Other drugs
Service not separately priced by Part B

D **J8520** Capecitabine, oral, 150 mg   N1 ASC N
BETOS: O1D   Chemotherapy
Drugs: CAPECITABINE, XELODA

D **J8521** Capecitabine, oral, 500 mg   N1 ASC N
BETOS: O1D   Chemotherapy
Drugs: CAPECITABINE, XELODA

D **J8530** Cyclophosphamide; oral, 25 mg   N1 ASC N
BETOS: O1D   Chemotherapy
Drugs: CYCLOPHOSPHAMIDE
Coding Clinic: 2002, Q1

D **J8540** Dexamethasone, oral, 0.25 mg   N1 ASC N
BETOS: O1E   Other drugs
Statute: 1861(s)2T
Drugs: DEXAMETHASONE

D **J8560** Etoposide; oral, 50 mg   K2 ASC K
BETOS: O1D   Chemotherapy
Drugs: ETOPOSIDE

C **J8562** Fludarabine phosphate, oral, 10 mg   E2
BETOS: O1D   Chemotherapy
Coding Clinic: 2011, Q1

D **J8565** Gefitinib, oral, 250 mg   E2
BETOS: O1E   Other drugs
Service not separately priced by Part B
Coding Clinic: 2014, Q4

D **J8597** Antiemetic drug, oral, not otherwise specified   N1 ASC N
BETOS: O1D   Chemotherapy
Statute: 1861s2T

D **J8600** Melphalan; oral, 2 mg   N1 ASC N
BETOS: O1D   Chemotherapy
Drugs: ALKERAN

D **J8610** Methotrexate; oral, 2.5 mg   N1 ASC N
BETOS: O1D   Chemotherapy
Drugs: METHOTREXATE, RHEUMATREX, TREXALL

C **J8650** Nabilone, oral, 1 mg   K2 ASC K
BETOS: O1E   Other drugs

D **J8655** Netupitant 300 mg and palonosetron 0.5 mg   K2 ASC G
BETOS: O1E   Other drugs
Drugs: AKYNZEO
Coding Clinic: 2016, Q1

D **J8670** Rolapitant, oral, 1 mg   K2 ASC K
BETOS: O1E   Other drugs

D **J8700** Temozolomide, oral, 5 mg   K2 ASC K
BETOS: O1D   Chemotherapy
Drugs: TEMODAR, TEMOZOLOMIDE

C **J8705** Topotecan, oral, 0.25 mg   K2 ASC K
BETOS: O1D   Chemotherapy
Drugs: HYCAMTIN, ORAL
Coding Clinic: 2008, Q4; 2009, Q1

D **J8999** Prescription drug, oral, chemotherapeutic, NOS   B
BETOS: O1D   Chemotherapy

♂ Male only   ♀ Female only   **A** Age   A2 - Z3 = ASC Payment indicator   A - Y = APC Status indicator
ASC = ASC-approved procedure   **DME** Paid under the DME fee schedule   **MIPS** MIPS code

J7799 - J8999

DRUGS ADMINISTERED OTHER THAN ORAL METHOD (J0120-J8999)

NOTES

CHEMOTHERAPY DRUGS (J9000-J9999)

CHEMOTHERAPY DRUGS, ADMINISTERED BY INJECTION (J9000-J9999), SEE ALSO CHEMOTHERAPY DRUGS, ORAL ADMINISTRATION (J8501-J8999)

D J9000 Injection, doxorubicin hydrochloride, 10 mg N1 ASC N
BETOS: O1D Chemotherapy
Drugs: ADRIAMYCIN, DOXORUBICIN HCL, DOXORUBICIN HCL (LYO)
Coding Clinic: 2007, Q4

D J9015 Injection, aldesleukin, per single use vial K2 ASC K
BETOS: O1D Chemotherapy
Coding Clinic: 2005, Q2

C J9017 Injection, arsenic trioxide, 1 mg K2 ASC K
BETOS: O1D Chemotherapy
Drugs: TRISENOX
Coding Clinic: 2002, Q1; 2002, Q2; 2005, Q2

D J9019 Injection, asparaginase (Erwinaze), 1,000 IU K2 ASC K
BETOS: O1D Chemotherapy
Drugs: ERWINAZE

D J9020 Injection, asparaginase, not otherwise specified, 10,000 units N1 ASC N
BETOS: O1D Chemotherapy

● **C** J9022 Injection, atezolizumab, 10 mg
BETOS: O1D Chemotherapy

● **C** J9023 Injection, avelumab, 10 mg
BETOS: O1E Other drugs

C J9025 Injection, azacitidine, 1 mg K2 ASC K
BETOS: O1D Chemotherapy
Drugs: AZACITIDINE, AZACITIDINE (VIDAZA)

C J9027 Injection, clofarabine, 1 mg K2 ASC K
BETOS: O1E Other drugs
Drugs: CLOFARABINE, CLOLAR

D J9031 BCG (intravesical) per instillation K2 ASC K
BETOS: O1D Chemotherapy
Drugs: TICE BCG

C J9032 Injection, belinostat, 10 mg K2 ASC G
BETOS: O1D Chemotherapy
Drugs: BELEODAQ
Coding Clinic: 2016, Q1

C J9033 Injection, bendamustine HCL (treanda), 1 mg K2 ASC K
BETOS: O1D Chemotherapy
Drugs: TREANDA
Coding Clinic: 2008, Q4

C J9034 Injection, bendamustine HCL (bendeka), 1 mg K2 ASC G
BETOS: O1D Chemotherapy
Drugs: BENDEKA
Coding Clinic: 2017, Q1

C J9035 Injection, bevacizumab, 10 mg K2 ASC K
BETOS: O1E Other drugs
Drugs: AVASTIN
Coding Clinic: 2013, Q1; 2013, Q3

C J9039 Injection, blinatumomab, 1 microgram K2 ASC G
BETOS: O1D Chemotherapy
Drugs: BLINCYTO
Coding Clinic: 2016, Q1

D J9040 Injection, bleomycin sulfate, 15 units N1 ASC N
BETOS: O1D Chemotherapy
Drugs: BLEO 15K, BLEOMYCIN, BLEOMYCIN SULFATE

C J9041 Injection, bortezomib, 0.1 mg K2 ASC K
BETOS: O1E Other drugs
Drugs: VELCADE
Coding Clinic: 2005, Q1; 2005, Q2

C J9042 Injection, brentuximab vedotin, 1 mg K2 ASC K
BETOS: O1D Chemotherapy
Drugs: ADCETRIS

C J9043 Injection, cabazitaxel, 1 mg K2 ASC K
BETOS: O1D Chemotherapy
Drugs: JEVTANA

D J9045 Injection, carboplatin, 50 mg N1 ASC N
BETOS: O1D Chemotherapy
Drugs: CARBOPLATIN

C J9047 Injection, carfilzomib, 1 mg K2 ASC K
BETOS: O1D Chemotherapy
Drugs: KYPROLIS
Coding Clinic: 2013, Q4

D J9050 Injection, carmustine, 100 mg K2 ASC K
BETOS: O1D Chemotherapy
Drugs: BICNU

C J9055 Injection, cetuximab, 10 mg K2 ASC K
BETOS: O1E Other drugs
Drugs: ERBITUX
Coding Clinic: 2005, Q2

D J9060 Injection, cisplatin, powder or solution, 10 mg N1 ASC N
BETOS: O1D Chemotherapy
Drugs: CISPLATIN
Coding Clinic: 2011, Q1

D J9065 Injection, cladribine, per 1 mg K2 ASC K
BETOS: O1D Chemotherapy
Drugs: CLADRIBINE

D J9070 Cyclophosphamide, 100 mg K2 ASC K
BETOS: O1D Chemotherapy
Drugs: CYCLOPHOSPHAMIDE
Coding Clinic: 2011, Q1

C J9098 Injection, cytarabine liposome, 10 mg K2 ASC K
BETOS: O1E Other drugs
Drugs: DEPOCYT

D J9100 Injection, cytarabine, 100 mg N1 ASC N
BETOS: O1D Chemotherapy
Drugs: CYTARABINE
Coding Clinic: 2011, Q1

D J9120 Injection, dactinomycin, 0.5 mg K2 ASC K
BETOS: O1D Chemotherapy
Drugs: COSMEGEN

D J9130 Dacarbazine, 100 mg N1 ASC N
BETOS: O1D Chemotherapy
Drugs: DACARBAZINE
Coding Clinic: 2011, Q1

D J9145 Injection, daratumumab, 10 mg K2 ASC G
BETOS: O1D Chemotherapy
Drugs: DARZALEX

D J9150 Injection, daunorubicin, 10 mg K2 ASC K
BETOS: O1D Chemotherapy
Drugs: DAUNORUBICIN HCL

D J9151 Injection, daunorubicin Citrate, liposomal formulation, 10 mg K2 ASC K
BETOS: O1D Chemotherapy

C J9155 Injection, degarelix, 1 mg K2 ASC K
BETOS: O1E Other drugs
Drugs: FIRMAGON

C J9160 Injection, denileukin diftitox, 300 micrograms E1 ASC
BETOS: O1E Other drugs
Coding Clinic: 2005, Q2

D J9165 Injection, diethylstilbestrol diphosphate, 250 mg E2
BETOS: O1D Chemotherapy

D J9171 Injection, docetaxel, 1 mg K2 ASC K
BETOS: O1E Other drugs
Drugs: DOCEFREZ, DOCETAXEL, TAXOTERE

D J9175 Injection, Elliotts' B solution, 1 ml N1 ASC N
BETOS: O1E Other drugs

C J9176 Injection, elotuzumab, 1 mg K2 ASC G
BETOS: O1E Other drugs
Drugs: EMPLICITI

C J9178 Injection, epirubicin HCl, 2 mg N1 ASC N
BETOS: O1E Other drugs
Drugs: ELLENCE, EPIRUBICIN

C J9179 Injection, eribulin mesylate, 0.1 mg K2 ASC K
BETOS: O1D Chemotherapy
Drugs: HALAVEN

D J9181 Injection, etoposide, 10 mg N1 ASC N
BETOS: O1D Chemotherapy
Drugs: ETOPOPHOS, ETOPOSIDE, TOPOSAR

D J9185 Injection, fludarabine phosphate, 50 mg N1 ASC N
BETOS: O1D Chemotherapy
Drugs: FLUDARABINE PHOSPHATE

D J9190 Injection, fluorouracil, 500 mg N1 ASC N
BETOS: O1D Chemotherapy
Drugs: ADRUCIL, FLUOROURACIL

D J9200 Injection, floxuridine, 500 mg K2 ASC K
BETOS: O1D Chemotherapy
Drugs: FLOXURIDINE

D J9201 Injection, gemcitabine hydrochloride, 200 mg N1 ASC N
BETOS: O1D Chemotherapy
Drugs: GEMCITABINE, GEMCITABINE HCL, GEMCITABINE HYDROCHLORIDE, GEMZAR

D J9202 Goserelin acetate implant, per 3.6 mg K2 ASC K
BETOS: O1D Chemotherapy
Drugs: ZOLADEX

● **C** J9203 Injection, gemtuzumab ozogamicin, 0.1 mg
BETOS: O1D Chemotherapy

D J9205 Injection, irinotecan liposome, 1 mg K2 ASC G
BETOS: O1D Chemotherapy
Drugs: ONIVYDE 43MG/10ML PER VIAL

D J9206 Injection, irinotecan, 20 mg N1 ASC N
BETOS: O1D Chemotherapy
Drugs: CAMPTOSAR, IRINOTECAN HCL

C J9207 Injection, ixabepilone, 1 mg K2 ASC K
BETOS: O1D Chemotherapy
Drugs: IXABEPILONE, IXEMPRA KIT
Coding Clinic: 2008, Q4

D J9208 Injection, ifosfamide, 1 gram K2 ASC K
BETOS: O1D Chemotherapy
Drugs: IFEX, IFOSFAMIDE

D J9209 Injection, mesna, 200 mg N1 ASC N
BETOS: O1D Chemotherapy
Drugs: MESNA, MESNEX

D J9211 Injection, idarubicin hydrochloride, 5 mg K2 ASC K
BETOS: O1D Chemotherapy
Drugs: IDAMYCIN PFS, IDARUBICIN

D J9212 Injection, interferon alfacon-1, recombinant, 1 microgram E2
BETOS: O1E Other drugs

D J9213 Injection, interferon, alfa-2a, recombinant, 3 million units K2 ASC K
BETOS: O1D Chemotherapy

D J9214 Injection, interferon, alfa-2b, recombinant, 1 million units K2 ASC K
BETOS: O1D Chemotherapy
Drugs: INTRON-A

D J9215 Injection, interferon, alfa-N3, (human leukocyte derived), 250,000 IU E2
BETOS: O1D Chemotherapy

▲ Revised code ● New code **C** Carrier judgment **D** Special coverage instructions apply
I Not payable by Medicare **M** Non-covered by Medicare **S** Non-covered by Medicare statute AHA Coding Clinic®

D J9216 Injection, interferon, gamma 1-b, 3 million units   K2 ASC K
BETOS: O1D   Chemotherapy
Coding Clinic: 2005, Q2

D J9217 Leuprolide acetate (for depot suspension), 7.5 mg   K2 ASC K
BETOS: O1D   Chemotherapy
Drugs: ELIGARD, LUPRON DEPOT 4-MONTH, 30MG , LUPRON DEPOT 6-MONTH, 45MG , LUPRON DEPOT 7.5 MG KIT, LUPRON DEPOT-3 MONTH 22.5MG KIT, LUPRON DEPOT-PED 15MG, LUPRON DEPOT-PED 7.5MG

D J9218 Leuprolide acetate, per 1 mg   K2 ASC K
BETOS: O1D   Chemotherapy
Drugs: LEUPROLIDE ACETATE, LEUPROLIDE ACETATE INJ

D J9219 Leuprolide acetate implant, 65 mg   K2 ASC K
BETOS: O1D   Chemotherapy
Coding Clinic: 2001, Q4

D J9225 Histrelin implant (Vantas), 50 mg   K2 ASC K
BETOS: O1D   Chemotherapy
Drugs: VANTAS IMPLANT

D J9226 Histrelin implant (Supprelin LA), 50 mg   K2 ASC K
BETOS: O1D   Chemotherapy
Drugs: SUPPRELIN LA IMPLANT
Coding Clinic: 2008, Q1

C J9228 Injection, ipilimumab, 1 mg   K2 ASC K
BETOS: O1D   Chemotherapy
Drugs: YERVOY

D J9230 Injection, mechlorethamine hydrochloride, (nitrogen mustard), 10 mg   K2 ASC K
BETOS: O1D   Chemotherapy
Drugs: MUSTARGEN

D J9245 Injection, melphalan hydrochloride, 50 mg   K2 ASC K
BETOS: O1D   Chemotherapy
Drugs: ALKERAN, EVOMELA, MELPHALAN

D J9250 Methotrexate sodium, 5 mg   N1 ASC N
BETOS: O1D   Chemotherapy
Drugs: METHOTREXATE, METHOTREXATE POWDER 1GM IN 50ML SD VIAL (P.F.), METHOTREXATE SODIUM

D J9260 Methotrexate sodium, 50 mg   N1 ASC N
BETOS: O1D   Chemotherapy
Drugs: METHOTREXATE, METHOTREXATE POWDER 1GM IN 50ML SD VIAL (P.F.), METHOTREXATE SODIUM

C J9261 Injection, nelarabine, 50 mg   K2 ASC K
BETOS: O1E   Other drugs
Drugs: ARRANON

C J9262 Injection, omacetaxine mepesuccinate, 0.01 mg   K2 ASC K
BETOS: O1D   Chemotherapy
Coding Clinic: 2013, Q4

C J9263 Injection, oxaliplatin, 0.5 mg   K2 ASC K
BETOS: O1D   Chemotherapy
Drugs: ELOXATIN, OXALIPLATIN
Coding Clinic: 2009, Q1

C J9264 Injection, paclitaxel protein-bound particles, 1 mg   K2 ASC K
BETOS: O1E   Other drugs
Drugs: ABRAXANE

D J9266 Injection, pegaspargase, per single dose vial   K2 ASC K
BETOS: O1D   Chemotherapy
Drugs: ONCASPAR
Coding Clinic: 2002, Q2

D J9267 Injection, paclitaxel, 1 mg   N1 ASC N
BETOS: O1D   Chemotherapy
Drugs: PACLITAXEL

D J9268 Injection, pentostatin, 10 mg   K2 ASC K
BETOS: O1D   Chemotherapy
Drugs: NIPENT

D J9270 Injection, plicamycin, 2.5 mg   N1 ASC N
BETOS: O1D   Chemotherapy

C J9271 Injection, pembrolizumab, 1 mg   K2 ASC G
BETOS: O1D   Chemotherapy
Drugs: KEYTRUDA
Coding Clinic: 2016, Q1

D J9280 Injection, mitomycin, 5 mg   K2 ASC K
BETOS: O1D   Chemotherapy
Drugs: MITOMYCIN
Coding Clinic: 2011, Q1; 2014, Q2; 2016, Q4

● **C J9285** Injection, olaratumab, 10 mg
BETOS: O1D   Chemotherapy

D J9293 Injection, mitoxantrone hydrochloride, per 5 mg   K2 ASC K
BETOS: O1D   Chemotherapy
Drugs: MITOXANTRONE HYDROCHLORIDE

C J9295 Injection, necitumumab, 1 mg   K2 ASC G
BETOS: O1D   Chemotherapy
Drugs: PORTRAZZA

D J9299 Injection, nivolumab, 1 mg   K2 ASC G
BETOS: O1D   Chemotherapy
Drugs: OPDIVO
Coding Clinic: 2016, Q1

C J9301 Injection, obinutuzumab, 10 mg   K2 ASC K
BETOS: O1D   Chemotherapy
Drugs: GAZYVA

C J9302 Injection, ofatumumab, 10 mg   K2 ASC K
BETOS: O1D   Chemotherapy
Drugs: ARZERRA
Coding Clinic: 2011, Q1

C J9303 Injection, panitumumab, 10 mg   K2 ASC K
BETOS: O1D   Chemotherapy
Drugs: PANITUMUMAB
Coding Clinic: 2008, Q1

♂ Male only   ♀ Female only   Ⓐ Age   A2 - Z3 = ASC Payment indicator   A - Y = APC Status indicator
ASC = ASC-approved procedure   DME Paid under the DME fee schedule   MIPS MIPS code

C **J9305** Injection, pemetrexed, 10 mg K2 ASC K
BETOS: O1E   Other drugs
Drugs: ALIMTA
Coding Clinic: 2005, Q2

C **J9306** Injection, pertuzumab, 1 mg K2 ASC K
BETOS: O1D   Chemotherapy
Drugs: PERJETA
Coding Clinic: 2013, Q4

C **J9307** Injection, pralatrexate, 1 mg K2 ASC K
BETOS: O1E   Other drugs
Drugs: FOLOTYN
Coding Clinic: 2011, Q1

C **J9308** Injection, ramucirumab, 5 mg K2 ASC K
BETOS: O1D   Chemotherapy
Drugs: CYRAMZA
Coding Clinic: 2016, Q1

D **J9310** Injection, rituximab, 100 mg K2 ASC K
BETOS: O1D   Chemotherapy
Drugs: RITUXAN
Coding Clinic: 2013, Q1; 2013, Q3

C **J9315** Injection, romidepsin, 1 mg K2 ASC K
BETOS: O1D   Chemotherapy
Drugs: ISTODAX (ROMIDEPSIN)
Coding Clinic: 2011, Q1

D **J9320** Injection, streptozocin, 1 gram K2 ASC K
BETOS: O1D   Chemotherapy
Drugs: ZANOSAR

C **J9325** Injection, talimogene laherparepvec, per
1 million plaque forming units K2 ASC G
BETOS: O1E   Other drugs
Drugs: IMLYGIC

C **J9328** Injection, temozolomide, 1 mg K2 ASC K
BETOS: O1D   Chemotherapy
Drugs: TEMODAR IV

C **J9330** Injection, temsirolimus, 1 mg K2 ASC K
BETOS: O1D   Chemotherapy
Drugs: TEMSIROLIMUS
Coding Clinic: 2008, Q4

D **J9340** Injection, thiotepa, 15 mg K2 ASC K
BETOS: O1D   Chemotherapy

C **J9351** Injection, topotecan, 0.1 mg K2 ASC K
BETOS: O1D   Chemotherapy
Drugs: HYCAMTIN, TOPOTECAN,
TOPOTECAN HCL
Coding Clinic: 2011, Q1

C **J9352** Injection, trabectedin, 0.1 mg K2 ASC G
BETOS: O1D   Chemotherapy
Drugs: YONDELIS

C **J9354** Injection, ado-trastuzumab emtansine,
1 mg K2 ASC K
BETOS: O1D   Chemotherapy
Drugs: KADCYLA
Coding Clinic: 2013, Q4

C **J9355** Injection, trastuzumab, 10 mg K2 ASC K
BETOS: O1E   Other drugs
Drugs: HERCEPTIN
Coding Clinic: 2006, Q2

D **J9357** Injection, valrubicin, intravesical,
200 mg K2 ASC K
BETOS: O1E   Other drugs
Drugs: VALSTAR

D **J9360** Injection, vinblastine sulfate, 1 mg N1 ASC N
BETOS: O1D   Chemotherapy
Drugs: VINBLASTINE SULFATE

D **J9370** Vincristine sulfate, 1 mg N1 ASC N
BETOS: O1D   Chemotherapy
Drugs: VINCRISTINE SULFATE
Coding Clinic: 2011, Q1

C **J9371** Injection, vincristine sulfate liposome,
1 mg K2 ASC K
BETOS: O1D   Chemotherapy
Drugs: VINCRISTINE SULFATE
Coding Clinic: 2013, Q4; 2014, Q1

D **J9390** Injection, vinorelbine tartrate,
10 mg N1 ASC N
BETOS: O1D   Chemotherapy
Drugs: NAVELBINE, VINORELBINE
TARTRATE
Coding Clinic: 2005, Q2

C **J9395** Injection, fulvestrant, 25 mg K2 ASC K
BETOS: O1E   Other drugs
Drugs: FASLODEX

C **J9400** Injection, ziv-aflibercept, 1 mg K2 ASC K
BETOS: O1E   Other drugs
Drugs: ZALTRAP
Coding Clinic: 2013, Q4

D **J9600** Injection, porfimer sodium, 75 mg K2 ASC K
BETOS: O1D   Chemotherapy

D **J9999** Not otherwise classified, antineoplastic
drugs N1 ASC N
BETOS: O1D   Chemotherapy
Coding Clinic: 2010, Q3; 2012, Q4; 2013,
Q1; 2017, Q1

▲ Revised code   ● New code   C Carrier judgment   D Special coverage instructions apply
I Not payable by Medicare   M Non-covered by Medicare   S Non-covered by Medicare statute   AHA Coding Clinic®

NOTES

NOTES

DURABLE MEDICAL EQUIPMENT (DME) (K0001-K0900)

WHEELCHAIRS, COMPONENTS, AND ACCESSORIES (K0001-K0195)

C **K0001** Standard wheelchair **DME** Y
BETOS: D1D Wheelchairs
DME Modifier: RR

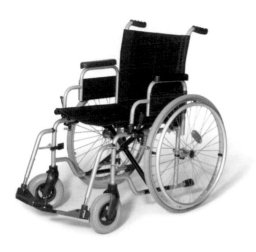

Wheelchair

C **K0002** Standard hemi (low seat) wheelchair **DME** Y
BETOS: D1D Wheelchairs
DME Modifier: RR

C **K0003** Lightweight wheelchair **DME** Y
BETOS: D1D Wheelchairs
DME Modifier: RR

C **K0004** High strength, lightweight wheelchair **DME** Y
BETOS: D1D Wheelchairs
DME Modifier: RR

C **K0005** Ultralightweight wheelchair **DME** Y
BETOS: D1D Wheelchairs
DME Modifier: NU,RR,UE

C **K0006** Heavy duty wheelchair **DME** Y
BETOS: D1D Wheelchairs
DME Modifier: RR

C **K0007** Extra heavy duty wheelchair **DME** Y
BETOS: D1D Wheelchairs
DME Modifier: RR

D **K0008** Custom manual wheelchair/base Y
BETOS: D1D Wheelchairs

C **K0009** Other manual wheelchair/base **DME** Y
BETOS: D1D Wheelchairs
DME Modifier: RR

C **K0010** Standard - weight frame motorized/power wheelchair **DME** Y
BETOS: D1D Wheelchairs
DME Modifier: RR

C **K0011** Standard - weight frame motorized/power wheelchair with programmable control parameters for speed adjustment, tremor dampening, acceleration control and braking **DME** Y
BETOS: D1D Wheelchairs
DME Modifier: RR

C **K0012** Lightweight portable motorized/power wheelchair **DME** Y
BETOS: D1D Wheelchairs
DME Modifier: RR

D **K0013** Custom motorized/power wheelchair base Y
BETOS: D1D Wheelchairs

C **K0014** Other motorized/power wheelchair base Y
BETOS: D1D Wheelchairs

C **K0015** Detachable, non-adjustable height armrest, replacement only, each **DME** Y
BETOS: D1D Wheelchairs
DME Modifier: RR
Pub: 100-4, Chap. 23, 60.3

C **K0017** Detachable, adjustable height armrest, base, replacement only, each **DME** Y
BETOS: D1D Wheelchairs
DME Modifier: NU,RR,UE

C **K0018** Detachable, adjustable height armrest, upper portion, replacement only, each **DME** Y
BETOS: D1D Wheelchairs
DME Modifier: NU,RR,UE

C **K0019** Arm pad, replacement only, each **DME** Y
BETOS: D1D Wheelchairs
DME Modifier: NU,RR,UE

C **K0020** Fixed, adjustable height armrest, pair **DME** Y
BETOS: D1D Wheelchairs
DME Modifier: NU,RR,UE

C **K0037** High mount flip-up footrest, replacement only, each **DME** Y
BETOS: D1D Wheelchairs
DME Modifier: NU,RR,UE

C **K0038** Leg strap, each **DME** Y
BETOS: D1D Wheelchairs
DME Modifier: NU,RR,UE

C **K0039** Leg strap, H style, each **DME** Y
BETOS: D1D Wheelchairs
DME Modifier: NU,RR,UE

C **K0040** Adjustable angle footplate, each **DME** Y
BETOS: D1D Wheelchairs
DME Modifier: NU,RR,UE

C K0041 Large size footplate, each DME Y
BETOS: D1D Wheelchairs
DME Modifier: NU,RR,UE

C K0042 Standard size footplate, replacement only, each DME Y
BETOS: D1D Wheelchairs
DME Modifier: NU,RR,UE

C K0043 Footrest, lower extension tube, replacement only, each DME Y
BETOS: D1D Wheelchairs
DME Modifier: NU,RR,UE

C K0044 Footrest, upper hanger bracket, replacement only, each DME Y
BETOS: D1D Wheelchairs
DME Modifier: NU,RR,UE

C K0045 Footrest, complete assembly, replacement only, each DME Y
BETOS: D1D Wheelchairs
DME Modifier: NU,RR,UE

C K0046 Elevating leg rest, lower extension tube, replacement only, each DME Y
BETOS: D1D Wheelchairs
DME Modifier: NU,RR,UE

C K0047 Elevating leg rest, upper hanger bracket, replacement only, each DME Y
BETOS: D1D Wheelchairs
DME Modifier: NU,RR,UE

C K0050 Ratchet assembly, replacement only DME Y
BETOS: D1D Wheelchairs
DME Modifier: NU,RR,UE

C K0051 Cam release assembly, footrest or leg rest, replacement only, each DME Y
BETOS: D1D Wheelchairs
DME Modifier: NU,RR,UE

C K0052 Swingaway, detachable footrests, replacement only, each DME Y
BETOS: D1D Wheelchairs
DME Modifier: NU,RR,UE

C K0053 Elevating footrests, articulating (telescoping), each DME Y
BETOS: D1D Wheelchairs
DME Modifier: NU,RR,UE

C K0056 Seat height less than 17" or equal to or greater than 21" for a high strength, lightweight, or ultralightweight wheelchair DME Y
BETOS: D1D Wheelchairs
DME Modifier: NU,RR,UE

C K0065 Spoke protectors, each DME Y
BETOS: D1D Wheelchairs
DME Modifier: NU,RR,UE

C K0069 Rear wheel assembly, complete, with solid tire, spokes or molded, replacement only, each DME Y
BETOS: D1D Wheelchairs
DME Modifier: NU,RR,UE

C K0070 Rear wheel assembly, complete, with pneumatic tire, spokes or molded, replacement only, each DME Y
BETOS: D1D Wheelchairs
DME Modifier: RR

C K0071 Front caster assembly, complete, with pneumatic tire, replacement only, each DME Y
BETOS: D1D Wheelchairs
DME Modifier: NU,RR,UE

C K0072 Front caster assembly, complete, with semi-pneumatic tire, replacement only, each DME Y
BETOS: D1D Wheelchairs
DME Modifier: NU,RR,UE

C K0073 Caster pin lock, each DME Y
BETOS: D1D Wheelchairs
DME Modifier: NU,RR,UE

C K0077 Front caster assembly, complete, with solid tire, replacement only, each DME Y
BETOS: D1D Wheelchairs
DME Modifier: NU,RR,UE

C K0098 Drive belt for power wheelchair, replacement only DME Y
BETOS: D1D Wheelchairs
DME Modifier: NU,RR,UE

C K0105 IV hanger, each DME Y
BETOS: D1D Wheelchairs
DME Modifier: NU,RR,UE

C K0108 Wheelchair component or accessory, not otherwise specified Y
BETOS: D1D Wheelchairs

D K0195 Elevating leg rests, pair (for use with capped rental wheelchair base) DME Y
BETOS: D1D Wheelchairs
DME Modifier: RR
Pub: 100-4, Chap. 23, 60.3

INFUSION PUMPS AND SUPPLIES (K0455-K0605)

D K0455 Infusion pump used for uninterrupted parenteral administration of medication, (e.g., epoprostenol or treprostinol) DME Y
BETOS: D1E Other DME
DME Modifier: RR

▲ Revised code ● New code **C** Carrier judgment **D** Special coverage instructions apply
I Not payable by Medicare **M** Non-covered by Medicare **S** Non-covered by Medicare statute AHA Coding Clinic®

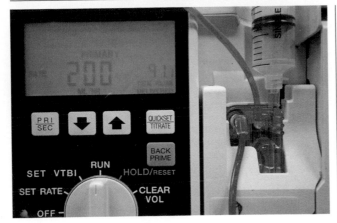

Infusion pump

D K0462 Temporary replacement for patient owned equipment being repaired, any type Y
BETOS: D1E Other DME

D K0552 Supplies for external non-insulin drug infusion pump, syringe type cartridge, sterile, each DME Y
BETOS: D1E Other DME

• **D K0553** Supply allowance for therapeutic continuous glucose monitor (CGM), includes all supplies and accessories, 1 month supply = 1 Unit Of Service DME Y
BETOS: D1E Other DME
Coding Clinic: 2017, Q2

• **D K0554** Receiver (monitor), dedicated, for use with therapeutic glucose continuous monitor system DME Y
BETOS: D1E Other DME
DME Modifier: NU,RR,UE
Coding Clinic: 2017, Q2

C K0601 Replacement battery for external infusion pump owned by patient, silver oxide, 1.5 volt, each DME Y
BETOS: D1E Other DME
DME Modifier: NU
Coding Clinic: 2003, Q2

C K0602 Replacement battery for external infusion pump owned by patient, silver oxide, 3 volt, each DME Y
BETOS: D1E Other DME
DME Modifier: NU
Coding Clinic: 2003, Q2

C K0603 Replacement battery for external infusion pump owned by patient, alkaline, 1.5 volt, each DME Y
BETOS: D1E Other DME
DME Modifier: NU
Coding Clinic: 2003, Q2

C K0604 Replacement battery for external infusion pump owned by patient, lithium, 3.6 volt, each DME Y

BETOS: D1E Other DME
DME Modifier: NU
Coding Clinic: 2003, Q2

C K0605 Replacement battery for external infusion pump owned by patient, lithium, 4.5 volt, each DME Y
BETOS: D1E Other DME
DME Modifier: NU
Coding Clinic: 2003, Q2

AUTOMATED EXTERNAL DEFIBRILLATOR AND SUPPLIES (K0606-K0609)

C K0606 Automatic external defibrillator, with integrated electrocardiogram analysis, garment type DME Y
BETOS: D1E Other DME
DME Modifier: RR

C K0607 Replacement battery for automated external defibrillator, garment type only, each DME Y
BETOS: D1E Other DME
DME Modifier: RR

C K0608 Replacement garment for use with automated external defibrillator, each DME Y
BETOS: D1E Other DME
DME Modifier: NU,RR,UE

C K0609 Replacement electrodes for use with automated external defibrillator, garment type only, each DME Y
BETOS: D1E Other DME
DME Modifier: KF

MISCELLANEOUS DME AND ACCESSORIES (K0669-K0746)

C K0669 Wheelchair accessory, wheelchair seat or back cushion, does not meet specific code criteria or no written coding verification from DME PDAC Y
BETOS: D1D Wheelchairs

C K0672 Addition to lower extremity orthosis, removable soft interface, all components, replacement only, each DME A
BETOS: D1F Prosthetic/orthotic devices

C K0730 Controlled dose inhalation drug delivery system DME Y
BETOS: D1E Other DME
DME Modifier: RR

C K0733 Power wheelchair accessory, 12 to 24 amp hour sealed lead acid battery, each (e.g., gel cell, absorbed glassmat) DME Y
BETOS: D1D Wheelchairs
DME Modifier: NU,RR,UE
Pub: 100-4, Chap. 23, 60.3

C **K0738** Portable gaseous oxygen system, rental; home compressor used to fill portable oxygen cylinders; includes portable containers, regulator, flowmeter, humidifier, cannula or mask, and tubing **DME** Y
BETOS: D1C   Oxygen and supplies
DME Modifier: RR

C **K0739** Repair or nonroutine service for durable medical equipment other than oxygen equipment requiring the skill of a technician, labor component, per 15 minutes   Y
BETOS: D1E   Other DME

M **K0740** Repair or nonroutine service for oxygen equipment requiring the skill of a technician, labor component, per 15 minutes   E1
BETOS: D1C   Oxygen and supplies
Service not separately priced by Part B

C **K0743** Suction pump, home model, portable, for use on wounds   Y
BETOS: D1E   Other DME

C **K0744** Absorptive wound dressing for use with suction pump, home model, portable, pad size 16 square inches or less   A
BETOS: D1E   Other DME

C **K0745** Absorptive wound dressing for use with suction pump, home model, portable, pad size more than 16 square inches but less than or equal to 48 square inches   A
BETOS: D1E   Other DME

C **K0746** Absorptive wound dressing for use with suction pump, home model, portable, pad size greater than 48 square inches   A
BETOS: D1E   Other DME

POWER OPERATED VEHICLES (K0800-K0812)

C **K0800** Power operated vehicle, group 1 standard, patient weight capacity up to and including 300 pounds **DME** Y
BETOS: D1D   Wheelchairs
DME Modifier: NU,RR,UE
Pub: 100-4, Chap. 12, 30.6.15.4; 100-4, Chap. 23, 60.3

C **K0801** Power operated vehicle, group 1 heavy duty, patient weight capacity 301 to 450 pounds **DME** Y
BETOS: D1D   Wheelchairs
DME Modifier: NU,RR,UE

C **K0802** Power operated vehicle, group 1 very heavy duty, patient weight capacity 451 to 600 pounds **DME** Y
BETOS: D1D   Wheelchairs
DME Modifier: NU,RR,UE

C **K0806** Power operated vehicle, group 2 standard, patient weight capacity up to and including 300 pounds **DME** Y

BETOS: D1D   Wheelchairs
DME Modifier: NU,RR,UE

C **K0807** Power operated vehicle, group 2 heavy duty, patient weight capacity 301 to 450 pounds **DME** Y
BETOS: D1D   Wheelchairs
DME Modifier: NU,RR,UE

C **K0808** Power operated vehicle, group 2 very heavy duty, patient weight capacity 451 to 600 pounds **DME** Y
BETOS: D1D   Wheelchairs
DME Modifier: NU,RR,UE

C **K0812** Power operated vehicle, not otherwise classified   Y
BETOS: D1D   Wheelchairs

WHEELCHAIRS, POWER OPERATED (K0813-K0899)

C **K0813** Power wheelchair, group 1 standard, portable, sling/solid seat and back, patient weight capacity up to and including 300 pounds **DME** Y
BETOS: D1D   Wheelchairs
DME Modifier: RR

C **K0814** Power wheelchair, group 1 standard, portable, captains chair, patient weight capacity up to and including 300 pounds **DME** Y
BETOS: D1D   Wheelchairs
DME Modifier: RR

C **K0815** Power wheelchair, group 1 standard, sling/solid seat and back, patient weight capacity up to and including 300 pounds **DME** Y
BETOS: D1D   Wheelchairs
DME Modifier: RR

C **K0816** Power wheelchair, group 1 standard, captains chair, patient weight capacity up to and including 300 pounds **DME** Y
BETOS: D1D   Wheelchairs
DME Modifier: RR

C **K0820** Power wheelchair, group 2 standard, portable, sling/solid seat/back, patient weight capacity up to and including 300 pounds **DME** Y
BETOS: D1D   Wheelchairs
DME Modifier: RR

C **K0821** Power wheelchair, group 2 standard, portable, captains chair, patient weight capacity up to and including 300 pounds **DME** Y
BETOS: D1D   Wheelchairs
DME Modifier: RR

C **K0822** Power wheelchair, group 2 standard, sling/solid seat/back, patient weight capacity up to and including 300 pounds   DME Y
BETOS: D1D   Wheelchairs
DME Modifier: RR

C **K0823** Power wheelchair, group 2 standard, captains chair, patient weight capacity up to and including 300 pounds   DME Y
BETOS: D1D   Wheelchairs
DME Modifier: RR

C **K0824** Power wheelchair, group 2 heavy duty, sling/solid seat/back, patient weight capacity 301 to 450 pounds   DME Y
BETOS: D1D   Wheelchairs
DME Modifier: RR

C **K0825** Power wheelchair, group 2 heavy duty, captains chair, patient weight capacity 301 to 450 pounds   DME Y
BETOS: D1D   Wheelchairs
DME Modifier: RR

C **K0826** Power wheelchair, group 2 very heavy duty, sling/solid seat/back, patient weight capacity 451 to 600 pounds   DME Y
BETOS: D1D   Wheelchairs
DME Modifier: RR

C **K0827** Power wheelchair, group 2 very heavy duty, captains chair, patient weight capacity 451 to 600 pounds   DME Y
BETOS: D1D   Wheelchairs
DME Modifier: RR

C **K0828** Power wheelchair, group 2 extra heavy duty, sling/solid seat/back, patient weight capacity 601 pounds or more   DME Y
BETOS: D1D   Wheelchairs
DME Modifier: RR

C **K0829** Power wheelchair, group 2 extra heavy duty, captains chair, patient weight 601 pounds or more   DME Y
BETOS: D1D   Wheelchairs
DME Modifier: RR

C **K0830** Power wheelchair, group 2 standard, seat elevator, sling/solid seat/back, patient weight capacity up to and including 300 pounds   Y
BETOS: D1D   Wheelchairs

C **K0831** Power wheelchair, group 2 standard, seat elevator, captains chair, patient weight capacity up to and including 300 pounds   Y
BETOS: D1D   Wheelchairs

C **K0835** Power wheelchair, group 2 standard, single power option, sling/solid seat/back, patient weight capacity up to and including 300 pounds   DME Y
BETOS: D1D   Wheelchairs
DME Modifier: RR

C **K0836** Power wheelchair, group 2 standard, single power option, captains chair, patient weight capacity up to and including 300 pounds   DME Y
BETOS: D1D   Wheelchairs
DME Modifier: RR

C **K0837** Power wheelchair, group 2 heavy duty, single power option, sling/solid seat/back, patient weight capacity 301 to 450 pounds   DME Y
BETOS: D1D   Wheelchairs
DME Modifier: RR

C **K0838** Power wheelchair, group 2 heavy duty, single power option, captains chair, patient weight capacity 301 to 450 pounds   DME Y
BETOS: D1D   Wheelchairs
DME Modifier: RR

C **K0839** Power wheelchair, group 2 very heavy duty, single power option, sling/solid seat/back, patient weight capacity 451 to 600 pounds   DME Y
BETOS: D1D   Wheelchairs
DME Modifier: RR

C **K0840** Power wheelchair, group 2 extra heavy duty, single power option, sling/solid seat/back, patient weight capacity 601 pounds or more   DME Y
BETOS: D1D   Wheelchairs
DME Modifier: RR

C **K0841** Power wheelchair, group 2 standard, multiple power option, sling/solid seat/back, patient weight capacity up to and including 300 pounds   DME Y
BETOS: D1D   Wheelchairs
DME Modifier: RR

C **K0842** Power wheelchair, group 2 standard, multiple power option, captains chair, patient weight capacity up to and including 300 pounds   DME Y
BETOS: D1D   Wheelchairs
DME Modifier: RR

C **K0843** Power wheelchair, group 2 heavy duty, multiple power option, sling/solid seat/back, patient weight capacity 301 to 450 pounds   DME Y
BETOS: D1D   Wheelchairs
DME Modifier: RR

C **K0848** Power wheelchair, group 3 standard, sling/solid seat/back, patient weight capacity up to and including 300 pounds   DME Y
BETOS: D1D   Wheelchairs
DME Modifier: RR

♂ Male only   ♀ Female only   A Age   A2 - Z3 = ASC Payment indicator   A - Y = APC Status indicator
ASC = ASC-approved procedure   DME Paid under the DME fee schedule   MIPS MIPS code

C **K0849** Power wheelchair, group 3 standard, captains chair, patient weight capacity up to and including 300 pounds DME Y
BETOS: D1D Wheelchairs
DME Modifier: RR

C **K0850** Power wheelchair, group 3 heavy duty, sling/solid seat/back, patient weight capacity 301 to 450 pounds DME Y
BETOS: D1D Wheelchairs
DME Modifier: RR

C **K0851** Power wheelchair, group 3 heavy duty, captains chair, patient weight capacity 301 to 450 pounds DME Y
BETOS: D1D Wheelchairs
DME Modifier: RR

C **K0852** Power wheelchair, group 3 very heavy duty, sling/solid seat/back, patient weight capacity 451 to 600 pounds DME Y
BETOS: D1D Wheelchairs
DME Modifier: RR

C **K0853** Power wheelchair, group 3 very heavy duty, captains chair, patient weight capacity 451 to 600 pounds DME Y
BETOS: D1D Wheelchairs
DME Modifier: RR

C **K0854** Power wheelchair, group 3 extra heavy duty, sling/solid seat/back, patient weight capacity 601 pounds or more DME Y
BETOS: D1D Wheelchairs
DME Modifier: RR

C **K0855** Power wheelchair, group 3 extra heavy duty, captains chair, patient weight capacity 601 pounds or more DME Y
BETOS: D1D Wheelchairs
DME Modifier: RR

C **K0856** Power wheelchair, group 3 standard, single power option, sling/solid seat/back, patient weight capacity up to and including 300 pounds DME Y
BETOS: D1D Wheelchairs
DME Modifier: RR

C **K0857** Power wheelchair, group 3 standard, single power option, captains chair, patient weight capacity up to and including 300 pounds DME Y
BETOS: D1D Wheelchairs
DME Modifier: RR

C **K0858** Power wheelchair, group 3 heavy duty, single power option, sling/solid seat/back, patient weight 301 to 450 pounds DME Y
BETOS: D1D Wheelchairs
DME Modifier: RR

C **K0859** Power wheelchair, group 3 heavy duty, single power option, captains chair, patient weight capacity 301 to 450 pounds DME Y

BETOS: D1D Wheelchairs
DME Modifier: RR

C **K0860** Power wheelchair, group 3 very heavy duty, single power option, sling/solid seat/back, patient weight capacity 451 to 600 pounds DME Y
BETOS: D1D Wheelchairs
DME Modifier: RR

C **K0861** Power wheelchair, group 3 standard, multiple power option, sling/solid seat/back, patient weight capacity up to and including 300 pounds DME Y
BETOS: D1D Wheelchairs
DME Modifier: RR

C **K0862** Power wheelchair, group 3 heavy duty, multiple power option, sling/solid seat/back, patient weight capacity 301 to 450 pounds DME Y
BETOS: D1D Wheelchairs
DME Modifier: RR

C **K0863** Power wheelchair, group 3 very heavy duty, multiple power option, sling/solid seat/back, patient weight capacity 451 to 600 pounds DME Y
BETOS: D1D Wheelchairs
DME Modifier: RR

C **K0864** Power wheelchair, group 3 extra heavy duty, multiple power option, sling/solid seat/back, patient weight capacity 601 pounds or more DME Y
BETOS: D1D Wheelchairs
DME Modifier: RR

C **K0868** Power wheelchair, group 4 standard, sling/solid seat/back, patient weight capacity up to and including 300 pounds Y
BETOS: D1D Wheelchairs

C **K0869** Power wheelchair, group 4 standard, captains chair, patient weight capacity up to and including 300 pounds Y
BETOS: D1D Wheelchairs

C **K0870** Power wheelchair, group 4 heavy duty, sling/solid seat/back, patient weight capacity 301 to 450 pounds Y
BETOS: D1D Wheelchairs

C **K0871** Power wheelchair, group 4 very heavy duty, sling/solid seat/back, patient weight capacity 451 to 600 pounds Y
BETOS: D1D Wheelchairs

C **K0877** Power wheelchair, group 4 standard, single power option, sling/solid seat/back, patient weight capacity up to and including 300 pounds Y
BETOS: D1D Wheelchairs

C **K0878** Power wheelchair, group 4 standard, single power option, captains chair, patient weight capacity up to and including 300 pounds   Y

    BETOS: D1D   Wheelchairs

C **K0879** Power wheelchair, group 4 heavy duty, single power option, sling/solid seat/back, patient weight capacity 301 to 450 pounds   Y

    BETOS: D1D   Wheelchairs

C **K0880** Power wheelchair, group 4 very heavy duty, single power option, sling/solid seat/back, patient weight 451 to 600 pounds   Y

    BETOS: D1D   Wheelchairs

C **K0884** Power wheelchair, group 4 standard, multiple power option, sling/solid seat/back, patient weight capacity up to and including 300 pounds   Y

    BETOS: D1D   Wheelchairs

C **K0885** Power wheelchair, group 4 standard, multiple power option, captains chair, patient weight capacity up to and including 300 pounds   Y

    BETOS: D1D   Wheelchairs

C **K0886** Power wheelchair, group 4 heavy duty, multiple power option, sling/solid seat/back, patient weight capacity 301 to 450 pounds   Y

    BETOS: D1D   Wheelchairs

C **K0890** Power wheelchair, group 5 pediatric, single power option, sling/solid seat/back, patient weight capacity up to and including 125 pounds   Ⓐ Y

    BETOS: D1D   Wheelchairs

C **K0891** Power wheelchair, group 5 pediatric, multiple power option, sling/solid seat/back, patient weight capacity up to and including 125 pounds   Ⓐ Y

    BETOS: D1D   Wheelchairs

C **K0898** Power wheelchair, not otherwise classified Y

    BETOS: D1D   Wheelchairs

C **K0899** Power mobility device, not coded by DME PDAC or does not meet criteria   Y

    BETOS: D1D   Wheelchairs

    Service not separately priced by Part B

    Pub: 100-4, Chap. 12, 30.6.15.4

CUSTOMIZED DME, OTHER THAN WHEELCHAIR (K0900)

D **K0900** Customized durable medical equipment, other than wheelchair   Y

    BETOS: D1E   Other DME

NOTES

ORTHOTIC PROCEDURES AND SERVICES (L0112-L4631)

CERVICAL ORTHOTICS (L0112-L0174)

C L0112 Cranial-cervical orthosis (CCO), congenital torticollis type, with or without soft interface material, adjustable range of motion joint, custom fabricated **DME** A

BETOS: D1F Prosthetic/orthotic devices

C L0113 Cranial-cervical orthosis (CCO), torticollis type, with or without joint, with or without soft interface material, prefabricated, includes fitting and adjustment **DME** A

BETOS: D1F Prosthetic/orthotic devices

Coding Clinic: 2008, Q4

C L0120 Cervical, flexible, non-adjustable, prefabricated, off-the-shelf (foam collar) **DME** A

BETOS: D1F Prosthetic/orthotic devices

C L0130 Cervical, flexible, thermoplastic collar, molded to patient **DME** A

BETOS: D1F Prosthetic/orthotic devices

C L0140 Cervical, semi-rigid, adjustable (plastic collar) **DME** A

BETOS: D1F Prosthetic/orthotic devices

C L0150 Cervical, semi-rigid, adjustable molded chin cup (plastic collar with mandibular/occipital piece) **DME** A

BETOS: D1F Prosthetic/orthotic devices

C L0160 Cervical, semi-rigid, wire frame occipital/mandibular support, prefabricated, off-the-shelf **DME** A

BETOS: D1F Prosthetic/orthotic devices

C L0170 Cervical, collar, molded to patient model **DME** A

BETOS: D1F Prosthetic/orthotic devices

C L0172 Cervical, collar, semi-rigid thermoplastic foam, two-piece, prefabricated, off-the-shelf **DME** A

BETOS: D1F Prosthetic/orthotic devices

C L0174 Cervical, collar, semi-rigid, thermoplastic foam, two piece with thoracic extension, prefabricated, off-the-shelf **DME** A

BETOS: D1F Prosthetic/orthotic devices

CERVICAL ORTHOTICS MULTI-POST COLLAR (L0180-L0200)

C L0180 Cervical, multiple post collar, occipital/mandibular supports, adjustable **DME** A

BETOS: D1F Prosthetic/orthotic devices

C L0190 Cervical, multiple post collar, occipital/mandibular supports, adjustable cervical bars (SOMI, Guilford, Taylor types) **DME** A

BETOS: D1F Prosthetic/orthotic devices

C L0200 Cervical, multiple post collar, occipital/mandibular supports, adjustable cervical bars, and thoracic extension **DME** A

BETOS: D1F Prosthetic/orthotic devices

THORACIC RIB BELTS (L0220)

C L0220 Thoracic, rib belt, custom fabricated **DME** A

BETOS: D1F Prosthetic/orthotic devices

THORACIC-LUMBAR-SACRAL ORTHOTICS (TLSO) (L0450-L0492), SEE ALSO LOW-PROFILE ADDITIONS, THORACIC-LUMBAR-SACRAL ORTHOTICS (L1200-L1290)

C L0450 Thoracic-lumbar-sacral orthosis (TLSO), flexible, provides trunk support, upper thoracic region, produces intracavitary pressure to reduce load on the intervertebral disks with rigid stays or panel(s), includes shoulder straps and closures, prefabricated, off-the-shelf **DME** A

BETOS: D1F Prosthetic/orthotic devices

C L0452 Thoracic-lumbar-sacral orthosis (TLSO), flexible, provides trunk support, upper thoracic region, produces intracavitary pressure to reduce load on the intervertebral disks with rigid stays or panel(s), includes shoulder straps and closures, custom fabricated **DME** A

BETOS: D1F Prosthetic/orthotic devices

C L0454 Thoracic-lumbar-sacral orthosis (TLSO), flexible, provides trunk support, extends from sacrococcygeal junction to above T-9 vertebra, restricts gross trunk motion in the sagittal plane, produces intracavitary pressure to reduce load on the intervertebral disks with rigid stays or panel(s), includes shoulder straps and closures, prefabricated item that has been trimmed, bent, molded, assembled, or otherwise customized to fit a specific patient by an individual with expertise **DME** A

BETOS: D1F Prosthetic/orthotic devices

C L0455 Thoracic-lumbar-sacral orthosis (TLSO), flexible, provides trunk support, extends from sacrococcygeal junction to above T-9 vertebra, restricts gross trunk motion in the sagittal plane, produces intracavitary pressure to reduce load on the intervertebral disks with rigid stays or panel(s), includes shoulder straps and closures, prefabricated, off-the-shelf **DME** A

BETOS: D1F Prosthetic/orthotic devices

C L0456 Thoracic-lumbar-sacral orthosis (TLSO), flexible, provides trunk support, thoracic region, rigid posterior panel and soft anterior apron, extends from the sacrococcygeal junction and terminates just inferior to the scapular spine, restricts gross trunk motion in the sagittal plane, produces intracavitary

---

♂ Male only   ♀ Female only   **A** Age   A2 - Z3 = ASC Payment indicator   A - Y = APC Status indicator

ASC = ASC-approved procedure   **DME** Paid under the DME fee schedule   **MIPS** MIPS code

pressure to reduce load on the intervertebral disks, includes straps and closures, prefabricated item that has been trimmed, bent, molded, assembled, or otherwise customized to fit a specific patient by an individual with expertise [DME] A

BETOS: D1F   Prosthetic/orthotic devices

C **L0457** Thoracic-lumbar-sacral orthosis (TLSO), flexible, provides trunk support, thoracic region, rigid posterior panel and soft anterior apron, extends from the sacrococcygeal junction and terminates just inferior to the scapular spine, restricts gross trunk motion in the sagittal plane, produces intracavitary pressure to reduce load on the intervertebral disks, includes straps and closures, prefabricated, off-the-shelf [DME] A

BETOS: D1F   Prosthetic/orthotic devices

C **L0458** Thoracic-lumbar-sacral orthosis (TLSO), triplanar control, modular segmented spinal system, two rigid plastic shells, posterior extends from the sacrococcygeal junction and terminates just inferior to the scapular spine, anterior extends from the symphysis pubis to the xiphoid, soft liner, restricts gross trunk motion in the sagittal, coronal, and transverse planes, lateral strength is provided by overlapping plastic and stabilizing closures, includes straps and closures, prefabricated, includes fitting and adjustment [DME] A

BETOS: D1F   Prosthetic/orthotic devices

C **L0460** Thoracic-lumbar-sacral orthosis (TLSO), triplanar control, modular segmented spinal system, two rigid plastic shells, posterior extends from the sacrococcygeal junction and terminates just inferior to the scapular spine, anterior extends from the symphysis pubis to the sternal notch, soft liner, restricts gross trunk motion in the sagittal, coronal, and transverse planes, lateral strength is provided by overlapping plastic and stabilizing closures, includes straps and closures, prefabricated item that has been trimmed, bent, molded, or otherwise customized to fit a specific patient by an individual with expertise [DME] A

BETOS: D1F   Prosthetic/orthotic devices

C **L0462** Thoracic-lumbar-sacral orthosis (TLSO), triplanar control, modular segmented spinal system, three rigid plastic shells, posterior extends from the sacrococcygeal junction and terminates just inferior to the scapular spine, anterior extends from the symphysis pubis to the sternal notch, soft liner, restricts gross trunk motion in the sagittal, coronal, and transverse planes, lateral strength is provided by overlapping plastic and stabilizing closures, includes straps and

closures, prefabricated, includes fitting and adjustment [DME] A

BETOS: D1F   Prosthetic/orthotic devices

C **L0464** Thoracic-lumbar-sacral orthosis (TLSO), triplanar control, modular segmented spinal system, four rigid plastic shells, posterior extends from sacrococcygeal junction and terminates just inferior to scapular spine, anterior extends from symphysis pubis to the sternal notch, soft liner, restricts gross trunk motion in sagittal, coronal, and transverse planes, lateral strength is provided by overlapping plastic and stabilizing closures, includes straps and closures, prefabricated, includes fitting and adjustment [DME] A

BETOS: D1F   Prosthetic/orthotic devices

C **L0466** Thoracic-lumbar-sacral orthosis (TLSO), sagittal control, rigid posterior frame and flexible soft anterior apron with straps, closures and padding, restricts gross trunk motion in sagittal plane, produces intracavitary pressure to reduce load on intervertebral disks, prefabricated item that has been trimmed, bent, molded, assembled, or otherwise customized to fit a specific patient by an individual with expertise [DME] A

BETOS: D1F   Prosthetic/orthotic devices

C **L0467** Thoracic-lumbar-sacral orthosis (TLSO), sagittal control, rigid posterior frame and flexible soft anterior apron with straps, closures and padding, restricts gross trunk motion in sagittal plane, produces intracavitary pressure to reduce load on intervertebral disks, prefabricated, off-the-shelf [DME] A

BETOS: D1F   Prosthetic/orthotic devices

C **L0468** Thoracic-lumbar-sacral orthosis (TLSO), sagittal-coronal control, rigid posterior frame and flexible soft anterior apron with straps, closures and padding, extends from sacrococcygeal junction over scapulae, lateral strength provided by pelvic, thoracic, and lateral frame pieces, restricts gross trunk motion in sagittal, and coronal planes, produces intracavitary pressure to reduce load on intervertebral disks, prefabricated item that has been trimmed, bent, molded, assembled, or otherwise customized to fit a specific patient by an individual with expertise [DME] A

BETOS: D1F   Prosthetic/orthotic devices

C **L0469** Thoracic-lumbar-sacral orthosis (TLSO), sagittal-coronal control, rigid posterior frame and flexible soft anterior apron with straps, closures and padding, extends from sacrococcygeal junction over scapulae, lateral strength provided by pelvic, thoracic, and lateral frame pieces, restricts gross trunk motion in sagittal and coronal planes, produces intracavitary pressure to reduce load on intervertebral disks, prefabricated, off-the-shelf `DME` A

BETOS: D1F   Prosthetic/orthotic devices

[C] **L0470** Thoracic-lumbar-sacral orthosis (TLSO), triplanar control, rigid posterior frame and flexible soft anterior apron with straps, closures and padding, extends from sacrococcygeal junction to scapula, lateral strength provided by pelvic, thoracic, and lateral frame pieces, rotational strength provided by subclavicular extensions, restricts gross trunk motion in sagittal, coronal, and transverse planes, provides intracavitary pressure to reduce load on the intervertebral disks, includes fitting and shaping the frame, prefabricated, includes fitting and adjustment `DME` A

BETOS: D1F   Prosthetic/orthotic devices

[C] **L0472** Thoracic-lumbar-sacral orthosis (TLSO), triplanar control, hyperextension, rigid anterior and lateral frame extends from symphysis pubis to sternal notch with two anterior components (one pubic and one sternal), posterior and lateral pads with straps and closures, limits spinal flexion, restricts gross trunk motion in sagittal, coronal, and transverse planes, includes fitting and shaping the frame, prefabricated, includes fitting and adjustment `DME` A

BETOS: D1F   Prosthetic/orthotic devices

[C] **L0480** Thoracic-lumbar-sacral orthosis (TLSO), triplanar control, one piece rigid plastic shell without interface liner, with multiple straps and closures, posterior extends from sacrococcygeal junction and terminates just inferior to scapular spine, anterior extends from symphysis pubis to sternal notch, anterior or posterior opening, restricts gross trunk motion in sagittal, coronal, and transverse planes, includes a carved plaster or CAD-CAM model, custom fabricated `DME` A

BETOS: D1F   Prosthetic/orthotic devices

[C] **L0482** Thoracic-lumbar-sacral orthosis (TLSO), triplanar control, one piece rigid plastic shell with interface liner, multiple straps and closures, posterior extends from sacrococcygeal junction and terminates just inferior to scapular spine, anterior extends from symphysis pubis to sternal notch, anterior or posterior opening, restricts gross trunk motion in sagittal, coronal, and transverse planes, includes a carved plaster or CAD-CAM model, custom fabricated `DME` A

BETOS: D1F   Prosthetic/orthotic devices

[C] **L0484** Thoracic-lumbar-sacral orthosis (TLSO), triplanar control, two piece rigid plastic shell without interface liner, with multiple straps and closures, posterior extends from

sacrococcygeal junction and terminates just inferior to scapular spine, anterior extends from symphysis pubis to sternal notch, lateral strength is enhanced by overlapping plastic, restricts gross trunk motion in the sagittal, coronal, and transverse planes, includes a carved plaster or CAD-CAM model, custom fabricated `DME` A

BETOS: D1F   Prosthetic/orthotic devices

[C] **L0486** Thoracic-lumbar-sacral orthosis (TLSO), triplanar control, two piece rigid plastic shell with interface liner, multiple straps and closures, posterior extends from sacrococcygeal junction and terminates just inferior to scapular spine, anterior extends from symphysis pubis to sternal notch, lateral strength is enhanced by overlapping plastic, restricts gross trunk motion in the sagittal, coronal, and transverse planes, includes a carved plaster or CAD-CAM model, custom fabricated `DME` A

BETOS: D1F   Prosthetic/orthotic devices

[C] **L0488** Thoracic-lumbar-sacral orthosis (TLSO), triplanar control, one piece rigid plastic shell with interface liner, multiple straps and closures, posterior extends from sacrococcygeal junction and terminates just inferior to scapular spine, anterior extends from symphysis pubis to sternal notch, anterior or posterior opening, restricts gross trunk motion in sagittal, coronal, and transverse planes, prefabricated, includes fitting and adjustment `DME` A

BETOS: D1F   Prosthetic/orthotic devices

[C] **L0490** Thoracic-lumbar-sacral orthosis (TLSO), sagittal-coronal control, one piece rigid plastic shell, with overlapping reinforced anterior, with multiple straps and closures, posterior extends from sacrococcygeal junction and terminates at or before the T-9 vertebra, anterior extends from symphysis pubis to xiphoid, anterior opening, restricts gross trunk motion in sagittal and coronal planes, prefabricated, includes fitting and adjustment `DME` A

BETOS: D1F   Prosthetic/orthotic devices

[C] **L0491** Thoracic-lumbar-sacral orthosis (TLSO), sagittal-coronal control, modular segmented spinal system, two rigid plastic shells, posterior extends from the sacrococcygeal junction and terminates just inferior to the scapular spine, anterior extends from the symphysis pubis to the xiphoid, soft liner, restricts gross trunk motion in the sagittal and coronal planes, lateral strength is provided by overlapping plastic and stabilizing closures, includes straps and closures, prefabricated, includes fitting and adjustment `DME` A

BETOS: D1F   Prosthetic/orthotic devices

ⓒ **L0492** Thoracic-lumbar-sacral orthosis (TLSO), sagittal-coronal control, modular segmented spinal system, three rigid plastic shells, posterior extends from the sacrococcygeal junction and terminates just inferior to the scapular spine, anterior extends from the symphysis pubis to the xiphoid, soft liner, restricts gross trunk motion in the sagittal and coronal planes, lateral strength is provided by overlapping plastic and stabilizing closures, includes straps and closures, prefabricated, includes fitting and adjustment DME A

BETOS: D1F   Prosthetic/orthotic devices

SACRAL ORTHOTICS (L0621-L0624)

ⓒ **L0621** Sacroiliac orthosis (SO), flexible, provides pelvic-sacral support, reduces motion about the sacroiliac joint, includes straps, closures, may include pendulous abdomen design, prefabricated, off-the-shelf DME A

BETOS: D1F   Prosthetic/orthotic devices

ⓒ **L0622** Sacroiliac orthosis (SO), flexible, provides pelvic-sacral support, reduces motion about the sacroiliac joint, includes straps, closures, may include pendulous abdomen design, custom fabricated DME A

BETOS: D1F   Prosthetic/orthotic devices

ⓒ **L0623** Sacroiliac orthosis (SO), provides pelvic-sacral support, with rigid or semi-rigid panels over the sacrum and abdomen, reduces motion about the sacroiliac joint, includes straps, closures, may include pendulous abdomen design, prefabricated, off-the-shelf DME A

BETOS: D1F   Prosthetic/orthotic devices

ⓒ **L0624** Sacroiliac orthosis (SO), provides pelvic-sacral support, with rigid or semi-rigid panels placed over the sacrum and abdomen, reduces motion about the sacroiliac joint, includes straps, closures, may include pendulous abdomen design, custom fabricated DME A

BETOS: D1F   Prosthetic/orthotic devices

LUMBAR ORTHOTICS (L0625-L0627), SEE ALSO LUMBAR ORTHOTICS SAGITTAL CONTROL (L0641, L0642)

ⓒ **L0625** Lumbar orthosis (LO), flexible, provides lumbar support, posterior extends from L-1 to below L-5 vertebra, produces intracavitary pressure to reduce load on the intervertebral discs, includes straps, closures, may include pendulous abdomen design, shoulder straps, stays, prefabricated, off-the-shelf DME A

BETOS: D1F   Prosthetic/orthotic devices

Thoracic-lumbar-sacral orthosis

ⓒ **L0626** Lumbar orthosis (LO), sagittal control, with rigid posterior panel(s), posterior extends from L-1 to below L-5 vertebra, produces intracavitary pressure to reduce load on the intervertebral discs, includes straps, closures, may include padding, stays, shoulder straps, pendulous abdomen design, prefabricated item that has been trimmed, bent, molded, assembled, or otherwise customized to fit a specific patient by an individual with expertise DME A

BETOS: D1F   Prosthetic/orthotic devices

ⓒ **L0627** Lumbar orthosis (LO), sagittal control, with rigid anterior and posterior panels, posterior extends from L-1 to below L-5 vertebra, produces intracavitary pressure to reduce load on the intervertebral discs, includes straps, closures, may include padding, shoulder straps, pendulous abdomen design, prefabricated item that has been trimmed, bent, molded, assembled, or otherwise customized to fit a specific patient by an individual with expertise DME A

BETOS: D1F   Prosthetic/orthotic devices

LUMBAR-SACRAL ORTHOTICS (L0628-L0640), SEE ALSO LUMBAR-SACRAL ORTHOTICS SAGITTAL CONTROL (L0643-L0651)

C **L0628** Lumbar-sacral orthosis (LSO), flexible, provides lumbo-sacral support, posterior extends from sacrococcygeal junction to T-9 vertebra, produces intracavitary pressure to reduce load on the intervertebral discs, includes straps, closures, may include stays, shoulder straps, pendulous abdomen design, prefabricated, off-the-shelf ▪DME▪ A

BETOS: D1F   Prosthetic/orthotic devices

Lumbar-sacral orthosis

C **L0629** Lumbar-sacral orthosis (LSO), flexible, provides lumbo-sacral support, posterior extends from sacrococcygeal junction to T-9 vertebra, produces intracavitary pressure to reduce load on the intervertebral discs, includes straps, closures, may include stays, shoulder straps, pendulous abdomen design, custom fabricated ▪DME▪ A

BETOS: D1F   Prosthetic/orthotic devices

C **L0630** Lumbar-sacral orthosis (LSO), sagittal control, with rigid posterior panel(s), posterior extends from sacrococcygeal junction to T-9 vertebra, produces intracavitary pressure to reduce load on the intervertebral discs, includes straps, closures, may include padding, stays, shoulder straps, pendulous abdomen design, prefabricated item that has been trimmed, bent, molded, assembled, or

otherwise customized to fit a specific patient by an individual with expertise ▪DME▪ A

BETOS: D1F   Prosthetic/orthotic devices

C **L0631** Lumbar-sacral orthosis (LSO), sagittal control, with rigid anterior and posterior panels, posterior extends from sacrococcygeal junction to T-9 vertebra, produces intracavitary pressure to reduce load on the intervertebral discs, includes straps, closures, may include padding, shoulder straps, pendulous abdomen design, prefabricated item that has been trimmed, bent, molded, assembled, or otherwise customized to fit a specific patient by an individual with expertise ▪DME▪ A

BETOS: D1F   Prosthetic/orthotic devices

C **L0632** Lumbar-sacral orthosis (LSO), sagittal control, with rigid anterior and posterior panels, posterior extends from sacrococcygeal junction to T-9 vertebra, produces intracavitary pressure to reduce load on the intervertebral discs, includes straps, closures, may include padding, shoulder straps, pendulous abdomen design, custom fabricated ▪DME▪ A

BETOS: D1F   Prosthetic/orthotic devices

C **L0633** Lumbar-sacral orthosis (LSO), sagittal-coronal control, with rigid posterior frame/panel(s), posterior extends from sacrococcygeal junction to T-9 vertebra, lateral strength provided by rigid lateral frame/panels, produces intracavitary pressure to reduce load on intervertebral discs, includes straps, closures, may include padding, stays, shoulder straps, pendulous abdomen design, prefabricated item that has been trimmed, bent, molded, assembled, or otherwise customized to fit a specific patient by an individual with expertise ▪DME▪ A

BETOS: D1F   Prosthetic/orthotic devices

C **L0634** Lumbar-sacral orthosis (LSO), sagittal-coronal control, with rigid posterior frame/panel(s), posterior extends from sacrococcygeal junction to T-9 vertebra, lateral strength provided by rigid lateral frame/panel(s), produces intracavitary pressure to reduce load on intervertebral discs, includes straps, closures, may include padding, stays, shoulder straps, pendulous abdomen design, custom fabricated ▪DME▪ A

BETOS: D1F   Prosthetic/orthotic devices

C **L0635** Lumbar-sacral orthosis (LSO), sagittal-coronal control, lumbar flexion, rigid posterior frame/panel(s), lateral articulating design to flex the lumbar spine, posterior extends from sacrococcygeal junction to T-9 vertebra, lateral strength provided by rigid lateral frame/panel(s), produces intracavitary pressure to reduce load on intervertebral discs, includes straps, closures, may include

L0636 - L0649

ORTHOTIC PROCEDURES AND SERVICES (L0112-L4631)

padding, anterior panel, pendulous abdomen design, prefabricated, includes fitting and adjustment DME A

BETOS: D1F   Prosthetic/orthotic devices

C L0636 Lumbar-sacral orthosis (LSO), sagittal-coronal control, lumbar flexion, rigid posterior frame/panels, lateral articulating design to flex the lumbar spine, posterior extends from sacrococcygeal junction to T-9 vertebra, lateral strength provided by rigid lateral frame/panels, produces intracavitary pressure to reduce load on intervertebral discs, includes straps, closures, may include padding, anterior panel, pendulous abdomen design, custom fabricated DME A

BETOS: D1F   Prosthetic/orthotic devices

C L0637 Lumbar-sacral orthosis (LSO), sagittal-coronal control, with rigid anterior and posterior frame/panels, posterior extends from sacrococcygeal junction to T-9 vertebra, lateral strength provided by rigid lateral frame/panels, produces intracavitary pressure to reduce load on intervertebral discs, includes straps, closures, may include padding, shoulder straps, pendulous abdomen design, prefabricated item that has been trimmed, bent, molded, assembled, or otherwise customized to fit a specific patient by an individual with expertise DME A

BETOS: D1F   Prosthetic/orthotic devices

C L0638 Lumbar-sacral orthosis (LSO), sagittal-coronal control, with rigid anterior and posterior frame/panels, posterior extends from sacrococcygeal junction to T-9 vertebra, lateral strength provided by rigid lateral frame/panels, produces intracavitary pressure to reduce load on intervertebral discs, includes straps, closures, may include padding, shoulder straps, pendulous abdomen design, custom fabricated DME A

BETOS: D1F   Prosthetic/orthotic devices

C L0639 Lumbar-sacral orthosis (LSO), sagittal-coronal control, rigid shell(s)/panel(s), posterior extends from sacrococcygeal junction to T-9 vertebra, anterior extends from symphysis pubis to xyphoid, produces intracavitary pressure to reduce load on the intervertebral discs, overall strength is provided by overlapping rigid material and stabilizing closures, includes straps, closures, may include soft interface, pendulous abdomen design, prefabricated item that has been trimmed, bent, molded, assembled, or otherwise customized to fit a specific patient by an individual with expertise DME A

BETOS: D1F   Prosthetic/orthotic devices

C L0640 Lumbar-sacral orthosis (LSO), sagittal-coronal control, rigid shell(s)/panel(s), posterior extends from sacrococcygeal

junction to T-9 vertebra, anterior extends from symphysis pubis to xyphoid, produces intracavitary pressure to reduce load on the intervertebral discs, overall strength is provided by overlapping rigid material and stabilizing closures, includes straps, closures, may include soft interface, pendulous abdomen design, custom fabricated DME A

BETOS: D1F   Prosthetic/orthotic devices

LUMBAR ORTHOTICS SAGITTAL CONTROL (L0641, L0642), SEE ALSO LUMBAR ORTHOTICS (L0625-L0627)

C L0641 Lumbar orthosis (LO), sagittal control, with rigid posterior panel(s), posterior extends from L-1 to below L-5 vertebra, produces intracavitary pressure to reduce load on the intervertebral discs, includes straps, closures, may include padding, stays, shoulder straps, pendulous abdomen design, prefabricated, off-the-shelf DME A

BETOS: D1F   Prosthetic/orthotic devices

C L0642 Lumbar orthosis (LO), sagittal control, with rigid anterior and posterior panels, posterior extends from L-1 to below L-5 vertebra, produces intracavitary pressure to reduce load on the intervertebral discs, includes straps, closures, may include padding, shoulder straps, pendulous abdomen design, prefabricated, off-the-shelf DME A

BETOS: D1F   Prosthetic/orthotic devices

LUMBAR-SACRAL ORTHOTICS SAGITTAL CONTROL (L0643-L0651), SEE ALSO LUMBAR-SACRAL ORTHOTICS (L0628-L0640)

C L0643 Lumbar-sacral orthosis (LSO), sagittal control, with rigid posterior panel(s), posterior extends from sacrococcygeal junction to T-9 vertebra, produces intracavitary pressure to reduce load on the intervertebral discs, includes straps, closures, may include padding, stays, shoulder straps, pendulous abdomen design, prefabricated, off-the-shelf DME A

BETOS: D1F   Prosthetic/orthotic devices

C L0648 Lumbar-sacral orthosis (LSO), sagittal control, with rigid anterior and posterior panels, posterior extends from sacrococcygeal junction to T-9 vertebra, produces intracavitary pressure to reduce load on the intervertebral discs, includes straps, closures, may include padding, shoulder straps, pendulous abdomen design, prefabricated, off-the-shelf DME A

BETOS: D1F   Prosthetic/orthotic devices

C L0649 Lumbar-sacral orthosis (LSO), sagittal-coronal control, with rigid posterior frame/panel(s), posterior extends from sacrococcygeal junction to T-9 vertebra, lateral strength provided by rigid lateral frame/panels, produces intracavitary pressure to reduce load on intervertebral discs, includes straps, closures, may include padding, stays, shoulder straps, pendulous abdomen design, prefabricated, off-the-shelf   `DME` A

BETOS: D1F   Prosthetic/orthotic devices

C L0650 Lumbar-sacral orthosis (LSO), sagittal-coronal control, with rigid anterior and posterior frame/panel(s), posterior extends from sacrococcygeal junction to T-9 vertebra, lateral strength provided by rigid lateral frame/panel(s), produces intracavitary pressure to reduce load on intervertebral discs, includes straps, closures, may include padding, shoulder straps, pendulous abdomen design, prefabricated, off-the-shelf   `DME` A

BETOS: D1F   Prosthetic/orthotic devices

C L0651 Lumbar-sacral orthosis (LSO), sagittal-coronal control, rigid shell(s)/panel(s), posterior extends from sacrococcygeal junction to T-9 vertebra, anterior extends from symphysis pubis to xyphoid, produces intracavitary pressure to reduce load on the intervertebral discs, overall strength is provided by overlapping rigid material and stabilizing closures, includes straps, closures, may include soft interface, pendulous abdomen design, prefabricated, off-the-shelf   `DME` A

BETOS: D1F   Prosthetic/orthotic devices

CERVICAL-THORACIC-LUMBAR-SACRAL ORTHOTICS (L0700, L0710)

C L0700 Cervical-thoracic-lumbar-sacral orthosis (CTLSO), anterior-posterior-lateral control, molded to patient model, (Minerva type)   `DME` A

BETOS: D1F   Prosthetic/orthotic devices

C L0710 Cervical-thoracic-lumbar-sacral orthosis (CTLSO), anterior-posterior-lateral-control, molded to patient model, with interface material, (Minerva type)   `DME` A

BETOS: D1F   Prosthetic/orthotic devices

CERVICAL HALO PROCEDURES (L0810-L0861)

C L0810 Halo procedure, cervical halo incorporated into jacket vest   `DME` A

BETOS: D1F   Prosthetic/orthotic devices

C L0820 Halo procedure, cervical halo incorporated into plaster body jacket   `DME` A

BETOS: D1F   Prosthetic/orthotic devices

C L0830 Halo procedure, cervical halo incorporated into Milwaukee type orthosis   `DME` A

BETOS: D1F   Prosthetic/orthotic devices

C L0859 Addition to halo procedure, magnetic resonance image compatible systems, rings and pins, any material   `DME` A

BETOS: D1F   Prosthetic/orthotic devices

C L0861 Addition to halo procedure, replacement liner/interface material   `DME` A

BETOS: D1F   Prosthetic/orthotic devices

ACCESSORIES FOR SPINAL ORTHOTICS INCLUDING THORACIC-LUMBAR-SACRAL ORTHOSES (TLSO) (L0970-L0999)

C L0970 Thoracic-lumbar-sacral orthosis (TLSO), corset front   `DME` A

BETOS: D1F   Prosthetic/orthotic devices

C L0972 Lumbar-sacral orthsis (LSO), corset front   `DME` A

BETOS: D1F   Prosthetic/orthotic devices

C L0974 Thoracic-lumbar-sacral orthosis (TLSO), full corset   `DME` A

BETOS: D1F   Prosthetic/orthotic devices

C L0976 Lumbar-sacral orthosis (LSO), full corset   `DME` A

BETOS: D1F   Prosthetic/orthotic devices

C L0978 Axillary crutch extension   `DME` A

BETOS: D1F   Prosthetic/orthotic devices

C L0980 Peroneal straps, prefabricated, off-the-shelf, pair   `DME` A

BETOS: D1F   Prosthetic/orthotic devices

C L0982 Stocking supporter grips, prefabricated, off-the-shelf, set of four (4)   `DME` A

BETOS: D1F   Prosthetic/orthotic devices

C L0984 Protective body sock, prefabricated, off-the-shelf, each   `DME` A

BETOS: D1F   Prosthetic/orthotic devices

C L0999 Addition to spinal orthosis, not otherwise specified   A

BETOS: D1F   Prosthetic/orthotic devices

SCOLIOSIS ORTHOTIC DEVICES INCLUDING CERVICAL-THORACIC-LUMBAR-SACRAL ORTHOSES (CTLSO) (L1000-L1120)

C L1000 Cervical-thoracic-lumbar-sacral orthosis (CTLSO) (Milwaukee), inclusive of furnishing initial orthosis, including model   `DME` A

BETOS: D1F   Prosthetic/orthotic devices

C L1001 Cervical-thoracic-lumbar-sacral orthosis (CTLSO), immobilizer, infant size, prefabricated, includes fitting and adjustment   `DME` A

BETOS: D1F   Prosthetic/orthotic devices

C L1005 Tension based scoliosis orthosis and accessory pads, includes fitting and adjustment   `DME` A

BETOS: D1F   Prosthetic/orthotic devices

Coding Clinic: 2002, Q1

♂ Male only   ♀ Female only   **Ⓐ** Age   A2 - Z3 = ASC Payment indicator   A - Y = APC Status indicator

ASC = ASC-approved procedure   `DME` Paid under the DME fee schedule   `MIPS` MIPS code

C **L1010** Addition to cervical-thoracic-lumbar-sacral orthosis (CTLSO) or scoliosis orthosis, axilla sling **DME** A
BETOS: D1F Prosthetic/orthotic devices

C **L1020** Addition to cervical-thoracic-lumbar-sacral-orthosis (CTLSO), or scoliosis orthosis, kyphosis pad **DME** A
BETOS: D1F Prosthetic/orthotic devices

C **L1025** Addition to cervical-thoracic-lumbar-sacral-orthosis (CTLSO), or scoliosis orthosis, kyphosis pad, floating **DME** A
BETOS: D1F Prosthetic/orthotic devices

C **L1030** Addition to cervical-thoracic-lumbar-sacral-orthosis (CTLSO), or scoliosis orthosis, lumbar bolster pad **DME** A
BETOS: D1F Prosthetic/orthotic devices

C **L1040** Addition to cervical-thoracic-lumbar-sacral-orthosis (CTLSO), or scoliosis orthosis, lumbar or lumbar rib pad **DME** A
BETOS: D1F Prosthetic/orthotic devices

C **L1050** Addition to cervical-thoracic-lumbar-sacral-orthosis (CTLSO), or scoliosis orthosis, sternal pad **DME** A
BETOS: D1F Prosthetic/orthotic devices

C **L1060** Addition to cervical-thoracic-lumbar-sacral-orthosis (CTLSO), or scoliosis orthosis, thoracic pad **DME** A
BETOS: D1F Prosthetic/orthotic devices

C **L1070** Addition to cervical-thoracic-lumbar-sacral-orthosis (CTLSO), or scoliosis orthosis, trapezius sling **DME** A
BETOS: D1F Prosthetic/orthotic devices

C **L1080** Addition to cervical-thoracic-lumbar-sacral-orthosis (CTLSO), or scoliosis orthosis, outrigger **DME** A
BETOS: D1F Prosthetic/orthotic devices

C **L1085** Addition to cervical-thoracic-lumbar-sacral-orthosis (CTLSO), or scoliosis orthosis, outrigger, bilateral with vertical extensions **DME** A
BETOS: D1F Prosthetic/orthotic devices

C **L1090** Addition to cervical-thoracic-lumbar-sacral-orthosis (CTLSO), or scoliosis orthosis, lumbar sling **DME** A
BETOS: D1F Prosthetic/orthotic devices

C **L1100** Addition to cervical-thoracic-lumbar-sacral-orthosis (CTLSO), or scoliosis orthosis, ring flange, plastic or leather **DME** A
BETOS: D1F Prosthetic/orthotic devices

C **L1110** Addition to cervical-thoracic-lumbar-sacral-orthosis (CTLSO), or scoliosis orthosis, ring flange, plastic or leather, molded to patient model **DME** A
BETOS: D1F Prosthetic/orthotic devices

C **L1120** Addition to cervical-thoracic-lumbar-sacral-orthosis (CTLSO), scoliosis orthosis, cover for upright, each **DME** A
BETOS: D1F Prosthetic/orthotic devices

LOW-PROFILE ADDITIONS, THORACIC-LUMBAR-SACRAL ORTHOTICS (L1200-L1290), SEE ALSO THORACIC-LUMBAR-SACRAL (TLSO) ORTHOTICS (L0450-L0492)

C **L1200** Thoracic-lumbar-sacral-orthosis (TLSO), inclusive of furnishing initial orthosis only **DME** A
BETOS: D1F Prosthetic/orthotic devices

C **L1210** Addition to thoracic-lumbar-sacral orthosis (TLSO), (low profile), lateral thoracic extension **DME** A
BETOS: D1F Prosthetic/orthotic devices

C **L1220** Addition to thoracic-lumbar-sacral orthosis (TLSO), (low profile), anterior thoracic extension **DME** A
BETOS: D1F Prosthetic/orthotic devices

C **L1230** Addition to thoracic-lumbar-sacral orthosis (TLSO), (low profile), milwaukee type superstructure **DME** A
BETOS: D1F Prosthetic/orthotic devices

C **L1240** Addition to thoracic-lumbar-sacral orthosis (TLSO), (low profile), lumbar derotation pad **DME** A
BETOS: D1F Prosthetic/orthotic devices

C **L1250** Addition to thoracic-lumbar-sacral orthosis (TLSO), (low profile), anterior asis pad **DME** A
BETOS: D1F Prosthetic/orthotic devices

C **L1260** Addition to thoracic-lumbar-sacral orthosis (TLSO), (low profile), anterior thoracic derotation pad **DME** A
BETOS: D1F Prosthetic/orthotic devices

C **L1270** Addition to thoracic-lumbar-sacral orthosis (TLSO), (low profile), abdominal pad **DME** A
BETOS: D1F Prosthetic/orthotic devices

C **L1280** Addition to thoracic-lumbar-sacral orthosis (TLSO), (low profile), rib gusset (elastic), each **DME** A
BETOS: D1F Prosthetic/orthotic devices

C **L1290** Addition to thoracic-lumbar-sacral orthosis (TLSO), (low profile), lateral trochanteric pad **DME** A
BETOS: D1F Prosthetic/orthotic devices

OTHER SCOLIOSIS AND SPINAL ORTHOTICS AND PROCEDURES (L1300-L1499)

C **L1300** Other scoliosis procedure, body jacket molded to patient model **DME** A
BETOS: D1F Prosthetic/orthotic devices

C **L1310** Other scoliosis procedure, post-operative body jacket **DME** A
BETOS: D1F Prosthetic/orthotic devices

C **L1499** Spinal orthosis, not otherwise specified A
BETOS: D1F   Prosthetic/orthotic devices

HIP ORTHOTICS (L1600-L1690)

C **L1600** Hip orthosis (HO), abduction control of hip joints, flexible, Frejka type with cover, prefabricated item that has been trimmed, bent, molded, assembled, or otherwise customized to fit a specific patient by an individual with expertise   DME A
BETOS: D1F   Prosthetic/orthotic devices

C **L1610** Hip orthosis (HO), abduction control of hip joints, flexible, (Frejka cover only), prefabricated item that has been trimmed, bent, molded, assembled, or otherwise customized to fit a specific patient by an individual with expertise   DME A
BETOS: D1F   Prosthetic/orthotic devices

C **L1620** Hip orthosis (HO), abduction control of hip joints, flexible, (Pavlik harness), prefabricated item that has been trimmed, bent, molded, assembled, or otherwise customized to fit a specific patient by an individual with expertise   DME A
BETOS: D1F   Prosthetic/orthotic devices

C **L1630** Hip orthosis (HO), abduction control of hip joints, semi-flexible (Von Rosen type), custom fabricated   DME A
BETOS: D1F   Prosthetic/orthotic devices

C **L1640** Hip orthosis (HO), abduction control of hip joints, static, pelvic band or spreader bar, thigh cuffs, custom fabricated   DME A
BETOS: D1F   Prosthetic/orthotic devices

C **L1650** Hip orthosis (HO), abduction control of hip joints, static, adjustable, (Ilfeld type), prefabricated, includes fitting and adjustment   DME A
BETOS: D1F   Prosthetic/orthotic devices

C **L1652** Hip orthosis (HO), bilateral thigh cuffs with adjustable abductor spreader bar, adult size, prefabricated, includes fitting and adjustment, any type   DME A
BETOS: D1F   Prosthetic/orthotic devices

C **L1660** Hip orthosis (HO), abduction control of hip joints, static, plastic, prefabricated, includes fitting and adjustment   DME A
BETOS: D1F   Prosthetic/orthotic devices

C **L1680** Hip orthosis (HO), abduction control of hip joints, dynamic, pelvic control, adjustable hip motion control, thigh cuffs (Rancho hip action type), custom fabricated   DME A
BETOS: D1F   Prosthetic/orthotic devices

C **L1685** Hip orthosis (HO), abduction control of hip joint, postoperative hip abduction type, custom fabricated   DME A
BETOS: D1F   Prosthetic/orthotic devices

C **L1686** Hip orthosis (HO), abduction control of hip joint, postoperative hip abduction type, prefabricated, includes fitting and adjustment   DME A
BETOS: D1F   Prosthetic/orthotic devices

C **L1690** Combination, bilateral, lumbar-sacral-hip-femur orthosis (LSHFO) providing adduction and internal rotation control, prefabricated, includes fitting and adjustment   DME A
BETOS: D1F   Prosthetic/orthotic devices

LEGG PERTHES ORTHOTICS (L1700-L1755)

C **L1700** Legg Perthes orthosis, (Toronto type), custom fabricated   DME A
BETOS: D1F   Prosthetic/orthotic devices

C **L1710** Legg Perthes orthosis, (Newington type), custom fabricated   DME A
BETOS: D1F   Prosthetic/orthotic devices

C **L1720** Legg Perthes orthosis, trilateral, (Tachdjian type), custom fabricated   DME A
BETOS: D1F   Prosthetic/orthotic devices

C **L1730** Legg Perthes orthosis, (Scottish Rite type), custom fabricated   DME A
BETOS: D1F   Prosthetic/orthotic devices

C **L1755** Legg Perthes orthosis, (Patten bottom type), custom fabricated   DME A
BETOS: D1F   Prosthetic/orthotic devices

KNEE ORTHOTICS (L1810-L1860)

C **L1810** Knee orthosis (KO), elastic with joints, prefabricated item that has been trimmed, bent, molded, assembled, or otherwise customized to fit a specific patient by an individual with expertise   DME A
BETOS: D1F   Prosthetic/orthotic devices

C **L1812** Knee orthosis (KO), elastic with joints, prefabricated, off-the-shelf   DME A
BETOS: D1F   Prosthetic/orthotic devices

C **L1820** Knee orthosis (KO), elastic with condylar pads and joints, with or without patellar control, prefabricated, includes fitting and adjustment   DME A
BETOS: D1F   Prosthetic/orthotic devices

C **L1830** Knee orthosis (KO), immobilizer, canvas longitudinal, prefabricated, off-the-shelf   DME A
BETOS: D1F   Prosthetic/orthotic devices

♂ Male only   ♀ Female only   Ⓐ Age   A2 - Z3 = ASC Payment indicator   A - Y = APC Status indicator
ASC = ASC-approved procedure   DME Paid under the DME fee schedule   MIPS MIPS code

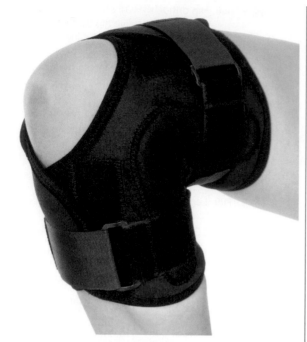

Knee orthosis

C L1831 Knee orthosis (KO), locking knee joint(s), positional orthosis, prefabricated, includes fitting and adjustment **DME** A

    BETOS: D1F   Prosthetic/orthotic devices

C L1832 Knee orthosis (KO), adjustable knee joints (unicentric or polycentric), positional orthosis, rigid support, prefabricated item that has been trimmed, bent, molded, assembled, or otherwise customized to fit a specific patient by an individual with expertise **DME** A

    BETOS: D1F   Prosthetic/orthotic devices

C L1833 Knee orthosis (KO), adjustable knee joints (unicentric or polycentric), positional orthosis, rigid support, prefabricated, off-the shelf **DME** A

    BETOS: D1F   Prosthetic/orthotic devices

C L1834 Knee orthosis (KO), without knee joint, rigid, custom fabricated **DME** A

    BETOS: D1F   Prosthetic/orthotic devices

C L1836 Knee orthosis (KO), rigid, without joint(s), includes soft interface material, prefabricated, off-the-shelf **DME** A

    BETOS: D1F   Prosthetic/orthotic devices

C L1840 Knee orthosis (KO), derotation, medial-lateral, anterior cruciate ligament, custom fabricated **DME** A

    BETOS: D1F   Prosthetic/orthotic devices

C L1843 Knee orthosis (KO), single upright, thigh and calf, with adjustable flexion and extension joint (unicentric or polycentric), medial-lateral and rotation control, with or without varus/valgus adjustment, prefabricated item that has been trimmed, bent, molded, assembled,

or otherwise customized to fit a specific patient by an individual with expertise **DME** A

    BETOS: D1F   Prosthetic/orthotic devices

C L1844 Knee orthosis (KO), single upright, thigh and calf, with adjustable flexion and extension joint (unicentric or polycentric), medial-lateral and rotation control, with or without varus/valgus adjustment, custom fabricated **DME** A

    BETOS: D1F   Prosthetic/orthotic devices

C L1845 Knee orthosis (KO), double upright, thigh and calf, with adjustable flexion and extension joint (unicentric or polycentric), medial-lateral and rotation control, with or without varus/valgus adjustment, prefabricated item that has been trimmed, bent, molded, assembled, or otherwise customized to fit a specific patient by an individual with expertise **DME** A

    BETOS: D1F   Prosthetic/orthotic devices

C L1846 Knee orthosis (KO), double upright, thigh and calf, with adjustable flexion and extension joint (unicentric or polycentric), medial-lateral and rotation control, with or without varus/valgus adjustment, custom fabricated **DME** A

    BETOS: D1F   Prosthetic/orthotic devices

C L1847 Knee orthosis (KO), double upright with adjustable joint, with inflatable air support chamber(s), prefabricated item that has been trimmed, bent, molded, assembled, or otherwise customized to fit a specific patient by an individual with expertise **DME** A

    BETOS: D1F   Prosthetic/orthotic devices

C L1848 Knee orthosis (KO), double upright with adjustable joint, with inflatable air support chamber(s), prefabricated, off-the-shelf **DME** A

    BETOS: D1F   Prosthetic/orthotic devices

C L1850 Knee orthosis (KO), swedish type, prefabricated, off-the-shelf **DME** A

    BETOS: D1F   Prosthetic/orthotic devices

C L1851 Knee orthosis (KO), single upright, thigh and calf, with adjustable flexion and extension joint (unicentric or polycentric), medial-lateral and rotation control, with or without varus/valgus adjustment, prefabricated, off-the-shelf **DME** A

    BETOS: D1F   Prosthetic/orthotic devices

C L1852 Knee orthosis (KO), double upright, thigh and calf, with adjustable flexion and extension joint (unicentric or polycentric), medial-lateral and rotation control, with or without varus/valgus adjustment, prefabricated, off-the-shelf **DME** A

    BETOS: D1F   Prosthetic/orthotic devices

C L1860 Knee orthosis (KO), modification of supracondylar prosthetic socket, custom fabricated (SK) **DME** A

    BETOS: D1F   Prosthetic/orthotic devices

▲ Revised code   ● New code   **C** Carrier judgment   **D** Special coverage instructions apply

I Not payable by Medicare   **M** Non-covered by Medicare   **S** Non-covered by Medicare statute   AHA Coding Clinic®

ANKLE-FOOT ORTHOTICS (L1900-L1990), SEE ALSO ANKLE-FOOT ORTHOTICS (L2106-L2116)

C L1900 Ankle-foot orthosis (AFO), spring wire, dorsiflexion assist calf band, custom fabricated DME A
BETOS: D1F Prosthetic/orthotic devices

C L1902 Ankle orthosis (AO), ankle gauntlet or similar, with or without joints, prefabricated, off-the-shelf DME A
BETOS: D1F Prosthetic/orthotic devices

C L1904 Ankle orthosis (AO), ankle gauntlet or similar, with or without joints (AO), custom fabricated DME A
BETOS: D1F Prosthetic/orthotic devices

C L1906 Ankle-foot orthosis (AFO), multiligamentous ankle support, prefabricated, off-the-shelf DME A
BETOS: D1F Prosthetic/orthotic devices

C L1907 Ankle orthosis (AO), supramalleolar with straps, with or without interface/pads, custom fabricated DME A
BETOS: D1F Prosthetic/orthotic devices

C L1910 Ankle-foot orthosis (AFO), posterior, single bar, clasp attachment to shoe counter, prefabricated, includes fitting and adjustment DME A
BETOS: D1F Prosthetic/orthotic devices

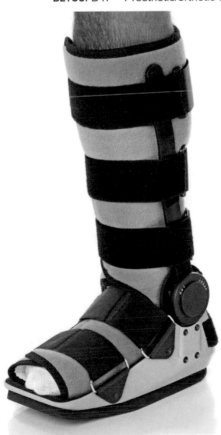
Ankle-foot orthosis

C L1920 Ankle-foot orthosis (AFO), single upright with static or adjustable stop (phelps or perlstein type), custom fabricated DME A
BETOS: D1F Prosthetic/orthotic devices

C L1930 Ankle-foot orthosis (AFO), plastic or other material, prefabricated, includes fitting and adjustment DME A
BETOS: D1F Prosthetic/orthotic devices

C L1932 Ankle-foot orthosis (AFO), rigid anterior tibial section, total carbon fiber or equal material, prefabricated, includes fitting and adjustment DME A
BETOS: D1F Prosthetic/orthotic devices

C L1940 Ankle-foot orthosis (AFO), plastic or other material, custom fabricated DME A
BETOS: D1F Prosthetic/orthotic devices

C L1945 Ankle-foot orthosis (AFO), plastic, rigid anterior tibial section (floor reaction), custom fabricated DME A
BETOS: D1F Prosthetic/orthotic devices

C L1950 Ankle-foot orthosis (AFO), spiral, (institute of rehabilitative medicine type), plastic, custom fabricated DME A
BETOS: D1F Prosthetic/orthotic devices

C L1951 Ankle-foot orthosis (AFO), spiral, (institute of rehabilitative medicine type), plastic or other material, prefabricated, includes fitting and adjustment DME A
BETOS: D1F Prosthetic/orthotic devices

C L1960 Ankle-foot orthosis (AFO), posterior solid ankle, plastic, custom fabricated DME A
BETOS: D1F Prosthetic/orthotic devices

C L1970 Ankle-foot orthosis (AFO), plastic with ankle joint, custom fabricated DME A
BETOS: D1F Prosthetic/orthotic devices

C L1971 Ankle-foot orthosis (AFO), plastic or other material with ankle joint, prefabricated, includes fitting and adjustment DME A
BETOS: D1F Prosthetic/orthotic devices

C L1980 Ankle-foot orthosis (AFO), single upright free plantar dorsiflexion, solid stirrup, calf band/cuff (single bar 'BK' orthosis), custom fabricated DME A
BETOS: D1F Prosthetic/orthotic devices

C L1990 Ankle-foot orthosis (AFO), double upright free plantar dorsiflexion, solid stirrup, calf band/cuff (double bar 'BK' orthosis), custom fabricated DME A
BETOS: D1F Prosthetic/orthotic devices

KNEE-ANKLE-FOOT ORTHOTICS (L2000-L2038), SEE ALSO KNEE-ANKLE-FOOT ORTHOTICS (L2126-L2136)

C L2000 Knee-ankle-foot orthosis (KAFO), single upright, free knee, free ankle, solid stirrup, thigh and calf bands/cuffs (single bar 'AK' orthosis), custom fabricated DME A

BETOS: D1F Prosthetic/orthotic devices

C L2005 Knee-ankle-foot orthosis (KAFO), any material, single or double upright, stance control, automatic lock and swing phase release, any type activation, includes ankle joint, any type, custom fabricated DME A

BETOS: D1F Prosthetic/orthotic devices

C L2010 Knee-ankle-foot orthosis (KAFO), single upright, free ankle, solid stirrup, thigh and calf bands/cuffs (single bar 'AK' orthosis), without knee joint, custom fabricated DME A

BETOS: D1F Prosthetic/orthotic devices

C L2020 Knee-ankle-foot orthosis (KAFO), double upright, free ankle, solid stirrup, thigh and calf bands/cuffs (double bar 'AK' orthosis), custom fabricated DME A

BETOS: D1F Prosthetic/orthotic devices

C L2030 Knee-ankle-foot orthosis (KAFO), double upright, free ankle, solid stirrup, thigh and calf bands/cuffs, (double bar 'AK' orthosis), without knee joint, custom fabricated DME A

BETOS: D1F Prosthetic/orthotic devices

C L2034 Knee-ankle-foot orthosis (KAFO), full plastic, single upright, with or without free motion knee, medial lateral rotation control, with or without free motion ankle, custom fabricated DME A

BETOS: D1F Prosthetic/orthotic devices

C L2035 Knee-ankle-foot orthosis (KAFO), full plastic, static (pediatric size), without free motion ankle, prefabricated, includes fitting and adjustment DME Ⓐ A

BETOS: D1F Prosthetic/orthotic devices

C L2036 Knee-ankle-foot orthosis (KAFO), full plastic, double upright, with or without free motion knee, with or without free motion ankle, custom fabricated DME A

BETOS: D1F Prosthetic/orthotic devices

C L2037 Knee-ankle-foot orthosis (KAFO), full plastic, single upright, with or without free motion knee, with or without free motion ankle, custom fabricated DME A

BETOS: D1F Prosthetic/orthotic devices

C L2038 Knee-ankle-foot orthosis (KAFO), full plastic, with or without free motion knee, multi-axis ankle, custom fabricated DME A

BETOS: D1F Prosthetic/orthotic devices

HIP-KNEE-ANKLE-FOOT ORTHOTICS (L2040-L2090)

C L2040 Hip-knee-ankle-foot orthosis (HKAFO), torsion control, bilateral rotation straps, pelvic band/belt, custom fabricated DME A

BETOS: D1F Prosthetic/orthotic devices

C L2050 Hip-knee-ankle-foot orthosis (HKAFO), torsion control, bilateral torsion cables, hip joint, pelvic band/belt, custom fabricated DME A

BETOS: D1F Prosthetic/orthotic devices

C L2060 Hip-knee-ankle-foot orthosis (HKAFO), torsion control, bilateral torsion cables, ball bearing hip joint, pelvic band/ belt, custom fabricated DME A

BETOS: D1F Prosthetic/orthotic devices

C L2070 Hip-knee-ankle-foot orthosis (HKAFO), torsion control, unilateral rotation straps, pelvic band/belt, custom fabricated DME A

BETOS: D1F Prosthetic/orthotic devices

C L2080 Hip-knee-ankle-foot orthosis (HKAFO), torsion control, unilateral torsion cable, hip joint, pelvic band/belt, custom fabricated DME A

BETOS: D1F Prosthetic/orthotic devices

C L2090 Hip-knee-ankle-foot orthosis (HKAFO), torsion control, unilateral torsion cable, ball bearing hip joint, pelvic band/ belt, custom fabricated DME A

BETOS: D1F Prosthetic/orthotic devices

ANKLE-FOOT ORTHOTICS (L2106-L2116), SEE ALSO ANKLE-FOOT ORTHOTICS (L1900-L1990)

C L2106 Ankle-foot orthosis (AFO), fracture orthosis, tibial fracture cast orthosis, thermoplastic type casting material, custom fabricated DME A

BETOS: D1F Prosthetic/orthotic devices

C L2108 Ankle-foot orthosis (AFO), fracture orthosis, tibial fracture cast orthosis, custom fabricated DME A

BETOS: D1F Prosthetic/orthotic devices

C L2112 Ankle-foot orthosis (AFO), fracture orthosis, tibial fracture orthosis, soft, prefabricated, includes fitting and adjustment DME A

BETOS: D1F Prosthetic/orthotic devices

C L2114 Ankle-foot orthosis (AFO), fracture orthosis, tibial fracture orthosis, semi-rigid, prefabricated, includes fitting and adjustment DME A

BETOS: D1F Prosthetic/orthotic devices

C L2116 Ankle-foot orthosis (AFO), fracture orthosis, tibial fracture orthosis, rigid, prefabricated, includes fitting and adjustment DME A

BETOS: D1F Prosthetic/orthotic devices

KNEE-ANKLE-FOOT ORTHOTICS (L2126-L2136), SEE ALSO
KNEE-ANKLE-FOOT ORTHOTICS (L2000-L2038)

C L2126 Knee-ankle-foot orthosis (KAFO), fracture orthosis, femoral fracture cast orthosis, thermoplastic type casting material, custom fabricated **DME** A
BETOS: D1F   Prosthetic/orthotic devices

C L2128 Knee-ankle-foot orthosis (KAFO), fracture orthosis, femoral fracture cast orthosis, custom fabricated **DME** A
BETOS: D1F   Prosthetic/orthotic devices

C L2132 Knee-ankle-foot orthosis (KAFO), fracture orthosis, femoral fracture cast orthosis, soft, prefabricated, includes fitting and adjustment **DME** A
BETOS: D1F   Prosthetic/orthotic devices

C L2134 Knee-ankle-foot orthosis (KAFO), fracture orthosis, femoral fracture cast orthosis, semi-rigid, prefabricated, includes fitting and adjustment **DME** A
BETOS: D1F   Prosthetic/orthotic devices

C L2136 Knee-ankle-foot orthosis (KAFO), fracture orthosis, femoral fracture cast orthosis, rigid, prefabricated, includes fitting and adjustment **DME** A
BETOS: D1F   Prosthetic/orthotic devices

ADDITIONS, LOWER EXTREMITY, FRACTURE ORTHOTICS
(L2180-L2192)

C L2180 Addition to lower extremity fracture orthosis, plastic shoe insert with ankle joints **DME** A
BETOS: D1F   Prosthetic/orthotic devices

C L2182 Addition to lower extremity fracture orthosis, drop lock knee joint **DME** A
BETOS: D1F   Prosthetic/orthotic devices

C L2184 Addition to lower extremity fracture orthosis, limited motion knee joint **DME** A
BETOS: D1F   Prosthetic/orthotic devices

C L2186 Addition to lower extremity fracture orthosis, adjustable motion knee joint, lerman type **DME** A
BETOS: D1F   Prosthetic/orthotic devices

C L2188 Addition to lower extremity fracture orthosis, quadrilateral brim **DME** A
BETOS: D1F   Prosthetic/orthotic devices

C L2190 Addition to lower extremity fracture orthosis, waist belt **DME** A
BETOS: D1F   Prosthetic/orthotic devices

C L2192 Addition to lower extremity fracture orthosis, hip joint, pelvic band, thigh flange, and pelvic belt **DME** A
BETOS: D1F   Prosthetic/orthotic devices

ADDITIONS, LOWER EXTREMITY ORTHOTICS (L2200-L2397)

C L2200 Addition to lower extremity, limited ankle motion, each joint **DME** A
BETOS: D1F   Prosthetic/orthotic devices

C L2210 Addition to lower extremity, dorsiflexion assist (plantar flexion resist), each joint **DME** A
BETOS: D1F   Prosthetic/orthotic devices

C L2220 Addition to lower extremity, dorsiflexion and plantar flexion assist/resist, each joint **DME** A
BETOS: D1F   Prosthetic/orthotic devices

C L2230 Addition to lower extremity, split flat caliper stirrups and plate attachment **DME** A
BETOS: D1F   Prosthetic/orthotic devices

C L2232 Addition to lower extremity orthosis, rocker bottom for total contact Ankle-foot orthosis (AFO), for custom fabricated orthosis only **DME** A
BETOS: D1F   Prosthetic/orthotic devices

C L2240 Addition to lower extremity, round caliper and plate attachment **DME** A
BETOS: D1F   Prosthetic/orthotic devices

C L2250 Addition to lower extremity, foot plate, molded to patient model, stirrup attachment **DME** A
BETOS: D1F   Prosthetic/orthotic devices

C L2260 Addition to lower extremity, reinforced solid stirrup (Scott-Craig type) **DME** A
BETOS: D1F   Prosthetic/orthotic devices

C L2265 Addition to lower extremity, long tongue stirrup **DME** A
BETOS: D1F   Prosthetic/orthotic devices

C L2270 Addition to lower extremity, varus/valgus correction ('T') strap, padded/lined or malleolus pad **DME** A
BETOS: D1F   Prosthetic/orthotic devices

C L2275 Addition to lower extremity, varus/valgus correction, plastic modification, padded/lined **DME** A
BETOS: D1F   Prosthetic/orthotic devices

C L2280 Addition to lower extremity, molded inner boot **DME** A
BETOS: D1F   Prosthetic/orthotic devices

C L2300 Addition to lower extremity, abduction bar (bilateral hip involvement), jointed, adjustable **DME** A
BETOS: D1F   Prosthetic/orthotic devices

C L2310 Addition to lower extremity, abduction bar-straight **DME** A
BETOS: D1F   Prosthetic/orthotic devices

C L2320 Addition to lower extremity, non-molded lacer, for custom fabricated orthosis only **DME** A
BETOS: D1F   Prosthetic/orthotic devices

♂ Male only   ♀ Female only   **A** Age   A2 - Z3 = ASC Payment indicator   A - Y = APC Status indicator
ASC = ASC-approved procedure   **DME** Paid under the DME fee schedule   **MIPS** MIPS code

C L2330 Addition to lower extremity, lacer molded to patient model, for custom fabricated orthosis only **DME** A
BETOS: D1F   Prosthetic/orthotic devices

C L2335 Addition to lower extremity, anterior swing band **DME** A
BETOS: D1F   Prosthetic/orthotic devices

C L2340 Addition to lower extremity, pre-tibial shell, molded to patient model **DME** A
BETOS: D1F   Prosthetic/orthotic devices

C L2350 Addition to lower extremity, prosthetic type, (BK) socket, molded to patient model, (used for 'PTB' 'AFO' orthoses) **DME** A
BETOS: D1F   Prosthetic/orthotic devices

C L2360 Addition to lower extremity, extended steel shank **DME** A
BETOS: D1F   Prosthetic/orthotic devices

C L2370 Addition to lower extremity, Patten bottom **DME** A
BETOS: D1F   Prosthetic/orthotic devices

C L2375 Addition to lower extremity, torsion control, ankle joint and half solid stirrup **DME** A
BETOS: D1F   Prosthetic/orthotic devices

C L2380 Addition to lower extremity, torsion control, straight knee joint, each joint **DME** A
BETOS: D1F   Prosthetic/orthotic devices

C L2385 Addition to lower extremity, straight knee joint, heavy duty, each joint **DME** A
BETOS: D1F   Prosthetic/orthotic devices

C L2387 Addition to lower extremity, polycentric knee joint, for custom fabricated Knee-ankle-foot orthosis (KAFO), each joint **DME** A
BETOS: D1F   Prosthetic/orthotic devices

C L2390 Addition to lower extremity, offset knee joint, each joint **DME** A
BETOS: D1F   Prosthetic/orthotic devices

C L2395 Addition to lower extremity, offset knee joint, heavy duty, each joint **DME** A
BETOS: D1F   Prosthetic/orthotic devices

C L2397 Addition to lower extremity orthosis, suspension sleeve **DME** A
BETOS: D1F   Prosthetic/orthotic devices

ORTHOTIC ADDITIONS TO KNEE JOINTS (L2405-L2492)

C L2405 Addition to knee joint, drop lock, each **DME** A
BETOS: D1F   Prosthetic/orthotic devices

C L2415 Addition to knee lock with integrated release mechanism (bail, cable, or equal), any material, each joint **DME** A
BETOS: D1F   Prosthetic/orthotic devices

C L2425 Addition to knee joint, disc or dial lock for adjustable knee flexion, each joint **DME** A
BETOS: D1F   Prosthetic/orthotic devices

C L2430 Addition to knee joint, ratchet lock for active and progressive knee extension, each joint **DME** A
BETOS: D1F   Prosthetic/orthotic devices

C L2492 Addition to knee joint, lift loop for drop lock ring **DME** A
BETOS: D1F   Prosthetic/orthotic devices

ADDITIONS, WEIGHT-BEARING, LOWER EXTREMITIES (L2500-L2550)

C L2500 Addition to lower extremity, thigh/weight bearing, gluteal/ ischial weight bearing, ring **DME** A
BETOS: D1F   Prosthetic/orthotic devices

C L2510 Addition to lower extremity, thigh/weight bearing, quadri- lateral brim, molded to patient model **DME** A
BETOS: D1F   Prosthetic/orthotic devices

C L2520 Addition to lower extremity, thigh/weight bearing, quadri- lateral brim, custom fitted **DME** A
BETOS: D1F   Prosthetic/orthotic devices

C L2525 Addition to lower extremity, thigh/weight bearing, ischial containment/narrow M-L brim molded to patient model **DME** A
BETOS: D1F   Prosthetic/orthotic devices

C L2526 Addition to lower extremity, thigh/weight bearing, ischial containment/narrow M-L brim, custom fitted **DME** A
BETOS: D1F   Prosthetic/orthotic devices

C L2530 Addition to lower extremity, thigh-weight bearing, lacer, non-molded **DME** A
BETOS: D1F   Prosthetic/orthotic devices

C L2540 Addition to lower extremity, thigh/weight bearing, lacer, molded to patient model **DME** A
BETOS: D1F   Prosthetic/orthotic devices

C L2550 Addition to lower extremity, thigh/weight bearing, high roll cuff **DME** A
BETOS: D1F   Prosthetic/orthotic devices

ADDITIONS, PELVIC AND/OR THORACIC CONTROL, LOWER EXTREMITIES (L2570-L2680)

C L2570 Addition to lower extremity, pelvic control, hip joint, Clevis-type two position joint, each **DME** A
BETOS: D1F   Prosthetic/orthotic devices

C L2580 Addition to lower extremity, pelvic control, pelvic sling **DME** A
BETOS: D1F   Prosthetic/orthotic devices

C L2600 Addition to lower extremity, pelvic control, hip joint, Clevis-type, or thrust bearing, free, each **DME** A
BETOS: D1F   Prosthetic/orthotic devices

C **L2610** Addition to lower extremity, pelvic control, hip joint, Clevis-type or thrust bearing, lock, each **DME** A

BETOS: D1F   Prosthetic/orthotic devices

C **L2620** Addition to lower extremity, pelvic control, hip joint, heavy duty, each **DME** A

BETOS: D1F   Prosthetic/orthotic devices

C **L2622** Addition to lower extremity, pelvic control, hip joint, adjustable flexion, each **DME** A

BETOS: D1F   Prosthetic/orthotic devices

C **L2624** Addition to lower extremity, pelvic control, hip joint, adjustable flexion, extension, abduction control, each **DME** A

BETOS: D1F   Prosthetic/orthotic devices

C **L2627** Addition to lower extremity, pelvic control, plastic, molded to patient model, reciprocating hip joint and cables **DME** A

BETOS: D1F   Prosthetic/orthotic devices

C **L2628** Addition to lower extremity, pelvic control, metal frame, reciprocating hip joint and cables **DME** A

BETOS: D1F   Prosthetic/orthotic devices

C **L2630** Addition to lower extremity, pelvic control, band and belt, unilateral **DME** A

BETOS: D1F   Prosthetic/orthotic devices

C **L2640** Addition to lower extremity, pelvic control, band and belt, bilateral **DME** A

BETOS: D1F   Prosthetic/orthotic devices

C **L2650** Addition to lower extremity, pelvic and thoracic control, gluteal pad, each **DME** A

BETOS: D1F   Prosthetic/orthotic devices

C **L2660** Addition to lower extremity, thoracic control, thoracic band **DME** A

BETOS: D1F   Prosthetic/orthotic devices

C **L2670** Addition to lower extremity, thoracic control, paraspinal uprights **DME** A

BETOS: D1F   Prosthetic/orthotic devices

C **L2680** Addition to lower extremity, thoracic control, lateral support uprights **DME** A

BETOS: D1F   Prosthetic/orthotic devices

OTHER LOWER EXTREMITY ADDITIONS (L2750-L2999)

C **L2750** Addition to lower extremity orthosis, plating chrome or nickel, per bar **DME** A

BETOS: D1F   Prosthetic/orthotic devices

C **L2755** Addition to lower extremity orthosis, high strength, lightweight material, all hybrid lamination/prepreg composite, per segment, for custom fabricated orthosis only **DME** A

BETOS: D1F   Prosthetic/orthotic devices

C **L2760** Addition to lower extremity orthosis, extension, per extension, per bar (for lineal adjustment for growth) **DME** A

BETOS: D1F   Prosthetic/orthotic devices

C **L2768** Orthotic side bar disconnect device, per bar **DME** A

BETOS: D1F   Prosthetic/orthotic devices

Coding Clinic: 2002, Q1

C **L2780** Addition to lower extremity orthosis, non-corrosive finish, per bar **DME** A

BETOS: D1F   Prosthetic/orthotic devices

C **L2785** Addition to lower extremity orthosis, drop lock retainer, each **DME** A

BETOS: D1F   Prosthetic/orthotic devices

C **L2795** Addition to lower extremity orthosis, knee control, full kneecap **DME** A

BETOS: D1F   Prosthetic/orthotic devices

C **L2800** Addition to lower extremity orthosis, knee control, knee cap, medial or lateral pull, for use with custom fabricated orthosis only **DME** A

BETOS: D1F   Prosthetic/orthotic devices

C **L2810** Addition to lower extremity orthosis, knee control, condylar pad **DME** A

BETOS: D1F   Prosthetic/orthotic devices

C **L2820** Addition to lower extremity orthosis, soft interface for molded plastic, below knee section **DME** A

BETOS: D1F   Prosthetic/orthotic devices

C **L2830** Addition to lower extremity orthosis, soft interface for molded plastic, above knee section **DME** A

BETOS: D1F   Prosthetic/orthotic devices

C **L2840** Addition to lower extremity orthosis, tibial length sock, fracture or equal, each **DME** A

BETOS: D1F   Prosthetic/orthotic devices

C **L2850** Addition to lower extremity orthosis, femoral length sock, fracture or equal, each **DME** A

BETOS: D1F   Prosthetic/orthotic devices

I **L2861** Addition to lower extremity joint, knee or ankle, concentric adjustable torsion style mechanism for custom fabricated orthotics only, each E1

BETOS: D1F   Prosthetic/orthotic devices

Service not separately priced by Part B

C **L2999** Lower extremity orthosis, not otherwise specified A

BETOS: D1F   Prosthetic/orthotic devices

FOOT INSERTS, REMOVABLE (L3000-L3031)

D **L3000** Foot, insert, removable, molded to patient model, 'UCB' type, Berkeley Shell, each **DME** A

BETOS: D1F   Prosthetic/orthotic devices

Service not separately priced by Part B

Pub: 100-2, Chap. 15, 290

♂ Male only   ♀ Female only   **A** Age   A2 - Z3 = ASC Payment indicator   A - Y = APC Status indicator

ASC = ASC-approved procedure   **DME** Paid under the DME fee schedule   **MIPS** MIPS code

D **L3001** Foot, insert, removable, molded to patient model, Spenco, each **DME** A
BETOS: D1F Prosthetic/orthotic devices
Service not separately priced by Part B
Pub: 100-2, Chap. 15, 290

D **L3002** Foot, insert, removable, molded to patient model, Plastazote or equal, each **DME** A
BETOS: D1F Prosthetic/orthotic devices
Service not separately priced by Part B
Pub: 100-2, Chap. 15, 290

D **L3003** Foot, insert, removable, molded to patient model, silicone gel, each **DME** A
BETOS: D1F Prosthetic/orthotic devices
Service not separately priced by Part B
Pub: 100-2, Chap. 15, 290

D **L3010** Foot, insert, removable, molded to patient model, longitudinal arch support, each **DME** A
BETOS: D1F Prosthetic/orthotic devices
Service not separately priced by Part B
Pub: 100-2, Chap. 15, 290

D **L3020** Foot, insert, removable, molded to patient model, longitudinal/ metatarsal support, each **DME** A
BETOS: D1F Prosthetic/orthotic devices
Service not separately priced by Part B
Pub: 100-2, Chap. 15, 290

D **L3030** Foot, insert, removable, formed to patient foot, each **DME** A
BETOS: D1F Prosthetic/orthotic devices
Service not separately priced by Part B
Pub: 100-2, Chap. 15, 290

C **L3031** Foot, insert/plate, removable, addition to lower extremity orthosis, high strength, lightweight material, all hybrid lamination/ prepreg composite, each **DME** A
BETOS: D1F Prosthetic/orthotic devices
Service not separately priced by Part B

FOOT ARCH SUPPORTS (L3040-L3090)

D **L3040** Foot, arch support, removable, premolded, longitudinal, each **DME** A
BETOS: D1F Prosthetic/orthotic devices
Service not separately priced by Part B
Pub: 100-2, Chap. 15, 290

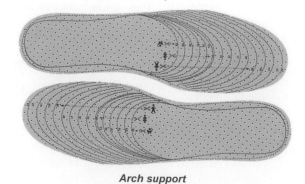

Arch support

D **L3050** Foot, arch support, removable, premolded, metatarsal, each **DME** A
BETOS: D1F Prosthetic/orthotic devices
Service not separately priced by Part B
Pub: 100-2, Chap. 15, 290

D **L3060** Foot, arch support, removable, premolded, longitudinal/ metatarsal, each **DME** A
BETOS: D1F Prosthetic/orthotic devices
Service not separately priced by Part B
Pub: 100-2, Chap. 15, 290

D **L3070** Foot, plastic, silicone or equal, heel stabilizer, prefabricated, off-the-shelf, each **DME** A
BETOS: D1F Prosthetic/orthotic devices
Service not separately priced by Part B
Pub: 100-2, Chap. 15, 290

D **L3080** Foot, arch support, non-removable attached to shoe, metatarsal, each **DME** A
BETOS: D1F Prosthetic/orthotic devices
Service not separately priced by Part B
Pub: 100-2, Chap. 15, 290

D **L3090** Foot, arch support, non-removable attached to shoe, longitudinal/metatarsal, each **DME** A
BETOS: D1F Prosthetic/orthotic devices
Service not separately priced by Part B
Pub: 100-2, Chap. 15, 290

REPOSITIONING FOOT ORTHOTICS (L3100-L3170)

D **L3100** Hallus-valgus night dynamic splint, prefabricated, off-the-shelf **DME** A
BETOS: D1F Prosthetic/orthotic devices
Service not separately priced by Part B
Pub: 100-2, Chap. 15, 290

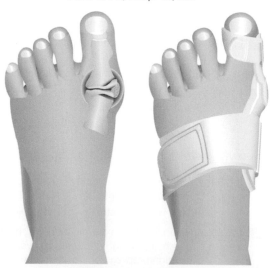

Hallux valgus splint

D **L3140** Foot, abduction rotation bar, including shoes **DME** A
BETOS: D1F Prosthetic/orthotic devices
Service not separately priced by Part B
Pub: 100-2, Chap. 15, 290

▲ Revised code   ● New code   **C** Carrier judgment   **D** Special coverage instructions apply
I Not payable by Medicare   **M** Non-covered by Medicare   **S** Non-covered by Medicare statute   AHA Coding Clinic®

D **L3150** Foot, abduction rotation bar, without shoes `DME` A
BETOS: D1F   Prosthetic/orthotic devices
Service not separately priced by Part B
Pub: 100-2, Chap. 15, 290

C **L3160** Foot, adjustable shoe-styled positioning device A
BETOS: D1F   Prosthetic/orthotic devices
Service not separately priced by Part B

D **L3170** Foot, plastic, silicone or equal, heel stabilizer, prafabricated, off-the-shelf, each `DME` A
BETOS: D1F   Prosthetic/orthotic devices
Service not separately priced by Part B
Pub: 100-2, Chap. 15, 290

ORTHOPEDIC SHOES (L3201-L3207)

D **L3201** Orthopedic shoe, Oxford with supinator or pronator, infant Ⓐ A
BETOS: D1F   Prosthetic/orthotic devices
Service not separately priced by Part B
Pub: 100-2, Chap. 15, 290

D **L3202** Orthopedic shoe, Oxford with supinator or pronator, child Ⓐ A
BETOS: D1F   Prosthetic/orthotic devices
Service not separately priced by Part B
Pub: 100-2, Chap. 15, 290

D **L3203** Orthopedic shoe, Oxford with supinator or pronator, junior Ⓐ A
BETOS: D1F   Prosthetic/orthotic devices
Service not separately priced by Part B
Pub: 100-2, Chap. 15, 290

D **L3204** Orthopedic shoe, hightop with supinator or pronator, infant Ⓐ A
BETOS: D1F   Prosthetic/orthotic devices
Service not separately priced by Part B
Pub: 100-2, Chap. 15, 290

D **L3206** Orthopedic shoe, hightop with supinator or pronator, child Ⓐ A
BETOS: D1F   Prosthetic/orthotic devices
Service not separately priced by Part B
Pub: 100-2, Chap. 15, 290

D **L3207** Orthopedic shoe, hightop with supinator or pronator, junior Ⓐ A
BETOS: D1F   Prosthetic/orthotic devices
Service not separately priced by Part B
Pub: 100-2, Chap. 15, 290

SURGICAL BOOTS (L3208-L3211)

D **L3208** Surgical boot, each, infant Ⓐ A
BETOS: D1F   Prosthetic/orthotic devices
Service not separately priced by Part B

D **L3209** Surgical boot, each, child Ⓐ A
BETOS: D1F   Prosthetic/orthotic devices
Service not separately priced by Part B

D **L3211** Surgical boot, each, junior Ⓐ A
BETOS: D1F   Prosthetic/orthotic devices
Service not separately priced by Part B

BENESCH BOOTS (L3212-L3214)

D **L3212** Benesch boot, pair, infant Ⓐ A
BETOS: D1F   Prosthetic/orthotic devices
Service not separately priced by Part B

D **L3213** Benesch boot, pair, child Ⓐ A
BETOS: D1F   Prosthetic/orthotic devices
Service not separately priced by Part B

D **L3214** Benesch boot, pair, junior Ⓐ A
BETOS: D1F   Prosthetic/orthotic devices
Service not separately priced by Part B

OTHER ORTHOPEDIC FOOTWEAR (L3215-L3265)

S **L3215** Orthopedic footwear, ladies shoe, Oxford, each ♀ E1
BETOS: D1F   Prosthetic/orthotic devices
Service not separately priced by Part B
Statute: 1862A8

S **L3216** Orthopedic footwear, ladies shoe, depth inlay, each ♀ E1
BETOS: D1F   Prosthetic/orthotic devices
Service not separately priced by Part B
Statute: 1862A8

S **L3217** Orthopedic footwear, ladies shoe, hightop, depth inlay, each ♀ E1
BETOS: D1F   Prosthetic/orthotic devices
Service not separately priced by Part B
Statute: 1862A8

S **L3219** Orthopedic footwear, mens shoe, Oxford, each ♂ E1
BETOS: D1F   Prosthetic/orthotic devices
Service not separately priced by Part B
Statute: 1862A8

S **L3221** Orthopedic footwear, mens shoe, depth inlay, each ♂ E1
BETOS: D1F   Prosthetic/orthotic devices
Service not separately priced by Part B
Statute: 1862A8

S **L3222** Orthopedic footwear, mens shoe, hightop, depth inlay, each ♂ E1
BETOS: D1F   Prosthetic/orthotic devices
Service not separately priced by Part B
Statute: 1862A8

D **L3224** Orthopedic footwear, woman's shoe, Oxford, used as an integral part of a brace (orthosis) ♀ `DME` A
BETOS: D1F   Prosthetic/orthotic devices
Pub: 100-2, Chap. 15, 290

D **L3225** Orthopedic footwear, man's shoe, Oxford, used as an integral part of a brace (orthosis) ♂ `DME` A

♂ Male only   ♀ Female only   Ⓐ Age   A2 - Z3 = ASC Payment indicator   A - Y = APC Status indicator
ASC = ASC-approved procedure   `DME` Paid under the DME fee schedule   `MIPS` MIPS code

CPT® is a registered trademark of the American Medical Association. All rights reserved.

315

ORTHOTIC PROCEDURES AND SERVICES (L0112-L4631)

L3230 - L3410

BETOS: D1F   Prosthetic/orthotic devices
Pub: 100-2, Chap. 15, 290

D **L3230** Orthopedic footwear, custom shoe, depth inlay, each   A

BETOS: D1F   Prosthetic/orthotic devices
Service not separately priced by Part B
Pub: 100-2, Chap. 15, 290

D **L3250** Orthopedic footwear, custom molded shoe, removable inner mold, prosthetic shoe, each   A

BETOS: D1F   Prosthetic/orthotic devices
Service not separately priced by Part B
Pub: 100-2, Chap. 15, 290

D **L3251** Foot, shoe molded to patient model, silicone shoe, each   A

BETOS: D1F   Prosthetic/orthotic devices
Service not separately priced by Part B
Pub: 100-2, Chap. 15, 290

D **L3252** Foot, shoe molded to patient model, Plastazote (or similar), custom fabricated, each   A

BETOS: D1F   Prosthetic/orthotic devices
Service not separately priced by Part B
Pub: 100-2, Chap. 15, 290

D **L3253** Foot, molded shoe Plastazote (or similar) custom fitted, each   A

BETOS: D1F   Prosthetic/orthotic devices
Service not separately priced by Part B
Pub: 100-2, Chap. 15, 290

D **L3254** Non-standard size or width   A

BETOS: D1F   Prosthetic/orthotic devices
Service not separately priced by Part B
Pub: 100-2, Chap. 15, 290

D **L3255** Non-standard size or length   A

BETOS: D1F   Prosthetic/orthotic devices
Service not separately priced by Part B
Pub: 100-2, Chap. 15, 290

D **L3257** Orthopedic footwear, additional charge for split size   A

BETOS: D1F   Prosthetic/orthotic devices
Service not separately priced by Part B
Pub: 100-2, Chap. 15, 290

D **L3260** Surgical boot/shoe, each   E1

BETOS: D1F   Prosthetic/orthotic devices
Service not separately priced by Part B

C **L3265** Plastazote sandal, each   A

BETOS: D1F   Prosthetic/orthotic devices
Service not separately priced by Part B

SHOE LIFTS (L3300-L3334)

D **L3300** Lift, elevation, heel, tapered to metatarsals, per inch   DME A

BETOS: D1F   Prosthetic/orthotic devices
Service not separately priced by Part B
Pub: 100-2, Chap. 15, 290

D **L3310** Lift, elevation, heel and sole, neoprene, per inch   DME A

BETOS: D1F   Prosthetic/orthotic devices
Service not separately priced by Part B
Pub: 100-2, Chap. 15, 290

D **L3320** Lift, elevation, heel and sole, cork, per inch A

BETOS: D1F   Prosthetic/orthotic devices
Service not separately priced by Part B
Pub: 100-2, Chap. 15, 290

D **L3330** Lift, elevation, metal extension (skate) DME A

BETOS: D1F   Prosthetic/orthotic devices
Service not separately priced by Part B
Pub: 100-2, Chap. 15, 290

D **L3332** Lift, elevation, inside shoe, tapered, up to one-half inch   DME A

BETOS: D1F   Prosthetic/orthotic devices
Service not separately priced by Part B
Pub: 100-2, Chap. 15, 290

D **L3334** Lift, elevation, heel, per inch   DME A

BETOS: D1F   Prosthetic/orthotic devices
Service not separately priced by Part B
Pub: 100-2, Chap. 15, 290

SHOE WEDGES (L3340-L3420)

D **L3340** Heel wedge, SACH   DME A

BETOS: D1F   Prosthetic/orthotic devices
Service not separately priced by Part B
Pub: 100-2, Chap. 15, 290

D **L3350** Heel wedge   DME A

BETOS: D1F   Prosthetic/orthotic devices
Service not separately priced by Part B
Pub: 100-2, Chap. 15, 290

D **L3360** Sole wedge, outside sole   DME A

BETOS: D1F   Prosthetic/orthotic devices
Service not separately priced by Part B
Pub: 100-2, Chap. 15, 290

D **L3370** Sole wedge, between sole   DME A

BETOS: D1F   Prosthetic/orthotic devices
Service not separately priced by Part B
Pub: 100-2, Chap. 15, 290

D **L3380** Clubfoot wedge   DME A

BETOS: D1F   Prosthetic/orthotic devices
Service not separately priced by Part B
Pub: 100-2, Chap. 15, 290

D **L3390** Outflare wedge   DME A

BETOS: D1F   Prosthetic/orthotic devices
Service not separately priced by Part B
Pub: 100-2, Chap. 15, 290

D **L3400** Metatarsal bar wedge, rocker   DME A

BETOS: D1F   Prosthetic/orthotic devices
Service not separately priced by Part B
Pub: 100-2, Chap. 15, 290

D **L3410** Metatarsal bar wedge, between sole   DME A

BETOS: D1F   Prosthetic/orthotic devices

▲ Revised code   ● New code   **C** Carrier judgment   **D** Special coverage instructions apply
I Not payable by Medicare   **M** Non-covered by Medicare   **S** Non-covered by Medicare statute   AHA Coding Clinic®

Service not separately priced by Part B
Pub: 100-2, Chap. 15, 290

D L3420 Full sole and heel wedge, between sole **DME** A
BETOS: D1F   Prosthetic/orthotic devices
Service not separately priced by Part B
Pub: 100-2, Chap. 15, 290

SHOE HEELS (L3430-L3485)

D L3430 Heel, counter, plastic reinforced **DME** A
BETOS: D1F   Prosthetic/orthotic devices
Service not separately priced by Part B
Pub: 100-2, Chap. 15, 290

D L3440 Heel, counter, leather reinforced **DME** A
BETOS: D1F   Prosthetic/orthotic devices
Service not separately priced by Part B
Pub: 100-2, Chap. 15, 290

D L3450 Heel, SACH cushion type **DME** A
BETOS: D1F   Prosthetic/orthotic devices
Service not separately priced by Part B
Pub: 100-2, Chap. 15, 290

D L3455 Heel, new leather, standard **DME** A
BETOS: D1F   Prosthetic/orthotic devices
Service not separately priced by Part B
Pub: 100-2, Chap. 15, 290

D L3460 Heel, new rubber, standard **DME** A
BETOS: D1F   Prosthetic/orthotic devices
Service not separately priced by Part B
Pub: 100-2, Chap. 15, 290

D L3465 Heel, Thomas with wedge **DME** A
BETOS: D1F   Prosthetic/orthotic devices
Service not separately priced by Part B
Pub: 100-2, Chap. 15, 290

D L3470 Heel, Thomas extended to ball **DME** A
BETOS: D1F   Prosthetic/orthotic devices
Service not separately priced by Part B
Pub: 100-2, Chap. 15, 290

D L3480 Heel, pad and depression for spur **DME** A
BETOS: D1F   Prosthetic/orthotic devices
Service not separately priced by Part B
Pub: 100-2, Chap. 15, 290

D L3485 Heel, pad, removable for spur A
BETOS: D1F   Prosthetic/orthotic devices
Service not separately priced by Part B
Pub: 100-2, Chap. 15, 290

OTHER ORTHOPEDIC SHOE ADDITIONS (L3500-L3595)

D L3500 Orthopedic shoe addition, insole, leather **DME** A
BETOS: D1F   Prosthetic/orthotic devices
Service not separately priced by Part B
Pub: 100-2, Chap. 15, 290

D L3510 Orthopedic shoe addition, insole, rubber **DME** A
BETOS: D1F   Prosthetic/orthotic devices

Service not separately priced by Part B
Pub: 100-2, Chap. 15, 290

D L3520 Orthopedic shoe addition, insole, felt covered with leather **DME** A
BETOS: D1F   Prosthetic/orthotic devices
Service not separately priced by Part B
Pub: 100-2, Chap. 15, 290

D L3530 Orthopedic shoe addition, sole, half **DME** A
BETOS: D1F   Prosthetic/orthotic devices
Service not separately priced by Part B
Pub: 100-2, Chap. 15, 290

D L3540 Orthopedic shoe addition, sole, full **DME** A
BETOS: D1F   Prosthetic/orthotic devices
Service not separately priced by Part B
Pub: 100-2, Chap. 15, 290

D L3550 Orthopedic shoe addition, toe tap standard **DME** A
BETOS: D1F   Prosthetic/orthotic devices
Service not separately priced by Part B
Pub: 100-2, Chap. 15, 290

D L3560 Orthopedic shoe addition, toe tap, horseshoe **DME** A
BETOS: D1F   Prosthetic/orthotic devices
Service not separately priced by Part B
Pub: 100-2, Chap. 15, 290

D L3570 Orthopedic shoe addition, special extension to instep (leather with eyelets) **DME** A
BETOS: D1F   Prosthetic/orthotic devices
Service not separately priced by Part B
Pub: 100-2, Chap. 15, 290

D L3580 Orthopedic shoe addition, convert instep to velcro closure **DME** A
BETOS: D1F   Prosthetic/orthotic devices
Service not separately priced by Part B
Pub: 100-2, Chap. 15, 290

D L3590 Orthopedic shoe addition, convert firm shoe counter to soft counter **DME** A
BETOS: D1F   Prosthetic/orthotic devices
Service not separately priced by Part B
Pub: 100-2, Chap. 15, 290

D L3595 Orthopedic shoe addition, March bar **DME** A
BETOS: D1F   Prosthetic/orthotic devices
Service not separately priced by Part B
Pub: 100-2, Chap. 15, 290

ORTHOSIS TRANSFERS (L3600-L3649)

D L3600 Transfer of an orthosis from one shoe to another, caliper plate, existing **DME** A
BETOS: D1F   Prosthetic/orthotic devices
Service not separately priced by Part B
Pub: 100-2, Chap. 15, 290

D L3610 Transfer of an orthosis from one shoe to another, caliper plate, new **DME** A
BETOS: D1F   Prosthetic/orthotic devices

Service not separately priced by Part B
Pub: 100-2, Chap. 15, 290

D L3620 Transfer of an orthosis from one shoe to another, solid stirrup, existing DME A
BETOS: D1F   Prosthetic/orthotic devices
Service not separately priced by Part B
Pub: 100-2, Chap. 15, 290

D L3630 Transfer of an orthosis from one shoe to another, solid stirrup, new DME A
BETOS: D1F   Prosthetic/orthotic devices
Service not separately priced by Part B
Pub: 100-2, Chap. 15, 290

D L3640 Transfer of an orthosis from one shoe to another, dennis browne splint (Riveton), both shoes DME A
BETOS: D1F   Prosthetic/orthotic devices
Service not separately priced by Part B
Pub: 100-2, Chap. 15, 290

D L3649 Orthopedic shoe, modification, addition or transfer, not otherwise specified A
BETOS: D1F   Prosthetic/orthotic devices
Service not separately priced by Part B
Pub: 100-2, Chap. 15, 290

SHOULDER ORTHOTICS (L3650-L3678)

C L3650 Shoulder orthosis (SO), figure of eight design abduction restrainer, prefabricated, off-the-shelf DME A
BETOS: D1F   Prosthetic/orthotic devices

C L3660 Shoulder orthosis (SO), figure of eight design abduction restrainer, canvas and webbing, prefabricated, off-the-shelf DME A
BETOS: D1F   Prosthetic/orthotic devices

C L3670 Shoulder orthosis (SO), acromio/clavicular (canvas and webbing type), prefabricated, off-the-shelf DME A
BETOS: D1F   Prosthetic/orthotic devices

C L3671 Shoulder orthosis (SO), shoulder joint design, without joints, may include soft interface, straps, custom fabricated, includes fitting and adjustment DME A
BETOS: D1F   Prosthetic/orthotic devices

C L3674 Shoulder orthosis (SO), abduction positioning (airplane design), thoracic component and support bar, with or without nontorsion joint/turnbuckle, may include soft interface, straps, custom fabricated, includes fitting and adjustment DME A
BETOS: D1F   Prosthetic/orthotic devices

C L3675 Shoulder orthosis (SO), vest type abduction restrainer, canvas webbing type or equal, prefabricated, off-the-shelf DME A
BETOS: D1F   Prosthetic/orthotic devices

D L3677 Shoulder orthosis (SO), shoulder joint design, without joints, may include soft interface, straps, prefabricated item that has

been trimmed, bent, molded, assembled, or otherwise customized to fit a specific patient by an individual with expertise A
BETOS: Z2   Undefined codes
Service not separately priced by Part B
Coding Clinic: 2002, Q1

C L3678 Shoulder orthosis (SO), shoulder joint design, without joints, may include soft interface, straps, prefabricated, off-the-shelf A
BETOS: D1F   Prosthetic/orthotic devices

ELBOW ORTHOTICS (L3702-L3762)

C L3702 Elbow orthosis (EO), without joints, may include soft interface, straps, custom fabricated, includes fitting and adjustment DME A
BETOS: D1F   Prosthetic/orthotic devices

C L3710 Elbow orthosis (EO), elastic with metal joints, prefabricated, off-the-shelf DME A
BETOS: D1F   Prosthetic/orthotic devices

C L3720 Elbow orthosis (EO), double upright with forearm/arm cuffs, free motion, custom fabricated DME A
BETOS: D1F   Prosthetic/orthotic devices

C L3730 Elbow orthosis (EO), double upright with forearm/arm cuffs, extension/ flexion assist, custom fabricated DME A
BETOS: D1F   Prosthetic/orthotic devices

C L3740 Elbow orthosis (EO), double upright with forearm/arm cuffs, adjustable position lock with active control, custom fabricated DME A
BETOS: D1F   Prosthetic/orthotic devices

▲ **C L3760** Elbow orthosis (EO), with adjustable position locking joint(s), prefabricated, item that has been trimmed, bent, molded, assembled, or otherwise customized to fit a specific patient by an individual with expertise DME A
BETOS: D1F   Prosthetic/orthotic devices

● **C L3761** Elbow orthosis (EO), with adjustable position locking joint(s), prefabricated, off-the-shelf
BETOS: D1F   Prosthetic/orthotic devices

C L3762 Elbow orthosis (EO), rigid, without joints, includes soft interface material, prefabricated, off-the-shelf DME A
BETOS: D1F   Prosthetic/orthotic devices

ELBOW-WRIST-HAND-FINGER ORTHOTICS (L3763-L3766)

C L3763 Elbow-wrist-hand orthosis (EWHO), rigid, without joints, may include soft interface, straps, custom fabricated, includes fitting and adjustment DME A
BETOS: D1F   Prosthetic/orthotic devices

C L3764 Elbow-wrist-hand orthosis (EWHO), includes one or more nontorsion joints, elastic bands, turnbuckles, may include soft interface,

▲ Revised code   ● New code   C Carrier judgment   D Special coverage instructions apply
I Not payable by Medicare   M Non-covered by Medicare   S Non-covered by Medicare statute   AHA Coding Clinic®

318

CPT® is a registered trademark of the American Medical Association. All rights reserved.

straps, custom fabricated, includes fitting and adjustment **DME** A

BETOS: D1F   Prosthetic/orthotic devices

C **L3765** Elbow-wrist-hand-finger orthosis (EWHFO), rigid, without joints, may include soft interface, straps, custom fabricated, includes fitting and adjustment **DME** A

BETOS: D1F   Prosthetic/orthotic devices

C **L3766** Elbow-wrist-hand-finger orthosis (EWHFO), includes one or more nontorsion joints, elastic bands, turnbuckles, may include soft interface, straps, custom fabricated, includes fitting and adjustment **DME** A

BETOS: D1F   Prosthetic/orthotic devices

WRIST-HAND-FINGER ORTHOTICS (L3806-L3904)

C **L3806** Wrist-hand-finger orthosis (WHFO), includes one or more nontorsion joint(s), turnbuckles, elastic bands/springs, may include soft interface material, straps, custom fabricated, includes fitting and adjustment **DME** A

BETOS: D1F   Prosthetic/orthotic devices

C **L3807** Wrist-hand-finger orthosis (WHFO), without joint(s), prefabricated item that has been trimmed, bent, molded, assembled, or otherwise customized to fit a specific patient by an individual with expertise **DME** A

BETOS: D1F   Prosthetic/orthotic devices

C **L3808** Wrist-hand-finger orthosis (WHFO), rigid without joints, may include soft interface material; straps, custom fabricated, includes fitting and adjustment **DME** A

BETOS: D1F   Prosthetic/orthotic devices

C **L3809** Wrist-hand-finger orthosis (WHFO), without joint(s), prefabricated, off-the-shelf, any type **DME** A

BETOS: D1F   Prosthetic/orthotic devices

I **L3891** Addition to upper extremity joint, wrist or elbow, concentric adjustable torsion style mechanism for custom fabricated orthotics only, each E1

BETOS: D1F   Prosthetic/orthotic devices
Service not separately priced by Part B

C **L3900** Wrist-hand-finger orthosis (WHFO), dynamic flexor hinge, reciprocal wrist extension/ flexion, finger flexion/extension, wrist or finger driven, custom fabricated **DME** A

BETOS: D1F   Prosthetic/orthotic devices

C **L3901** Wrist-hand-finger orthosis (WHFO), dynamic flexor hinge, reciprocal wrist extension/ flexion, finger flexion/extension, cable driven, custom fabricated **DME** A

BETOS: D1F   Prosthetic/orthotic devices

C **L3904** Wrist-hand-finger orthosis (WHFO), external powered, electric, custom fabricated **DME** A

BETOS: D1F   Prosthetic/orthotic devices

WRIST-HAND ORTHOTICS (L3905-L3908)

C **L3905** Wrist-hand orthosis (WHO), includes one or more nontorsion joints, elastic bands, turnbuckles, may include soft interface, straps, custom fabricated, includes fitting and adjustment **DME** A

BETOS: D1F   Prosthetic/orthotic devices

C **L3906** Wrist-hand orthosis (WHO), without joints, may include soft interface, straps, custom fabricated, includes fitting and adjustment **DME** A

BETOS: D1F   Prosthetic/orthotic devices

C **L3908** Wrist-hand orthosis (WHO), wrist extension control cock-up, non molded, prefabricated, off-the-shelf **DME** A

BETOS: D1F   Prosthetic/orthotic devices

ADDITIONAL MISCELLANEOUS ORTHOTICS, UPPER EXTREMITIES (L3912-L3956)

C **L3912** Hand-finger orthosis (HFO), flexion glove with elastic finger control, prefabricated, off-the-shelf **DME** A

BETOS: D1F   Prosthetic/orthotic devices

C **L3913** Hand-finger orthosis (HFO), without joints, may include soft interface, straps, custom fabricated, includes fitting and adjustment **DME** A

BETOS: D1F   Prosthetic/orthotic devices

C **L3915** Wrist-hand orthosis (WHO), includes one or more nontorsion joint(s), elastic bands, turnbuckles, may include soft interface, straps, prefabricated item that has been trimmed, bent, molded, assembled, or otherwise customized to fit a specific patient by an individual with expertise **DME** A

BETOS: D1F   Prosthetic/orthotic devices

C **L3916** Wrist-hand orthosis (WHO), includes one or more nontorsion joint(s), elastic bands, turnbuckles, may include soft interface, straps, prefabricated, off-the-shelf **DME** A

BETOS: D1F   Prosthetic/orthotic devices

C **L3917** Hand orthosis (HO), metacarpal fracture orthosis, prefabricated item that has been trimmed, bent, molded, assembled, or otherwise customized to fit a specific patient by an individual with expertise **DME** A

BETOS: D1F   Prosthetic/orthotic devices

C **L3918** Hand orthosis (HO), metacarpal fracture orthosis, prefabricated, off-the-shelf **DME** A

BETOS: D1F   Prosthetic/orthotic devices

C **L3919** Hand orthosis (HO), without joints, may include soft interface, straps, custom fabricated, includes fitting and adjustment **DME** A

BETOS: D1F   Prosthetic/orthotic devices

L3921 - L3976

ORTHOTIC PROCEDURES AND SERVICES (L0112-L4631)

C **L3921** Hand-finger orthosis (HFO), includes one or more nontorsion joints, elastic bands, turnbuckles, may include soft interface, straps, custom fabricated, includes fitting and adjustment **DME** A
BETOS: D1F   Prosthetic/orthotic devices

C **L3923** Hand-finger orthosis (HFO), without joints, may include soft interface, straps, prefabricated item that has been trimmed, bent, molded, assembled, or otherwise customized to fit a specific patient by an individual with expertise **DME** A
BETOS: D1F   Prosthetic/orthotic devices

C **L3924** Hand-finger orthosis (HFO), without joints, may include soft interface, straps, prefabricated, off-the-shelf **DME** A
BETOS: D1F   Prosthetic/orthotic devices

C **L3925** Finger orthosis (FO), proximal interphalangeal (PIP)/distal interphalangeal (DIP), non torsion joint/spring, extension/flexion, may include soft interface material, prefabricated, off-the-shelf **DME** A
BETOS: D1F   Prosthetic/orthotic devices

C **L3927** Finger orthosis (FO), proximal interphalangeal (PIP)/distal interphalangeal (DIP), without joint/spring, extension/flexion (e.g., static or ring type), may include soft interface material, prefabricated, off-the-shelf **DME** A
BETOS: D1F   Prosthetic/orthotic devices

C **L3929** Hand-finger orthosis (HFO), includes one or more nontorsion joint(s), turnbuckles, elastic bands/springs, may include soft interface material, straps, prefabricated item that has been trimmed, bent, molded, assembled, or otherwise customized to fit a specific patient by an individual with expertise **DME** A
BETOS: D1F   Prosthetic/orthotic devices

C **L3930** Hand-finger orthosis (HFO), includes one or more nontorsion joint(s), turnbuckles, elastic bands/springs, may include soft interface material, straps, prefabricated, off-the-shelf **DME** A
BETOS: D1F   Prosthetic/orthotic devices

C **L3931** Wrist-hand-finger orthosis (WHFO), includes one or more nontorsion joint(s), turnbuckles, elastic bands/springs, may include soft interface material, straps, prefabricated, includes fitting and adjustment **DME** A
BETOS: D1F   Prosthetic/orthotic devices

C **L3933** Finger orthosis (FO), without joints, may include soft interface, custom fabricated, includes fitting and adjustment **DME** A
BETOS: D1F   Prosthetic/orthotic devices

C **L3935** Finger orthosis (FO), nontorsion joint, may include soft interface, custom fabricated, includes fitting and adjustment **DME** A
BETOS: D1F   Prosthetic/orthotic devices

C **L3956** Addition of joint to upper extremity orthosis, any material; per joint **DME** A
BETOS: D1F   Prosthetic/orthotic devices

SHOULDER-ELBOW-WRIST-HAND ORTHOTICS (L3960-L3973)

C **L3960** Shoulder-elbow-wrist-hand orthosis (SEWHO), abduction positioning, airplane design, prefabricated, includes fitting and adjustment **DME** A
BETOS: D1F   Prosthetic/orthotic devices

C **L3961** Shoulder-elbow-wrist-hand orthosis (SEWHO), shoulder cap design, without joints, may include soft interface, straps, custom fabricated, includes fitting and adjustment **DME** A
BETOS: D1F   Prosthetic/orthotic devices

C **L3962** Shoulder-elbow-wrist-hand orthosis (SEWHO), abduction positioning, erb's palsey design, prefabricated, includes fitting and adjustment **DME** A
BETOS: D1F   Prosthetic/orthotic devices

C **L3967** Shoulder-elbow-wrist-hand orthosis (SEWHO), abduction positioning (airplane design), thoracic component and support bar, without joints, may include soft interface, straps, custom fabricated, includes fitting and adjustment **DME** A
BETOS: D1F   Prosthetic/orthotic devices

C **L3971** Shoulder-elbow-wrist-hand orthosis (SEWHO), shoulder cap design, includes one or more nontorsion joints, elastic bands, turnbuckles, may include soft interface, straps, custom fabricated, includes fitting and adjustment **DME** A
BETOS: D1F   Prosthetic/orthotic devices

C **L3973** Shoulder-elbow-wrist-hand orthosis (SEWHO), abduction positioning (airplane design), thoracic component and support bar, includes one or more nontorsion joints, elastic bands, turnbuckles, may include soft interface, straps, custom fabricated, includes fitting and adjustment **DME** A
BETOS: D1F   Prosthetic/orthotic devices

SHOULDER-ELBOW-WRIST-HAND-FINGER ORTHOTICS (L3975-L3978)

C **L3975** Shoulder-elbow-wrist-hand-finger (SEWHF) orthosis, shoulder cap design, without joints, may include soft interface, straps, custom fabricated, includes fitting and adjustment **DME** A
BETOS: D1F   Prosthetic/orthotic devices

C **L3976** Shoulder-elbow-wrist-hand-finger (SEWHF) orthosis, abduction positioning (airplane design), thoracic component and support bar, without joints, may include soft interface, straps, custom fabricated, includes fitting and adjustment **DME** A
BETOS: D1F   Prosthetic/orthotic devices

C **L3977** Shoulder-elbow-wrist-hand-finger (SEWHF) orthosis, shoulder cap design, includes one or more nontorsion joints, elastic bands, turnbuckles, may include soft interface, straps, custom fabricated, includes fitting and adjustment **DME** A

BETOS: D1F   Prosthetic/orthotic devices

C **L3978** Shoulder-elbow-wrist-hand-finger (SEWHF) orthosis, abduction positioning (airplane design), thoracic component and support bar, includes one or more nontorsion joints, elastic bands, turnbuckles, may include soft interface, straps, custom fabricated, includes fitting and adjustment **DME** A

BETOS: D1F   Prosthetic/orthotic devices

FRACTURE, ADDITION, AND UNSPECIFIED ORTHOTICS, UPPER EXTREMITIES (L3980-L3999)

C **L3980** Upper extremity fracture orthosis, humeral, prefabricated, includes fitting and adjustment **DME** A

BETOS: D1F   Prosthetic/orthotic devices

C **L3981** Upper extremity fracture orthosis, humeral, prefabricated, includes shoulder cap design, with or without joints, forearm section, may include soft interface, straps, includes fitting and adjustments **DME** A

BETOS: D1F   Prosthetic/orthotic devices

C **L3982** Upper extremity fracture orthosis, radius/ulnar, prefabricated, includes fitting and adjustment **DME** A

BETOS: D1F   Prosthetic/orthotic devices

C **L3984** Upper extremity fracture orthosis, wrist, prefabricated, includes fitting and adjustment **DME** A

BETOS: D1F   Prosthetic/orthotic devices

C **L3995** Addition to upper extremity orthosis, sock, fracture or equal, each **DME** A

BETOS: D1F   Prosthetic/orthotic devices

C **L3999** Upper limb orthosis, not otherwise specified   A

BETOS: D1F   Prosthetic/orthotic devices

ORTHOTIC REPLACEMENT PARTS OR REPAIR (L4000-L4210)

C **L4000** Replace girdle for spinal orthosis (Cervical-thoracic-lumbar-sacral orthosis (CTLSO) or Shoulder orthosis (SO)) **DME** A

BETOS: D1F   Prosthetic/orthotic devices

C **L4002** Replacement strap, any orthosis, includes all components, any length, any type **DME** A

BETOS: D1F   Prosthetic/orthotic devices

C **L4010** Replace trilateral socket brim **DME** A

BETOS: D1F   Prosthetic/orthotic devices

C **L4020** Replace quadrilateral socket brim, molded to patient model **DME** A

BETOS: D1F   Prosthetic/orthotic devices

C **L4030** Replace quadrilateral socket brim, custom fitted **DME** A

BETOS: D1F   Prosthetic/orthotic devices

C **L4040** Replace molded thigh lacer, for custom fabricated orthosis only **DME** A

BETOS: D1F   Prosthetic/orthotic devices

C **L4045** Replace non-molded thigh lacer, for custom fabricated orthosis only **DME** A

BETOS: D1F   Prosthetic/orthotic devices

C **L4050** Replace molded calf lacer, for custom fabricated orthosis only **DME** A

BETOS: D1F   Prosthetic/orthotic devices

C **L4055** Replace non-molded calf lacer, for custom fabricated orthosis only **DME** A

BETOS: D1F   Prosthetic/orthotic devices

C **L4060** Replace high roll cuff **DME** A

BETOS: D1F   Prosthetic/orthotic devices

C **L4070** Replace proximal and distal upright for KAFO **DME** A

BETOS: D1F   Prosthetic/orthotic devices

C **L4080** Replace metal bands KAFO, proximal thigh **DME** A

BETOS: D1F   Prosthetic/orthotic devices

C **L4090** Replace metal bands KAFO-AFO, calf or distal thigh **DME** A

BETOS: D1F   Prosthetic/orthotic devices

C **L4100** Replace leather cuff KAFO, proximal thigh **DME** A

BETOS: D1F   Prosthetic/orthotic devices

C **L4110** Replace leather cuff KAFO-AFO, calf or distal thigh **DME** A

BETOS: D1F   Prosthetic/orthotic devices

C **L4130** Replace pretibial shell **DME** A

BETOS: D1F   Prosthetic/orthotic devices

D **L4205** Repair of orthotic device, labor component, per 15 minutes   A

BETOS: D1F   Prosthetic/orthotic devices

D **L4210** Repair of orthotic device, repair or replace minor parts   A

BETOS: D1F   Prosthetic/orthotic devices

OTHER LOWER EXTREMITY ORTHOTICS (L4350-L4631)

C **L4350** Ankle control orthosis, stirrup style, rigid, includes any type interface (e.g., pneumatic, gel), prefabricated, off-the-shelf **DME** A

BETOS: D1F   Prosthetic/orthotic devices

C **L4360** Walking boot, pneumatic and/or vacuum, with or without joints, with or without interface material, prefabricated item that has been trimmed, bent, molded, assembled, or otherwise customized to fit a specific patient by an individual with expertise **DME** A

BETOS: D1F   Prosthetic/orthotic devices

♂ Male only   ♀ Female only   🅐 Age   A2 - Z3 = ASC Payment indicator   A - Y = APC Status indicator

ASC = ASC-approved procedure   **DME** Paid under the DME fee schedule   **MIPS** MIPS code

ORTHOTIC PROCEDURES AND SERVICES (L0112-L4631) — L4361 - L4631

C **L4361** Walking boot, pneumatic and/or vacuum, with or without joints, with or without interface material, prefabricated, off-the-shelf **DME** A

BETOS: D1F Prosthetic/orthotic devices

C **L4370** Pneumatic full leg splint, prefabricated, off-the-shelf **DME** A

BETOS: D1F Prosthetic/orthotic devices

C **L4386** Walking boot, non-pneumatic, with or without joints, with or without interface material, prefabricated item that has been trimmed, bent, molded, assembled, or otherwise customized to fit a specific patient by an individual with expertise **DME** A

BETOS: D1F Prosthetic/orthotic devices

C **L4387** Walking boot, non-pneumatic, with or without joints, with or without interface material, prefabricated, off-the-shelf **DME** A

BETOS: D1F Prosthetic/orthotic devices

C **L4392** Replacement, soft interface material, static AFO **DME** A

BETOS: D1F Prosthetic/orthotic devices

C **L4394** Replace soft interface material, foot drop splint **DME** A

BETOS: D1F Prosthetic/orthotic devices

C **L4396** Static or dynamic Ankle-foot orthosis (AFO), including soft interface material, adjustable for fit, for positioning, may be used for minimal ambulation, prefabricated item that has been trimmed, bent, molded, assembled, or otherwise customized to fit a specific patient by an individual with expertise **DME** A

BETOS: D1F Prosthetic/orthotic devices

C **L4397** Static or dynamic Ankle-foot orthosis (AFO), including soft interface material, adjustable for fit, for positioning, may be used for minimal ambulation, prefabricated, off-the-shelf **DME** A

BETOS: D1F Prosthetic/orthotic devices

C **L4398** Foot drop splint, recumbent positioning device, prefabricated, off-the-shelf **DME** A

BETOS: D1F Prosthetic/orthotic devices

C **L4631** Ankle-foot orthosis (AFO), walking boot type, varus/valgus correction, rocker bottom, anterior tibial shell, soft interface, custom arch support, plastic or other material, includes straps and closures, custom fabricated **DME** A

BETOS: D1F Prosthetic/orthotic devices

NOTES

NOTES

PROSTHETIC PROCEDURES (L5000-L9900)

PARTIAL FOOT PROSTHETICS (L5000-L5020)

D L5000 Partial foot, shoe insert with longitudinal arch, toe filler   DME A
BETOS: D1F   Prosthetic/orthotic devices

D L5010 Partial foot, molded socket, ankle height, with toe filler   DME A
BETOS: D1F   Prosthetic/orthotic devices
Pub: 100-2, Chap. 15, 290

D L5020 Partial foot, molded socket, tibial tubercle height, with toe filler   DME A
BETOS: D1F   Prosthetic/orthotic devices
Pub: 100-2, Chap. 15, 290

ANKLE PROSTHETICS (L5050, L5060)

C L5050 Ankle, Symes, molded socket, SACH foot   DME A
BETOS: D1F   Prosthetic/orthotic devices

C L5060 Ankle, Symes, metal frame, molded leather socket, articulated ankle/foot   DME A
BETOS: D1F   Prosthetic/orthotic devices

BELOW THE KNEE PROSTHETICS (L5100, L5105)

C L5100 Below knee, molded socket, shin, SACH foot   DME A
BETOS: D1F   Prosthetic/orthotic devices

C L5105 Below knee, plastic socket, joints and thigh lacer, SACH foot   DME A
BETOS: D1F   Prosthetic/orthotic devices

KNEE DISARTICULATION PROSTHETICS (L5150, L5160)

C L5150 Knee disarticulation (or through knee), molded socket, external knee joints, shin, SACH foot   DME A
BETOS: D1F   Prosthetic/orthotic devices

C L5160 Knee disarticulation (or through knee), molded socket, bent knee configuration, external knee joints, shin, SACH foot   DME A
BETOS: D1F   Prosthetic/orthotic devices

ABOVE THE KNEE PROSTHETICS (L5200-L5230)

C L5200 Above knee, molded socket, single axis constant friction knee, shin, SACH foot   DME A
BETOS: D1F   Prosthetic/orthotic devices

C L5210 Above knee, short prosthesis, no knee joint ('stubbies'), with foot blocks, no ankle joints, each   DME A
BETOS: D1F   Prosthetic/orthotic devices

C L5220 Above knee, short prosthesis, no knee joint ('stubbies'), with articulated ankle/foot, dynamically aligned, each   DME A
BETOS: D1F   Prosthetic/orthotic devices

C L5230 Above knee, for proximal femoral focal deficiency, constant friction knee, shin, SACH foot   DME A
BETOS: D1F   Prosthetic/orthotic devices

HIP DISARTICULATION PROSTHETICS (L5250, L5270)

C L5250 Hip disarticulation, Canadian type; molded socket, hip joint, single axis constant friction knee, shin, SACH foot   DME A
BETOS: D1F   Prosthetic/orthotic devices

C L5270 Hip disarticulation, tilt table type; molded socket, locking hip joint, single axis constant friction knee, shin, SACH foot   DME A
BETOS: D1F   Prosthetic/orthotic devices

ENDOSKELETAL PROSTHETICS, LOWER LIMBS (L5280-L5341)

C L5280 Hemipelvectomy, Canadian type; molded socket, hip joint, single axis constant friction knee, shin, SACH foot   DME A
BETOS: D1F   Prosthetic/orthotic devices

C L5301 Below knee, molded socket, shin, SACH foot, endoskeletal system   DME A
BETOS: D1F   Prosthetic/orthotic devices
Coding Clinic: 2002, Q1

C L5312 Knee disarticulation (or through knee), molded socket, single axis knee, pylon, SACH foot, endoskeletal system   DME A
BETOS: D1F   Prosthetic/orthotic devices

C L5321 Above knee, molded socket, open end, SACH foot, endoskeletal system, single axis knee   DME A
BETOS: D1F   Prosthetic/orthotic devices
Coding Clinic: 2002, Q1

C L5331 Hip disarticulation, Canadian type, molded socket, endoskeletal system, hip joint, single axis knee, SACH foot   DME A
BETOS: D1F   Prosthetic/orthotic devices
Coding Clinic: 2002, Q1

C L5341 Hemipelvectomy, Canadian type, molded socket, endoskeletal system, hip joint, single axis knee, SACH foot   DME A
BETOS: D1F   Prosthetic/orthotic devices
Coding Clinic: 2002, Q1

PROSTHETIC FITTING, IMMEDIATE POSTSURGICAL OR EARLY, LOWER LIMBS (L5400-L5460)

C L5400 Immediate post surgical or early fitting, application of initial rigid dressing, including fitting, alignment, suspension, and one cast change, below knee   DME A
BETOS: D1F   Prosthetic/orthotic devices

C **L5410** Immediate post surgical or early fitting, application of initial rigid dressing, including fitting, alignment and suspension, below knee, each additional cast change and realignment **DME** A

BETOS: D1F   Prosthetic/orthotic devices

C **L5420** Immediate post surgical or early fitting, application of initial rigid dressing, including fitting, alignment and suspension and one cast change 'AK' or knee disarticulation **DME** A

BETOS: D1F   Prosthetic/orthotic devices

C **L5430** Immediate post surgical or early fitting, application of initial rigid dressing, incl. fitting, alignment and suspension, 'AK' or knee disarticulation, each additional cast change and realignment **DME** A

BETOS: D1F   Prosthetic/orthotic devices

C **L5450** Immediate post surgical or early fitting, application of non-weight bearing rigid dressing, below knee **DME** A

BETOS: D1F   Prosthetic/orthotic devices

C **L5460** Immediate post surgical or early fitting, application of non-weight bearing rigid dressing, above knee **DME** A

BETOS: D1F   Prosthetic/orthotic devices

SUPPLY, INITIAL PROSTHESIS (L5500-L5505)

C **L5500** Initial, below knee 'PTB' type socket, non-alignable system, pylon, no cover, SACH foot, plaster socket, direct formed **DME** A

BETOS: D1F   Prosthetic/orthotic devices
Pub: 100-2, Chap. 1, 40

C **L5505** Initial, above knee - knee disarticulation, ischial level socket, non-alignable system, pylon, no cover, SACH foot, plaster socket, direct formed **DME** A

BETOS: D1F   Prosthetic/orthotic devices
Pub: 100-2, Chap. 1, 40

SUPPLY, PREPARATORY PROSTHESIS (L5510-L5600)

C **L5510** Preparatory, below knee 'PTB' type socket, non-alignable system, pylon, no cover, SACH foot, plaster socket, molded to model **DME** A

BETOS: D1F   Prosthetic/orthotic devices

C **L5520** Preparatory, below knee 'PTB' type socket, non-alignable system, pylon, no cover, SACH foot, thermoplastic or equal, direct formed **DME** A

BETOS: D1F   Prosthetic/orthotic devices

C **L5530** Preparatory, below knee 'PTB' type socket, non-alignable system, pylon, no cover, SACH foot, thermoplastic or equal, molded to model **DME** A

BETOS: D1F   Prosthetic/orthotic devices

C **L5535** Preparatory, below knee 'PTB' type socket, non-alignable system, no cover, SACH foot, prefabricated, adjustable open end socket **DME** A

BETOS: D1F   Prosthetic/orthotic devices

C **L5540** Preparatory, below knee 'PTB' type socket, non-alignable system, pylon, no cover, SACH foot, laminated socket, molded to model **DME** A

BETOS: D1F   Prosthetic/orthotic devices

C **L5560** Preparatory, above knee- knee disarticulation, ischial level socket, non-alignable system, pylon, no cover, SACH foot, plaster socket, molded to model **DME** A

BETOS: D1F   Prosthetic/orthotic devices

C **L5570** Preparatory, above knee - knee disarticulation, ischial level socket, non-alignable system, pylon, no cover, SACH foot, thermoplastic or equal, direct formed **DME** A

BETOS: D1F   Prosthetic/orthotic devices

C **L5580** Preparatory, above knee - knee disarticulation ischial level socket, non-alignable system, pylon, no cover, SACH foot, thermoplastic or equal, molded to model **DME** A

BETOS: D1F   Prosthetic/orthotic devices

C **L5585** Preparatory, above knee - knee disarticulation, ischial level socket, non-alignable system, pylon, no cover, SACH foot, prefabricated adjustable open end socket **DME** A

BETOS: D1F   Prosthetic/orthotic devices

C **L5590** Preparatory, above knee - knee disarticulation ischial level socket, non-alignable system, pylon no cover, SACH foot, laminated socket, molded to model **DME** A

BETOS: D1F   Prosthetic/orthotic devices

C **L5595** Preparatory, hip disarticulation-hemipelvectomy, pylon, no cover, SACH foot, thermoplastic or equal, molded to patient model **DME** A

BETOS: D1F   Prosthetic/orthotic devices

C **L5600** Preparatory, hip disarticulation-hemipelvectomy, pylon, no cover, SACH foot, laminated socket, molded to patient model **DME** A

BETOS: D1F   Prosthetic/orthotic devices

ENDOSKELETAL PROSTHETIC ADDITIONS, LOWER EXTREMITIES (L5610-L5617)

C **L5610** Addition to lower extremity, endoskeletal system, above knee, hydracadence system **DME** A

BETOS: D1F   Prosthetic/orthotic devices

▲ Revised code   ● New code   **C** Carrier judgment   **D** Special coverage instructions apply

I Not payable by Medicare   **M** Non-covered by Medicare   **S** Non-covered by Medicare statute   AHA Coding Clinic®

C **L5611** Addition to lower extremity, endoskeletal system, above knee - knee disarticulation, 4 bar linkage, with friction swing phase control   DME A

BETOS: D1F   Prosthetic/orthotic devices

C **L5613** Addition to lower extremity, endoskeletal system, above knee-knee disarticulation, 4 bar linkage, with hydraulic swing phase control   DME A

BETOS: D1F   Prosthetic/orthotic devices

C **L5614** Addition to lower extremity, exoskeletal system, above knee-knee disarticulation, 4 bar linkage, with pneumatic swing phase control   DME A

BETOS: D1F   Prosthetic/orthotic devices

C **L5616** Addition to lower extremity, endoskeletal system, above knee, universal multiplex system, friction swing phase control   DME A

BETOS: D1F   Prosthetic/orthotic devices

C **L5617** Addition to lower extremity, quick change self-aligning unit, above knee or below knee, each   DME A

BETOS: D1F   Prosthetic/orthotic devices

TEST SOCKET PROSTHETIC ADDITIONS, LOWER EXTREMITIES (L5618-L5628)

C **L5618** Addition to lower extremity, test socket, Symes   DME A

BETOS: D1F   Prosthetic/orthotic devices

C **L5620** Addition to lower extremity, test socket, below knee   DME A

BETOS: D1F   Prosthetic/orthotic devices

C **L5622** Addition to lower extremity, test socket, knee disarticulation   DME A

BETOS: D1F   Prosthetic/orthotic devices

C **L5624** Addition to lower extremity, test socket, above knee   DME A

BETOS: D1F   Prosthetic/orthotic devices

C **L5626** Addition to lower extremity, test socket, hip disarticulation   DME A

BETOS: D1F   Prosthetic/orthotic devices

C **L5628** Addition to lower extremity, test socket, hemipelvectomy   DME A

BETOS: D1F   Prosthetic/orthotic devices

VARIOUS PROSTHETIC SOCKETS (L5629-L5653)

C **L5629** Addition to lower extremity, below knee, acrylic socket   DME A

BETOS: D1F   Prosthetic/orthotic devices

C **L5630** Addition to lower extremity, Symes type, expandable wall socket   DME A

BETOS: D1F   Prosthetic/orthotic devices

C **L5631** Addition to lower extremity, above knee or knee disarticulation, acrylic socket   DME A

BETOS: D1F   Prosthetic/orthotic devices

C **L5632** Addition to lower extremity, Symes type, 'PTB' brim design socket   DME A

BETOS: D1F   Prosthetic/orthotic devices

C **L5634** Addition to lower extremity, Symes type, posterior opening (Canadian) socket   DME A

BETOS: D1F   Prosthetic/orthotic devices

C **L5636** Addition to lower extremity, Symes type, medial opening socket   DME A

BETOS: D1F   Prosthetic/orthotic devices

C **L5637** Addition to lower extremity, below knee, total contact   DME A

BETOS: D1F   Prosthetic/orthotic devices

C **L5638** Addition to lower extremity, below knee, leather socket   DME A

BETOS: D1F   Prosthetic/orthotic devices

C **L5639** Addition to lower extremity, below knee, wood socket   DME A

BETOS: D1F   Prosthetic/orthotic devices

C **L5640** Addition to lower extremity, knee disarticulation, leather socket   DME A

BETOS: D1F   Prosthetic/orthotic devices

C **L5642** Addition to lower extremity, above knee, leather socket   DME A

BETOS: D1F   Prosthetic/orthotic devices

C **L5643** Addition to lower extremity, hip disarticulation, flexible inner socket, external frame   DME A

BETOS: D1F   Prosthetic/orthotic devices

C **L5644** Addition to lower extremity, above knee, wood socket   DME A

BETOS: D1F   Prosthetic/orthotic devices

C **L5645** Addition to lower extremity, below knee, flexible inner socket, external frame   DME A

BETOS: D1F   Prosthetic/orthotic devices

C **L5646** Addition to lower extremity, below knee, air, fluid, gel or equal, cushion socket   DME A

BETOS: D1F   Prosthetic/orthotic devices

C **L5647** Addition to lower extremity, below knee suction socket   DME A

BETOS: D1F   Prosthetic/orthotic devices

C **L5648** Addition to lower extremity, above knee, air, fluid, gel or equal, cushion socket   DME A

BETOS: D1F   Prosthetic/orthotic devices

C **L5649** Addition to lower extremity, ischial containment/narrow M-L socket   DME A

BETOS: D1F   Prosthetic/orthotic devices

C **L5650** Additions to lower extremity, total contact, above knee or knee disarticulation socket   DME A

BETOS: D1F   Prosthetic/orthotic devices

C **L5651** Addition to lower extremity, above knee, flexible inner socket, external frame   DME A

BETOS: D1F   Prosthetic/orthotic devices

♂ Male only   ♀ Female only   Ⓐ Age   A2 - Z3 = ASC Payment indicator   A - Y = APC Status indicator
ASC = ASC-approved procedure   DME Paid under the DME fee schedule   MIPS MIPS code

C L5652 Addition to lower extremity, suction suspension, above knee or knee disarticulation socket `DME` A
BETOS: D1F Prosthetic/orthotic devices

C L5653 Addition to lower extremity, knee disarticulation, expandable wall socket `DME` A
BETOS: D1F Prosthetic/orthotic devices

SOCKET INSERT, SUSPENSIONS, AND OTHER PROSTHETIC ADDITIONS (L5654-L5699)

C L5654 Addition to lower extremity, socket insert, Symes, (Kemblo, Pelite, Aliplast, Plastazote or equal) `DME` A
BETOS: D1F Prosthetic/orthotic devices

C L5655 Addition to lower extremity, socket insert, below knee (Kemblo, Pelite, Aliplast, Plastazote or equal) `DME` A
BETOS: D1F Prosthetic/orthotic devices

C L5656 Addition to lower extremity, socket insert, knee disarticulation (Kemblo, Pelite, Aliplast, Plastazote or equal) `DME` A
BETOS: D1F Prosthetic/orthotic devices

C L5658 Addition to lower extremity, socket insert, above knee (Kemblo, Pelite, Aliplast, Plastazote or equal) `DME` A
BETOS: D1F Prosthetic/orthotic devices

C L5661 Addition to lower extremity, socket insert, multi-durometer Symes `DME` A
BETOS: D1F Prosthetic/orthotic devices

C L5665 Addition to lower extremity, socket insert, multi-durometer, below knee `DME` A
BETOS: D1F Prosthetic/orthotic devices

C L5666 Addition to lower extremity, below knee, cuff suspension `DME` A
BETOS: D1F Prosthetic/orthotic devices

C L5668 Addition to lower extremity, below knee, molded distal cushion `DME` A
BETOS: D1F Prosthetic/orthotic devices

C L5670 Addition to lower extremity, below knee, molded supracondylar suspension ('PTS' or similar) `DME` A
BETOS: D1F Prosthetic/orthotic devices

C L5671 Addition to lower extremity, below knee / above knee suspension locking mechanism (shuttle, lanyard or equal), excludes socket insert `DME` A
BETOS: D1F Prosthetic/orthotic devices
Coding Clinic: 2002, Q1

C L5672 Addition to lower extremity, below knee, removable medial brim suspension `DME` A
BETOS: D1F Prosthetic/orthotic devices

C L5673 Addition to lower extremity, below knee/ above knee, custom fabricated from existing mold or prefabricated, socket insert, silicone gel, elastomeric or equal, for use with locking mechanism `DME` A
BETOS: D1F Prosthetic/orthotic devices

C L5676 Additions to lower extremity, below knee, knee joints, single axis, pair `DME` A
BETOS: D1F Prosthetic/orthotic devices

C L5677 Additions to lower extremity, below knee, knee joints, polycentric, pair `DME` A
BETOS: D1F Prosthetic/orthotic devices

C L5678 Additions to lower extremity, below knee, joint covers, pair `DME` A
BETOS: D1F Prosthetic/orthotic devices

C L5679 Addition to lower extremity, below knee/ above knee, custom fabricated from existing mold or prefabricated, socket insert, silicone gel, elastomeric or equal, not for use with locking mechanism `DME` A
BETOS: D1F Prosthetic/orthotic devices

C L5680 Addition to lower extremity, below knee, thigh lacer, nonmolded `DME` A
BETOS: D1F Prosthetic/orthotic devices

C L5681 Addition to lower extremity, below knee/ above knee, custom fabricated socket insert for congenital or atypical traumatic amputee, silicone gel, elastomeric or equal, for use with or without locking mechanism, initial only (for other than initial, use code L5673 or L5679) `DME` A
BETOS: D1F Prosthetic/orthotic devices

C L5682 Addition to lower extremity, below knee, thigh lacer, gluteal/ischial, molded `DME` A
BETOS: D1F Prosthetic/orthotic devices

C L5683 Addition to lower extremity, below knee/ above knee, custom fabricated socket insert for other than congenital or atypical traumatic amputee, silicone gel, elastomeric or equal, for use with or without locking mechanism, initial only (for other than initial, use code L5673 or L5679) `DME` A
BETOS: D1F Prosthetic/orthotic devices

C L5684 Addition to lower extremity, below knee, fork strap `DME` A
BETOS: D1F Prosthetic/orthotic devices

C L5685 Addition to lower extremity prosthesis, below knee, suspension/sealing sleeve, with or without valve, any material, each `DME` A
BETOS: D1F Prosthetic/orthotic devices

C L5686 Addition to lower extremity, below knee, back check (extension control) `DME` A
BETOS: D1F Prosthetic/orthotic devices

C L5688 Addition to lower extremity, below knee, waist belt, webbing `DME` A
BETOS: D1F Prosthetic/orthotic devices

C L5690 Addition to lower extremity, below knee, waist belt, padded and lined `DME` A
BETOS: D1F Prosthetic/orthotic devices

C **L5692** Addition to lower extremity, above knee, pelvic control belt, light **DME** A
BETOS: D1F   Prosthetic/orthotic devices

C **L5694** Addition to lower extremity, above knee, pelvic control belt, padded and lined **DME** A
BETOS: D1F   Prosthetic/orthotic devices

C **L5695** Addition to lower extremity, above knee, pelvic control, sleeve suspension, neoprene or equal, each **DME** A
BETOS: D1F   Prosthetic/orthotic devices

C **L5696** Addition to lower extremity, above knee or knee disarticulation, pelvic joint **DME** A
BETOS: D1F   Prosthetic/orthotic devices

C **L5697** Addition to lower extremity, above knee or knee disarticulation, pelvic band **DME** A
BETOS: D1F   Prosthetic/orthotic devices

C **L5698** Addition to lower extremity, above knee or knee disarticulation, Silesian bandage **DME** A
BETOS: D1F   Prosthetic/orthotic devices

C **L5699** All lower extremity prostheses, shoulder harness **DME** A
BETOS: D1F   Prosthetic/orthotic devices

REPLACEMENT SOCKETS (L5700-L5703)

C **L5700** Replacement, socket, below knee, molded to patient model **DME** A
BETOS: D1F   Prosthetic/orthotic devices

C **L5701** Replacement, socket, above knee/knee disarticulation, including attachment plate, molded to patient model **DME** A
BETOS: D1F   Prosthetic/orthotic devices

C **L5702** Replacement, socket, hip disarticulation, including hip joint, molded to patient model **DME** A
BETOS: D1F   Prosthetic/orthotic devices

C **L5703** Ankle, Symes, molded to patient model, socket without solid ankle cushion heel (SACH) foot, replacement only **DME** A
BETOS: D1F   Prosthetic/orthotic devices

CUSTOM-SHAPED PROTECTIVE COVERS (L5704-L5707)

C **L5704** Custom shaped protective cover, below knee **DME** A
BETOS: D1F   Prosthetic/orthotic devices

C **L5705** Custom shaped protective cover, above knee **DME** A
BETOS: D1F   Prosthetic/orthotic devices

C **L5706** Custom shaped protective cover, knee disarticulation **DME** A
BETOS: D1F   Prosthetic/orthotic devices

C **L5707** Custom shaped protective cover, hip disarticulation **DME** A
BETOS: D1F   Prosthetic/orthotic devices

EXOSKELETAL KNEE-SHIN SYSTEM ADDITIONS (L5710-L5780)

C **L5710** Addition, exoskeletal knee-shin system, single axis, manual lock **DME** A
BETOS: D1F   Prosthetic/orthotic devices

C **L5711** Additions exoskeletal knee-shin system, single axis, manual lock, ultra-light material **DME** A
BETOS: D1F   Prosthetic/orthotic devices

C **L5712** Addition, exoskeletal knee-shin system, single axis, friction swing and stance phase control (safety knee) **DME** A
BETOS: D1F   Prosthetic/orthotic devices

C **L5714** Addition, exoskeletal knee-shin system, single axis, variable friction swing phase control **DME** A
BETOS: D1F   Prosthetic/orthotic devices

C **L5716** Addition, exoskeletal knee-shin system, polycentric, mechanical stance phase lock **DME** A
BETOS: D1F   Prosthetic/orthotic devices

C **L5718** Addition, exoskeletal knee-shin system, polycentric, friction swing and stance phase control **DME** A
BETOS: D1F   Prosthetic/orthotic devices

C **L5722** Addition, exoskeletal knee-shin system, single axis, pneumatic swing, friction stance phase control **DME** A
BETOS: D1F   Prosthetic/orthotic devices

C **L5724** Addition, exoskeletal knee-shin system, single axis, fluid swing phase control **DME** A
BETOS: D1F   Prosthetic/orthotic devices

C **L5726** Addition, exoskeletal knee-shin system, single axis, external joints fluid swing phase control **DME** A
BETOS: D1F   Prosthetic/orthotic devices

C **L5728** Addition, exoskeletal knee-shin system, single axis, fluid swing and stance phase control **DME** A
BETOS: D1F   Prosthetic/orthotic devices

C **L5780** Addition, exoskeletal knee-shin system, single axis, pneumatic/hydra pneumatic swing phase control **DME** A
BETOS: D1F   Prosthetic/orthotic devices

VACUUM PUMPS, LOWER LIMB PROSTHETIC ADDITIONS (L5781, L5782)

C **L5781** Addition to lower limb prosthesis, vacuum pump, residual limb volume management and moisture evacuation system **DME** A
BETOS: D1F   Prosthetic/orthotic devices

C **L5782** Addition to lower limb prosthesis, vacuum pump, residual limb volume management and moisture evacuation system, heavy duty **DME** A
BETOS: D1F   Prosthetic/orthotic devices

♂ Male only   ♀ Female only   **A** Age   A2 - Z3 = ASC Payment indicator   A - Y = APC Status indicator
ASC = ASC-approved procedure   **DME** Paid under the DME fee schedule   **MIPS** MIPS code

OTHER EXOSKELETAL ADDITIONS (L5785-L5795)

C L5785 Addition, exoskeletal system, below knee, ultra-light material (titanium, carbon fiber or equal) **DME** A

BETOS: D1F   Prosthetic/orthotic devices

C L5790 Addition, exoskeletal system, above knee, ultra-light material (titanium, carbon fiber or equal) **DME** A

BETOS: D1F   Prosthetic/orthotic devices

C L5795 Addition, exoskeletal system, hip disarticulation, ultra-light material (titanium, carbon fiber or equal) **DME** A

BETOS: D1F   Prosthetic/orthotic devices

ENDOSKELETAL KNEE OR HIP SYSTEM ADDITIONS (L5810-L5966)

C L5810 Addition, endoskeletal knee-shin system, single axis, manual lock **DME** A

BETOS: D1F   Prosthetic/orthotic devices

C L5811 Addition, endoskeletal knee-shin system, single axis, manual lock, ultra-light material **DME** A

BETOS: D1F   Prosthetic/orthotic devices

C L5812 Addition, endoskeletal knee-shin system, single axis, friction swing and stance phase control (safety knee) **DME** A

BETOS: D1F   Prosthetic/orthotic devices

C L5814 Addition, endoskeletal knee-shin system, polycentric, hydraulic swing phase control, mechanical stance phase lock **DME** A

BETOS: D1F   Prosthetic/orthotic devices

C L5816 Addition, endoskeletal knee-shin system, polycentric, mechanical stance phase lock **DME** A

BETOS: D1F   Prosthetic/orthotic devices

C L5818 Addition, endoskeletal knee-shin system, polycentric, friction swing, and stance phase control **DME** A

BETOS: D1F   Prosthetic/orthotic devices

C L5822 Addition, endoskeletal knee-shin system, single axis, pneumatic swing, friction stance phase control **DME** A

BETOS: D1F   Prosthetic/orthotic devices

C L5824 Addition, endoskeletal knee-shin system, single axis, fluid swing phase control **DME** A

BETOS: D1F   Prosthetic/orthotic devices

C L5826 Addition, endoskeletal knee-shin system, single axis, hydraulic swing phase control, with miniature high activity frame **DME** A

BETOS: D1F   Prosthetic/orthotic devices

C L5828 Addition, endoskeletal knee-shin system, single axis, fluid swing and stance phase control **DME** A

BETOS: D1F   Prosthetic/orthotic devices

C L5830 Addition, endoskeletal knee-shin system, single axis, pneumatic/ swing phase control **DME** A

BETOS: D1F   Prosthetic/orthotic devices

C L5840 Addition, endoskeletal knee/shin system, 4-bar linkage or multiaxial, pneumatic swing phase control **DME** A

BETOS: D1F   Prosthetic/orthotic devices

C L5845 Addition, endoskeletal, knee-shin system, stance flexion feature, adjustable **DME** A

BETOS: D1F   Prosthetic/orthotic devices

C L5848 Addition to endoskeletal knee-shin system, fluid stance extension, dampening feature, with or without adjustability **DME** A

BETOS: D1F   Prosthetic/orthotic devices

C L5850 Addition, endoskeletal system, above knee or hip disarticulation, knee extension assist **DME** A

BETOS: D1F   Prosthetic/orthotic devices

C L5855 Addition, endoskeletal system, hip disarticulation, mechanical hip extension assist **DME** A

BETOS: D1F   Prosthetic/orthotic devices

C L5856 Addition to lower extremity prosthesis, endoskeletal knee-shin system, microprocessor control feature, swing and stance phase, includes electronic sensor(s), any type **DME** A

BETOS: D1F   Prosthetic/orthotic devices

C L5857 Addition to lower extremity prosthesis, endoskeletal knee-shin system, microprocessor control feature, swing phase only, includes electronic sensor(s), any type **DME** A

BETOS: D1F   Prosthetic/orthotic devices

C L5858 Addition to lower extremity prosthesis, endoskeletal knee shin system, microprocessor control feature, stance phase only, includes electronic sensor(s), any type **DME** A

BETOS: D1F   Prosthetic/orthotic devices

C L5859 Addition to lower extremity prosthesis, endoskeletal knee-shin system, powered and programmable flexion/extension assist control, includes any type motor(s) **DME** A

BETOS: D1F   Prosthetic/orthotic devices

▲ Revised code   ● New code   **C** Carrier judgment   **D** Special coverage instructions apply

I Not payable by Medicare   **M** Non-covered by Medicare   **S** Non-covered by Medicare statute   AHA Coding Clinic®

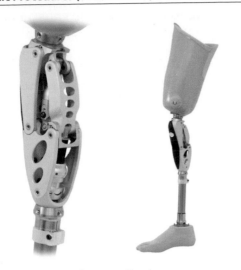

Leg prosthesis

C **L5910** Addition, endoskeletal system, below knee, alignable system **DME** A
BETOS: D1F   Prosthetic/orthotic devices

C **L5920** Addition, endoskeletal system, above knee or hip disarticulation, alignable system **DME** A
BETOS: D1F   Prosthetic/orthotic devices

C **L5925** Addition, endoskeletal system, above knee, knee disarticulation or hip disarticulation, manual lock **DME** A
BETOS: D1F   Prosthetic/orthotic devices

C **L5930** Addition, endoskeletal system, high activity knee control frame **DME** A
BETOS: D1F   Prosthetic/orthotic devices

C **L5940** Addition, endoskeletal system, below knee, ultra-light material (titanium, carbon fiber or equal) **DME** A
BETOS: D1F   Prosthetic/orthotic devices

C **L5950** Addition, endoskeletal system, above knee, ultra-light material (titanium, carbon fiber or equal) **DME** A
BETOS: D1F   Prosthetic/orthotic devices

C **L5960** Addition, endoskeletal system, hip disarticulation, ultra-light material (titanium, carbon fiber or equal) **DME** A
BETOS: D1F   Prosthetic/orthotic devices

C **L5961** Addition, endoskeletal system, polycentric hip joint, pneumatic or hydraulic control, rotation control, with or without flexion and/or extension control **DME** A
BETOS: D1F   Prosthetic/orthotic devices

C **L5962** Addition, endoskeletal system, below knee, flexible protective outer surface covering system **DME** A
BETOS: D1F   Prosthetic/orthotic devices

C **L5964** Addition, endoskeletal system, above knee, flexible protective outer surface covering system **DME** A
BETOS: D1F   Prosthetic/orthotic devices

C **L5966** Addition, endoskeletal system, hip disarticulation, flexible protective outer surface covering system **DME** A
BETOS: D1F   Prosthetic/orthotic devices

ANKLE AND/OR FOOT PROSTHETICS AND ADDITIONS (L5968-L5999)

C **L5968** Addition to lower limb prosthesis, multiaxial ankle with swing phase active dorsiflexion feature **DME** A
BETOS: D1F   Prosthetic/orthotic devices

C **L5969** Addition, endoskeletal ankle-foot or ankle system, power assist, includes any type motor(s) A
BETOS: D1F   Prosthetic/orthotic devices

C **L5970** All lower extremity prostheses, foot, external keel, SACH foot **DME** A
BETOS: D1F   Prosthetic/orthotic devices

C **L5971** All lower extremity prosthesis, solid ankle cushion heel (SACH) foot, replacement only **DME** A
BETOS: D1F   Prosthetic/orthotic devices

C **L5972** All lower extremity prostheses, foot, flexible keel **DME** A
BETOS: D1F   Prosthetic/orthotic devices

C **L5973** Endoskeletal ankle-foot system, microprocessor controlled feature, dorsiflexion and/or plantar flexion control, includes power source **DME** A
BETOS: D1F   Prosthetic/orthotic devices

C **L5974** All lower extremity prostheses, foot, single axis ankle/foot **DME** A
BETOS: D1F   Prosthetic/orthotic devices

C **L5975** All lower extremity prosthesis, combination single axis ankle and flexible keel foot **DME** A
BETOS: D1F   Prosthetic/orthotic devices

C **L5976** All lower extremity prostheses, energy storing foot (seattle carbon copy II or equal) **DME** A
BETOS: D1F   Prosthetic/orthotic devices

C **L5978** All lower extremity prostheses, foot, multiaxial ankle/foot **DME** A
BETOS: D1F   Prosthetic/orthotic devices

C **L5979** All lower extremity prosthesis, multi-axial ankle, dynamic response foot, one piece system **DME** A
BETOS: D1F   Prosthetic/orthotic devices

C **L5980** All lower extremity prostheses, flex foot system **DME** A
BETOS: D1F   Prosthetic/orthotic devices

C **L5981** All lower extremity prostheses, flex-walk system or equal **DME** A
BETOS: D1F   Prosthetic/orthotic devices

♂ Male only   ♀ Female only   **A** Age   A2 - Z3 = ASC Payment indicator   A - Y = APC Status indicator
ASC = ASC-approved procedure   **DME** Paid under the DME fee schedule   **MIPS** MIPS code

C L5982 All exoskeletal lower extremity prostheses, axial rotation unit DME A
BETOS: D1F   Prosthetic/orthotic devices

C L5984 All endoskeletal lower extremity prosthesis, axial rotation unit, with or without adjustability DME A
BETOS: D1F   Prosthetic/orthotic devices

C L5985 All endoskeletal lower extremity prostheses, dynamic prosthetic pylon DME A
BETOS: D1F   Prosthetic/orthotic devices

C L5986 All lower extremity prostheses, multi-axial rotation unit ('MCP' or equal) DME A
BETOS: D1F   Prosthetic/orthotic devices

C L5987 All lower extremity prosthesis, shank foot system with vertical loading pylon DME A
BETOS: D1F   Prosthetic/orthotic devices

C L5988 Addition to lower limb prosthesis, vertical shock reducing pylon feature DME A
BETOS: D1F   Prosthetic/orthotic devices

C L5990 Addition to lower extremity prosthesis, user adjustable heel height DME A
BETOS: D1F   Prosthetic/orthotic devices
Coding Clinic: 2002, Q1

C L5999 Lower extremity prosthesis, not otherwise specified A
BETOS: D1F   Prosthetic/orthotic devices

PARTIAL HAND PROSTHETICS (L6000-L6026)

C L6000 Partial hand, thumb remaining DME A
BETOS: D1F   Prosthetic/orthotic devices

C L6010 Partial hand, little and/or ring finger remaining DME A
BETOS: D1F   Prosthetic/orthotic devices

C L6020 Partial hand, no finger remaining DME A
BETOS: D1F   Prosthetic/orthotic devices

C L6026 Transcarpal/metacarpal or partial hand disarticulation prosthesis, external power, self-suspended, inner socket with removable forearm section, electrodes and cables, two batteries, charger, myoelectric control of terminal device, excludes terminal device(s) DME A
BETOS: D1F   Prosthetic/orthotic devices

WRIST DISARTICULATION, HAND PROSTHETICS (L6050-L6055)

C L6050 Wrist disarticulation, molded socket, flexible elbow hinges, triceps pad DME A
BETOS: D1F   Prosthetic/orthotic devices

C L6055 Wrist disarticulation, molded socket with expandable interface, flexible elbow hinges, triceps pad DME A
BETOS: D1F   Prosthetic/orthotic devices

BELOW ELBOW, FOREARM AND HAND PROSTHETICS (L6100-L6130)

C L6100 Below elbow, molded socket, flexible elbow hinge, triceps pad DME A
BETOS: D1F   Prosthetic/orthotic devices

C L6110 Below elbow, molded socket, (Muenster or Northwestern suspension types) DME A
BETOS: D1F   Prosthetic/orthotic devices

C L6120 Below elbow, molded double wall split socket, step-up hinges, half cuff DME A
BETOS: D1F   Prosthetic/orthotic devices

C L6130 Below elbow, molded double wall split socket, stump activated locking hinge, half cuff DME A
BETOS: D1F   Prosthetic/orthotic devices

ELBOW DISARTICULATION, FOREARM AND HAND PROSTHETICS (L6200-L6205)

C L6200 Elbow disarticulation, molded socket, outside locking hinge, forearm DME A
BETOS: D1F   Prosthetic/orthotic devices

C L6205 Elbow disarticulation, molded socket with expandable interface, outside locking hinges, forearm DME A
BETOS: D1F   Prosthetic/orthotic devices

ABOVE ELBOW, FOREARM AND HAND PROSTHETICS (L6250)

C L6250 Above elbow, molded double wall socket, internal locking elbow, forearm DME A
BETOS: D1F   Prosthetic/orthotic devices

SHOULDER DISARTICULATION, ARM AND HAND PROSTHETICS (L6300-L6320)

C L6300 Shoulder disarticulation, molded socket, shoulder bulkhead, humeral section, internal locking elbow, forearm DME A
BETOS: D1F   Prosthetic/orthotic devices

C L6310 Shoulder disarticulation, passive restoration (complete prosthesis) DME A
BETOS: D1F   Prosthetic/orthotic devices

C L6320 Shoulder disarticulation, passive restoration (shoulder cap only) DME A
BETOS: D1F   Prosthetic/orthotic devices

INTERSCAPULAR THORACIC, ARM, AND HAND PROSTHETICS (L6350-L6370)

C L6350 Interscapular thoracic, molded socket, shoulder bulkhead, humeral section, internal locking elbow, forearm DME A
BETOS: D1F   Prosthetic/orthotic devices

C L6360 Interscapular thoracic, passive restoration (complete prosthesis) DME A
BETOS: D1F   Prosthetic/orthotic devices

CPT® is a registered trademark of the American Medical Association. All rights reserved.

C **L6370** Interscapular thoracic, passive restoration (shoulder cap only) `DME` A
BETOS: D1F Prosthetic/orthotic devices

PROSTHETIC FITTING, IMMEDIATE POSTSURGICAL OR EARLY, UPPER LIMBS (L6380-L6388)

C **L6380** Immediate post surgical or early fitting, application of initial rigid dressing, including fitting alignment and suspension of components, and one cast change, wrist disarticulation or below elbow `DME` A
BETOS: D1F Prosthetic/orthotic devices

C **L6382** Immediate post surgical or early fitting, application of initial rigid dressing including fitting alignment and suspension of components, and one cast change, elbow disarticulation or above elbow `DME` A
BETOS: D1F Prosthetic/orthotic devices

C **L6384** Immediate post surgical or early fitting, application of initial rigid dressing including fitting alignment and suspension of components, and one cast change, shoulder disarticulation or interscapular thoracic `DME` A
BETOS: D1F Prosthetic/orthotic devices

C **L6386** Immediate post surgical or early fitting, each additional cast change and realignment `DME` A
BETOS: D1F Prosthetic/orthotic devices

C **L6388** Immediate post surgical or early fitting, application of rigid dressing only `DME` A
BETOS: D1F Prosthetic/orthotic devices

MOLDED SOCKET ENDOSKELETAL PROSTHETIC SYSTEM, UPPER LIMBS (L6400-L6570)

C **L6400** Below elbow, molded socket, endoskeletal system, including soft prosthetic tissue shaping `DME` A
BETOS: D1F Prosthetic/orthotic devices

C **L6450** Elbow disarticulation, molded socket, endoskeletal system, including soft prosthetic tissue shaping `DME` A
BETOS: D1F Prosthetic/orthotic devices

C **L6500** Above elbow, molded socket, endoskeletal system, including soft prosthetic tissue shaping `DME` A
BETOS: D1F Prosthetic/orthotic devices

C **L6550** Shoulder disarticulation, molded socket, endoskeletal system, including soft prosthetic tissue shaping `DME` A
BETOS: D1F Prosthetic/orthotic devices

C **L6570** Interscapular thoracic, molded socket, endoskeletal system, including soft prosthetic tissue shaping `DME` A
BETOS: D1F Prosthetic/orthotic devices

PREPARATORY PROSTHETIC, UPPER LIMBS (L6580-L6590)

C **L6580** Preparatory, wrist disarticulation or below elbow, single wall plastic socket, friction wrist, flexible elbow hinges, figure of eight harness, humeral cuff, Bowden cable control, USMC or equal pylon, no cover, molded to patient model `DME` A
BETOS: D1F Prosthetic/orthotic devices

C **L6582** Preparatory, wrist disarticulation or below elbow, single wall socket, friction wrist, flexible elbow hinges, figure of eight harness, humeral cuff, Bowden cable control, USMC or equal pylon, no cover, direct formed `DME` A
BETOS: D1F Prosthetic/orthotic devices

C **L6584** Preparatory, elbow disarticulation or above elbow, single wall plastic socket, friction wrist, locking elbow, figure of eight harness, fair lead cable control, USMC or equal pylon, no cover, molded to patient model `DME` A
BETOS: D1F Prosthetic/orthotic devices

C **L6586** Preparatory, elbow disarticulation or above elbow, single wall socket, friction wrist, locking elbow, figure of eight harness, fair lead cable control, USMC or equal pylon, no cover, direct formed `DME` A
BETOS: D1F Prosthetic/orthotic devices

C **L6588** Preparatory, shoulder disarticulation or interscapular thoracic, single wall plastic socket, shoulder joint, locking elbow, friction wrist, chest strap, fair lead cable control, USMC or equal pylon, no cover, molded to patient model `DME` A
BETOS: D1F Prosthetic/orthotic devices

C **L6590** Preparatory, shoulder disarticulation or interscapular thoracic, single wall socket, shoulder joint, locking elbow, friction wrist, chest strap, fair lead cable control, USMC or equal pylon, no cover, direct formed `DME` A
BETOS: D1F Prosthetic/orthotic devices

UPPER EXTREMITY PROSTHETIC ADDITIONS (L6600-L6698)

C **L6600** Upper extremity additions, polycentric hinge, pair `DME` A
BETOS: D1F Prosthetic/orthotic devices

C **L6605** Upper extremity additions, single pivot hinge, pair `DME` A
BETOS: D1F Prosthetic/orthotic devices

C **L6610** Upper extremity additions, flexible metal hinge, pair `DME` A
BETOS: D1F Prosthetic/orthotic devices

C **L6611** Addition to upper extremity prosthesis, external powered, additional switch, any type `DME` A
BETOS: D1F Prosthetic/orthotic devices

C **L6615** Upper extremity addition, disconnect locking wrist unit `DME` A
BETOS: D1F Prosthetic/orthotic devices

♂ Male only   ♀ Female only   Ⓐ Age   A2 - Z3 = ASC Payment indicator   A - Y = APC Status indicator
ASC = ASC-approved procedure   `DME` Paid under the DME fee schedule   `MIPS` MIPS code

C L6616 Upper extremity addition, additional disconnect insert for locking wrist unit, each [DME] A
    BETOS: D1F   Prosthetic/orthotic devices

C L6620 Upper extremity addition, flexion/extension wrist unit, with or without friction [DME] A
    BETOS: D1F   Prosthetic/orthotic devices

C L6621 Upper extremity prosthesis addition, flexion/extension wrist with or without friction, for use with external powered terminal device [DME] A
    BETOS: D1F   Prosthetic/orthotic devices

C L6623 Upper extremity addition, spring assisted rotational wrist unit with latch release [DME] A
    BETOS: D1F   Prosthetic/orthotic devices

C L6624 Upper extremity addition, flexion/extension and rotation wrist unit [DME] A
    BETOS: D1F   Prosthetic/orthotic devices

C L6625 Upper extremity addition, rotation wrist unit with cable lock [DME] A
    BETOS: D1F   Prosthetic/orthotic devices

C L6628 Upper extremity addition, quick disconnect hook adapter, Otto Bock or equal [DME] A
    BETOS: D1F   Prosthetic/orthotic devices

C L6629 Upper extremity addition, quick disconnect lamination collar with coupling piece, Otto Bock or equal [DME] A
    BETOS: D1F   Prosthetic/orthotic devices

C L6630 Upper extremity addition, stainless steel, any wrist [DME] A
    BETOS: D1F   Prosthetic/orthotic devices

C L6632 Upper extremity addition, latex suspension sleeve, each [DME] A
    BETOS: D1F   Prosthetic/orthotic devices

C L6635 Upper extremity addition, lift assist for elbow [DME] A
    BETOS: D1F   Prosthetic/orthotic devices

C L6637 Upper extremity addition, nudge control elbow lock [DME] A
    BETOS: D1F   Prosthetic/orthotic devices

C L6638 Upper extremity addition to prosthesis, electric locking feature, only for use with manually powered elbow [DME] A
    BETOS: D1F   Prosthetic/orthotic devices

C L6640 Upper extremity additions, shoulder abduction joint, pair [DME] A
    BETOS: D1F   Prosthetic/orthotic devices

C L6641 Upper extremity addition, excursion amplifier, pulley type [DME] A
    BETOS: D1F   Prosthetic/orthotic devices

C L6642 Upper extremity addition, excursion amplifier, lever type [DME] A
    BETOS: D1F   Prosthetic/orthotic devices

C L6645 Upper extremity addition, shoulder flexion-abduction joint, each [DME] A
    BETOS: D1F   Prosthetic/orthotic devices

C L6646 Upper extremity addition, shoulder joint, multipositional locking, flexion, adjustable abduction friction control, for use with body powered or external powered system [DME] A
    BETOS: D1F   Prosthetic/orthotic devices

C L6647 Upper extremity addition, shoulder lock mechanism, body powered actuator [DME] A
    BETOS: D1F   Prosthetic/orthotic devices

C L6648 Upper extremity addition, shoulder lock mechanism, external powered actuator [DME] A
    BETOS: D1F   Prosthetic/orthotic devices

C L6650 Upper extremity addition, shoulder universal joint, each [DME] A
    BETOS: D1F   Prosthetic/orthotic devices

C L6655 Upper extremity addition, standard control cable, extra [DME] A
    BETOS: D1F   Prosthetic/orthotic devices

C L6660 Upper extremity addition, heavy duty control cable [DME] A
    BETOS: D1F   Prosthetic/orthotic devices

C L6665 Upper extremity addition, Teflon, or equal, cable lining [DME] A
    BETOS: D1F   Prosthetic/orthotic devices

C L6670 Upper extremity addition, hook to hand, cable adapter [DME] A
    BETOS: D1F   Prosthetic/orthotic devices

C L6672 Upper extremity addition, harness, chest or shoulder, saddle type [DME] A
    BETOS: D1F   Prosthetic/orthotic devices

C L6675 Upper extremity addition, harness, (e.g., figure of eight type), single cable design [DME] A
    BETOS: D1F   Prosthetic/orthotic devices

C L6676 Upper extremity addition, harness, (e.g., figure of eight type), dual cable design [DME] A
    BETOS: D1F   Prosthetic/orthotic devices

C L6677 Upper extremity addition, harness, triple control, simultaneous operation of terminal device and elbow [DME] A
    BETOS: D1F   Prosthetic/orthotic devices

C L6680 Upper extremity addition, test socket, wrist disarticulation or below elbow [DME] A
    BETOS: D1F   Prosthetic/orthotic devices

C L6682 Upper extremity addition, test socket, elbow disarticulation or above elbow [DME] A
    BETOS: D1F   Prosthetic/orthotic devices

C L6684 Upper extremity addition, test socket, shoulder disarticulation or interscapular thoracic [DME] A
    BETOS: D1F   Prosthetic/orthotic devices

▲ Revised code   ● New code   C Carrier judgment   D Special coverage instructions apply
I Not payable by Medicare   M Non-covered by Medicare   S Non-covered by Medicare statute   AHA Coding Clinic®

C L6686 Upper extremity addition, suction socket `DME` A
BETOS: D1F   Prosthetic/orthotic devices

C L6687 Upper extremity addition, frame type socket, below elbow or wrist disarticulation `DME` A
BETOS: D1F   Prosthetic/orthotic devices

C L6688 Upper extremity addition, frame type socket, above elbow or elbow disarticulation `DME` A
BETOS: D1F   Prosthetic/orthotic devices

C L6689 Upper extremity addition, frame type socket, shoulder disarticulation `DME` A
BETOS: D1F   Prosthetic/orthotic devices

C L6690 Upper extremity addition, frame type socket, interscapular-thoracic `DME` A
BETOS: D1F   Prosthetic/orthotic devices

C L6691 Upper extremity addition, removable insert, each `DME` A
BETOS: D1F   Prosthetic/orthotic devices

C L6692 Upper extremity addition, silicone gel insert or equal, each `DME` A
BETOS: D1F   Prosthetic/orthotic devices

C L6693 Upper extremity addition, locking elbow, forearm counterbalance `DME` A
BETOS: D1F   Prosthetic/orthotic devices

C L6694 Addition to upper extremity prosthesis, below elbow/above elbow, custom fabricated from existing mold or prefabricated, socket insert, silicone gel, elastomeric or equal, for use with locking mechanism `DME` A
BETOS: D1F   Prosthetic/orthotic devices

C L6695 Addition to upper extremity prosthesis, below elbow/above elbow, custom fabricated from existing mold or prefabricated, socket insert, silicone gel, elastomeric or equal, not for use with locking mechanism `DME` A
BETOS: D1F   Prosthetic/orthotic devices

C L6696 Addition to upper extremity prosthesis, below elbow/above elbow, custom fabricated socket insert for congenital or atypical traumatic amputee, silicone gel, elastomeric or equal, for use with or without locking mechanism, initial only (for other than initial, use code L6694 or L6695) `DME` A
BETOS: D1F   Prosthetic/orthotic devices

C L6697 Addition to upper extremity prosthesis, below elbow/above elbow, custom fabricated socket insert for other than congenital or atypical traumatic amputee, silicone gel, elastomeric or equal, for use with or without locking mechanism, initial only (for other than initial, use code L6694 or L6695) `DME` A
BETOS: D1F   Prosthetic/orthotic devices

C L6698 Addition to upper extremity prosthesis, below elbow/above elbow, lock mechanism, excludes socket insert `DME` A
BETOS: D1F   Prosthetic/orthotic devices

TERMINAL DEVICES AND ADDITIONS (L6703-L6882)

C L6703 Terminal device, passive hand/mitt, any material, any size `DME` A
BETOS: D1F   Prosthetic/orthotic devices

C L6704 Terminal device, sport/recreational/work attachment, any material, any size `DME` A
BETOS: D1F   Prosthetic/orthotic devices

C L6706 Terminal device, hook, mechanical, voluntary opening, any material, any size, lined or unlined `DME` A
BETOS: D1F   Prosthetic/orthotic devices

C L6707 Terminal device, hook, mechanical, voluntary closing, any material, any size, lined or unlined `DME` A
BETOS: D1F   Prosthetic/orthotic devices

C L6708 Terminal device, hand, mechanical, voluntary opening, any material, any size `DME` A
BETOS: D1F   Prosthetic/orthotic devices

C L6709 Terminal device, hand, mechanical, voluntary closing, any material, any size `DME` A
BETOS: D1F   Prosthetic/orthotic devices

C L6711 Terminal device, hook, mechanical, voluntary opening, any material, any size, lined or unlined, pediatric `DME` ⒶA
BETOS: D1F   Prosthetic/orthotic devices
Coding Clinic: 2008, Q4

C L6712 Terminal device, hook, mechanical, voluntary closing, any material, any size, lined or unlined, pediatric `DME` ⒶA
BETOS: D1F   Prosthetic/orthotic devices
Coding Clinic: 2008, Q4

C L6713 Terminal device, hand, mechanical, voluntary opening, any material, any size, pediatric `DME` ⒶA
BETOS: D1F   Prosthetic/orthotic devices
Coding Clinic: 2008, Q4

C L6714 Terminal device, hand, mechanical, voluntary closing, any material, any size, pediatric `DME` ⒶA
BETOS: D1F   Prosthetic/orthotic devices
Coding Clinic: 2008, Q4

C L6715 Terminal device, multiple articulating digit, includes motor(s), initial issue or replacement `DME` A
BETOS: D1F   Prosthetic/orthotic devices

C L6721 Terminal device, hook or hand, heavy duty, mechanical, voluntary opening, any material, any size, lined or unlined `DME` A
BETOS: D1F   Prosthetic/orthotic devices
Coding Clinic: 2008, Q4

C L6722 Terminal device, hook or hand, heavy duty, mechanical, voluntary closing, any material, any size, lined or unlined `DME` A
BETOS: D1F   Prosthetic/orthotic devices
Coding Clinic: 2008, Q4

♂ Male only   ♀ Female only   Ⓐ Age   A2 - Z3 = ASC Payment indicator   A - Y = APC Status indicator
ASC = ASC-approved procedure   `DME` Paid under the DME fee schedule   `MIPS` MIPS code

D **L6805** Addition to terminal device, modifier wrist unit DME A

    BETOS: D1F Prosthetic/orthotic devices

D **L6810** Addition to terminal device, precision pinch device DME A

    BETOS: D1F Prosthetic/orthotic devices

C **L6880** Electric hand, switch or myoelectric controlled, independently articulating digits, any grasp pattern or combination of grasp patterns, includes motor(s) DME A

    BETOS: D1F Prosthetic/orthotic devices

C **L6881** Automatic grasp feature, addition to upper limb electric prosthetic terminal device DME A

    BETOS: D1F Prosthetic/orthotic devices
    Coding Clinic: 2002, Q1

D **L6882** Microprocessor control feature, addition to upper limb prosthetic terminal device DME A

    BETOS: D1F Prosthetic/orthotic devices
    Coding Clinic: 2002, Q1

REPLACEMENT SOCKETS, UPPER LIMBS (L6883-L6885)

C **L6883** Replacement socket, below elbow/wrist disarticulation, molded to patient model, for use with or without external power DME A

    BETOS: D1F Prosthetic/orthotic devices

C **L6884** Replacement socket, above elbow/elbow disarticulation, molded to patient model, for use with or without external power DME A

    BETOS: D1F Prosthetic/orthotic devices

C **L6885** Replacement socket, shoulder disarticulation/interscapular thoracic, molded to patient model, for use with or without external power DME A

    BETOS: D1F Prosthetic/orthotic devices

HAND RESTORATION PROSTHETICS AND ADDITIONS (L6890-L6915)

C **L6890** Addition to upper extremity prosthesis, glove for terminal device, any material, prefabricated, includes fitting and adjustment DME A

    BETOS: D1F Prosthetic/orthotic devices

C **L6895** Addition to upper extremity prosthesis, glove for terminal device, any material, custom fabricated DME A

    BETOS: D1F Prosthetic/orthotic devices

C **L6900** Hand restoration (casts, shading and measurements included), partial hand, with glove, thumb or one finger remaining DME A

    BETOS: D1F Prosthetic/orthotic devices

C **L6905** Hand restoration (casts, shading and measurements included), partial hand, with glove, multiple fingers remaining DME A

    BETOS: D1F Prosthetic/orthotic devices

C **L6910** Hand restoration (casts, shading and measurements included), partial hand, with glove, no fingers remaining DME A

    BETOS: D1F Prosthetic/orthotic devices

C **L6915** Hand restoration (shading, and measurements included), replacement glove for above DME A

    BETOS: D1F Prosthetic/orthotic devices

EXTERNAL POWER UPPER LIMB PROSTHETICS (L6920-L6975)

C **L6920** Wrist disarticulation, external power, self-suspended inner socket, removable forearm shell, Otto Bock or equal, switch, cables, two batteries and one charger, switch control of terminal device DME A

    BETOS: D1F Prosthetic/orthotic devices

C **L6925** Wrist disarticulation, external power, self-suspended inner socket, removable forearm shell, Otto Bock or equal electrodes, cables, two batteries and one charger, myoelectronic control of terminal device DME A

    BETOS: D1F Prosthetic/orthotic devices

C **L6930** Below elbow, external power, self-suspended inner socket, removable forearm shell, Otto Bock or equal switch, cables, two batteries and one charger, switch control of terminal device DME A

    BETOS: D1F Prosthetic/orthotic devices

C **L6935** Below elbow, external power, self-suspended inner socket, removable forearm shell, Otto Bock or equal electrodes, cables, two batteries and one charger, myoelectronic control of terminal device DME A

    BETOS: D1F Prosthetic/orthotic devices

C **L6940** Elbow disarticulation, external power, molded inner socket, removable humeral shell, outside locking hinges, forearm, Otto Bock or equal switch, cables, two batteries and one charger, switch control of terminal device DME A

    BETOS: D1F Prosthetic/orthotic devices

C **L6945** Elbow disarticulation, external power, molded inner socket, removable humeral shell, outside locking hinges, forearm, Otto Bock or equal electrodes, cables, two batteries and one charger, myoelectronic control of terminal device DME A

    BETOS: D1F Prosthetic/orthotic devices

C **L6950** Above elbow, external power, molded inner socket, removable humeral shell, internal locking elbow, forearm, Otto Bock or equal switch, cables, two batteries and one charger, switch control of terminal device DME A

    BETOS: D1F Prosthetic/orthotic devices

▲ Revised code   ● New code   **C** Carrier judgment   **D** Special coverage instructions apply
I Not payable by Medicare   **M** Non-covered by Medicare   **S** Non-covered by Medicare statute   AHA Coding Clinic®

C **L6955** Above elbow, external power, molded inner socket, removable humeral shell, internal locking elbow, forearm, Otto Bock or equal electrodes, cables, two batteries and one charger, myoelectronic control of terminal device **DME** A

    BETOS: D1F   Prosthetic/orthotic devices

C **L6960** Shoulder disarticulation, external power, molded inner socket, removable shoulder shell, shoulder bulkhead, humeral section, mechanical elbow, forearm, Otto Bock or equal switch, cables, two batteries and one charger, switch control of terminal device **DME** A

    BETOS: D1F   Prosthetic/orthotic devices

C **L6965** Shoulder disarticulation, external power, molded inner socket, removable shoulder shell, shoulder bulkhead, humeral section, mechanical elbow, forearm, Otto Bock or equal electrodes, cables, two batteries and one charger, myoelectronic control of terminal device **DME** A

    BETOS: D1F   Prosthetic/orthotic devices

C **L6970** Interscapular-thoracic, external power, molded inner socket, removable shoulder shell, shoulder bulkhead, humeral section, mechanical elbow, forearm, Otto Bock or equal switch, cables, two batteries and one charger, switch control of terminal device **DME** A

    BETOS: D1F   Prosthetic/orthotic devices

C **L6975** Interscapular-thoracic, external power, molded inner socket, removable shoulder shell, shoulder bulkhead, humeral section, mechanical elbow, forearm, Otto Bock or equal electrodes, cables, two batteries and one charger, myoelectronic control of terminal device **DME** A

    BETOS: D1F   Prosthetic/orthotic devices

ELECTRIC HAND OR HOOK AND ADDITIONS (L7007-L7045)

C **L7007** Electric hand, switch or myoelectric controlled, adult **DME** Ⓐ A

    BETOS: D1F   Prosthetic/orthotic devices

C **L7008** Electric hand, switch or myoelectric, controlled, pediatric **DME** Ⓐ A

    BETOS: D1F   Prosthetic/orthotic devices

C **L7009** Electric hook, switch or myoelectric controlled, adult **DME** Ⓐ A

    BETOS: D1F   Prosthetic/orthotic devices

C **L7040** Prehensile actuator, switch controlled **DME** A

    BETOS: D1F   Prosthetic/orthotic devices

C **L7045** Electric hook, switch or myoelectric controlled, pediatric **DME** Ⓐ A

    BETOS: D1F   Prosthetic/orthotic devices

ELECTRONIC ELBOW AND ADDITIONS (L7170-L7259)

C **L7170** Electronic elbow, Hosmer or equal, switch controlled **DME** A

    BETOS: D1F   Prosthetic/orthotic devices

C **L7180** Electronic elbow, microprocessor sequential control of elbow and terminal device **DME** A

    BETOS: D1F   Prosthetic/orthotic devices

C **L7181** Electronic elbow, microprocessor simultaneous control of elbow and terminal device **DME** A

    BETOS: D1F   Prosthetic/orthotic devices

C **L7185** Electronic elbow, adolescent, Variety Village or equal, switch controlled **DME** A

    BETOS: D1F   Prosthetic/orthotic devices

C **L7186** Electronic elbow, child, Variety Village or equal, switch controlled **DME** Ⓐ A

    BETOS: D1F   Prosthetic/orthotic devices

C **L7190** Electronic elbow, adolescent, Variety Village or equal, myoelectronically controlled **DME** A

    BETOS: D1F   Prosthetic/orthotic devices

C **L7191** Electronic elbow, child, Variety Village or equal, myoelectronically controlled **DME** Ⓐ A

    BETOS: D1F   Prosthetic/orthotic devices

C **L7259** Electronic wrist rotator, any type **DME** A

    BETOS: D1F   Prosthetic/orthotic devices

BATTERIES AND ACCESSORIES (L7360-L7368)

C **L7360** Six volt battery, each **DME** A

    BETOS: D1F   Prosthetic/orthotic devices

C **L7362** Battery charger, six volt, each **DME** A

    BETOS: D1F   Prosthetic/orthotic devices

C **L7364** Twelve volt battery, each **DME** A

    BETOS: D1F   Prosthetic/orthotic devices

C **L7366** Battery charger, twelve volt, each **DME** A

    BETOS: D1F   Prosthetic/orthotic devices

C **L7367** Lithium ion battery, rechargeable, replacement **DME** A

    BETOS: D1F   Prosthetic/orthotic devices

C **L7368** Lithium ion battery charger, replacement only **DME** A

    BETOS: D1F   Prosthetic/orthotic devices

ADDITIONS FOR UPPER EXTREMITY PROSTHETICS (L7400-L7405)

C **L7400** Addition to upper extremity prosthesis, below elbow/wrist disarticulation, ultralight material (titanium, carbon fiber or equal) **DME** A

    BETOS: D1F   Prosthetic/orthotic devices

♂ Male only   ♀ Female only   Ⓐ Age   A2 - Z3 = ASC Payment indicator   A - Y = APC Status indicator

ASC = ASC-approved procedure   **DME** Paid under the DME fee schedule   **MIPS** MIPS code

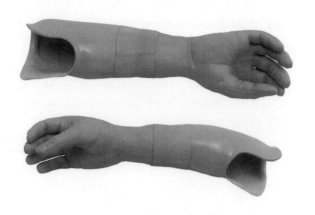

Arm prosthesis

C L7401 Addition to upper extremity prosthesis, above elbow disarticulation, ultralight material (titanium, carbon fiber or equal) DME A
  BETOS: D1F   Prosthetic/orthotic devices

C L7402 Addition to upper extremity prosthesis, shoulder disarticulation/interscapular thoracic, ultralight material (titanium, carbon fiber or equal) DME A
  BETOS: D1F   Prosthetic/orthotic devices

C L7403 Addition to upper extremity prosthesis, below elbow/wrist disarticulation, acrylic material DME A
  BETOS: D1F   Prosthetic/orthotic devices

C L7404 Addition to upper extremity prosthesis, above elbow disarticulation, acrylic material DME A
  BETOS: D1F   Prosthetic/orthotic devices

C L7405 Addition to upper extremity prosthesis, shoulder disarticulation/interscapular thoracic, acrylic material DME A
  BETOS: D1F   Prosthetic/orthotic devices

UPPER EXTREMITY PROSTHETICS, NOT OTHERWISE SPECIFIED (NOS) (L7499)

C L7499 Upper extremity prosthesis, not otherwise specified A
  BETOS: D1F   Prosthetic/orthotic devices

PROSTHETIC REPAIR (L7510, L7520)

D L7510 Repair of prosthetic device, repair or replace minor parts A
  BETOS: D1F   Prosthetic/orthotic devices

C L7520 Repair prosthetic device, labor component, per 15 minutes A
  BETOS: D1F   Prosthetic/orthotic devices

PROSTHETIC DONNING SLEEVE (L7600)

S L7600 Prosthetic donning sleeve, any material, each E1

  BETOS: D1F   Prosthetic/orthotic devices
  Service not separately priced by Part B
  Statute: 1862(1)(a)

GASKET OR SEAL WITH PROSTHETIC (L7700)

● **C L7700** Gasket or seal, for use with prosthetic socket insert, any type, each
  BETOS: D1F   Prosthetic/orthotic devices

PENILE PROSTHETICS (L7900, L7902)

S L7900 Male vacuum erection system ♂ E1
  BETOS: D1F   Prosthetic/orthotic devices
  Service not separately priced by Part B
  Statute: 1834a

S L7902 Tension ring, for vacuum erection device, any type, replacement only, each E1
  BETOS: D1F   Prosthetic/orthotic devices
  Service not separately priced by Part B
  Statute: 1834a

BREAST PROSTHETICS AND ACCESSORIES (L8000-L8039), SEE ALSO PROSTHETIC BREAST IMPLANT (L8600)

D L8000 Breast prosthesis, mastectomy bra, without integrated breast prosthesis form, any size, any type ♀ DME A
  BETOS: D1F   Prosthetic/orthotic devices

D L8001 Breast prosthesis, mastectomy bra, with integrated breast prosthesis form, unilateral, any size, any type ♀ DME A
  BETOS: D1F   Prosthetic/orthotic devices
  Coding Clinic: 2002, Q1

D L8002 Breast prosthesis, mastectomy bra, with integrated breast prosthesis form, bilateral, any size, any type ♀ DME A
  BETOS: D1F   Prosthetic/orthotic devices
  Coding Clinic: 2002, Q1

D L8010 Breast prosthesis, mastectomy sleeve ♀ A
  BETOS: D1F   Prosthetic/orthotic devices
  Service not separately priced by Part B

D L8015 External breast prosthesis garment, with mastectomy form, post mastectomy ♀ DME A
  BETOS: D1F   Prosthetic/orthotic devices

D L8020 Breast prosthesis, mastectomy form ♀ DME A
  BETOS: D1F   Prosthetic/orthotic devices

D L8030 Breast prosthesis, silicone or equal, without integral adhesive ♀ DME A
  BETOS: D1F   Prosthetic/orthotic devices

D L8031 Breast prosthesis, silicone or equal, with integral adhesive ♀ DME A
  BETOS: D1F   Prosthetic/orthotic devices

C L8032 Nipple prosthesis, reusable, any type, each ♀ DME A
  BETOS: D1F   Prosthetic/orthotic devices

D **L8035** Custom breast prosthesis, post mastectomy, molded to patient model ♀ DME A
BETOS: D1F Prosthetic/orthotic devices

C **L8039** Breast prosthesis, not otherwise specified ♀ A
BETOS: D1F Prosthetic/orthotic devices

FACIAL AND EXTERNAL EAR PROSTHETICS (L8040-L8049)

C **L8040** Nasal prosthesis, provided by a non-physician DME A
BETOS: D1F Prosthetic/orthotic devices
DME Modifier: KM,KN

C **L8041** Midfacial prosthesis, provided by a non-physician DME A
BETOS: D1F Prosthetic/orthotic devices
DME Modifier: KM,KN

C **L8042** Orbital prosthesis, provided by a non-physician DME A
BETOS: D1F Prosthetic/orthotic devices
DME Modifier: KM,KN

C **L8043** Upper facial prosthesis, provided by a non-physician DME A
BETOS: D1F Prosthetic/orthotic devices
DME Modifier: KM,KN

C **L8044** Hemi-facial prosthesis, provided by a non-physician DME A
BETOS: D1F Prosthetic/orthotic devices
DME Modifier: KM,KN

C **L8045** Auricular prosthesis, provided by a non-physician DME A
BETOS: D1F Prosthetic/orthotic devices
DME Modifier: KM,KN

C **L8046** Partial facial prosthesis, provided by a non-physician DME A
BETOS: D1F Prosthetic/orthotic devices
DME Modifier: KM,KN

C **L8047** Nasal septal prosthesis, provided by a non-physician DME A
BETOS: D1F Prosthetic/orthotic devices
DME Modifier: KM,KN

C **L8048** Unspecified maxillofacial prosthesis, by report, provided by a non-physician A
BETOS: D1F Prosthetic/orthotic devices

C **L8049** Repair or modification of maxillofacial prosthesis, labor component, 15 minute increments, provided by a non-physician A
BETOS: D1F Prosthetic/orthotic devices

HERNIA TRUSSES (L8300-L8330)

D **L8300** Truss, single with standard pad DME A
BETOS: D1F Prosthetic/orthotic devices

D **L8310** Truss, double with standard pads DME A
BETOS: D1F Prosthetic/orthotic devices

D **L8320** Truss, addition to standard pad, water pad DME A
BETOS: D1F Prosthetic/orthotic devices

D **L8330** Truss, addition to standard pad, scrotal pad ♂ DME A
BETOS: D1F Prosthetic/orthotic devices

PROSTHETIC SHEATHS, SOCKS, AND SHRINKERS (L8400-L8485)

D **L8400** Prosthetic sheath, below knee, each DME A
BETOS: D1F Prosthetic/orthotic devices

D **L8410** Prosthetic sheath, above knee, each DME A
BETOS: D1F Prosthetic/orthotic devices

D **L8415** Prosthetic sheath, upper limb, each DME A
BETOS: D1F Prosthetic/orthotic devices

C **L8417** Prosthetic sheath/sock, including a gel cushion layer, below knee or above knee, each DME A
BETOS: D1F Prosthetic/orthotic devices

D **L8420** Prosthetic sock, multiple ply, below knee, each DME A
BETOS: D1F Prosthetic/orthotic devices

D **L8430** Prosthetic sock, multiple ply, above knee, each DME A
BETOS: D1F Prosthetic/orthotic devices

D **L8435** Prosthetic sock, multiple ply, upper limb, each DME A
BETOS: D1F Prosthetic/orthotic devices

D **L8440** Prosthetic shrinker, below knee, each DME A
BETOS: D1F Prosthetic/orthotic devices

D **L8460** Prosthetic shrinker, above knee, each DME A
BETOS: D1F Prosthetic/orthotic devices

D **L8465** Prosthetic shrinker, upper limb, each DME A
BETOS: D1F Prosthetic/orthotic devices

D **L8470** Prosthetic sock, single ply, fitting, below knee, each DME A
BETOS: D1F Prosthetic/orthotic devices

D **L8480** Prosthetic sock, single ply, fitting, above knee, each DME A
BETOS: D1F Prosthetic/orthotic devices

D **L8485** Prosthetic sock, single ply, fitting, upper limb, each DME A
BETOS: D1F Prosthetic/orthotic devices

UNLISTED PROSTHETIC PROCEDURES (L8499)

C **L8499** Unlisted procedure for miscellaneous prosthetic services A
BETOS: D1F Prosthetic/orthotic devices

VOICE PROSTHETICS AND ACCESSORIES (L8500-L8515)

D **L8500** Artificial larynx, any type DME A
BETOS: D1F Prosthetic/orthotic devices

♂ Male only   ♀ Female only   **A** Age   A2 - Z3 = ASC Payment indicator   A - Y = APC Status indicator
ASC = ASC-approved procedure   DME Paid under the DME fee schedule   MIPS MIPS code

CPT® is a registered trademark of the American Medical Association. All rights reserved.

339

D **L8501** Tracheostomy speaking valve   DME A
   BETOS: D1F   Prosthetic/orthotic devices

C **L8505** Artificial larynx replacement battery/
   accessory, any type   A
   BETOS: D1F   Prosthetic/orthotic devices
   Coding Clinic: 2002, Q1

C **L8507** Tracheo-esophageal voice prosthesis,
   patient inserted, any type, each   DME A
   BETOS: D1F   Prosthetic/orthotic devices
   Coding Clinic: 2002, Q1

C **L8509** Tracheo-esophageal voice prosthesis,
   inserted by a licensed health care provider,
   any type   DME A
   BETOS: D1F   Prosthetic/orthotic devices
   Coding Clinic: 2002, Q1

D **L8510** Voice amplifier   DME A
   BETOS: D1F   Prosthetic/orthotic devices
   Coding Clinic: 2002, Q1

C **L8511** Insert for indwelling tracheoesophageal
   prosthesis, with or without valve,
   replacement only, each   DME A
   BETOS: D1F   Prosthetic/orthotic devices

C **L8512** Gelatin capsules or equivalent, for use
   with tracheoesophageal voice prosthesis,
   replacement only, per 10   DME A
   BETOS: D1F   Prosthetic/orthotic devices

C **L8513** Cleaning device used with
   tracheoesophageal voice prosthesis,
   pipet, brush, or equal, replacement only,
   each   DME A
   BETOS: D1F   Prosthetic/orthotic devices

C **L8514** Tracheoesophageal puncture dilator,
   replacement only, each   DME A
   BETOS: D1F   Prosthetic/orthotic devices

C **L8515** Gelatin capsule, application device for use
   with tracheoesophageal voice prosthesis,
   each   DME A
   BETOS: D1F   Prosthetic/orthotic devices

**PROSTHETIC BREAST IMPLANT (L8600), SEE ALSO BREAST
PROSTHETICS AND ACCESSORIES (L8000-L8039)**

D **L8600** Implantable breast prosthesis, silicone or
   equal   N1 ♀ DME ASC N
   BETOS: D1F   Prosthetic/orthotic devices

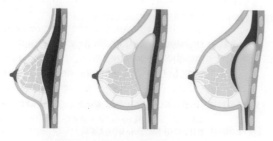

Breast prosthesis augmentation

BULKING AGENTS (L8603-L8607)

D **L8603** Injectable bulking agent, collagen
   implant, urinary tract, 2.5 ml syringe,
   includes shipping and necessary
   supplies   N1 DME ASC N
   BETOS: D1F   Prosthetic/orthotic devices

C **L8604** Injectable bulking agent, dextranomer/
   hyaluronic acid copolymer implant, urinary
   tract, 1 ml, includes shipping and necessary
   supplies   N1 ASC N
   BETOS: D1F   Prosthetic/orthotic devices
   Service not separately priced by Part B
   Coding Clinic: 2008, Q4

C **L8605** Injectable bulking agent, dextranomer/
   hyaluronic acid copolymer implant, anal
   canal, 1 ml, includes shipping and necessary
   supplies   N1 DME ASC N
   BETOS: D1F   Prosthetic/orthotic devices

D **L8606** Injectable bulking agent, synthetic implant,
   urinary tract, 1 ml syringe, includes shipping
   and necessary supplies   N1 DME ASC N
   BETOS: D1F   Prosthetic/orthotic devices

D **L8607** Injectable bulking agent for vocal cord
   medialization, 0.1 ml, includes shipping and
   necessary supplies   N1 DME ASC N
   BETOS: D1F   Prosthetic/orthotic devices

**IMPLANTABLE EYE AND EAR PROSTHETICS AND
ACCESSORIES (L8609-L8629)**

C **L8609** Artificial cornea   N1 DME ASC N
   BETOS: D1F   Prosthetic/orthotic devices

D **L8610** Ocular implant   N1 DME ASC N
   BETOS: D1F   Prosthetic/orthotic devices

D **L8612** Aqueous shunt   N1 DME ASC N
   BETOS: D1F   Prosthetic/orthotic devices

D **L8613** Ossicula implant   N1 DME ASC N
   BETOS: D1F   Prosthetic/orthotic devices

D **L8614** Cochlear device, includes all internal and
   external components   N1 DME ASC N
   BETOS: D1F   Prosthetic/orthotic devices
   Coding Clinic: 2001, Q1; 2002, Q3; 2003,
   Q4
   Pub: 100-4, Chap. 14, 40.8

D **L8615** Headset/headpiece for use with cochlear
   implant device, replacement   DME A
   BETOS: D1F   Prosthetic/orthotic devices

D **L8616** Microphone for use with cochlear implant
   device, replacement   DME A
   BETOS: D1F   Prosthetic/orthotic devices

D **L8617** Transmitting coil for use with cochlear
   implant device, replacement   DME A
   BETOS: D1F   Prosthetic/orthotic devices

▲ Revised code   ● New code   **C** Carrier judgment   **D** Special coverage instructions apply
I Not payable by Medicare   **M** Non-covered by Medicare   **S** Non-covered by Medicare statute   AHA Coding Clinic®

▲ D **L8618** Transmitter cable for use with cochlear implant device or auditory osseointegrated device, replacement `DME` A

   BETOS: D1F   Prosthetic/orthotic devices

D **L8619** Cochlear implant, external speech processor and controller, integrated system, replacement `DME` A

   BETOS: D1F   Prosthetic/orthotic devices

Cochlear device

C **L8621** Zinc air battery for use with cochlear implant device and auditory osseointegrated sound processors, replacement, each `DME` A

   BETOS: D1F   Prosthetic/orthotic devices

C **L8622** Alkaline battery for use with cochlear implant device, any size, replacement, each `DME` A

   BETOS: D1F   Prosthetic/orthotic devices

C **L8623** Lithium ion battery for use with cochlear implant device speech processor, other than ear level, replacement, each `DME` A

   BETOS: D1F   Prosthetic/orthotic devices

▲ C **L8624** Lithium ion battery for use with cochlear implant or auditory osseointegrated device speech processor, ear level, replacement, each `DME` A

   BETOS: D1F   Prosthetic/orthotic devices

● D **L8625** External recharging system for battery for use with cochlear implant or auditory osseointegrated device, replacement only, each

   BETOS: D1F   Prosthetic/orthotic devices

D **L8627** Cochlear implant, external speech processor, component, replacement `DME` A

   BETOS: D1F   Prosthetic/orthotic devices

D **L8628** Cochlear implant, external controller component, replacement `DME` A

   BETOS: D1F   Prosthetic/orthotic devices

D **L8629** Transmitting coil and cable, integrated, for use with cochlear implant device, replacement `DME` A

   BETOS: D1F   Prosthetic/orthotic devices

IMPLANTABLE HAND AND FEET PROSTHETICS (L8630-L8659)

D **L8630** Metacarpophalangeal joint implant N1 `DME` ASC N

   BETOS: D1F   Prosthetic/orthotic devices

D **L8631** Metacarpal phalangeal joint replacement, two or more pieces, metal (e.g., stainless steel or cobalt chrome), ceramic-like material (e.g., pyrocarbon), for surgical implantation (all sizes, includes entire system) N1 `DME` ASC N

   BETOS: D1F   Prosthetic/orthotic devices

D **L8641** Metatarsal joint implant N1 `DME` ASC N

   BETOS: D1F   Prosthetic/orthotic devices

D **L8642** Hallux implant N1 `DME` ASC N

   BETOS: D1F   Prosthetic/orthotic devices

D **L8658** Interphalangeal joint spacer, silicone or equal, each N1 `DME` ASC N

   BETOS: D1F   Prosthetic/orthotic devices

D **L8659** Interphalangeal finger joint replacement, 2 or more pieces, metal (e.g., stainless steel or cobalt chrome), ceramic-like material (e.g., pyrocarbon) for surgical implantation, any size N1 `DME` ASC N

   BETOS: D1F   Prosthetic/orthotic devices

VASCULAR IMPLANTS (L8670)

D **L8670** Vascular graft material, synthetic, implant N1 `DME` ASC N

   BETOS: D1F   Prosthetic/orthotic devices

IMPLANTABLE NEUROSTIMULATORS AND COMPONENTS (L8679-L8689)

D **L8679** Implantable neurostimulator, pulse generator, any type N1 `DME` ASC N

   BETOS: D1F   Prosthetic/orthotic devices

I **L8680** Implantable neurostimulator electrode, each E1

   BETOS: D1F   Prosthetic/orthotic devices
   Service not separately priced by Part B

D **L8681** Patient programmer (external) for use with implantable programmable neurostimulator pulse generator, replacement only `DME` A

   BETOS: D1F   Prosthetic/orthotic devices

D **L8682** Implantable neurostimulator radiofrequency receiver N1 `DME` ASC N

   BETOS: D1F   Prosthetic/orthotic devices

D **L8683** Radiofrequency transmitter (external) for use with implantable neurostimulator radiofrequency receiver `DME` A

   BETOS: D1F   Prosthetic/orthotic devices

D **L8684** Radiofrequency transmitter (external) for use with implantable sacral root neurostimulator receiver for bowel and bladder management, replacement `DME` A

   BETOS: D1F   Prosthetic/orthotic devices

♂ Male only	♀ Female only	Ⓐ Age	A2 - Z3 = ASC Payment indicator	A - Y = APC Status indicator
	ASC = ASC-approved procedure	`DME` Paid under the DME fee schedule		`MIPS` MIPS code

I L8685 Implantable neurostimulator pulse generator, single array, rechargeable, includes extension   E1
> **BETOS:** D1F Prosthetic/orthotic devices
> Service not separately priced by Part B

I L8686 Implantable neurostimulator pulse generator, single array, non-rechargeable, includes extension   E1
> **BETOS:** D1F Prosthetic/orthotic devices
> Service not separately priced by Part B

I L8687 Implantable neurostimulator pulse generator, dual array, rechargeable, includes extension   E1
> **BETOS:** D1F Prosthetic/orthotic devices
> Service not separately priced by Part B

I L8688 Implantable neurostimulator pulse generator, dual array, non-rechargeable, includes extension   E1
> **BETOS:** D1F Prosthetic/orthotic devices
> Service not separately priced by Part B

D L8689 External recharging system for battery (internal) for use with implantable neurostimulator, replacement only   DME A
> **BETOS:** D1F Prosthetic/orthotic devices

MISCELLANEOUS ORTHOTIC AND PROSTHETIC SERVICES AND SUPPLIES (L8690-L9900)

C L8690 Auditory osseointegrated device, includes all internal and external components   N1 DME ASC N
> **BETOS:** D1F Prosthetic/orthotic devices
> **Coding Clinic:** 2007, Q1
> **Pub:** 100-4, Chap. 14, 40.8

▲ **C L8691** Auditory osseointegrated device, external sound processor, excludes transducer/actuator, replacement only, each   DME A
> **BETOS:** D1F Prosthetic/orthotic devices

S L8692 Auditory osseointegrated device, external sound processor, used without osseointegration, body worn, includes headband or other means of external attachment   E1
> **BETOS:** D1F Prosthetic/orthotic devices
> Service not separately priced by Part B
> Statute: 1862(a)(7)

C L8693 Auditory osseointegrated device abutment, any length, replacement only   DME A
> **BETOS:** D1F Prosthetic/orthotic devices

● **C L8694** Auditory osseointegrated device, transducer/actuator, replacement only, each
> **BETOS:** D1F Prosthetic/orthotic devices

D L8695 External recharging system for battery (external) for use with implantable neurostimulator, replacement only   DME A
> **BETOS:** D1F Prosthetic/orthotic devices

D L8696 Antenna (external) for use with implantable diaphragmatic/phrenic nerve stimulation device, replacement, each   DME A
> **BETOS:** D1F Prosthetic/orthotic devices

C L8699 Prosthetic implant, not otherwise specified   N1 ASC N
> **BETOS:** D1F Prosthetic/orthotic devices

C L9900 Orthotic and prosthetic supply, accessory, and/or service component of another HCPCS "L" code   N1 ASC N
> **BETOS:** D1F Prosthetic/orthotic devices

NOTES

NOTES

MEDICAL SERVICES (M0075-M0301)

MISCELLANEOUS MEDICAL SERVICES (M0075-M0301)

M **M0075** Cellular therapy   E1
    BETOS: Y2   Other - non-Medicare fee schedule
    Service not separately priced by Part B

M **M0076** Prolotherapy   E1
    BETOS: Y2   Other - non-Medicare fee schedule
    Service not separately priced by Part B

M **M0100** Intragastric hypothermia using gastric freezing   E1
    BETOS: P1G   Major procedure - other
    Service not separately priced by Part B

M **M0300** IV chelation therapy (chemical endarterectomy)   E1
    BETOS: Y2   Other - non-Medicare fee schedule
    Service not separately priced by Part B
    Pub: 100-3, Chap. 1, 20.21; 100-3, Chap. 1, 20.22

M **M0301** Fabric wrapping of abdominal aneurysm   E1
    BETOS: P1G   Major procedure - other
    Service not separately priced by Part B
    Coding Clinic: 2009, Q2

♂ Male only   ♀ Female only   **A** Age   A2 - Z3 = ASC Payment indicator   A - Y = APC Status indicator

ASC = ASC-approved procedure   **DME** Paid under the DME fee schedule   **MIPS** MIPS code

NOTES

PATHOLOGY AND LABORATORY SERVICES (P2028-P9615)

LABORATORY TESTS OF BLOOD AND HAIR (P2028-P2038)

D P2028 Cephalin floculation, blood   A
BETOS: T1H   Lab tests - other (non-Medicare fee schedule)
Other carrier priced

D P2029 Congo red, blood   A
BETOS: T1H   Lab tests - other (non-Medicare fee schedule)
Other carrier priced

M P2031 Hair analysis (excluding arsenic)   E1
BETOS: T1H   Lab tests - other (non-Medicare fee schedule)
Service not separately priced by Part B

D P2033 Thymol turbidity, blood   A
BETOS: T1H   Lab tests - other (non-Medicare fee schedule)
Other carrier priced

D P2038 Mucoprotein, blood (seromucoid) (medical necessity procedure)   A
BETOS: T1H   Lab tests - other (non-Medicare fee schedule)
Price subject to national limitation amount

PAP SMEARS (P3000, P3001)

D P3000 Screening Papanicolaou smear, cervical or vaginal, up to three smears, by technician under physician supervision   ♀ A
BETOS: T1H   Lab tests - other (non-Medicare fee schedule)
Price subject to national limitation amount

D P3001 Screening Papanicolaou smear, cervical or vaginal, up to three smears, requiring interpretation by physician   ♀ B
BETOS: T1G   Lab tests - other (Medicare fee schedule)
Price established using national RVUs

URINE BACTERIAL CULTURE AND SENSITIVITY STUDIES (P7001)

I P7001 Culture, bacterial, urine; quantitative, sensitivity study   E1
BETOS: T1H   Lab tests - other (non-Medicare fee schedule)
Service not separately priced by Part B

BLOOD AND BLOOD PRODUCTS, WITH ASSOCIATED PROCEDURES (P9010-P9100)

D P9010 Blood (whole), for transfusion, per unit   R
BETOS: T1H   Lab tests - other (non-Medicare fee schedule)
Reasonable charge
Coding Clinic: 2004, Q3

Pub: 100-1, Chap. 3, 20.5; 100-1, Chap. 3, 20.5.2; 100-1, Chap. 3, 20.5.3; 100-2, Chap. 1, 10; 100-4, Chap. 3, 40.2.2

D P9011 Blood, split unit   R
BETOS: T1H   Lab tests - other (non-Medicare fee schedule)
Reasonable charge
Coding Clinic: 2004, Q3; 2005, Q2
Pub: 100-1, Chap. 3, 20.5; 100-1, Chap. 3, 20.5.2; 100-1, Chap. 3, 20.5.3; 100-2, Chap. 1, 10; 100-4, Chap. 3, 40.2.2; 100-4, Chap. 4, 231.4

D P9012 Cryoprecipitate, each unit   R
BETOS: T1H   Lab tests - other (non-Medicare fee schedule)
Reasonable charge
Coding Clinic: 2004, Q3
Pub: 100-2, Chap. 1, 10; 100-4, Chap. 3, 40.2.2

D P9016 Red blood cells, leukocytes reduced, each unit   R
BETOS: T1H   Lab tests - other (non-Medicare fee schedule)
Reasonable charge
Coding Clinic: 2004, Q3; 2004, Q4
Pub: 100-2, Chap. 1, 10; 100-4, Chap. 3, 40.2.2

D P9017 Fresh frozen plasma (single donor), frozen within 8 hours of collection, each unit   R
BETOS: T1H   Lab tests - other (non-Medicare fee schedule)
Reasonable charge
Coding Clinic: 2004, Q3
Pub: 100-2, Chap. 1, 10; 100-4, Chap. 3, 40.2.2

D P9019 Platelets, each unit   R
BETOS: T1H   Lab tests - other (non-Medicare fee schedule)
Reasonable charge
Coding Clinic: 2004, Q3
Pub: 100-2, Chap. 1, 10; 100-4, Chap. 3, 40.2.2

D P9020 Platelet rich plasma, each unit   R
BETOS: T1H   Lab tests - other (non-Medicare fee schedule)
Reasonable charge
Coding Clinic: 2004, Q3
Pub: 100-4, Chap. 3, 40.2.2

D P9021 Red blood cells, each unit   R
BETOS: T1H   Lab tests - other (non-Medicare fee schedule)
Reasonable charge
Coding Clinic: 2004, Q3; 2004, Q4
Pub: 100-1, Chap. 3, 20.5; 100-1, Chap. 3, 20.5.2; 100-1, Chap. 3, 20.5.3; 100-2, Chap. 1, 10; 100-4, Chap. 3, 40.2.2

D P9022 Red blood cells, washed, each unit   R
BETOS: T1H   Lab tests - other (non-Medicare fee schedule)

Reasonable charge
Coding Clinic: 2004, Q3
Pub: 100-1, Chap. 3, 20.5; 100-1, Chap. 3, 20.5.2; 100-1, Chap. 3, 20.5.3; 100-2, Chap. 1, 10; 100-4, Chap. 3, 40.2.2

D P9023 Plasma, pooled multiple donor, solvent/detergent treated, frozen, each unit   R
BETOS: T1H   Lab tests - other
(non-Medicare fee schedule)
Reasonable charge
Coding Clinic: 2004, Q3
Pub: 100-2, Chap. 1, 10; 100-4, Chap. 3, 40.2.2

D P9031 Platelets, leukocytes reduced, each unit   R
BETOS: T1H   Lab tests - other
(non-Medicare fee schedule)
Reasonable charge
Coding Clinic: 2004, Q3
Pub: 100-2, Chap. 1, 10; 100-4, Chap. 3, 40.2.2

D P9032 Platelets, irradiated, each unit   R
BETOS: T1H   Lab tests - other
(non-Medicare fee schedule)
Reasonable charge
Coding Clinic: 2004, Q3; 2005, Q2
Pub: 100-2, Chap. 1, 10; 100-4, Chap. 3, 40.2.2

D P9033 Platelets, leukocytes reduced, irradiated, each unit   R
BETOS: T1H   Lab tests - other
(non-Medicare fee schedule)
Reasonable charge
Coding Clinic: 2004, Q3; 2005, Q2
Pub: 100-2, Chap. 1, 10; 100-4, Chap. 3, 40.2.2

D P9034 Platelets, pheresis, each unit   R
BETOS: T1H   Lab tests - other
(non-Medicare fee schedule)
Reasonable charge
Coding Clinic: 2004, Q3
Pub: 100-2, Chap. 1, 10; 100-4, Chap. 3, 40.2.2

D P9035 Platelets, pheresis, leukocytes reduced, each unit   R
BETOS: T1H   Lab tests - other
(non-Medicare fee schedule)
Reasonable charge
Coding Clinic: 2004, Q3
Pub: 100-2, Chap. 1, 10; 100-4, Chap. 3, 40.2.2

D P9036 Platelets, pheresis, irradiated, each unit   R
BETOS: T1H   Lab tests - other
(non-Medicare fee schedule)
Reasonable charge
Coding Clinic: 2004, Q3; 2005, Q2
Pub: 100-2, Chap. 1, 10; 100-4, Chap. 3, 40.2.2

D P9037 Platelets, pheresis, leukocytes reduced, irradiated, each unit   R

BETOS: T1H   Lab tests - other
(non-Medicare fee schedule)
Reasonable charge
Coding Clinic: 2004, Q3; 2005, Q2
Pub: 100-2, Chap. 1, 10; 100-4, Chap. 3, 40.2.2

D P9038 Red blood cells, irradiated, each unit   R
BETOS: T1H   Lab tests - other
(non-Medicare fee schedule)
Reasonable charge
Coding Clinic: 2004, Q3; 2005, Q2
Pub: 100-1, Chap. 3, 20.5; 100-1, Chap. 3, 20.5.2; 100-1, Chap. 3, 20.5.3; 100-2, Chap. 1, 10; 100-4, Chap. 3, 40.2.2

D P9039 Red blood cells, deglycerolized, each unit   R
BETOS: T1H   Lab tests - other
(non-Medicare fee schedule)
Reasonable charge
Coding Clinic: 2004, Q3
Pub: 100-2, Chap. 1, 10; 100-4, Chap. 3, 40.2.2

D P9040 Red blood cells, leukocytes reduced, irradiated, each unit   R
BETOS: T1H   Lab tests - other
(non-Medicare fee schedule)
Reasonable charge
Coding Clinic: 2004, Q3; 2005, Q2
Pub: 100-2, Chap. 1, 10; 100-4, Chap. 3, 40.2.2

C P9041 Infusion, albumin (human), 5%, 50 ml   K2 ASC K
BETOS: T1H   Lab tests - other
(non-Medicare fee schedule)
Reasonable charge
Drugs: ALBUKED 5, ALBUMIN, ALBUMIN (HUMAN), ALBUMIN 5%, 12.5 G IN 250 ML, ALBUMIN 5%, 25 G IN 500 ML, ALBUMIN 5%, 25GR, ALBUMIN 5%, 5 G IN 100 ML, ALBUMIN, 12.5GR, ALBUMIN-ZLB, ALBUMINAR-5, ALBURX, ALBUTEIN 5%, ALBUTEIN®, ALBUTEIN® 5% ALBUMIN 500 ML, BUMINATE, PLASBUMIN-5
Coding Clinic: 2004, Q3
Pub: 100-2, Chap. 1, 10; 100-4, Chap. 3, 40.2.2

D P9043 Infusion, plasma protein fraction (human), 5%, 50 ml   R
BETOS: T1H   Lab tests - other
(non-Medicare fee schedule)
Reasonable charge
Coding Clinic: 2004, Q3
Pub: 100-2, Chap. 1, 10; 100-4, Chap. 3, 40.2.2

D P9044 Plasma, cryoprecipitate reduced, each unit R
BETOS: T1H   Lab tests - other
(non-Medicare fee schedule)
Reasonable charge
Coding Clinic: 2004, Q3
Pub: 100-2, Chap. 1, 10; 100-4, Chap. 3, 40.2.2

C **P9045** Infusion, albumin (human), 5%, 250 ml   K2 ASC K

BETOS: Y2   Other - non-Medicare fee schedule

Reasonable charge

Drugs: ALBUKED 5, ALBUMIN, ALBUMIN (HUMAN), ALBUMIN 5%, 12.5 G IN 250 ML, ALBUMIN 5%, 25 G IN 500 ML, ALBUMIN 5%, 25GR, ALBUMIN 5%, 5 G IN 100 ML, ALBUMIN, 12.5GR, ALBUMIN-ZLB, ALBUMINAR-5, ALBURX, ALBUTEIN® 5% ALBUMIN 500 ML, ALBUTEIN® 5%, BUMINATE, PLASBUMIN-5

Coding Clinic: 2002, Q1; 2004, Q3

Pub: 100-2, Chap. 1, 10; 100-4, Chap. 3, 40.2.2

C **P9046** Infusion, albumin (human), 25%, 20 ml   K2 ASC K

BETOS: Y2   Other - non-Medicare fee schedule

Reasonable charge

Drugs: ALBUKED 25, ALBUMIN, ALBUMIN (HUMAN), ALBUMIN 25%, 12.5 G IN 50 ML, ALBUMIN 25%, 25 G IN 100 ML, ALBUMIN-ALPINE, ALBUMINAR-25, ALBURX, ALBUTEIN 25%, ALBUTEIN®, ALBUTEIN® 25% ALBUMIN 100 ML, BUMINATE, FLEXBUMIN, KEDBUMIN, PLASBUMIN-25

Coding Clinic: 2002, Q1; 2004, Q3

Pub: 100-2, Chap. 1, 10; 100-4, Chap. 3, 40.2.2

C **P9047** Infusion, albumin (human), 25%, 50 ml   K2 ASC K

BETOS: Y2   Other - non-Medicare fee schedule

Reasonable charge

Drugs: ALBUKED 25, ALBUMIN, ALBUMIN (HUMAN), ALBUMIN (HUMAN) 25%, ALBUMIN 25%, 12.5 G IN 50 ML, ALBUMIN 25%, 25 G IN 100 ML, ALBUMIN-ZLB, ALBUMINAR-25, ALBURX, ALBUTEIN® 25%, ALBUTEIN® 25% ALBUMIN 100 ML, BUMINATE, FLEXBUMIN, HUMAN ALBUMIN GRIFOLS, KEDBUMIN, PLASBUMIN-25

Coding Clinic: 2002, Q1; 2004, Q3

Pub: 100-2, Chap. 1, 10; 100-4, Chap. 3, 40.2.2

C **P9048** Infusion, plasma protein fraction (human), 5%, 250 ml   R

BETOS: Y2   Other - non-Medicare fee schedule

Reasonable charge

Coding Clinic: 2002, Q1; 2004, Q3

Pub: 100-2, Chap. 1, 10; 100-4, Chap. 3, 40.2.2

C **P9050** Granulocytes, pheresis, each unit   E2

BETOS: Z2   Undefined codes

Reasonable charge

Coding Clinic: 2002, Q1; 2004, Q3

Pub: 100-2, Chap. 1, 10; 100-4, Chap. 3, 40.2.2

D **P9051** Whole blood or red blood cells, leukocytes reduced, CMV-negative, each unit   R

BETOS: T1H   Lab tests - other (non-Medicare fee schedule)

Reasonable charge

Statute: 1833T

Coding Clinic: 2004, Q3

Pub: 100-2, Chap. 1, 10; 100-4, Chap. 3, 40.2.2

D **P9052** Platelets, HLA-matched leukocytes reduced, apheresis/pheresis, each unit   R

BETOS: T1H   Lab tests - other (non-Medicare fee schedule)

Reasonable charge

Statute: 1833T

Coding Clinic: 2004, Q3

Pub: 100-2, Chap. 1, 10; 100-4, Chap. 3, 40.2.2

D **P9053** Platelets, pheresis, leukocytes reduced, CMV-negative, irradiated, each unit   R

BETOS: T1H   Lab tests - other (non-Medicare fee schedule)

Reasonable charge

Statute: 1833T

Coding Clinic: 2004, Q3; 2005, Q2

Pub: 100-2, Chap. 1, 10; 100-4, Chap. 3, 40.2.2

D **P9054** Whole blood or red blood cells, leukocytes reduced, frozen, deglycerol, washed, each unit   R

BETOS: T1H   Lab tests - other (non-Medicare fee schedule)

Reasonable charge

Statute: 1833T

Coding Clinic: 2004, Q3

Pub: 100-2, Chap. 1, 10; 100-4, Chap. 3, 40.2.2

D **P9055** Platelets, leukocytes reduced, CMV-negative, apheresis/pheresis, each unit   R

BETOS: T1H   Lab tests - other (non-Medicare fee schedule)

Reasonable charge

Statute: 1833T

Coding Clinic: 2004, Q3

Pub: 100-2, Chap. 1, 10; 100-4, Chap. 3, 40.2.2

D **P9056** Whole blood, leukocytes reduced, irradiated, each unit   R

BETOS: T1H   Lab tests - other (non-Medicare fee schedule)

Reasonable charge

Statute: 1833T

Coding Clinic: 2004, Q3; 2005, Q2

Pub: 100-2, Chap. 1, 10; 100-4, Chap. 3, 40.2.2

D **P9057** Red blood cells, frozen/deglycerolized/washed, leukocytes reduced, irradiated, each unit   R

♂ Male only   ♀ Female only   Ⓐ Age   A2 - Z3 = ASC Payment indicator   A - Y = APC Status indicator

ASC = ASC-approved procedure   **DME** Paid under the DME fee schedule   **MIPS** MIPS code

BETOS: T1H   Lab tests - other
(non-Medicare fee schedule)
Reasonable charge
Statute: 1833T
Coding Clinic: 2004, Q3; 2005, Q2
Pub: 100-2, Chap. 1, 10; 100-4, Chap. 3, 40.2.2

D **P9058** Red blood cells, leukocytes reduced, CMV-negative, irradiated, each unit   R
BETOS: T1H   Lab tests - other
(non-Medicare fee schedule)
Reasonable charge
Statute: 1833T
Coding Clinic: 2004, Q3; 2005, Q2
Pub: 100-2, Chap. 1, 10; 100-4, Chap. 3, 40.2.2

D **P9059** Fresh frozen plasma between 8-24 hours of collection, each unit   R
BETOS: T1H   Lab tests - other
(non-Medicare fee schedule)
Reasonable charge
Statute: 1833T
Coding Clinic: 2004, Q3
Pub: 100-2, Chap. 1, 10; 100-4, Chap. 3, 40.2.2

D **P9060** Fresh frozen plasma, donor retested, each unit   R
BETOS: T1H   Lab tests - other
(non-Medicare fee schedule)
Reasonable charge
Statute: 1833T
Coding Clinic: 2004, Q3
Pub: 100-2, Chap. 1, 10; 100-4, Chap. 3, 40.2.2

D **P9070** Plasma, pooled multiple donor, pathogen reduced, frozen, each unit   R
BETOS: T1H   Lab tests - other
(non-Medicare fee schedule)
Reasonable charge
Statute: 1833T
Coding Clinic: 2016, Q1

D **P9071** Plasma (single donor), pathogen reduced, frozen, each unit   R
BETOS: T1H   Lab tests - other
(non-Medicare fee schedule)
Reasonable charge
Statute: 1833T
Coding Clinic: 2016, Q1

● **D** **P9073** Platelets, pheresis, pathogen-reduced, each unit
BETOS: T1H   Lab tests - other
(non-Medicare fee schedule)
Reasonable charge
Statute: 1833T

● **D** **P9100** Pathogen(s) test for platelets
BETOS: T1H   Lab tests - other
(non-Medicare fee schedule)
Other carrier priced

SPECIMEN COLLECTION, TRAVEL ALLOWANCE (P9603, P9604)

D **P9603** Travel allowance one-way in connection with medically necessary laboratory specimen collection drawn from home bound or nursing home bound patient; prorated miles actually travelled   A
BETOS: Y2   Other - non-Medicare fee schedule
Price established by carriers
Pub: 100-4, Chap. 16, 60.2

D **P9604** Travel allowance one-way in connection with medically necessary laboratory specimen collection drawn from home bound or nursing home bound patient; prorated trip charge   A
BETOS: Y2   Other - non-Medicare fee schedule
Price established by carriers
Pub: 100-4, Chap. 16, 60.2

SPECIMEN COLLECTION, CATHETERIZATION (P9612, P9615)

D **P9612** Catheterization for collection of specimen, single patient, all places of service   A
BETOS: T1H   Lab tests - other
(non-Medicare fee schedule)
Other carrier priced
Coding Clinic: 2007, Q3

D **P9615** Catheterization for collection of specimen(s) (multiple patients)   N
BETOS: T1H   Lab tests - other
(non-Medicare fee schedule)
Other carrier priced
Pub: 100-4, Chap. 16, 60.1.4

NOTES

NOTES

TEMPORARY CODES (Q0035-Q9983)

MISCELLANEOUS DRUGS AND TESTS (Q0035-Q0144)

D **Q0035** Cardiokymography — Q1

BETOS: T2D Other tests - other

Price established using national RVUs

D **Q0081** Infusion therapy, using other than chemotherapeutic drugs, per visit — B

BETOS: P6C Minor procedures - other (Medicare fee schedule)

Service not separately priced by Part B

Coding Clinic: 2002, Q1; 2002, Q2; 2002, Q4; 2004, Q1; 2004, Q2; 2004, Q4; 2005, Q1; 2006, Q4

C **Q0083** Chemotherapy administration by other than infusion technique only (e.g., subcutaneous, intramuscular, push), per visit — B

BETOS: O1D Chemotherapy

Service not separately priced by Part B

Coding Clinic: 2002, Q1; 2004, Q1; 2004, Q4; 2005, Q1; 2006, Q4

D **Q0084** Chemotherapy administration by infusion technique only, per visit — B

BETOS: O1D Chemotherapy

Service not separately priced by Part B

Coding Clinic: 2002, Q1; 2004, Q1; 2004, Q2; 2004, Q4; 2005, Q1; 2006, Q4

C **Q0085** Chemotherapy administration by both infusion technique and other technique(s) (e.g., subcutaneous, intramuscular, push), per visit — B

BETOS: O1D Chemotherapy

Service not separately priced by Part B

Coding Clinic: 2002, Q1; 2004, Q1; 2004, Q4; 2006, Q4

D **Q0091** Screening Papanicolaou smear; obtaining, preparing and conveyance of cervical or vaginal smear to laboratory — ♀ S

BETOS: P6C Minor procedures - other (Medicare fee schedule)

Coding Clinic: 2002, Q4; 2008, Q4

Price established using national RVUs

D **Q0092** Set-up portable X-ray equipment — N

BETOS: I1F Standard imaging - other

Price established using national RVUs

C **Q0111** Wet mounts, including preparations of vaginal, cervical or skin specimens — A

BETOS: T1H Lab tests - other (non-Medicare fee schedule)

Price subject to national limitation amount

C **Q0112** All potassium hydroxide (KOH) preparations — A

BETOS: T1H Lab tests - other (non-Medicare fee schedule)

Price subject to national limitation amount

C **Q0113** Pinworm examinations — A

BETOS: T1H Lab tests - other (non-Medicare fee schedule)

Price subject to national limitation amount

C **Q0114** Fern test — ♀ A

BETOS: T1H Lab tests - other (non-Medicare fee schedule)

Price subject to national limitation amount

C **Q0115** Post-coital direct, qualitative examinations of vaginal or cervical mucous — ♀ A

BETOS: T1H Lab tests - other (non-Medicare fee schedule)

Price subject to national limitation amount

C **Q0138** Injection, ferumoxytol, for treatment of iron deficiency anemia, 1 mg (non-ESRD use) — K2 ASC K

BETOS: O1E Other drugs

Drugs: FERAHEME

C **Q0139** Injection, ferumoxytol, for treatment of iron deficiency anemia, 1 mg (for ESRD on dialysis) — K2 ASC K

BETOS: O1E Other drugs

Drugs: FERAHEME

M **Q0144** Azithromycin dihydrate, oral, capsules/powder, 1 gram — E1

BETOS: O1E Other drugs

Service not separately priced by Part B

CHEMOTHERAPY ANTI-EMETIC MEDICATIONS (Q0161-Q0181), SEE ALSO CHEMOTHERAPY MEDICATIONS (Q5101-Q5102)

C **Q0161** Chlorpromazine hydrochloride, 5 mg, oral, FDA-approved prescription anti-emetic, for use as a complete therapeutic substitute for an IV anti-emetic at the time of chemotherapy treatment, not to exceed a 48-hour dosage regimen — N1 ASC N

BETOS: O1D Chemotherapy

Coding Clinic: 2014, Q1

D **Q0162** Ondansetron 1 mg, oral, FDA-approved prescription anti-emetic, for use as a complete therapeutic substitute for an IV anti-emetic at the time of chemotherapy treatment, not to exceed a 48-hour dosage regimen — N1 ASC N

BETOS: O1D Chemotherapy

Statute: 4557

Drugs: ONDANSETRON, ONDANSETRON HCL, ONDANSETRON ODT, ZOFRAN, ZOFRAN ODT

D **Q0163** Diphenhydramine hydrochloride, 50 mg, oral, FDA-approved prescription anti-emetic, for use as a complete therapeutic substitute for an IV anti-emetic at time of chemotherapy treatment not to exceed a 48-hour dosage regimen — N1 ASC N

BETOS: O1D Chemotherapy

Statute: 4557

Drugs: DIPHENHYDRAMINE HCL

Coding Clinic: 2012, Q2

♂ Male only ♀ Female only Ⓐ Age A2 - Z3 = ASC Payment indicator A - Y = APC Status indicator

ASC = ASC-approved procedure **DME** Paid under the DME fee schedule **MIPS** MIPS code

D **Q0164** Prochlorperazine maleate, 5 mg, oral, FDA-approved prescription anti-emetic, for use as a complete therapeutic substitute for an IV anti-emetic at the time of chemotherapy treatment, not to exceed a 48-hour dosage regimen N1 ASC N

  BETOS: O1D Chemotherapy
  Statute: 4557
  Drugs: PROCHLORPERAZINE MALEATE

D **Q0166** Granisetron hydrochloride, 1 mg, oral, FDA-approved prescription anti-emetic, for use as a complete therapeutic substitute for an IV anti-emetic at the time of chemotherapy treatment, not to exceed a 24-hour dosage regimen N1 ASC N

  BETOS: O1D Chemotherapy
  Statute: 4557
  Drugs: GRANISETRON HCL

D **Q0167** Dronabinol, 2.5 mg, oral, FDA-approved prescription anti-emetic, for use as a complete therapeutic substitute for an IV anti-emetic at the time of chemotherapy treatment, not to exceed a 48-hour dosage regimen N1 ASC N

  BETOS: O1D Chemotherapy
  Statute: 4557
  Drugs: DRONABINOL, MARINOL

D **Q0169** Promethazine hydrochloride, 12.5 mg, oral, FDA-approved prescription anti-emetic, for use as a complete therapeutic substitute for an IV anti-emetic at the time of chemotherapy treatment, not to exceed a 48-hour dosage regimen N1 ASC N

  BETOS: O1D Chemotherapy
  Statute: 4557
  Drugs: PROMETHAZINE HCL

D **Q0173** Trimethobenzamide hydrochloride, 250 mg, oral, FDA-approved prescription anti-emetic, for use as a complete therapeutic substitute for an IV anti-emetic at the time of chemotherapy treatment, not to exceed a 48-hour dosage regimen N1 ASC N

  BETOS: O1D Chemotherapy
  Statute: 4557

D **Q0174** Thiethylperazine maleate, 10 mg, oral, FDA-approved prescription anti-emetic, for use as a complete therapeutic substitute for an IV anti-emetic at the time of chemotherapy treatment, not to exceed a 48-hour dosage regimen E2

  BETOS: O1D Chemotherapy
  Statute: 4557

D **Q0175** Perphenazine, 4 mg, oral, FDA-approved prescription anti-emetic, for use as a complete therapeutic substitute for an IV anti-emetic at the time of chemotherapy treatment, not to exceed a 48-hour dosage regimen N1 ASC N

  BETOS: O1D Chemotherapy
  Statute: 4557

D **Q0177** Hydroxyzine pamoate, 25 mg, oral, FDA-approved prescription anti-emetic, for use as a complete therapeutic substitute for an IV anti-emetic at the time of chemotherapy treatment, not to exceed a 48-hour dosage regimen N1 ASC N

  BETOS: O1D Chemotherapy
  Statute: 4557

D **Q0180** Dolasetron mesylate, 100 mg, oral, FDA-approved prescription anti-emetic, for use as a complete therapeutic substitute for an IV anti-emetic at the time of chemotherapy treatment, not to exceed a 24-hour dosage regimen N1 ASC N

  BETOS: O1D Chemotherapy
  Statute: 4557

D **Q0181** Unspecified oral dosage form, FDA-approved prescription anti-emetic, for use as a complete therapeutic substitute for a IV anti-emetic at the time of chemotherapy treatment, not to exceed a 48-hour dosage regimen N1 ASC N

  BETOS: O1D Chemotherapy
  Statute: 4557
  Coding Clinic: 2012, Q2

VENTRICULAR ASSIST DEVICES (Q0477-Q0509)

● **D** **Q0477** Power module patient cable for use with electric or electric/pneumatic ventricular assist device, replacement only

  BETOS: D1F Prosthetic/orthotic devices

D **Q0478** Power adapter for use with electric or electric/pneumatic ventricular assist device, vehicle type DME A

  BETOS: D1F Prosthetic/orthotic devices

D **Q0479** Power module for use with electric or electric/pneumatic ventricular assist device, replacement only DME A

  BETOS: D1F Prosthetic/orthotic devices

D **Q0480** Driver for use with pneumatic ventricular assist device, replacement only DME A

  BETOS: D1F Prosthetic/orthotic devices
  Coding Clinic: 2005, Q3

D **Q0481** Microprocessor control unit for use with electric ventricular assist device, replacement only DME A

  BETOS: D1F Prosthetic/orthotic devices
  Coding Clinic: 2005, Q3

D **Q0482** Microprocessor control unit for use with electric/pneumatic combination ventricular assist device, replacement only DME A

  BETOS: D1F Prosthetic/orthotic devices
  Coding Clinic: 2005, Q3

D **Q0483** Monitor/display module for use with electric ventricular assist device, replacement only DME A

▲ Revised code ● New code **C** Carrier judgment **D** Special coverage instructions apply
J Not payable by Medicare **M** Non-covered by Medicare **S** Non-covered by Medicare statute AHA Coding Clinic®

BETOS: D1F   Prosthetic/orthotic devices
Coding Clinic: 2005, Q3

D **Q0484** Monitor/display module for use with electric or electric/pneumatic ventricular assist device, replacement only   **DME** A
BETOS: D1F   Prosthetic/orthotic devices
Coding Clinic: 2005, Q3

D **Q0485** Monitor control cable for use with electric ventricular assist device, replacement only   **DME** A
BETOS: D1F   Prosthetic/orthotic devices
Coding Clinic: 2005, Q3

D **Q0486** Monitor control cable for use with electric/ pneumatic ventricular assist device, replacement only   **DME** A
BETOS: D1F   Prosthetic/orthotic devices
Coding Clinic: 2005, Q3

D **Q0487** Leads (pneumatic/electrical) for use with any type electric/pneumatic ventricular assist device, replacement only   **DME** A
BETOS: D1F   Prosthetic/orthotic devices
Coding Clinic: 2005, Q3

D **Q0488** Power pack base for use with electric ventricular assist device, replacement only A
BETOS: D1F   Prosthetic/orthotic devices
Coding Clinic: 2005, Q3

D **Q0489** Power pack base for use with electric/ pneumatic ventricular assist device, replacement only   **DME** A
BETOS: D1F   Prosthetic/orthotic devices
Coding Clinic: 2005, Q3

D **Q0490** Emergency power source for use with electric ventricular assist device, replacement only   **DME** A
BETOS: D1F   Prosthetic/orthotic devices
Coding Clinic: 2005, Q3

D **Q0491** Emergency power source for use with electric/pneumatic ventricular assist device, replacement only   **DME** A
BETOS: D1F   Prosthetic/orthotic devices
Coding Clinic: 2005, Q3

D **Q0492** Emergency power supply cable for use with electric ventricular assist device, replacement only   **DME** A
BETOS: D1F   Prosthetic/orthotic devices
Coding Clinic: 2005, Q3

D **Q0493** Emergency power supply cable for use with electric/pneumatic ventricular assist device, replacement only   **DME** A
BETOS: D1F   Prosthetic/orthotic devices
Coding Clinic: 2005, Q3

D **Q0494** Emergency hand pump for use with electric or electric/pneumatic ventricular assist device, replacement only   **DME** A
BETOS: D1F   Prosthetic/orthotic devices
Coding Clinic: 2005, Q3

D **Q0495** Battery/power pack charger for use with electric or electric/pneumatic ventricular assist device, replacement only   **DME** A
BETOS: D1F   Prosthetic/orthotic devices
Coding Clinic: 2005, Q3

D **Q0496** Battery, other than lithium-ion, for use with electric or electric/pneumatic ventricular assist device, replacement only   **DME** A
BETOS: D1F   Prosthetic/orthotic devices
Coding Clinic: 2005, Q3

D **Q0497** Battery clips for use with electric or electric/ pneumatic ventricular assist device, replacement only   **DME** A
BETOS: D1F   Prosthetic/orthotic devices
Coding Clinic: 2005, Q3

D **Q0498** Holster for use with electric or electric/ pneumatic ventricular assist device, replacement only   **DME** A
BETOS: D1F   Prosthetic/orthotic devices
Coding Clinic: 2005, Q3

D **Q0499** Belt/vest/bag for use to carry external peripheral components of any type ventricular assist device, replacement only   **DME** A
BETOS: D1F   Prosthetic/orthotic devices
Coding Clinic: 2005, Q3

D **Q0500** Filters for use with electric or electric/ pneumatic ventricular assist device, replacement only   **DME** A
BETOS: D1F   Prosthetic/orthotic devices
Coding Clinic: 2005, Q3

D **Q0501** Shower cover for use with electric or electric/pneumatic ventricular assist device, replacement only   **DME** A
BETOS: D1F   Prosthetic/orthotic devices
Coding Clinic: 2005, Q3

D **Q0502** Mobility cart for pneumatic ventricular assist device, replacement only   **DME** A
BETOS: D1F   Prosthetic/orthotic devices
Coding Clinic: 2005, Q3

D **Q0503** Battery for pneumatic ventricular assist device, replacement only, each   **DME** A
BETOS: D1F   Prosthetic/orthotic devices
Coding Clinic: 2005, Q3

D **Q0504** Power adapter for pneumatic ventricular assist device, replacement only, vehicle type   **DME** A
BETOS: D1F   Prosthetic/orthotic devices
Coding Clinic: 2005, Q3

D **Q0506** Battery, lithium-ion, for use with electric or electric/pneumatic ventricular assist device, replacement only   **DME** A
BETOS: D1F   Prosthetic/orthotic devices

D **Q0507** Miscellaneous supply or accessory for use with an external ventricular assist device A
BETOS: D1F   Prosthetic/orthotic devices

Q0508 - Q2040 *(side margin)*

TEMPORARY CODES (Q0035-Q9983) *(side margin)*

D Q0508 Miscellaneous supply or accessory for use with an implanted ventricular assist device A
BETOS: D1F Prosthetic/orthotic devices

D Q0509 Miscellaneous supply or accessory for use with any implanted ventricular assist device for which payment was not made under Medicare Part A A
BETOS: D1F Prosthetic/orthotic devices

PHARMACY SUPPLY AND DISPENSING FEES (Q0510-Q0514)

D Q0510 Pharmacy supply fee for initial immunosuppressive drug(s), first month following transplant B
BETOS: O1E Other drugs

D Q0511 Pharmacy supply fee for oral anti-cancer, oral anti-emetic or immunosuppressive drug(s); for the first prescription in a 30-day period B
BETOS: O1E Other drugs

D Q0512 Pharmacy supply fee for oral anti-cancer, oral anti-emetic or immunosuppressive drug(s); for a subsequent prescription in a 30-day period B
BETOS: O1E Other drugs

D Q0513 Pharmacy dispensing fee for inhalation drug(s); per 30 days B
BETOS: O1E Other drugs

D Q0514 Pharmacy dispensing fee for inhalation drug(s); per 90 days B
BETOS: O1E Other drugs

MISCELLANEOUS DRUG AND NEW TECHNOLOGY CODES (Q0515-Q2028)

D Q0515 Injection, sermorelin acetate, 1 microgram E2
BETOS: O1E Other drugs

D Q1004 New technology intraocular lens category 4 as defined in Federal Register notice E1
BETOS: D1F Prosthetic/orthotic devices
Other carrier priced

D Q1005 New technology intraocular lens category 5 as defined in Federal Register notice E1
BETOS: D1F Prosthetic/orthotic devices
Other carrier priced

D Q2004 Irrigation solution for treatment of bladder calculi, for example renacidin, per 500 ml N1 ASC N
BETOS: O1E Other drugs
Statute: 1861S2B

D Q2009 Injection, fosphenytoin, 50 mg phenytoin equivalent N1 ASC N
BETOS: O1E Other drugs
Statute: 1861S2B

D Q2017 Injection, teniposide, 50 mg K2 ASC K
BETOS: O1D Chemotherapy
Statute: 1861S2B

D Q2026 Injection, Radiesse, 0.1 ml N1 ASC N
BETOS: O1E Other drugs
Coding Clinic: 2010, Q3
Pub: 100-4, Chap. 32, 260.2.2

D Q2028 Injection, sculptra, 0.5 mg N1 ASC N
BETOS: O1E Other drugs
Coding Clinic: 2014, Q1

INFLUENZA VIRUS VACCINES (Q2034-Q2039)

D Q2034 Influenza virus vaccine, split-virus, for intramuscular use (Agriflu) L1 ASC L
BETOS: O1G Influenza immunization
Coding Clinic: 2012, Q3

D Q2035 Influenza virus vaccine, split-virus, when administered to individuals 3 years of age and older, for intramuscular use (Afluria) L1 Ⓐ ASC L
BETOS: O1G Influenza immunization
Drugs: AFLURIA 2016/2017, AFLURIA 2017/2018
Coding Clinic: 2010, Q4; 2011, Q1
Pub: 100-2, Chap. 15, 50.4.4.2

D Q2036 Influenza virus vaccine, split-virus, when administered to individuals 3 years of age and older, for intramuscular use (Flulaval) L1 Ⓐ ASC L
BETOS: O1G Influenza immunization
Coding Clinic: 2010, Q4; 2011, Q1

D Q2037 Influenza virus vaccine, split-virus, when administered to individuals 3 years of age and older, for intramuscular use (Fluvirin) L1 Ⓐ ASC L
BETOS: O1G Influenza immunization
Drugs: FLUVIRIN 2016/2017, FLUVIRIN 2017/2018
Coding Clinic: 2010, Q4; 2011, Q1

D Q2038 Influenza virus vaccine, split-virus, when administered to individuals 3 years of age and older, for intramuscular use (Fluzone) L1 Ⓐ ASC L
BETOS: O1G Influenza immunization
Coding Clinic: 2010, Q4; 2011, Q1

D Q2039 Influenza virus vaccine, not otherwise specified L1 Ⓐ ASC L
BETOS: O1G Influenza immunization
Coding Clinic: 2010, Q4; 2011, Q1

OTHER DRUGS AND SERVICE FEES (Q2040-Q3031)

● C Q2040 Tisagenlecleucel, up to 250 million car-positive viable T cells, including leukapheresis and dose preparation procedures, per infusion
BETOS: O1E Other drugs
Coding Clinic: 2011, Q1; 2012, Q1

▲ Revised code   ● New code   **C** Carrier judgment   **D** Special coverage instructions apply
J Not payable by Medicare   **M** Non-covered by Medicare   **S** Non-covered by Medicare statute   AHA Coding Clinic®

D **Q2043** Sipuleucel-T, minimum of 50 million autologous CD54+ cells activated with PAP-GM-CSF, including leukapheresis and all other preparatory procedures, per infusion   K2 ASC K
BETOS: P1G   Major procedure - other
Drugs: PROVENGE®
Coding Clinic: 2012, Q1; 2012, Q2

C **Q2049** Injection, doxorubicin hydrochloride, liposomal, imported Lipodox, 10 mg   K2 ASC K
BETOS: O1D   Chemotherapy
Coding Clinic: 2012, Q3

D **Q2050** Injection, doxorubicin hydrochloride, liposomal, not otherwise specified, 10 mg   K2 ASC K
BETOS: O1D   Chemotherapy
Drugs: DOXIL, DOXORUBICIN HCL, LIPOSOMAL,
Coding Clinic: 2013, Q3; 2013, Q4

D **Q2052** Services, supplies and accessories used in the home under the Medicare intravenous immune globulin (IVIG) demonstration   E1
BETOS: O1E   Other drugs
Other carrier priced
Coding Clinic: 2014, Q2

D **Q3001** Radioelements for brachytherapy, any type, each   B
BETOS: P7A   Oncology - radiation therapy
Other carrier priced

C **Q3014** Telehealth originating site facility fee   A
BETOS: Y2   Other - non-Medicare fee schedule
Pub: 100-4, Chap. 12, 190.6

D **Q3027** Injection, interferon beta-1a, 1 mcg for intramuscular use   K2 ASC K
BETOS: O1E   Other drugs
Drugs: AVONEX, AVONEX PEN
Coding Clinic: 2014, Q1

I **Q3028** Injection, interferon beta-1a, 1 mcg for subcutaneous use   E1
BETOS: O1E   Other drugs
Service not separately priced by Part B

D **Q3031** Collagen skin test   N1 ASC N
BETOS: D1A   Medical/surgical supplies
Price established using national RVUs

CAST AND SPLINT SUPPLIES (Q4001-Q4051)

C **Q4001** Casting supplies, body cast adult, with or without head, plaster   DME Ⓐ B
BETOS: D1A   Medical/surgical supplies
Coding Clinic: 2002, Q2

C **Q4002** Cast supplies, body cast adult, with or without head, fiberglass   DME Ⓐ B
BETOS: D1A   Medical/surgical supplies

C **Q4003** Cast supplies, shoulder cast, adult (11 years +), plaster   DME Ⓐ B
BETOS: D1A   Medical/surgical supplies

C **Q4004** Cast supplies, shoulder cast, adult (11 years +), fiberglass   DME Ⓐ B
BETOS: D1A   Medical/surgical supplies

C **Q4005** Cast supplies, long arm cast, adult (11 years +), plaster   DME Ⓐ B
BETOS: D1A   Medical/surgical supplies

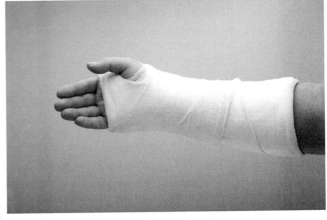

Arm cast

C **Q4006** Cast supplies, long arm cast, adult (11 years +), fiberglass   DME Ⓐ B
BETOS: D1A   Medical/surgical supplies

C **Q4007** Cast supplies, long arm cast, pediatric (0-10 years), plaster   DME Ⓐ B
BETOS: D1A   Medical/surgical supplies

C **Q4008** Cast supplies, long arm cast, pediatric (0-10 years), fiberglass   DME Ⓐ B
BETOS: D1A   Medical/surgical supplies

C **Q4009** Cast supplies, short arm cast, adult (11 years +), plaster   DME Ⓐ B
BETOS: D1A   Medical/surgical supplies

C **Q4010** Cast supplies, short arm cast, adult (11 years +), fiberglass   DME Ⓐ B
BETOS: D1A   Medical/surgical supplies

C **Q4011** Cast supplies, short arm cast, pediatric (0-10 years), plaster   DME Ⓐ B
BETOS: D1A   Medical/surgical supplies

C **Q4012** Cast supplies, short arm cast, pediatric (0-10 years), fiberglass   DME Ⓐ B
BETOS: D1A   Medical/surgical supplies

C **Q4013** Cast supplies, gauntlet cast (includes lower forearm and hand), adult (11 years +), plaster   DME Ⓐ B
BETOS: D1A   Medical/surgical supplies

C **Q4014** Cast supplies, gauntlet cast (includes lower forearm and hand), adult (11 years +), fiberglass   DME Ⓐ B
BETOS: D1A   Medical/surgical supplies

C **Q4015** Cast supplies, gauntlet cast (includes lower forearm and hand), pediatric (0-10 years), plaster DME Ⓐ B

BETOS: D1A Medical/surgical supplies

C **Q4016** Cast supplies, gauntlet cast (includes lower forearm and hand), pediatric (0-10 years), fiberglass DME Ⓐ B

BETOS: D1A Medical/surgical supplies

C **Q4017** Cast supplies, long arm splint, adult (11 years +), plaster DME Ⓐ B

BETOS: D1A Medical/surgical supplies

C **Q4018** Cast supplies, long arm splint, adult (11 years +), fiberglass DME Ⓐ B

BETOS: D1A Medical/surgical supplies

C **Q4019** Cast supplies, long arm splint, pediatric (0-10 years), plaster DME Ⓐ B

BETOS: D1A Medical/surgical supplies

C **Q4020** Cast supplies, long arm splint, pediatric (0-10 years), fiberglass DME Ⓐ B

BETOS: D1A Medical/surgical supplies

C **Q4021** Cast supplies, short arm splint, adult (11 years +), plaster DME Ⓐ B

BETOS: D1A Medical/surgical supplies

C **Q4022** Cast supplies, short arm splint, adult (11 years +), fiberglass DME Ⓐ B

BETOS: D1A Medical/surgical supplies

C **Q4023** Cast supplies, short arm splint, pediatric (0-10 years), plaster DME Ⓐ B

BETOS: D1A Medical/surgical supplies

C **Q4024** Cast supplies, short arm splint, pediatric (0-10 years), fiberglass DME Ⓐ B

BETOS: D1A Medical/surgical supplies

C **Q4025** Cast supplies, hip spica (one or both legs), adult (11 years +), plaster DME Ⓐ B

BETOS: D1A Medical/surgical supplies

C **Q4026** Cast supplies, hip spica (one or both legs), adult (11 years +), fiberglass DME Ⓐ B

BETOS: D1A Medical/surgical supplies

C **Q4027** Cast supplies, hip spica (one or both legs), pediatric (0-10 years), plaster DME Ⓐ B

BETOS: D1A Medical/surgical supplies

C **Q4028** Cast supplies, hip spica (one or both legs), pediatric (0-10 years), fiberglass DME Ⓐ B

BETOS: D1A Medical/surgical supplies

C **Q4029** Cast supplies, long leg cast, adult (11 years +), plaster DME Ⓐ B

BETOS: D1A Medical/surgical supplies

C **Q4030** Cast supplies, long leg cast, adult (11 years +), fiberglass DME Ⓐ B

BETOS: D1A Medical/surgical supplies

C **Q4031** Cast supplies, long leg cast, pediatric (0-10 years), plaster DME Ⓐ B

BETOS: D1A Medical/surgical supplies

C **Q4032** Cast supplies, long leg cast, pediatric (0-10 years), fiberglass DME Ⓐ B

BETOS: D1A Medical/surgical supplies

C **Q4033** Cast supplies, long leg cylinder cast, adult (11 years +), plaster DME Ⓐ B

BETOS: D1A Medical/surgical supplies

C **Q4034** Cast supplies, long leg cylinder cast, adult (11 years +), fiberglass DME Ⓐ B

BETOS: D1A Medical/surgical supplies

C **Q4035** Cast supplies, long leg cylinder cast, pediatric (0-10 years), plaster DME Ⓐ B

BETOS: D1A Medical/surgical supplies

C **Q4036** Cast supplies, long leg cylinder cast, pediatric (0-10 years), fiberglass DME Ⓐ B

BETOS: D1A Medical/surgical supplies

C **Q4037** Cast supplies, short leg cast, adult (11 years +), plaster DME Ⓐ B

BETOS: D1A Medical/surgical supplies

C **Q4038** Cast supplies, short leg cast, adult (11 years +), fiberglass DME Ⓐ B

BETOS: D1A Medical/surgical supplies

C **Q4039** Cast supplies, short leg cast, pediatric (0-10 years), plaster DME Ⓐ B

BETOS: D1A Medical/surgical supplies

C **Q4040** Cast supplies, short leg cast, pediatric (0-10 years), fiberglass DME Ⓐ B

BETOS: D1A Medical/surgical supplies

C **Q4041** Cast supplies, long leg splint, adult (11 years +), plaster DME Ⓐ B

BETOS: D1A Medical/surgical supplies

C **Q4042** Cast supplies, long leg splint, adult (11 years +), fiberglass DME Ⓐ B

BETOS: D1A Medical/surgical supplies

C **Q4043** Cast supplies, long leg splint, pediatric (0-10 years), plaster DME Ⓐ B

BETOS: D1A Medical/surgical supplies

C **Q4044** Cast supplies, long leg splint, pediatric (0-10 years), fiberglass DME Ⓐ B

BETOS: D1A Medical/surgical supplies

C **Q4045** Cast supplies, short leg splint, adult (11 years +), plaster DME Ⓐ B

BETOS: D1A Medical/surgical supplies

C **Q4046** Cast supplies, short leg splint, adult (11 years +), fiberglass DME Ⓐ B

BETOS: D1A Medical/surgical supplies

C **Q4047** Cast supplies, short leg splint, pediatric (0-10 years), plaster DME Ⓐ B

BETOS: D1A Medical/surgical supplies

C **Q4048** Cast supplies, short leg splint, pediatric (0-10 years), fiberglass DME Ⓐ B

BETOS: D1A Medical/surgical supplies

▲ Revised code   ● New code   C Carrier judgment   D Special coverage instructions apply

I Not payable by Medicare   M Non-covered by Medicare   S Non-covered by Medicare statute   AHA Coding Clinic®

C **Q4049** Finger splint, static   DME B
    BETOS: D1A   Medical/surgical supplies
    Coding Clinic: 2007, Q2

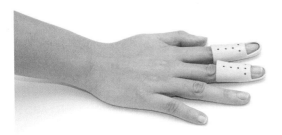

Finger splint

C **Q4050** Cast supplies, for unlisted types and materials of casts   B
    BETOS: D1A   Medical/surgical supplies
    Other carrier priced

C **Q4051** Splint supplies, miscellaneous (includes thermoplastics, strapping, fasteners, padding and other supplies)   B
    BETOS: D1A   Medical/surgical supplies
    Other carrier priced
    Coding Clinic: 2002, Q2

MISCELLANEOUS DRUGS (Q4074-Q4082)

C **Q4074** Iloprost, inhalation solution, FDA-approved final product, non-compounded, administered through DME, unit dose form, up to 20 micrograms   Y
    BETOS: D1G   Drugs administered through DME
    Drugs: VENTAVIS

D **Q4081** Injection, epoetin alfa, 100 units (for ESRD on dialysis)   N
    BETOS: O1E   Other drugs
    Other carrier priced
    Drugs: EPOGEN, PROCRIT
    Pub: 100-4, Chap. 8, 60.4; 100-4, Chap. 8, 60.4.1; 100-4, Chap. 8, 60.4.4.1: 100-4, Chap. 8, 60.4.4.2 ; 100-4, Chap. 8, 60.4.5.1

C **Q4082** Drug or biological, not otherwise classified, Part B drug competitive acquisition program (CAP)   B
    BETOS: D1E   Other DME

SKIN SUBSTITUTES AND BIOLOGICALS (Q4100-Q4182)

C **Q4100** Skin substitute, not otherwise specified   N1 ASC N
    BETOS: O1E   Other drugs
    Coding Clinic: 2010, Q1; 2012, Q2

C **Q4101** Apligraf, per square centimeter   N1 ASC N
    BETOS: O1E   Other drugs
    Drugs: APLIGRAF
    Coding Clinic: 2010, Q1; 2011, Q1; 2012, Q2

C **Q4102** Oasis wound matrix, per square centimeter   N1 ASC N
    BETOS: O1E   Other drugs
    Drugs: OASIS WOUND MATRIX
    Coding Clinic: 2010, Q1; 2011, Q1; 2012, Q2; 2012, Q3

C **Q4103** Oasis burn matrix, per square centimeter   N1 ASC N
    BETOS: O1E   Other drugs
    Coding Clinic: 2010, Q1; 2011, Q1; 2012, Q2

C **Q4104** Integra bilayer matrix wound dressing (BMWD), per square centimeter   N1 ASC N
    BETOS: O1E   Other drugs
    Coding Clinic: 2010, Q1; 2011, Q1; 2012, Q2; 2014, Q3

C **Q4105** Integra dermal regeneration template (DRT) or integra omnigraft dermal regeneration matrix, per square centimeter   N1 ASC N
    BETOS: O1E   Other drugs
    Coding Clinic: 2010, Q1; 2011, Q1; 2012, Q2

C **Q4106** Dermagraft, per square centimeter   N1 ASC N
    BETOS: O1E   Other drugs
    Drugs: DERMAGRAFT
    Coding Clinic: 2010, Q1; 2011, Q1; 2012, Q2

C **Q4107** GRAFTJACKET, per square centimeter   N1 ASC N
    BETOS: O1E   Other drugs
    Drugs: GRAFTJACKET STD
    Coding Clinic: 2010, Q1; 2011, Q1; 2012, Q2

C **Q4108** Integra matrix, per square centimeter   N1 ASC N
    BETOS: O1E   Other drugs
    Coding Clinic: 2010, Q1; 2011, Q1; 2012, Q2

C **Q4110** PriMatrix, per square centimeter   N1 ASC N
    BETOS: O1E   Other drugs
    Coding Clinic: 2010, Q1; 2011, Q1; 2012, Q2

C **Q4111** GammaGraft, per square centimeter   N1 ASC N
    BETOS: O1E   Other drugs
    Drugs: GAMMAGRAFT
    Coding Clinic: 2010, Q1; 2011, Q1; 2012, Q2

C **Q4112** Cymetra, injectable, 1 cc   N1 ASC N
    BETOS: O1E   Other drugs
    Drugs: CYMETRA
    Coding Clinic: 2010, Q1; 2011, Q1; 2012, Q2

♂ Male only   ♀ Female only   **A** Age   A2 - Z3 = ASC Payment indicator   A - Y = APC Status indicator
ASC = ASC-approved procedure   **DME** Paid under the DME fee schedule   **MIPS** MIPS code

C **Q4113** GRAFTJACKET XPRESS, injectable, 1 cc   N1 ASC N
BETOS: O1E   Other drugs
Drugs: GRAFTJACKET XPRESS
Coding Clinic: 2010, Q1; 2011, Q1; 2012, Q2

C **Q4114** Integra flowable wound matrix, injectable, 1 cc   N1 ASC N
BETOS: O1E   Other drugs
Coding Clinic: 2010, Q1; 2012, Q2

C **Q4115** AlloSkin, per square centimeter   N1 ASC N
BETOS: O1E   Other drugs
Drugs: ALLOSKIN
Coding Clinic: 2010, Q1; 2011, Q1; 2012, Q2

C **Q4116** AlloDerm, per square centimeter   N1 ASC N
BETOS: O1E   Other drugs
Drugs: ALLODERM, ALLODERM SELECT, ALLODERM SELECT CONTOUR
Coding Clinic: 2010, Q1; 2011, Q1; 2012, Q2

C **Q4117** HYALOMATRIX, per square centimeter   N1 ASC N
BETOS: O1E   Other drugs

C **Q4118** MatriStem micromatrix, 1 mg   N1 ASC N
BETOS: O1E   Other drugs
Coding Clinic: 2011, Q1; 2012, Q2; 2013, Q4

C **Q4121** TheraSkin, per square centimeter   N1 ASC N
BETOS: O1E   Other drugs
Drugs: THERASKIN
Coding Clinic: 2011, Q1; 2012, Q2

C **Q4122** DermACELL, per square centimeter   N1 ASC N
BETOS: O1E   Other drugs
Coding Clinic: 2012, Q1; 2012, Q2

C **Q4123** AlloSkin RT, per square centimeter N1 ASC N
BETOS: O1E   Other drugs
Drugs: ALLOSKIN RT

C **Q4124** OASIS ultra tri-layer wound matrix, per square centimeter   N1 ASC N
BETOS: O1E   Other drugs
Coding Clinic: 2012, Q2

C **Q4125** Arthroflex, per square centimeter   N1 ASC N
BETOS: O1E   Other drugs

C **Q4126** MemoDerm, DermaSpan, TranZgraft or InteguPly, per square centimeter   N1 ASC N
BETOS: O1E   Other drugs

C **Q4127** Talymed, per square centimeter   N1 ASC N
BETOS: O1E   Other drugs

C **Q4128** FlexHD, AllopatchHD, or MatrixHD, per square centimeter   N1 ASC N
BETOS: O1E   Other drugs

C **Q4130** Strattice TM, per square centimeter   N1 ASC N
BETOS: O1E   Other drugs
Coding Clinic: 2012, Q2

C **Q4131** Epifix or epicord, per square centimeter   N1 ASC N
BETOS: O1E   Other drugs
Drugs: EPICORD , EPIFIX, EPIFIX AMNIOTIC MEMBRANE ALLOGRAFT

▲ **C** **Q4132** Grafix CORE and GrafixPL CORE, per square centimeter   N1 ASC N
BETOS: O1E   Other drugs
Drugs: GRAFIX CORE

▲ **C** **Q4133** Grafix prime and Grafixpl prime, per square centimeter   N1 ASC N
BETOS: O1E   Other drugs
Drugs: GRAFIX PRIME

C **Q4134** Hmatrix, per square centimeter   N1 ASC N
BETOS: O1E   Other drugs

C **Q4135** Mediskin, per square centimeter   N1 ASC N
BETOS: O1E   Other drugs

C **Q4136** E-Z Derm, per square centimeter   N1 ASC N
BETOS: O1E   Other drugs

C **Q4137** AMNIOEXCEL or BioDExCel, per square centimeter   N1 ASC N
BETOS: O1E   Other drugs

C **Q4138** BioDFence dryflex, per square centimeter   N1 ASC N
BETOS: O1E   Other drugs
Coding Clinic: 2014, Q1

C **Q4139** AmnioMatrix or biodmatrix, injectable, 1 cc   N1 ASC N
BETOS: O1E   Other drugs
Coding Clinic: 2014, Q1

C **Q4140** Biodfence, per square centimeter   N1 ASC N
BETOS: O1E   Other drugs
Coding Clinic: 2014, Q1

C **Q4141** AlloSkin AC, per square centimeter N1 ASC N
BETOS: O1E   Other drugs
Coding Clinic: 2014, Q1

C **Q4142** XCM BIOLOGIC tissue matrix, per square centimeter   N1 ASC N
BETOS: O1E   Other drugs
Coding Clinic: 2014, Q1

C **Q4143** Repriza, per square centimeter   N1 ASC N
BETOS: O1E   Other drugs
Coding Clinic: 2014, Q1

C **Q4145** EpiFix, injectable, 1 mg   N1 ASC N
BETOS: O1E   Other drugs
Coding Clinic: 2014, Q1

C **Q4146** Tensix, per square centimeter   N1 ASC N
BETOS: O1E   Other drugs
Coding Clinic: 2014, Q1

C **Q4147** Architect, Architect PX, or Architect FX, extracellular matrix, per square centimeter   N1 ASC N
BETOS: O1E   Other drugs
Coding Clinic: 2014, Q1

▲ Revised code   ● New code   **C** Carrier judgment   **D** Special coverage instructions apply
I Not payable by Medicare   **M** Non-covered by Medicare   **S** Non-covered by Medicare statute   AHA Coding Clinic®

▲ **C** **Q4148** NEOX CORD 1K, NEOX CORD RT, or CLARIXCORD 1K, per square centimeter N1 ASC N
BETOS: O1E Other drugs
Coding Clinic: 2014, Q1

C **Q4149** Excellagen, 0.1 cc N1 ASC N
BETOS: O1E Other drugs
Coding Clinic: 2014, Q1

C **Q4150** Allowrap DS or Dry, per square centimeter N1 ASC N
BETOS: O1E Other drugs
Coding Clinic: 2014, Q4

C **Q4151** AmnioBand or Guardian, per square centimeter N1 ASC N
BETOS: O1E Other drugs
Coding Clinic: 2014, Q4

C **Q4152** DermaPure, per square centimeter N1 ASC N
BETOS: O1E Other drugs
Coding Clinic: 2014, Q4

C **Q4153** Dermavest and plurivest, per square centimeter N1 ASC N
BETOS: O1E Other drugs
Coding Clinic: 2014, Q4; 2016, Q1

C **Q4154** Biovance, per square centimeter N1 ASC N
BETOS: O1E Other drugs
Coding Clinic: 2014, Q4

C **Q4155** NeoxFlo or clarixFlo, 1 mg N1 ASC N
BETOS: O1E Other drugs
Coding Clinic: 2014, Q4

▲ **C** **Q4156** NEOX 100 or CLARIX 100, per square centimeter N1 ASC N
BETOS: O1E Other drugs
Coding Clinic: 2014, Q4

C **Q4157** Revitalon, per square centimeter N1 ASC N
BETOS: O1E Other drugs
Coding Clinic: 2014, Q4

▲ **C** **Q4158** Kerecis Omega3, per square centimeter N1 ASC N
BETOS: O1E Other drugs
Coding Clinic: 2014, Q4

C **Q4159** Affinity, per square centimeter N1 ASC N
BETOS: O1E Other drugs
Coding Clinic: 2014, Q4

C **Q4160** NuShield, per square centimeter N1 ASC N
BETOS: O1E Other drugs
Coding Clinic: 2014, Q4

C **Q4161** Bio-ConneKt wound matrix, per square centimeter N1 ASC N
BETOS: O1E Other drugs
Coding Clinic: 2016, Q1

▲ **C** **Q4162** WoundEx Flow, BioSkin Flow, 0.5 cc N1 ASC N
BETOS: O1E Other drugs
Coding Clinic: 2016, Q1

▲ **C** **Q4163** WoundEx, BioSkin, per square centimeter N1 ASC N
BETOS: O1E Other drugs
Coding Clinic: 2016, Q1

C **Q4164** Helicoll, per square centimeter N1 ASC N
BETOS: O1E Other drugs
Coding Clinic: 2016, Q1

C **Q4165** Keramatrix, per square centimeter N1 ASC N
BETOS: O1E Other drugs
Coding Clinic: 2016, Q1

C **Q4166** Cytal, per square centimeter N1 ASC N
BETOS: O1E Other drugs
Coding Clinic: 2017, Q1

C **Q4167** Truskin, per square centimeter N1 ASC N
BETOS: O1E Other drugs
Coding Clinic: 2017, Q1

C **Q4168** Amnioband, 1 mg N1 ASC N
BETOS: O1E Other drugs
Coding Clinic: 2017, Q1

C **Q4169** Artacent wound, per square centimeter N1 ASC N
BETOS: O1E Other drugs
Coding Clinic: 2017, Q1

C **Q4170** Cygnus, per square centimeter N1 ASC N
BETOS: O1E Other drugs
Coding Clinic: 2017, Q1

C **Q4171** Interfyl, 1 mg N1 ASC N
BETOS: O1E Other drugs
Coding Clinic: 2017, Q1

C **Q4172** Puraply or puraply am, per square centimeter K2 ASC G
BETOS: O1E Other drugs

C **Q4173** Palingen or palingen xplus, per square centimeter N1 ASC N
BETOS: O1E Other drugs
Coding Clinic: 2017, Q1

C **Q4174** Palingen or promatrx, 0.36 mg per 0.25 cc N1 ASC N
BETOS: O1E Other drugs
Coding Clinic: 2017, Q1

C **Q4175** Miroderm, per square centimeter N1 ASC N
BETOS: O1E Other drugs
Coding Clinic: 2017, Q1

● **C** **Q4176** Neopatch, per square centimeter
BETOS: O1E Other drugs

● **C** **Q4177** Floweramnioflo, 0.1 cc
BETOS: O1E Other drugs

● **C** **Q4178** Floweramniopatch, per square centimeter
BETOS: O1E Other drugs

● **C** **Q4179** Flowerderm, per square centimeter
BETOS: O1E Other drugs

● **C** **Q4180** Revita, per square centimeter
BETOS: O1E Other drugs

♂ Male only   ♀ Female only   **A** Age   A2 - Z3 = ASC Payment indicator   A - Y = APC Status indicator
ASC = ASC-approved procedure   **DME** Paid under the DME fee schedule   **MIPS** MIPS code

- ● C **Q4181** Amnio wound, per square centimeter
  BETOS: O1E   Other drugs

- ● C **Q4182** Transcyte, per square centimeter
  BETOS: O1E   Other drugs

HOSPICE AND HOME HEALTH CARE (Q5001-Q5010)

D **Q5001** Hospice or home health care provided in patient's home/residence   B
BETOS: Y2   Other - non-Medicare fee schedule
Service not separately priced by Part B
Pub: 100-4, Chap. 10, 40.2; 100-4, Chap. 11, 30.3

D **Q5002** Hospice or home health care provided in assisted living facility   B
BETOS: Y2   Other - non-Medicare fee schedule
Service not separately priced by Part B

D **Q5003** Hospice care provided in nursing long term care facility (LTC) or non-skilled nursing facility (NF)   B
BETOS: Y2   Other - non-Medicare fee schedule
Service not separately priced by Part B

D **Q5004** Hospice care provided in skilled nursing facility (SNF)   B
BETOS: Y2   Other - non-Medicare fee schedule
Service not separately priced by Part B

D **Q5005** Hospice care provided in inpatient hospital B
BETOS: Y2   Other - non-Medicare fee schedule
Service not separately priced by Part B

D **Q5006** Hospice care provided in inpatient hospice facility   B
BETOS: Y2   Other - non-Medicare fee schedule
Service not separately priced by Part B

D **Q5007** Hospice care provided in long term care facility   B
BETOS: Y2   Other - non-Medicare fee schedule
Service not separately priced by Part B

D **Q5008** Hospice care provided in inpatient psychiatric facility   B
BETOS: Y2   Other - non-Medicare fee schedule
Service not separately priced by Part B

D **Q5009** Hospice or home health care provided in place not otherwise specified (NOS)   B
BETOS: Y2   Other - non-Medicare fee schedule
Service not separately priced by Part B
Pub: 100-4, Chap. 10, 40.2

D **Q5010** Hospice home care provided in a hospice facility   B
BETOS: Y2   Other - non-Medicare fee schedule
Service not separately priced by Part B

CHEMOTHERAPY MEDICATIONS (Q5101-Q5102), SEE ALSO CHEMOTHERAPY ANTI-EMETIC MEDICATIONS (Q0161-Q0181)

D **Q5101** Injection, filgrastim (G-CSF), biosimilar, 1 microgram   K2 ASC G
BETOS: O1E   Other drugs
Drugs: ZARXIO (FILGRASTIM-SNDZ)
Coding Clinic: 2016, Q2

D **Q5102** Injection, infliximab, biosimilar, 10 mg   K2 ASC G
BETOS: O1E   Other drugs
Drugs: INFLECTRA
Coding Clinic: 2016, Q2; 2017, Q3

CONTRAST AGENTS/DIAGNOSTIC IMAGING (Q9950-Q9983), SEE ALSO IMAGING STUDIES (S8030-S8092)

C **Q9950** Injection, sulfur hexafluoride lipid microspheres, per ml   K2 ASC G
BETOS: I1F   Standard imaging - other
Other carrier priced
Drugs: LUMASON
Coding Clinic: 2016, Q1; 2016, Q4

D **Q9951** Low osmolar contrast material, 400 or greater mg/ml iodine concentration, per ml   N1 ASC N
BETOS: I1E   Standard imaging - nuclear medicine
Coding Clinic: 2012, Q3
Pub: 100-4, Chap. 13, 40

D **Q9953** Injection, iron-based magnetic resonance contrast agent, per ml   N1 ASC N
BETOS: I1F   Standard imaging - other
Other carrier priced
Coding Clinic: 2012, Q3

D **Q9954** Oral magnetic resonance contrast agent, per 100 ml   N1 ASC N
BETOS: I1F   Standard imaging - other
Other carrier priced
Coding Clinic: 2012, Q3

C **Q9955** Injection, perflexane lipid microspheres, per ml   N1 ASC N
BETOS: I1F   Standard imaging - other
Other carrier priced
Coding Clinic: 2012, Q3

C **Q9956** Injection, octafluoropropane microspheres, per ml   N1 ASC N
BETOS: I1F   Standard imaging - other
Other carrier priced
Drugs: OPTISON
Coding Clinic: 2012, Q3

▲ Revised code   ● New code   C Carrier judgment   D Special coverage instructions apply
I Not payable by Medicare   M Non-covered by Medicare   S Non-covered by Medicare statute   AHA Coding Clinic®

C Q9957 Injection, perflutren lipid microspheres, per ml   N1 ASC N
BETOS: I1F   Standard imaging - other
Other carrier priced
Drugs: DEFINITY
Coding Clinic: 2012, Q3

D Q9958 High osmolar contrast material, up to 149 mg/ml iodine concentration, per ml N1 ASC N
BETOS: I1E   Standard imaging - nuclear medicine
Drugs: CONRAY 30, CYSTO-CONRAY II, CYSTOGRAFIN, CYSTOGRAFIN-DILUTE
Coding Clinic: 2011, Q4; 2012, Q3

D Q9959 High osmolar contrast material, 150-199 mg/ml iodine concentration, per ml   N1 ASC N
BETOS: I1E   Standard imaging - nuclear medicine
Coding Clinic: 2012, Q3

D Q9960 High osmolar contrast material, 200-249 mg/ml iodine concentration, per ml   N1 ASC N
BETOS: I1E   Standard imaging - nuclear medicine
Drugs: CONRAY 43
Coding Clinic: 2012, Q3

D Q9961 High osmolar contrast material, 250-299 mg/ml iodine concentration, per ml   N1 ASC N
BETOS: I1E   Standard imaging - nuclear medicine
Drugs: CHOLOGRAFIN MEGLUMINE, CONRAY
Coding Clinic: 2012, Q3

D Q9962 High osmolar contrast material, 300-349 mg/ml iodine concentration, per ml   N1 ASC N
BETOS: I1E   Standard imaging - nuclear medicine
Coding Clinic: 2012, Q3

D Q9963 High osmolar contrast material, 350-399 mg/ml iodine concentration, per ml   N1 ASC N
BETOS: I1E   Standard imaging - nuclear medicine
Drugs: GASTROGRAFIN, MD GASTROVIEW, MD-76R, SINOGRAFIN
Coding Clinic: 2012, Q3

D Q9964 High osmolar contrast material, 400 or greater mg/ml iodine concentration, per ml   N1 ASC N
BETOS: I1E   Standard imaging - nuclear medicine
Coding Clinic: 2011, Q4; 2012, Q3

D Q9965 Low osmolar contrast material, 100-199 mg/ml iodine concentration, per ml   N1 ASC N
BETOS: I1E   Standard imaging - nuclear medicine
Drugs: OMNIPAQUE 140, OMNIPAQUE 180
Coding Clinic: 2011, Q4; 2012, Q3

D Q9966 Low osmolar contrast material, 200-299 mg/ml iodine concentration, per ml   N1 ASC N

BETOS: I1E   Standard imaging - nuclear medicine
Drugs: ISOVUE-200, ISOVUE-250, ISOVUE-250 MULTIPACK, ISOVUE-M-200, OMNIPAQUE, OMNIPAQUE 240, OPTIRAY 240, ULTRAVIST 240, VISIPAQUE 270
Coding Clinic: 2012, Q3

D Q9967 Low osmolar contrast material, 300-399 mg/ml iodine concentration, per ml   N1 ASC N
BETOS: I1E   Standard imaging - nuclear medicine
Drugs: HEXABRIX 320, HEXABRIX 320 MGL/ML, 100ML VOLUME, HEXABRIX 320 MGL/ML, 200ML VOLUME, HEXABRIX 320 MGL/ML, 50ML VOLUME, ISOVUE-300, ISOVUE-300 MULTI PACK, ISOVUE-370, ISOVUE-370 MULTI PACK, ISOVUE-M-300, OMNIPAQUE, OMNIPAQUE 300, OMNIPAQUE 350, OPTIRAY 300, OPTIRAY 320, OPTIRAY 350, OXILAN 300, OXILAN 350, ULTRAVIST 300, ULTRAVIST 370, VISIPAQUE, VISIPAQUE 320
Coding Clinic: 2011, Q4; 2012, Q3

C Q9968 Injection, non-radioactive, non-contrast, visualization adjunct (e.g., methylene blue, isosulfan blue), 1 mg   K2 ASC K
BETOS: I1E   Standard imaging - nuclear medicine

D Q9969 Tc-99m from non-highly enriched uranium source, full cost recovery add-on, per study dose   K
BETOS: Y1   Other - Medicare fee schedule

D Q9982 Flutemetamol f18, diagnostic, per study dose, up to 5 millicuries   K2 ASC G
BETOS: I1E   Standard imaging - nuclear medicine
Service not separately priced by Part B
Coding Clinic: 2016, Q2

D Q9983 Florbetaben f18, diagnostic, per study dose, up to 8.1 millicuries   K2 ASC G
BETOS: I1E   Standard imaging - nuclear medicine
Service not separately priced by Part B
Coding Clinic: 2016, Q2

♂ Male only   ♀ Female only   **A** Age   A2 - Z3 = ASC Payment indicator   A - Y = APC Status indicator
ASC = ASC-approved procedure   **DME** Paid under the DME fee schedule   **MIPS** MIPS code

NOTES

DIAGNOSTIC RADIOLOGY SERVICES
(R0070-R0076)

TRANSPORTATION, PORTABLE RADIOLOGY EQUIPMENT
(R0070-R0076)

D **R0070** Transportation of portable X-ray equipment
and personnel to home or nursing home, per
trip to facility or location, one patient seen B
BETOS: I1F   Standard imaging - other
Price established by carriers

D **R0075** Transportation of portable X-ray equipment
and personnel to home or nursing home,
per trip to facility or location, more than one
patient seen B
BETOS: I1F   Standard imaging - other
Price established by carriers

D **R0076** Transportation of portable EKG to facility or
location, per patient B
BETOS: I1F   Standard imaging - other
Price established by carriers

♂ Male only   ♀ Female only   **Ⓐ** Age   A2 - Z3 = ASC Payment indicator   A - Y = APC Status indicator
ASC = ASC-approved procedure   **DME** Paid under the DME fee schedule   **MIPS** MIPS code

NOTES

TEMPORARY NATIONAL CODES (NON-MEDICARE) (S0012-S9999)

NON-MEDICARE DRUG CODES (S0012-S0197)

S0012 Butorphanol tartrate, nasal spray, 25 mg
BETOS: Z2 Undefined codes
Service not separately priced by Part B

S0014 Tacrine hydrochloride, 10 mg
BETOS: Z2 Undefined codes
Service not separately priced by Part B

S0017 Injection, aminocaproic acid, 5 grams
BETOS: Z2 Undefined codes
Service not separately priced by Part B

S0020 Injection, bupivicaine hydrochloride, 30 ml
BETOS: Z2 Undefined codes
Service not separately priced by Part B

S0021 Injection, cefoperazone sodium, 1 gram
BETOS: Z2 Undefined codes
Service not separately priced by Part B

S0023 Injection, cimetidine hydrochloride, 300 mg
BETOS: Z2 Undefined codes
Service not separately priced by Part B

S0028 Injection, famotidine, 20 mg
BETOS: Z2 Undefined codes
Service not separately priced by Part B

S0030 Injection, metronidazole, 500 mg
BETOS: Z2 Undefined codes
Service not separately priced by Part B

S0032 Injection, nafcillin sodium, 2 grams
BETOS: Z2 Undefined codes
Service not separately priced by Part B

S0034 Injection, ofloxacin, 400 mg
BETOS: Z2 Undefined codes
Service not separately priced by Part B

S0039 Injection, sulfamethoxazole and trimethoprim, 10 ml
BETOS: Z2 Undefined codes
Service not separately priced by Part B

S0040 Injection, ticarcillin disodium and clavulanate potassium, 3.1 grams
BETOS: Z2 Undefined codes
Service not separately priced by Part B

S0073 Injection, aztreonam, 500 mg
BETOS: Z2 Undefined codes
Service not separately priced by Part B

S0074 Injection, cefotetan disodium, 500 mg
BETOS: Z2 Undefined codes
Service not separately priced by Part B

S0077 Injection, clindamycin phosphate, 300 mg
BETOS: Z2 Undefined codes
Service not separately priced by Part B

S0078 Injection, fosphenytoin sodium, 750 mg
BETOS: Z2 Undefined codes
Service not separately priced by Part B

S0080 Injection, pentamidine isethionate, 300 mg
BETOS: Z2 Undefined codes
Service not separately priced by Part B

S0081 Injection, piperacillin sodium, 500 mg
BETOS: Z2 Undefined codes
Service not separately priced by Part B

S0088 Imatinib, 100 mg
BETOS: Z2 Undefined codes
Service not separately priced by Part B

S0090 Sildenafil citrate, 25 mg Ⓐ
BETOS: Z2 Undefined codes
Service not separately priced by Part B

S0091 Granisetron hydrochloride, 1 mg (for circumstances falling under the Medicare statute, use Q0166)
BETOS: Z2 Undefined codes
Service not separately priced by Part B

S0092 Injection, hydromorphone hydrochloride, 250 mg (loading dose for infusion pump)
BETOS: Z2 Undefined codes
Service not separately priced by Part B

S0093 Injection, morphine sulfate, 500 mg (loading dose for infusion pump)
BETOS: Z2 Undefined codes
Service not separately priced by Part B

S0104 Zidovudine, oral, 100 mg
BETOS: Z2 Undefined codes
Service not separately priced by Part B

S0106 Bupropion HCL sustained release tablet, 150 mg, per bottle of 60 tablets
BETOS: Z2 Undefined codes
Service not separately priced by Part B

S0108 Mercaptopurine, oral, 50 mg
BETOS: Z2 Undefined codes
Service not separately priced by Part B

S0109 Methadone, oral, 5 mg
BETOS: Z2 Undefined codes
Service not separately priced by Part B

S0117 Tretinoin, topical, 5 grams
BETOS: Z2 Undefined codes
Service not separately priced by Part B

S0119 Ondansetron, oral, 4 mg (for circumstances falling under the Medicare statute, use HCPCS Q code)
BETOS: Z2 Undefined codes
Service not separately priced by Part B

S0122 Injection, menotropins, 75 IU
BETOS: Z2 Undefined codes
Service not separately priced by Part B

♂ Male only   ♀ Female only   Ⓐ Age   A2 - Z3 = ASC Payment indicator   A - Y = APC Status indicator
ASC = ASC-approved procedure   **DME** Paid under the DME fee schedule   **MIPS** MIPS code

S0126 - S0190 (side tab)

TEMPORARY NATIONAL CODES (NON-MEDICARE) (S0012-S9999) (side tab)

❙ S0126 Injection, follitropin alfa, 75 IU ♀
BETOS: Z2   Undefined codes
Service not separately priced by Part B

❙ S0128 Injection, follitropin beta, 75 IU
BETOS: Z2   Undefined codes
Service not separately priced by Part B

❙ S0132 Injection, ganirelix acetate, 250 mcg ♀
BETOS: Z2   Undefined codes
Service not separately priced by Part B

❙ S0136 Clozapine, 25 mg
BETOS: Z2   Undefined codes
Service not separately priced by Part B

❙ S0137 Didanosine (ddi), 25 mg
BETOS: Z2   Undefined codes
Service not separately priced by Part B

❙ S0138 Finasteride, 5 mg ♂
BETOS: Z2   Undefined codes
Service not separately priced by Part B

❙ S0139 Minoxidil, 10 mg
BETOS: Z2   Undefined codes
Service not separately priced by Part B

❙ S0140 Saquinavir, 200 mg
BETOS: Z2   Undefined codes
Service not separately priced by Part B

❙ S0142 Colistimethate sodium, inhalation solution administered through DME, concentrated form, per mg
BETOS: Z2   Undefined codes
Service not separately priced by Part B

❙ S0145 Injection, pegylated interferon alfa-2a, 180 mcg per ml
BETOS: Z2   Undefined codes
Service not separately priced by Part B

❙ S0148 Injection, pegylated interferon alfa-2b, 10 mcg
BETOS: Z2   Undefined codes
Service not separately priced by Part B

❙ S0155 Sterile dilutant for epoprostenol, 50 ml
BETOS: Z2   Undefined codes
Service not separately priced by Part B

❙ S0156 Exemestane, 25 mg
BETOS: Z2   Undefined codes
Service not separately priced by Part B

❙ S0157 Becaplermin gel 0.01%, 0.5 gm
BETOS: Z2   Undefined codes
Service not separately priced by Part B

❙ S0160 Dextroamphetamine sulfate, 5 mg
BETOS: Z2   Undefined codes
Service not separately priced by Part B

❙ S0164 Injection, pantoprazole sodium, 40 mg
BETOS: Z2   Undefined codes
Service not separately priced by Part B

❙ S0166 Injection, olanzapine, 2.5 mg
BETOS: Z2   Undefined codes
Service not separately priced by Part B

❙ S0169 Calcitrol, 0.25 microgram
BETOS: Z2   Undefined codes
Service not separately priced by Part B

❙ S0170 Anastrozole, oral, 1 mg
BETOS: Z2   Undefined codes
Service not separately priced by Part B

❙ S0171 Injection, bumetanide, 0.5 mg
BETOS: Z2   Undefined codes
Service not separately priced by Part B

❙ S0172 Chlorambucil, oral, 2 mg
BETOS: Z2   Undefined codes
Service not separately priced by Part B

❙ S0174 Dolasetron mesylate, oral 50 mg (for circumstances falling under the Medicare statute, use Q0180)
BETOS: Z2   Undefined codes
Service not separately priced by Part B

❙ S0175 Flutamide, oral, 125 mg
BETOS: Z2   Undefined codes
Service not separately priced by Part B

❙ S0176 Hydroxyurea, oral, 500 mg
BETOS: Z2   Undefined codes
Service not separately priced by Part B

❙ S0177 Levamisole hydrochloride, oral, 50 mg
BETOS: Z2   Undefined codes
Service not separately priced by Part B

❙ S0178 Lomustine, oral, 10 mg
BETOS: Z2   Undefined codes
Service not separately priced by Part B

❙ S0179 Megestrol acetate, oral, 20 mg
BETOS: Z2   Undefined codes
Service not separately priced by Part B

❙ S0182 Procarbazine hydrochloride, oral, 50 mg
BETOS: Z2   Undefined codes
Service not separately priced by Part B

❙ S0183 Prochlorperazine maleate, oral, 5 mg (for circumstances falling under the medicare statute, use Q0164)
BETOS: Z2   Undefined codes
Service not separately priced by Part B

❙ S0187 Tamoxifen citrate, oral, 10 mg
BETOS: Z2   Undefined codes
Service not separately priced by Part B

❙ S0189 Testosterone pellet, 75 mg
BETOS: Z2   Undefined codes
Service not separately priced by Part B

❙ S0190 Mifepristone, oral, 200 mg ♀
BETOS: Z2   Undefined codes
Service not separately priced by Part B

▲ Revised code   ● New code   **C** Carrier judgment   **D** Special coverage instructions apply
❙ Not payable by Medicare   **M** Non-covered by Medicare   **S** Non-covered by Medicare statute   AHA Coding Clinic®

CPT® is a registered trademark of the American Medical Association. All rights reserved.

S0191 Misoprostol, oral, 200 mcg
BETOS: Z2 Undefined codes
Service not separately priced by Part B

S0194 Dialysis/stress vitamin supplement, oral, 100 capsules
BETOS: Z2 Undefined codes
Service not separately priced by Part B

S0197 Prenatal vitamins, 30-day supply ♀
BETOS: Z2 Undefined codes
Service not separately priced by Part B

MISCELLANEOUS PROVIDER SERVICES (S0199-S0400), SEE ALSO MISCELLANEOUS PROVIDER SERVICES AND SUPPLIES (S0630-S3722)

S0199 Medically-induced abortion by oral ingestion of medication including all associated services and supplies (e.g., patient counseling, office visits, confirmation of pregnancy by HCG, ultrasound to confirm duration of pregnancy, ultrasound to confirm completion of abortion) except drugs ♀
BETOS: Z2 Undefined codes
Service not separately priced by Part B

S0201 Partial hospitalization services, less than 24 hours, per diem
BETOS: Z2 Undefined codes
Service not separately priced by Part B

S0207 Paramedic intercept, non-hospital-based ALS service (non-voluntary), non-transport
BETOS: Z2 Undefined codes
Service not separately priced by Part B

S0208 Paramedic intercept, hospital-based ALS service (non-voluntary), non-transport
BETOS: Z2 Undefined codes
Service not separately priced by Part B

S0209 Wheelchair van, mileage, per mile
BETOS: Z2 Undefined codes
Service not separately priced by Part B

S0215 Non-emergency transportation; mileage, per mile
BETOS: Z2 Undefined codes
Service not separately priced by Part B

S0220 Medical conference by a physician with interdisciplinary team of health professionals or representatives of community agencies to coordinate activities of patient care (patient is present); approximately 30 minutes
BETOS: Z2 Undefined codes
Service not separately priced by Part B

S0221 Medical conference by a physician with interdisciplinary team of health professionals or representatives of community agencies to coordinate activities of patient care (patient is present); approximately 60 minutes
BETOS: Z2 Undefined codes
Service not separately priced by Part B

S0250 Comprehensive geriatric assessment and treatment planning performed by assessment team Ⓐ
BETOS: Z2 Undefined codes
Service not separately priced by Part B

S0255 Hospice referral visit (advising patient and family of care options) performed by nurse, social worker, or other designated staff
BETOS: Z2 Undefined codes
Service not separately priced by Part B

S0257 Counseling and discussion regarding advance directives or end of life care planning and decisions, with patient and/or surrogate (list separately in addition to code for appropriate evaluation and management service)
BETOS: Z2 Undefined codes
Service not separately priced by Part B

S0260 History and physical (outpatient or office) related to surgical procedure (list separately in addition to code for appropriate evaluation and management service)
BETOS: Z2 Undefined codes
Service not separately priced by Part B

S0265 Genetic counseling, under physician supervision, each 15 minutes
BETOS: Z2 Undefined codes
Service not separately priced by Part B

S0270 Physician management of patient home care, standard monthly case rate (per 30 days)
BETOS: Z2 Undefined codes
Service not separately priced by Part B

S0271 Physician management of patient home care, hospice monthly case rate (per 30 days)
BETOS: Z2 Undefined codes
Service not separately priced by Part B

S0272 Physician management of patient home care, episodic care monthly case rate (per 30 days)
BETOS: Z2 Undefined codes
Service not separately priced by Part B

S0273 Physician visit at member's home, outside of a capitation arrangement
BETOS: Z2 Undefined codes
Service not separately priced by Part B

S0274 Nurse practitioner visit at member's home, outside of a capitation arrangement
BETOS: Z2 Undefined codes
Service not separately priced by Part B

S0280 Medical home program, comprehensive care coordination and planning, initial plan
BETOS: Z2 Undefined codes
Service not separately priced by Part B

S0281 - S0512

TEMPORARY NATIONAL CODES (NON-MEDICARE) (S0012-S9999)

I **S0281** Medical home program, comprehensive care coordination and planning, maintenance of plan
BETOS: Z2   Undefined codes
Service not separately priced by Part B

I **S0285** Colonoscopy consultation performed prior to a screening colonoscopy procedure
BETOS: Z2   Undefined codes
Service not separately priced by Part B
Coding Clinic: 2016, Q2

I **S0302** Completed early periodic screening diagnosis and treatment (EPSDT) service (list in addition to code for appropriate evaluation and management service) Ⓐ
BETOS: Z2   Undefined codes
Service not separately priced by Part B

I **S0310** Hospitalist services (list separately in addition to code for appropriate evaluation and management service)
BETOS: Z2   Undefined codes
Service not separately priced by Part B

I **S0311** Comprehensive management and care coordination for advanced illness, per calendar month
BETOS: Z2   Undefined codes
Service not separately priced by Part B
Coding Clinic: 2016, Q2

I **S0315** Disease management program; initial assessment and initiation of the program
BETOS: Z2   Undefined codes
Service not separately priced by Part B

I **S0316** Disease management program, follow-up/ reassessment
BETOS: Z2   Undefined codes
Service not separately priced by Part B

I **S0317** Disease management program; per diem
BETOS: Z2   Undefined codes
Service not separately priced by Part B

I **S0320** Telephone calls by a registered nurse to a disease management program member for monitoring purposes; per month
BETOS: Z2   Undefined codes
Service not separately priced by Part B

I **S0340** Lifestyle modification program for management of coronary artery disease, including all supportive services; first quarter / stage
BETOS: Z2   Undefined codes
Service not separately priced by Part B

I **S0341** Lifestyle modification program for management of coronary artery disease, including all supportive services; second or third quarter / stage
BETOS: Z2   Undefined codes
Service not separately priced by Part B

I **S0342** Lifestyle modification program for management of coronary artery disease, including all supportive services; fourth quarter / stage
BETOS: Z2   Undefined codes
Service not separately priced by Part B

I **S0353** Treatment planning and care coordination management for cancer, initial treatment
BETOS: Z2   Undefined codes
Service not separately priced by Part B

I **S0354** Treatment planning and care coordination management for cancer, established patient with a change of regimen
BETOS: Z2   Undefined codes
Service not separately priced by Part B

I **S0390** Routine foot care; removal and/or trimming of corns, calluses and/or nails and preventive maintenance in specific medical conditions (e.g., diabetes), per visit
BETOS: Z2   Undefined codes
Service not separately priced by Part B

I **S0395** Impression casting of a foot performed by a practitioner other than the manufacturer of the orthotic
BETOS: Z2   Undefined codes
Service not separately priced by Part B

I **S0400** Global fee for extracorporeal shock wave lithotripsy treatment of kidney stone(s)
BETOS: Z2   Undefined codes
Service not separately priced by Part B

VISION SUPPLIES (S0500-S0596)

I **S0500** Disposable contact lens, per lens
BETOS: Z2   Undefined codes
Service not separately priced by Part B

I **S0504** Single vision prescription lens (safety, athletic, or sunglass), per lens
BETOS: Z2   Undefined codes
Service not separately priced by Part B

I **S0506** Bifocal vision prescription lens (safety, athletic, or sunglass), per lens
BETOS: Z2   Undefined codes
Service not separately priced by Part B

I **S0508** Trifocal vision prescription lens (safety, athletic, or sunglass), per lens
BETOS: Z2   Undefined codes
Service not separately priced by Part B

I **S0510** Non-prescription lens (safety, athletic, or sunglass), per lens
BETOS: Z2   Undefined codes
Service not separately priced by Part B

I **S0512** Daily wear specialty contact lens, per lens
BETOS: Z2   Undefined codes
Service not separately priced by Part B

▲ Revised code   ● New code   **C** Carrier judgment   **D** Special coverage instructions apply
I Not payable by Medicare   **M** Non-covered by Medicare   **S** Non-covered by Medicare statute   AHA Coding Clinic®

S0514 Color contact lens, per lens
BETOS: Z2   Undefined codes
Service not separately priced by Part B

S0515 Scleral lens, liquid bandage device, per lens
BETOS: Z2   Undefined codes
Service not separately priced by Part B

S0516 Safety eyeglass frames
BETOS: Z2   Undefined codes
Service not separately priced by Part B

S0518 Sunglasses frames
BETOS: Z2   Undefined codes
Service not separately priced by Part B

S0580 Polycarbonate lens (list this code in addition to the basic code for the lens)
BETOS: Z2   Undefined codes
Service not separately priced by Part B

S0581 Nonstandard lens (list this code in addition to the basic code for the lens)
BETOS: Z2   Undefined codes
Service not separately priced by Part B

S0590 Integral lens service, miscellaneous services reported separately
BETOS: Z2   Undefined codes
Service not separately priced by Part B

S0592 Comprehensive contact lens evaluation
BETOS: Z2   Undefined codes
Service not separately priced by Part B

S0595 Dispensing new spectacle lenses for patient supplied frame
BETOS: Z2   Undefined codes
Service not separately priced by Part B

S0596 Phakic intraocular lens for correction of refractive error
BETOS: Z2   Undefined codes
Service not separately priced by Part B

SCREENINGS AND EXAMINATIONS (S0601-S0622)

S0601 Screening proctoscopy
BETOS: Z2   Undefined codes
Service not separately priced by Part B

S0610 Annual gynecological examination, new patient ♀
BETOS: Z2   Undefined codes
Service not separately priced by Part B

S0612 Annual gynecological examination, established patient ♀
BETOS: Z2   Undefined codes
Service not separately priced by Part B

S0613 Annual gynecological examination; clinical breast examination without pelvic evaluation ♀
BETOS: Z2   Undefined codes
Service not separately priced by Part B

S0618 Audiometry for hearing aid evaluation to determine the level and degree of hearing loss
BETOS: Z2   Undefined codes
Service not separately priced by Part B

S0620 Routine ophthalmological examination including refraction; new patient
BETOS: Z2   Undefined codes
Service not separately priced by Part B

S0621 Routine ophthalmological examination including refraction; established patient
BETOS: Z2   Undefined codes
Service not separately priced by Part B

S0622 Physical exam for college, new or established patient (list separately in addition to appropriate evaluation and management code) Ⓐ
BETOS: Z2   Undefined codes
Service not separately priced by Part B

MISCELLANEOUS PROVIDER SERVICES AND SUPPLIES (S0630-S3722), SEE ALSO MISCELLANEOUS PROVIDER SERVICES (S0199-S0400)

S0630 Removal of sutures; by a physician other than the physician who originally closed the wound
BETOS: Z2   Undefined codes
Service not separately priced by Part B

S0800 Laser in situ keratomileusis (LASIK)
BETOS: Z2   Undefined codes
Service not separately priced by Part B

S0810 Photorefractive keratectomy (PRK)
BETOS: Z2   Undefined codes
Service not separately priced by Part B

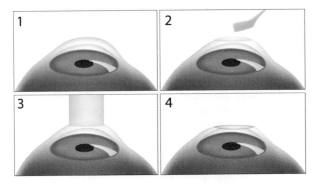

Phototherapeutic keratectomy

S0812 Phototherapeutic keratectomy (PTK)
BETOS: Z2   Undefined codes
Service not separately priced by Part B

S1001 Deluxe item, patient aware (list in addition to code for basic item)
BETOS: Z2   Undefined codes
Service not separately priced by Part B
Pub: 100-2, Chap. 1, 10.1.4

♂ Male only   ♀ Female only   Ⓐ Age   A2 - Z3 = ASC Payment indicator   A - Y = APC Status indicator
ASC = ASC-approved procedure   **DME** Paid under the DME fee schedule   **MIPS** MIPS code

I S1002 Customized item (list in addition to code for basic item)

BETOS: Z2   Undefined codes
Service not separately priced by Part B

I S1015 IV tubing extension set

BETOS: Z2   Undefined codes
Service not separately priced by Part B

I S1016 Non-PVC (polyvinyl chloride) intravenous administration set, for use with drugs that are not stable in PVC e.g. paclitaxel

BETOS: Z2   Undefined codes
Service not separately priced by Part B

I S1030 Continuous noninvasive glucose monitoring device, purchase (for physician interpretation of data, use CPT® code)

BETOS: Z2   Undefined codes
Service not separately priced by Part B

I S1031 Continuous noninvasive glucose monitoring device, rental, including sensor, sensor replacement, and download to monitor (for physician interpretation of data, use CPT® code)

BETOS: Z2   Undefined codes
Service not separately priced by Part B

I S1034 Artificial pancreas device system (e.g., low glucose suspend (LGS) feature) including continuous glucose monitor, blood glucose device, insulin pump and computer algorithm that communicates with all of the devices

BETOS: Z2   Undefined codes
Service not separately priced by Part B

I S1035 Sensor; invasive (e.g., subcutaneous), disposable, for use with artificial pancreas device system

BETOS: Z2   Undefined codes
Service not separately priced by Part B

I S1036 Transmitter; external, for use with artificial pancreas device system

BETOS: Z2   Undefined codes
Service not separately priced by Part B

I S1037 Receiver (monitor); external, for use with artificial pancreas device system

BETOS: Z2   Undefined codes
Service not separately priced by Part B

I S1040 Cranial remolding orthosis, pediatric, rigid, with soft interface material, custom fabricated, includes fitting and adjustment(s) Ⓐ

BETOS: Z2   Undefined codes
Service not separately priced by Part B

I S1090 Mometasone furoate sinus implant, 370 micrograms

BETOS: Z2   Undefined codes
Service not separately priced by Part B

I S2053 Transplantation of small intestine and liver allografts

BETOS: Z2   Undefined codes
Service not separately priced by Part B

I S2054 Transplantation of multivisceral organs

BETOS: Z2   Undefined codes
Service not separately priced by Part B

I S2055 Harvesting of donor multivisceral organs, with preparation and maintenance of allografts; from cadaver donor

BETOS: Z2   Undefined codes
Service not separately priced by Part B

I S2060 Lobar lung transplantation

BETOS: Z2   Undefined codes
Service not separately priced by Part B

I S2061 Donor lobectomy (lung) for transplantation, living donor

BETOS: Z2   Undefined codes
Service not separately priced by Part B

I S2065 Simultaneous pancreas kidney transplantation

BETOS: Z2   Undefined codes
Service not separately priced by Part B

I S2066 Breast reconstruction with gluteal artery perforator (GAP) flap, including harvesting of the flap, microvascular transfer, closure of donor site and shaping the flap into a breast, unilateral ♀

BETOS: Z2   Undefined codes
Service not separately priced by Part B

I S2067 Breast reconstruction of a single breast with "stacked" deep inferior epigastric perforator (DIEP) flap(s) and/or gluteal artery perforator (GAP) flap(s), including harvesting of the flap(s), microvascular transfer, closure of donor site(s) and shaping the flap into a breast, unilateral ♀

BETOS: Z2   Undefined codes
Service not separately priced by Part B

I S2068 Breast reconstruction with deep inferior epigastric perforator (DIEP) flap or superficial inferior epigastric artery (SIEA) flap, including harvesting of the flap, microvascular transfer, closure of donor site and shaping the flap into a breast, unilateral ♀

BETOS: Z2   Undefined codes
Service not separately priced by Part B

I S2070 Cystourethroscopy, with ureteroscopy and/or pyeloscopy; with endoscopic laser treatment of ureteral calculi (includes ureteral catheterization)

BETOS: Z2   Undefined codes
Service not separately priced by Part B

I S2079 Laparoscopic esophagomyotomy (Heller type)

BETOS: Z2   Undefined codes
Service not separately priced by Part B

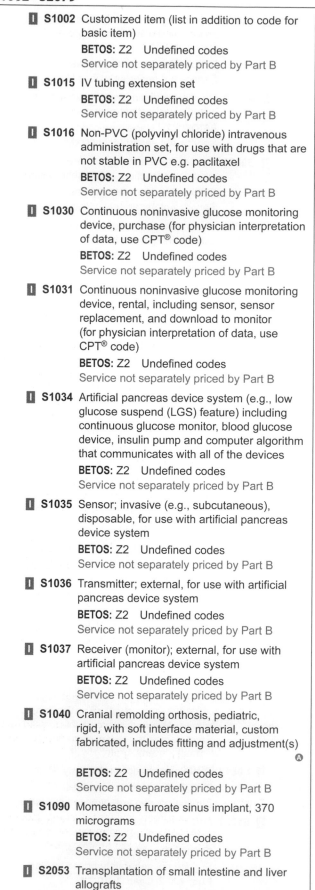

▲ Revised code   ● New code   **C** Carrier judgment   **D** Special coverage instructions apply
I Not payable by Medicare   **M** Non-covered by Medicare   **S** Non-covered by Medicare statute   AHA Coding Clinic®

■ **S2080** Laser-assisted uvulopalatoplasty (LAUP)
BETOS: Z2 Undefined codes
Service not separately priced by Part B

■ **S2083** Adjustment of gastric band diameter via subcutaneous port by injection or aspiration of saline
BETOS: Z2 Undefined codes
Service not separately priced by Part B

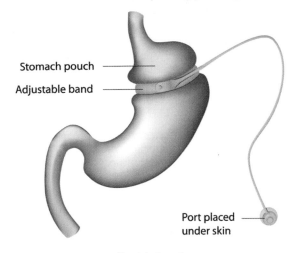

Stomach pouch

Adjustable band

Port placed under skin

Gastric band

■ **S2095** Transcatheter occlusion or embolization for tumor destruction, percutaneous, any method, using yttrium-90 microspheres
BETOS: Z2 Undefined codes
Service not separately priced by Part B

■ **S2102** Islet cell tissue transplant from pancreas; allogeneic
BETOS: Z2 Undefined codes
Service not separately priced by Part B

■ **S2103** Adrenal tissue transplant to brain
BETOS: Z2 Undefined codes
Service not separately priced by Part B

■ **S2107** Adoptive immunotherapy i.e. development of specific anti-tumor reactivity (e.g., tumor-infiltrating lymphocyte therapy) per course of treatment
BETOS: Z2 Undefined codes
Service not separately priced by Part B

■ **S2112** Arthroscopy, knee, surgical for harvesting of cartilage (chondrocyte cells)
BETOS: Z2 Undefined codes
Service not separately priced by Part B

■ **S2115** Osteotomy, periacetabular, with internal fixation
BETOS: Z2 Undefined codes
Service not separately priced by Part B

■ **S2117** Arthroereisis, subtalar
BETOS: Z2 Undefined codes
Service not separately priced by Part B

■ **S2118** Metal-on-metal total hip resurfacing, including acetabular and femoral components
BETOS: Z2 Undefined codes
Service not separately priced by Part B

■ **S2120** Low density lipoprotein (LDL) apheresis using heparin-induced extracorporeal LDL precipitation
BETOS: Z2 Undefined codes
Service not separately priced by Part B

■ **S2140** Cord blood harvesting for transplantation, allogeneic
BETOS: Z2 Undefined codes
Service not separately priced by Part B

■ **S2142** Cord blood-derived stem-cell transplantation, allogeneic
BETOS: Z2 Undefined codes
Service not separately priced by Part B

■ **S2150** Bone marrow or blood-derived stem cells (peripheral or umbilical), allogeneic or autologous, harvesting, transplantation, and related complications; including: pheresis and cell preparation/storage; marrow ablative therapy; drugs, supplies, hospitalization with outpatient follow-up; medical/surgical, diagnostic, emergency, and rehabilitative services; and the number of days of pre-and post-transplant care in the global definition
BETOS: Z2 Undefined codes
Service not separately priced by Part B

■ **S2152** Solid organ(s), complete or segmental, single organ or combination of organs; deceased or living donor(s), procurement, transplantation, and related complications; including: drugs; supplies; hospitalization with outpatient follow-up; medical/surgical, diagnostic, emergency, and rehabilitative services, and the number of days of pre- and post-transplant care in the global definition
BETOS: Z2 Undefined codes
Service not separately priced by Part B

■ **S2202** Echosclerotherapy
BETOS: Z2 Undefined codes
Service not separately priced by Part B

■ **S2205** Minimally invasive direct coronary artery bypass surgery involving mini-thoracotomy or mini-sternotomy surgery, performed under direct vision; using arterial graft(s), single coronary arterial graft
BETOS: Z2 Undefined codes
Service not separately priced by Part B

■ **S2206** Minimally invasive direct coronary artery bypass surgery involving mini-thoracotomy or mini-sternotomy surgery, performed under direct vision; using arterial graft(s), two coronary arterial grafts
BETOS: Z2 Undefined codes
Service not separately priced by Part B

♂ Male only   ♀ Female only   🅐 Age   A2 - Z3 = ASC Payment indicator   A - Y = APC Status indicator
ASC = ASC-approved procedure   **DME** Paid under the DME fee schedule   **MIPS** MIPS code

I S2207 Minimally invasive direct coronary artery bypass surgery involving mini-thoracotomy or mini-sternotomy surgery, performed under direct vision; using venous graft only, single coronary venous graft
BETOS: Z2 Undefined codes
Service not separately priced by Part B

I S2208 Minimally invasive direct coronary artery bypass surgery involving mini-thoracotomy or mini-sternotomy surgery, performed under direct vision; using single arterial and venous graft(s), single venous graft
BETOS: Z2 Undefined codes
Service not separately priced by Part B

I S2209 Minimally invasive direct coronary artery bypass surgery involving mini-thoracotomy or mini-sternotomy surgery, performed under direct vision; using two arterial grafts and single venous graft
BETOS: Z2 Undefined codes
Service not separately priced by Part B

I S2225 Myringotomy, laser-assisted
BETOS: Z2 Undefined codes
Service not separately priced by Part B

I S2230 Implantation of magnetic component of semi-implantable hearing device on ossicles in middle ear
BETOS: Z2 Undefined codes
Service not separately priced by Part B

I S2235 Implantation of auditory brain stem implant
BETOS: Z2 Undefined codes
Service not separately priced by Part B

I S2260 Induced abortion, 17 to 24 weeks ♀
BETOS: Z2 Undefined codes
Service not separately priced by Part B

I S2265 Induced abortion, 25 to 28 weeks ♀
BETOS: Z2 Undefined codes
Service not separately priced by Part B

I S2266 Induced abortion, 29 to 31 weeks ♀
BETOS: Z2 Undefined codes
Service not separately priced by Part B

I S2267 Induced abortion, 32 weeks or greater ♀
BETOS: Z2 Undefined codes
Service not separately priced by Part B

I S2300 Arthroscopy, shoulder, surgical; with thermally-induced capsulorrhaphy
BETOS: Z2 Undefined codes
Service not separately priced by Part B

I S2325 Hip core decompression
BETOS: Z2 Undefined codes
Service not separately priced by Part B
Coding Clinic: 2017, Q3

I S2340 Chemodenervation of abductor muscle(s) of vocal cord
BETOS: Z2 Undefined codes
Service not separately priced by Part B

I S2341 Chemodenervation of adductor muscle(s) of vocal cord
BETOS: Z2 Undefined codes
Service not separately priced by Part B

I S2342 Nasal endoscopy for post-operative debridement following functional endoscopic sinus surgery, nasal and/or sinus cavity(s), unilateral or bilateral
BETOS: Z2 Undefined codes
Service not separately priced by Part B

I S2348 Decompression procedure, percutaneous, of nucleus pulposus of intervertebral disc, using radiofrequency energy, single or multiple levels, lumbar
BETOS: Z2 Undefined codes
Service not separately priced by Part B

I S2350 Diskectomy, anterior, with decompression of spinal cord and/or nerve root(s), including osteophytectomy; lumbar, single interspace
BETOS: Z2 Undefined codes
Service not separately priced by Part B

I S2351 Diskectomy, anterior, with decompression of spinal cord and/or nerve root(s), including osteophytectomy; lumbar, each additional interspace (list separately in addition to code for primary procedure)
BETOS: Z2 Undefined codes
Service not separately priced by Part B

I S2400 Repair, congenital diaphragmatic hernia in the fetus using temporary tracheal occlusion, procedure performed in utero ♀ Ⓐ
BETOS: Z2 Undefined codes
Service not separately priced by Part B

I S2401 Repair, urinary tract obstruction in the fetus, procedure performed in utero ♀ Ⓐ
BETOS: Z2 Undefined codes
Service not separately priced by Part B

I S2402 Repair, congenital cystic adenomatoid malformation in the fetus, procedure performed in utero ♀ Ⓐ
BETOS: Z2 Undefined codes
Service not separately priced by Part B

I S2403 Repair, extralobar pulmonary sequestration in the fetus, procedure performed in utero ♀ Ⓐ
BETOS: Z2 Undefined codes
Service not separately priced by Part B

I S2404 Repair, myelomeningocele in the fetus, procedure performed in utero ♀ Ⓐ
BETOS: Z2 Undefined codes
Service not separately priced by Part B

I S2405 Repair of sacrococcygeal teratoma in the fetus, procedure performed in utero ♀ Ⓐ
BETOS: Z2 Undefined codes
Service not separately priced by Part B

S2409 Repair, congenital malformation of fetus, procedure performed in utero, not otherwise classified ♀ Ⓐ
  BETOS: Z2　Undefined codes
  Service not separately priced by Part B

S2411 Fetoscopic laser therapy for treatment of twin-to-twin transfusion syndrome Ⓐ
  BETOS: Z2　Undefined codes
  Service not separately priced by Part B

S2900 Surgical techniques requiring use of robotic surgical system (list separately in addition to code for primary procedure)
  BETOS: Z2　Undefined codes
  Service not separately priced by Part B
  Coding Clinic: 2010, Q1

S3000 Diabetic indicator; retinal eye exam, dilated, bilateral
  BETOS: Z2　Undefined codes
  Service not separately priced by Part B

S3005 Performance measurement, evaluation of patient self assessment, depression
  BETOS: Z2　Undefined codes
  Service not separately priced by Part B

S3600 STAT laboratory request (situations other than S3601)
  BETOS: Z2　Undefined codes
  Service not separately priced by Part B

S3601 Emergency STAT laboratory charge for patient who is homebound or residing in a nursing facility
  BETOS: Z2　Undefined codes
  Service not separately priced by Part B

S3620 Newborn metabolic screening panel, includes test kit, postage and the laboratory tests specified by the state for inclusion in this panel (e.g., galactose; hemoglobin, electrophoresis; hydroxyprogesterone, 17-D; phenylalanine (PKU); and thyroxine, total) Ⓐ
  BETOS: Z2　Undefined codes
  Service not separately priced by Part B

S3630 Eosinophil count, blood, direct
  BETOS: Z2　Undefined codes
  Service not separately priced by Part B

S3645 HIV-1 antibody testing of oral mucosal transudate
  BETOS: Z2　Undefined codes
  Service not separately priced by Part B

S3650 Saliva test, hormone level; during menopause ♀
  BETOS: Z2　Undefined codes
  Service not separately priced by Part B

S3652 Saliva test, hormone level; to assess preterm labor risk ♀
  BETOS: Z2　Undefined codes
  Service not separately priced by Part B

S3655 Antisperm antibodies test (Immunobead®) ♀
  BETOS: Z2　Undefined codes
  Service not separately priced by Part B

S3708 Gastrointestinal fat absorption study
  BETOS: Z2　Undefined codes
  Service not separately priced by Part B

S3722 Dose optimization by area under the curve (AUC) analysis, for infusional 5-fluorouracil
  BETOS: Z2　Undefined codes
  Service not separately priced by Part B

GENETIC TESTING (S3800-S3870)

S3800 Genetic testing for amyotrophic lateral sclerosis (ALS)
  BETOS: Z2　Undefined codes
  Service not separately priced by Part B

S3840 DNA analysis for germline mutations of the RET proto-oncogene for susceptibility to multiple endocrine neoplasia type 2
  BETOS: Z2　Undefined codes
  Service not separately priced by Part B

S3841 Genetic testing for retinoblastoma
  BETOS: Z2　Undefined codes
  Service not separately priced by Part B

S3842 Genetic testing for Von Hippel-Lindau disease
  BETOS: Z2　Undefined codes
  Service not separately priced by Part B

S3844 DNA analysis of the Connexin 26 gene (GJB2) for susceptibility to congenital, profound deafness
  BETOS: Z2　Undefined codes
  Service not separately priced by Part B

S3845 Genetic testing for alpha-thalassemia
  BETOS: Z2　Undefined codes
  Service not separately priced by Part B

S3846 Genetic testing for hemoglobin E beta-thalassemia
  BETOS: Z2　Undefined codes
  Service not separately priced by Part B

S3849 Genetic testing for Niemann-Pick disease
  BETOS: Z2　Undefined codes
  Service not separately priced by Part B

S3850 Genetic testing for sickle cell anemia
  BETOS: Z2　Undefined codes
  Service not separately priced by Part B

S3852 DNA analysis for APOE epsilon 4 allele for susceptibility to Alzheimer's disease
  BETOS: Z2　Undefined codes
  Service not separately priced by Part B

S3853 Genetic testing for myotonic muscular dystrophy
  BETOS: Z2　Undefined codes
  Service not separately priced by Part B

♂ Male only　　♀ Female only　　Ⓐ Age　　A2 - Z3 = ASC Payment indicator　　A - Y = APC Status indicator
ASC = ASC-approved procedure　　**DME** Paid under the DME fee schedule　　**MIPS** MIPS code

I **S3854** Gene expression profiling panel for use in the management of breast cancer treatment
BETOS: Z2   Undefined codes
Service not separately priced by Part B
Coding Clinic: 2016, Q2

I **S3861** Genetic testing, sodium channel, voltage-gated, type V, alpha subunit (SCN5A) and variants for suspected brugada syndrome
BETOS: Z2   Undefined codes
Service not separately priced by Part B

I **S3865** Comprehensive gene sequence analysis for hypertrophic cardiomyopathy
BETOS: Z2   Undefined codes
Service not separately priced by Part B

I **S3866** Genetic analysis for a specific gene mutation for hypertrophic cardiomyopathy (HCM) in an individual with a known HCM mutation in the family
BETOS: Z2   Undefined codes
Service not separately priced by Part B

I **S3870** Comparative genomic hybridization (CGH) microarray testing for developmental delay, autism spectrum disorder and/or intellectual disability
BETOS: Z2   Undefined codes
Service not separately priced by Part B

MISCELLANEOUS TESTS (S3900-S3904)

I **S3900** Surface electromyography (EMG)
BETOS: Z2   Undefined codes
Service not separately priced by Part B

I **S3902** Ballistocardiogram
BETOS: Z2   Undefined codes
Service not separately priced by Part B

I **S3904** Masters two step
BETOS: Z2   Undefined codes
Service not separately priced by Part B

ASSORTED OBSTETRICAL AND FERTILITY SERVICES (S4005-S4989)

I **S4005** Interim labor facility global (labor occurring but not resulting in delivery) ♀
BETOS: Z2   Undefined codes
Service not separately priced by Part B

I **S4011** In vitro fertilization; including but not limited to identification and incubation of mature oocytes, fertilization with sperm, incubation of embryo(s), and subsequent visualization for determination of development ♀
BETOS: Z2   Undefined codes
Service not separately priced by Part B

I **S4013** Complete cycle, gamete intrafallopian transfer (GIFT), case rate ♀
BETOS: Z2   Undefined codes
Service not separately priced by Part B

I **S4014** Complete cycle, zygote intrafallopian transfer (ZIFT), case rate ♀
BETOS: Z2   Undefined codes
Service not separately priced by Part B

I **S4015** Complete in vitro fertilization cycle, not otherwise specified, case rate ♀
BETOS: Z2   Undefined codes
Service not separately priced by Part B

I **S4016** Frozen in vitro fertilization cycle, case rate ♀
BETOS: Z2   Undefined codes
Service not separately priced by Part B

I **S4017** Incomplete cycle, treatment cancelled prior to stimulation, case rate ♀
BETOS: Z2   Undefined codes
Service not separately priced by Part B

I **S4018** Frozen embryo transfer procedure cancelled before transfer, case rate ♀
BETOS: Z2   Undefined codes
Service not separately priced by Part B

I **S4020** In vitro fertilization procedure cancelled before aspiration, case rate ♀
BETOS: Z2   Undefined codes
Service not separately priced by Part B

I **S4021** In vitro fertilization procedure cancelled after aspiration, case rate ♀
BETOS: Z2   Undefined codes
Service not separately priced by Part B

I **S4022** Assisted oocyte fertilization, case rate ♀
BETOS: Z2   Undefined codes
Service not separately priced by Part B

I **S4023** Donor egg cycle, incomplete, case rate ♀
BETOS: Z2   Undefined codes
Service not separately priced by Part B

I **S4025** Donor services for in vitro fertilization (sperm or embryo), case rate ♀
BETOS: Z2   Undefined codes
Service not separately priced by Part B

I **S4026** Procurement of donor sperm from sperm bank ♂
BETOS: Z2   Undefined codes
Service not separately priced by Part B

I **S4027** Storage of previously frozen embryos ♀
BETOS: Z2   Undefined codes
Service not separately priced by Part B

I **S4028** Microsurgical epididymal sperm aspiration (MESA) ♂
BETOS: Z2   Undefined codes
Service not separately priced by Part B

I **S4030** Sperm procurement and cryopreservation services; initial visit ♂
BETOS: Z2   Undefined codes
Service not separately priced by Part B

I **S4031** Sperm procurement and cryopreservation services; subsequent visit ♂

▲ Revised code   ● New code   **C** Carrier judgment   **D** Special coverage instructions apply
I Not payable by Medicare   **M** Non-covered by Medicare   **S** Non-covered by Medicare statute   AHA Coding Clinic®

S4035 Stimulated intrauterine insemination (IUI), case rate ♀
BETOS: Z2   Undefined codes
Service not separately priced by Part B

S4037 Cryopreserved embryo transfer, case rate ♀
BETOS: Z2   Undefined codes
Service not separately priced by Part B

S4040 Monitoring and storage of cryopreserved embryos, per 30 days ♀
BETOS: Z2   Undefined codes
Service not separately priced by Part B

S4042 Management of ovulation induction (interpretation of diagnostic tests and studies, non-face-to-face medical management of the patient), per cycle ♀
BETOS: Z2   Undefined codes
Service not separately priced by Part B

S4981 Insertion of levonorgestrel-releasing intrauterine system ♀
BETOS: Z2   Undefined codes
Service not separately priced by Part B

S4989 Contraceptive intrauterine device (e.g., Progestacert IUD), including implants and supplies ♀
BETOS: Z2   Undefined codes
Service not separately priced by Part B

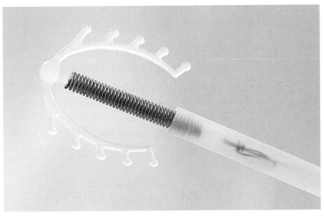

Intrauterine device

MISCELLANEOUS MEDICATIONS AND THERAPEUTIC SUBSTANCES (S4990-S5014)

S4990 Nicotine patches, legend
BETOS: Z2   Undefined codes
Service not separately priced by Part B

S4991 Nicotine patches, non-legend
BETOS: Z2   Undefined codes
Service not separately priced by Part B

S4993 Contraceptive pills for birth control ♀
BETOS: Z2   Undefined codes
Service not separately priced by Part B

BETOS: Z2   Undefined codes
Service not separately priced by Part B

S4995 Smoking cessation gum
BETOS: Z2   Undefined codes
Service not separately priced by Part B

S5000 Prescription drug, generic
BETOS: Z2   Undefined codes
Service not separately priced by Part B

S5001 Prescription drug, brand name
BETOS: Z2   Undefined codes
Service not separately priced by Part B

S5010 5% dextrose and 0.45% normal saline, 1000 ml
BETOS: Z2   Undefined codes
Service not separately priced by Part B

S5012 5% dextrose with potassium chloride, 1000 ml
BETOS: Z2   Undefined codes
Service not separately priced by Part B

S5013 5% dextrose/0.45% normal saline with potassium chloride and magnesium sulfate, 1000 ml
BETOS: Z2   Undefined codes
Service not separately priced by Part B

S5014 5% dextrose/0.45% normal saline with potassium chloride and magnesium sulfate, 1500 ml
BETOS: Z2   Undefined codes
Service not separately priced by Part B

VARIOUS HOME CARE SERVICES (S5035-S5199)

S5035 Home infusion therapy, routine service of infusion device (e.g., pump maintenance)
BETOS: Z2   Undefined codes
Service not separately priced by Part B

S5036 Home infusion therapy, repair of infusion device (e.g., pump repair)
BETOS: Z2   Undefined codes
Service not separately priced by Part B

S5100 Day care services, adult; per 15 minutes Ⓐ
BETOS: Z2   Undefined codes
Service not separately priced by Part B

S5101 Day care services, adult; per half day Ⓐ
BETOS: Z2   Undefined codes
Service not separately priced by Part B

S5102 Day care services, adult; per diem Ⓐ
BETOS: Z2   Undefined codes
Service not separately priced by Part B

S5105 Day care services, center-based; services not included in program fee, per diem
BETOS: Z2   Undefined codes
Service not separately priced by Part B

S5108 Home care training to home care client, per 15 minutes
BETOS: Z2   Undefined codes
Service not separately priced by Part B

♂ Male only   ♀ Female only   Ⓐ Age   A2 - Z3 = ASC Payment indicator   A - Y = APC Status indicator
ASC = ASC-approved procedure   **DME** Paid under the DME fee schedule   **MIPS** MIPS code

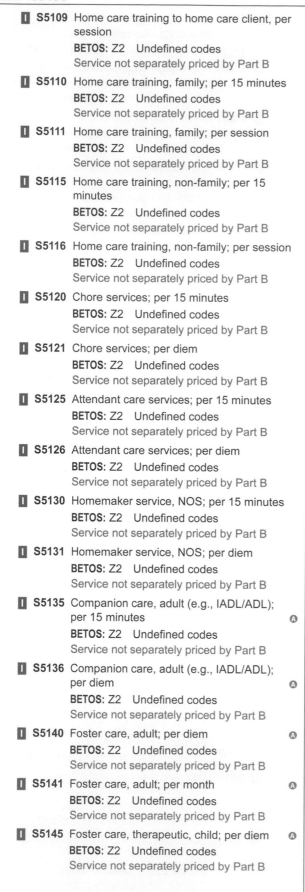

S5109 Home care training to home care client, per session
BETOS: Z2   Undefined codes
Service not separately priced by Part B

S5110 Home care training, family; per 15 minutes
BETOS: Z2   Undefined codes
Service not separately priced by Part B

S5111 Home care training, family; per session
BETOS: Z2   Undefined codes
Service not separately priced by Part B

S5115 Home care training, non-family; per 15 minutes
BETOS: Z2   Undefined codes
Service not separately priced by Part B

S5116 Home care training, non-family; per session
BETOS: Z2   Undefined codes
Service not separately priced by Part B

S5120 Chore services; per 15 minutes
BETOS: Z2   Undefined codes
Service not separately priced by Part B

S5121 Chore services; per diem
BETOS: Z2   Undefined codes
Service not separately priced by Part B

S5125 Attendant care services; per 15 minutes
BETOS: Z2   Undefined codes
Service not separately priced by Part B

S5126 Attendant care services; per diem
BETOS: Z2   Undefined codes
Service not separately priced by Part B

S5130 Homemaker service, NOS; per 15 minutes
BETOS: Z2   Undefined codes
Service not separately priced by Part B

S5131 Homemaker service, NOS; per diem
BETOS: Z2   Undefined codes
Service not separately priced by Part B

S5135 Companion care, adult (e.g., IADL/ADL); per 15 minutes Ⓐ
BETOS: Z2   Undefined codes
Service not separately priced by Part B

S5136 Companion care, adult (e.g., IADL/ADL); per diem Ⓐ
BETOS: Z2   Undefined codes
Service not separately priced by Part B

S5140 Foster care, adult; per diem Ⓐ
BETOS: Z2   Undefined codes
Service not separately priced by Part B

S5141 Foster care, adult; per month Ⓐ
BETOS: Z2   Undefined codes
Service not separately priced by Part B

S5145 Foster care, therapeutic, child; per diem Ⓐ
BETOS: Z2   Undefined codes
Service not separately priced by Part B

S5146 Foster care, therapeutic, child; per month Ⓐ
BETOS: Z2   Undefined codes
Service not separately priced by Part B

S5150 Unskilled respite care, not hospice; per 15 minutes
BETOS: Z2   Undefined codes
Service not separately priced by Part B

S5151 Unskilled respite care, not hospice; per diem
BETOS: Z2   Undefined codes
Service not separately priced by Part B

S5160 Emergency response system; installation and testing
BETOS: Z2   Undefined codes
Service not separately priced by Part B

S5161 Emergency response system; service fee, per month (excludes installation and testing)
BETOS: Z2   Undefined codes
Service not separately priced by Part B

S5162 Emergency response system; purchase only
BETOS: Z2   Undefined codes
Service not separately priced by Part B

S5165 Home modifications; per service
BETOS: Z2   Undefined codes
Service not separately priced by Part B

S5170 Home delivered meals, including preparation; per meal
BETOS: Z2   Undefined codes
Service not separately priced by Part B

S5175 Laundry service, external, professional; per order
BETOS: Z2   Undefined codes
Service not separately priced by Part B

S5180 Home health respiratory therapy, initial evaluation
BETOS: Z2   Undefined codes
Service not separately priced by Part B

S5181 Home health respiratory therapy, NOS, per diem
BETOS: Z2   Undefined codes
Service not separately priced by Part B

S5185 Medication reminder service, non-face-to-face; per month
BETOS: Z2   Undefined codes
Service not separately priced by Part B

S5190 Wellness assessment, performed by non-physician
BETOS: Z2   Undefined codes
Service not separately priced by Part B

S5199 Personal care item, NOS, each
BETOS: Z2   Undefined codes
Service not separately priced by Part B

HOME INFUSION THERAPY (S5497-S5523), SEE ALSO
HOME INFUSION THERAPY (S9325-S9379); HOME THERAPY
SERVICES (S9490-S9810)

S5497 Home infusion therapy, catheter care /
maintenance, not otherwise classified;
includes administrative services, professional
pharmacy services, care coordination, and
all necessary supplies and equipment (drugs
and nursing visits coded separately), per
diem
BETOS: Z2   Undefined codes
Service not separately priced by Part B

S5498 Home infusion therapy, catheter care /
maintenance, simple (single lumen), includes
administrative services, professional
pharmacy services, care coordination and all
necessary supplies and equipment, (drugs
and nursing visits coded separately), per
diem
BETOS: Z2   Undefined codes
Service not separately priced by Part B

S5501 Home infusion therapy, catheter care /
maintenance, complex (more than one
lumen), includes administrative services,
professional pharmacy services, care
coordination, and all necessary supplies and
equipment (drugs and nursing visits coded
separately), per diem
BETOS: Z2   Undefined codes
Service not separately priced by Part B

S5502 Home infusion therapy, catheter care /
maintenance, implanted access device,
includes administrative services, professional
pharmacy services, care coordination and all
necessary supplies and equipment, (drugs
and nursing visits coded separately), per
diem (use this code for interim maintenance
of vascular access not currently in use)
BETOS: Z2   Undefined codes
Service not separately priced by Part B

S5517 Home infusion therapy, all supplies
necessary for restoration of catheter patency
or declotting
BETOS: Z2   Undefined codes
Service not separately priced by Part B

S5518 Home infusion therapy, all supplies
necessary for catheter repair
BETOS: Z2   Undefined codes
Service not separately priced by Part B

S5520 Home infusion therapy, all supplies (including
catheter) necessary for a peripherally
inserted central venous catheter (PICC) line
insertion
BETOS: Z2   Undefined codes
Service not separately priced by Part B

S5521 Home infusion therapy, all supplies (including
catheter) necessary for a midline catheter
insertion
BETOS: Z2   Undefined codes
Service not separately priced by Part B

S5522 Home infusion therapy, insertion of
peripherally inserted central venous catheter
(PICC), nursing services only (no supplies or
catheter included)
BETOS: Z2   Undefined codes
Service not separately priced by Part B

S5523 Home infusion therapy, insertion of midline
venous catheter, nursing services only (no
supplies or catheter included)
BETOS: Z2   Undefined codes
Service not separately priced by Part B

INSULIN AND DELIVERY DEVICES (S5550-S5571)

S5550 Insulin, rapid onset, 5 units
BETOS: Z2   Undefined codes
Service not separately priced by Part B

S5551 Insulin, most rapid onset (Lispro or Aspart);
5 units
BETOS: Z2   Undefined codes
Service not separately priced by Part B

S5552 Insulin, intermediate acting (NPH or LENTE);
5 units
BETOS: Z2   Undefined codes
Service not separately priced by Part B

S5553 Insulin, long acting; 5 units
BETOS: Z2   Undefined codes
Service not separately priced by Part B

S5560 Insulin delivery device, reusable pen; 1.5 ml
size
BETOS: Z2   Undefined codes
Service not separately priced by Part B

S5561 Insulin delivery device, reusable pen; 3 ml
size
BETOS: Z2   Undefined codes
Service not separately priced by Part B

S5565 Insulin cartridge for use in insulin delivery
device other than pump; 150 units
BETOS: Z2   Undefined codes
Service not separately priced by Part B

S5566 Insulin cartridge for use in insulin delivery
device other than pump; 300 units
BETOS: Z2   Undefined codes
Service not separately priced by Part B

S5570 Insulin delivery device, disposable pen
(including insulin); 1.5 ml size
BETOS: Z2   Undefined codes
Service not separately priced by Part B

S5571 Insulin delivery device, disposable pen
(including insulin); 3 ml size
BETOS: Z2   Undefined codes
Service not separately priced by Part B

♂ Male only   ♀ Female only   Ⓐ Age   A2 - Z3 = ASC Payment indicator   A - Y = APC Status indicator
ASC = ASC-approved procedure   **DME** Paid under the DME fee schedule   **MIPS** MIPS code

IMAGING STUDIES (S8030-S8092), SEE ALSO CONTRAST AGENTS/DIAGNOSTIC IMAGING (Q9950-Q9983)

I S8030 Scleral application of tantalum ring(s) for localization of lesions for proton beam therapy
BETOS: Z2   Undefined codes
Service not separately priced by Part B

I S8035 Magnetic source imaging
BETOS: Z2   Undefined codes
Service not separately priced by Part B

I S8037 Magnetic resonance cholangiopancreatography (MRCP)
BETOS: Z2   Undefined codes
Service not separately priced by Part B

I S8040 Topographic brain mapping
BETOS: Z2   Undefined codes
Service not separately priced by Part B

I S8042 Magnetic resonance imaging (MRI), low-field
BETOS: Z2   Undefined codes
Service not separately priced by Part B

I S8055 Ultrasound guidance for multifetal pregnancy reduction(s), technical component (only to be used when the physician doing the reduction procedure does not perform the ultrasound, guidance is included in the CPT® code for multifetal pregnancy reduction - 59866)   ♀
BETOS: Z2   Undefined codes
Service not separately priced by Part B

I S8080 Scintimammography (radioimmunoscintigraphy of the breast), unilateral, including supply of radiopharmaceutical   ♀
BETOS: Z2   Undefined codes
Service not separately priced by Part B

I S8085 Fluorine-18 fluorodeoxyglucose (F-18 FDG) imaging using dual-head coincidence detection system (non-dedicated PET scan)
BETOS: Z2   Undefined codes
Service not separately priced by Part B

I S8092 Electron beam computed tomography (also known as ultrafast CT, cine CT)
BETOS: Z2   Undefined codes
Service not separately priced by Part B

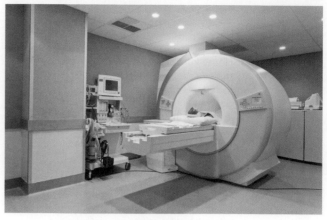
CT Scanner

ASSISTED BREATHING SUPPLIES (S8096-S8210), SEE ALSO BREATHING AIDS (A7000-A7048); INTERMITTENT POSITIVE PRESSURE BREATHING DEVICES (E0500; OTHER BREATHING AIDS (E0605, E0606)

I S8096 Portable peak flow meter
BETOS: Z2   Undefined codes
Service not separately priced by Part B

I S8097 Asthma kit (including but not limited to portable peak expiratory flow meter, instructional video, brochure, and/or spacer)
BETOS: Z2   Undefined codes
Service not separately priced by Part B

I S8100 Holding chamber or spacer for use with an inhaler or nebulizer; without mask
BETOS: Z2   Undefined codes
Service not separately priced by Part B

I S8101 Holding chamber or spacer for use with an inhaler or nebulizer; with mask
BETOS: Z2   Undefined codes
Service not separately priced by Part B

I S8110 Peak expiratory flow rate (physician services)
BETOS: Z2   Undefined codes
Service not separately priced by Part B

I S8120 Oxygen contents, gaseous, 1 unit equals 1 cubic foot
BETOS: Z2   Undefined codes
Service not separately priced by Part B

I S8121 Oxygen contents, liquid, 1 unit equals 1 pound
BETOS: Z2   Undefined codes
Service not separately priced by Part B

I S8130 Interferential current stimulator, 2 channel
BETOS: Z2   Undefined codes
Service not separately priced by Part B

I S8131 Interferential current stimulator, 4 channel
BETOS: Z2   Undefined codes
Service not separately priced by Part B

▲ Revised code   ● New code   **C** Carrier judgment   **D** Special coverage instructions apply
I Not payable by Medicare   **M** Non-covered by Medicare   **S** Non-covered by Medicare statute   AHA Coding Clinic®

S8185 Flutter device
BETOS: Z2   Undefined codes
Service not separately priced by Part B

S8186 Swivel adapter
BETOS: Z2   Undefined codes
Service not separately priced by Part B

S8189 Tracheostomy supply, not otherwise classified
BETOS: Z2   Undefined codes
Service not separately priced by Part B

S8210 Mucus trap
BETOS: Z2   Undefined codes
Service not separately priced by Part B

MISCELLANEOUS SUPPLIES AND SERVICES (S8265-S9152), SEE ALSO MISCELLANEOUS SUPPLIES AND SERVICES (S9381-S9485)

S8265 Haberman feeder for cleft lip/palate
BETOS: Z2   Undefined codes
Service not separately priced by Part B

S8270 Enuresis alarm, using auditory buzzer and/or vibration device
BETOS: Z2   Undefined codes
Service not separately priced by Part B

S8301 Infection control supplies, not otherwise specified
BETOS: Z2   Undefined codes
Service not separately priced by Part B

S8415 Supplies for home delivery of infant   Ⓐ
BETOS: Z2   Undefined codes
Service not separately priced by Part B

S8420 Gradient pressure aid (sleeve and glove combination), custom made
BETOS: Z2   Undefined codes
Service not separately priced by Part B

S8421 Gradient pressure aid (sleeve and glove combination), ready made
BETOS: Z2   Undefined codes
Service not separately priced by Part B

S8422 Gradient pressure aid (sleeve), custom made, medium weight
BETOS: Z2   Undefined codes
Service not separately priced by Part B

S8423 Gradient pressure aid (sleeve), custom made, heavy weight
BETOS: Z2   Undefined codes
Service not separately priced by Part B

S8424 Gradient pressure aid (sleeve), ready made
BETOS: Z2   Undefined codes
Service not separately priced by Part B

S8425 Gradient pressure aid (glove), custom made, medium weight
BETOS: Z2   Undefined codes
Service not separately priced by Part B

S8426 Gradient pressure aid (glove), custom made, heavy weight
BETOS: Z2   Undefined codes
Service not separately priced by Part B

S8427 Gradient pressure aid (glove), ready made
BETOS: Z2   Undefined codes
Service not separately priced by Part B

S8428 Gradient pressure aid (gauntlet), ready made
BETOS: Z2   Undefined codes
Service not separately priced by Part B

S8429 Gradient pressure exterior wrap
BETOS: Z2   Undefined codes
Service not separately priced by Part B

S8430 Padding for compression bandage, roll
BETOS: Z2   Undefined codes
Service not separately priced by Part B

S8431 Compression bandage, roll
BETOS: Z2   Undefined codes
Service not separately priced by Part B

S8450 Splint, prefabricated, digit (specify digit by use of modifier)
BETOS: Z2   Undefined codes
Service not separately priced by Part B

S8451 Splint, prefabricated, wrist or ankle
BETOS: Z2   Undefined codes
Service not separately priced by Part B

S8452 Splint, prefabricated, elbow
BETOS: Z2   Undefined codes
Service not separately priced by Part B

S8460 Camisole, post-mastectomy
BETOS: Z2   Undefined codes
Service not separately priced by Part B

S8490 Insulin syringes (100 syringes, any size)
BETOS: Z2   Undefined codes
Service not separately priced by Part B

S8930 Electrical stimulation of auricular acupuncture points; each 15 minutes of personal one-on-one contact with the patient
BETOS: Z2   Undefined codes
Service not separately priced by Part B

S8940 Equestrian/hippotherapy, per session
BETOS: Z2   Undefined codes
Service not separately priced by Part B

S8948 Application of a modality (requiring constant provider attendance) to one or more areas; low-level laser; each 15 minutes
BETOS: Z2   Undefined codes
Service not separately priced by Part B

S8950 Complex lymphedema therapy, each 15 minutes
BETOS: Z2   Undefined codes
Service not separately priced by Part B

♂ Male only	♀ Female only	Ⓐ Age	A2 - Z3 = ASC Payment indicator	A - Y = APC Status indicator
ASC = ASC-approved procedure		**DME** Paid under the DME fee schedule		**MIPS** MIPS code

S8990 Physical or manipulative therapy performed for maintenance rather than restoration
BETOS: Z2   Undefined codes
Service not separately priced by Part B

S8999 Resuscitation bag (for use by patient on artificial respiration during power failure or other catastrophic event)
BETOS: Z2   Undefined codes
Service not separately priced by Part B

S9001 Home uterine monitor with or without associated nursing services   ♀
BETOS: Z2   Undefined codes
Service not separately priced by Part B

S9007 Ultrafiltration monitor
BETOS: Z2   Undefined codes
Service not separately priced by Part B

S9024 Paranasal sinus ultrasound
BETOS: Z2   Undefined codes
Service not separately priced by Part B

S9025 Omnicardiogram/cardiointegram
BETOS: Z2   Undefined codes
Service not separately priced by Part B

S9034 Extracorporeal shockwave lithotripsy for gall stones (if performed with ERCP, use 43265)
BETOS: Z2   Undefined codes
Service not separately priced by Part B

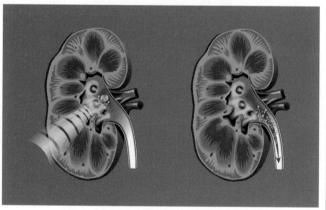

Extracorporeal shock wave lithotripsy

S9055 Procuren or other growth factor preparation to promote wound healing
BETOS: Z2   Undefined codes
Service not separately priced by Part B

S9056 Coma stimulation per diem
BETOS: Z2   Undefined codes
Service not separately priced by Part B

S9061 Home administration of aerosolized drug therapy (e.g., pentamidine); administrative services, professional pharmacy services, care coordination, all necessary supplies and equipment (drugs and nursing visits coded separately), per diem
BETOS: Z2   Undefined codes
Service not separately priced by Part B

S9083 Global fee urgent care centers
BETOS: Z2   Undefined codes
Service not separately priced by Part B

S9088 Services provided in an urgent care center (list in addition to code for service)
BETOS: Z2   Undefined codes
Service not separately priced by Part B

S9090 Vertebral axial decompression, per session
BETOS: Z2   Undefined codes
Service not separately priced by Part B

S9097 Home visit for wound care
BETOS: Z2   Undefined codes
Service not separately priced by Part B

S9098 Home visit, phototherapy services (e.g., Bili-lite), including equipment rental, nursing services, blood draw, supplies, and other services, per diem
BETOS: Z2   Undefined codes
Service not separately priced by Part B

S9110 Telemonitoring of patient in their home, including all necessary equipment; computer system, connections, and software; maintenance; patient education and support; per month
BETOS: Z2   Undefined codes
Service not separately priced by Part B

S9117 Back school, per visit
BETOS: Z2   Undefined codes
Service not separately priced by Part B

S9122 Home health aide or certified nurse assistant, providing care in the home; per hour
BETOS: Z2   Undefined codes
Service not separately priced by Part B

S9123 Nursing care, in the home; by registered nurse, per hour (use for general nursing care only, not to be used when CPT® codes 99500-99602 can be used)
BETOS: Z2   Undefined codes
Service not separately priced by Part B

S9124 Nursing care, in the home; by licensed practical nurse, per hour
BETOS: Z2   Undefined codes
Service not separately priced by Part B

S9125 Respite care, in the home, per diem
BETOS: Z2   Undefined codes
Service not separately priced by Part B

S9126 Hospice care, in the home, per diem
BETOS: Z2   Undefined codes
Service not separately priced by Part B

S9127 Social work visit, in the home, per diem
BETOS: Z2   Undefined codes
Service not separately priced by Part B

S9128 Speech therapy, in the home, per diem
BETOS: Z2   Undefined codes
Service not separately priced by Part B

▲ Revised code   ● New code   **C** Carrier judgment   **D** Special coverage instructions apply
I Not payable by Medicare   **M** Non-covered by Medicare   **S** Non-covered by Medicare statute   AHA Coding Clinic®

S9129 Occupational therapy, in the home, per diem
BETOS: Z2 Undefined codes
Service not separately priced by Part B

S9131 Physical therapy; in the home, per diem
BETOS: Z2 Undefined codes
Service not separately priced by Part B

S9140 Diabetic management program, follow-up visit to non-MD provider
BETOS: Z2 Undefined codes
Service not separately priced by Part B

S9141 Diabetic management program, follow-up visit to MD provider
BETOS: Z2 Undefined codes
Service not separately priced by Part B

S9145 Insulin pump initiation, instruction in initial use of pump (pump not included)
BETOS: Z2 Undefined codes
Service not separately priced by Part B

S9150 Evaluation by ocularist
BETOS: Z2 Undefined codes
Service not separately priced by Part B

S9152 Speech therapy, re-evaluation
BETOS: Z2 Undefined codes
Service not separately priced by Part B

HOME MANAGEMENT OF PREGNANCY (S9208-S9214)

S9208 Home management of preterm labor, including administrative services, professional pharmacy services, care coordination, and all necessary supplies or equipment (drugs and nursing visits coded separately), per diem (do not use this code with any home infusion per diem code) ♀
BETOS: Z2 Undefined codes
Service not separately priced by Part B

S9209 Home management of preterm premature rupture of membranes (PPROM), including administrative services, professional pharmacy services, care coordination, and all necessary supplies or equipment (drugs and nursing visits coded separately), per diem (do not use this code with any home infusion per diem code) ♀
BETOS: Z2 Undefined codes
Service not separately priced by Part B

S9211 Home management of gestational hypertension, includes administrative services, professional pharmacy services, care coordination and all necessary supplies and equipment (drugs and nursing visits coded separately); per diem (do not use this code with any home infusion per diem code) ♀
BETOS: Z2 Undefined codes
Service not separately priced by Part B

S9212 Home management of postpartum hypertension, includes administrative services, professional pharmacy services, care coordination, and all necessary supplies and equipment (drugs and nursing visits coded separately), per diem (do not use this code with any home infusion per diem code) ♀
BETOS: Z2 Undefined codes
Service not separately priced by Part B

S9213 Home management of preeclampsia, includes administrative services, professional pharmacy services, care coordination, and all necessary supplies and equipment (drugs and nursing services coded separately); per diem (do not use this code with any home infusion per diem code) ♀
BETOS: Z2 Undefined codes
Service not separately priced by Part B

S9214 Home management of gestational diabetes, includes administrative services, professional pharmacy services, care coordination, and all necessary supplies and equipment (drugs and nursing visits coded separately); per diem (do not use this code with any home infusion per diem code) ♀
BETOS: Z2 Undefined codes
Service not separately priced by Part B

HOME INFUSION THERAPY (S9325-S9379), SEE ALSO HOME INFUSION THERAPY (S5497-S5523); HOME THERAPY SERVICES (S9490-S9810)

S9325 Home infusion therapy, pain management infusion; administrative services, professional pharmacy services, care coordination, and all necessary supplies and equipment, (drugs and nursing visits coded separately), per diem (do not use this code with S9326, S9327 or S9328)
BETOS: Z2 Undefined codes
Service not separately priced by Part B

S9326 Home infusion therapy, continuous (twenty-four hours or more) pain management infusion; administrative services, professional pharmacy services, care coordination and all necessary supplies and equipment (drugs and nursing visits coded separately), per diem
BETOS: Z2 Undefined codes
Service not separately priced by Part B

S9327 Home infusion therapy, intermittent (less than twenty-four hours) pain management infusion; administrative services, professional pharmacy services, care coordination, and all necessary supplies and equipment (drugs and nursing visits coded separately), per diem
BETOS: Z2 Undefined codes
Service not separately priced by Part B

♂ Male only   ♀ Female only   Ⓐ Age   A2 - Z3 = ASC Payment indicator   A - Y = APC Status indicator
ASC = ASC-approved procedure   **DME** Paid under the DME fee schedule   **MIPS** MIPS code

▌ S9328 Home infusion therapy, implanted pump pain management infusion; administrative services, professional pharmacy services, care coordination, and all necessary supplies and equipment (drugs and nursing visits coded separately), per diem
BETOS: Z2   Undefined codes
Service not separately priced by Part B

▌ S9329 Home infusion therapy, chemotherapy infusion; administrative services, professional pharmacy services, care coordination, and all necessary supplies and equipment (drugs and nursing visits coded separately), per diem (do not use this code with S9330 or S9331)
BETOS: Z2   Undefined codes
Service not separately priced by Part B

▌ S9330 Home infusion therapy, continuous (twenty-four hours or more) chemotherapy infusion; administrative services, professional pharmacy services, care coordination, and all necessary supplies and equipment (drugs and nursing visits coded separately), per diem
BETOS: Z2   Undefined codes
Service not separately priced by Part B

▌ S9331 Home infusion therapy, intermittent (less than twenty-four hours) chemotherapy infusion; administrative services, professional pharmacy services, care coordination, and all necessary supplies and equipment (drugs and nursing visits coded separately), per diem
BETOS: Z2   Undefined codes
Service not separately priced by Part B

▌ S9335 Home therapy, hemodialysis; administrative services, professional pharmacy services, care coordination, and all necessary supplies and equipment (drugs and nursing services coded separately), per diem
BETOS: Z2   Undefined codes
Service not separately priced by Part B

▌ S9336 Home infusion therapy, continuous anticoagulant infusion therapy (e.g., Heparin), administrative services, professional pharmacy services, care coordination and all necessary supplies and equipment (drugs and nursing visits coded separately), per diem
BETOS: Z2   Undefined codes
Service not separately priced by Part B

▌ S9338 Home infusion therapy, immunotherapy, administrative services, professional pharmacy services, care coordination, and all necessary supplies and equipment (drugs and nursing visits coded separately), per diem
BETOS: Z2   Undefined codes
Service not separately priced by Part B

▌ S9339 Home therapy; peritoneal dialysis, administrative services, professional pharmacy services, care coordination and all necessary supplies and equipment (drugs and nursing visits coded separately), per diem
BETOS: Z2   Undefined codes
Service not separately priced by Part B

▌ S9340 Home therapy; enteral nutrition; administrative services, professional pharmacy services, care coordination, and all necessary supplies and equipment (enteral formula and nursing visits coded separately), per diem
BETOS: Z2   Undefined codes
Service not separately priced by Part B

▌ S9341 Home therapy; enteral nutrition via gravity; administrative services, professional pharmacy services, care coordination, and all necessary supplies and equipment (enteral formula and nursing visits coded separately), per diem
BETOS: Z2   Undefined codes
Service not separately priced by Part B

▌ S9342 Home therapy; enteral nutrition via pump; administrative services, professional pharmacy services, care coordination, and all necessary supplies and equipment (enteral formula and nursing visits coded separately), per diem
BETOS: Z2   Undefined codes
Service not separately priced by Part B

▌ S9343 Home therapy; enteral nutrition via bolus; administrative services, professional pharmacy services, care coordination, and all necessary supplies and equipment (enteral formula and nursing visits coded separately), per diem
BETOS: Z2   Undefined codes
Service not separately priced by Part B

▌ S9345 Home infusion therapy, anti-hemophilic agent infusion therapy (e.g., Factor VIII); administrative services, professional pharmacy services, care coordination, and all necessary supplies and equipment (drugs and nursing visits coded separately), per diem
BETOS: Z2   Undefined codes
Service not separately priced by Part B

▌ S9346 Home infusion therapy, alpha-1-proteinase inhibitor (e.g., Prolastin); administrative services, professional pharmacy services, care coordination, and all necessary supplies and equipment (drugs and nursing visits coded separately), per diem
BETOS: Z2   Undefined codes
Service not separately priced by Part B

▲ Revised code   ● New code   **C** Carrier judgment   **D** Special coverage instructions apply
▌ Not payable by Medicare   **M** Non-covered by Medicare   **S** Non-covered by Medicare statute   AHA Coding Clinic®

■ **S9347** Home infusion therapy, uninterrupted, long-term, controlled rate intravenous or subcutaneous infusion therapy (e.g., epoprostenol); administrative services, professional pharmacy services, care coordination, and all necessary supplies and equipment (drugs and nursing visits coded separately), per diem

BETOS: Z2   Undefined codes
Service not separately priced by Part B

■ **S9348** Home infusion therapy, sympathomimetic/ inotropic agent infusion therapy (e.g., Dobutamine); administrative services, professional pharmacy services, care coordination, all necessary supplies and equipment (drugs and nursing visits coded separately), per diem

BETOS: Z2   Undefined codes
Service not separately priced by Part B

■ **S9349** Home infusion therapy, tocolytic infusion therapy; administrative services, professional pharmacy services, care coordination, and all necessary supplies and equipment (drugs and nursing visits coded separately), per diem

BETOS: Z2   Undefined codes
Service not separately priced by Part B

■ **S9351** Home infusion therapy, continuous or intermittent anti-emetic infusion therapy; administrative services, professional pharmacy services, care coordination, and all necessary supplies and equipment (drugs and visits coded separately), per diem

BETOS: Z2   Undefined codes
Service not separately priced by Part B

■ **S9353** Home infusion therapy, continuous insulin infusion therapy; administrative services, professional pharmacy services, care coordination, and all necessary supplies and equipment (drugs and nursing visits coded separately), per diem

BETOS: Z2   Undefined codes
Service not separately priced by Part B

■ **S9355** Home infusion therapy, chelation therapy; administrative services, professional pharmacy services, care coordination, and all necessary supplies and equipment (drugs and nursing visits coded separately), per diem

BETOS: Z2   Undefined codes
Service not separately priced by Part B

■ **S9357** Home infusion therapy, enzyme replacement intravenous therapy; (e.g., Imiglucerase); administrative services, professional pharmacy services, care coordination, and all necessary supplies and equipment (drugs and nursing visits coded separately), per diem

BETOS: Z2   Undefined codes
Service not separately priced by Part B

■ **S9359** Home infusion therapy, anti-tumor necrosis factor intravenous therapy; (e.g., Infliximab); administrative services, professional pharmacy services, care coordination, and all necessary supplies and equipment (drugs and nursing visits coded separately), per diem

BETOS: Z2   Undefined codes
Service not separately priced by Part B

■ **S9361** Home infusion therapy, diuretic intravenous therapy; administrative services, professional pharmacy services, care coordination, and all necessary supplies and equipment (drugs and nursing visits coded separately), per diem

BETOS: Z2   Undefined codes
Service not separately priced by Part B

■ **S9363** Home infusion therapy, anti-spasmotic therapy; administrative services, professional pharmacy services, care coordination, and all necessary supplies and equipment (drugs and nursing visits coded separately), per diem

BETOS: Z2   Undefined codes
Service not separately priced by Part B

■ **S9364** Home infusion therapy, total parenteral nutrition (TPN); administrative services, professional pharmacy services, care coordination, and all necessary supplies and equipment including standard TPN formula (lipids, specialty amino acid formulas, drugs other than in standard formula and nursing visits coded separately), per diem (do not use with home infusion codes S9365-S9368 using daily volume scales)

BETOS: Z2   Undefined codes
Service not separately priced by Part B

■ **S9365** Home infusion therapy, total parenteral nutrition (TPN); one liter per day, administrative services, professional pharmacy services, care coordination, and all necessary supplies and equipment including standard TPN formula (lipids, specialty amino acid formulas, drugs other than in standard formula and nursing visits coded separately), per diem

BETOS: Z2   Undefined codes
Service not separately priced by Part B

■ **S9366** Home infusion therapy, total parenteral nutrition (TPN); more than one liter but no more than two liters per day, administrative services, professional pharmacy services, care coordination, and all necessary supplies and equipment including standard TPN formula (lipids, specialty amino acid formulas, drugs other than in standard formula and nursing visits coded separately), per diem

BETOS: Z2   Undefined codes
Service not separately priced by Part B

♂ Male only   ♀ Female only   Ⓐ Age   A2 - Z3 = ASC Payment indicator   A - Y = APC Status indicator
ASC = ASC-approved procedure   **DME** Paid under the DME fee schedule   **MIPS** MIPS code

■ **S9367** Home infusion therapy, total parenteral nutrition (TPN); more than two liters but no more than three liters per day, administrative services, professional pharmacy services, care coordination, and all necessary supplies and equipment including standard TPN formula (lipids, specialty amino acid formulas, drugs other than in standard formula and nursing visits coded separately), per diem
BETOS: Z2 Undefined codes
Service not separately priced by Part B

■ **S9368** Home infusion therapy, total parenteral nutrition (TPN); more than three liters per day, administrative services, professional pharmacy services, care coordination, and all necessary supplies and equipment including standard TPN formula (lipids, specialty amino acid formulas, drugs other than in standard formula and nursing visits coded separately), per diem
BETOS: Z2 Undefined codes
Service not separately priced by Part B

■ **S9370** Home therapy, intermittent anti-emetic injection therapy; administrative services, professional pharmacy services, care coordination, and all necessary supplies and equipment (drugs and nursing visits coded separately), per diem
BETOS: Z2 Undefined codes
Service not separately priced by Part B

■ **S9372** Home therapy; intermittent anticoagulant injection therapy (e.g., Heparin); administrative services, professional pharmacy services, care coordination, and all necessary supplies and equipment (drugs and nursing visits coded separately), per diem (do not use this code for flushing of infusion devices with Heparin to maintain patency)
BETOS: Z2 Undefined codes
Service not separately priced by Part B

■ **S9373** Home infusion therapy, hydration therapy; administrative services, professional pharmacy services, care coordination, and all necessary supplies and equipment (drugs and nursing visits coded separately), per diem (do not use with hydration therapy codes S9374-S9377 using daily volume scales)
BETOS: Z2 Undefined codes
Service not separately priced by Part B

■ **S9374** Home infusion therapy, hydration therapy; one liter per day, administrative services, professional pharmacy services, care coordination, and all necessary supplies and equipment (drugs and nursing visits coded separately), per diem
BETOS: Z2 Undefined codes
Service not separately priced by Part B

■ **S9375** Home infusion therapy, hydration therapy; more than one liter but no more than two liters per day, administrative services, professional pharmacy services, care coordination, and all necessary supplies and equipment (drugs and nursing visits coded separately), per diem
BETOS: Z2 Undefined codes
Service not separately priced by Part B

■ **S9376** Home infusion therapy, hydration therapy; more than two liters but no more than three liters per day, administrative services, professional pharmacy services, care coordination, and all necessary supplies and equipment (drugs and nursing visits coded separately), per diem
BETOS: Z2 Undefined codes
Service not separately priced by Part B

■ **S9377** Home infusion therapy, hydration therapy; more than three liters per day, administrative services, professional pharmacy services, care coordination, and all necessary supplies (drugs and nursing visits coded separately), per diem
BETOS: Z2 Undefined codes
Service not separately priced by Part B

■ **S9379** Home infusion therapy, infusion therapy, not otherwise classified; administrative services, professional pharmacy services, care coordination, and all necessary supplies and equipment (drugs and nursing visits coded separately), per diem
BETOS: Z2 Undefined codes
Service not separately priced by Part B

MISCELLANEOUS SUPPLIES AND SERVICES (S9381-S9485), SEE ALSO MISCELLANEOUS SUPPLIES AND SERVICES (S8265-S9152)

■ **S9381** Delivery or service to high risk areas requiring escort or extra protection, per visit
BETOS: Z2 Undefined codes
Service not separately priced by Part B

■ **S9401** Anticoagulation clinic, inclusive of all services except laboratory tests, per session
BETOS: Z2 Undefined codes
Service not separately priced by Part B

■ **S9430** Pharmacy compounding and dispensing services
BETOS: Z2 Undefined codes
Service not separately priced by Part B

■ **S9433** Medical food nutritionally complete, administered orally, providing 100% of nutritional intake
BETOS: Z2 Undefined codes
Service not separately priced by Part B
Coding Clinic: 2008, Q4

▲ Revised code   ● New code   C Carrier judgment   D Special coverage instructions apply
■ Not payable by Medicare   M Non-covered by Medicare   S Non-covered by Medicare statute   AHA Coding Clinic®

■ **S9434** Modified solid food supplements for inborn errors of metabolism
BETOS: Z2 Undefined codes
Service not separately priced by Part B

■ **S9435** Medical foods for inborn errors of metabolism
BETOS: Z2 Undefined codes
Service not separately priced by Part B

■ **S9436** Childbirth preparation/lamaze classes, non-physician provider, per session ♀
BETOS: Z2 Undefined codes
Service not separately priced by Part B

■ **S9437** Childbirth refresher classes, non-physician provider, per session ♀
BETOS: Z2 Undefined codes
Service not separately priced by Part B

■ **S9438** Cesarean birth classes, non-physician provider, per session ♀
BETOS: Z2 Undefined codes
Service not separately priced by Part B

■ **S9439** VBAC (vaginal birth after cesarean) classes, non-physician provider, per session ♀
BETOS: Z2 Undefined codes
Service not separately priced by Part B

■ **S9441** Asthma education, non-physician provider, per session
BETOS: Z2 Undefined codes
Service not separately priced by Part B

■ **S9442** Birthing classes, non-physician provider, per session ♀
BETOS: Z2 Undefined codes
Service not separately priced by Part B

■ **S9443** Lactation classes, non-physician provider, per session ♀
BETOS: Z2 Undefined codes
Service not separately priced by Part B

■ **S9444** Parenting classes, non-physician provider, per session
BETOS: Z2 Undefined codes
Service not separately priced by Part B

■ **S9445** Patient education, not otherwise classified, non-physician provider, individual, per session
BETOS: Z2 Undefined codes
Service not separately priced by Part B

■ **S9446** Patient education, not otherwise classified, non-physician provider, group, per session
BETOS: Z2 Undefined codes
Service not separately priced by Part B

■ **S9447** Infant safety (including CPR) classes, non-physician provider, per session
BETOS: Z2 Undefined codes
Service not separately priced by Part B

■ **S9449** Weight management classes, non-physician provider, per session
BETOS: Z2 Undefined codes
Service not separately priced by Part B

■ **S9451** Exercise classes, non-physician provider, per session
BETOS: Z2 Undefined codes
Service not separately priced by Part B

■ **S9452** Nutrition classes, non-physician provider, per session
BETOS: Z2 Undefined codes
Service not separately priced by Part B

■ **S9453** Smoking cessation classes, non-physician provider, per session
BETOS: Z2 Undefined codes
Service not separately priced by Part B

■ **S9454** Stress management classes, non-physician provider, per session
BETOS: Z2 Undefined codes
Service not separately priced by Part B

■ **S9455** Diabetic management program, group session
BETOS: Z2 Undefined codes
Service not separately priced by Part B

■ **S9460** Diabetic management program, nurse visit
BETOS: Z2 Undefined codes
Service not separately priced by Part B

■ **S9465** Diabetic management program, dietitian visit
BETOS: Z2 Undefined codes
Service not separately priced by Part B

■ **S9470** Nutritional counseling, dietitian visit
BETOS: Z2 Undefined codes
Service not separately priced by Part B

■ **S9472** Cardiac rehabilitation program, non-physician provider, per diem
BETOS: Z2 Undefined codes
Service not separately priced by Part B

■ **S9473** Pulmonary rehabilitation program, non-physician provider, per diem
BETOS: Z2 Undefined codes
Service not separately priced by Part B

■ **S9474** Enterostomal therapy by a registered nurse certified in enterostomal therapy, per diem
BETOS: Z2 Undefined codes
Service not separately priced by Part B

■ **S9475** Ambulatory setting substance abuse treatment or detoxification services, per diem
BETOS: Z2 Undefined codes
Service not separately priced by Part B

■ **S9476** Vestibular rehabilitation program, non-physician provider, per diem
BETOS: Z2 Undefined codes
Service not separately priced by Part B

■ **S9480** Intensive outpatient psychiatric services, per diem
BETOS: Z2 Undefined codes
Service not separately priced by Part B

S9482 Family stabilization services, per 15 minutes
BETOS: Z2 Undefined codes
Service not separately priced by Part B

S9484 Crisis intervention mental health services, per hour
BETOS: Z2 Undefined codes
Service not separately priced by Part B

S9485 Crisis intervention mental health services, per diem
BETOS: Z2 Undefined codes
Service not separately priced by Part B

HOME THERAPY SERVICES (S9490-S9810), SEE ALSO HOME INFUSION THERAPY (S9325-S9379); HOME INFUSION THERAPY (S5497-S5523)

S9490 Home infusion therapy, corticosteroid infusion; administrative services, professional pharmacy services, care coordination, and all necessary supplies and equipment (drugs and nursing visits coded separately), per diem
BETOS: Z2 Undefined codes
Service not separately priced by Part B

S9494 Home infusion therapy, antibiotic, antiviral, or antifungal therapy; administrative services, professional pharmacy services, care coordination, and all necessary supplies and equipment (drugs and nursing visits coded separately), per diem (do not use this code with home infusion codes for hourly dosing schedules S9497-S9504)
BETOS: Z2 Undefined codes
Service not separately priced by Part B

S9497 Home infusion therapy, antibiotic, antiviral, or antifungal therapy; once every 3 hours; administrative services, professional pharmacy services, care coordination, and all necessary supplies and equipment (drugs and nursing visits coded separately), per diem
BETOS: Z2 Undefined codes
Service not separately priced by Part B

S9500 Home infusion therapy, antibiotic, antiviral, or antifungal therapy; once every 24 hours; administrative services, professional pharmacy services, care coordination, and all necessary supplies and equipment (drugs and nursing visits coded separately), per diem
BETOS: Z2 Undefined codes
Service not separately priced by Part B

S9501 Home infusion therapy, antibiotic, antiviral, or antifungal therapy; once every 12 hours; administrative services, professional pharmacy services, care coordination, and all necessary supplies and equipment (drugs and nursing visits coded separately), per diem

BETOS: Z2 Undefined codes
Service not separately priced by Part B

S9502 Home infusion therapy, antibiotic, antiviral, or antifungal therapy; once every 8 hours, administrative services, professional pharmacy services, care coordination, and all necessary supplies and equipment (drugs and nursing visits coded separately), per diem
BETOS: Z2 Undefined codes
Service not separately priced by Part B

S9503 Home infusion therapy, antibiotic, antiviral, or antifungal; once every 6 hours; administrative services, professional pharmacy services, care coordination, and all necessary supplies and equipment (drugs and nursing visits coded separately), per diem
BETOS: Z2 Undefined codes
Service not separately priced by Part B

S9504 Home infusion therapy, antibiotic, antiviral, or antifungal; once every 4 hours; administrative services, professional pharmacy services, care coordination, and all necessary supplies and equipment (drugs and nursing visits coded separately), per diem
BETOS: Z2 Undefined codes
Service not separately priced by Part B

S9529 Routine venipuncture for collection of specimen(s), single home bound, nursing home, or skilled nursing facility patient
BETOS: Z2 Undefined codes
Service not separately priced by Part B

S9537 Home therapy; hematopoietic hormone injection therapy (e.g., erythropoietin, G-CSF, GM-CSF); administrative services, professional pharmacy services, care coordination, and all necessary supplies and equipment (drugs and nursing visits coded separately), per diem
BETOS: Z2 Undefined codes
Service not separately priced by Part B

S9538 Home transfusion of blood product(s); administrative services, professional pharmacy services, care coordination and all necessary supplies and equipment (blood products, drugs, and nursing visits coded separately), per diem
BETOS: Z2 Undefined codes
Service not separately priced by Part B

S9542 Home injectable therapy, not otherwise classified, including administrative services, professional pharmacy services, care coordination, and all necessary supplies and equipment (drugs and nursing visits coded separately), per diem
BETOS: Z2 Undefined codes
Service not separately priced by Part B

▲ Revised code   ● New code   **C** Carrier judgment   **D** Special coverage instructions apply
I Not payable by Medicare   **M** Non-covered by Medicare   **S** Non-covered by Medicare statute   AHA Coding Clinic®

S9558 Home injectable therapy; growth hormone, including administrative services, professional pharmacy services, care coordination, and all necessary supplies and equipment (drugs and nursing visits coded separately), per diem
BETOS: Z2   Undefined codes
Service not separately priced by Part B

S9559 Home injectable therapy, interferon, including administrative services, professional pharmacy services, care coordination, and all necessary supplies and equipment (drugs and nursing visits coded separately), per diem
BETOS: Z2   Undefined codes
Service not separately priced by Part B

S9560 Home injectable therapy; hormonal therapy (e.g., Leuprolide, Goserelin), including administrative services, professional pharmacy services, care coordination, and all necessary supplies and equipment (drugs and nursing visits coded separately), per diem
BETOS: Z2   Undefined codes
Service not separately priced by Part B

S9562 Home injectable therapy, Palivizumab, including administrative services, professional pharmacy services, care coordination, and all necessary supplies and equipment (drugs and nursing visits coded separately), per diem
BETOS: Z2   Undefined codes
Service not separately priced by Part B

S9590 Home therapy, irrigation therapy (e.g., sterile irrigation of an organ or anatomical cavity); including administrative services, professional pharmacy services, care coordination, and all necessary supplies and equipment (drugs and nursing visits coded separately), per diem
BETOS: Z2   Undefined codes
Service not separately priced by Part B

S9810 Home therapy; professional pharmacy services for provision of infusion, specialty drug administration, and/or disease state management, not otherwise classified, per hour (do not use this code with any per diem code)
BETOS: Z2   Undefined codes
Service not separately priced by Part B

VARIOUS SERVICES, FEES, AND COSTS (S9900-S9999)

S9900 Services by a Journal-listed Christian Science practitioner for the purpose of healing, per diem
BETOS: Z2   Undefined codes
Service not separately priced by Part B

S9901 Services by a journal-listed Christian Science nurse, per hour
BETOS: Z2   Undefined codes
Service not separately priced by Part B

S9960 Ambulance service, conventional air service, nonemergency transport, one-way (fixed wing)
BETOS: O1A   Ambulance
Service not separately priced by Part B

S9961 Ambulance service, conventional air service, nonemergency transport, one-way (rotary wing)
BETOS: O1A   Ambulance
Service not separately priced by Part B

S9970 Health club membership, annual
BETOS: Z2   Undefined codes
Service not separately priced by Part B

S9975 Transplant related lodging, meals and transportation, per diem
BETOS: Z2   Undefined codes
Service not separately priced by Part B

S9976 Lodging, per diem, not otherwise classified
BETOS: Z2   Undefined codes
Service not separately priced by Part B

S9977 Meals, per diem, not otherwise specified
BETOS: Z2   Undefined codes
Service not separately priced by Part B

S9981 Medical records copying fee, administrative
BETOS: Z2   Undefined codes
Service not separately priced by Part B

S9982 Medical records copying fee, per page
BETOS: Z2   Undefined codes
Service not separately priced by Part B

S9986 Not medically necessary service (patient is aware that service not medically necessary)
BETOS: Z2   Undefined codes
Service not separately priced by Part B

S9988 Services provided as part of a Phase I clinical trial
BETOS: Z2   Undefined codes
Service not separately priced by Part B

S9989 Services provided outside of the United States of America (list in addition to code(s) for service(s))
BETOS: Z2   Undefined codes
Service not separately priced by Part B

S9990 Services provided as part of a Phase II clinical trial
BETOS: Z2   Undefined codes
Service not separately priced by Part B

S9991 Services provided as part of a Phase III clinical trial
BETOS: Z2   Undefined codes
Service not separately priced by Part B

♂ Male only   ♀ Female only   🅐 Age   A2 - Z3 = ASC Payment indicator   A - Y = APC Status indicator
ASC = ASC-approved procedure   **DME** Paid under the DME fee schedule   **MIPS** MIPS code

I **S9992** Transportation costs to and from trial location and local transportation costs (e.g., fares for taxicab or bus) for clinical trial participant and one caregiver/companion

BETOS: Z2 Undefined codes
Service not separately priced by Part B

I **S9994** Lodging costs (e.g., hotel charges) for clinical trial participant and one caregiver/companion

BETOS: Z2 Undefined codes
Service not separately priced by Part B

I **S9996** Meals for clinical trial participant and one caregiver/companion

BETOS: Z2 Undefined codes
Service not separately priced by Part B

I **S9999** Sales tax

BETOS: Z2 Undefined codes
Service not separately priced by Part B
Coding Clinic: 2009, Q2

▲ Revised code ● New code **C** Carrier judgment **D** Special coverage instructions apply
I Not payable by Medicare **M** Non-covered by Medicare **S** Non-covered by Medicare statute AHA Coding Clinic®

NOTES

NOTES

NATIONAL CODES ESTABLISHED FOR STATE MEDICAID AGENCIES (T1000-T5999)

NURSING SERVICES (T1000-T1005), SEE ALSO ADDITIONAL NURSING SERVICES (T1030-T1031)

T1000 Private duty / independent nursing service(s) - licensed, up to 15 minutes
BETOS: Z2 Undefined codes
Service not separately priced by Part B
Coding Clinic: 2009, Q2

T1001 Nursing assessment / evaluation
BETOS: Z2 Undefined codes
Service not separately priced by Part B

T1002 RN services, up to 15 minutes
BETOS: Z2 Undefined codes
Service not separately priced by Part B

T1003 LPN/LVN services, up to 15 minutes
BETOS: Z2 Undefined codes
Service not separately priced by Part B

T1004 Services of a qualified nursing aide, up to 15 minutes
BETOS: Z2 Undefined codes
Service not separately priced by Part B

T1005 Respite care services, up to 15 minutes
BETOS: Z2 Undefined codes
Service not separately priced by Part B

ALCOHOL AND SUBSTANCE ABUSE SERVICES (T1006-T1012)

T1006 Alcohol and/or substance abuse services, family/couple counseling
BETOS: Z2 Undefined codes
Service not separately priced by Part B

T1007 Alcohol and/or substance abuse services, treatment plan development and/or modification
BETOS: Z2 Undefined codes
Service not separately priced by Part B

T1009 Child sitting services for children of the individual receiving alcohol and/or substance abuse services
BETOS: Z2 Undefined codes
Service not separately priced by Part B

T1010 Meals for individuals receiving alcohol and/or substance abuse services (when meals not included in the program)
BETOS: Z2 Undefined codes
Service not separately priced by Part B

T1012 Alcohol and/or substance abuse services, skills development
BETOS: Z2 Undefined codes
Service not separately priced by Part B

OTHER SERVICES (T1013-T1018)

T1013 Sign language or oral interpretive services, per 15 minutes
BETOS: Z2 Undefined codes
Service not separately priced by Part B

T1014 Telehealth transmission, per minute, professional services bill separately
BETOS: Z2 Undefined codes
Service not separately priced by Part B

T1015 Clinic visit/encounter, all-inclusive
BETOS: Z2 Undefined codes
Service not separately priced by Part B
Coding Clinic: 2002, Q1

T1016 Case management, each 15 minutes
BETOS: Z2 Undefined codes
Service not separately priced by Part B

T1017 Targeted case management, each 15 minutes
BETOS: Z2 Undefined codes
Service not separately priced by Part B

T1018 School-based individualized education program (IEP) services, bundled
BETOS: Z2 Undefined codes
Service not separately priced by Part B

HOME HEALTH SERVICES (T1019-T1022)

T1019 Personal care services, per 15 minutes, not for an inpatient or resident of a hospital, nursing facility, ICF/MR or IMD, part of the individualized plan of treatment (code may not be used to identify services provided by home health aide or certified nurse assistant)
BETOS: Z2 Undefined codes
Service not separately priced by Part B

T1020 Personal care services, per diem, not for an inpatient or resident of a hospital, nursing facility, ICF/MR or IMD, part of the individualized plan of treatment (code may not be used to identify services provided by home health aide or certified nurse assistant)
BETOS: Z2 Undefined codes
Service not separately priced by Part B

T1021 Home health aide or certified nurse assistant, per visit
BETOS: Z2 Undefined codes
Service not separately priced by Part B

T1022 Contracted home health agency services, all services provided under contract, per day
BETOS: Z2 Undefined codes
Service not separately priced by Part B

♂ Male only   ♀ Female only   🅐 Age   A2 - Z3 = ASC Payment indicator   A - Y = APC Status indicator
ASC = ASC-approved procedure   **DME** Paid under the DME fee schedule   **MIPS** MIPS code

SCREENINGS, ASSESSMENTS, AND TREATMENTS, INDIVIDUAL AND FAMILY (T1023-T1029)

T1023 Screening to determine the appropriateness of consideration of an individual for participation in a specified program, project or treatment protocol, per encounter
BETOS: Z2   Undefined codes
Service not separately priced by Part B

T1024 Evaluation and treatment by an integrated, specialty team contracted to provide coordinated care to multiple or severely handicapped children, per encounter Ⓐ
BETOS: Z2   Undefined codes
Service not separately priced by Part B

T1025 Intensive, extended multidisciplinary services provided in a clinic setting to children with complex medical, physical, mental and psychosocial impairments, per diem Ⓐ
BETOS: Z2   Undefined codes
Service not separately priced by Part B

T1026 Intensive, extended multidisciplinary services provided in a clinic setting to children with complex medical, physical, medical and psychosocial impairments, per hour Ⓐ
BETOS: Z2   Undefined codes
Service not separately priced by Part B

T1027 Family training and counseling for child development, per 15 minutes
BETOS: Z2   Undefined codes
Service not separately priced by Part B

T1028 Assessment of home, physical and family environment, to determine suitability to meet patient's medical needs
BETOS: Z2   Undefined codes
Service not separately priced by Part B

T1029 Comprehensive environmental lead investigation, not including laboratory analysis, per dwelling
BETOS: Z2   Undefined codes
Service not separately priced by Part B

ADDITIONAL NURSING SERVICES (T1030, T1031), SEE ALSO NURSING SERVICES (T1000-T1005)

T1030 Nursing care, in the home, by registered nurse, per diem
BETOS: Z2   Undefined codes
Service not separately priced by Part B

T1031 Nursing care, in the home, by licensed practical nurse, per diem
BETOS: Z2   Undefined codes
Service not separately priced by Part B

BEHAVIORAL HEALTH SERVICES (T1040, T1041)

T1040 Medicaid certified community behavioral health clinic services, per diem
BETOS: Z2   Undefined codes
Service not separately priced by Part B

T1041 Medicaid certified community behavioral health clinic services, per month
BETOS: Z2   Undefined codes
Service not separately priced by Part B

MISCELLANEOUS SERVICES AND SUPPLIES (T1502-T1999)

T1502 Administration of oral, intramuscular and/or subcutaneous medication by health care agency/professional, per visit
BETOS: Z2   Undefined codes
Service not separately priced by Part B

T1503 Administration of medication, other than oral and/or injectable, by a health care agency/professional, per visit
BETOS: Z2   Undefined codes
Service not separately priced by Part B

T1505 Electronic medication compliance management device, includes all components and accessories, not otherwise classified
BETOS: Z2   Undefined codes
Service not separately priced by Part B

T1999 Miscellaneous therapeutic items and supplies, retail purchases, not otherwise classified; identify product in "remarks"
BETOS: Z2   Undefined codes
Service not separately priced by Part B

TRANSPORTATION SERVICES (T2001-T2007)

T2001 Non-emergency transportation; patient attendant/escort
BETOS: Z2   Undefined codes
Service not separately priced by Part B

T2002 Non-emergency transportation; per diem
BETOS: Z2   Undefined codes
Service not separately priced by Part B

T2003 Non-emergency transportation; encounter/trip
BETOS: Z2   Undefined codes
Service not separately priced by Part B

T2004 Non-emergency transport; commercial carrier, multi-pass
BETOS: Z2   Undefined codes
Service not separately priced by Part B

T2005 Non-emergency transportation; stretcher van
BETOS: Z2   Undefined codes
Service not separately priced by Part B

T2007 Transportation waiting time, air ambulance and non-emergency vehicle, one-half (1/2) hour increments
BETOS: Z2   Undefined codes
Service not separately priced by Part B

▲ Revised code   ● New code   C Carrier judgment   D Special coverage instructions apply
I Not payable by Medicare   M Non-covered by Medicare   S Non-covered by Medicare statute   AHA Coding Clinic®

PREADMISSION SCREENING (T2010, T2011)

▐ **T2010** Preadmission screening and resident review (PASRR) level I identification screening, per screen
BETOS: Z2   Undefined codes
Service not separately priced by Part B

▐ **T2011** Preadmission screening and resident review (PASRR) level II evaluation, per evaluation
BETOS: Z2   Undefined codes
Service not separately priced by Part B

WAIVER SERVICES (T2012-T2041)

▐ **T2012** Habilitation, educational; waiver, per diem
BETOS: Z2   Undefined codes
Service not separately priced by Part B

▐ **T2013** Habilitation, educational, waiver; per hour
BETOS: Z2   Undefined codes
Service not separately priced by Part B

▐ **T2014** Habilitation, prevocational, waiver; per diem
BETOS: Z2   Undefined codes
Service not separately priced by Part B

▐ **T2015** Habilitation, prevocational, waiver; per hour
BETOS: Z2   Undefined codes
Service not separately priced by Part B

▐ **T2016** Habilitation, residential, waiver; per diem
BETOS: Z2   Undefined codes
Service not separately priced by Part B

▐ **T2017** Habilitation, residential, waiver; 15 minutes
BETOS: Z2   Undefined codes
Service not separately priced by Part B

▐ **T2018** Habilitation, supported employment, waiver; per diem
BETOS: Z2   Undefined codes
Service not separately priced by Part B

▐ **T2019** Habilitation, supported employment, waiver; per 15 minutes
BETOS: Z2   Undefined codes
Service not separately priced by Part B

▐ **T2020** Day habilitation, waiver; per diem
BETOS: Z2   Undefined codes
Service not separately priced by Part B

▐ **T2021** Day habilitation, waiver; per 15 minutes
BETOS: Z2   Undefined codes
Service not separately priced by Part B

▐ **T2022** Case management, per month
BETOS: Z2   Undefined codes
Service not separately priced by Part B

▐ **T2023** Targeted case management; per month
BETOS: Z2   Undefined codes
Service not separately priced by Part B

▐ **T2024** Service assessment/plan of care development, waiver

BETOS: Z2   Undefined codes
Service not separately priced by Part B

▐ **T2025** Waiver services; not otherwise specified (NOS)
BETOS: Z2   Undefined codes
Service not separately priced by Part B

▐ **T2026** Specialized childcare, waiver; per diem
BETOS: Z2   Undefined codes
Service not separately priced by Part B

▐ **T2027** Specialized childcare, waiver; per 15 minutes
BETOS: Z2   Undefined codes
Service not separately priced by Part B

▐ **T2028** Specialized supply, not otherwise specified, waiver
BETOS: Z2   Undefined codes
Service not separately priced by Part B

▐ **T2029** Specialized medical equipment, not otherwise specified, waiver
BETOS: Z2   Undefined codes
Service not separately priced by Part B

▐ **T2030** Assisted living, waiver; per month
BETOS: Z2   Undefined codes
Service not separately priced by Part B

▐ **T2031** Assisted living; waiver, per diem
BETOS: Z2   Undefined codes
Service not separately priced by Part B

▐ **T2032** Residential care, not otherwise specified (NOS), waiver; per month
BETOS: Z2   Undefined codes
Service not separately priced by Part B

▐ **T2033** Residential care, not otherwise specified (NOS), waiver; per diem
BETOS: Z2   Undefined codes
Service not separately priced by Part B

▐ **T2034** Crisis intervention, waiver; per diem
BETOS: Z2   Undefined codes
Service not separately priced by Part B

▐ **T2035** Utility services to support medical equipment and assistive technology/devices, waiver
BETOS: Z2   Undefined codes
Service not separately priced by Part B

▐ **T2036** Therapeutic camping, overnight, waiver; each session
BETOS: Z2   Undefined codes
Service not separately priced by Part B

▐ **T2037** Therapeutic camping, day, waiver; each session
BETOS: Z2   Undefined codes
Service not separately priced by Part B

▐ **T2038** Community transition, waiver; per service
BETOS: Z2   Undefined codes
Service not separately priced by Part B

♂ Male only   ♀ Female only   Ⓐ Age   A2 - Z3 = ASC Payment indicator   A - Y = APC Status indicator
ASC = ASC-approved procedure   **DME** Paid under the DME fee schedule   **MIPS** MIPS code

I **T2039** Vehicle modifications, waiver; per service
    BETOS: Z2   Undefined codes
    Service not separately priced by Part B

I **T2040** Financial management, self-directed, waiver; per 15 minutes
    BETOS: Z2   Undefined codes
    Service not separately priced by Part B

I **T2041** Supports brokerage, self-directed, waiver; per 15 minutes
    BETOS: Z2   Undefined codes
    Service not separately priced by Part B

HOSPICE CARE (T2042-T2046)

I **T2042** Hospice routine home care; per diem
    BETOS: Z2   Undefined codes
    Service not separately priced by Part B

I **T2043** Hospice continuous home care; per hour
    BETOS: Z2   Undefined codes
    Service not separately priced by Part B

I **T2044** Hospice inpatient respite care; per diem
    BETOS: Z2   Undefined codes
    Service not separately priced by Part B

I **T2045** Hospice general inpatient care; per diem
    BETOS: Z2   Undefined codes
    Service not separately priced by Part B

I **T2046** Hospice long term care, room and board only; per diem
    BETOS: Z2   Undefined codes
    Service not separately priced by Part B

LONG-TERM RESIDENTIAL CARE (T2048)

I **T2048** Behavioral health; long-term care residential (non-acute care in a residential treatment program where stay is typically longer than 30 days), with room and board, per diem
    BETOS: Z2   Undefined codes
    Service not separately priced by Part B

NON-EMERGENCY TRANSPORTATION FEES (T2049)

I **T2049** Non-emergency transportation; stretcher van, mileage; per mile
    BETOS: Z2   Undefined codes
    Service not separately priced by Part B

SERVICES RELATED TO BREAST MILK (T2101)

I **T2101** Human breast milk processing, storage and distribution only ♀
    BETOS: Z2   Undefined codes
    Service not separately priced by Part B

INCONTINENCE SUPPLIES (T4521-T4544)

M **T4521** Adult sized disposable incontinence product, brief/diaper, small, each
    BETOS: D1A   Medical/surgical supplies
    Service not separately priced by Part B

M **T4522** Adult sized disposable incontinence product, brief/diaper, medium, each
    BETOS: D1A   Medical/surgical supplies
    Service not separately priced by Part B

M **T4523** Adult sized disposable incontinence product, brief/diaper, large, each
    BETOS: D1A   Medical/surgical supplies
    Service not separately priced by Part B

M **T4524** Adult sized disposable incontinence product, brief/diaper, extra large, each
    BETOS: D1A   Medical/surgical supplies
    Service not separately priced by Part B

M **T4525** Adult sized disposable incontinence product, protective underwear/pull-on, small size, each
    BETOS: D1A   Medical/surgical supplies
    Service not separately priced by Part B

M **T4526** Adult sized disposable incontinence product, protective underwear/pull-on, medium size, each
    BETOS: D1A   Medical/surgical supplies
    Service not separately priced by Part B

M **T4527** Adult sized disposable incontinence product, protective underwear/pull-on, large size, each
    BETOS: D1A   Medical/surgical supplies
    Service not separately priced by Part B

M **T4528** Adult sized disposable incontinence product, protective underwear/pull-on, extra large size, each
    BETOS: D1A   Medical/surgical supplies
    Service not separately priced by Part B

M **T4529** Pediatric sized disposable incontinence product, brief/diaper, small/medium size, each Ⓐ
    BETOS: D1A   Medical/surgical supplies
    Service not separately priced by Part B

M **T4530** Pediatric sized disposable incontinence product, brief/diaper, large size, each Ⓐ
    BETOS: D1A   Medical/surgical supplies
    Service not separately priced by Part B

M **T4531** Pediatric sized disposable incontinence product, protective underwear/pull-on, small/medium size, each Ⓐ
    BETOS: D1A   Medical/surgical supplies
    Service not separately priced by Part B

M **T4532** Pediatric sized disposable incontinence product, protective underwear/pull-on, large size, each Ⓐ
    BETOS: D1A   Medical/surgical supplies
    Service not separately priced by Part B

M **T4533** Youth-sized disposable incontinence product, brief/diaper, each

---

▲ Revised code   ● New code   **C** Carrier judgment   **D** Special coverage instructions apply

I Not payable by Medicare   **M** Non-covered by Medicare   **S** Non-covered by Medicare statute   AHA Coding Clinic®

BETOS: D1A   Medical/surgical supplies
Service not separately priced by Part B

M **T4534** Youth-sized disposable incontinence product, protective underwear/pull-on, each
BETOS: D1A   Medical/surgical supplies
Service not separately priced by Part B

M **T4535** Disposable liner/shield/guard/pad/ undergarment, for incontinence, each
BETOS: D1A   Medical/surgical supplies
Service not separately priced by Part B

M **T4536** Incontinence product, protective underwear/ pull-on, reusable, any size, each
BETOS: D1A   Medical/surgical supplies
Service not separately priced by Part B

M **T4537** Incontinence product, protective underpad, reusable, bed size, each
BETOS: D1A   Medical/surgical supplies
Service not separately priced by Part B

M **T4538** Diaper service, reusable diaper, each diaper
BETOS: D1A   Medical/surgical supplies
Service not separately priced by Part B

M **T4539** Incontinence product, diaper/brief, reusable, any size, each
BETOS: D1A   Medical/surgical supplies
Service not separately priced by Part B

M **T4540** Incontinence product, protective underpad, reusable, chair size, each
BETOS: D1A   Medical/surgical supplies
Service not separately priced by Part B

I **T4541** Incontinence product, disposable underpad, large, each
BETOS: Z2   Undefined codes
Service not separately priced by Part B

I **T4542** Incontinence product, disposable underpad, small size, each
BETOS: Z2   Undefined codes
Service not separately priced by Part B

M **T4543** Adult sized disposable incontinence product, protective brief/diaper, above extra large, each
BETOS: D1A   Medical/surgical supplies
Service not separately priced by Part B

M **T4544** Adult sized disposable incontinence product, protective underwear/pull-on, above extra large, each   Ⓐ
BETOS: D1A   Medical/surgical supplies
Service not separately priced by Part B

OTHER AND UNSPECIFIED SUPPLIES (T5001, T5999)

I **T5001** Positioning seat for persons with special orthopedic needs
BETOS: Z2   Undefined codes
Service not separately priced by Part B

I **T5999** Supply, not otherwise specified
BETOS: Z2   Undefined codes
Service not separately priced by Part B

♂ Male only   ♀ Female only   Ⓐ Age   A2 - Z3 = ASC Payment indicator   A - Y = APC Status indicator
ASC = ASC-approved procedure   **DME** Paid under the DME fee schedule   **MIPS** MIPS code

NOTES

VISION SERVICES (V2020-V2799)

SPECTACLE FRAMES (V2020, V2025)

D **V2020** Frames, purchases `DME` A
BETOS: D1F   Prosthetic/orthotic devices

M **V2025** Deluxe frame E1
BETOS: D1F   Prosthetic/orthotic devices
Service not separately priced by Part B

LENSES, SINGLE VISION (V2100-V2199)

C **V2100** Sphere, single vision, plano to plus or minus 4.00, per lens `DME` A
BETOS: D1F   Prosthetic/orthotic devices

C **V2101** Sphere, single vision, plus or minus 4.12 to plus or minus 7.00d, per lens `DME` A
BETOS: D1F   Prosthetic/orthotic devices

C **V2102** Sphere, single vision, plus or minus 7.12 to plus or minus 20.00d, per lens `DME` A
BETOS: D1F   Prosthetic/orthotic devices

C **V2103** Spherocylinder, single vision, plano to plus or minus 4.00d sphere, .12 to 2.00d cylinder, per lens `DME` A
BETOS: D1F   Prosthetic/orthotic devices

C **V2104** Spherocylinder, single vision, plano to plus or minus 4.00d sphere, 2.12 to 4.00d cylinder, per lens `DME` A
BETOS: D1F   Prosthetic/orthotic devices

C **V2105** Spherocylinder, single vision, plano to plus or minus 4.00d sphere, 4.25 to 6.00d cylinder, per lens `DME` A
BETOS: D1F   Prosthetic/orthotic devices

C **V2106** Spherocylinder, single vision, plano to plus or minus 4.00d sphere, over 6.00d cylinder, per lens `DME` A
BETOS: D1F   Prosthetic/orthotic devices

C **V2107** Spherocylinder, single vision, plus or minus 4.25 to plus or minus 7.00 sphere, .12 to 2.00d cylinder, per lens `DME` A
BETOS: D1F   Prosthetic/orthotic devices

C **V2108** Spherocylinder, single vision, plus or minus 4.25d to plus or minus 7.00d sphere, 2.12 to 4.00d cylinder, per lens `DME` A
BETOS: D1F   Prosthetic/orthotic devices

C **V2109** Spherocylinder, single vision, plus or minus 4.25 to plus or minus 7.00d sphere, 4.25 to 6.00d cylinder, per lens `DME` A
BETOS: D1F   Prosthetic/orthotic devices

C **V2110** Spherocylinder, single vision, plus or minus 4.25 to 7.00d sphere, over 6.00d cylinder, per lens `DME` A
BETOS: D1F   Prosthetic/orthotic devices

C **V2111** Spherocylinder, single vision, plus or minus 7.25 to plus or minus 12.00d sphere, .25 to 2.25d cylinder, per lens `DME` A
BETOS: D1F   Prosthetic/orthotic devices

C **V2112** Spherocylinder, single vision, plus or minus 7.25 to plus or minus 12.00d sphere, 2.25d to 4.00d cylinder, per lens `DME` A
BETOS: D1F   Prosthetic/orthotic devices

C **V2113** Spherocylinder, single vision, plus or minus 7.25 to plus or minus 12.00d sphere, 4.25 to 6.00d cylinder, per lens `DME` A
BETOS: D1F   Prosthetic/orthotic devices

C **V2114** Spherocylinder, single vision, sphere over plus or minus 12.00d, per lens `DME` A
BETOS: D1F   Prosthetic/orthotic devices

C **V2115** Lenticular, (Myodisc), per lens, single vision `DME` A
BETOS: D1F   Prosthetic/orthotic devices

C **V2118** Aniseikonic lens, single vision `DME` A
BETOS: D1F   Prosthetic/orthotic devices

D **V2121** Lenticular lens, per lens, single `DME` A
BETOS: D1F   Prosthetic/orthotic devices

C **V2199** Not otherwise classified, single vision lens A
BETOS: D1F   Prosthetic/orthotic devices

LENSES, BIFOCALS (V2200-V2299)

C **V2200** Sphere, bifocal, plano to plus or minus 4.00d, per lens `DME` A
BETOS: D1F   Prosthetic/orthotic devices

C **V2201** Sphere, bifocal, plus or minus 4.12 to plus or minus 7.00d, per lens `DME` A
BETOS: D1F   Prosthetic/orthotic devices

C **V2202** Sphere, bifocal, plus or minus 7.12 to plus or minus 20.00d, per lens `DME` A
BETOS: D1F   Prosthetic/orthotic devices

C **V2203** Spherocylinder, bifocal, plano to plus or minus 4.00d sphere, .12 to 2.00d cylinder, per lens `DME` A
BETOS: D1F   Prosthetic/orthotic devices

C **V2204** Spherocylinder, bifocal, plano to plus or minus 4.00d sphere, 2.12 to 4.00d cylinder, per lens `DME` A
BETOS: D1F   Prosthetic/orthotic devices

C **V2205** Spherocylinder, bifocal, plano to plus or minus 4.00d sphere, 4.25 to 6.00d cylinder, per lens `DME` A
BETOS: D1F   Prosthetic/orthotic devices

C **V2206** Spherocylinder, bifocal, plano to plus or minus 4.00d sphere, over 6.00d cylinder, per lens `DME` A
BETOS: D1F   Prosthetic/orthotic devices

C **V2207** Spherocylinder, bifocal, plus or minus 4.25 to plus or minus 7.00d sphere, .12 to 2.00d cylinder, per lens `DME` A
BETOS: D1F   Prosthetic/orthotic devices

♂ Male only   ♀ Female only   **A** Age   A2 - Z3 = ASC Payment indicator   A - Y = APC Status indicator
ASC = ASC-approved procedure   `DME` Paid under the DME fee schedule   `MIPS` MIPS code

V2208 Spherocylinder, bifocal, plus or minus 4.25 to plus or minus 7.00d sphere, 2.12 to 4.00d cylinder, per lens ▫DME A
BETOS: D1F Prosthetic/orthotic devices

V2209 Spherocylinder, bifocal, plus or minus 4.25 to plus or minus 7.00d sphere, 4.25 to 6.00d cylinder, per lens ▫DME A
BETOS: D1F Prosthetic/orthotic devices

V2210 Spherocylinder, bifocal, plus or minus 4.25 to plus or minus 7.00d sphere, over 6.00d cylinder, per lens ▫DME A
BETOS: D1F Prosthetic/orthotic devices

V2211 Spherocylinder, bifocal, plus or minus 7.25 to plus or minus 12.00d sphere, .25 to 2.25d cylinder, per lens ▫DME A
BETOS: D1F Prosthetic/orthotic devices

V2212 Spherocylinder, bifocal, plus or minus 7.25 to plus or minus 12.00d sphere, 2.25 to 4.00d cylinder, per lens ▫DME A
BETOS: D1F Prosthetic/orthotic devices

V2213 Spherocylinder, bifocal, plus or minus 7.25 to plus or minus 12.00d sphere, 4.25 to 6.00d cylinder, per lens ▫DME A
BETOS: D1F Prosthetic/orthotic devices

V2214 Spherocylinder, bifocal, sphere over plus or minus 12.00d, per lens ▫DME A
BETOS: D1F Prosthetic/orthotic devices

V2215 Lenticular (Myodisc), per lens, bifocal ▫DME A
BETOS: D1F Prosthetic/orthotic devices

V2218 Aniseikonic, per lens, bifocal ▫DME A
BETOS: D1F Prosthetic/orthotic devices

V2219 Bifocal seg width over 28 mm ▫DME A
BETOS: D1F Prosthetic/orthotic devices

V2220 Bifocal add over 3.25d ▫DME A
BETOS: D1F Prosthetic/orthotic devices

V2221 Lenticular lens, per lens, bifocal ▫DME A
BETOS: D1F Prosthetic/orthotic devices

V2299 Specialty bifocal (by report) A
BETOS: D1F Prosthetic/orthotic devices

LENSES, TRIFOCAL (V2300-V2399)

V2300 Sphere, trifocal, plano to plus or minus 4.00d, per lens ▫DME A
BETOS: D1F Prosthetic/orthotic devices

V2301 Sphere, trifocal, plus or minus 4.12 to plus or minus 7.00d, per lens ▫DME A
BETOS: D1F Prosthetic/orthotic devices

V2302 Sphere, trifocal, plus or minus 7.12 to plus or minus 20.00, per lens ▫DME A
BETOS: D1F Prosthetic/orthotic devices

V2303 Spherocylinder, trifocal, plano to plus or minus 4.00d sphere, .12-2.00d cylinder, per lens ▫DME A
BETOS: D1F Prosthetic/orthotic devices

V2304 Spherocylinder, trifocal, plano to plus or minus 4.00d sphere, 2.25-4.00d cylinder, per lens ▫DME A
BETOS: D1F Prosthetic/orthotic devices

V2305 Spherocylinder, trifocal, plano to plus or minus 4.00d sphere, 4.25 to 6.00 cylinder, per lens ▫DME A
BETOS: D1F Prosthetic/orthotic devices

V2306 Spherocylinder, trifocal, plano to plus or minus 4.00d sphere, over 6.00d cylinder, per lens ▫DME A
BETOS: D1F Prosthetic/orthotic devices

V2307 Spherocylinder, trifocal, plus or minus 4.25 to plus or minus 7.00d sphere, .12 to 2.00d cylinder, per lens ▫DME A
BETOS: D1F Prosthetic/orthotic devices

V2308 Spherocylinder, trifocal, plus or minus 4.25 to plus or minus 7.00d sphere, 2.12 to 4.00d cylinder, per lens ▫DME A
BETOS: D1F Prosthetic/orthotic devices

V2309 Spherocylinder, trifocal, plus or minus 4.25 to plus or minus 7.00d sphere, 4.25 to 6.00d cylinder, per lens ▫DME A
BETOS: D1F Prosthetic/orthotic devices

V2310 Spherocylinder, trifocal, plus or minus 4.25 to plus or minus 7.00d sphere, over 6.00d cylinder, per lens ▫DME A
BETOS: D1F Prosthetic/orthotic devices

V2311 Spherocylinder, trifocal, plus or minus 7.25 to plus or minus 12.00d sphere, .25 to 2.25d cylinder, per lens ▫DME A
BETOS: D1F Prosthetic/orthotic devices

V2312 Spherocylinder, trifocal, plus or minus 7.25 to plus or minus 12.00d sphere, 2.25 to 4.00d cylinder, per lens ▫DME A
BETOS: D1F Prosthetic/orthotic devices

V2313 Spherocylinder, trifocal, plus or minus 7.25 to plus or minus 12.00d sphere, 4.25 to 6.00d cylinder, per lens ▫DME A
BETOS: D1F Prosthetic/orthotic devices

V2314 Spherocylinder, trifocal, sphere over plus or minus 12.00d, per lens ▫DME A
BETOS: D1F Prosthetic/orthotic devices

V2315 Lenticular, (Myodisc), per lens, trifocal ▫DME A
BETOS: D1F Prosthetic/orthotic devices

V2318 Aniseikonic lens, trifocal ▫DME A
BETOS: D1F Prosthetic/orthotic devices

V2319 Trifocal seg width over 28 mm ▫DME A
BETOS: D1F Prosthetic/orthotic devices

V2320 Trifocal add over 3.25d ▫DME A
BETOS: D1F Prosthetic/orthotic devices

V2321 Lenticular lens, per lens, trifocal ▫DME A
BETOS: D1F Prosthetic/orthotic devices

C V2399 Specialty trifocal (by report)   A
BETOS: D1F   Prosthetic/orthotic devices

LENSES, ASPHERICAL AND VARIABLE SPHERICITY (V2410-V2499)

C V2410 Variable asphericity lens, single vision, full field, glass or plastic, per lens   DME   A
BETOS: D1F   Prosthetic/orthotic devices

C V2430 Variable asphericity lens, bifocal, full field, glass or plastic, per lens   DME   A
BETOS: D1F   Prosthetic/orthotic devices

C V2499 Variable sphericity lens, other type   A
BETOS: D1F   Prosthetic/orthotic devices

ASSORTED CONTACT LENSES (V2500-V2599)

C V2500 Contact lens, PMMA, spherical, per lens   DME   A
BETOS: D1F   Prosthetic/orthotic devices

C V2501 Contact lens, PMMA, toric or prism ballast, per lens   DME   A
BETOS: D1F   Prosthetic/orthotic devices

C V2502 Contact lens, PMMA, bifocal, per lens   DME   A
BETOS: D1F   Prosthetic/orthotic devices

C V2503 Contact lens, PMMA, color vision deficiency, per lens   DME   A
BETOS: D1F   Prosthetic/orthotic devices

C V2510 Contact lens, gas permeable, spherical, per lens   DME   A
BETOS: D1F   Prosthetic/orthotic devices

C V2511 Contact lens, gas permeable, toric, prism ballast, per lens   DME   A
BETOS: D1F   Prosthetic/orthotic devices

C V2512 Contact lens, gas permeable, bifocal, per lens   DME   A
BETOS: D1F   Prosthetic/orthotic devices

C V2513 Contact lens, gas permeable, extended wear, per lens   DME   A
BETOS: D1F   Prosthetic/orthotic devices

D V2520 Contact lens, hydrophilic, spherical, per lens   DME   A
BETOS: D1F   Prosthetic/orthotic devices

D V2521 Contact lens, hydrophilic, toric, or prism ballast, per lens   DME   A
BETOS: D1F   Prosthetic/orthotic devices

D V2522 Contact lens, hydrophilic, bifocal, per lens   DME   A
BETOS: D1F   Prosthetic/orthotic devices

D V2523 Contact lens, hydrophilic, extended wear, per lens   DME   A
BETOS: D1F   Prosthetic/orthotic devices

C V2530 Contact lens, scleral, gas impermeable, per lens (for contact lens modification, see 92325)   DME   A
BETOS: D1F   Prosthetic/orthotic devices

D V2531 Contact lens, scleral, gas permeable, per lens (for contact lens modification, see 92325)   DME   A
BETOS: D1F   Prosthetic/orthotic devices

C V2599 Contact lens, other type   A
BETOS: D1F   Prosthetic/orthotic devices

LOW AND NEAR VISION AIDS (V2600-V2615)

C V2600 Hand-held low vision aids and other nonspectacle mounted aids   A
BETOS: D1F   Prosthetic/orthotic devices

C V2610 Single lens spectacle mounted low vision aids   A
BETOS: D1F   Prosthetic/orthotic devices

C V2615 Telescopic and other compound lens system, including distance vision telescopic, near vision telescopes and compound microscopic lens system   A
BETOS: D1F   Prosthetic/orthotic devices

EYE PROSTHETICS AND SERVICES (V2623-V2629)

D V2623 Prosthetic eye, plastic, custom   DME   A
BETOS: D1F   Prosthetic/orthotic devices

C V2624 Polishing/resurfacing of ocular prosthesis   DME   A
BETOS: D1F   Prosthetic/orthotic devices

C V2625 Enlargement of ocular prosthesis   DME   A
BETOS: D1F   Prosthetic/orthotic devices

C V2626 Reduction of ocular prosthesis   DME   A
BETOS: D1F   Prosthetic/orthotic devices

D V2627 Scleral cover shell   DME   A
BETOS: D1F   Prosthetic/orthotic devices

C V2628 Fabrication and fitting of ocular conformer   DME   A
BETOS: D1F   Prosthetic/orthotic devices

C V2629 Prosthetic eye, other type   A
BETOS: D1F   Prosthetic/orthotic devices

LENSES, INTRAOCULAR (V2630-V2632)

D V2630 Anterior chamber intraocular lens   N1 DME ASC N
BETOS: D1F   Prosthetic/orthotic devices

D V2631 Iris supported intraocular lens   N1 DME ASC N
BETOS: D1F   Prosthetic/orthotic devices

D V2632 Posterior chamber intraocular lens   N1 DME ASC N
BETOS: D1F   Prosthetic/orthotic devices
Pub: 100-4, Chap. 32, 120.2

VISION SERVICES (V2700-V2799)

C V2700 Balance lens, per lens   DME   A
BETOS: D1F   Prosthetic/orthotic devices

M **V2702** Deluxe lens feature   E1
BETOS: D1F   Prosthetic/orthotic devices
Service not separately priced by Part B

C **V2710** Slab off prism, glass or plastic,
per lens   DME A
BETOS: D1F   Prosthetic/orthotic devices

C **V2715** Prism, per lens   DME A
BETOS: D1F   Prosthetic/orthotic devices

C **V2718** Press-on lens, Fresnell prism, per lens   DME A
BETOS: D1F   Prosthetic/orthotic devices

C **V2730** Special base curve, glass or plastic,
per lens   DME A
BETOS: D1F   Prosthetic/orthotic devices

D **V2744** Tint, photochromatic, per lens   DME A
BETOS: D1F   Prosthetic/orthotic devices

D **V2745** Addition to lens; tint, any color, solid,
gradient or equal, excludes photochromatic,
any lens material, per lens   DME A
BETOS: D1F   Prosthetic/orthotic devices

D **V2750** Anti-reflective coating, per lens   DME A
BETOS: D1F   Prosthetic/orthotic devices

D **V2755** U-V lens, per lens   DME A
BETOS: D1F   Prosthetic/orthotic devices

C **V2756** Eye glass case   E1
BETOS: Z2   Undefined codes
Service not separately priced by Part B

C **V2760** Scratch resistant coating, per lens   DME E1
BETOS: D1F   Prosthetic/orthotic devices

D **V2761** Mirror coating, any type, solid, gradient or
equal, any lens material, per lens   B
BETOS: D1F   Prosthetic/orthotic devices

D **V2762** Polarization, any lens material,
per lens   DME E1
BETOS: D1F   Prosthetic/orthotic devices

C **V2770** Occluder lens, per lens   DME A
BETOS: D1F   Prosthetic/orthotic devices

C **V2780** Oversize lens, per lens   DME A
BETOS: D1F   Prosthetic/orthotic devices

C **V2781** Progressive lens, per lens   B
BETOS: D1F   Prosthetic/orthotic devices
Service not separately priced by Part B

D **V2782** Lens, index 1.54 to 1.65 plastic or 1.60 to
1.79 glass, excludes polycarbonate,
per lens   DME A
BETOS: D1F   Prosthetic/orthotic devices

D **V2783** Lens, index greater than or equal to 1.66
plastic or greater than or equal to 1.80 glass,
excludes polycarbonate, per lens   DME A
BETOS: D1F   Prosthetic/orthotic devices

D **V2784** Lens, polycarbonate or equal, any index,
per lens   DME A
BETOS: D1F   Prosthetic/orthotic devices

C **V2785** Processing, preserving and transporting
corneal tissue   F4 ASC F
BETOS: D1F   Prosthetic/orthotic devices
Pub: 100-4, Chap. 4, 200.1

D **V2786** Specialty occupational multifocal lens, per
lens   DME E1
BETOS: D1F   Prosthetic/orthotic devices

S **V2787** Astigmatism correcting function of intraocular
lens   E1
BETOS: Z2   Undefined codes
Service not separately priced by Part B
Statute: 1862(a)(7)
Pub: 100-4, Chap. 32, 120.1; 100-4, Chap. 32,
120.2

S **V2788** Presbyopia correcting function of intraocular
lens   E1
BETOS: Z2   Undefined codes
Service not separately priced by Part B
Statute: 1862(a)(7)
Pub: 100-4, Chap. 32, 120.1; 100-4, Chap. 32,
120.2

C **V2790** Amniotic membrane for surgical
reconstruction, per procedure   N1 ASC N
BETOS: Z2   Undefined codes
Other carrier priced
Pub: 100-4, Chap. 4, 200.4

C **V2797** Vision supply, accessory and/or service
component of another HCPCS vision
code   E1
BETOS: D1F   Prosthetic/orthotic devices
Service not separately priced by Part B

C **V2799** Vision item or service, miscellaneous   A
BETOS: D1F   Prosthetic/orthotic devices

▲ Revised code   ● New code   **C** Carrier judgment   **D** Special coverage instructions apply
I Not payable by Medicare   **M** Non-covered by Medicare   **S** Non-covered by Medicare statute   AHA Coding Clinic®

NOTES

NOTES

HEARING SERVICES (V5008-V5364)

HEARING ASSESSMENTS AND EVALUATIONS (V5008-V5020)

[M] V5008 Hearing screening   E1
BETOS: O1F   Hearing and speech services
Service not separately priced by Part B

[S] V5010 Assessment for hearing aid   E1
BETOS: O1F   Hearing and speech services
Service not separately priced by Part B
Statute: 1862A7

[S] V5011 Fitting/orientation/checking of hearing aid   E1
BETOS: O1F   Hearing and speech services
Service not separately priced by Part B
Statute: 1862A7

[S] V5014 Repair/modification of a hearing aid   E1
BETOS: O1F   Hearing and speech services
Service not separately priced by Part B
Statute: 1862A7

[S] V5020 Conformity evaluation   E1
BETOS: O1F   Hearing and speech services
Service not separately priced by Part B
Statute: 1862A7

HEARING AID, MONAURAL (V5030-V5060)

[S] V5030 Hearing aid, monaural, body worn, air
conduction   E1
BETOS: O1F   Hearing and speech services
Service not separately priced by Part B
Statute: 1862A7

[S] V5040 Hearing aid, monaural, body worn, bone
conduction   E1
BETOS: O1F   Hearing and speech services
Service not separately priced by Part B
Statute: 1862A7

[S] V5050 Hearing aid, monaural, in the ear   E1
BETOS: O1F   Hearing and speech services
Service not separately priced by Part B
Statute: 1862A7

[S] V5060 Hearing aid, monaural, behind the ear   E1
BETOS: O1F   Hearing and speech services
Service not separately priced by Part B
Statute: 1862A7

MISCELLANEOUS HEARING SERVICES AND SUPPLIES (V5070-V5110)

[S] V5070 Glasses, air conduction   E1
BETOS: O1F   Hearing and speech services
Service not separately priced by Part B
Statute: 1862A7

[S] V5080 Glasses, bone conduction   E1
BETOS: O1F   Hearing and speech services
Service not separately priced by Part B
Statute: 1862A7

[S] V5090 Dispensing fee, unspecified hearing aid   E1
BETOS: O1F   Hearing and speech services
Service not separately priced by Part B
Statute: 1862A7

[S] V5095 Semi-implantable middle ear hearing
prosthesis   E1
BETOS: O1F   Hearing and speech services
Service not separately priced by Part B
Statute: 1862A7

[S] V5100 Hearing aid, bilateral, body worn   E1
BETOS: O1F   Hearing and speech services
Service not separately priced by Part B
Statute: 1862A7

[S] V5110 Dispensing fee, bilateral   E1
BETOS: O1F   Hearing and speech services
Service not separately priced by Part B
Statute: 1862A7

HEARING AIDS (V5120-V5267)

[S] V5120 Binaural, body   E1
BETOS: O1F   Hearing and speech services
Service not separately priced by Part B
Statute: 1862A7

[S] V5130 Binaural, in the ear   E1
BETOS: O1F   Hearing and speech services
Service not separately priced by Part B
Statute: 1862A7

[S] V5140 Binaural, behind the ear   E1
BETOS: O1F   Hearing and speech services
Service not separately priced by Part B
Statute: 1862A7

[S] V5150 Binaural, glasses   E1
BETOS: O1F   Hearing and speech services
Service not separately priced by Part B
Statute: 1862A7

[S] V5160 Dispensing fee, binaural   E1
BETOS: O1F   Hearing and speech services
Service not separately priced by Part B
Statute: 1862A7

[S] V5170 Hearing aid, CROS, in the ear   E1
BETOS: O1F   Hearing and speech services
Service not separately priced by Part B
Statute: 1862A7

[S] V5180 Hearing aid, CROS, behind the ear   E1
BETOS: O1F   Hearing and speech services
Service not separately priced by Part B
Statute: 1862A7

[S] V5190 Hearing aid, CROS, glasses   E1
BETOS: O1F   Hearing and speech services
Service not separately priced by Part B
Statute: 1862A7

[S] V5200 Dispensing fee, CROS   E1
BETOS: O1F   Hearing and speech services
Service not separately priced by Part B
Statute: 1862A7

♂ Male only   ♀ Female only   🅐 Age   A2 - Z3 = ASC Payment indicator   A - Y = APC Status indicator
ASC = ASC-approved procedure   **DME** Paid under the DME fee schedule   **MIPS** MIPS code

S V5210 Hearing aid, BICROS, in the ear   E1
BETOS: O1F   Hearing and speech services
Service not separately priced by Part B
Statute: 1862A7

S V5220 Hearing aid, BICROS, behind the ear   E1
BETOS: O1F   Hearing and speech services
Service not separately priced by Part B
Statute: 1862A7

S V5230 Hearing aid, BICROS, glasses   E1
BETOS: O1F   Hearing and speech services
Service not separately priced by Part B
Statute: 1862A7

S V5240 Dispensing fee, BICROS   E1
BETOS: O1F   Hearing and speech services
Service not separately priced by Part B
Statute: 1862A7

S V5241 Dispensing fee, monaural hearing aid, any type   E1
BETOS: O1F   Hearing and speech services
Service not separately priced by Part B
Statute: 1862A7
Coding Clinic: 2002, Q1

S V5242 Hearing aid, analog, monaural, CIC (completely in the ear canal)   E1
BETOS: O1F   Hearing and speech services
Service not separately priced by Part B
Statute: 1862A7
Coding Clinic: 2002, Q1

S V5243 Hearing aid, analog, monaural, ITC (in the canal)   E1
BETOS: O1F   Hearing and speech services
Service not separately priced by Part B
Statute: 1862A7
Coding Clinic: 2002, Q1

S V5244 Hearing aid, digitally programmable analog, monaural, CIC   E1
BETOS: O1F   Hearing and speech services
Service not separately priced by Part B
Statute: 1862A7
Coding Clinic: 2002, Q1

S V5245 Hearing aid, digitally programmable, analog, monaural, ITC   E1
BETOS: O1F   Hearing and speech services
Service not separately priced by Part B
Statute: 1862A7
Coding Clinic: 2002, Q1

S V5246 Hearing aid, digitally programmable analog, monaural, ITE (in the ear)   E1
BETOS: O1F   Hearing and speech services
Service not separately priced by Part B
Statute: 1862A7
Coding Clinic: 2002, Q1

S V5247 Hearing aid, digitally programmable analog, monaural, BTE (behind the ear)   E1
BETOS: O1F   Hearing and speech services

Service not separately priced by Part B
Statute: 1862A7
Coding Clinic: 2002, Q1

S V5248 Hearing aid, analog, binaural, CIC   E1
BETOS: O1F   Hearing and speech services
Service not separately priced by Part B
Statute: 1862A7
Coding Clinic: 2002, Q1

S V5249 Hearing aid, analog, binaural, ITC   E1
BETOS: O1F   Hearing and speech services
Service not separately priced by Part B
Statute: 1862A7
Coding Clinic: 2002, Q1

S V5250 Hearing aid, digitally programmable analog, binaural, CIC   E1
BETOS: O1F   Hearing and speech services
Service not separately priced by Part B
Statute: 1862A7
Coding Clinic: 2002, Q1

S V5251 Hearing aid, digitally programmable analog, binaural, ITC   E1
BETOS: O1F   Hearing and speech services
Service not separately priced by Part B
Statute: 1862A7
Coding Clinic: 2002, Q1

S V5252 Hearing aid, digitally programmable, binaural, ITE   E1
BETOS: O1F   Hearing and speech services
Service not separately priced by Part B
Statute: 1862A7
Coding Clinic: 2002, Q1

S V5253 Hearing aid, digitally programmable, binaural, BTE   E1
BETOS: O1F   Hearing and speech services
Service not separately priced by Part B
Statute: 1862A7
Coding Clinic: 2002, Q1

S V5254 Hearing aid, digital, monaural, CIC   E1
BETOS: O1F   Hearing and speech services
Service not separately priced by Part B
Statute: 1862A7
Coding Clinic: 2002, Q1

S V5255 Hearing aid, digital, monaural, ITC   E1
BETOS: O1F   Hearing and speech services
Service not separately priced by Part B
Statute: 1862A7
Coding Clinic: 2002, Q1

S V5256 Hearing aid, digital, monaural, ITE   E1
BETOS: O1F   Hearing and speech services
Service not separately priced by Part B
Statute: 1862A7
Coding Clinic: 2002, Q1

S V5257 Hearing aid, digital, monaural, BTE   E1
BETOS: O1F   Hearing and speech services
Service not separately priced by Part B

▲ Revised code   ● New code   **C** Carrier judgment   **D** Special coverage instructions apply
I Not payable by Medicare   **M** Non-covered by Medicare   **S** Non-covered by Medicare statute   AHA Coding Clinic®

Statute: 1862A7
Coding Clinic: 2002, Q1

S **V5258** Hearing aid, digital, binaural, CIC   E1
BETOS: O1F   Hearing and speech services
Service not separately priced by Part B
Statute: 1862A7
Coding Clinic: 2002, Q1

S **V5259** Hearing aid, digital, binaural, ITC   E1
BETOS: O1F   Hearing and speech services
Service not separately priced by Part B
Statute: 1862A7
Coding Clinic: 2002, Q1

S **V5260** Hearing aid, digital, binaural, ITE   E1
BETOS: O1F   Hearing and speech services
Service not separately priced by Part B
Statute: 1862A7
Coding Clinic: 2002, Q1

S **V5261** Hearing aid, digital, binaural, BTE   E1
BETOS: O1F   Hearing and speech services
Service not separately priced by Part B
Statute: 1862A7
Coding Clinic: 2002, Q1

S **V5262** Hearing aid, disposable, any type,
monaural   E1
BETOS: O1F   Hearing and speech services
Service not separately priced by Part B
Statute: 1862A7
Coding Clinic: 2002, Q1

S **V5263** Hearing aid, disposable, any type,
binaural   E1
BETOS: O1F   Hearing and speech services
Service not separately priced by Part B
Statute: 1862A7
Coding Clinic: 2002, Q1

S **V5264** Ear mold/insert, not disposable, any type   E1
BETOS: O1F   Hearing and speech services
Service not separately priced by Part B
Statute: 1862A7
Coding Clinic: 2002, Q1

S **V5265** Ear mold/insert, disposable, any type   E1
BETOS: O1F   Hearing and speech services
Service not separately priced by Part B
Statute: 1862A7
Coding Clinic: 2002, Q1

S **V5266** Battery for use in hearing device   E1
BETOS: O1F   Hearing and speech services
Service not separately priced by Part B
Statute: 1862A7
Coding Clinic: 2002, Q1

S **V5267** Hearing aid or assistive listening device/
supplies/accessories, not
otherwise specified   E1
BETOS: O1F   Hearing and speech services
Service not separately priced by Part B
Statute: 1862A7
Coding Clinic: 2002, Q1

ASSISTIVE HEARING DEVICES (V5268-V5290)

S **V5268** Assistive listening device, telephone
amplifier, any type   E1
BETOS: O1F   Hearing and speech services
Service not separately priced by Part B
Statute: 1862A7
Coding Clinic: 2002, Q1

S **V5269** Assistive listening device, alerting,
any type   E1
BETOS: O1F   Hearing and speech services
Service not separately priced by Part B
Statute: 1862A7
Coding Clinic: 2002, Q1

S **V5270** Assistive listening device, television
amplifier, any type   E1
BETOS: O1F   Hearing and speech services
Service not separately priced by Part B
Statute: 1862A7
Coding Clinic: 2002, Q1

S **V5271** Assistive listening device, television caption
decoder   E1
BETOS: O1F   Hearing and speech services
Service not separately priced by Part B
Statute: 1862A7
Coding Clinic: 2002, Q1

S **V5272** Assistive listening device, TDD   E1
BETOS: O1F   Hearing and speech services
Service not separately priced by Part B
Statute: 1862A7
Coding Clinic: 2002, Q1

S **V5273** Assistive listening device, for use with
cochlear implant   E1
BETOS: O1F   Hearing and speech services
Service not separately priced by Part B
Statute: 1862A7
Coding Clinic: 2002, Q1

S **V5274** Assistive listening device, not otherwise
specified   E1
BETOS: O1F   Hearing and speech services
Service not separately priced by Part B
Statute: 1862A7
Coding Clinic: 2002, Q1

S **V5275** Ear impression, each   E1
BETOS: O1F   Hearing and speech services
Service not separately priced by Part B
Statute: 1862A7
Coding Clinic: 2002, Q1

S **V5281** Assistive listening device, personal FM/DM
system, monaural, (1 receiver, transmitter,
microphone), any type   E1
BETOS: O1F   Hearing and speech services
Service not separately priced by Part B
Statute: 1862a7

S **V5282** Assistive listening device, personal FM/DM
system, binaural, (2 receivers, transmitter,
microphone), any type   E1

BETOS: O1F   Hearing and speech services
Service not separately priced by Part B
Statute: 1862a7

S V5283 Assistive listening device, personal FM/DM neck, loop induction receiver   E1
BETOS: O1F   Hearing and speech services
Service not separately priced by Part B
Statute: 1862a7

S V5284 Assistive listening device, personal FM/DM, ear level receiver   E1
BETOS: O1F   Hearing and speech services
Service not separately priced by Part B
Statute: 1862a7

S V5285 Assistive listening device, personal FM/DM, direct audio input receiver   E1
BETOS: O1F   Hearing and speech services
Service not separately priced by Part B
Statute: 1862a7

S V5286 Assistive listening device, personal blue tooth FM/DM receiver   E1
BETOS: O1F   Hearing and speech services
Service not separately priced by Part B
Statute: 1862a7

S V5287 Assistive listening device, personal FM/DM receiver, not otherwise specified   E1
BETOS: O1F   Hearing and speech services
Service not separately priced by Part B
Statute: 1862a7

S V5288 Assistive listening device, personal FM/DM transmitter assistive listening device   E1
BETOS: O1F   Hearing and speech services
Service not separately priced by Part B
Statute: 1862a7

S V5289 Assistive listening device, personal FM/DM adapter/boot coupling device for receiver, any type   E1
BETOS: O1F   Hearing and speech services
Service not separately priced by Part B
Statute: 1862a7

S V5290 Assistive listening device, transmitter microphone, any type   E1
BETOS: O1F   Hearing and speech services
Service not separately priced by Part B
Statute: 1862a7

OTHER AND MISCELLANEOUS HEARING SERVICES AND SUPPLIES (V5298, V5299)

S V5298 Hearing aid, not otherwise classified   E1
BETOS: O1F   Hearing and speech services
Service not separately priced by Part B
Statute: 1862A7

D V5299 Hearing service, miscellaneous   B
BETOS: O1F   Hearing and speech services
Price established by carriers

SPEECH-RELATED SCREENINGS AND COMMUNICATION DEVICE REPAIR (V5336-V5364)

S V5336 Repair/modification of augmentative communicative system or device (excludes adaptive hearing aid)   E1
BETOS: O1F   Hearing and speech services
Service not separately priced by Part B
Statute: 1862A7

S V5362 Speech screening   E1
BETOS: O1F   Hearing and speech services
Service not separately priced by Part B
Statute: 1862(a)(7)

S V5363 Language screening   E1
BETOS: O1F   Hearing and speech services
Service not separately priced by Part B
Statute: 1862(a)(7)

S V5364 Dysphagia screening   E1
BETOS: O1F   Hearing and speech services
Service not separately priced by Part B
Statute: 1862(a)(7)

NOTES

NOTES

Appendix A: Table of Drugs and Biologicals

Generic and brand-name drugs found throughout the Table of Drugs are from the latest CMS updates and have also been validated for accuracy. Please check the CMS website and the FDA website for the most up-to-date information on coverage and validity of drugs.

Caution: Never code directly from the Table of Drugs and Biologicals. Always cross-reference the code to the Tabular List before final code assignment.

Questions regarding coding and billing guidance should be submitted to the insurer in whose jurisdiction a claim would be filed. For private sector health insurance systems, please contact the individual private insurance entity. For Medicaid systems, please contact the Medicaid Agency in the state in which the claim is being filed. For Medicare, contact the Medicare contractor.

IA - Intra-arterial administration
IV - Intravenous administration
IM - Intramuscular administration

IT - Intrathecal
SC - Subcutaneous administration
INH - Administration by inhaled solution

VAR - Various routes of administration
OTH - Other routes of administration
ORAL - Administered orally

Intravenous administration includes all methods, such as gravity infusion, injections, and timed pushes into blood vessels, usually veins. IM refers to injections into muscles; IT to injections into the spinal column; and SC injections into tissues (not muscle) under the skin. The 'VAR' posting denotes various routes of administration and is used for drugs that are commonly administered into joints, cavities, tissues, or topical applications, in addition to other parenteral administrations. Listings posted with 'OTH' indicate other administration methods, such as intraocular injections, suppositories or catheter injections.

DRUG NAME	UNIT PER	ROUTE	CODE
A.P.L.®, *SEE* CHORIONIC GONADOTROPIN	-	-	-
ABATACEPT	10 mg	IV	J0129
ABBOKINASE®, *SEE* UROKINASE	-	-	-
ABCIXIMAB	10 mg	IV	J0130
ABELCET®	10 mg	IV	J0287
ABILIFY MAINTENA®	1 mg	IM	J0401
ABLC, *SEE* AMPHOTERICIN B	-	-	-
ABOBOTULINUM TYPE A	5 units	IM	J0586
ACCUNEB®	1 mg	INH	J7611
ACCUNEB®	1 mg	INH	J7613
ACEPHEN®	10 mg	IV	J0131
ACETADOTE®	100 mg	IV	J0132
ACETAMINOPHEN	10 mg	IV	J0131
ACETAZOLAMIDE SODIUM	up to 500 mg	IM, IV	J1120
ACETYLCYSTEINE, INJECTION	100 mg	IV	J0132
ACETYLCYSTEINE, UNIT DOSE FORM	per gram	INH	J7604, J7608
ACHROMYCIN®, *SEE* TETRACYCLINE	-	-	-
ACLASTA®	1 mg	IV	J3489
ACTAMIN®	10 mg	IV	J0131
ACTEMRA®	1 mg	IV	J3262
ACTH GEL®	up to 40 units	IV, IM, SC	J0800
ACTH-40 HP®	up to 40 units	IV, IM, SC	J0800
ACTH-80®	up to 40 units	IV, IM, SC	J0800
ACTHAR GEL®	up to 40 units	IV, IM, SC	J0800
ACTHAR®	up to 40 units	IV, IM, SC	J0800
ACTHREL®	1 mcg	IM	J0795
ACTIMMUNE®	3 million units	SC	J9216
ACTIVASE®	1 mg	IV	J2997
ACYCLOVIR	5 mg	VAR, IV	J0133
ACYS-5®	100 mg	IV	J0132
ACYS-5®	per gram	INH	J7608

DRUG NAME	UNIT PER	ROUTE	CODE
ADAGEN®	25 IU	IM	J2504
ADALIMUMAB	20 mg	SC	J0135
ADBEON®	per 3 mg	IM	J0702
ADCETRIS®	1 mg	IV	J9042
ADENOCARD®	1 mg	IV	J0153
ADENOSCAN®	1 mg	IV	J0153
ADENOSINE	1 mg	IV	J0153
ADO-TRASTUZUMAB EMTANSINE	1 mg	IV	J9354
ADRENACLICK TWO-PACK®	0.1 mg	SC, IM	J0171
ADRENALIN CHLORIDE®, *SEE* ADRENALIN, EPINEPHRINE	-	-	-
ADRENALIN®	0.1 mg	SC, IM	J0171
ADRENALIN, EPINEPHRINE	0.1 mg	SC, IM	J0171
ADRIAMYCIN PFS®	10 mg	IV	J9000
ADRIAMYCIN PFS®, *SEE* DOXORUBICIN HCL	-	-	-
ADRIAMYCIN RDF®	10 mg	IV	J9000
ADRIAMYCIN RDF®, *SEE* DOXORUBICIN HCL	-	-	-
ADRIAMYCIN®	10 mg	IV	J9000
ADRUCIL®	500 mg	IV	J9190
ADRUCIL®, *SEE* FLUOROURACIL	-	-	-
ADYNOVATE®	1 IU	IV	J7207
ADVATE®	per IU	IV	J7185
ADVATE®	per IU	IV	J7192
AEROLATE III®	per 40 mg	IV	J2810
AEROLATE JR®	per 40 mg	IV	J2810
AEROLATE SR®	per 40 mg	IV	J2810
AFLIBERCEPT	1 mg	OTH	J0178
AGALSIDASE BETA	1 mg	IV	J0180
AGGRASTAT®	0.25 mg	IM, IV	J3246
AGGRASTAT®, *SEE* TIROFIBAN HYDROCHLORIDE	-	-	-
A-HYDROCORT®, *SEE* HYDROCORTISONE SODIUM PHOSPHATE	-	-	-
AKINETON®, *SEE* BIPERIDEN LACTATE	-	-	-

DRUG NAME	UNIT PER	ROUTE	CODE
ALATROFLOXACIN MESYLATE, INJECTION	100 mg	IV	J0200
ALBUTEROL	0.5 mg	INH	J7620
ALBUTEROL, CONCENTRATED FORM	1 mg	INH	J7610, J7611
ALBUTEROL, UNIT DOSE FORM	1 mg	INH	J7609, J7613
ALDESLEUKIN	per single use vial	IM, IV	J9015
ALDURAZYME®	0.1 mg	IV	J1931
ALEFACEPT	0.5 mg	IM, IV	J0215
ALFERON N®	250, 000 IU	IM	J9215
ALFERON N®, SEE INTERFERON ALFA-N3 (HUMAN LEUKOVYTE DERIVED)	-	-	-
ALGLUCERASE	per 10 units	IV	J0205
ALGLUCOSIDASE ALFA	10 mg	IV	J0220, J0221
ALIMTA®	10 mg	IV	J9305
ALKABAN-AQ®, SEE VINBLASTINE SULFATE	-	-	-
ALKERAN®	2 mg	ORAL	J8600
ALKERAN®	50 mg	IV	J9245
ALKERAN®, SEE MELPHALAN, ORAL	-	-	-
ALLERMAX®	50 mg	ORAL	Q0163
ALOXI®	25 mcg	IV	J2469
ALPHA 1-PROTEINASE INHIBITOR, HUMAN	10 mg	IV	J0256, J0257
ALPHANATE®	PER FACTOR VIII IU	IV	J7186
ALPHANINE SD	per 1 IU	IV	J7194
ALPROLIX	1 IU	IV	J7201
ALPROSTADIL, INJECTION	1.25 mcg	OTH	J0270
ALPROSTADIL, URETHRAL SUPPOSITORY	each	OTH	J0275
ALSUMA®	6 mg	SC	J3030
ALTEPLASE RECOMBINANT	1 mg	IV	J2997
ALUPENT®	10 mg	OTH, INH	J7668
ALUPENT®	10 mg	OTH	J7669
ALUPENT®, SEE METAPROTERENOL SULFATE OR METAPROTERENOL, COMPOUNDED	-	-	-
AMBISOME®	10 mg	IV	J0289
AMCORT®, SEE TRIAMCINOLONE DIACETATE	-	-	-
AMELUZ®	10 mg	OTH	J7345
A-METHAPRED®, SEE METHYLPREDNISOLONE SODIUM SUCCINATE	-	-	-

DRUG NAME	UNIT PER	ROUTE	CODE
AMEVIVE®	0.5 mg	IM, IV	J0215
AMGEN®, SEE INTERFERON ALPHACON-1 RECOMBINANT	-	-	-
AMIFOSTINE	500 mg	IV	J0207
AMIKACIN SULFATE	100 mg	INJ	J0278
AMIKIN PEDIATRIC®	100 mg	INJ	J0278
AMIKIN®	100 mg	INJ	J0278
AMINOLEVULINATE	1 gm	OTH	J7309
AMINOLEVULINIC ACID HCL	unit dose (354 mg)	OTH	J7308
AMINOLEVULINIC ACID HCL, 10% GEL	10 mg	OTH	J7345
AMINOPHYLLINE/AMINOPHYLLIN	up to 250 mg	IV	J0280
AMIODARONE HCL	30 mg	IV	J0282
AMITRIPTYLINE HCL	up to 20 mg	IM	J1320
AMOBARBITAL	up to 125 mg	IM, IV	J0300
AMPHADASE®	up to 150 units	SC, IV	J3470
AMPHOCIN®	50 mg	IV	J0285
AMPHOCIN®, SEE AMPHOTERICIN B	-	-	-
AMPHOTEC®	10 mg	IV	J0288
AMPHOTERICIN B	50 mg	IV	J0285
AMPHOTERICIN B, LIPID COMPLEX	10 mg	IV	J0287, J0289
AMPICILLIN SODIUM	up to 500 mg	IM, IV	J0290
AMPICILLIN SODIUM/SULBACTAM SODIUM	per 1.5 gm	IM, IV	J0295
AMYTAL®	up to 125 mg	IM, IV	J0300
AMYTAL®, SEE AMOBARBITAL	-	-	-
ANABOLIN LA 100®, SEE NANDROLONE DECANOATE	-	-	-
ANASCORP®	up to 120 mg	IV	J0716
ANASCORP®, SEE CENTRUROIDES IMMUNE F(AB)	-	-	-
ANASPAZ®	up to 0.25 mg	SC, IM, IV	J1980
ANCEF®	500 mg	IV, IM	J0690
ANCEF®, SEE CEFAZOLIN SODIUM	-	-	-
ANDREST 90-4®, SEE TESTOSTERONE ENANTHATE AND ESTRADIOL VALERATE	-	-	-
ANDRO L.A. 200®, SEE TESTOSTERONE ENANTHATE	-	-	-
ANDRO/FEM®, SEE TESTOSTERONE CYPIONATE AND ESTRADIOL CYPIONATE	-	-	-
ANDRO-CYP®, SEE TESTOSTERONE CYPIONATE	-	-	-

DRUG NAME	UNIT PER	ROUTE	CODE
ANDRO-CYP 200®, *SEE* TESTOSTERONE CYPIONATE	-	-	-
ANDRO-ESTRO 90-4®, *SEE* TESTOSTERONE ENANTHATE AND ESTRADIOL VALERATE	-	-	-
ANDROGYN L.A.®, *SEE* TESTOSTERONE ENANTHATE AND ESTRADIOL VALERATE	-	-	-
ANDROLONE-D 100®, *SEE* NANDROLONE DECANOATE	-	-	-
ANDRONAQ-LA®, *SEE* TESTOSTERONE CYPIONATE	-	-	-
ANDRONATE-100®, *SEE* TESTOSTERONE CYPIONATE	-	-	-
ANDRONATE-200®, *SEE* TESTOSTERONE CYPIONATE	-	-	-
ANDROPOSITORY 100®, *SEE* TESTOSTERONE ENANTHATE	-	-	-
ANDRYL 200®, *SEE* TESTOSTERONE ENANTHATE	-	-	-
ANECTINE®	up to 20 mg	IV, IM	J0330
ANECTINE®, *SEE* SUCCINYLCHOLINE CHLORIDE	-	-	-
ANERGAN 25®, *SEE* PROMETHAZINE HCL	-	-	-
ANERGAN 50®, *SEE* PROMETHAZINE HCL	-	-	-
ANESTACAINE®	10 mg	IV	J2001
ANGIOMAX®	1 mg	IV	J0583
ANIDULAFUNGIN	1 mg	IV	J0348
ANISTREPLASE	30 units	IV	J0350
ANTI D (RHO) IMMUNOGLOBULIN®	50 mg	IM	J2788
ANTI D (RHO) IMMUNOGLOBULIN®	1 dose package, 300 mcg	IM	J2790
ANTIFLEX®	up to 60 mg	IV, IM	J2360
ANTI-INHIBITOR	per IU	IV	J7198
ANTISPAS®, *SEE* DICYCLOMINE HCL	-	-	-
ANTITHROMBIN III (HUMAN)	per IU	IV	J7197
ANTITHROMBIN RECOMBINANT	50 IU	IV	J7196
ANTIZOL®	15 mg	INJ	J1451
ANX®	25 mg	ORAL	Q0177
ANZEMET®	10 mg	IV	J1260
ANZEMET®	100 mg	ORAL	Q0180
ANZEMET®, *SEE* DOLASETRON MESYLATE INJECTION	-	-	-
APOKYN®	1 mg	SC	J0364
APOMORPHINE HYDROCHLORIDE	1 mg	SC	J0364
APRESOLINE®	up to 20 mg	IV, IM	J0360
APRESOLINE®, *SEE* HYDRALAZINE HCL	-	-	-

DRUG NAME	UNIT PER	ROUTE	CODE
APROTININ	10, 000 kiu	INJ	J0365
AQUAMEPHYTON®, *SEE* VITAMIN K	-	-	-
AQUAPHYLLIN®	per 40 mg	IV	J2810
ARALAST NP®	10 mg	IV	J0256
ARALAST®	10 mg	IV	J0256
ARALEN®	up to 250 mg	IM	J0390
ARALEN®, *SEE* CHLOROQUINE HCL	-	-	-
ARAMINE®, *SEE* METARAMINOL BITARTRATE	-	-	-
ARANESP ALBUMIN FREE® (NON-ESRD)	1 mcg	IV, SC	J0881
ARANESP ALBUMIN FREE® (FOR ESRD)	1 mcg	IV, SC	J0882
ARANESP SURECLICK® (NON-ESRD)	1 mcg	IV, SC	J0881
ARANESP SURECLICK® (FOR ESRD)	1 mcg	IV, SC	J0882
ARANESP® (NON-ESRD)	1 mcg	IV, SC	J0881
ARANESP® (FOR ESRD)	1 mcg	IV, SC	J0882
ARBUTAMINE	1 mg	IV	J0395
ARCALYST®	1 mg	SC	J2793
AREDIA®	per 30 mg	IV	J2430
AREDIA®, *SEE* PAMIDRONATE DISODIUM	-	-	-
ARFORMOTEROL TARTRATE	15 mcg	INH	J7605
ARGATROBAN (NON-ESRD USE)	1 mg	IV	J0883
ARGATROBAN (ESRD)	1 mg	IV	J0884
ARIDOL®	5 mg	INH	J7665
ARIDOL®, *SEE* MANNITOL	-	-	-
ARIPIPRAZOLE	0.25 mg	IM	J0400
ARIPIPRAZOLE, EXTENDED RELEASE	1 mg	INJ	J0401
ARIPIPRAZOLE LAUROXIL	1 mg	IM	J1942
ARISTADA®	1 mg	IM	J1942
ARISTOCORT FORTE®, *SEE* TRIAMCINOLONE DIACETATE	-	-	-
ARISTOCORT INTRALESIONAL®, *SEE* TRIAMCINOLONE DIACETATE	-	-	-
ARISTOCORT®	1 mg	INJ	J3300
ARISTOCORT®	per 10 mg	IM	J3301
ARISTOCORT®	per 5 mg	IM	J3302
ARISTOCORT®	per 5 mg	VAR	J3303
ARISTOSPAN INTRA-ARTICULAR®, *SEE* TRIAMCINOLONE HEXACETONIDE	-	-	-
ARISTOSPAN INTRALESIONAL®, *SEE* TRIAMCINOLONE HEXACETONIDE	-	-	-
ARIXTRA®	0.5 mg	SC	J1652
ARRANON®	50 mg	IV	J9261
APREPITANT	5 mg	Oral	J8501
ARRESTIN®, *SEE* TRIMETHOBENZAMIDE HCL	-	-	-
ARSENIC TRIOXIDE	1 mg	IV	J9017
ARZERRA®	10 mg	IV	J9302

DRUG NAME	UNIT PER	ROUTE	CODE
ARZERRA®, *SEE* OFATUMUMAB	-	-	-
ASPARAGINASE	1, 000 units	IV, IM	J9019
ASPARAGINASE	10, 000 units	IM	J9020
ASTAGRAF XL®	0.1 mg	ORAL	J7508
ASTRAMORPH PF®, *SEE* MORPHINE SULFATE	-	-	-
ATARAX®	up to 25 mg	IM	J3410
ATARAX®	25 mg	ORAL	Q0177
ATEZOLIZUMAB	10 mg	IV	J9022
ATGAM®	250 mg	IV	J7504
ATGAM®, *SEE* LYMPHOCYTE IMMUNE GLOBULIN	-	-	-
ATIVAN®	2 mg	IM, IV	J2060
ATIVAN®, *SEE* LORAZEPAM	-	-	-
ATREZA®	0.01 mg	IV, IM, SC	J0461
ATROPEN®	0.01 mg	IV, IM, SC	J0461
ATROPINE SULFATE	0.01 mg	IV, IM, SC	J0461
ATROPINE, CONCENTRATED FORM	per mg	INH	J7635
ATROPINE, UNIT DOSE FORM	per mg	INH	J7636
ATROVENT HFA®	per mg	INH	J7644
ATROVENT®	per mg	INH	J7644
ATROVENT®, *SEE* IPRATROPIUM BROMIDE	-	-	-
ATRYN®	per IU	IV	J7196
ATRYN®, *SEE* ANTITHROMBIN RECOMBINANT	-	-	-
AUROTHIOGLUCOSE	up to 50 mg	IM	J2910
AUTOLOGOUS CULTURED CHONDROCYTES IMPLANT	each	OTH	J7330
AUTOPLEX T®	per IU	IV	J7198
AUTOPLEX T®, *SEE* HEMOPHILIA CLOTTING FACTORS	-	-	-
AUVI-Q®	0.1 mg	SC, IM	J0171
AVASTIN®	10 mg	IV	J9035
AVEED®	1 mg	IM	J3145
AVELOX I.V®	100 mg	IV	J2280
AVELOX®	100 mg	IV	J2280
AVELUMAB	10 mg	IV	J9023
AVONEX®, *SEE* INTERFERON BETA-1A	-	-	-
AXUMIN®	1 mCi	-	A9588
AZACITIDINE	1 mg	SC	J9025
AZASAN®	50 mg	ORAL	J7500
AZASAN®	100 mg	IV	J7501
AZATHIOPRINE	50 mg	ORAL	J7500
AZATHIOPRINE, PARENTERAL	100 mg	IV	J7501
AZITHROMYCIN 3 DAY DOSE PACK®	500 mg	IV	J0456
AZITHROMYCIN 3 DAY DOSE PACK®	1 gm	ORAL	Q0144

DRUG NAME	UNIT PER	ROUTE	CODE
AZITHROMYCIN 5 DAY DOSE PACK®	500 mg	IV	J0456
AZITHROMYCIN 5 DAY DOSE PACK®	1 gm	ORAL	Q0144
AZITHROMYCIN, DIHYDRATE	1 gm	ORAL	Q0144
AZITHROMYCIN, INJECTION	500 mg	IV	J0456
AZTREONAM	500 mg	IV, IM	S0073
BACLOFEN	10 mg	IT	J0475
BACLOFEN FOR INTRATHECAL TRIAL	50 mcg	OTH	J0476
BACTOCILL®	up to 250 mg	IM, IV	J2700
BACTOCILL®, *SEE* OXACILLIN SODIUM	-	-	-
BAL IN OIL®	per 100 mg	IM	J0470
BAL IN OIL®, *SEE* DIMERCAPROL	-	-	-
BANFLEX®	up to 60 mg	IV, IM	J2360
BANFLEX®, *SEE* ORPHENADRINE CITRATE	-	-	-
BANOPHEN®	50 mg	ORAL	Q0163
BASILIXIMAB	20 mg	IV	J0480
BAYCADRON ELIXER®	0.25 mg	ORAL	J8540
BAYCADRON®	1 mg	IM	J1094
BAYRHO D FULL DOSE®	1 dose package, 300 mcg	IM	J2790
BAYRHO D MINI-DOSE®	50 mg	IM	J2788
BAYTET®	up to 250 units	IM	J1670
BCG (BACILLUS CALMETTE AND GUÉRIN), LIVE	per vial instillation	IV	J9031
BEBULIN VH®	per IU	IV	J7194
BEBULIN®	per IU	IV	J7194
BECLOMETHASONE INHALATION SOLUTION, UNIT DOSE FORM	per mg	INH	J7622
BELATACEPT	1 mg	IV	J0485
BELEODAQ®	10 mg	IV	J9032
BELIMUMAB	10 mg	IV	J0490
BELINOSTAT	10 mg	IV	J9032
BENA-D 10®, *SEE* DIPHENHYDRAMINE HCL	-	-	-
BENA-D 50®, *SEE* DIPHENHYDRAMINE HCL	-	-	-
BENADRYL®	50 mg	ORAL	Q0163
BENADRYL®, *SEE* DIPHENHYDRAMINE HCL	-	-	-
BENAHIST 10®, *SEE* DIPHENHYDRAMINE HCL	-	-	-
BENAHIST 50®, *SEE* DIPHENHYDRAMINE HCL	-	-	-
BEN-ALLERGIN-50®, *SEE* DIPHENHYDRAMINE HCL	-	-	-
BENDAMUSTINE HCL	1 mg	IV	J9033, J9034
BENDEKA®	1 mg	IV	J9034

DRUG NAME	UNIT PER	ROUTE	CODE
BENEFIX®	per IU	IV	J7195
BENLYSTA®	10 mg	IV	J0490
BENLYSTA®, SEE BELIMUMAB	-	-	-
BENOJECT-10®, SEE DIPHENHYDRAMINE HCL	-	-	-
BENOJECT-50®, SEE DIPHENHYDRAMINE HCL	-	-	-
BENTYL®	up to 20 mg	IM	J0500
BENTYL®, SEE DICYCLOMINE HCL	-	-	-
BENZACOT®	up to 200 mg	IM	J3250
BENZACOT®	250 mg	ORAL	Q0173
BENZTROPINE MESYLATE	per 1 mg	IM, IV	J0515
BERINERT®	10 units	IV	J0597
BERUBIGEN®, SEE VITAMIN B-12 CYANOCOBALAMIN	-	-	-
BETA PHOS AC®	per 3 mg	IM	J0702
BETALIN 12®, SEE VITAMIN B-12 CYANOCOBALAMIN	-	-	-
BETAMETHASONE ACETATE & BETAMETHASONE SODIUM PHOSPHATE	per 3 mg	IM	J0702
BETAMETHASONE INHALATION SOLUTION, UNIT DOSE FORM	per mg	INH	J7624
BETASERON®	0.25 mg	SC	J1830
BETASERON®, SEE INTERFERON BETA-1B	-	-	-
BETHANECHOL CHLORIDE	up to 5 mg	SC	J0520
BETHKIS®	300 mg	INH	J7682
BEVACIZUMAB	10 mg	IV	J9035
BEZLOTOXUMAB	10 mg	IV	J0565
BICILLIN C-R 900/300®, SEE PENICILLIN G PROCAINE AND PENICILLIN G BENZATHINE	-	-	-
BICILLIN C-R®, SEE PENICILLIN G BENZATHINE AND PENICILLIN G PROCAINE	-	-	-
BICILLIN C-R.	100, 000 units	IM	J0558
BICILLIN L-A®, SEE PENICILLIN G BENZATHINE	-	-	-
BICILLIN L-A.	100, 000 units	IM	J0561
BICNU®	100 mg	IV	J9050
BICNU®, SEE CARMUSTINE	-	-	-
BIPERIDEN LACTATE	per 5 mg	IM, IV	J0190
BITOLTEROL MESYLATE, CONCENTRATED FORM	per mg	INH	J7628
BITOLTEROL MESYLATE, UNIT DOSE FORM	per mg	INH	J7629

DRUG NAME	UNIT PER	ROUTE	CODE
BIVALIRUDIN	1 mg	IV	J0583
BIVIGAM®	500 mg	IV	J1556
BLENOXANE®, SEE BLEOMYCIN SULFATE	-	-	-
BLEOMYCIN SULFATE	15 units	IM, IV, SC	J9040
BLINATUMOMAB	1 microgram	IV	J9039
BLOXIVERZ®	up to 0.5 mg	IM, IV, SC	J2710
BONDRONAT®	1 mg	IV	J1740
BONIVA®	1 mg	IV	J1740
BORTEZOMIB	0.1 mg	IV	J9041
BOTOX COSMETIC®	1 unit	IM	J0585
BOTOX®	1 unit	IM	J0585
BOTOX®, SEE ONABOTULINUMTOXINA	-	-	-
BRAVELLE®	75 IU	OTH	J3355
BRENTUXIMAB VEDOTIN	1 mg	IV	J9042
BRETHINE®, SEE TERBUTALINE SULFATE	-	-	-
BRICANYL SUBCUTANEOUS®, SEE TERBUTALINE SULFATE	-	-	-
BROMPHENIRAMINE MALEATE	per 10 mg	IM, SC, IV	J0945
BRONKOSOL®, SEE ALSO ISOETHARINE HCL	-	-	-
BROVANA®	15 mcg	INH	J7605
BUDESONIDE INHALATION SOLUTION, CONCENTRATED FORM	0.25 mg	INH	J7633, J7634
BUDESONIDE INHALATION SOLUTION, UNIT DOSE FORM	0.5 mg	INH	J7626, J7627
BUNAVAIL®	<=3 mg	ORAL	J0572
BUNAVAIL®	>3 mg but <=6 mg	ORAL	J0573
BUNAVAIL®	>6 mg but <=10 mg	ORAL	J0574
BUNAVAIL®	>10 mg	ORAL	J0575
BUPRENEX®	1 mg	ORAL	J0571
BUPRENEX®	0.1 mg	IM	J0592
BUPRENORPHINE	74.2 mg	Implant	J0570
BUPRENORPHINE HYDROCHLORIDE	0.1 mg	IM	J0592
BUPRENORPHINE/NALOXONE	1 mg	ORAL	J0571
BUPRENORPHINE/NALOXONE	<=3 mg	ORAL	J0572
BUPRENORPHINE/NALOXONE	>3 mg but <=6 mg	ORAL	J0573
BUPRENORPHINE/NALOXONE	>6 mg but <=10 mg	ORAL	J0574
BUPRENORPHINE/NALOXONE	>10 mg	ORAL	J0575
BUSULFAN	1 mg	IV	J0594
BUSULFAN	2 mg	ORAL	J8510
BUSULFEX®	1 mg	IV	J0594

DRUG NAME	UNIT PER	ROUTE	CODE
BUSULFEX®	2 mg	ORAL	J8510
BUTORPHANOL TARTRATE	1 mg	IM	J0595
C1 ESTERASE INHIBITOR	10 units	IV	J0596-J0598
CABAZITAXEL	1 mg	IV	J9043
CABERGOLINE	0.25 mg	ORAL	J8515
CAFCIT®	5 mg	IV	J0706
CAFCIT®, SEE CAFFEINE CITRATE	-	-	-
CAFFEINE CITRATE	5 mg	IV	J0706
CAINE-1®, SEE LIDOCAINE HCL	-	-	-
CAINE-2®, SEE LIDOCAINE HCL	-	-	-
CALCIJEX®, SEE CALCITRIOL	-	-	-
CALCIMAR®, SEE CALCITONIN-SALMON	-	-	-
CALCITONIN-SALMON	up to 400 units	SC, IM	J0630
CALCITRIOL	0.1 mcg	IM	J0636
CALCIUM DISODIUM VERSENATE®, SEE EDETATE CALCIUM DISODIUM	-	-	-
CALCIUM DISODIUM VERSENATE.	up to 1000 mg	IV, SC, IM	J0600
CALCIUM GLUCONATE	per 10 ml	IV	J0610
CALCIUM GLYCEROPHOSPHATE & CALCIUM LACTATE	per 10 ml	IM, SC	J0620
CALDOLOR®	100 mg	IV	J1741
CALDOLOR®, SEE IBUPROFEN	-	-	-
CALPHOSAN®, SEE CALCIUM GLYCEROPHOSPHATE AND CALCIUM LACTATE	-	-	-
CAMPATH®	10 mg	IV	J0202
CAMPTOSAR®	20 mg	IV	J9206
CAMPTOSAR®, SEE IRINOTECAN	-	-	-
CANAKINUMAB	1 mg	SC	J0638
CANCIDAS®	5 mg	IV	J0637
CANGRELOR	1 mg	INJ	C9460
CAPECITABINE	150 mg	ORAL	J8520
CAPECITABINE	500 mg	ORAL	J8521
CAPITAL® W/CODINE	per 30 mg	IM, IV, SC	J0745
CAPSAICIN PATCH	per sq cm	OTH	J7336
CARBACOT®	up to 10 ml	IV, IM	J2800
CARBIDOPA/LEVODOPA	5 mg/20 mg	OTH	J7340
CARBOCAINE HCL®	per 10 ml	VAR	J0670
CARBOCAINE WITH NEO-COBEFRIN®, SEE MEPIVACAINE HCL	-	-	-
CARBOCAINE®	per 10 ml	VAR	J0670
CARBOCAINE®, SEE MEPIVACAINE	-	-	-
CARBOPLATIN	50 mg	IV	J9045

DRUG NAME	UNIT PER	ROUTE	CODE
CARBOPLATIN NOVAPLUS®	50 mg	IV	J9045
CARDOXIN®	up to 0.5 mg	IM, IV	J1160
CARFILZOMIB	1 mg	IV	J9047
CARMUSTINE	100 mg	IV	J9050
CARNITOR®	per 1 gm	IV	J1955
CARNITOR®, SEE LEVOCARNITINE	-	-	-
CARTICEL®	each	OTH	J7330
CARTICEL®, SEE AUTOLOGOUS CULTURED CHONDROCYTES	-	-	-
CASPOFUNGIN ACETATE	5 mg	IV	J0637
CATAPRES®	1 mg	epidural	J0735
CAVERJECT IMPULSE®	1.25 mcg	OTH	J0270
CAVERJECT®	1.25 mcg	OTH	J0270
CAYSTON®, SEE AZTREONAM	-	-	-
CEFADYL®, SEE CEPHAPIRIN SODIUM	-	-	-
CEFAZOLIN SODIUM	500 mg	IV, IM	J0690
CEFEPIME HYDROCHLORIDE	500 mg	IV	J0692
CEFIZOX®, SEE CEFTIZOXIME SODIUM	-	-	-
CEFOTAXIME SODIUM	per 1 g	IV, IM	J0698
CEFOXITIN SODIUM	1 g	IV, IM	J0694
CEFTAROLINE FOSAMIL	10 mg	INJ	J0712
CEFTAZIDIME	per 500 mg	IM, IV	J0713
CEFTAZIDIME AND AVIBACTAM	0.5 g/0.125 g	IV	J0714
CEFTIN®	per 750 mg	IM, IV	J0697
CEFTIZOXIME SODIUM	per 500 mg	IV, IM	J0715
CEFTOLOZANE 50 MG AND TAZOBACTAM 25 MG	-	IV	J0695
CEFTRIAXONE SODIUM	per 250 mg	IV, IM	J0696
CEFUROXIME SODIUM, STERILE	per 750 mg	IM, IV	J0697
CELESTONE PHOSPHATE®	per 3 mg	IM	J0702
CELESTONE SOLUSPAN®	per 3 mg	IM	J0702
CELESTONE SOLUSPAN®, SEE BETAMETHASONE ACETATE AND BETAMETHASONE SODIUM PHOSPHATE	-	-	-
CELESTONE®	per 3 mg	IM	J0702
CELLCEPT®	250 mg	ORAL	J7517
CENACORT A-40®, SEE TRIAMCINOLONE ACETONIDE	-	-	-
CENACORT FORTE®, SEE TRIAMCINOLONE DIACETATE	-	-	-
CENTRUROIDES IMMUNE F(AB)	up to 120 mg	IV	J0716

DRUG NAME	UNIT PER	ROUTE	CODE
CEPHALOTHIN SODIUM	up to 1 g	IM, IV	J1890
CEPHAPIRIN SODIUM	up to 1 g	IV, IM	J0710
CEPROTIN®	10 IU	IV	J2724
CEPTAZ®	per 500 mg	IM, IV	J0713
CEREBYX®	50 mg	IV	Q2009
CEREDASE®, SEE ALGLUCERASE	-	-	-
CEREZYME®	10 units	IV	J1786
CERTOLIZUMAB PEGOL	1 mg	SC	J0717
CERUBIDINE®	10 mg	IV	J9150
CERUBIDINE®, SEE DAUNORUBICIN HCL	-	-	-
CESAMET®	1 mg	ORAL	J8650
CETRAXAL®	6 mg	OTH	J7342
CETUXIMAB	10 mg	IV	J9055
CHEALAMIDE®, SEE ENDRATE ETHYLENEDIAMINE-TETRA-ACETIC ACID	-	-	-
CHLORAMPHENICOL SODIUM SUCCINATE	up to 1 g	IV	J0720
CHLORDIAZEPOXIDE HCL	up to 100 mg	IM, IV	J1990
CHLOROMYCETIN SODIUM SUCCINATE®	up to 1 g	IV	J0720
CHLOROMYCETIN SODIUM SUCCINATE®, SEE CHLORAMPHENICOL SODIUM SUCCINATE	-	-	-
CHLOROPROCAINE HCL	per 30 ml	VAR	J2400
CHLOROQUINE HCL	up to 250 mg	IM	J0390
CHLOROTHIAZIDE SODIUM	per 500 mg	IV	J1205
CHLORPROMAZINE HCL	5 mg	ORAL	Q0161
CHLORPROMAZINE HCL	up to 50 mg	IM, IV	J3230
CHOLINE C-11	up to 20 mCi	IV	A9515
CHOREX-5®, SEE CHORIONIC GONADOTROPIN	-	-	-
CHOREX-10®, SEE CHORIONIC GONADOTROPIN	-	-	-
CHORIGNON®, SEE CHORIONIC GONADOTROPIN	-	-	-
CHORIONIC GONADOTROPIN	per 1, 000 USP units	IM	J0725
CHORON 10®, SEE CHORIONIC GONADOTROPIN	-	-	-
CIDOFOVIR	375 mg	IV	J0740
CILASTATIN SODIUM, IMIPENEM	per 250 mg	IV, IM	J0743

DRUG NAME	UNIT PER	ROUTE	CODE
CINACALCET, ORAL (FOR ESRD ON DIALYSIS)	1 mg	ORAL	J0604
CIPROFLOXACIN OTIC SUSPENSION	6 mg	OTH	J7342
CIMZIA®	1 mg	SC	J0717
CIMZIA®, SEE CERTOLIZUMAB PEGOL	-	-	-
CINQAIR®	1 mg	IV	J2786
CINRYZE®	10 units	IV	J0598
CINRYZE®, SEE C1 ESTERASE INHIBITOR	-	-	-
CIPRO IV®, SEE CIPROFLOXACIN	-	-	-
CIPRO®	200 mg	IV	J0744
CIPRODEX®	6 mg	OTH	J7342
CIPROFLOXACIN	200 mg	IV	J0706
CISPLATIN, POWDER OR SOLUTION	per 10 mg	IV	J9060
CLADRIBINE	per mg	IV	J9065
CLADRIBINE NOVAPLUS®	per mg	IV	J9065
CLAFORAN®	per 1 g	IV, IM	J0698
CLEXANE FORTE®	10 mg	SC	J1650
CLEXANE®	10 mg	SC	J1650
CLOFARABINE	1 mg	IV	J9027
CLOLAR®	1 mg	IV	J9027
CLONIDINE HYDROCHLORIDE	1 mg	epidural	J0735
COAGADEX®	1 IU	IV	J7175
COBEX®, SEE VITAMIN B-12 CYANOCOBALAMIN	-	-	-
CODEINE PHOSPHATE	per 30 mg	IM, IV, SC	J0745
COGENTIN®	per 1 mg	IM, IV	J0515
COGENTIN®, SEE BENZTROPINE MESYLATE	-	-	-
COLISTIMETHATE SODIUM	up to 150 mg	IM, IV	J0770
COLLAGENASE, CLOSTRIDIUM HISTOLYTICUM	0.01 mg	OTH	J0775
COLY-MYCIN M®	up to 150 mg	IM, IV	J0770
COLY-MYCIN M®, SEE COLISTIMETHATE SODIUM	-	-	-
COMBIVENT RESPIMAT®	0.5 mg	INH	J7620
COMBIVENT®	0.5 mg	INH	J7620
COMPA-Z®, SEE PROCHLORPERAZINE	-	-	-
COMPAZINE®, SEE PROCHLORPERAZINE	-	-	-
COMPOUNDED DRUG, NOT OTHERWISE CLASSIFIED	-	-	J7999
COMPOZ NIGHTTIME SLEEP AID®	50 mg	ORAL	Q0163
COPAXONE®	20 mg	SC	J1595
COPPER CONTRACEPTIVE, INTRAUTERINE	each	OTH	J7300

DRUG NAME	UNIT PER	ROUTE	CODE
CORDARONE®	30 mg	IV	J0282
CORDARONE®, SEE AMIODARONE HCL	-	-	-
CORGONJECT-5®, SEE CHORIONIC GONADOTROPIN	-	-	-
CORTICORELIN OVINE TRIFLUTATE	1 mcg	IV	J0795
CORTICOTROPIN	up to 40 units	IV, IM, SC	J0800
CORVERT®	1 mg	IV	J1742
COSMEGEN®	0.5 mg	IV	J9120
COSMEGEN®, SEE DACTINOMYCIN	-	-	-
COSYNTROPIN	per 0.25 mg	IM, IV	J0833, J0834
COTOLONE®	up to 1 ml	IM	J2650
COTOLONE®	5 mg	ORAL	J7510
COTRANZINE®, SEE PROCHLORPERAZINE	-	-	-
CROFAB®	up to 1 gram	IV	J0840
CROFAB®, SEE CROTALIDAE POLYVALENT IMMUNE FAB	-	-	-
CROMOLYN SODIUM	per 10 mg	INH	J7631, J7632
CROTALIDAE POLYVALENT IMMUNE FAB	up to 1 gram	IV	J0840
CRYOSERV®	50%, 50 ml	OTH	J1212
CRYSTICILLIN 300 A.S.®, SEE PENICILLIN G PROCAINE	-	-	-
CRYSTICILLIN 600 A.S.®, SEE PENICILLIN G PROCAINE	-	-	-
CUBICIN®	1 mg	IV	J0878
CUVITRU®	100 mg	IV	J1555
CYCLOPHOSPHAMIDE	100 mg	IV	J9070
CYCLOPHOSPHAMIDE, ORAL	25 mg	ORAL	J8530
CYCLOSPORINE, ORAL	25 mg	ORAL	J7515
CYCLOSPORINE, ORAL	100 mg	ORAL	J7502
CYCLOSPORINE, PARENTERAL	250 mg	IV	J7516
CYSTOSPAZ®	up to 0.25 mg	SC, IM, IV	J1980
CYTARABINE	100 mg	SC, IV	J9100
CYTARABINE LIPOSOME	10 mg	IT	J9098
CYTOGAM®	per vial	IV	J0850
CYTOMEGALOVIRUS IMMUNE GLOBULIN INTRAVENOUS(HUMAN)	per vial	IV	J0850
CYTOSAR U®	100 mg	SC, IV	J9100
CYTOVENE®	500 mg	IV	J1570
CYTOVENE®	4.5 mg	OTH	J7310
CYTOVENE®, SEE GANCICLOVIR SODIUM	-	-	-
CYTOXAN LYOPHILIZED®, SEE CYCLOPHOSPHAMIDE	-	-	-

DRUG NAME	UNIT PER	ROUTE	CODE
CYTOXAN®, SEE CYCLOPHOSPHAMIDE	-	-	-
D GAM ANTI D®	1 dose package, 300 mcg	IM	J2790
D.H.E. 45®, SEE DIHYDROERGOTAMINE	-	-	-
D-5-W, INFUSION	1000 cc	IV	J7070
DACARBAZINE	100 mg	IV	J9130
DACLIZUMAB	25 mg	IV	J7513
DACOGEN®	1 mg	IV	J0894
DACTINOMYCIN	0.5 mg	IV	J9120
DALALONE L.A.®, SEE DEXAMETHASONE ACETATE	-	-	-
DALALONE®, SEE DEXAMETHASONE SODIUM PHOSPHATE	-	-	-
DALBAVANCIN	5 mg	IV	J0875
DALTEPARIN SODIUM	per 2500 IU	SC	J1645
DALVANCE®	10 mg	IV	J0875
DAPTOMYCIN	1 mg	IV	J0878
DARATUMUMAB	10 mg	IV	J9145
DARBEPOETIN ALFA	1 mcg	IV, SC	J0881, J0882
DARZALEX®	10 mg	IV	J9145
DAUNORUBICIN CITRATE, LIPOSOMAL FORMULATION	10 mg	IV	J9151
DAUNORUBICIN HCL	10 mg	IV	J9150
DAUNOXOME®, SEE DAUNORUBICIN CITRATE	-	-	-
DDAVP®	1 mcg	IV, SC	J2597
DDAVP®, SEE DESMOPRESSIN ACETATE	-	-	-
DECADRON PHOSPHATE®	1 mg	IM, IV, OTH	J1100
DECADRON PHOSPHATE®, SEE DEXAMETHASONE SODIUM PHOSPHATE	-	-	-
DECADRON®	0.25 mg	ORAL	J8540
DECADRON®, SEE DEXAMETHASONE SODIUM PHOSPHATE	-	-	-
DECADRON-LA®, SEE DEXAMETHASONE ACETATE	-	-	-
DECA-DURABOLIN®, SEE NANDROLONE DECANOATE	-	-	-
DECAJECT®, SEE DEXAMETHASONE SODIUM PHOSPHATE	-	-	-
DECAJECT-L.A.®, SEE DEXAMETHASONE ACETATE	-	-	-
DECITABINE	1 mg	IV	J0894
DECOLONE-50®, SEE NANDROLONE DECANOATE	-	-	-
DECOLONE-100®, SEE NANDROLONE DECANOATE	-	-	-

DRUG NAME	UNIT PER	ROUTE	CODE
DE-COMBEROL®, *SEE* TESTOSTERONE CYPIONATE AND ESTRADIOL CYPIONATE	-	-	-
DEFEROXAMINE MESYLATE	500 mg	IM, SC, IV	J0895
DEGARELIX	1 mg	SC	J9155
DEHIST®, *SEE* BROMPHENIRAMINE MALEATE	-	-	-
DEKPAK 13 DAY TAPERPAK®	0.25 mg	ORAL	J8540
DELADUMONE OB®, *SEE* TESTOSTERONE ENANTHATE AND ESTRADIOL VALERATE	-	-	-
DELADUMONE®, *SEE* TESTOSTERONE ENANTHATE AND ESTRADIOL VALERATE	-	-	-
DELATEST®, *SEE* TESTOSTERONE ENANTHATE	-	-	-
DELATESTADIOL®, *SEE* TESTOSTERONE ENANTHATE AND ESTRADIOL VALERATE	-	-	-
DELATESTRYL®	1 mg	IM	J3121
DELATESTRYL®, *SEE* TESTOSTERONE ENANTHATE	-	-	-
DELESTROGEN®	up to 10 mg	IM	J1380
DELESTROGEN®, *SEE* ESTRADIOL VALERATE	-	-	-
DELTA-CORTEF®, *SEE* PREDNISOLONE, ORAL	-	-	-
DEMADEX I.V.®	10 mg/ml	IV	J3265
DEMADEX®	10 mg/ml	IV	J3265
DEMADEX®, *SEE* TORSEMIDE	-	-	-
DEMEROL HCL®	per 100 mg	IM, IV, SC	J2175
DEMEROL HCL®, *SEE* MEPERIDINE HCL	-	-	-
DENILEUKIN DIFTITOX	300 mcg	IV	J9160
DENOSUMAB	1 mg	SC	J0897
DEPANDROGYN®, *SEE* TESTOSTERONE CYPIONATE AND ESTRADIOL CYPIONATE	-	-	-
DEPGYNOGEN®, *SEE* DEPO-ESTRADIOL CYPIONATE	-	-	-
DEPMEDALONE 40®, *SEE* METHYLPREDNISOLONE ACETATE	-	-	-
DEPMEDALONE 80®, *SEE* METHYLPREDNISOLONE ACETATE	-	-	-
DEPO ESTRADIOL®	up to 5 mg	IM	J1000
DEPO TESTOSTERONE®	1 mg	IM	J1071
DEPOCYT®	10 mg	IT	J9098
DEPO-ESTRADIOL CYPIONATE	up to 5 mg	IM	J1000
DEPOGEN®, *SEE* DEPO-ESTRADIOL CYPIONATE	-	-	-

DRUG NAME	UNIT PER	ROUTE	CODE
DEPO-MEDROL®, *SEE* METHYLPREDNISOLONE ACETATE	-	-	-
DEPOPRED-40®, *SEE* METHYLPREDNISOLONE ACETATE	-	-	-
DEPOPRED-80®, *SEE* METHYLPREDNISOLONE ACETATE	-	-	-
DEPO-PROVERA®, *SEE* MEDROXYPROGESTERONE ACETATE	-	-	-
DEPOTEST®, *SEE* TESTOSTERONE CYPIONATE	-	-	-
DEPO-TESTADIOL®, *SEE* TESTOSTERONE CYPIONATE AND ESTRADIOL CYPIONATE	-	-	-
DEPOTESTOGEN®, *SEE* TESTOSTERONE CYPIONATE AND ESTRADIOL CYPIONATE	-	-	-
DEPO-TESTOSTERONE®, *SEE* TESTOSTERONE CYPIONATE	-	-	-
DESFERAL MESYLATE®, *SEE* DEFEROXAMINE MESYLATE	-	-	-
DESFERAL®	500 mg	IM, SC, IV	J0895
DESMOPRESSIN ACETATE	1 mcg	IV, SC	J2597
DEXACEN LA-8®, *SEE* DEXAMETHASONE ACETATE	-	-	-
DEXACEN-4®, *SEE* DEXAMETHASONE SODIUM PHOSPHATE	-	-	-
DEXAMETHASONE ACETATE	1 mg	IM	J1094
DEXAMETHASONE INTENSOL®	0.25 mg	ORAL	J8540
DEXAMETHASONE INTENSOL®	1 mg	IM	J1094
DEXAMETHASONE SODIUM PHOSPHATE	1 mg	IM, IV, OTH	J1100
DEXAMETHASONE, CONCENTRATED FORM	per mg	INH	J7637
DEXAMETHASONE, INTRAVITREAL IMPLANT	0.1 mg	OTH	J7312
DEXAMETHASONE, ORAL	0.25 mg	ORAL	J8540
DEXAMETHASONE, UNIT FORM	per mg	INH	J7638
DEXASONE L.A.®, *SEE* DEXAMETHASONE ACETATE	-	-	-
DEXASONE®, *SEE* DEXAMETHASONE SODIUM PHOSPHATE	-	-	-
DEXFERRUM®	50 mg	IV	J1750
DEXFERRUM®, *SEE* IRON DEXTRAN	-	-	-
DEXONE LA®, *SEE* DEXAMETHASONE ACETATE	-	-	-
DEXONE®, *SEE* DEXAMETHASONE SODIUM PHOSPHATE	-	-	-
DEXPAK®	0.25 mg	ORAL	J8540
DEXRAZOXANE HYDROCHLORIDE	250 mg	IV	J1190
DEXTRAN 40	500 ml	IV	J7100
DEXTRAN 75	500 ml	IV	J7110
DEXTROSE 5%/LACTATED RINGERS	up to 1000 cc	IV	J7121

DRUG NAME	UNIT PER	ROUTE	CODE
DEXTROSE 5%/NORMAL SALINE SOLUTION,	500 ml = 1 unit	IV	J7042
DEXTROSE/WATER (5%)	500 ml = 1 unit	IV	J7060
D-GAM ANTI-D®	50 mg	IM	J2788
DIAMOX®, *SEE* ACETAZOLAMIDE SODIUM	-	-	-
DIAQUA 2®	up to 20 mg	IM, IV	J1940
DIAZEPAM	up to 5 mg	IM, IV	J3360
DIAZOXIDE	up to 300 mg	IV	J1730
DIBENT®	up to 20 mg	IM	J0500
DIBENT®, *SEE* DICYCLOMINE HCL	-	-	-
DICLOFENAC SODIUM	0.5 mg	IV	J1130
DICYCLOCOT®	up to 20 mg	IM	J0500
DICYCLOMINE HCL	up to 20 mg	IM	J0500
DIDRONEL IV®	per 300 mg	IV	J1436
DIDRONEL®	per 300 mg	IV	J1436
DIDRONEL®, *SEE* ETIDRONATE DISODIUM	-	-	-
DIETHYLSTILBESTROL DIPHOSPHATE	250 mg	IV	J9165
DIFLUCAN®	200 mg	IV	J1450
DIFLUCAN®, *SEE* FLUCONAZOLE	-	-	-
DIGIBIND®	per vial	IM, IV	J1162
DIGIFAB®	per vial	IM, IV	J1162
DIGITEK®	up to 0.5 mg	IM, IV	J1160
DIGOXIN	up to 0.5 mg	IM, IV	J1160
DIGOXIN IMMUNE FAB (OVINE)	per vial	IM, IV	J1162
DIHYDREX®, *SEE* DIPHENHYDRAMINE HCL	-	-	-
DIHYDROERGOTAMINE MESYLATE	per 1 mg	IM, IV	J1110
DILANTIN®	per 50 mg	IM, IV	J1165
DILANTIN®, *SEE* PHENYTOIN SODIUM	-	-	-
DILAUDID®	up to 4 mg	SC, IM, IV	J1170
DILOCAINE®, *SEE* LIDOCAINE HCL	-	-	-
DILOMINE®, *SEE* DICYCLOMINE HCL	-	-	-
DILOR®, *SEE* DYPHYLLINE	-	-	-
DIMENHYDRINATE	up to 50 mg	IM, IV	J1240
DIMERCAPROL	per 100 mg	IM	J0470
DIMETHYL SULFOXIDE®, *SEE* DMSO, DIMETHYLSULFOXIDE	-	-	-
DINATE®, *SEE* DIMENHYDRINATE	-	-	-

DRUG NAME	UNIT PER	ROUTE	CODE
DIOVAL 40®, *SEE* ESTRADIOL VALERATE	-	-	-
DIOVAL XX®, *SEE* ESTRADIOL VALERATE	-	-	-
DIOVAL®, *SEE* ESTRADIOL VALERATE	-	-	-
DIPHEDRYL®	50 mg	ORAL	Q0163
DIPHENACEN-50®, *SEE* DIPHENHYDRAMINE HCL	-	-	-
DIPHENHIST®	50 mg	ORAL	Q0163
DIPHENHYDRAMINE HCL, INJECTION	up to 50 mg	IV, IM	J1200
DIPHENHYDRAMINE HCL, ORAL	50 mg	ORAL	Q0163
DIPRIVAN®	10 mg	IV	J2704
DIPYRIDAMOLE	per 10 mg	IV	J1245
DISOTATE®	per 150 mg	IV	J3520
DISOTATE®, *SEE* ENDRATE ETHYLENEDIAMINE-TETRA-ACETIC ACID	-	-	-
DI-SPAZ®, *SEE* DICYCLOMINE HCL	-	-	-
DITATE-DS®, *SEE* TESTOSTERONE ENANTHATE AND ESTRADIOL VALERATE	-	-	-
DIURIL SODIUM®	per 500 mg	IV	J1205
DIURIL SODIUM®, *SEE* CHLOROTHIAZIDE SODIUM	-	-	-
DIURIL®	per 500 mg	IV	J1205
D-MED 80®, *SEE* METHYLPREDNISOLONE ACETATE	-	-	-
DMSO, DIMETHYL SULFOXIDE	50%, 50 ml	OTH	J1212
DOBUTAMINE HCL	per 250 mg	IV	J1250
DOBUTREX®	per 250 mg	IV	J1250
DOBUTREX®, *SEE* DOBUTAMINE HCL	-	-	-
DOCEFREZ®	1 mg	IV	J9171
DOLASETRON MESYLATE, INJECTION	10 mg	IV	J9171
DOLASETRON MESYLATE, TABLETS	100 mg	ORAL	Q0180
DOLOPHINE HCL®, *SEE* METHADONE HCL	-	-	-
DOLOPHINE®	up to 10 mg	IM, SC	J1230
DOMMANATE®, *SEE* DIMENHYDRINATE	-	-	-
DONBAX®, *SEE* DORIPENEM	-	-	-
DOPAMINE HCL	40 mg	INJ	J1265
DORIBAX®	10 mg	IV	J1267
DORIBAX®, *SEE* DORIPENEM	-	-	-
DORIPENEM	10 mg	IV	J1267
DORNASE ALPHA, UNIT DOSE FORM	per mg	INH	J7639
DOSTINEX®	0.25 mg	ORAL	J8515

DRUG NAME	UNIT PER	ROUTE	CODE
DOXERCALCIFEROL	1 mcg	IV	J1270
DOXIL®	10 mg	IV	Q2050
DOXIL®, SEE DOXORUBICIN HCL, LIPID	-	-	-
DOXORUBICIN HCL	10 mg	IV	J9000
DRAMAMINE®	up to 50 mg	IM, IV	J1240
DRAMAMINE®, SEE DIMENHYDRINATE	-	-	-
DRAMANATE®, SEE DIMENHYDRINATE	-	-	-
DRAMILIN®, SEE DIMENHYDRINATE	-	-	-
DRAMOCEN®, SEE DIMENHYDRINATE	-	-	-
DRAMOJECT®	up to 50 mg	IM, IV	J1240
DRAMOJECT®, SEE DIMENHYDRINATE	-	-	-
DRONABINOL, ORAL	2.5 mg	ORAL	Q0167
DROPERIDOL	up to 5 mg	IM, IV	J1790
DROPERIDOL AND FENTANYL CITRATE	up to 2 ml ampule	IM, IV	J1810
DRUG ADMINISTERED THROUGH A METERED DOSE INHALER	-	INH	J3535
DTIC-DOME®, SEE DACARBAZINE	-	-	-
DUONEB®, SEE ALBUTEROL	-	-	-
DUOPA®	5 mg/10 mg	OTH	J7340
DUOVAL P.A.®, SEE TESTOSTERONE ENANTHATE AND ESTRADIOL VALERATE	-	-	-
DURACILLIN A.S.®, SEE PENICILLIN G PROCAINE	-	-	-
DURACLON®	1 mg	epidural	J0735
DURACLON®, SEE CLONIDINE HYDROCHLORIDE	-	-	-
DURA-ESTRIN®, SEE DEPO-ESTRADIOL CYPIONATE	-	-	-
DURAGEN-10®, SEE ESTRADIOL VALERATE	-	-	-
DURAGEN-20®, SEE ESTRADIOL VALERATE	-	-	-
DURAGEN-40®, SEE ESTRADIOL VALERATE	-	-	-
DURALONE-40®, SEE METHYLPREDNISOLONE ACETATE	-	-	-
DURALONE-80®, SEE METHYLPREDNISOLONE ACETATE	-	-	-
DURALUTIN®, SEE HYDROXYPROGESTERONE CAPROATE	-	-	-
DURAMORPH®, SEE MORPHINE SULFATE	-	-	-
DURATEST-100®, SEE TESTOSTERONE CYPIONATE	-	-	-
DURATEST-200®, SEE TESTOSTERONE CYPIONATE	-	-	-

DRUG NAME	UNIT PER	ROUTE	CODE
DURATESTRIN®, SEE TESTOSTERONE CYPIONATE AND ESTRADIOL CYPIONATE	-	-	-
DURATHATE-200®, SEE TESTOSTERONE ENANTHATE	-	-	-
DURVALUMAB	10 mg	IV	C9492
DYLIX	up to 500 mg	IM	J1180
DYLOJECT®	0.5 mg	IV	J1130
DYMENATE®	up to 50 mg	IM, IV	J1240
DYMENATE®, SEE DIMENHYDRINATE	-	-	-
DYNACIN®	1 mg	IV	J2265
DYPHYLLINE	up to 500 mg	IM	J1180
DYSPORT®	5 units	IM	J0586
DYSPORT®, SEE ABOBOTULINUMTOXINTYPEA	-	-	-
DYTUSS®	50 mg	ORAL	Q0163
ECALLANTIDE	1 mg	SC	J1290
ECULIZUMAB	10 mg	IV	J1300
EDETATE CALCIUM DISODIUM	up to 1000 mg	IV, SC, IM	J0600
EDETATE DISODIUM	per 150 mg	IV	J3520
EDEX®	1.25 mcg	OTH	J0270
ELAPRASE®	1 mg	IV	J1743
ELAVIL®, SEE AMITRIPTYLINE HCL	-	-	-
ELELYSO®	10 units	IV	J3060
ELIGARD®	per 1 mg	IM	J9218
ELITEK®	0.5 mg	IV	J2783
ELIXOPHYLLIN®	per 40 mg	IV	J2810
ELLENCE®	2 mg	INJ	J9178
ELLENCE®, SEE EPIRUBICIN HCL	-	-	-
ELLIOTTS B SOLUTION	1 ml	OTH	J9175
ELOCTATE WITH FC FUSION PROTEIN®	per IU	IV	J7192
ELOSULFASE ALFA	1 mg	IV	J1322
ELOTUZUMAB	1 mg	IV	J9176
ELOXATIN®	0.5 mg	IV	J9263
ELSPAR	1000 IU	IM	J9019
EMEND 2-DAY®	5 mg	ORAL	J8501
EMEND 3-DAY	5 mg	ORAL	J8501
EMEND®	5 mg	ORAL	J8501
EMPLICITI®	1 mg	IV	J9176
ENBREL®	25 mg	IM, IV	J1438
ENBREL PREFILLED SYRINGE®	25 mg	IM, IV	J1438
ENBREL®, SEE ETANERCEPT	-	-	-
ENBREL SURECLICK®	25 mg	IM, IV	J1438
ENDACOF C®	per 30 mg	IM, IV, SC	J0745
ENDEP®, SEE AMITRIPTYLINE HCL	-	-	-

DRUG NAME	UNIT PER	ROUTE	CODE
ENDRATE ETHYLENEDIAMINE-TETRA-ACETIC ACID®, *SEE* EDETATE DISODIUM	-	-	-
ENDRATE®	per 150 mg	IV	J3520
ENFUVIRTIDE	1 mg	SC	J1324
ENOVIL®, *SEE* AMITRIPTYLINE HCL	-	-	-
ENOXAPARIN SODIUM	10 mg	SC	J1650
ENTOCORT EC®	0.5 mg	INH	J7626
ENTOCORT EC®	0.25 mg	INH	J7633
ENVARSUS XR®	0.25mg	ORAL	J7503
EOVIST®, *SEE* GADOXETATE DISODIUM	-	-	-
EPIKLOR®	per 2 mEq	IV	J3480
EPINEPHRINE, ADRENALIN	0.1 mg	SC, IM	J0171
EPIPEN 2-PAK®	0.1 mg	SC, IM	J0171
EPIPEN JR 2-PAK®	0.1 mg	SC, IM	J0171
EPIRUBICIN HYDROCHLORIDE	2 mg	-	J9178
EPOETIN ALFA	1000 units	IV, SC	Q4081
EPOETIN BETA, ESRD USE	1 mcg	IV	J0887
EPOETIN BETA, NON-ESRD USE	1 mcg	IV	J0888
EPOGEN®	1000 units	IV	J0885
EPOGEN®	1000 units	IV, SC	Q4081
EPOPROSTENOL	0.5 mg	IV	J1325
EPSOM SALT®	500 mg	IV, IM	J3475
EPTIFIBATIDE, INJECTION	5 mg	IM, IV	J1327
ERAXIS®	1 mg	IV	J0348
ERBITUX®	10 mg	IV	J9055
ERGONOVINE MALEATE	up to 0.2 mg	IM, IV	J1330
ERIBULIN MESYLATE	0.1 mg	IV	J9179
ERTAPENEM SODIUM	500 mg	IM, IV	J1335
ERWINASE®, *SEE* ASPARAGINASE	-	-	-
ERYTHROCIN®	500 mg	IV	J1364
ERYTHROMYCIN LACTOBIONATE	500 mg	IV	J1364
ESTRA-D®, *SEE* DEPO-ESTRADIOL CYPIONATE	-	-	-
ESTRADIOL CYPIONATE®, *SEE* DEPO-ESTRADIOL CYPIONATE	-	-	-
ESTRADIOL L.A. 20®, *SEE* ESTRADIOL VALERATE	-	-	-
ESTRADIOL L.A. 40®, *SEE* ESTRADIOL VALERATE	-	-	-
ESTRADIOL L.A.®, *SEE* ESTRADIOL VALERATE	-	-	-
ESTRADIOL VALERATE	up to 10 mg	IM	J1380
ESTRA-L 20®, *SEE* ESTRADIOL VALERATE	-	-	-
ESTRA-L 40®, *SEE* ESTRADIOL VALERATE	-	-	-

DRUG NAME	UNIT PER	ROUTE	CODE
ESTRA-TESTRIN®, *SEE* TESTOSTERONE ENANTHATE AND ESTRADIOL VALERATE	-	-	-
ESTRO-CYP®, *SEE* DEPO-ESTRADIOL CYPIONATE	-	-	-
ESTROGEN, CONJUGATED	per 25 mg	IV, IM	J1410
ESTROJECT L.A.®, *SEE* DEPO-ESTRADIOL CYPIONATE	-	-	-
ESTRONE	per 1 mg	IM	J1435
ESTRONE 5®, *SEE* ESTRONE	-	-	-
ESTRONE AQUEOUS®, *SEE* ESTRONE	-	-	-
ESTRONOL®, *SEE* ESTRONE	-	-	-
ESTRONOL-L.A.®, *SEE* DEPO-ESTRADIOL CYPIONATE	-	-	-
ETANERCEPT, INJECTION	25 mg	IM, IV	J1438
ETELCALCETIDE	0.1 mg	IV	J0606
ETEPLIRSEN	10 mg	IV	J1428
ETHAMOLIN®	100 mg	INJ	J1430
ETHANOLAMINE	100 mg	INJ	J1430
ETHYOL®	500 mg	IV	J0207
ETHYOL®, *SEE* AMIFOSTINE	-	-	-
ETIDRONATE DISODIUM	per 300 mg	IV	J1436
ETONOGESTREL IMPLANT	each	OTH	J7307
ETOPOPHOS®, *SEE* ETOPOSIDE	-	-	-
ETOPOSIDE	10 mg	IV	J9181
EUFLEXXA®	per dose	OTH	J7323
ETOPOSIDE, ORAL	50 mg	ORAL	J8560
EVEROLIMUS, ORAL	0.25 mg	ORAL	J7527
EVERONE®, *SEE* TESTOSTERONE ENANTHATE	-	-	-
EVZIO®	per 1 mg	IM, IV, SC	J2310
EXTAVIA®	0.25 mg	SC	J1830
EYLEA®	1 mg	OTH	J0178
FABRAZYME®	1 mg	IV	J0180
FACTOR IX (ANTI-HEMOPHILIC FACTOR, PURIFIED, NON-RECOMBINANT)	per IU	IV	J7193
FACTOR IX (ANTI-HEMOPHILIC FACTOR, RECOMBINANT)	1 IU	IV	J7195, J7200 - J7201
FACTOR IX, COMPLEX	per IU	IV	J7194
FACTOR VIIA (COAGULATION FACTOR, RECOMBINANT)	1 mcg	IV	J7189
FACTOR VIII (ANTI-HEMOPHILIC FACTOR, HUMAN)	per IU	IV	J7190
FACTOR VIII (ANTI-HEMOPHILIC FACTOR, PORCINE)	per IU	IV	J7191
FACTOR VIII (ANTI-HEMOPHILIC FACTOR, RECOMBINANT)	per IU	IV	J7182, J7185, J7192, J7188

DRUG NAME	UNIT PER	ROUTE	CODE
FACTOR VIII, (ANTIHEMOPHILIC FACTOR, RECOMBINANT), (AFSTYLA)	1 i.u.	IV	J7210
FACTOR VIII, (ANTIHEMOPHILIC FACTOR, RECOMBINANT), (KOVALTRY)	1 IU	IV	J7211
FACTOR VIII, (ANTIHEMOPHILIC FACTOR, RECOMBINANT), (NUWIQ)	1 IU	IV	J7209
FACTOR VIII, (ANTIHEMOPHILIC FACTOR, RECOMBINANT), PEGYLATED	1 IU	IV	J7207
FACTOR VIII FC FUSION (RECOMBINANT)	per IU	IV	J7205
FACTOR IX, ALBUMIN FUSION PROTEIN, (RECOMBINANT)	1 IU	IV	J7202
FACTOR X, (HUMAN)	1 IU	IV	J7175
FACTOR XIII A-SUBUNIT (RECOMBINANT)	per IU	IV	J7181
FACTORS, OTHER HEMOPHILIA CLOTTING	per IU	IV	J7196
FACTREL®, SEE GONADORELIN HCL	-	-	-
FASLODEX®	25 mg	IM	J9395
FEIBA NF®, FEIBA VH IMMUNO®	per IU	IV	J7198
FENTANYL CITRATE	0.1 mg	IM, IV	J3010
FERAHEME® (NON-ESRD USE)	1 mg	INJ	Q0138
FERAHEME® (FOR ESRD ON DIALYSIS)	1 mg	INJ	Q0139
FERAHEME®, SEE FERUMOXYTOL	-	-	-
FERRIC CARBOXYMALTOSE	1 mg	IV	J1439
FERRIC PYROPHOSPHATE CITRATE SOLUTION	0.1 mg of iron	IV	J1443
FERRLECIT®	12.5 mg	IV	J2916
FERRLECIT®, SEE SODIUM FERRICGLUCONATE COMPLEX IN SUCROSE INJECTION	-	-	-
FERUMOXYTOL	1 mg	INJ	Q0138, Q0139
FEVERALL®	10 mg	IV	J0131
FILGRASTIM (G-CSF)	1 mcg	SC, IV	J1442, Q5101
FILGRASTIM (TBO)	1 mcg	SC, IV	J1447
FIRAZYR®	1 mg	SC	J1744
FIRAZYR®, SEE ICATIBANT	-	-	-
FIRMAGON®	1 mg	SC	J9155
FIRMAGON®, SEE DEGARELIX	-	-	-
FIRST PROGESTERONE MC10®	per 50 mg	IM	J2675
FIRST-VANCOMYCIN®	500 mg	IV, IM	J3370
FLEBOGAMMA DIF®	500 mg	IV	J1572
FLEBOGAMMA®	500 mg	IV	J1572
FLEXOJECT®	up to 60 mg	IV, IM	J2360
FLEXOJECT®, SEE ORPHENADRINE CITRATE	-	-	-

DRUG NAME	UNIT PER	ROUTE	CODE
FLEXON®	up to 60 mg	IV, IM	J2360
FLEXON®, SEE ORPHENADRINE CITRATE	-	-	-
FLOLAN®	0.5 mg	IV	J1325
FLOLAN®, SEE EPOPROSTENOL	-	-	-
FLORBETABEN F18	up to 8.1 millicuries	IV	Q9983
FLOXURIDINE	500 mg	IV	J9200
FLUCICLOVINE F-18	1 mCi	IV	A9588
FLUCONAZOLE	200 mg	IV	J1450
FLUDARA®, SEE FLUDARABINE PHOSPHATE	-	-	-
FLUDARABINE PHOSPHATE	1 mg	ORAL	J8562
FLUDARABINE PHOSPHATE	50 mg	IV	J9185
FLUNISOLIDE INHALATION SOLUTION, UNIT DOSE FORM	per mg	INH	J7641
FLUOCINOLONE	0.01 mg	OTH	J7311, J7313
FLUOROURACIL	500 mg	IV	J9190
FLUPHENAZINE DECANOATE	up to 25 mg	IV	J2680
FLUTEMETAMOL F18	up to 5 millicuries	IV	Q9982
FOLEX PFS®, SEE METHOTREXATE SODIUM	-	-	-
FOLEX®, SEE METHOTREXATE SODIUM	-	-	-
FOLLUTEIN®, SEE CHORIONIC GONADOTROPIN	-	-	-
FOLOTYN®	1 mg	IV	J9307
FOLOTYN®, SEE PRALATREXATE	-	-	-
FOMEPIZOLE	15 mg	INJ	J1451
FOMIVIRSEN SODIUM	1.65 mg	Intraocular	J1452
FONDAPARINUX SODIUM	0.5 mg	SC	J1652
FORADIL AEROLIZER®	20 mcg	INH	J7606
FORMOTEROL	12 mcg	INH	J7640
FORMOTEROL FUMARATE	20 mcg	INH	J7606
FORTAZ ADD VANTAGE®	per 500 mg	IM, IV	J0713
FORTAZ TWISTVIAL®	per 500 mg	IM, IV	J0713
FORTAZ®	per 500 mg	IM, IV	J0713
FORTAZ®, SEE CEFTAZIDIME	-	-	-
FORTEO®	10 mcg	SC	J3110
FOSAPREPITANT	1 mg	IV	J1453
FOSCARNET SODIUM	per 1,000 mg	IV	J1455
FOSCAVIR®	per 1,000 mg	IV	J1455
FOSCAVIR®, SEE FOSCARNET SODIUM	-	-	-
FOSPHENYTOIN	50 mg	IV	Q2009

DRUG NAME	UNIT PER	ROUTE	CODE
FRAGMIN®	per 2500 IU	SC	J1645
FUDR®	500 mg	IV	J9200
FUDR®, *SEE* FLOXURIDINE	-	-	-
FULVESTRANT	25 mg	IM	J9395
FUNGIZONE INTRAVENOUS®, *SEE* AMPHOTERICIN B	-	-	-
FUNGIZONE®	50 mg	IV	J0285
FUROMIDE M.D.®, *SEE* FUROSEMIDE	-	-	-
FUROSEMIDE	up to 20 mg	IM, IV	J1940
FUSILEV®	0.5 mg	IV	J0641
FUZEON®	1 mg	SC	J1324
GABLOFEN®	10 mg	IT	J0475
GABLOFEN®	50 mcg	OTH	J0476
GADOXETATE DISODIUM	1 ml	IV	A9581
GALLIUM NITRATE	1 mg	IV	J1457
GALLIUM GA-68, DOTATATE	0.1 mCi	-	A9587
GALSULFASE	1 mg	IV	J1458
GAMASTAN®, *SEE* GAMMA GLOBULIN AND IMMUNE GLOBULIN	-	-	-
GAMMA GLOBULIN	1 cc	IM	J1460
GAMMA GLOBULIN	over 10 cc	IM	J1560
GAMMAGARD® LIQUID	500 mg	IV	J1568
GAMMAKED®	500 mg	IV	J1561
GAMMAPLEX®	500 mg	IV	J1557
GAMULIN RH®	50 mg	IM	J2788
GAMULIN RH®	1 dose package, 300 mcg	IM	J2790
GAMULIN RH®, *SEE* RHO(D) IMMUNE GLOBULIN	-	-	-
GAMUNEX	500 mg	IV	J1561
GAMUNEX C®	500 mg	IV	J1561
GANCICLOVIR SODIUM	500 mg	IV	J1570
GANCICLOVIR, IMPLANT	4.5 mg	OTH	J7310
GARAMYCIN®	up to 80 mg	IM, IV	J1580
GARAMYCIN, GENTAMICIN	up to 80 mg	IM, IV	J1580
GASTROCROM®	per 10 mg	INH	J7631
GAZYVA®	10 mg	INJ	J9301
GEFITINIB	250 mg	ORAL	J8565
GEL-ONE®	per dose	OTH	J7326
GEMCITABINE HCL	200 mg	IV	J9201
GEMSAR®, *SEE* GEMCITABINE HCL	-	-	-
GEMTUZUMAB OZOGAMICIN	0.1 mg	IV	J9203
GENESA®, *SEE* ARBUTAMINE	-	-	-
GENGRAF®	25 mg	ORAL	J7515
GENGRAF®	250 mg	IV	J7516

DRUG NAME	UNIT PER	ROUTE	CODE
GENGRAF®	100 mg	ORAL	J7502
GENOTROPIN MINIQUICK®	1 mg	SC	J2941
GENOTROPIN®	1 mg	SC	J2941
GENTAMICIN SULFATE®, *SEE* GARAMYCIN, GENTAMICIN	-	-	-
GENTRAN 75®, *SEE* DEXTRAN 75	-	-	-
GENTRAN®, *SEE* DEXTRAN 40	-	-	-
GEODON®	10 mg	IM	J3486
GEREF®, *SEE* SERMORELIN ACETATE	-	-	-
GESTEROL 50®, *SEE* PROGESTERONE	-	-	-
GENVISC® 850	0.1 mg	IV	J7328
GENVISC®	1 mg	OTH	J7320
GLASSIA®	10 mg	IV	J0257
GLATIRAMER ACETATE	20 mg	SC	J1595
GLIADEL®	100 mg	IV	J9050
GLUCAGEN HYPOKIT®	per 1 mg	SC, IM, IV	J1610
GLUCAGEN®	per 1 mg	SC, IM, IV	J1610
GLUCAGON EMERGENCY KIT FOR LOW BLOOD SUGAR®	per 1 mg	SC, IM, IV	J1610
GLUCAGON HCL	per 1 mg	SC, IM, IV	J1610
GLUKOR®, *SEE* CHORIONIC GONADOTROPIN	-	-	-
GLYCOPYRROLATE, CONCENTRATED FORM	per 1 mg	INH	J7642
GLYCOPYRROLATE, UNIT DOSE FORM	per 1 mg	INH	J7643
GOLD SODIUM THIOMALATE	up to 50 mg	IM	J1600
GOLIMUMAB	1 mg	IV	J1602
GONADORELIN HCL	per 100 mcg	SC, IV	J1620
GONIC®, *SEE* CHORIONIC GONADOTROPIN	-	-	-
GOSERELIN ACETATE IMPLANT	per 3.6 mg	SC	J9202
GRANISETRON, EXTENDED RELEASE	0.1 mg	IV	J1627
GRANISETRON HCL, INJECTION	100 mcg	IV	J1626
GRANISETRON HCL, ORAL	1 mg	ORAL	Q0166
GRANISOL®, *SEE* GRANISETRON HYDROCHLORIDE	100 mcg	IV	J1626
GYNOGEN L.A. A10®, *SEE* ESTRADIOL VALERATE	-	-	-
GYNOGEN L.A. A20®, *SEE* ESTRADIOL VALERATE	-	-	-
GYNOGEN L.A. A40®, *SEE* ESTRADIOL VALERATE	-	-	-
H.P. ACTHA GEL®	up to 40 units	IV, IM, SC	J0800
HALAVEN®	0.1 mg	IV	J9179

DRUG NAME	UNIT PER	ROUTE	CODE
HALAVEN®, *SEE* ERIBULIN MESYLATE	-	-	-
HALDOL DECANOATE®	per 50 mg	IM	J1631
HALDOL®	up to 5 mg	IM, IV	J1630
HALDOL®, *SEE* HALOPERIDOL	-	-	-
HALOPERIDOL	up to 5 mg	IM, IV	J1630
HALOPERIDOL DECANOATE	per 50 mg	IM	J1631
HECTORAL®, *SEE* DOXERCALCIFEROL	-	-	-
HECTOROL®	1 mcg	IV	J1270
HELIXATE FS®	per IU	IV	J7185
HELIXATE FS®	per IU	IV	J7192
HEMANGEOL®	up to 1 mg	IV	J1800
HEMIN	1 mg	INJ	J1640
HEMOFIL M®, *SEE* FACTOR VIII	-	-	-
HEMOFIL-M®	per IU	IV	J7190
HEMOPHILIA CLOTTING FACTORS(E.G., ANTI-INHIBITORS)	per IU	IV	J7198
HEMOPHILIA CLOTTING FACTORS, NOC	per IU	IV	J7199
HEPAGAM B	0.5 ml	IM	J1571
HEPAGAM B	0.5 ml	IV	J1573
HEPAGAM B®	0.5 ml	IV	J1573
HEPARIN SODIUM	1, 000 units	IV, SC	J1644
HEPARIN SODIUM (HEPARIN LOCK FLUSH)	10 units	IV	J1642
HEP-LOCK U/P®, *SEE* HEPARIN SODIUM (HEPARIN LOCK FLUSH)	-	-	-
HEP-LOCK®, *SEE* HEPARIN SODIUM (HEPARIN LOCK FLUSH)	-	-	-
HERCEPTIN®	10 mg	IV	J9355
HERCEPTIN®, *SEE* TRASTUZUMAB	-	-	-
HEXADROL PHOSPHATE®, *SEE* DEXAMETHASONE SODIUM PHOSPHATE	-	-	-
HISTAJECT®	per 10 mg	IM, SC, IV	J0945
HISTAJECT®, *SEE* BROMPHENIRAMINE MALEATE	-	-	-
HISTRELIN ACETATE	10 mcg	INJ	J1675
HISTRELIN IMPLANT	50 mg	OTH	J9225
HIZENTRA®	100 mg	SC	J1559
HIZENTRA®, *SEE* IMMUNE GLOBULIN	-	-	-
HUMAN FIBRINOGEN CONCENTRATE	100 mg	IV	J7178
HUMAN SECRETIN®	1 mcg	IV	J2850
HUMATE-P®	per IU	IV	J7187
HUMATROPE®	1 mg	SC	J2941
HUMATROPEN®	1 mg	SC	J2941
HUMIRA®	20 mg	SC	J0135
HYALGAN®	per dose	OTH	J7321

DRUG NAME	UNIT PER	ROUTE	CODE
HYALURONAN OR DERIVATIVE	per dose	OTH	J7326
HYALURONAN OR DERIVATIVE	per dose	IV	J7327
HYALURONAN OR DERIVITIVE	0.1 mg	OTH	J7328
HYALURONAN OR DERIVATIVE	1 mg	OTH	J7322
HYALURONAN OR DERIVATIVE	1 mg	OTH	J7325
HYALURONIDASE	up to 150 units	SC, IV	J3470
HYALURONIDASE RECOMBINANT	1 usp	SC	J3473
HYALURONIDASE, (HYQVIA)	100 mg	IV	J1575
HYALURONIDASE, OVINE	up to 999 units	VAR	J3471
HYALURONIDASE, OVINE	per 1000 units	VAR	J3472
HYATE:C®, *SEE* FACTOR VIII (ANTI-HEMOPHILIC FACTOR (PORCINE))	-	-	-
HYBOLIN DECANOATE®, *SEE* NANDROLONE DECANOATE	-	-	-
HYCAMTIN®	0.25 mg	Oral	J8705
HYCAMTIN®	0.1 mg	IV	J9351
HYCAMTIN®, *SEE* TOPOTECAN	-	-	-
HYDASE®	up to 150 units	SC, IV	J3470
HYDRALAZINE HCL	up to 20 mg	IV, IM	J0360
HYDROCORTISONE ACETATE	up to 25 mg	IV, IM, SC	J1700
HYDROCORTISONE SODIUM PHOSPHATE	up to 50 mg	IV, IM, SC	J1710
HYDROCORTISONE SUCCINATE SODIUM	up to 100 mg	IV, IM, SC	J1720
HYDROCORTONE ACETATE®, *SEE* HYDROCORTISONE ACETATE	-	-	-
HYDROCORTONE PHOSPHATE®, *SEE* HYDROCORTISONE SODIUM PHOSPHATE	-	-	-
HYDROMORPHONE HCL	up to 4 mg	SC, IM, IV	J1170
HYDROXYPROGESTERONE CAPROATE, (MAKENA)	10 mg	IV	J1726
HYDROXYPROGESTERONE CAPROATE, NOT OTHERWISE SPECIFIED	10 mg	IV	J1729
HYDROXYZINE HCL	up to 25 mg	IM	J3410
HYDROXYZINE PAMOATE	25 mg	ORAL	Q0177
HYLAN G-F 20	1 mg	OTH	J7325
HYLENEX®	up to 150 units	SC, IV	J3470
HYLENEX®	1 usp	SC	J3473
HYMOVIS®	1 mg	OTH	J7322
HYOSCYAMINE SULFATE	up to 0.25 mg	SC, IM, IV	J1980

DRUG NAME	UNIT PER	ROUTE	CODE
HYPERRHO S/D FULL DOSE®	1 dose package, 300 mcg	IM	J2790
HYPERRHO SD MINI DOSE®	50 mg	IM	J2788
HYPERSTAT IV®, *SEE* DIAZOXIDE	-	-	-
HYPERSTAT®	up to 300 mg	IV	J1730
HYPERTET S/D®	up to 250 units	IM	J1670
HYPER-TET®, *SEE* TETANUS IMMUNE GLOBULIN, HUMAN	-	-	-
HYQVIA®	1 cc	IM	J1460
HYQVIA®	over 10 cc	IM	J1560
HYREXIN-50®, *SEE* DIPHENHYDRAMINE HCL	-	-	-
HYZINE-50®, *SEE* HYDROXYZINE HCL	-	-	-
IBANDRONATE SODIUM	1 mg	IV	J1740
IBUPROFEN	100 mg	IV	J1741
IBUTILIDE FUMARATE	1 mg	IV	J1742
ICATIBANT	1 mg	SC	J1744
IDAMYCIN PFS®	5 mg	IV	J9211
IDAMYCIN®	5 mg	IV	J9211
IDAMYCIN®, *SEE* IDARUBICIN HCL	-	-	-
IDARUBICIN HCL	5 mg	IV	J9211
IDELVION®	1 IU	IV	J7202
IDURSULFASE	1 mg	IV	J1743
IFEX®	1 g	IV	J9208
IFEX®, *SEE* IFOSFAMIDE	-	-	-
IFOSFAMIDE	1 g	IV	J9208
ILARIS®	1 mg	SC	J0638
ILARIS®, *SEE* CANAKINUMAB	-	-	-
ILOPROST	20 mcg	INH	Q4074
ILUVIEN®	each	OTH	J7311
IMFERON®, *SEE* IRON DEXTRAN	-	-	-
IMFINZI®	10 mg	IV	C9492
IMIGLUCERASE	10 units	IV	J1786
IMITREX®	6 mg	SC	J3030
IMITREX STATDOSE®	6 mg	SC	J3030
IMLYGIC®	1 million PFU	IV	J9325
IMMUNE GLOBULIN, BIVIGAM	500 mg	IV	J1556
IMMUNE GLOBULIN, CUVITRU	100 mg	IV	J1555
IMMUNE GLOBULIN, FLEBOGAMMA	500 mg	IV	J1572
IMMUNE GLOBULIN, GAMMAGARD LIQUID	500 mg	IV	J1569
IMMUNE GLOBULIN, GAMMAPLEX	500 mg	IV	J1557
IMMUNE GLOBULIN, GAMUNEX	500 mg	IV	J1561
IMMUNE GLOBULIN, HEPAGAM B	0.5 ml	IV	J1573
IMMUNE GLOBULIN, HEPAGAM B	0.5 ml	IM	J1571

DRUG NAME	UNIT PER	ROUTE	CODE
IMMUNE GLOBULIN, HIZENTRA	100 mg	SC	J1559
IMMUNE GLOBULIN, NOS	500 mg	IV	J1566, J1599
IMMUNE GLOBULIN, OCTAGAM	500 mg	IV	J1568
IMMUNE GLOBULIN, PRIVIGEN	500 mg	IV	J1459
IMMUNE GLOBULIN, RHOPHYLAC	100 IU	IM	J2791
IMMUNE GLOBULIN, SUBCUTANEOUS	100 mg	SC	J1562
IMMUNOSUPPRESSIVE DRUG, NOT OTHERWISE CLASSIFIED	-	-	J7599
IMPLANON®	each	OTH	J7307
IMURAN®	50 mg	ORAL	J7500
IMURAN®	100 mg	IV	J7501
IMURAN®, *SEE* AZATHIOPRINE	-	-	-
INAPSINE®	up to 5 mg	IM, IV	J1790
INAPSINE®, *SEE* DROPERIDOL	-	-	-
INCOBOTULINUMTOXIN TYPE A	1 unit	IM	J0588
INCRELEX®	1 mg	SC	J2170
INDERAL LA®	up to 1 mg	IV	J1800
INDERAL XL®	up to 1 mg	IV	J1800
INDERAL®	up to 1 mg	IV	J1800
INDERAL®, *SEE* PROPRANOLOL HCL	-	-	-
INFED®	50 mg	IV	J1750
INFED®, *SEE* IRON DEXTRAN	-	-	-
INFERGEN®, *SEE* INTERFERON ALFACON-1, RECOMBINANT	-	-	-
INFLECTRA®	10 mg	IV	Q5102
INFLIXIMAB, BIOSIMILAR	10 mg	IV	Q5102
INFLIXIMAB, INJECTION	10 mg	IM, IV	J1745
INJECTAFER®	1 mg	IV	J1439
INNOPRAN XL®	up to 1 mg	IV	J1800
INNOVAR®, *SEE* DROPERIDOL AND FENTANYL CITRATE	-	-	-
INSULIN	5 units	SC	J1815
INSULIN LISPRO	50 units	SC	J1817
INTAL®, *SEE* CROMOLYN SODIUM	-	-	-
INTEGRILIN®	5 mg	IM, IV	J1327
INTEGRILIN, INJECTION®, *SEE* EPTIFIBATIDE	-	-	-
INTERFERON ALFA-2A, RECOMBINANT	3 million units	SC, IM	J9213
INTERFERON ALFA-2B, RECOMBINANT	1 million units	SC, IM	J9214
INTERFERON ALFA-N3 (HUMAN LEUKOCYTE DERIVED)	250, 000 IU	IM	J9215
INTERFERON ALPHACON-1, RECOMBINANT	1 mcg	SC	J9212
INTERFERON BETA-1A	30 mcg	IM	J1826
INTERFERON BETA-1A	1 mcg	IM	Q3027
INTERFERON BETA-1A	1 mcg	SC	Q3028
INTERFERON BETA-1B	0.25 mg	SC	J1830

DRUG NAME	UNIT PER	ROUTE	CODE
INTERFERON GAMMA-1B	3 million units	SC	J9216
INTRAUTERINE COPPER CONTRACEPTIVE®, *SEE* COPPER CONTRACEPTIVE, INTRAUTERINE	-	-	-
INTRON A®	1 million units	SC, IM	J9214
INTROPIN®	40 mg	INJ	J1265
INVANZ®	500 mg	IM, IV	J1335
INVEGA SUSTENNA®, *SEE* PALIPERIDONE PALMITATE	-	-	-
INVEGA®	1 mg	IM	J2426
IPILIMUMAB	1 mg	IV	J9228
IPRATROPIUM BROMIDE, UNIT DOSE FORM	per mg	INH	J7644, J7645
IRESSA®	250 mg	ORAL	J8565
IRINOTECAN	20 mg	IV	J9206
IRINOTECAN LIPOSOME	1 mg	IV	J9205
IRON DEXTRAN	50 mg	IV	J1750
IRON SUCROSE	1 mg	IV	J1756
IRRIGATION SOLUTION FOR TX OF BLADDER CALCULI	per 50 ml	OTH	Q2004
ISAVUCONAZONIUM	1 mg	IV	J1833
ISOCAINE HCL®, *SEE* MEPIVACAINE HCL	-	-	-
ISOETHARINE HCL, CONCENTRATED FORM	per mg	INH	J7647, J7648
ISOETHARINE HCL, UNIT DOSE FORM	per mg	INH	J7649, J7650
ISOPROTERENOL HCL, CONCENTRATED FORM	per mg	INH	J7657, J7658
ISOPROTERENOL HCL, UNIT DOSE FORM	per mg	INH	J7659, J7660
ISTODAX®	1 mg	IV	J9315
ISTODAX®, *SEE* ROMIDEPSIN	-	-	-
ISUPREL HCL®	1 mg	INH	J7658
ISUPREL HCL®	1 mg	INH	J7659
ITRACONAZOLE	50 mg	IV	J1835
IXABEPILONE	1 mg	IV	J9207
IXEMPRA®	1 mg	IV	J9207
IXEMPRA®, *SEE* IXABEPILONE	-	-	-
JENAMICIN®, *SEE* GARAMYCIN, GENTAMICIN	-	-	-
JETREA®	0.125 mg	IV	J7316
JEVTANA®	1 mg	IV	J9043
JEVTANA®, *SEE* CABAZITAXEL	-	-	-
KABIKINASE®, *SEE* STREPTOKINASE	-	-	-
KADCYLA®	1 mg	IV	J9354
KADIAN®	10 mg	INJ	J2274
KAL POTASSIUM 99®	per 2 mEq	IV	J3480
KALBITOR®	1 mg	SC	J1290

DRUG NAME	UNIT PER	ROUTE	CODE
KALBITOR®, *SEE* ECALLANTIDE	-	-	-
KALEINATE®, *SEE* CALCIUM GLUCONATE	-	-	-
KANAMYCIN SULFATE	up to 75 mg	IM, IV	J1850
KANAMYCIN SULFATE	up to 500 mg	IM, IV	J1840
KANUMA®	1 mg	IV	J2840
KAOCHLOR S-F®	per 2 mEq	IV	J3480
KAON-CL®	per 2 mEq	IV	J3480
KAY CIEL®	per 2 mEq	IV	J3480
K-DUR®	per 2 mEq	IV	J3480
KEFLIN®, *SEE* CEPHALOTHIN SODIUM	-	-	-
KEFUROX®	per 750 mg	IM, IV	J0697
KEFZOL®	500 mg	IV, IM	J0690
KEFZOL®, *SEE* CEFAZOLIN SODIUM	-	-	-
KENAJECT-40®, *SEE* TRIAMCINOLONE ACETONIDE	-	-	-
KENALOG-10®, *SEE* TRIAMCINOLONE ACETONIDE	-	-	-
KENALOG-40®, *SEE* TRIAMCINOLONE ACETONIDE	-	-	-
KEPIVANCE®	50 mcg	IV	J2425
KEPPRA®	10 mg	IV	J1953
KEPPRA®, *SEE* LEVETIRACETAM	-	-	-
KESTRONE 5®, *SEE* ESTRONE	-	-	-
KETOROLAC TROMETHAMINE	per 15 mg	IM, IV	J1885
KEY-PRED-SP®, *SEE* PREDNISOLONE	-	-	-
KEYTRUDA®	1 mg	IV	J9271
K-FLEX®, *SEE* ORPHENADRINE CITRATE	-	-	-
KINEVAC®	5 mcg	IV	J2805
KINLYTIC®	5, 000 IU vial	IV	J3364
KINLYTIC®	250, 000 IU vial	IV	J3365
KLEBCIL®, *SEE* KANAMYCIN SULFATE	-	-	-
K-LOR®	per 2 mEq	IV	J3480
KLOR-CON®	per 2 mEq	IV	J3480
KOATE-DVI®	per IU	IV	J7190
KOATE-HP®, *SEE* FACTOR VIII	-	-	-
KOGENATE FS®	per IU	IV	J7192
KONAKION®, *SEE* VITAMIN K, PHYTONADIONE, ETC.	-	-	-
KRYSTEXXA®	1 mg	IV	J2507
KYLEENA®	19.5 mg	OTH	J7296
KYPROLIS®	1 mg	IV	J9047
KYTRIL®, *SEE* GRANISETRON HCL	-	-	-
L.A.E. 20®, *SEE* ESTRADIOL VALERATE	-	-	-

DRUG NAME	UNIT PER	ROUTE	CODE
LAETRILE, AMYGDALIN, VITAMIN B-17	per dose	INJ	J3570
LANOXIN®	up to 0.5 mg	IM, IV	J1160
LANOXIN®, SEE DIGOXIN	-	-	-
LANREOTIDE	1 mg	SC	J1930
LARONIDASE	0.1 mg	IV	J1931
LASIX®	up to 20 mg	IM, IV	J1940
LASIX®, SEE FUROSEMIDE	-	-	-
L-CAINE®, SEE LIDOCAINE HCL	-	-	-
LEMTRADA®	10 mg	IV	J0202
LEPIRUDIN	50 mg	IV	J1945
LEUCOVORIN CALCIUM	per 50 mg	IM, IV	J0640
LEUKINE®	50 mcg	IV	J2820
LEUKINE®, SEE SARGRAMOSTIM (GM-CSF)	-	-	-
LEUPROLIDE ACETATE	per 1 mg	IM	J9218
LEUPROLIDE ACETATE (FOR DEPOT SUSPENSION)	per 3.75 mg	IM	J1950
LEUPROLIDE ACETATE (FOR DEPOT SUSPENSION)	7.5 mg	IM	J9217
LEUPROLIDE ACETATE IMPLANT	65 mg	OTH	J9219
LEUSTATIN®, SEE CLADRIBINE	-	-	-
LEVALBUTEROL HCL, CONCENTRATED FORM	0.5 mg	INH	J7607, J7612
LEVALBUTEROL HCL, UNIT DOSE FORM	0.5 mg	INH	J7614, J7615
LEVAQUIN I.U.®, SEE LEVOFLOXACIN	-	-	-
LEVAQUIN®	250 mg	IV	J1956
LEVETIRACETAM	10 mg	IV	J1953
LEVOCARNITINE	per 1 gm	IV	J1955
LEVO-DROMORAN®, SEE LEVORPHANOL TARTRATE	-	-	-
LEVOFLOXACIN	250 mg	IV	J1956
LEVOLEUCOVORIN CALCIUM	0.5 mg	IV	J0641
LEVONORGESTREL IMPLANT	each	OTH	J7306
LEVONORGESTREL-RELEASING INTRAUTERINE CONTRACEPTIVE	52 mg	OTH	J7297, J7298
LEVONORGESTREL-RELEASING INTRAUTERINE CONTRACEPTIVE SYSTEM	19.5 mg	OTH	J7296
LEVORPHANOL TARTRATE	up to 2 mg	SC, IV	J1960
LEVSIN®, SEE HYOSCYAMINE SULFATE	-	-	-
LEVULAN KERASTICK®	unit dose (354 mg)	OTH	J7308
LEVULAN KERASTICK®, SEE AMINOLEVULINIC ACID HCL	-	-	-
LEXISCAN®	0.1 mg	IV	J2785
LEXISCAN®, SEE REGADENOSON	-	-	-
LIBERIM D®	50 mg	IM	J2788

DRUG NAME	UNIT PER	ROUTE	CODE
LIBERIM D®	1 dose package, 300 mcg	IM	J2790
LIBRITABS®	up to 100 mg	IM, IV	J1990
LIBRIUM®	up to 100 mg	IM, IV	J1990
LIBRIUM®, SEE CHLORDIAZEPOXIDE HCL	-	-	-
LIDOCAINE HCL	10 mg	IV	J2001
LIDOJECT-1®, SEE LIDOCAINE HCL	-	-	-
LIDOJECT-2®, SEE LIDOCAINE HCL	-	-	-
LILETTA®	52 mg	OTH	J7297
LINCOCIN®	up to 300 mg	IV	J2010
LINCOCIN®, SEE LINCOMYCIN HCL	-	-	-
LINCOMYCIN HCL	up to 300 mg	IV	J2010
LINCOREX®	up to 300 mg	IV	J2010
LINEZOLID	200 mg	IV	J2020
LIORESAL INTRATHECAL®	10 mg	IT	J0475
LIORESAL INTRATHECAL®	50 mcg	OTH	J0476
LIORESAL®	10 mg	IT	J0475
LIORESAL®	50 mcg	OTH	J0476
LIORESAL®, SEE BACLOFEN	-	-	-
LIPODOX®	10 mg	IV	Q2050
LIQUAEMIN SODIUM®, SEE HEPARIN SODIUM	-	-	-
LMD (10%)®, SEE DEXTRAN 40	-	-	-
LMD®	500 ml	IV	J7100
LORAZEPAM	2 mg	IM, IV	J2060
LOVENOX HP®	10 mg	SC	J1650
LOVENOX®	10 mg	SC	J1650
LOVENOX®, SEE ENOXAPARIN SODIUM	-	-	-
LUCENTIS®	0.1 mg	OTH	J2778
LUFYLLIN®, SEE DYPHYLLINE	-	-	-
LUMASON®	per ml	IV	Q9950
LUMIZYME®	10 mg	IV	J0221
LUNELLE®, SEE MEDROXYPROGESTERONE ACETATE/ ESTRADIOL CYPIONATE	-	-	-
LUPRON DEPOT®	per 3.75 mg	IM	J1950
LUPRON DEPOT®	7.5 mg	IM	J9217
LUPRON®	per 1 mg	IM	J9218
LYMPHOCYTE IMMUNE GLOBULIN, ANTI-THYMOCYTE GLOBULIN, EQUINE	250 mg	IV	J7504

DRUG NAME	UNIT PER	ROUTE	CODE
LYMPHOCYTE IMMUNE GLOBULIN, ANTI-THYMOCYTE GLOBULIN, RABBIT	25 mg	IV	J7511
LYOPHILIZED®, SEE CYCLOPHOSPHAMIDE, LYOPHILIZED	-	-	-
MACUGEN®	0.3 mg	OTH	J2503
MAGNESIUM SULFATE	500 mg	-	J3475
MAKENA®, SEE HYDROXYPROGESTERONE CAPROATE	-	-	-
MANNITOL	25% in 50 ml	IV	J2150
MANNITOL	5 mg	INH	J7665
MAPAP®	10 mg	IV	J0131
MARINOL®	2.5 mg	ORAL	Q0167
MARMINE®, SEE DIMENHYDRINATE	-	-	-
MARQIBO®	1 mg	IV	J9371
MAXIPIME®	500 mg	IV	J0692
MECASERMIN	1 mg	SC	J2170
MECHLORETHAMINE HCL (NITROGEN MUSTARD), HN2	10 mg	IV	J9230
MEDRALONE 40®, SEE METHYLPREDNISOLONE ACETATE	-	-	-
MEDRALONE 80®, SEE METHYLPREDNISOLONE ACETATE	-	-	-
MEDROL DOSEPAK®	20 mg	IM	J1020
MEDROL DOSEPAK®	40 mg	IM	J1030
MEDROL DOSEPAK®	80 mg	IM	J1040
MEDROL DOSEPAK®	up to 40 mg	IM, IV	J2920
MEDROL DOSEPAK®	up to 125 mg	IM, IV	J2930
MEDROL DOSEPAK®	per 4 mg	ORAL	J7509
MEDROL®, SEE METHYLPREDNISOLONE ACETATE	-	-	-
MEDROXYPROGESTERONE ACETATE	1 mg	IM	J1050
MEFOXIN®	1 g	IV, IM	J0694
MEFOXIN®, SEE CEFOXITIN SODIUM	-	-	-
MELPHALAN HCL	50 mg	IV	J9245
MELPHALAN, ORAL	2 mg	ORAL	J8600
MENOJECT LA®, SEE TESTOSTERONE CYPIONATE AND ESTRADIOL CYPIONATE	-	-	-
MEPERIDINE AND PROMETHAZINE HCL	up to 50 mg	IM, IV	J2180
MEPERIDINE HCL	per 100 mg	IM, IV, SC	J2175
MEPIVACAINE HCL	per 10 ml	VAR	J0670
MEPOLIZUMAB	1 mg	IV	J2182
MEROPENEM	100 mg	IV	J2185
MERREM®	100 mg	IV	J2185
MESNA	200 mg	IV	J9209

DRUG NAME	UNIT PER	ROUTE	CODE
MESNEX®	200 mg	IV	J9209
METAPROTERENOL SULFATE, CONCENTRATED FORM	per 10 mg	INH	J7667, J7668
METAPROTERENOL SULFATE, UNIT DOSE FORM	per 10 mg	INH	J7669, J7670
METARAMINOL BITARTRATE	per 10 mg	IV, IM, SC	J0380
METASTRON®, SEE STRONTIUM-89 CHLORIDE	-	-	-
METHACHOLINE CHLORIDE	1 mg	INH	J7674
METHADONE HCL	up to 10 mg	IM, SC	J1230
METHERGINE®	0.2 mg	IV	J2210
METHERGINE®, SEE METHYLERGONOVINE MALEATE	-	-	-
METHOCARBAMOL	up to 10 ml	IV, IM	J2800
METHOTREXATE LPF®, SEE METHOTREXATE SODIUM	-	-	-
METHOTREXATE SODIUM	5 mg	IV, IM, IT, IA	J9250
METHOTREXATE SODIUM	50 mg	IV, IM, IT, IA	J9260
METHOTREXATE, ORAL	2.5 mg	ORAL	J8610
METHYLDOPATE HYDROCHLORIDE	up to 250 mg	IV	J0210
METHYLERGONOVINE MALEATE	UP TO 0.2 mg	IV, IM	J2210
METHYLNALTREXONE	0.1 mg	SC	J2212
METHYLPREDNISOLONE ACETATE	20 mg	IM	J1020
METHYLPREDNISOLONE ACETATE	40 mg	IM	J1030
METHYLPREDNISOLONE ACETATE	80 mg	IM	J1040
METHYLPREDNISOLONE SODIUM SUCCINATE	up to 40 mg	IM, IV	J2920
METHYLPREDNISOLONE SODIUM SUCCINATE	up to 125 mg	IM, IV	J2930
METHYLPREDNISOLONE, ORAL	per 4 mg	ORAL	J7509
METOCLOPRAMIDE HCL	up to 10 mg	IV	J2765
METOZOLV ODT®	up to 10 mg	IV	J2765
METRODIN®	75 iu	SC	J3355
METVIXIA®, SEE AMINOLEVULINATE	-	-	-
MIACALCIN®	up to 400 units	SC, IM	J0630
MIACALCIN®, SEE CALCITONIN-SALMON	-	-	-
MICAFUNGIN SODIUM	1 mg	IV	J2248
MICRHOGAM ULTRA FILTERED PLUS®	50 mg	IM	J2788
MICRHOGAM ULTRA FILTERED PLUS®	1 dose package, 300 mcg	IM	J2790
MICRHOGAM®	50 mg	IM	J2788

DRUG NAME	UNIT PER	ROUTE	CODE
MICRHOGAM®	1 dose package, 300 mcg	IM	J2790
MIDAZOLAM HCL	per 1 mg	IM, IV	J2250
MILLIPRED DP®	up to 1 ml	IM	J2650
MILLIPRED DP®	5 mg	ORAL	J7510
MILLIPRED®	up to 1 ml	IM	J2650
MILLIPRED®	5 mg	ORAL	J7510
MILRINONE LACTATE	5 mg	IV	J2260
MINIGAMULIN RH®	50 mg	IM	J2788
MINIGAMULIN RH®	1 dose package, 300 mcg	IM	J2790
MINOCIN®	1 mg	IV	J2265
MINOCINE®, SEE MINOCYCLINE HYDROCHLORIDE	-	-	-
MINOCYCLINE HYDROCHLORIDE	1 mg	IV	J2265
MIO-REL®	up to 60 mg	IV, IM	J2360
MIRCERA®	1 mcg	IV	J0887
MIRCERA®	1 mcg	IV	J0888
MITHRACIN®, SEE PLICAMYCIN	-	-	-
MITOMYCIN, OPTHALMIC	0.2 mg	OTH	J7315
MITOMYCIN	5 mg	IV	J9280
MITOSOL®, SEE MITOMYCIN	-	-	-
MITOXANTRONE HCL	per 5 mg	IV	J9293
MONARC-M®	per IU	IV	J7190
MONOCLATE-P®	per IU	IV	J7190
MONOCLATE-P®, SEE FACTOR VIII	-	-	-
MONOCLONAL ANTIBODIES, PARENTERAL	5 mg	IV	J7505
MONONINE	per IU	IV	J7194
MONONINE®	per IU	IV	J7193
MONONINE®, SEE FACTOR IX, PURIFIED, NON-RECOMBINANT	-	-	-
MONOVISC®	per dose	IV	J7327
MORPHINE SULFATE	up to 10 mg	IM, IV, SC	J2270
MORPHINE SULFATE	10 mg	SC, IM, IV	J2274
MOXIFLOXACIN	100 mg	IV	J2280
MOZOBIL®	1 mg	SC	J2562
MOZOBIL®, SEE PLERIXAFOR	-	-	-
M-PREDNISOL-40®, SEE METHYLPREDNISOLONE ACETATE	-	-	-
M-PREDNISOL-80®, SEE METHYLPREDNISOLONE ACETATE	-	-	-
MS CONTIN®	-	-	J2274
MUCOMYST®, SEE ACETYLCYSTEINE	-	-	-
MUROMONAB-CD3	5 mg	IV	J7505

DRUG NAME	UNIT PER	ROUTE	CODE
MUSE®	per dose	OTH	J0270
MUSE® URETHRAL SUPPOSITORY.	each	OTH	J0275
MUSTARGEN®	10 mg	IV	J9230
MUSTARGEN®, SEE MECHLORETHAMINE HCL	-	-	-
MUTAMYCIN®	5 mg	IV	J9280
MUTAMYCIN®, SEE MITOMYCIN	-	-	-
MYCAMINE®	1 mg	IV	J2248
MYCOPHENOLATE MOFETIL	250 mg	ORAL	J7517
MYCOPHENOLIC ACID	180 mg	ORAL	J7518
MYFORTIC®	180 mg	ORAL	J7518
MYLERAN®	2 mg	ORAL	J8510
MYLERAN®, SEE BUSULFAN	-	-	-
MYLOTARG®, SEE GEMTUZUMAB OZOGAMICIN	-	-	-
MYOBLOC®	100 units	IM	J0587
MYOBLOC®, SEE RIMABOTULINUMTOXINB	-	-	-
MYOCHRYSINE®, SEE GOLD SODIUM THIOMALATE	-	-	-
MYOLIN®	up to 60 mg	IV, IM	J2360
MYOLIN®, SEE ORPHENADRINE CITRATE	-	-	-
MYOZYME®	10 mg	IV	J0220
NABILONE	1 mg	ORAL	J8650
NAC®	100 mg	IV	J0132
NAC®	per gram	INH	J7608
NAGLAZYME®	1 mg	IV	J1458
NALBUPHINE HCL	per 10 mg	IM, IV, SC	J2300
NALOXONE HCL	per 1 mg	IM, IV, SC	J2310
NALTREXONE, DEPOT FORM	1 mg	IM	J2315
NANDROBOLIC L.A.®, SEE NANDROLONE DECANOATE	-	-	-
NANDROLONE DECANOATE	up to 50 mg	IM	J2320
NARCAN®	per 1 mg	IM, IV, SC	J2310
NARCAN®, SEE NALOXONE HCL	-	-	-
NAROPIN POLYAMP®	1 mg	OTH	J2795
NAROPIN SDV®	1 mg	OTH	J2795
NAROPIN®	1 mg	OTH	J2795
NASAHIST B®	per 10 mg	IM, SC, IV	J0945
NASAHIST B®, SEE BROMPHENIRAMINE MALEATE	-	-	-
NASAL VACCINE INHALATION	per dose	INH	J3530
NATALIZUMAB	1 mg	IV	J2323
NATRECOR®	0.1 mg	IV	J2325
NAVELBINE®	per 10 mg	IV	J9390

DRUG NAME	UNIT PER	ROUTE	CODE
NAVELBINE®, SEE VINORELBINE TARTRATE	-	-	-
ND STAT®, SEE BROMPHENIRAMINE MALEATE	-	-	-
NEBCIN®, SEE TOBRAMYCIN SULFATE	-	-	-
NEBUPENT®	per 300 mg	INH	J2545
NEBUPENT®	300 mg	OTH	J7676
NECITUMUMAB	1 mg	IV	J9295
NELARABINE	50 mg	IV	J9261
NEMBUTAL SODIUM SOLUTION®, SEE PENTOBARBITAL SODIUM	-	-	-
NEMBUTAL SODIUM®	per 50 mg	IM, IV, OTH	J2515
NEOCYTEN®, SEE ORPHENADRINE CITRATE	-	-	-
NEO-DURABOLIC®, SEE NANDROLONE DECANOATE	-	-	-
NEOQUESS®, SEE DICYCLOMINE HCL	-	-	-
NEORAL®	100 mg	ORAL	J7502
NEORAL®	25 mg	ORAL	J7515
NEORAL®	250 mg	IV	J7516
NEOSAR®	100 mg	IV	J9070
NEOSAR®, SEE CYCLOPHOSPHAMIDE	-	-	-
NEOSTIGMINE METHYLSULFATE	up to 0.5 mg	IM, IV, SC	J2710
NEOSYNEPHRINE®	up to 1 ml	SC, IM, IV	J2370
NERVOCAINE 1%®, SEE LIDOCAINE HCL	-	-	-
NERVOCAINE 2%®, SEE LIDOCAINE HCL	-	-	-
NESACAINE®, SEE CHLOROPROCAINE HCL	-	-	-
NESACAINE-MPF®, SEE CHLOROPROCAINE HCL	-	-	-
NESIRITIDE	0.1 mg	IV	J2325
NETSPOT®	0.1 mCi	IV	A9587
NETUPITANT/PALONOSETRON	300 mg/ 0.5 mg	ORAL	J8655
NEULASTA®	6 mg	SC	J2505
NEUMEGA®	5 mg	SC	J2355
NEUMEGA®, SEE OPRELVEKIN	-	-	-
NEUPOGEN®	1 mcg	SC, IV	J1442
NEUPOGEN®, SEE FILGRASTIM (G-CSF)	-	-	-
NEURACEQ®	up to 8.1 millicuries	IV	Q9983
NEUTREXIN®, SEE TRIMETREXATE GLUCURONATE	-	-	-
NEXPLANON®	-	-	J7307
NIPENT®	per 10 mg	IV	J9268

DRUG NAME	UNIT PER	ROUTE	CODE
NIPENT®, SEE PENTOSTATIN	-	-	-
NIVOLUMAB	1 mg	IV	J9299
NORDITROPIN FLEXPRO PEN®	1 mg	SC	J2941
NORFLEX®, SEE ORPHENADRINE CITRATE	-	-	-
NORZINE®, SEE THIETHYLPERAZINE MALEATE	-	-	-
NOT OTHERWISE CLASSIFIED DRUGS	-	-	J3490
NOT OTHERWISE CLASSIFIED DRUGS	-	other than INH administered thru DME	J7799
NOT OTHERWISE CLASSIFIED DRUGS	-	INH administered thru DME	J7699
NOT OTHERWISE CLASSIFIED DRUGS, ANTI-NEOPLASTIC	-	-	J9999
NOT OTHERWISE CLASSIFIED DRUGS, CHEMOTHERAPEUTIC	-	ORAL	J8999
NOT OTHERWISE CLASSIFIED DRUGS, IMMUNOSUPPRESSIVE	-	-	J7599
NOT OTHERWISE CLASSIFIED DRUGS, NONCHEMOTHERAPEUTIC	-	ORAL	J8499
NOVANTRONE®	per 5 mg	IV	J9293
NOVANTRONE®, SEE MITOXANTRONE HCL	-	-	-
NOVAREL®	per 1, 000 USP units	IM	J0725
NOVO SEVEN®, SEE FACTOR VIIA	-	-	-
NOVOEIGHT®	per IU	IV	J7182
NOVOSEVEN®	1 mcg	IV	J7189
NPH®, SEE INSULIN	-	-	-
NPLATE®	10 mcg	SC	J2796
NPLATE®, SEE ROMIPLOSTIM	-	-	-
NUBAIN®, SEE NALBUPHINE HCL	-	-	-
NUCALA®	1 mg	IV	J2182
NULECIT®	12.5 mg	IV	J2916
NULICAINE®, SEE LIDOCAINE HCL	-	-	-
NULOJIX®	1 mg	IV	J0485
NULOJIX®, SEE BELATACEPT	-	-	-
NUMORPHAN H.P.®, SEE OXYMORPHONE HCL	-	-	-
NUMORPHAN HCL®	up to 1 mg	IV, SC, IM	J2410
NUMORPHAN®, SEE OXYMORPHONE HCL	-	-	-
NUSINERSEN	0.1 mg	IV	J2326
NUTROPIN AQ NUSPIN 5®	1 mg	SC	J2941
NUTROPIN AQ NUSPIN 10®	1 mg	SC	J2941
NUTROPIN AQ NUSPIN 20®	1 mg	SC	J2941
NUTROPIN AQ PEN 10 CARTRIDGE®	1 mg	SC	J2941
NUTROPIN AQ PEN 20 CARTRIDGE®	1 mg	SC	J2941

DRUG NAME	UNIT PER	ROUTE	CODE
NUTROPIN®	1 mg	SC	J2941
NUVARING®	each	OTH	J7303
NUWIQ®	1 IU	IV	J7209
NYTOL QUICKCAPS®	50 mg	ORAL	Q0163
OBIZUR®	per IU	IV	J7191
OCRELIZUMAB	1 mg	IV	J2350
OCRIPLASMIN	0.125 mg	IV	J7316
OCTAGAM®	500 mg	IV	J1568
OCTREOTIDE ACETATE, INJECTION	1 mg	IM	J2353
OCTREOTIDE ACETATE, INJECTION	25 mcg	IV, SQ	J2354
OCULINUM®, *SEE* ONABOTULINUMTOXINA	-	-	-
OFATUMUMAB	10 mg	IV	J9302
OFIRMEV®, *SEE* ACETAMINOPHEN	-	-	-
OFIRMEV®	10 mg	IV	J0131
O-FLEX®, *SEE* ORPHENADRINE CITRATE	-	-	-
OFORTA®, *SEE* FLUDARABINE PHOSPHATE	-	-	-
OLANZAPINE	1 mg	IM	J2358
OLARATUMAB	10 mg	IV	J9285
OMACETAXINE MEPESUCCINATE	0.01 mg	IV	J9262
OMALIZUMAB	5 mg	SC	J2357
OMIDRIA®	4 ml vial	OTH	C9447
OMNIPEN-N®, *SEE* AMPICILLIN SODIUM	-	-	-
OMNITROPE® PEN 5 CARTRIDGE®	1 mg	SC	J2941
OMNITROPE® PEN 10 CARTRIDGE®	1 mg	SC	J2941
OMONTYS®, *SEE* PEGINESATIDE	-	-	-
ONABOTULINUMTOXINA	1 unit	IM	J0585
ONCASPAR®	per single dose vial	IM, IV	J9266
ONCASPAR®, *SEE* PEGASPARGASE	-	-	-
ONCOVIN®, *SEE* VINCRISTINE SULFATE	-	-	-
ONDANSETRON HCl	1 mg	IV	J2405
ONDANSETRON HCL, ORAL	1 mg	ORAL	Q0162
ONIVYDE®	1 mg	IV	J9205
ONMEL®	50 mg	IV	J1835
ONTAK®	300 mcg	IV	J9160
OPANA®	up to 1 mg	IV, SC, IM	J2410
OPRELVEKIN	5 mg	SC	J2355
ORAMINIC II®, *SEE* BROMPHENIRAMINE MALEATE	-	-	-
ORAPRED ODT®	5 mg	ORAL	J7510
ORAVERSE®	up to 5 mg	IM, IV	J2760
ORBACTIV®	10 mg	IV	J2407
ORENCIA®	10 mg	IV	J0129
ORENITRAM®	1 mg	IV, OTH	J3285

DRUG NAME	UNIT PER	ROUTE	CODE
ORFRO®	up to 60 mg	IV, IM	J2360
ORMAZINE®, *SEE* CHLORPROMAZINE HCL	-	-	-
ORPHENADRINE CITRATE	up to 60 mg	IV, IM	J2360
ORPHENATE®	up to 60 mg	IV, IM	J2360
ORPHENATE®, *SEE* ORPHENADRINE CITRATE	-	-	-
ORTHOCLONE OKT3®	5 mg	IV	J7505
ORTHOVISC®	per dose	OTH	J7324
OR-TYL®, *SEE* DICYCLOMINE HCL	-	-	-
OSMITROL®	25% in 50 ml	IV	J2150
OSMITROL®	5 mg	INH	J7665
OTIPRIO®	6 mg	OTH	J7342
OXACILLIN SODIUM	up to 250 mg	IM, IV	J2700
OXALIPLATIN	0.5 mg	IV	J9263
OXYMORPHONE HCL	up to 1 mg	IV, SC, IM	J2410
OXYTETRACYCLINE HCL	up to 50 mg	IM	J2460
OXYTOCIN	up to 10 units	IV, IM	J2590
OZURDEX®	0.1 mg	OTH	J7312
OZURDEX®, *SEE* DEXAMETHASONE, INTRAVITREAL IMPLANT	-	-	-
PACERONE®	30 mg	IV	J0282
PACLITAXEL	1 mg	IV	J9267
PACLITAXEL PROTEIN-BOUND PARTICLES	1 mg	IV	J9264
PALIFERMIN	50 mcg	IV	J2425
PALIPERIDONE PALMITATE	1 mg	IM	J2426
PALONOSETRON HCL	25 mcg	IV	J2469
PAMIDRONATE DISODIUM	per 30 mg	IV	J2430
PANHEMATIN®	1 mg	INJ	J1640
PANITUMUMAB	10 mg	IV	J9303
PAPAVERINE HCL	up to 60 mg	IV, IM	J2440
PARAGARD T 380 A®, *SEE* COPPER CONTRACEPTIVE, INTRAUTERINE	-	-	-
PARAGARD®	each	OTH	J7300
PARAPLATIN®	50 mg	IV	J9045
PARAPLATIN®, *SEE* CARBOPLATIN	-	-	-
PARICALCITOL, INJECTION	1 mcg	IV, IM	J2501
PASIREOTIDE LONG ACTING	1 mg	INJ	J2502
PARTOBULIN SDF®	50 mg	IM	J2788
PARTOBULIN SDF®	1 dose package, 300 mcg	IM	J2790
PEDIAPRED®	up to 1 ml	IM	J2650

DRUG NAME	UNIT PER	ROUTE	CODE
PEDIAPRED®	5 mg	ORAL	J7510
PEFOROMIST®, *SEE* FORMOTEROL FUMARATE	-	-	-
PEGADEMASE BOVINE	25 iu	-	J2504
PEGAPTANIB	0.3 mg	OTH	J2503
PEGASPARGASE	per single dose vial	IM, IV	J9266
PEGFILGRASTIM	6 mg	SC	J2505
PEGINESATIDE	0.1 mg	IV, SC	J0890
PEGLOTICASE	1 mg	IV	J2507
PEMETREXED	10 mg	IV	J9305
PENICILLIN G BENZATHINE	100, 000 units	IM	J0561
PENICILLIN G BENZATHINE AND PENICILLIN G PROCAINE	100, 000 units	IM	J0558
PENICILLIN G POTASSIUM	up to 600, 000 units	IM, IV	J2540
PENICILLIN G PROCAINE, AQUEOUS	up to 600, 000 units	IM, IV	J2510
PENTACARINAT®	per 300 mg	INH	J2545
PENTAM 300®	per 300 mg	INH	J2545
PENTAMIDINE ISETHIONATE	per 300 mg	INH	J2545, J7676
PENTASTARCH, 10%	100 ml	IV	J2513
PENTAZOCINE HCL	30 mg	IM, SC, IV	J3070
PENTOBARBITAL SODIUM	per 50 mg	IM, IV, OTH	J2515
PENTOSTATIN	per 10 mg	IV	J9268
PERAMIVIR	1 mg	INJ	J2547
PERFOROMIST®	20 mcg	INH	J7606
PERJETA®	1 mg	IV	J9306
PERMAPEN®, *SEE* PENICILLIN G BENZATHINE	-	-	-
PERMITIL®	25 mg	IM	J2680
PERPHENAZINE, INJECTION	up to 5 mg	IM, IV	J3310
PERPHENAZINE, TABLETS	4 mg	ORAL	Q0175
PERSANTINE IV®	per 10 mg	IV	J1245
PERSANTINE IV®, *SEE* DIPYRIDAMOLE	-	-	-
PERTUZUMAB	1 mg	IV	J9306
PFIZERPEN A.S.®, *SEE* PENICILLIN G PROCAINE	-	-	-
PFIZERPEN®	up to 600, 000 units	IM, IV	J2540
PFIZERPEN®, *SEE* PENICILLIN G POTASSIUM	-	-	-
PHARMORUBICIN PFS®	2 mg	IV	J9178
PHARMORUBICIN RDF®	2 mg	IV	J9178
PHENAZINE 25®, *SEE* PROMETHAZINE HCL	-	-	-

DRUG NAME	UNIT PER	ROUTE	CODE
PHENAZINE 50®, *SEE* PROMETHAZINE HCL	-	-	-
PHENERGAN®	up to 50 mg	IM, IV	J2550
PHENERGAN®	12.5 mg	ORAL	Q0169
PHENERGAN®, *SEE* PROMETHAZINE HCL	-	-	-
PHENOBARBITAL SODIUM	up to 120 mg	IM, IV	J2560
PHENTOLAMINE MESYLATE	up to 5 mg	IM, IV	J2760
PHENYLEPHRINE HCL	up to 1 ml	SC, IM, IV	J2370
PHENYTOIN SODIUM	per 50 mg	IM, IV	J1165
PHOTOFRIN®	75 mg	IV	J9600
PHOTOFRIN®, *SEE* PORFIMER SODIUM	-	-	-
PHYTONADIONE (VITAMIN K)	per 1 mg	IM, SC, IV	J3430
PIPERACILLIN/TAZOBACTAM SODIUM, INJECTION	1.125 g	IV	J2543
PITOCIN®	up to 10 units	IV, IM	J2590
PITOCIN®, *SEE* OXYTOCIN	-	-	-
PLANTINOL AQ®, *SEE* CISPLATIN	-	-	-
PLAS+SD®, *SEE* PLASMA, POOLED MULTIPLE DONOR	-	-	-
PLASMA, CRYOPRECIPITATE REDUCED	each unit	IV	P9044
PLASMA, POOLED MULTIPLE DONOR, PATHOGEN REDUCED, FROZEN	each unit	IV	P9070
PLASMA, POOLED MULTIPLE DONOR, SOLVENT/DETERGENT TREATED, FROZEN	each unit	IV	P9023
PLASMA (SINGLE DONOR), PATHOGEN REDUCED, FROZEN	each unit	IV	P9071
PLATINOL®, *SEE* CISPLATIN	-	-	-
PLERIXAFOR	1 mg	SC	J2562
PLICAMYCIN	2, 500 mcg	IV	J9270
POLOCAINE MPF®	per 10 ml	VAR	J0670
POLOCAINE®, *SEE* MEPIVACAINE HCL	-	-	-
PORFIMER SODIUM	75 mg	IV	J9600
PORTRAZZA®	1 mg	IV	J9295
POTASSIUM CHLORIDE	per 2 mEq	IV	J3480
POXI®	up to 100 mg	IM, IV	J1990
PRALATREXATE	1 mg	IV	J9307
PRALIDOXIME CHLORIDE	up to 1 g	IV, IM, SC	J2730
PREDCOR®, *SEE* PREDNISOLONE ACETATE	-	-	-
PREDICORT®, *SEE* PREDNISOLONE ACETATE	-	-	-
PREDNISOLONE ACETATE	up to 1 ml	IM	J2650

DRUG NAME	UNIT PER	ROUTE	CODE
PREDNISOLONE, ORAL	5 mg	ORAL	J7510
PREDNISONE	1 mg	ORAL	J7512
PREDOJECT-50®, SEE PREDNISOLONE ACETATE	-	-	-
PREGNYL®	per 1, 000 USP units	IM	J0725
PREGNYL®, SEE CHORIONIC GONADOTROPIN	-	-	-
PRELONE®	up to 1 ml	IM	J2650
PRELONE®	5 mg	ORAL	J7510
PREMARIN INTRAVENOUS®, SEE ESTROGEN, CONJUGATED	-	-	-
PREMARIN®	per 25 mg	IV, IM	J1410
PRESCRIPTION, CHEMOTHERAPEUTIC, NOT OTHERWISE SPECIFIED	-	ORAL	J8999
PRESCRIPTION, NONCHEMOTHERAPEUTIC, NOT OTHERWISE SPECIFIED	-	ORAL	J8499
PRI CORTIN 50®	up to 1 ml	IM	J2650
PRIALT®	1 mcg	OTH	J2278
PRI-CORTIN 50®, SEE PREDNISOLONE ACETATE	-	-	-
PRIMACOR®	5 mg	IV	J2260
PRIMACOR®, SEE MILRINONE LACTATE	-	-	-
PRIMAXIN I.M.®, SEE CILASTATIN SODIUM, IMIPENEM	-	-	-
PRIMAXIN I.V.®, SEE CILASTATIN SODIUM, IMIPENEM	-	-	-
PRIMAXIN IV®	per 250 mg	IV, IM	J0743
PRISCOLINE HCL®, SEE TOLAZOLINE HCL	-	-	-
PRISCOLINE®, SEE TOLAZOLINE HCL	-	-	-
PRIVIGEN®	500 mg	IV	J1459
PROAIR HFA®	1 mg	INH	J7611
PROAIR HFA®	1 mg	INH	J7613
PROBUPHINE®	74.2 mg	Implant	J0570
PROCAINAMIDE HCL	up to 1 g	IM, IV	J2690
PROCAN SR®	up to 1 g	IM, IV	J2690
PROCANBID®	up to 1 g	IM, IV	J2690
PROCHLORPERAZINE	up to 10 mg	IM, IV	J0780
PROCHLORPERAZINE MALEATE, ORAL	5 mg	ORAL	Q0164
PROCRIT®	1000 units	IV, OTH	J0885
PROCRIT®	1000 units	IV, SC	Q4081
PROFASI HP®, SEE CHORIONIC GONADOTROPIN	-	-	-
PROFILNINE HEAT-TREATED®, SEE FACTOR IX	-	-	-
PROFILNINE SD®	per IU	IV	J7194

DRUG NAME	UNIT PER	ROUTE	CODE
PROGEST®	per 50 mg	IM	J2675
PROGESTAJECT®, SEE PROGESTERONE	-	-	-
PROGESTERONE	per 50 mg	IM	J2675
PROGLYCEM®	up to 300 mg	IV	J1730
PROGRAF®	per 1 mg	ORAL	J7507
PROGRAF®	5 mg	IV	J7525
PROGRAF®, SEE TACROLIMUS, ORAL OR PARENTERAL	-	-	-
PROKINE®, SEE SARGRAMOSTIM (GM-CSF)	-	-	-
PROLASTIN®	10 mg	IV	J0256
PROLASTIN®, SEE ALPHA 1-PROTEINASE INHIBITOR, HUMAN	-	-	-
PROLASTIN-C®	10 mg	IV	J0256
PROLEUKIN®	per single use vial	IM, IV	J9015
PROLIXIN®	25 mg	IM	J2680
PROLIXIN DECANOATE®	25 mg	IM	J2680
PROLIXIN ENANTHATE®	25 mg	IM	J2680
PROMAZINE HCL	up to 25 mg	IM	J2950
PROMETHAZINE HCL, INJECTION	up to 50 mg	IM, IV	J2550
PROMETHAZINE HCL, ORAL	12.5 mg	ORAL	Q0169
PROMETRIUM®	per 50 mg	IM	J2675
PRONESTYL®, SEE PROCAINAMIDE HCL	-	-	-
PROP A TANE®	per 10 mg	IM, SC, IV	J0945
PROPLEX SX-T®, SEE FACTOR IX	-	-	-
PROPLEX T®	per IU	IV	J7194
PROPLEX T®, SEE FACTOR IX	-	-	-
PROPRANOLOL HCL	up to 1 mg	IV	J1800
PROREX-25®, SEE PROMETHAZINE HCL	-	-	-
PROREX-50®, SEE PROMETHAZINE HCL	-	-	-
PROSTAPHLIN®, SEE PROCAINAMIDE HCL	-	-	-
PROSTIGMIN BROMIDE®	up to 0.5 mg	IM, IV, SC	J2710
PROSTIGMIN®, SEE NEOSTIGMINE METHYLSULFATE	-	-	-
PROSTIN VR PEDIATRIC®	1.25 mcg	OTH	J0270
PROTAMINE SULFATE	per 10 mg	IV	J2720
PROTEIN C CONCENTRATE	10 IU	IV	J2724
PROTHAZINE®, SEE PROMETHAZINE HCL	-	-	-
PROTIRELIN	per 250 mcg	IV	J2725

DRUG NAME	UNIT PER	ROUTE	CODE
PROTOPAM CHLORIDE®	up to 1 g	IV, IM, SC	J2730
PROTOPAM CHLORIDE®, SEE PRALIDOXIME CHLORIDE	-	-	-
PROVENTIL HFA®	1 mg	INH	J7611
PROVENTIL HFA®	1 mg	INH	J7613
PROVENTIL®	1 mg	INH	J7611
PROVENTIL®	1 mg	INH	J7613
PROVENTIL®, SEE ALBUTEROL	-	-	-
PROVERA®	1 mg	IM	J1050
PROVOCHOLINE®	1 mg	INH	J7674
PROZINE-50®, SEE PROMAZINE HCL	-	-	-
PULMICORT RESPULES®, SEE BUDESONIDE	-	-	-
PULMOZYME®	per mg	INH	J7639
PYRIDOXINE HCL	100 mg	IM, IV	J3415
Q-PAP®	10 mg	IV	J0131
QUELICIN®	up to 20 mg	IV, IM	J0330
QUELICIN®, SEE SUCCINYLCHOLINE CHLORIDE	-	-	-
QUIBRON T/SR®	per 40 mg	IV	J2810
QUINUPRISTIN/DALFOPRISTIN	500 mg (150/350)	IV	J2770
QUTENZA®, SEE CAPSAICIN PATCH	-	-	-
RADIOPHARMACEUTICAL	per dose	OTH	A9597, A9598
RAMUCIRUMAB	5 mg	INJ	J9308
RANIBIZUMAB	0.1 mg	OTH	J2778
RANITIDINE HCL, INJECTION	25 mg	IV, IM	J2780
RAPAMUNE®	1 mg	Oral	J7520
RAPAMUNE®, SEE SIROLIMUS	-	-	-
RASBURICASE	0.5 mg	IV	J2783
REBIF®	30 mcg	IM	J1826
REBIF®	1 mcg	IM	Q3027
REBIF®	1 mcg	SC	Q3028
RECLAST®	1 mg	IV	J3489
RECOMBINATE®	per IU	IV	J7185
RECOMBINATE®	per IU	IV	J7192
RECOMBINATE®, SEE FACTOR VIII	-	-	-
REDISOL®, SEE VITAMIN B-12 CYANOCOBALAMIN	-	-	-
REGADENOSON	0.1 mg	IV	J2785
REGITINE®	up to 5 mg	IM, IV	J2760
REGITINE®, SEE PHENTOLAMINE MESYLATE	-	-	-
REGLAN®	up to 10 mg	IV	J2765
REGLAN®, SEE METOCLOPRAMIDE HCL	-	-	-
REGULAR®, SEE INSULIN	-	-	-

DRUG NAME	UNIT PER	ROUTE	CODE
RELEFACT TRH®, SEE PROTIRELIN	-	-	-
RELION VENTOLIN HFA®	1 mg	INH	J7611
RELION VENTOLIN HFA®	1 mg	INH	J7613
RELISTOR®	0.1 mg	SC	J2212
RELISTOR®, SEE METHYLNALTREXONE	-	-	-
REMICADE®	10 mg	IM, IV	J1745
REMICADE®, SEE INFLIXIMAB, INJECTION	-	-	-
REO PRO®, SEE ABCIXIMAB	-	-	-
REOPRO®	10 mg	IV	J0130
REP-PRED 40®, SEE METHYLPREDNISOLONE ACETATE	-	-	-
REP-PRED 80®, SEE METHYLPREDNISOLONE ACETATE	-	-	-
RESECTISOL®	5 mg	INH	J7665
RESECTISOL®	25% in 50 ml	IV	J2150
RESLIZUMAB	1 mg	IV	J2786
RETAVASE®	18.8 mg	IV	J2993
RETAVASE®, SEE RETEPLASE	-	-	-
RETEPLASE	18.8 mg	IV	J2993
RETROVIR®	10 mg	IV	J3485
RETROVIR®, SEE ZIDOVUDINE	-	-	-
RHEOMACRODEX®, SEE DEXTRAN 40	-	-	-
RHESONATIV®, SEE RHO(D) IMMUNE GLOBULIN, HUMAN	-	-	-
RHEUMATREX DOSE PACK®	2.5 mg	ORAL	J8610
RHEUMATREX DOSE PACK®	5 mg	IV, IM, IT, IA	J9250
RHEUMATREX DOSE PACK®	50 mg	IV, IM, IT, IA	J9260
RHO(D) IMMUNE GLOBULIN	100 iu	IM, IV	J2791
RHO(D) IMMUNE GLOBULIN, HUMAN	1 dose package, 300 mcg	IM	J2790
RHO(D) IMMUNE GLOBULIN, HUMAN	50 mg	IM	J2788
RHO(D)IMMUNE GLOBULIN, HUMAN, SOLVENT DETERGENT	100 IU	IV	J2792
RHOGAM ULTRA FILTERED PLUS®	50 mg	IM	J2788
RHOGAM ULTRA FILTERED PLUS®	1 dose package, 300 mcg	IM	J2790
RHOGAM®	50 mg	IM	J2788
RHOGAM®	1 dose package, 300 mcg	IM	J2790
RHOPHYLAC®	50 mg	IM	J2788
RHOPHYLAC®	1 dose package, 300 mcg	IM	J2790
RHOPHYLAC®	100 IU	IM	J2791
RIASTAP®	100 mg	IV	J7178

DRUG NAME	UNIT PER	ROUTE	CODE
RIASTAP®, *SEE* HUMAN FIBRINOGEN CONCENTRATE	-	-	-
RILONACEPT	1 mg	SC	J2793
RIMABOTULINUMTOXINB	100 units	IM	J0587
RIMSO 50®	50%, 50 ml	OTH	J1212
RINGERS LACTATE INFUSION	up to 1,000 cc	IV	J7120
RISPERDAL®	0.5 mg	IM	J2794
RISPERDAL CONSTA®	0.5 mg	IM	J2794
RISPERIDONE	0.5 mg	IM	J2794
RITUXAN®	100 mg	IV	J9310
RITUXAN®, *SEE* RITUXIMAB	-	-	-
RITUXIMAB	100 mg	IV	J9310
RIXUBIS®	per IU	IV	J7200
RIXUBIS®	per IU	IV	J7195
ROBAXIN®	up to 10 ml	IV, IM	J2800
ROCALTROL®	0.1 mcg	IM	J0636
ROCEPHIN®, *SEE* CEFTRIAXONE SODIUM	-	-	-
ROFERON-A®, *SEE* INTERFERON ALFA-2A, RECOMBINANT	-	-	-
ROLAPITANT HCL	1 mg	ORAL	J8670
ROMIDEPSIN	1 mg	IV	J9315
ROMIPLOSTIM	10 mcg	SC	J2796
ROPIVACAINE HYDROCHLORIDE	1 mg	OTH	J2795
RUBEX®	10 mg	IV	J9000
RUBEX®, *SEE* DOXORUBICIN HCL	-	-	-
RUBRAMIN PC®, *SEE* VITAMIN B-12 CYANOCOBALAMIN	-	-	-
RUM-K®	per 2 mEq	IV	J3480
SAIZEN®	1 mg	SC	J2941
SALINE SOLUTION	5% dextrose, 500 ml	IV	J7042
SALINE SOLUTION	infusion, 250 cc	IV	J7050
SALINE SOLUTION	infusion, 1,000 cc	IV	J7030
SALINE SOLUTION, STERILE	500 ml = 1 unit	IV, OTH	J7040
SAL-TROPINE®, *SEE* ATROPINE SULFATE	-	-	-
SANDIMMUNE®	100 mg	ORAL	J7502
SANDIMMUNE®	25 mg	ORAL	J7515
SANDIMMUNE®	250 mg	IV	J7516
SANDOSTATIN LAR DEPOT®	1 mg	IM	J2353
SANDOSTATIN®	25 mcg	IV, SQ	J2354
SARGRAMOSTIM (GM-CSF)	50 mcg	IV	J2820
SCANDONEST®	per 10 ml	VAR	J0670

DRUG NAME	UNIT PER	ROUTE	CODE
SCULPTRA	0.5 mg	IV	Q2028
SEBELIPASE ALFA	1 mg	IV	J2840
SECREFLO®	1mcg	IV	J2850
SECRETIN FERRING®	1mcg	IV	J2850
SELESTOJECT®	per 3 mg	IM	J0702
SERMORELIN ACETATE	1 mcg	SC	Q0515
SEROSTIM®	1 mg	SC	J2941
SILPHEN COUGH®	50 mg	ORAL	Q0163
SILTUXIMAB	10 mg	INJ	J2860
SIMPLY SLEEP®	50 mg	ORAL	Q0163
SIMPONI ARIA®	1 mg	IV	J1602
SIMPONI®	1 mg	IV	J1602
SIMULECT®	20 mg	IV	J0480
SINCALIDE	5 mcg	IV	J2805
SINUSOL-B®, *SEE* BROMPHENIRAMINE MALEATE	-	-	-
SIROLIMUS	1 mg	Oral	J7520
SITAVIG®	5 mg	IV	J0133
SIVEXTRO®	1 mg	IV	J3090
SKELEX®	up to 10 ml	IV, IM	J2800
SKYLA®	13.5 mg	OTH	J7301
SLEEPINAL®	50 mg	ORAL	Q0163
SLO PHYLLIN®, *SEE* THEOPHYLLINE	-	-	-
SODIUM FERRICGLUCONATE IN SUCROSE	12.5 mg	IV	J2916
SODIUM HYALURONATE	-	-	-
SODIUM HYALURONATE, EUFLEXXA®	per dose	OTH	J7323
SODIUM HYALURONATE, HYALGAN®	per dose	OTH	J7321
SODIUM HYALURONATE, ORTHOVISC®	per dose	OTH	J7324
SODIUM HYALURONATE, SUPARTZ®	per dose	OTH	J7321
SOLGANAL®, *SEE* AUROTHIOGLUCOSE	-	-	-
SOLIRIS®	10 mg	IV	J1300
SOLU-CORTEF®	up to 100 mg	IV, IM, SC	J1720
SOLU-CORTEF®, *SEE* HYDROCORTISONE SODIUM PHOSPHATE	-	-	-
SOLU-MEDROL®, *SEE* METHYLPREDNISOLONE SODIUM SUCCINATE	-	-	-
SOLUREX LA®, *SEE* DEXAMETHASONE ACETATE	-	-	-
SOLUREX®, *SEE* DEXAMETHASONE SODIUM PHOSPHATE	-	-	-
SOMATREM	1 mg	SC	J2940
SOMATROPIN	1 mg	SC	J2941
SOMATULIN DEPOT®, *SEE* LANREOTIDE	-	-	-

DRUG NAME	UNIT PER	ROUTE	CODE
SOMATULINE DEPOT®	1 mg	SC	J1930
SOMINEX®	50 mg	ORAL	Q0163
SOTALOL HYDROCHLORIDE (HCL)	1 mg	IV	C9482
SOTYLIZE®	1 mg	IV	C9482
SPARINE®, SEE PROMAZINE HCL	-	-	-
SPASMOJECT®, SEE DICYCLOMINE HCL	-	-	-
SPECTINOMYCIN HCL	up to 2 g	IM	J3320
SPORANOX®	50 mg	IV	J1835
SPORANOX®, SEE ITRACONAZOLE	-	-	-
STELARA®	1 mg	SC	J3357
STILPHOSTROL®, SEE DIETHYLSTILBESTROL DIPHOSPHATE	-	-	-
STREPTASE®, SEE STREPTOKINASE	-	-	-
STREPTOKINASE	per 250,000 IU	IV	J2995
STREPTOMYCIN	up to 1 g	IM	J3000
STREPTOMYCIN SULFATE®, SEE STREPTOMYCIN	-	-	-
STREPTOZOCIN	1 gm	IV	J9320
STRONTIUM-89 CHLORIDE	per millicurie	IV	A9600
SUBLIMAZE®	0.1 mg	IM, IV	J3010
SUBLIMAZE®, SEE FENTANYL CITRATE	-	-	-
SUBOXONE®	<=3 mg	ORAL	J0572
SUBOXONE®	>3 mg but <=6 mg	ORAL	J0573
SUBOXONE®	>6 mg but <=10 mg	ORAL	J0574
SUBOXONE®	>10 mg	ORAL	J0575
SUCCINYLCHOLINE CHLORIDE	up to 20 mg	IV, IM	J0330
SULFUR HEXAFLUORIDE LIPID MICROSPHERES	per ml	IV	Q9950
SUMATRIPTAN SUCCINATE	6 mg	SC	J3030
SUMAVEL DOSEPRO®	6 mg	SC	J3030
SUPARTZ®	per dose	OTH	J7321
SUPPRELIN®	10 mcg	INJ	J1675
SUPPRELIN LA®	50 mg	OTH	J9226
SUS-PHRINE®, SEE ADRENALIN, EPINEPHRINE	-	-	-
SYNERCID®	500 mg (150/350)	IV	J2770
SYNERCID®, SEE QUINUPRISTIN/DALFOPRISTIN	-	-	-
SYNKAVITE®, SEE PHYTONADIONE, (VITAMIN K)	-	-	-
SYNRIBO®	0.01 mg	IV	J9262
SYNTOCIONON®, SEE OXYTOCIN	-	-	-
SYNVISC ONE®	1 mg	OTH	J7325
SYTOBEX®, SEE VITAMIN B-12 CYANOCOBALAMIN	-	-	-

DRUG NAME	UNIT PER	ROUTE	CODE
TACROLIMUS, EXTENDED RELEASE (ENVARSUS XR®)	0.25 mg	ORAL	J7503
TACROLIMUS, ORAL, EXTENDED RELEASE	0.1 mg	ORAL	J7508
TACROLIMUS, ORAL, IMMEDIATE RELEASE	per 1 mg	ORAL	J7507
TACROLIMUS, PARENTERAL	5 mg	IV	J7525
TACTINAL®	10 mg	IV	J0131
TALADINE®	25 mg	IV, IM	J2780
TALIGLUCERACE ALFA	10 units	IV	J3060
TALIMOGENE LAHERPAREPVEC	1 million PFU	IV	J9325
TAXOL®	1 mg	IV	J9264
TAXOL®	1 mg	IV	J9267
TAXOL®, SEE PACLITAXEL	-	-	-
TAXOTERE®	1 mg	IV	J9171
TAXOTERE®, SEE DOCETAXEL	-	-	-
TAZICEF®	per 500 mg	IM, IV	J0713
TECHNETIUM TC SESTAMBI	per dose	OTH	A9500
TAZOCIN®	1.125 g	IV	J2543
TEEV®, SEE TESTOSTERONE ENANTHATE AND ESTRADIOL VALERATE	-	-	-
TEFLARO®	10 mg	INJ	J0712
TEFLARO®, SEE CEFTAROLINE FOSAMIL	-	-	-
TELAVANCIN	10 mg	IV	J3095
TEMODAR®	5 mg	ORAL	J8700
TEMODAR®	1 mg	IV	J9328
TEMOZOLOMIDE	1 mg	IV	J9328
TEMOZOLOMIDE	5 mg	ORAL	J8700
TEMPRA®	10 mg	IV	J0131
TEMSIROLIMUS	1 mg	IV	J9330
TENECTEPLASE	1 mg	IV	J3101
TENIPOSIDE	50 mg	IV	Q2017
TERBUTALINE SULFATE	up to 1 mg	SC, IV	J3105
TERBUTALINE SULFATE, CONCENTRATED FORM	per 1 mg	INH	J7680
TERBUTALINE SULFATE, UNIT DOSE FORM	per 1 mg	INH	J7681
TERIPARATIDE	10 mcg	SC	J3110
TERRAMYCIN IM®, SEE OXYTETRACYCLINE HCL	-	-	-
TESTA-C®, SEE TESTOSTERONE CYPIONATE	-	-	-
TESTADIATE®, SEE TESTOSTERONE ENANTHATE AND ESTRADIOL VALERATE	-	-	-
TESTADIATE-DEPO®, SEE TESTOSTERONE CYPIONATE	-	-	-

DRUG NAME	UNIT PER	ROUTE	CODE
TESTAJECT-LA®, *SEE* TESTOSTERONE CYPIONATE	-	-	-
TEST-ESTRO CYPIONATES®, *SEE* TESTOSTERONE CYPIONATE AND ESTRADIOL CYPIONATE	-	-	-
TEST-ESTRO-C®, *SEE* TESTOSTERONE CYPIONATE AND ESTRADIOL CYPIONATE	-	-	-
TESTOJECT-LA®, *SEE* TESTOSTERONE CYPIONATE	-	-	-
TESTONE LA 100®, *SEE* TESTOSTERONE ENANTHATE	-	-	-
TESTONE LA 200®, *SEE* TESTOSTERONE ENANTHATE	-	-	-
TESTOSTERONE CYPIONATE	1 mg	IM	J1071
TESTOSTERONE ENANTHATE	1 mg	IM	J3121
TESTOSTERONE UNDECANOATE	1 mg	IM	J3145
TESTRADIOL 90/4®, *SEE* TESTOSTERONE ENANTHATE AND ESTRADIOL VALERATE	-	-	-
TESTRIN PA®, *SEE* TESTOSTERONE ENANTHATE	-	-	-
TETANUS IMMUNE GLOBULIN, HUMAN	up to 250 units	IM	J1670
TETRACYCLINE	up to 250 mg	IM, IV	J0120
TEV TROPIN®, *SEE* SOMATROPIN	-	-	-
THALLOUS CHLORIDE TL 201	per MCI	IV	A9505
THEELIN AQUEOUS®, *SEE* ESTRONE	-	-	-
THEO 24®	per 40 mg	IV	J2810
THEO-DUR®, *SEE* THEOPHYLLINE	-	-	-
THEOBID®, *SEE* THEOPHYLLINE	per 40 mg	IV	J2810
THEOCHRON®	per 40 mg	IV	J2810
THEOCLEAR®, *SEE* THEOPHYLLINE	-	-	-
THEOLAIR®, *SEE* THEOPHYLLINE	-	-	-
THEOPHYLLINE	per 40 mg	IV	J2810
THEOVENT®, *SEE* THEOPHYLLINE	-	-	-
THERACYS®	per vial instillation	IV	J9031
THIAMINE HCL	100 mg	-	J3411
THIETHYLPERAZINE MALEATE, INJECTION	up to 10 mg	IM	J3280
THIETHYLPERAZINE MALEATE, ORAL	10 mg	ORAL	Q0174
THIOTEPA	15 mg	IV	J9340
THORAZINE®, *SEE* CHLORPROMAZINE	5 mg	ORAL	Q0161
THROMBATE III®	per IU	IV	J7197
THYMOGLOBULIN®	25 mg	IV	J7511
THYPINONE®, *SEE* PROTIRELIN	-	-	-
THYROGEN®	0.9 mg	IM, SC	J3240
THYROGEN®, *SEE* THYROTROPIN ALFA	-	-	-
THYROTROPIN ALFA, INJECTION	0.9 mg	IM, SC	J3240

DRUG NAME	UNIT PER	ROUTE	CODE
TICE® BCG LIVE	per vial instillation	IV	J9031
TICE BCG VACCINE®	per vial instillation	IV	J9031
TICON®	up to 200 mg	IM	J3250
TICON®	250 mg	ORAL	Q0173
TIGAN®	up to 200 mg	IM	J3250
TIGAN®	250 mg	ORAL	Q0173
TIGECYCLINE	1 mg	IV	J3243
TIJECT-20®, *SEE* TRIMETHOBENZAMIDE HCL	-	-	-
TINZAPARIN SODIUM	1000 IU	SC	J1655
TIROFIBAN HYDROCHLORIDE, INJECTION	0.25 mg	IM, IV	J3246
TNKASE®	1 mg	IV	J3101
TOBI PODHALER®	300 mg	INH	J7682
TOBI®	300 mg	INH	J7682
TOBRAMYCIN SULFATE	up to 80 mg	IM, IV	J3260
TOBRAMYCIN, INHALATION SOLUTION	300 mg	INH	J7682, J7685
TOCILIZUMAB	1 mg	IV	J3262
TOLAZOLINE HCL	up to 25 mg	IV	J2670
TOPOTECAN	0.25 mg	Oral	J8705
TOPOTECAN	0.1 mg	IV	J9351
TORADOL®, *SEE* KETOROLAC TROMETHAMINE	per 15 mg	IM, IV	J1885
TORADOL®, *SEE* KETOROLAC TROMETHAMINE	-	-	-
TORECAN®, *SEE* THIETHYLPERAZINE MALEATE	-	-	-
TORISEL®	1 mg	IV	J9330
TORISEL®, *SEE* TEMSIROLIMUS	-	-	-
TORNALATE®, *SEE* BITOLTEROL MESYLATE	-	-	-
TORSEMIDE	10 mg/ml	IV	J3265
TOTECT®	250 mg	IV	J1190
TRABECTEDIN	0.1 mg	IV	J9352
TRANQUIL®	50 mg	ORAL	Q0163
TRASTUZUMAB	10 mg	IV	J9355
TRASYLOL®, *SEE* APROTININ	-	-	-
TREANDA®	1 mg	IV	J9033
TREANDA®, *SEE* BENDAMUSTINE HCL	-	-	-
TRELSTAR®	3.75 mg	IM	C9016
TRELSTAR DEPOT®	3.75 mg	SC	J3315
TRELSTAR LA®	3.75 mg	SC	J3315
TREPROSTINIL	1 mg	IV, OTH	J3285
TRETTEN®	per IU	IV	J7181
TREXALL®	2.5 mg	ORAL	J8610

DRUG NAME	UNIT PER	ROUTE	CODE
TREXALL®	5 mg	IV, IM, IT, IA	J9250
TREXALL®	50 mg	IV, IM, IT, IA	J9260
TRIAM-A®, SEE TRIAMCINOLONE ACETONIDE	-	-	-
TRIAMCINOLONE ACETONIDE	1 mg	INJ	J3300
TRIAMCINOLONE ACETONIDE	per 10 mg	IM	J3301
TRIAMCINOLONE DIACETATE	per 5 mg	IM	J3302
TRIAMCINOLONE HEXACETONIDE	per 5 mg	VAR	J3303
TRIAMCINOLONE, CONCENTRATED FORM	per 1 mg	INH	J7683
TRIAMCINOLONE, UNIT DOSE	per 1 mg	INH	J7684
TRIAMINIC THIN STRIPS ALLERGY®, SEE DIPHENHYDRAMINE HCL	-	-	-
TRIESENCE®, SEE TRIAMCINOLONE ACETONIDE	-	-	-
TRIFLUPROMAZINE HCL	up to 20 mg	IM, IV	J3400
TRI-KORT®, SEE TRIAMCINOLONE ACETONIDE	-	-	-
TRILAFON®	4 mg	ORAL	Q0175
TRILAFON®, SEE PERPHENAZINE	-	-	-
TRILOG®, SEE TRIAMCINOLONE ACETONIDE	-	-	-
TRILONE®, SEE TRIAMCINOLONE DIACETATE	-	-	-
TRIMETHOBENZAMIDE HCL, INJECTION	up to 200 mg	IM	J3250
TRIMETHOBENZAMIDE HCL, ORAL	250 mg	ORAL	Q0173
TRIMETREXATE GLUCURONATE	per 25 mg	IV	J3305
TRIPTORELIN	3.75 mg	IM	C9016
TRIPTORELIN PAMOATE	3.75 mg	SC	J3315
TRISENOX®	1 mg	IV	J9017
TRISENOX®, SEE ARSENIC TRIOXIDE	-	-	-
TROBICIN®, SEE SPECTINOMYCIN HCL	-	-	-
TROVAN®, SEE ALATROFLOXACIN MESYLATE	-	-	-
TRUPHYLLINE®	up to 250 mg	IV	J0280
TRUXOPHYLLIN®	per 40 mg	IV	J2810
TWILITE®	50 mg	ORAL	Q0163
TYGACIL®	1 mg	IV	J3243
TYLENOL®	10 mg	IV	J0131
TYSABRI®	1 mg	IV	J2323
TYSABRI®, SEE NATALIZUMAB	-	-	-
TYVASO®	1.74 mg	INH	J7686
TYVASO REFILL KIT®	1.74 mg	INH	J7686
TYVASO STARTER KIT®	1.74 mg	INH	J7686
UCERIS®	0.25 mg	INH	J7633

DRUG NAME	UNIT PER	ROUTE	CODE
ULTRAZINE-10®, SEE PROCHLORPERAZINE	-	-	-
UNASYN®	per 1.5 gm	IM, IV	J0295
UNASYN®, SEE AMPICILLIN SODIUM/ SULBACTAM SODIUM	-	-	-
UNCLASSIFIED DRUGS (SEE ALSO NOT ELSEWHERE CLASSIFIED)	-	-	J3490
UNI DUR®	per 40 mg	IV	J2810
UNIPHYL®	per 40 mg	IV	J2810
UNISERTS®	10 mg	IV	J0131
UNISOM SLEEPGELS MAXIMUM STRENGTH®	50 mg	ORAL	Q0163
UNSPECIFIED ORAL ANTIEMETIC	-	-	Q0181
UREA	up to 40 g	IV	J3350
UREAPHIL®, SEE UREA	-	-	-
URECHOLINE®	up to 5 mg	SC	J0520
URECHOLINE®, SEE BETHANECHOL CHLORIDE	-	-	-
UROFOLLITROPIN	75 IU	OTH	J3355
UROKINASE	5, 000 IU vial	IV	J3364
UROKINASE	250, 000 IU vial	IV	J3365
USTEKINUMAB	1 mg	SC	J3357
USTEKINUMAB	1 mg	IV	J3358
VALERGEN 10®, SEE ESTRADIOL VALERATE	-	-	-
VALERGEN 20®, SEE ESTRADIOL VALERATE	-	-	-
VALERGEN 40®, SEE ESTRADIOL VALERATE	-	-	-
VALERTEST NO. 1®, SEE TESTOSTERONE ENANTHATE AND ESTRADIOL VALERATE	-	-	-
VALERTEST NO. 2®, SEE TESTOSTERONE ENANTHATE AND ESTRADIOL VALERATE	-	-	-
VALIUM®	up to 5 mg	IM, IV	J3360
VALIUM®, SEE DIAZEPAM	-	-	-
VALRUBICIN, INTRAVESICAL	200 mg	OTH	J9357
VALSTAR®	200 mg	OTH	J9357
VALSTAR®, SEE VALRUBICIN	-	-	-
VALU DRYL®	50 mg	ORAL	Q0163
VANATRIP®, SEE AMITRIPTYLINE HCL	-	-	-
VANCOCIN HCL PULVULES®	500 mg	IV, IM	J3370
VANCOCIN®, SEE VANCOMYCIN HCL	-	-	-
VANCOLED®, SEE VANCOMYCIN HCL	-	-	-
VANCOMYCIN HCL	500 mg	IV, IM	J3370
VANTAS®	10 mcg	INJ	J1675

DRUG NAME	UNIT PER	ROUTE	CODE
VANTAS®	50 mg	OTH	J9225
VARUBI®	1 mg	ORAL	J8670
VECTIBIX®	10 mg	IV	J9303
VEDOLIZUMAB	1 mg	INJ	J3380
VELAGLUCERASE ALFA	100 units	IV	J3385
VELBAN®, SEE VINBLASTINE SULFATE	-	-	-
VELCADE®	0.1 mg	IV	J9041
VELETRI®	0.5 mg	IV	J1325
VELSAR®, SEE VINBLASTINE SULFATE	-	-	-
VENOFER®	1 mg	IV	J1756
VENOFER®, SEE IRON SUCROSE	-	-	-
VENTAVIS®	20 mcg	INH	Q4074
VENTOLIN HFA®	1 mg	INH	J7611
VENTOLIN HFA®	1 mg	INH	J7613
VENTOLIN®, SEE ALBUTEROL	-	-	-
VEPESID®	50 mg	ORAL	J8560
VEPESID®	10 mg	IV	J9181
VEPESID®, SEE ETOPOSIDE AND ETOPOSIDE, ORAL	-	-	-
VERSED®	per 1 mg	IM, IV	J2250
VERTEPORFIN	0.1 mg	IV	J3396
VESPRIN®, SEE TRIFLUPROMAZINE HCL	-	-	-
VFEND®	10 mg	IV	J3465
V-GAN 25®, SEE PROMETHAZINE HCL	-	-	-
V-GAN 50®, SEE PROMETHAZINE HCL	-	-	-
VIADUR®	65 mg	OTH	J9219
VIADUR®, SEE LEUPROLIDE ACETATE IMPLANT	-	-	-
VIBATIV®	10 mg	IV	J3095
VIBATIV®, SEE TELAVANCIN	-	-	-
VIDAZA®	1 mg	SC	J9025
VIMIZIM®	1 mg	IV	J1322
VINBLASTINE SULFATE	1 mg	IV	J9360
VINCASAR PFS®, SEE VINCRISTINE SULFATE	-	-	-
VINCRISTINE SULFATE	1 mg	IV	J9370
VINCRISTINE SULFATE LIPOSOME	1 mg	IV	J9371
VINORELBINE TARTRATE	per 10 mg	IV	J9390
VISTACON®	up to 25 mg	IM	J3410
VISTACOT®	up to 25 mg	IM	J3410
VISTAJECT-25®, SEE HYDROXYZINE HCL	-	-	-
VISTAJECT-50®	up to 25 mg	IM	J3410
VISTARIL IM®, SEE HYDROXYZINE HYDROCHLORIDE	-	-	-

DRUG NAME	UNIT PER	ROUTE	CODE
VISTARIL®	25 mg	ORAL	Q0177
VISTAZINE®	up to 25 mg	IM	J3410
VISTIDE®, SEE CIDOFOVIR	-	-	-
VISUDYNE®	0.1 mg	IV	J3396
VISUDYNE®, SEE VERTEPORFIN	-	-	-
VITAMIN B-12 CYANOCOBALAMIN	up to 1,000 mcg	IM, SC	J3420
VITAMIN B1®	100 mg	IM, IV	J3411
VITAMIN K, PHYTONADIONE, MENADIONE, MENADIOL SODIUM DIPHOSPHATE	per 1 mg	IM, SC, IV	J3430
VITAPAP®	10 mg	IV	J0131
VITELLENESTREX®	100 mg	IM, IV	J3415
VITRASE®	up to 150 units	SC, IV	J3470
VITRASE®	up to 999 units	VAR	J3471
VITRASE®	per 1000 units	VAR	J3472
VITRAVENE®, SEE FOMIVIRSEN SODIUM	-	-	-
VIVAGLOBIN®, SEE IMMUNE GLOBULIN	-	-	-
VIZAMYL®	up to 5 millicuries	IV	Q9982
VON WILLEBRAND FACTOR	1 IU	IV	J7179
VON WILLEBRAND FACTOR COMPLEX, HUMAN	per IU	IV	J7187
VON WILLEBRAND FACTOR COMPLEX, HUMAN	Per IU	IV	J7183
VORICONAZOLE	10 mg	IV	J3465
VONVENDI®	1 IU	IV	J7179
VPRIV®	100 units	IV	J3385
VPRIV®, SEE VELAGLUCERASE ALFA	-	-	-
VUMON®	50 mg	IV	Q2017
WEHAMINE®, SEE DIMENHYDRINATE	-	-	-
WEHDRYL®, SEE DIPHENHYDRAMINE HCL	-	-	-
WELLCOVORIN®, SEE LEUCOVORIN CALCIUM	-	-	-
WILATE®	Per IU	IV	J7183
WILATE®, SEE VON WILLEBRAND FACTOR COMPLEX (HUMAN)	-	-	-
WIN RHO SD®, SEE RHO(D) IMMUGLOBULIN, HUMAN, SOLVENT DETERGENT	-	-	-
WINRHO SDF®	50 mg	IM	J2788
WINRHO SDF®	1 dose package, 300 mcg	IM	J2790
WYCILLIN®, SEE PENICILLIN G PROCAINE	-	-	-

DRUG NAME	UNIT PER	ROUTE	CODE
WYDASE®	up to 150 units	SC, IV	J3470
WYDASE®, *SEE* HYALURONIDASE	-	-	-
XELODA®	150 mg	ORAL	J8520
XELODA®	500 mg	ORAL	J8521
XELODA®, *SEE* CAPECITABINE	-	-	-
XEOMIN®	1 unit	IM	J0588
XEOMIN®, *SEE* INCOBOTULINUMTOXIN TYPE A	-	-	-
XGEVA®	1 mg	SC	J0897
XGEVA®, *SEE* DENOSUMAB	-	-	-
XIAFLEX®	0.01 mg	OTH	J0775
XIAFLEX®, *SEE* COLLAGENASE	-	-	-
XOLAIR®	5 mg	SC	J2357
XOPENEX CONCENTRATE®	0.5 mg	INH	J7612
XOPENEX CONCENTRATE®	0.5 mg	INH	J7614
XOPENEX HFA®	0.5 mg	INH	J7612
XOPENEX HFA®	0.5 mg	INH	J7614
XOPENEX®	0.5 mg	INH	J7612
XOPENEX®	0.5 mg	INH	J7614
XOPENEX®, *SEE* ALBUTEROL	-	-	-
XULANE®	each	OTH	J7304
XYLOCAINE HCL®	10 mg	IV	J2001
XYLOCAINE HCL®, *SEE* LIDOCAINE HCL	-	-	-
XYNTHA®	per IU	IV	J7185
XYNTHA®	per IU	IV	J7192
XYNTHA®, *SEE* FACTOR VIII (ANTI-HEMOPHILIC FACTOR, RECOMBINANT)	-	-	-
YERVOY®	1 mg	IV	J9228
YERVOY®, *SEE* IPILIMUMAB	-	-	-
YONDELIS®	0.1 mg	IV	J9352
Z SLEEP®	50 mg	ORAL	Q0163
ZALTRAP®	1 mg	IV	J9400
ZANOSAR®	1 gm	IV	J9320
ZANOSAR®, *SEE* STREPTOZOCIN	-	-	-
ZANTAC®	25 mg	IV, IM	J2780
ZANTAC®, *SEE* RANITIDINE HCL	-	-	-
ZEMA PAK®	0.25 mg	ORAL	J8540
ZEMAIRA®	10 mg	IV	J0256

DRUG NAME	UNIT PER	ROUTE	CODE
ZEMPLAR®	1 mcg	IV, IM	J2501
ZEMPLAR®, *SEE* PARICALCITOL	-	-	-
ZENAPAX®, *SEE* DACLIZUMAB	-	-	-
ZETRAN®, *SEE* DIAZEPAM	-	-	-
ZICONOTIDE	1 mcg	OTH	J2278
ZIDOVUDINE	10 mg	IV	J3485
ZINACEF®	per 750 mg	IM, IV	J0697
ZINECARD®	250 mg	IV	J1190
ZINPLAVA®	10 mg	IV	J0565
ZIPRASIDONE MESYLATE	10 mg	IM	J3486
ZITHROMAX IV®	500 mg	IV	J0456
ZITHROMAX TRI-PAK®	1 gm	ORAL	Q0144
ZITHROMAX Z-PAK®	1 gm	ORAL	Q0144
ZITHROMAX®	1 gm	ORAL	Q0144
ZIV-AFLIBERCEPT	1 mg	IV	J9400
ZMAX®	500 mg	IV	J0456
ZMAX®	1 gm	ORAL	Q0144
ZOFRAN ODT®	1 mg	IV	J2405
ZOFRAN ODT®	1 mg	ORAL	Q0162
ZOFRAN®	1 mg	IV	J2405
ZOFRAN®	1 mg	ORAL	Q0162
ZOLADEX®	per 3.6 mg	SC	J9202
ZOLEDRONIC ACID	1 mg	IV	J3489
ZOLICEF®, *SEE* CEFAZOLIN SODIUM	-	-	-
ZOMETA CONCENTRATE®	1 mg	IV	J3489
ZOMETA®	1 mg	IV	J3489
ZORBTIVE®	1 mg	SC	J2941
ZORTRESS®	0.25 mg	ORAL	J7527
ZOVIRAX®	5 mg	IV	J0133
ZUBSOLV®	<=3 mg	ORAL	J0572
ZUBSOLV®	>3 mg but <=6 mg	ORAL	J0573
ZUBSOLV®	>6 mg but <=10 mg	ORAL	J0574
ZUBSOLV®	>10 mg	ORAL	J0575
ZUPLENZ®	1 mg	IV	J2405
ZUPLENZ®	1 mg	ORAL	Q0162
ZYPREXA®	1 mg	IM	J2358
ZYVOX®	200 mg	IV	J2020

This page intentionally left blank

Appendix B: HCPCS Level II Modifiers

HCPCS Modifiers

Modifier	Description
A1	Dressing for one wound
A2	Dressing for two wounds
A3	Dressing for three wounds
A4	Dressing for four wounds
A5	Dressing for five wounds
A6	Dressing for six wounds
A7	Dressing for seven wounds
A8	Dressing for eight wounds
A9	Dressing for nine or more wounds
AA	Anesthesia services performed personally by anesthesiologist
AD	Medical supervision by a physician: more than four concurrent anesthesia procedures
AE	Registered dietician
AF	Specialty physician
AG	Primary physician
AH	Clinical psychologist
AI	Principal physician of record
AJ	Clinical social worker
AK	Non participating physician
AM	Physician, team member service
AO	Alternate payment method declined by provider of service
AP	Determination of refractive state was not performed in the course of diagnostic ophthalmological examination
AQ	Physician providing a service in an unlisted health professional shortage area (HPSA)
AR	Physician provider services in a physician scarcity area
AS	Physician assistant, nurse practitioner, or clinical nurse specialist services for assistant at surgery
AT	Acute treatment (this modifier should be used when reporting service 98940, 98941, 98942)
AU	Item furnished in conjunction with a urological, ostomy, or tracheostomy supply
AV	Item furnished in conjunction with a prosthetic device, prosthetic or orthotic
AW	Item furnished in conjunction with a surgical dressing
AX	Item furnished in conjunction with dialysis services
AY	Item or service furnished to an ESRD patient that is not for the treatment of ESRD

Modifier	Description
AZ	Physician providing a service in a dental health professional shortage area for the purpose of an electronic health record incentive payment
BA	Item furnished in conjunction with parenteral enteral nutrition (PEN) services
BL	Special acquisition of blood and blood products
BO	Orally administered nutrition, not by feeding tube
BP	The beneficiary has been informed of the purchase and rental options and has elected to purchase the item
BR	The beneficiary has been informed of the purchase and rental options and has elected to rent the item
BU	The beneficiary has been informed of the purchase and rental options and after 30 days has not informed the supplier of his/her decision
CA	Procedure payable only in the inpatient setting when performed emergently on an outpatient who expires prior to admission
CB	Service ordered by a renal dialysis facility (RDF) physician as part of the ESRD beneficiary's dialysis benefit, is not part of the composite rate, and is separately reimbursable
CC	Procedure code change (use 'CC' when the procedure code submitted was changed either for administrative reasons or because an incorrect code was filed)
CD	AMCC test has been ordered by an ESRD facility or MCP physician that is part of the composite rate and is not separately billable
CE	AMCC test has been ordered by an ESRD facility or MCP physician that is a composite rate test but is beyond the normal frequency covered under the rate and is separately reimbursable based on medical necessity
CF	AMCC test has been ordered by an ESRD facility or MCP physician that is not part of the composite rate and is separately billable
CG	Policy criteria applied
CH	0 percent impaired, limited or restricted
CI	At least 1 percent but less than 20 percent impaired, limited or restricted
CJ	At least 20 percent but less than 40 percent impaired, limited or restricted
CK	At least 40 percent but less than 60 percent impaired, limited or restricted
CL	At least 60 percent but less than 80 percent impaired, limited or restricted

Modifier	Description
CM	At least 80 percent but less than 100 percent impaired, limited or restricted
CN	100 percent impaired, limited or restricted
CR	Catastrophe/disaster related
CS	Item or service related, in whole or in part, to an illness, injury, or condition that was caused by or exacerbated by the effects, direct or indirect, of the 2010 oil spill in the Gulf of Mexico, including but not limited to subsequent clean-up activities
CT	Computed tomography services furnished using equipment that does not meet each of the attributes of the national electrical manufacturers association (NEMA) XR-29-2013 standard
DA	Oral health assessment by a licensed health professional other than a dentist
E1	Upper left, eyelid
E2	Lower left, eyelid
E3	Upper right, eyelid
E4	Lower right, eyelid
EA	Erythropoetic stimulating agent (ESA) administered to treat anemia due to anti-cancer chemotherapy
EB	Erythropoetic stimulating agent (ESA) administered to treat anemia due to anti-cancer radiotherapy
EC	Erythropoetic stimulating agent (ESA) administered to treat anemia not due to anti-cancer radiotherapy or anti-cancer chemotherapy
ED	Hematocrit level has exceeded 39% (or hemoglobin level has exceeded 13.0 g/dl) for 3 or more consecutive billing cycles immediately prior to and including the current cycle
EE	Hematocrit level has not exceeded 39% (or hemoglobin level has not exceeded 13.0 g/dl) for 3 or more consecutive billing cycles immediately prior to and including the current cycle
EJ	Subsequent claims for a defined course of therapy, e.g., EPO, sodium hyaluronate, infliximab
EM	Emergency reserve supply (for ESRD benefit only)
EP	Service provided as part of medicaid early periodic screening diagnosis and treatment (EPSDT) program
ET	Emergency services
EX	Expatriate beneficiary
EY	No physician or other licensed health care provider order for this item or service
F1	Left hand, second digit
F2	Left hand, third digit
F3	Left hand, fourth digit
F4	Left hand, fifth digit

Modifier	Description
F5	Right hand, thumb
F6	Right hand, second digit
F7	Right hand, third digit
F8	Right hand, fourth digit
F9	Right hand, fifth digit
FA	Left hand, thumb
FB	Item provided without cost to provider, supplier or practitioner, or full credit received for replaced device (examples, but not limited to, covered under warranty, replaced due to defect, free samples)
FC	Partial credit received for replaced device
FP	Service provided as part of family planning program
FX	X-ray taken using film
FY	X-ray taken using computed radiography technology/cassette-based imaging
G1	Most recent URR reading of less than 60
G2	Most recent URR reading of 60 to 64.9
G3	Most recent URR reading of 65 to 69.9
G4	Most recent URR reading of 70 to 74.9
G5	Most recent URR reading of 75 or greater
G6	ESRD patient for whom less than six dialysis sessions have been provided in a month
G7	Pregnancy resulted from rape or incest or pregnancy certified by physician as life threatening
G8	Monitored anesthesia care (MAC) for deep complex, complicated, or markedly invasive surgical procedure
G9	Monitored anesthesia care for patient who has history of severe cardio-pulmonary condition
GA	Waiver of liability statement issued as required by payer policy, individual case
GB	Claim being resubmitted for payment because it is no longer covered under a global payment demonstration
GC	This service has been performed in part by a resident under the direction of a teaching physician
GD	Units of service exceeds medically unlikely edit value and represents reasonable and necessary services
GE	This service has been performed by a resident without the presence of a teaching physician under the primary care exception
GF	Non-physician (e.g. nurse practitioner (NP), certified registered nurse anesthetist (CRNA), certified registered nurse (CRN), clinical nurse specialist (CNS), physician assistant (PA)) services in a critical access hospital
GG	Performance and payment of a screening mammogram and diagnostic mammogram on the same patient, same day

Modifier	Description
GH	Diagnostic mammogram converted from screening mammogram on same day
GJ	"Opt-out" physician or practitioner emergency or urgent service
GK	Reasonable and necessary item/service associated with a GA or GZ modifier
GL	Medically unnecessary upgrade provided instead of non-upgraded item, no charge, no advance beneficiary notice (ABN)
GM	Multiple patients on one ambulance trip
GN	Services delivered under an outpatient speech language pathology plan of care
GO	Services delivered under an outpatient occupational therapy plan of care
GP	Services delivered under an outpatient physical therapy plan of care
GQ	Via asynchronous telecommunications system
GR	This service was performed in whole or in part by a resident in a department of veterans affairs medical center or clinic, supervised in accordance with VA policy
GS	Dosage of erythropoietin stimulating agent has been reduced and maintained in response to hematocrit or hemoglobin level
GT	Via interactive audio and video telecommunication systems
GU	Waiver of liability statement issued as required by payer policy, routine notice
GV	Attending physician not employed or paid under arrangement by the patient's hospice provider
GW	Service not related to the hospice patient's terminal condition
GX	Notice of liability issued, voluntary under payer policy
GY	Item or service statutorily excluded, does not meet the definition of any Medicare benefit or, for non-Medicare insurers, is not a contract benefit
GZ	Item or service expected to be denied as not reasonable and necessary
H9	Court-ordered
HA	Child/adolescent program
HB	Adult program, Non-geriatric
HC	Adult program, geriatric
HD	Pregnant/parenting women's program
HE	Mental health program
HF	Substance abuse program
HG	Opioid addiction treatment program
HH	Integrated mental health/substance abuse program
HI	Integrated mental health and intellectual disability/developmental disabilities program
HJ	Employee assistance program

Modifier	Description
HK	Specialized mental health programs for high-risk populations
HL	Intern
HM	Less than bachelor degree level
HN	Bachelors degree level
HO	Masters degree level
HP	Doctoral level
HQ	Group setting
HR	Family/couple with client present
HS	Family/couple without client present
HT	Multi-disciplinary team
HU	Funded by child welfare agency
HV	Funded state addictions agency
HW	Funded by state mental health agency
HX	Funded by county/local agency
HY	Funded by juvenile justice agency
HZ	Funded by criminal justice agency
J1	Competitive acquisition program no-pay submission for a prescription number
J2	Competitive acquisition program, restocking of emergency drugs after emergency administration
J3	Competitive acquisition program (CAP), drug not available through CAP as written, reimbursed under average sales price methodology
J4	DMEPOS item subject to DMEPOS competitive bidding program that is furnished by a hospital upon discharge
JA	Administered intravenously
JB	Administered subcutaneously
JC	Skin substitute used as a graft
JD	Skin substitute not used as a graft
JE	Administered via dialysate
JG	Drug or biological acquired with 340b drug pricing program discount
JW	Drug amount discarded/not administered to any patient
K0	Lower extremity prosthesis functional level 0 - does not have the ability or potential to ambulate or transfer safely with or without assistance and a prosthesis does not enhance their quality of life or mobility.
K1	Lower extremity prosthesis functional level 1 - has the ability or potential to use a prosthesis for transfers or ambulation on level surfaces at fixed cadence. Typical of the limited and unlimited household ambulator.
K2	Lower extremity prosthesis functional level 2 - has the ability or potential for ambulation with the ability to traverse low level environmental barriers such as curbs, stairs or uneven surfaces. Typical of the limited community ambulator.

Modifier	Description
K3	Lower extremity prosthesis functional level 3 - has the ability or potential for ambulation with variable cadence. Typical of the community ambulator who has the ability to transverse most environmental barriers and may have vocational, therapeutic, or exercise activity that demands prosthetic utilization beyond simple locomotion.
K4	Lower extremity prosthesis functional level 4 - has the ability or potential for prosthetic ambulation that exceeds the basic ambulation skills, exhibiting high impact, stress, or energy levels, typical of the prosthetic demands of the child, active adult, or athlete.
KA	Add on option/accessory for wheelchair
KB	Beneficiary requested upgrade for ABN, more than 4 modifiers identified on claim
KC	Replacement of special power wheelchair interface
KD	Drug or biological infused through DME
KE	Bid under round one of the DMEPOS competitive bidding program for use with non-competitive bid base equipment
KF	Item designated by FDA as class III device
KG	DMEPOS item subject to DMEPOS competitive bidding program number 1
KH	DMEPOS item, initial claim, purchase or first month rental
KI	DMEPOS item, second or third month rental
KJ	DMEPOS item, parenteral enteral nutrition (PEN) pump or capped rental, months four to fifteen
KK	DMEPOS item subject to DMEPOS competitive bidding program number 2
KL	DMEPOS item delivered via mail
KM	Replacement of facial prosthesis including new impression/moulage
KN	Replacement of facial prosthesis using previous master model
KO	Single drug unit dose formulation
KP	First drug of a multiple drug unit dose formulation
KQ	Second or subsequent drug of a multiple drug unit dose formulation
KR	Rental item, billing for partial month
KS	Glucose monitor supply for diabetic beneficiary not treated with insulin
KT	Beneficiary resides in a competitive bidding area and travels outside that competitive bidding area and receives a competitive bid item
KU	DMEPOS item subject to DMEPOS competitive bidding program number 3
KV	DMEPOS item subject to DMEPOS competitive bidding program that is furnished as part of a professional service

Modifier	Description
KW	DMEPOS item subject to DMEPOS competitive bidding program number 4
KX	Requirements specified in the medical policy have been met
KY	DMEPOS item subject to DMEPOS competitive bidding program number 5
KZ	New coverage not implemented by managed care
LC	Left circumflex coronary artery
LD	Left anterior descending coronary artery
LL	Lease/rental (use the 'LL' modifier when DME equipment rental is to be applied against the purchase price)
LM	Left main coronary artery
LR	Laboratory round trip
LS	FDA-monitored intraocular lens implant
LT	Left side (used to identify procedures performed on the left side of the body)
M2	Medicare secondary payer (MSP)
MS	Six month maintenance and servicing fee for reasonable and necessary parts and labor which are not covered under any manufacturer or supplier warranty
NB	Nebulizer system, any type, FDA-cleared for use with specific drug
NR	New when rented (use the 'NR' modifier when DME which was new at the time of rental is subsequently purchased)
NU	New equipment
P1	A normal healthy patient
P2	A patient with mild systemic disease
P3	A patient with severe systemic disease
P4	A patient with severe systemic disease that is a constant threat to life
P5	A moribund patient who is not expected to survive without the operation
P6	A declared brain-dead patient whose organs are being removed for donor purposes
PA	Surgical or other invasive procedure on wrong body part
PB	Surgical or other invasive procedure on wrong patient
PC	Wrong surgery or other invasive procedure on patient
PD	Diagnostic or related non diagnostic item or service provided in a wholly owned or operated entity to a patient who is admitted as an inpatient within 3 days
PI	Positron emission tomography (PET) or PET/computed tomography (CT) to inform the initial treatment strategy of tumors that are biopsy proven or strongly suspected of being cancerous based on other diagnostic testing
PL	Progressive addition lenses

Modifier	Description
PM	Post mortem
PN	Non-excepted service provided at an off-campus, outpatient, provider-based department of a hospital
PO	Excepted service provided at an off-campus, outpatient, provider-based department of a hospital
PS	Positron emission tomography (PET) or PET/computed tomography (CT) to inform the subsequent treatment strategy of cancerous tumors when the beneficiary's treating physician determines that the PET study is needed to inform subsequent anti-tumor strategy
PT	Colorectal cancer screening test; converted to diagnostic test or other procedure
Q0	Investigational clinical service provided in a clinical research study that is in an approved clinical research study
Q1	Routine clinical service provided in a clinical research study that is in an approved clinical research study
Q2	Demonstration procedure/service
Q3	Live kidney donor surgery and related services
Q4	Service for ordering/referring physician qualifies as a service exemption
Q5	Service furnished under a reciprocal billing arrangement by a substitute physician or by a substitute physical therapist furnishing outpatient physical therapy services in a health professional shortage area, a medically underserved area, or a rural area
Q6	Service furnished under a fee-for-time compensation arrangement by a substitute physician or by a substitute physical therapist furnishing outpatient physical therapy services in a health professional shortage area, a medically underserved area, or a rural area
Q7	One class A finding
Q8	Two class B findings
Q9	One class B and two class C findings
QC	Single channel monitoring
QD	Recording and storage in solid state memory by a digital recorder
QE	Prescribed amount of oxygen is less than 1 liter per minute (LPM)
QF	Prescribed amount of oxygen exceeds 4 liters per minute (LPM) and portable oxygen is prescribed
QG	Prescribed amount of oxygen is greater than 4 liters per minute(LPM)
QH	Oxygen conserving device is being used with an oxygen delivery system
QJ	Services/items provided to a prisoner or patient in state or local custody, however the state or local government, as applicable, meets the requirements in 42 cfr 411.4 (b)

Modifier	Description
QK	Medical direction of two, three, or four concurrent anesthesia procedures involving qualified individuals
QL	Patient pronounced dead after ambulance called
QM	Ambulance service provided under arrangement by a provider of services
QN	Ambulance service furnished directly by a provider of services
QP	Documentation is on file showing that the laboratory test(s) was ordered individually or ordered as a CPT®-recognized panel other than automated profile codes 80002-80019, G0058, G0059, and G0060.
QQ	Ordering professional consulted a qualified clinical decision support mechanism for this service and the related data was provided to the furnishing professional
QS	Monitored anesthesia care service
QT	Recording and storage on tape by an analog tape recorder
QW	CLIA waived test
QX	CRNA service: with medical direction by a physician
QY	Medical direction of one certified registered nurse anesthetist (CRNA) by an anesthesiologist
QZ	CRNA service: without medical direction by a physician
RA	Replacement of a DME, orthotic or prosthetic item
RB	Replacement of a part of a DME, orthotic or prosthetic item furnished as part of a repair
RC	Right coronary artery
RD	Drug provided to beneficiary, but not administered "incident-to"
RE	Furnished in full compliance with FDA-mandated risk evaluation and mitigation strategy (REMS)
RI	Ramus intermedius coronary artery
RR	Rental (use the 'RR' modifier when DME is to be rented)
RT	Right side (used to identify procedures performed on the right side of the body)
SA	Nurse practitioner rendering service in collaboration with a physician
SB	Nurse midwife
SC	Medically necessary service or supply
SD	Services provided by registered nurse with specialized, highly technical home infusion training
SE	State and/or federally-funded programs/services

Modifier	Description
SF	Second opinion ordered by a professional review organization (PRO) per section 9401, p.l. 99-272 (100% reimbursement - no Medicare deductible or coinsurance)
SG	Ambulatory surgical center (ASC) facility service
SH	Second concurrently administered infusion therapy
SJ	Third or more concurrently administered infusion therapy
SK	Member of high risk population (use only with codes for immunization)
SL	State supplied vaccine
SM	Second surgical opinion
SN	Third surgical opinion
SQ	Item ordered by home health
SS	Home infusion services provided in the infusion suite of the IV therapy provider
ST	Related to trauma or injury
SU	Procedure performed in physician's office (to denote use of facility and equipment)
SV	Pharmaceuticals delivered to patient's home but not utilized
SW	Services provided by a certified diabetic educator
SY	Persons who are in close contact with member of high-risk population (use only with codes for immunization)
T1	Left foot, second digit
T2	Left foot, third digit
T3	Left foot, fourth digit
T4	Left foot, fifth digit
T5	Right foot, great toe
T6	Right foot, second digit
T7	Right foot, third digit
T8	Right foot, fourth digit
T9	Right foot, fifth digit
TA	Left foot, great toe
TB	Drug or biological acquired with 340b drug pricing program discount, reported for informational purposes
TC	Technical component; under certain circumstances, a charge may be made for the technical component alone; under those circumstances the technical component charge is identified by adding modifier 'TC' to the usual procedure number; technical component charges are institutional charges and not billed separately by physicians; however, portable X-ray suppliers only bill for technical component and should utilize modifier TC; the charge data from portable X-ray suppliers will then be used to build customary and prevailing profiles
TD	RN

Modifier	Description
TE	LPN/IVN
TF	Intermediate level of care
TG	Complex/high tech level of care
TH	Obstetrical treatment/services, prenatal or postpartum
TJ	Program group, child and/or adolescent
TK	Extra patient or passenger, non-ambulance
TL	Early intervention/individualized family service plan (IFSP)
TM	Individualized education program (IEP)
TN	Rural/outside providers' customary service area
TP	Medical transport, unloaded vehicle
TQ	Basic life support transport by a volunteer ambulance provider
TR	School-based individualized education program (IEP) services provided outside the public school district responsible for the student
TS	Follow-up service
TT	Individualized service provided to more than one patient in same setting
TU	Special payment rate, overtime
TV	Special payment rates, holidays/weekends
TW	Back-up equipment
U1	Medicaid level of care 1, as defined by each state
U2	Medicaid level of care 2, as defined by each state
U3	Medicaid level of care 3, as defined by each state
U4	Medicaid level of care 4, as defined by each state
U5	Medicaid level of care 5, as defined by each state
U6	Medicaid level of care 6, as defined by each state
U7	Medicaid level of care 7, as defined by each state
U8	Medicaid level of care 8, as defined by each state
U9	Medicaid level of care 9, as defined by each state
UA	Medicaid level of care 10, as defined by each state
UB	Medicaid level of care 11, as defined by each state
UC	Medicaid level of care 12, as defined by each state
UD	Medicaid level of care 13, as defined by each state
UE	Used durable medical equipment

Modifier	Description
UF	Services provided in the morning
UG	Services provided in the afternoon
UH	Services provided in the evening
UJ	Services provided at night
UK	Services provided on behalf of the client to someone other than the client (collateral relationship)
UN	Two patients served
UP	Three patients served
UQ	Four patients served
UR	Five patients served
US	Six or more patients served
V1	Demonstration modifier 1
V2	Demonstration modifier 2
V3	Demonstration modifier 3
V5	Vascular catheter (alone or with any other vascular access)
V6	Arteriovenous graft (or other vascular access not including a vascular catheter)
V7	Arteriovenous fistula only (in use with two needles)
VM	Medicare diabetes prevention program (MDPP) virtual make-up session
VP	Aphakic patient
X1	Continuous/broad services: for reporting services by clinicians, who provide the principal care for a patient, with no planned endpoint of the relationship; services in this category represent comprehensive care, dealing with the entire scope of patient problems, either directly or in a care coordination role; reporting clinician service examples include, but are not limited to: primary care, and clinicians providing comprehensive care to patients in addition to specialty care
X2	Continuous/focused services: for reporting services by clinicians whose expertise is needed for the ongoing management of a chronic disease or a condition that needs to be managed and followed with no planned endpoint to the relationship; reporting clinician service examples include but are not limited to: a rheumatologist taking care of the patient's rheumatoid arthritis longitudinally but not providing general primary care services
X3	Episodic/broad services: for reporting services by clinicians who have broad responsibility for the comprehensive needs of the patient that is limited to a defined period and circumstance such as a hospitalization; reporting clinician service examples include but are not limited to the hospitalist's services rendered providing comprehensive and general care to a patient while admitted to the hospital

Modifier	Description
X4	Episodic/focused services: for reporting services by clinicians who provide focused care on particular types of treatment limited to a defined period and circumstance; the patient has a problem, acute or chronic, that will be treated with surgery, radiation, or some other type of generally time-limited intervention; reporting clinician service examples include but are not limited to, the orthopedic surgeon performing a knee replacement and seeing the patient through the postoperative period
X5	Diagnostic services requested by another clinician: for reporting services by a clinician who furnishes care to the patient only as requested by another clinician or subsequent and related services requested by another clinician; this modifier is reported for patient relationships that may not be adequately captured by the above alternative categories; reporting clinician service examples include but are not limited to, the radiologist's interpretation of an imaging study requested by another clinician
XE	Separate encounter, a service that is distinct because it occurred during a separate encounter
XP	Separate practitioner, a service that is distinct because it was performed by a different practitioner
XS	Separate structure, a service that is distinct because it was performed on a separate organ/structure
XU	Unusual non-overlapping service, the use of a service that is distinct because it does not overlap usual components of the main service
ZA	Novartis/Sandoz
ZB	Pfizer/Hospira
ZC	Merck/Samsung Bioepis

Ambulance Modifiers

HCPCS Level II codes for ambulance services (A0021-A0999) must be reported with modifiers indicating pick-up origins and destinations. The modifier describing the arrangement (QM, QN) is listed first. The modifiers describing the origin and destination are listed second. Origin and destination modifiers are created by combining two alpha characters from the following list. Each alpha character, with the exception of X, represents either an origin or destination. Each pair of the alpha characters creates one modifier. The first position represents the origin and the second the destination. The modifiers most commonly used are:

Modifier	Description
D	Diagnostic or therapeutic site other than P or H when these are used as origin codes
E	Residential, domiciliary, custodial facility (other than 1819 facility)
G	Hospital-based dialysis facility
H	Hospital
I	Site of transfer (e.g., airport or helicopter pad) between modes of ambulance transport
J	Free standing ESRD facility
N	Skilled nursing facility (SNF)
P	Physician's office
R	Residence
S	Scene of accident or acute event
X	Intermediate stop at physician's office on way to hospital (destination code only)

Ambulatory Modifiers

CPT® Modifiers

Modifier	Description
25	Significant, separately identifiable evaluation and management service by the same physician or other qualified health care professional on the same day of the procedure or other service
27	Multiple outpatient hospital E/M encounters on the same date
50	Bilateral procedure
52	Reduced services
58	Staged or related procedure or service by the same physician or other qualified health care professional during the postoperative period
59	Distinct procedural service
73	Discontinued out-patient hospital/ambulatory surgery center (ASC) procedure prior to the administration of anesthesia
74	Discontinued out-patient hospital/ambulatory surgery center (ASC) procedure after administration of anesthesia
76	Repeat procedure or service by same physician or other qualified health care professional
77	Repeat procedure by another physician or other qualified health care professional
78	Unplanned return to the operating/procedure room by the same physician or other qualified health care professional following initial procedure for a related procedure during the postoperative period
79	Unrelated procedure or service by the same physician or other qualified health care professional during the postoperative period
91	Repeat clinical diagnostic laboratory test
96	Habilitative services
97	Rehabilitative services

LEVEL II (HCPCS/National) Modifiers

Modifier	Description
AI	Principal physician of record
E1	Upper left, eyelid
E2	Lower left, eyelid
E3	Upper right, eyelid
E4	Lower right, eyelid
F1	Left hand, second digit
F2	Left hand, third digit
F3	Left hand, fourth digit
F4	Left hand, fifth digit
F5	Right hand, thumb
F6	Right hand, second digit
F7	Right hand, third digit
F8	Right hand, fourth digit
F9	Right hand, fifth digit
FA	Left hand, thumb
GA	Waiver of liability statement issued as required by payer policy, individual case
GC	This service has been performed in part by a resident under the direction of a teaching physician
GE	This service has been performed by a resident without the presence of a teaching physician under the primary care exception
GV	Attending physician not employed or paid under arrangement by the patient's hospice provider
GW	Service not related to the hospice patient's terminal condition
LC	Left circumflex coronary artery

Modifier	Description
LD	Left anterior descending coronary artery
LM	Left main coronary artery
LT	Left side (used to identify procedures performed on the left side of the body)
QM	Ambulance service provided under arrangement by a provider of services
RC	Right coronary artery
RI	Ramus intermedius coronary artery
RT	Right side (used to identify procedures performed on the right side of the body)
T1	Left foot, second digit
T2	Left foot, third digit
T3	Left foot, fourth digit
T4	Left foot, fifth digit
T5	Right foot, great toe
T6	Right foot, second digit
T7	Right foot, third digit
T8	Right foot, fourth digit
T9	Right foot, fifth digit
TA	Left foot, great toe
ZA	Novartis/Sandoz
ZB	Pfizer/Hospira
ZC	Merck/Samsung Bioepis

Appendix C: List of Abbreviations

Abbreviation	Description
/	Or
<	Less than
<=	Less than equal to
>	Greater than
>=	Greater than equal to
AAA	Abdominal aortic aneurysm
AC	Alternating current
ACE	Angiotensin converting enzyme
AFO	Ankle-foot orthosis
AICC	Anti-inhibitor coagulant complex
AK	Above the knee
AKA	above knee amputation
ALS	advanced life support
AMP	ampule
ARB	Angiotensin receptor blocker
ART	arterial
ASC	ambulatory surgery center
ATT	attached
A-V	Arteriovenous
AVF	arteriovenous fistula
BICROS	bilateral routing of signals
BK	below the knee
BLS	basic life support
BMI	body mass index
BP	blood pressure
BTE	behind the ear (hearing aid)
CAD	coronary artery disease
CAPD	continuous ambulatory peritoneal dialysis
Carb	carbohydrate
CBC	complete blood count
cc	cubic centimeter
CCPD	continuous cycling peritoneal analysis
CGH	comparative genomic hybridization
CHF	congestive heart failure
CIC	completely in the canal (hearing aid)
CIM	Coverage Issue Manual
Cisd	closed
cm	centimeter
CMN	certificate of medical necessity
CMS	Centers for Medicare and Medicaid Services
CMV	Cytomegalovirus
Conc	concentrate
Conc	concentrated

Abbreviation	Description
Cont	continuous
CP	clinical psychologist
CPAP	continuous positive airway pressure
CPT®	Current Procedural Terminology
CRF	chronic renal failure
CRNA	certified registered nurse anesthetist
CROS	contralateral routing of signals
CSW	clinical social worker
CT	computed tomography
CTLSO	cervical-thoracic-lumbar-sacral orthosis
cu	cubic centimeter
DC	direct current
DI	diurnal rhythm
DLI	donor leukocyte infusion
DME	durable medical equipment
DME MAC	durable medical equipment Medicare administrative contractor
DMEPOS	durable medical equipment; prosthetic, orthotics, and other supplies
DMERC	durable medical equipment regional carrier
DR	diagnostic radiology
Dx	diagnosis
DX	diagnostic
DXA	dual-energy x-ray absorptiometry
e.g.	for example
Ea	each
ECF	extended care facility
EEG	electroencephalogram
EKG	electrocardiogram
EMG	electromyography
EO	elbow orthosis
EP	electrophysiologic
EPO	epoetin alfa
EPSDT	early periodic screening , diagnosis and treatment
ESRD	end-stage renal disease
Ex	extended
EXPER	experimental
Ext	external
F	french
FDA	Food and Drug Administration
FDG-PET	positron emission with tomography with 18 fluorodeoxyglucose

Abbreviation	Description
Fem	female
FO	finger orthosis
FPD	fixed partial denture
Fr	french
ft	foot
G-CSF	filgrastim (granulocyte colony-stimulating factor)
gm	gram (g)
H2O	water
HCL	hydrochloric acid, hydrochloride
HCPCS	Healthcare Common Procedural Coding System
HCT	hematocrit
HCV	Hepatitis C virus
HDL-C	High - density lipoprotein- cholesterol
HF	Heart Failure
HFO	hand-finger orthosis
HHA	home health agency
HI	high
HI-LO	high-low
HIT	home infusion therapy
HKAFO	hip-knee-ankle foot orthosis
HLA	human leukocyte antigen
HMES	heat and moisture exchange system
HNPCC	hereditary non-polyposis colorectal cancer
HO	hip orthosis
HPSA	health professional shortage area
HST	home sleep test
I-131	Iodine 131
IA	intra- arterial administration
lbs	pounds
ICF	intermediate care facility
ICU	intensive care unit
IM	intramuscular
in	inch
INF	infusion
INH	inhalation solution
INJ	injection
IOL	intraocular lens
ip	interphalangeal
IPD	intermittent peritoneal dialysis
IPPB	intermittent positive pressure breathing
IT	intrathecal administration
ITC	in the canal (hearing aid)
ITE	in the ear (hearing aid)
IU	international units

Abbreviation	Description
IV	intravenous
IVF	in vitro fertilization
IVP	Intrauterine pregnancy
KAFO	knee-ankle-foot orthosis
KO	knee orthosis
KOH	potassium hydroxide
L	left
LASIK	laser in situ keratomileusis
LAUP	laser assisted uvulopalatoplasty
LDL	low density lipoprotein
lbs	pounds
LDS	lipodystrophy syndrome
Lo	low
LOPS	loss of protective sensation
LPM	liters per minute
LPN/LVN	Licensed Practical Nurse/Licensed Vocational Nurse
LSO	lumbar-sacral orthosis
LTC	long term care facility
LVEF	left ventricular ejection fraction
MAC	Medicare administrative contractor
mcg	microgram
mCi	millicurie
MCM	Medicare Carriers Manual
MCP	metacarpophalangeal joint
mEq	milliequivalent
MESA	microsurgical epididymal sperm aspiration
mg	milligram
mgs	milligrams
MHT	megahertz
ml	milliliter
mm	millimeter
mmHg	millimeters of Mercury
mp	metacarpophalangeal
MRA	magnetic resonance angiography
MRI	magnetic resonance imaging
NA	sodium
NCI	National Cancer Institute
NEC	not elsewhere classified
NG	nasogastric
NH	nursing home
NMES	neuromuscular electrical stimulation
NOC	not otherwise classified
NOS	not otherwise specified
O2	oxygen
OBRA	Omnibus Budget Reconciliation Act

Abbreviation	Description
OMT	osteopathic manipulation therapy
OPPS	outpatient prospective payment system
ORAL	oral administration
OSA	obstructive sleep apnea
Ost	ostomy
OTH	other routes of administration
oz.	ounce
PA	physician's assistant
PAR	parenteral
PCA	patient controlled analgesia
PCH	pouch
PEN	parenteral and enteral nutrition
PENS	percutaneous electrical nerve stimulation
PET	positron emission tomography
PHP	pre-paid health plan
PHP	physician hospital plan
PI	paramedic intercept
PICC	peripherally inserted central venous catheter
PKR	photorefractive keratotomy
PNB	peripheral nerve block
Pow	powder
PPPS	personalized prevention plan of service
PQRS	physician quality reporting system
PRK	photoreactive keratectomy
PRO	peer review organization
PSA	prostate specific antigen
PSA	prostate specific antigen test
PTB	patellar tendon bearing
PTK	phototherapeutic keratectomy
PVC	polyvinyl chloride
R	right
Repl	replace
RN	registered nurse
RP	retrograde pyelogram
Rx	prescription
SACH	solid ankle, cushion heel
SC	subcutaneous
SCT	specialty care transport
SEO	shoulder-elbow orthosis
SEWHO	shoulder-elbow-wrist-hand orthosis
SEXA	single energy x- ray absorptiometry
SGD	speech generating device
SGD	sinus rhythm
SM	samarium
SNCT	sensory nerve conduction test

Abbreviation	Description
SNF	skilled nursing facility
SO	sacroiliac orthosis
SO	shoulder orthosis
Sol	solution
SQ	square
SR	screen
ST	standard
ST	sustained release
Syr	syrup
TABS	tablets
Tc	Technetium
Tc 99m	technetium isotope
TD	diphtheria toxoids vaccine
TDAP	diphtheria toxoids and acellular pertussis vaccine
TEE	Transesophageal echocardiography
TENS	transcutaneous electrical nerve stimulator
THKAO	thoracic-hip-knee-ankle orthosis
TLSO	thoracic-lumbar-sacral-orthosis
TM	temporomandibular
TMJ	temporomandibular joint
TPN	total parenteral nutrition
U	unit
uCi	microcurie
VAR	various routes of administration
w	with
w/	with
w/o	without
WAK	wearable artificial kidney
wc	wheelchair
WHFO	wrist-hand-finger orthotic
wk	week
Xe	xenon (isotope mass of xenon 133)

This page intentionally left blank

Appendix D: Place of Service/Type of Service

Place of Service

Code	Place of Service	Place of Service Description
01	Pharmacy	A facility or location where drugs and other medically related items and services are sold, dispensed, or otherwise provided directly to patients.
02	Telehealth	The location where health services and health related services are provided or received, through a telecommunication system.
03	School	A facility whose primary purpose is education.
04	Homeless Shelter	A facility or location whose primary purpose is to provide temporary housing to homeless individuals (e.g., emergency shelters, individual or family shelters).
05	Indian Health Service Free-standing Facility	A facility or location, owned and operated by the Indian Health Service, which provides diagnostic, therapeutic (surgical and non-surgical), and rehabilitation services to American Indians and Alaska Natives who do not require hospitalization.
06	Indian Health Service Provider-based Facility	A facility or location, owned and operated by the Indian Health Service, which provides diagnostic, therapeutic (surgical and non-surgical), and rehabilitation services rendered by, or under the supervision of, physicians to American Indians and Alaska Natives admitted as inpatients or outpatients.
07	Tribal 638 Free-standing Facility	A facility or location owned and operated by a federally recognized American Indian or Alaska Native tribe or tribal organization under a 638 agreement, which provides diagnostic, therapeutic (surgical and non-surgical), and rehabilitation services to tribal members who do not require hospitalization.
08	Tribal 638 Provider-based Facility	A facility or location owned and operated by a federally recognized American Indian or Alaska Native tribe or tribal organization under a 638 agreement, which provides diagnostic, therapeutic (surgical and non-surgical), and rehabilitation services to tribal members admitted as inpatients or outpatients.
09	Prison/ Correctional Facility	A prison, jail, reformatory, work farm, detention center, or any other similar facility maintained by either Federal, State or local authorities for the purpose of confinement or rehabilitation of adult or juvenile criminal offenders.
11	Office	Location, other than a hospital, skilled nursing facility (SNF), military treatment facility, community health center, State or local public health clinic, or intermediate care facility (ICF), where the health professional routinely provides health examinations, diagnosis, and treatment of illness or injury on an ambulatory basis.
12	Home	Location, other than a hospital or other facility, where the patient receives care in a private residence.
13	Assisted Living Facility	Congregate residential facility with self-contained living units providing assessment of each resident's needs and on-site support 24 hours a day, 7 days a week, with the capacity to deliver or arrange for services including some health care and other services.
14	Group Home	A residence, with shared living areas, where clients receive supervision and other services such as social and/or behavioral services, custodial service, and minimal services (e.g., medication administration).
15	Mobile Unit	A facility/unit that moves from place-to-place equipped to provide preventive, screening, diagnostic, and/or treatment services.
16	Temporary Lodging	A short term accommodation such as a hotel, camp ground, hostel, cruise ship or resort where the patient receives care, and which is not identified by any other POS code.
17	Walk-in Retail Health Clinic	A walk-in health clinic, other than an office, urgent care facility, pharmacy or independent clinic and not described by any other Place of Service code, that is located within a retail operation and provides, on an ambulatory basis, preventive and primary care services.
18	Place of Employment-Worksite	A location, not described by any other POS code, owned or operated by a public or private entity where the patient is employed, and where a health professional provides on-going or episodic occupational medical, therapeutic or rehabilitative services to the individual.
19	Off Campus-Outpatient Hospital	A portion of an off-campus hospital provider based department which provides diagnostic, therapeutic (both surgical and nonsurgical), and rehabilitation services to sick or injured persons who do not require hospitalization or institutionalization.

Code	Place of Service	Place of Service Description
20	Urgent Care Facility	Location, distinct from a hospital emergency room, an office, or a clinic, whose purpose is to diagnose and treat illness or injury for unscheduled, ambulatory patients seeking immediate medical attention.
21	Inpatient Hospital	A facility, other than psychiatric, which primarily provides diagnostic, therapeutic (both surgical and nonsurgical), and rehabilitation services by, or under, the supervision of physicians to patients admitted for a variety of medical conditions.
22	On Campus-Outpatient Hospital	A portion of a hospital's main campus which provides diagnostic, therapeutic (both surgical and nonsurgical), and rehabilitation services to sick or injured persons who do not require hospitalization or institutionalization.
23	Emergency Room-Hospital	A portion of a hospital where emergency diagnosis and treatment of illness or injury is provided.
24	Ambulatory Surgical Center	A freestanding facility, other than a physician's office, where surgical and diagnostic services are provided on an ambulatory basis.
25	Birthing Center	A facility, other than a hospital's maternity facilities or a physician's office, which provides a setting for labor, delivery, and immediate post-partum care as well as immediate care of new born infants.
26	Military Treatment Facility	A medical facility operated by one or more of the Uniformed Services. Military Treatment Facility (MTF) also refers to certain former U.S. Public Health Service (USPHS) facilities now designated as Uniformed Service Treatment Facilities (USTF).
31	Skilled Nursing Facility	A facility which primarily provides inpatient skilled nursing care and related services to patients who require medical, nursing, or rehabilitative services but does not provide the level of care or treatment available in a hospital.
32	Nursing Facility	A facility which primarily provides to residents skilled nursing care and related services for the rehabilitation of injured, disabled, or sick persons, or, on a regular basis, health-related care services above the level of custodial care to other than mentally retarded individuals.
33	Custodial Care Facility	A facility which provides room, board and other personal assistance services, generally on a long-term basis, and which does not include a medical component.
34	Hospice	A facility, other than a patient's home, in which palliative and supportive care for terminally ill patients and their families are provided.
41	Ambulance-Land	A land vehicle specifically designed, equipped and staffed for lifesaving and transporting the sick or injured.
42	Ambulance-Air or Water	An air or water vehicle specifically designed, equipped and staffed for lifesaving and transporting the sick or injured.
49	Independent Clinic	A location, not part of a hospital and not described by any other Place of Service code, that is organized and operated to provide preventive, diagnostic, therapeutic, rehabilitative, or palliative services to outpatients only.
50	Federally Qualified Health Center	A facility located in a medically underserved area that provides Medicare beneficiaries preventive primary medical care under the general direction of a physician.
51	Inpatient Psychiatric Facility	A facility that provides inpatient psychiatric services for the diagnosis and treatment of mental illness on a 24-hour basis, by or under the supervision of a physician.
52	Psychiatric Facility-Partial Hospitalization	A facility for the diagnosis and treatment of mental illness that provides a planned therapeutic program for patients who do not require full time hospitalization, but who need broader programs than are possible from outpatient visits to a hospital-based or hospital-affiliated facility.
53	Community Mental Health Center	A facility that provides the following services: outpatient services, including specialized outpatient services for children, the elderly, individuals who are chronically ill, and residents of the CMHC's mental health services area who have been discharged from inpatient treatment at a mental health facility; 24 hour a day emergency care services; day treatment, other partial hospitalization services, or psychosocial rehabilitation services; screening for patients being considered for admission to State mental health facilities to determine the appropriateness of such admission; and consultation and education services.
54	Intermediate Care Facility/Individuals with Intellectual Disabilities	A facility which primarily provides health-related care and services above the level of custodial care to mentally retarded individuals but does not provide the level of care or treatment available in a hospital or SNF.

Code	Place of Service	Place of Service Description
55	Residential Substance Abuse Treatment Facility	A facility which provides treatment for substance (alcohol and drug) abuse to live-in residents who do not require acute medical care. Services include individual and group therapy and counseling, family counseling, laboratory tests, drugs and supplies, psychological testing, and room and board.
56	Psychiatric Residential Treatment Center	A facility or distinct part of a facility for psychiatric care which provides a total 24-hour therapeutically planned and professionally staffed group living and learning environment.
57	Non-residential Substance Abuse Treatment Facility	A location which provides treatment for substance (alcohol and drug) abuse on an ambulatory basis. Services include individual and group therapy and counseling, family counseling, laboratory tests, drugs and supplies, and psychological testing.
60	Mass Immunization Center	A location where providers administer pneumococcal pneumonia and influenza virus vaccinations and submit these services as electronic media claims, paper claims, or using the roster billing method. This generally takes place in a mass immunization setting, such as, a public health center, pharmacy, or mall but may include a physician office setting.
61	Comprehensive Inpatient Rehabilitation Facility	A facility that provides comprehensive rehabilitation services under the supervision of a physician to inpatients with physical disabilities. Services include physical therapy, occupational therapy, speech pathology, social or psychological services, and orthotics and prosthetics services.
62	Comprehensive Outpatient Rehabilitation Facility	A facility that provides comprehensive rehabilitation services under the supervision of a physician to outpatients with physical disabilities. Services include physical therapy, occupational therapy, and speech pathology services.
65	End-Stage Renal Disease Treatment Facility	A facility other than a hospital, which provides dialysis treatment, maintenance, and/or training to patients or caregivers on an ambulatory or home-care basis.
71	Public Health Clinic	A facility maintained by either State or local health departments that provides ambulatory primary medical care under the general direction of a physician.
72	Rural Health Clinic	A certified facility which is located in a rural medically underserved area that provides ambulatory primary medical care under the general direction of a physician.
81	Independent Laboratory	A laboratory certified to perform diagnostic and/or clinical tests independent of an institution or a physician's office.
99	Other Place of Service	Other place of service not identified above.

Type of Service

Code	Type of Service
0	Whole Blood
1	Medical Care
2	Surgery
3	Consultation
4	Diagnostic Radiology
5	Diagnostic Laboratory
6	Therapeutic Radiology
7	Anesthesia
8	Assistant at Surgery
9	Other Medical Items or Services
A	Used DME
B	High Risk Screening Mammography
C	Low Risk Screening Mammography
D	Ambulance
E	Enteral/Parenteral Nutrients/Supplies
F	Ambulatory Surgical Center (Facility Usage for Surgical Services)

Code	Type of Service
G	Immunosuppressive Drugs
H	Hospice
J	Diabetic Shoes
K	Hearing Items and Services
L	ESRD Supplies
M	Monthly Capitation Payment for Dialysis
N	Kidney Donor
P	Lump Sum Purchase of DME, Prosthetics, Orthotics
Q	Vision Items or Services
R	Rental of DME
S	Surgical Dressings or Other Medical Supplies
T	Outpatient Mental Health Treatment Limitation
U	Occupational Therapy
V	Pneumococcal/Flu Vaccine
W	Physical Therapy

Appendix E: Payment Status Indicators

This status indicator list reflects proposed OPPS payment status indicators for CY 2018 available when this book was sent to press. Be sure to check the CMS site at www.cms.gov for final changes.

Status Indicator	Definition
A	Services furnished to a hospital outpatient that are paid under a fee schedule or payment system other than OPPS,* for example: — Ambulance Services • Separately Payable Clinical Diagnostic Laboratory Services • Separately Payable Non-Implantable Prosthetics and Orthotics • Physical, Occupational, and Speech Therapy • Diagnostic Mammography • Screening Mammography
B	Codes that are not recognized by OPPS when submitted on an outpatient hospital Part B bill type (12x and 13x).
C	Inpatient Procedures
D	Discontinued Codes
E1	Items and Services: Not covered by any Medicare outpatient benefit category Statutorily excluded by Medicare Not reasonable and necessary
E2	Items and Services for which pricing information and claims data are not available
F	Corneal Tissue Acquisition; Certain CRNA Services and Hepatitis B Vaccines
G	Pass-Through Drugs and Biologicals
H	Pass-Through Device Categories
J1	Hospital Part B services paid through a comprehensive APC
J2	Hospital Part B Services That May Be Paid Through a Comprehensive APC
K	Nonpass-Through Drugs and Nonimplantable Biologicals, Including Therapeutic Radiopharmaceuticals
L	Influenza Vaccine; Pneumococcal Pneumonia Vaccine
M	Items and Services Not Billable to the MAC
N	Items and Services Packaged into APC Rates
P	Partial Hospitalization
Q1	STV-Packaged Codes
Q2	T-Packaged Codes
Q3	Codes That May Be Paid Through a Composite APC
Q4	Conditionally packaged laboratory tests
R	Blood and Blood Products
S	Procedure or Service, Not Discounted when Multiple
T	Procedure or Service, Multiple Procedure Reduction Applies
U	Brachytherapy Sources
V	Clinic or Emergency Department Visit
Y	Non-Implantable Durable Medical Equipment

*Note – Payments "under a fee schedule or payment system other than OPPS" may be contractor priced.

This page intentionally left blank

Appendix F: ASC Payment Indicators

Indicator	Payment Indicator Definition
A2	Surgical procedure on ASC list in CY 2007; payment based on OPPS relative payment weight.
B5	Alternative code may be available; no payment made
D5	Deleted/discontinued code; no payment made.
F4	Corneal tissue acquisition, hepatitis B vaccine; paid at reasonable cost.
G2	Non office-based surgical procedure added in CY 2008 or later; payment based on OPPS relative payment weight.
H2	Brachytherapy source paid separately when provided integral to a surgical procedure on ASC list; payment based on OPPS rate.
J7	OPPS pass-through device paid separately when provided integral to a surgical procedure on ASC list; payment contractor-priced.
J8	Device-intensive procedure; paid at adjusted rate.
K2	Drugs and biologicals paid separately when provided integral to a surgical procedure on ASC list; payment based on OPPS rate.
K7	Unclassified drugs and biologicals; payment contractor-priced.
L1	Influenza vaccine; pneumococcal vaccine. Packaged item/service; no separate payment made.
L6	New Technology Intraocular Lens (NTIOL); special payment.
N1	Packaged service/item; no separate payment made.
P2	Office-based surgical procedure added to ASC list in CY 2008 or later with MPFS nonfacility PE RVUs; payment based on OPPS relative payment weight.
P3	Office-based surgical procedure added to ASC list in CY 2008 or later with MPFS nonfacility PE RVUs; payment based on MPFS nonfacility PE RVUs.
R2	Office-based surgical procedure added to ASC list in CY 2008 or later without MPFS nonfacility PE RVUs; payment based on OPPS relative payment weight.
Z2	Radiology or diagnostic service paid separately when provided integral to a surgical procedure on ASC list; payment based on OPPS relative payment weight.
Z3	Radiology or diagnostic service paid separately when provided integral to a surgical procedure on ASC list; payment based on MPFS nonfacility PE RVUs.

463

This page intentionally left blank

Appendix G: Column 1 and Column 2 Correct Coding Edits

Column 1	Column 2	Modifier
A9500	A9512	1
A9501	A9512	0
A9502	A9512	0
A9503	A9512	0
A9504	A9512	0
A9510	A9512	0
A9521	A9512	0
A9536	A9512	0
A9537	A9512	0
A9538	A9512	0
A9539	A9512	0
A9540	A9512	1
A9541	A9512	1
A9550	A9512	0
A9551	A9512	0
A9557	A9512	0
A9560	A9512	0
A9561	A9512	0
A9562	A9512	0
A9566	A9512	0
A9567	A9512	0
A9568	A9512	0
A9569	A9512	0
C5271	G0168	1
C5271	G0471	1
C5271	J0670	1
C5271	J2001	1
C5272	G0168	1
C5272	G0471	1
C5272	J0670	1
C5272	J2001	1
C5273	G0168	1
C5273	G0471	1
C5273	J0670	1
C5273	J2001	1
C5274	G0168	1
C5274	G0471	1
C5274	J0670	1
C5274	J2001	1
C5275	G0168	1
C5275	G0471	1
C5275	J0670	1

Column 1	Column 2	Modifier
C5275	J2001	1
C5276	G0168	1
C5276	G0471	1
C5276	J0670	1
C5276	J2001	1
C5277	G0168	1
C5277	G0471	1
C5277	J0670	1
C5277	J2001	1
C5278	G0168	1
C5278	G0471	1
C5278	J0670	1
C5278	J2001	1
C8906	C8903	1
C8906	C8904	1
C8906	C8905	1
C8907	C8903	1
C8907	C8904	1
C8907	C8905	1
C8908	C8903	1
C8908	C8904	1
C8908	C8905	1
C8921	C8922	1
C8923	C8924	1
C8923	C8929	0
C8928	C8923	1
C8928	C8924	1
C8928	C8925	1
C8928	C8927	0
C8928	C8929	1
C8928	C8930	0
C8929	C8924	1
C8930	C8929	1
C8931	C8932	0
C8931	J1642	1
C8932	J1642	1
C8933	C8931	0
C8933	C8932	0
C8933	J1642	1
C8934	C8935	0
C8934	J1642	1
C8935	J1642	1

Column 1	Column 2	Modifier
C8936	C8934	0
C8936	C8935	0
C8936	J1642	1
C8957	G0463	1
C8957	G0505	1
C9600	G0269	1
C9600	G0471	1
C9601	G0269	1
C9601	G0471	1
C9602	G0269	1
C9602	G0471	1
C9603	G0269	1
C9603	G0471	1
C9604	G0269	1
C9604	G0471	1
C9605	G0269	1
C9605	G0471	1
C9606	G0269	1
C9606	G0471	1
C9607	G0269	1
C9607	G0471	1
C9608	G0269	1
C9608	G0471	1
C9739	G0463	1
C9739	G0471	0
C9739	J2001	1
C9739	P9612	0
C9740	C9739	0
C9740	G0463	1
C9740	G0471	0
C9740	J2001	1
C9740	P9612	0
E0781	E0782	1
G0101	G0181	1
G0101	G0182	1
G0101	G0380	1
G0101	G0381	1
G0101	G0382	1
G0101	G0383	1
G0101	G0384	1
G0101	G0406	1
G0101	G0407	1

Column 1	Column 2	Modifier
G0101	G0408	1
G0101	G0425	1
G0101	G0426	1
G0101	G0427	1
G0101	G0463	1
G0101	G0505	1
G0101	G0508	1
G0101	G0509	1
G0104	G0105	0
G0104	G0106	1
G0104	G0120	1
G0104	G0121	0
G0104	G0181	1
G0104	G0182	1
G0104	G0380	1
G0104	G0381	1
G0104	G0382	1
G0104	G0383	1
G0104	G0384	1
G0104	G0406	1
G0104	G0407	1
G0104	G0408	1
G0104	G0425	1
G0104	G0426	1
G0104	G0427	1
G0104	G0463	1
G0104	G0471	1
G0104	G0505	1
G0104	G0508	1
G0104	G0509	1
G0105	G0181	1
G0105	G0182	1
G0105	G0380	1
G0105	G0381	1
G0105	G0382	1
G0105	G0383	1
G0105	G0384	1
G0105	G0406	1
G0105	G0407	1
G0105	G0408	1
G0105	G0425	1
G0105	G0426	1
G0105	G0427	1
G0105	G0463	1
G0105	G0471	1
G0105	G0505	1
G0105	G0508	1

Column 1	Column 2	Modifier
G0105	G0509	1
G0106	G0105	0
G0106	G0121	0
G0106	G0181	1
G0106	G0182	1
G0106	G0380	1
G0106	G0381	1
G0106	G0382	1
G0106	G0383	1
G0106	G0384	1
G0106	G0406	1
G0106	G0407	1
G0106	G0408	1
G0106	G0425	1
G0106	G0426	1
G0106	G0427	1
G0106	G0463	1
G0106	G0505	1
G0106	G0508	1
G0106	G0509	1
G0108	G0270	0
G0108	G0271	0
G0109	G0270	0
G0109	G0271	0
G0117	G0118	0
G0120	G0105	0
G0120	G0106	0
G0120	G0121	0
G0120	G0181	1
G0120	G0182	1
G0120	G0380	1
G0120	G0381	1
G0120	G0382	1
G0120	G0383	1
G0120	G0384	1
G0120	G0406	1
G0120	G0407	1
G0120	G0408	1
G0120	G0425	1
G0120	G0426	1
G0120	G0427	1
G0120	G0463	1
G0120	G0505	1
G0120	G0508	1
G0120	G0509	1
G0121	G0105	0
G0121	G0380	1

Column 1	Column 2	Modifier
G0121	G0381	1
G0121	G0382	1
G0121	G0383	1
G0121	G0384	1
G0121	G0406	1
G0121	G0407	1
G0121	G0408	1
G0121	G0425	1
G0121	G0426	1
G0121	G0427	1
G0121	G0463	1
G0121	G0471	1
G0121	G0505	1
G0121	G0508	1
G0121	G0509	1
G0123	P3000	0
G0124	G0141	0
G0124	G0147	0
G0124	G0148	0
G0124	P3000	0
G0124	P3001	0
G0127	G0380	1
G0127	G0381	1
G0127	G0382	1
G0127	G0383	1
G0127	G0384	1
G0127	G0406	1
G0127	G0407	1
G0127	G0408	1
G0127	G0425	1
G0127	G0426	1
G0127	G0427	1
G0127	G0463	1
G0127	G0471	1
G0127	G0505	1
G0127	G0508	1
G0127	G0509	1
G0141	G0123	0
G0141	G0143	0
G0141	G0144	0
G0141	P3000	0
G0145	G0147	0
G0145	G0148	0
G0148	G0147	0
G0151	G0281	1
G0151	G0283	1
G0151	G0329	1

Column 1	Column 2	Modifier
G0157	G0281	1
G0157	G0283	1
G0157	G0329	1
G0159	G0281	1
G0159	G0283	1
G0159	G0329	1
G0162	G0008	1
G0162	G0009	1
G0162	G0010	1
G0162	G0128	1
G0162	P9612	1
G0162	P9615	1
G0168	G0463	1
G0168	G0471	1
G0168	J0670	1
G0168	J2001	1
G0179	G0180	0
G0181	G0102	1
G0181	G0182	1
G0181	G0506	0
G0182	G0102	1
G0182	G0506	0
G0204	G0202	1
G0204	G0206	0
G0206	G0202	1
G0239	G0237	1
G0239	G0238	1
G0245	G0127	0
G0245	G0246	0
G0246	G0127	0
G0247	G0127	0
G0257	G0491	1
G0257	G0492	1
G0268	G0463	1
G0268	G0471	1
G0270	G0271	0
G0276	G0453	0
G0281	G0283	1
G0281	G0329	0
G0302	G0303	0
G0302	G0304	0
G0302	G0380	1
G0302	G0381	1
G0302	G0382	1
G0302	G0383	1
G0302	G0384	1
G0302	G0406	1

Column 1	Column 2	Modifier
G0302	G0407	1
G0302	G0408	1
G0302	G0425	1
G0302	G0426	1
G0302	G0427	1
G0302	G0463	1
G0302	G0505	1
G0302	G0508	1
G0302	G0509	1
G0303	G0304	0
G0303	G0380	1
G0303	G0381	1
G0303	G0382	1
G0303	G0383	1
G0303	G0384	1
G0303	G0406	1
G0303	G0407	1
G0303	G0408	1
G0303	G0425	1
G0303	G0426	1
G0303	G0427	1
G0303	G0463	1
G0303	G0505	1
G0303	G0508	1
G0303	G0509	1
G0304	G0380	1
G0304	G0381	1
G0304	G0382	1
G0304	G0383	1
G0304	G0384	1
G0304	G0406	1
G0304	G0407	1
G0304	G0408	1
G0304	G0425	1
G0304	G0426	1
G0304	G0427	1
G0304	G0463	1
G0304	G0505	1
G0304	G0508	1
G0304	G0509	1
G0305	G0380	1
G0305	G0381	1
G0305	G0382	1
G0305	G0383	1
G0305	G0384	1
G0305	G0406	1
G0305	G0407	1

Column 1	Column 2	Modifier
G0305	G0408	1
G0305	G0425	1
G0305	G0426	1
G0305	G0427	1
G0305	G0463	1
G0305	G0505	1
G0305	G0508	1
G0305	G0509	1
G0306	G0307	0
G0329	G0283	1
G0337	G0101	0
G0337	G0102	0
G0337	G0104	0
G0337	G0105	0
G0337	G0106	0
G0337	G0117	0
G0337	G0118	0
G0337	G0120	0
G0337	G0121	0
G0337	G0245	0
G0337	G0246	0
G0337	G0248	0
G0337	G0250	1
G0337	G0270	0
G0337	G0271	0
G0337	G0410	1
G0337	G0411	1
G0337	G0459	0
G0337	G0463	0
G0337	G0505	0
G0337	P3000	0
G0337	P3001	0
G0337	Q0091	0
G0339	G0340	1
G0339	G0459	0
G0339	G0463	0
G0339	G0471	0
G0339	G0500	0
G0339	G0505	0
G0339	G6002	0
G0339	G6003	1
G0339	G6004	1
G0339	G6005	1
G0339	G6006	1
G0339	G6007	1
G0339	G6008	1
G0339	G6009	1

Column 1	Column 2	Modifier	Column 1	Column 2	Modifier	Column 1	Column 2	Modifier
G0339	G6010	1	G0381	G0271	1	G0402	G0384	1
G0339	G6011	1	G0381	G0380	1	G0402	G0438	0
G0339	G6012	1	G0381	G0459	1	G0402	G0439	0
G0339	G6013	1	G0381	G0498	1	G0402	G0444	0
G0339	G6014	1	G0382	G0102	1	G0402	G0459	1
G0340	G0459	0	G0382	G0245	1	G0402	G0463	1
G0340	G0463	0	G0382	G0246	1	G0402	G0505	1
G0340	G0471	0	G0382	G0270	1	G0403	G0404	0
G0340	G0500	0	G0382	G0271	1	G0403	G0405	0
G0340	G0505	0	G0382	G0380	1	G0406	G0102	0
G0340	G6002	0	G0382	G0381	1	G0406	G0245	0
G0340	G6003	1	G0382	G0459	1	G0406	G0246	0
G0340	G6004	1	G0382	G0498	1	G0406	G0250	0
G0340	G6005	1	G0383	G0102	1	G0406	G0270	0
G0340	G6006	1	G0383	G0245	1	G0406	G0271	0
G0340	G6007	1	G0383	G0246	1	G0406	G0459	0
G0340	G6008	1	G0383	G0270	1	G0406	G0498	1
G0340	G6009	1	G0383	G0271	1	G0407	G0102	0
G0340	G6010	1	G0383	G0380	1	G0407	G0245	0
G0340	G6011	1	G0383	G0381	1	G0407	G0246	0
G0340	G6012	1	G0383	G0382	1	G0407	G0250	0
G0340	G6013	1	G0383	G0459	1	G0407	G0270	0
G0340	G6014	1	G0383	G0498	1	G0407	G0271	0
G0341	G0463	1	G0384	G0102	1	G0407	G0406	0
G0341	G0471	1	G0384	G0245	1	G0407	G0459	0
G0341	J0670	1	G0384	G0246	1	G0407	G0498	1
G0341	J1642	1	G0384	G0270	1	G0408	G0102	0
G0341	J1644	1	G0384	G0271	1	G0408	G0245	0
G0341	J2001	1	G0384	G0380	1	G0408	G0246	0
G0342	G0341	0	G0384	G0381	1	G0408	G0250	0
G0342	G0463	1	G0384	G0382	1	G0408	G0270	0
G0342	G0471	1	G0384	G0383	1	G0408	G0271	0
G0343	G0341	0	G0384	G0459	1	G0408	G0406	0
G0343	G0342	0	G0384	G0498	1	G0408	G0407	0
G0343	G0463	1	G0396	G0442	0	G0408	G0459	0
G0343	G0471	1	G0397	G0396	0	G0408	G0498	1
G0380	G0102	1	G0397	G0442	0	G0409	G0155	1
G0380	G0245	1	G0398	G0399	0	G0409	G0176	1
G0380	G0246	1	G0398	G0400	0	G0409	G0177	1
G0380	G0270	1	G0399	G0400	0	G0409	G0459	1
G0380	G0271	1	G0402	G0250	1	G0410	G0176	1
G0380	G0459	1	G0402	G0270	0	G0410	G0177	1
G0380	G0498	1	G0402	G0271	0	G0410	G0270	0
G0381	G0102	1	G0402	G0380	1	G0410	G0271	0
G0381	G0245	1	G0402	G0381	1	G0410	G0380	1
G0381	G0246	1	G0402	G0382	1	G0410	G0381	1
G0381	G0270	1	G0402	G0383	1	G0410	G0382	1

Column 1	Column 2	Modifier
G0410	G0383	1
G0410	G0384	1
G0410	G0459	0
G0410	G0463	1
G0410	G0505	1
G0411	G0176	1
G0411	G0177	1
G0411	G0270	0
G0411	G0271	0
G0411	G0380	1
G0411	G0381	1
G0411	G0382	1
G0411	G0383	1
G0411	G0384	1
G0411	G0410	1
G0411	G0459	0
G0411	G0463	1
G0411	G0505	1
G0412	G0463	1
G0412	G0471	1
G0413	G0463	1
G0413	G0471	1
G0414	G0463	1
G0414	G0471	1
G0415	G0413	1
G0415	G0463	1
G0415	G0471	1
G0420	G0421	1
G0422	G0423	1
G0422	G0471	1
G0423	G0471	1
G0424	G0237	0
G0424	G0238	0
G0424	G0239	0
G0424	G0406	1
G0424	G0407	1
G0424	G0408	1
G0424	G0422	1
G0424	G0423	1
G0424	G0471	1
G0425	G0102	0
G0425	G0245	0
G0425	G0246	0
G0425	G0250	1
G0425	G0270	0
G0425	G0271	0
G0425	G0406	0

Column 1	Column 2	Modifier
G0425	G0407	0
G0425	G0408	0
G0425	G0424	1
G0425	G0459	0
G0425	G0498	1
G0426	G0102	0
G0426	G0245	0
G0426	G0246	0
G0426	G0250	1
G0426	G0270	0
G0426	G0271	0
G0426	G0406	0
G0426	G0407	0
G0426	G0408	0
G0426	G0424	1
G0426	G0425	0
G0426	G0459	0
G0426	G0498	1
G0426	G0508	0
G0426	G0509	0
G0427	G0102	0
G0427	G0245	0
G0427	G0246	0
G0427	G0250	1
G0427	G0270	0
G0427	G0271	0
G0427	G0406	0
G0427	G0407	0
G0427	G0408	0
G0427	G0424	1
G0427	G0425	0
G0427	G0426	0
G0427	G0459	0
G0427	G0498	1
G0427	G0508	0
G0427	G0509	0
G0428	G0471	1
G0429	G0463	1
G0429	G0471	1
G0429	J2001	1
G0429	Q2026	0
G0438	G0250	1
G0438	G0270	0
G0438	G0271	0
G0438	G0380	1
G0438	G0381	1
G0438	G0382	1

Column 1	Column 2	Modifier
G0438	G0383	1
G0438	G0384	1
G0438	G0439	0
G0438	G0444	0
G0438	G0459	1
G0438	G0463	1
G0438	G0505	1
G0439	G0250	1
G0439	G0270	0
G0439	G0271	0
G0439	G0380	1
G0439	G0381	1
G0439	G0382	1
G0439	G0383	1
G0439	G0384	1
G0439	G0459	1
G0439	G0463	1
G0439	G0505	1
G0443	G0396	0
G0443	G0397	0
G0447	G0473	1
G0448	G0471	1
G0451	G0505	1
G0455	G0463	1
G0458	G0471	0
G0458	G0500	0
G0458	P9612	0
G0459	G0250	1
G0459	G0270	0
G0459	G0271	0
G0459	G0444	1
G0459	G0445	1
G0459	G0446	1
G0459	G0447	1
G0459	G0473	1
G0460	P9020	1
G0463	G0102	0
G0463	G0117	0
G0463	G0118	0
G0463	G0245	0
G0463	G0246	0
G0463	G0248	1
G0463	G0250	1
G0463	G0270	0
G0463	G0271	0
G0463	G0396	1
G0463	G0397	1

Column 1	Column 2	Modifier	Column 1	Column 2	Modifier	Column 1	Column 2	Modifier
G0463	G0442	1	G0492	G0381	1	G0505	G0443	1
G0463	G0443	1	G0492	G0382	1	G0505	G0444	1
G0463	G0444	1	G0492	G0383	1	G0505	G0445	1
G0463	G0445	1	G0492	G0384	1	G0505	G0446	1
G0463	G0446	1	G0492	G0406	1	G0505	G0447	1
G0463	G0447	1	G0492	G0407	1	G0505	G0459	0
G0463	G0459	0	G0492	G0408	1	G0505	G0473	1
G0463	G0473	1	G0492	G0425	1	G0508	G0102	0
G0463	G0505	1	G0492	G0426	1	G0508	G0245	0
G0471	G0463	1	G0492	G0427	1	G0508	G0246	0
G0471	J0670	1	G0492	G0463	1	G0508	G0250	1
G0471	J2001	1	G0492	G0471	1	G0508	G0270	0
G0471	P9612	0	G0492	G0505	1	G0508	G0271	0
G0471	P9615	0	G0492	G0508	1	G0508	G0406	0
G0475	G0432	0	G0492	G0509	1	G0508	G0407	0
G0475	G0433	0	G0498	G0463	1	G0508	G0408	0
G0480	G0659	0	G0498	J1644	1	G0508	G0424	1
G0481	G0480	0	G0500	G0380	1	G0508	G0459	0
G0481	G0659	0	G0500	G0381	1	G0508	G0509	0
G0482	G0480	0	G0500	G0382	1	G0509	G0102	0
G0482	G0481	0	G0500	G0383	1	G0509	G0245	0
G0482	G0659	0	G0500	G0384	1	G0509	G0246	0
G0483	G0480	0	G0500	G0406	1	G0509	G0250	1
G0483	G0481	0	G0500	G0407	1	G0509	G0270	0
G0483	G0482	0	G0500	G0408	1	G0509	G0271	0
G0483	G0659	0	G0500	G0425	1	G0509	G0406	0
G0491	G0270	0	G0500	G0426	1	G0509	G0407	0
G0491	G0271	0	G0500	G0427	1	G0509	G0408	0
G0491	G0380	1	G0500	G0463	1	G0509	G0424	1
G0491	G0381	1	G0505	G0102	0	G0509	G0459	0
G0491	G0382	1	G0505	G0117	0	G6001	G6017	1
G0491	G0383	1	G0505	G0118	0	G6002	G0459	0
G0491	G0384	1	G0505	G0245	0	G6002	G0463	1
G0491	G0406	1	G0505	G0246	0	G6002	G0471	0
G0491	G0407	1	G0505	G0248	1	G6002	G0500	0
G0491	G0408	1	G0505	G0250	1	G6002	G0505	1
G0491	G0425	1	G0505	G0270	0	G6002	G6001	0
G0491	G0426	1	G0505	G0271	0	G6002	G6017	1
G0491	G0427	1	G0505	G0396	1	G6003	G0459	0
G0491	G0463	1	G0505	G0397	1	G6003	G0463	1
G0491	G0471	1	G0505	G0406	0	G6003	G0471	0
G0491	G0505	1	G0505	G0407	0	G6003	G0500	0
G0491	G0508	1	G0505	G0408	0	G6003	G0505	1
G0491	G0509	1	G0505	G0425	0	G6004	G0459	0
G0492	G0270	0	G0505	G0426	0	G6004	G0463	1
G0492	G0271	0	G0505	G0427	0	G6004	G0471	0
G0492	G0380	1	G0505	G0442	1	G6004	G0500	0

Column 1	Column 2	Modifier
G6004	G0505	1
G6004	G6003	1
G6005	G0459	0
G6005	G0463	1
G6005	G0471	0
G6005	G0500	0
G6005	G0505	1
G6005	G6003	1
G6005	G6004	1
G6006	G0459	0
G6006	G0463	1
G6006	G0471	0
G6006	G0500	0
G6006	G0505	1
G6006	G6003	1
G6006	G6004	1
G6006	G6005	1
G6007	G0459	0
G6007	G0463	1
G6007	G0471	0
G6007	G0500	0
G6007	G0505	1
G6007	G6003	1
G6007	G6004	1
G6007	G6005	1
G6007	G6006	1
G6008	G0459	0
G6008	G0463	1
G6008	G0471	0
G6008	G0500	0
G6008	G0505	1
G6008	G6003	1
G6008	G6004	1
G6008	G6005	1
G6008	G6006	1
G6008	G6007	1
G6009	G0459	0
G6009	G0463	1
G6009	G0471	0
G6009	G0500	0
G6009	G0505	1
G6009	G6003	1
G6009	G6004	1
G6009	G6005	1
G6009	G6006	1
G6009	G6007	1
G6009	G6008	1

Column 1	Column 2	Modifier
G6010	G0459	0
G6010	G0463	1
G6010	G0471	0
G6010	G0500	0
G6010	G0505	1
G6010	G6003	1
G6010	G6004	1
G6010	G6005	1
G6010	G6006	1
G6010	G6007	1
G6010	G6008	1
G6010	G6009	1
G6011	G0459	0
G6011	G0463	1
G6011	G0471	0
G6011	G0500	0
G6011	G0505	1
G6011	G6003	1
G6011	G6004	1
G6011	G6005	1
G6011	G6006	1
G6011	G6007	1
G6011	G6008	1
G6011	G6009	1
G6011	G6010	1
G6012	G0459	0
G6012	G0463	1
G6012	G0471	0
G6012	G0500	0
G6012	G0505	1
G6012	G6003	1
G6012	G6004	1
G6012	G6005	1
G6012	G6006	1
G6012	G6007	1
G6012	G6008	1
G6012	G6009	1
G6012	G6010	1
G6012	G6011	1
G6013	G0459	0
G6013	G0463	1
G6013	G0471	0
G6013	G0500	0
G6013	G0505	1
G6013	G6003	1
G6013	G6004	1
G6013	G6005	1

Column 1	Column 2	Modifier
G6013	G6006	1
G6013	G6007	1
G6013	G6008	1
G6013	G6009	1
G6013	G6010	1
G6013	G6011	1
G6013	G6012	1
G6014	G0459	0
G6014	G0463	1
G6014	G0471	0
G6014	G0500	0
G6014	G0505	1
G6014	G6003	1
G6014	G6004	1
G6014	G6005	1
G6014	G6006	1
G6014	G6007	1
G6014	G6008	1
G6014	G6009	1
G6014	G6010	1
G6014	G6011	1
G6014	G6012	1
G6014	G6013	1
G6015	G0339	0
G6015	G0340	0
G6015	G0459	0
G6015	G0463	1
G6015	G0471	0
G6015	G0500	0
G6015	G0505	1
G6015	G6003	0
G6015	G6004	0
G6015	G6005	0
G6015	G6006	0
G6015	G6007	0
G6015	G6008	0
G6015	G6009	0
G6015	G6010	0
G6015	G6011	0
G6015	G6012	0
G6015	G6013	0
G6015	G6014	0
G6015	G6016	0
G6016	G0339	0
G6016	G0340	0
G6016	G0459	0
G6016	G0463	0

Column 1	Column 2	Modifier	Column 1	Column 2	Modifier	Column 1	Column 2	Modifier
G6016	G0471	0	P3001	G0383	1	P9036	P9021	1
G6016	G0505	0	P3001	G0384	1	P9036	P9022	1
G6016	G6003	1	P3001	G0406	1	P9036	P9031	1
G6016	G6004	1	P3001	G0407	1	P9036	P9034	1
G6016	G6005	1	P3001	G0408	1	P9036	P9035	1
G6016	G6006	1	P3001	G0425	1	P9036	P9039	1
G6016	G6007	1	P3001	G0426	1	P9037	P9010	1
G6016	G6008	1	P3001	G0427	1	P9037	P9011	1
G6016	G6009	1	P3001	G0463	1	P9037	P9016	1
G6016	G6010	1	P3001	G0505	1	P9037	P9019	1
G6016	G6011	1	P3001	G0508	1	P9037	P9020	1
G6016	G6012	1	P3001	G0509	1	P9037	P9021	1
G6016	G6013	1	P9011	P9010	1	P9037	P9022	1
G6016	G6014	1	P9011	P9021	0	P9037	P9031	1
G6017	G0459	1	P9011	P9022	0	P9037	P9034	1
G6017	G0463	1	P9011	P9039	0	P9037	P9035	1
G6017	G0471	1	P9022	P9010	1	P9037	P9039	1
G6017	G0500	1	P9022	P9016	1	P9038	P9010	1
G6017	G0505	1	P9022	P9021	1	P9038	P9011	1
J1560	J1460	0	P9022	P9039	1	P9038	P9016	1
J2790	J2792	1	P9032	P9010	1	P9038	P9019	1
J7298	J7297	0	P9032	P9011	1	P9038	P9020	1
P3000	G0380	1	P9032	P9016	1	P9038	P9021	1
P3000	G0381	1	P9032	P9019	1	P9038	P9022	1
P3000	G0382	1	P9032	P9020	1	P9038	P9031	1
P3000	G0383	1	P9032	P9021	1	P9038	P9034	1
P3000	G0384	1	P9032	P9022	1	P9038	P9035	1
P3000	G0406	1	P9032	P9031	1	P9038	P9039	1
P3000	G0407	1	P9032	P9034	1	P9039	P9010	1
P3000	G0408	1	P9032	P9035	1	P9039	P9016	1
P3000	G0425	1	P9032	P9039	1	P9039	P9021	1
P3000	G0426	1	P9033	P9010	1	P9040	P9010	1
P3000	G0427	1	P9033	P9011	1	P9040	P9011	1
P3000	G0463	1	P9033	P9016	1	P9040	P9016	1
P3000	G0505	1	P9033	P9019	1	P9040	P9019	1
P3000	G0508	1	P9033	P9020	1	P9040	P9020	1
P3000	G0509	1	P9033	P9021	1	P9040	P9021	1
P3001	G0123	0	P9033	P9022	1	P9040	P9022	1
P3001	G0141	0	P9033	P9031	1	P9040	P9031	1
P3001	G0143	0	P9033	P9034	1	P9040	P9034	1
P3001	G0144	0	P9033	P9035	1	P9040	P9035	1
P3001	G0145	0	P9033	P9039	1	P9040	P9039	1
P3001	G0147	0	P9036	P9010	1	P9603	P9604	1
P3001	G0148	0	P9036	P9011	1	P9612	P9615	0
P3001	G0380	1	P9036	P9016	1	Q0091	G0181	1
P3001	G0381	1	P9036	P9019	1	Q0091	G0182	1
P3001	G0382	1	P9036	P9020	1	Q0091	G0380	1

Column 1	Column 2	Modifier
Q0091	G0381	1
Q0091	G0382	1
Q0091	G0383	1
Q0091	G0384	1
Q0091	G0406	1
Q0091	G0407	1
Q0091	G0408	1
Q0091	G0425	1
Q0091	G0426	1
Q0091	G0427	1
Q0091	G0463	1
Q0091	G0505	1
Q0091	G0508	1
Q0091	G0509	1
Q1004	Q1005	1
Q2035	Q2034	0
Q2035	Q2036	0
Q2035	Q2037	0
Q2035	Q2038	0
Q2035	Q2039	0

Column 1	Column 2	Modifier
Q2036	Q2034	0
Q2036	Q2037	0
Q2036	Q2038	0
Q2036	Q2039	0
Q2037	Q2034	0
Q2037	Q2038	0
Q2037	Q2039	0
Q2038	Q2034	0
Q2038	Q2039	0
Q2039	Q2034	0
Q2043	G0380	1
Q2043	G0381	1
Q2043	G0382	1
Q2043	G0383	1
Q2043	G0384	1
Q2043	G0463	1
Q2043	G0471	1
Q2043	G0505	1
R0075	R0070	1

This page intentionally left blank

Appendix H: General Correct Coding Policies

CHAPTER XII SUPPLEMENTAL SERVICES

HCPCS LEVEL II CODES A0000 - V9999 FOR

NATIONAL CORRECT CODING INITIATIVE POLICY MANUAL FOR MEDICARE SERVICES

TABLE OF CONTENTS

Chapter XII Supplemental Services

HCPCS Level II Codes A0000 - V9999

A. Introduction

The principles of correct coding discussed in Chapter I apply to HCPCS codes in the range A0000-V9999. Several general guidelines are repeated in this chapter. However, those general guidelines from Chapter I not discussed in this chapter are nonetheless applicable.

Physicians *shall* report the HCPCS/CPT® code that describes the procedure performed to the greatest specificity possible. A HCPCS/CPT® code *shall* be reported only if all services described by the code are performed. A physician *shall* not report multiple HCPCS/CPT® codes if a single HCPCS/CPT® code exists that describes the services. This type of unbundling is incorrect coding.

HCPCS/CPT® codes include all services usually performed as part of the procedure as a standard of medical/surgical practice. A physician *shall* not separately report these services simply because HCPCS/CPT® codes exist for them.

Specific issues unique to HCPCS Level II codes are clarified in this chapter.

The HCPCS Level II codes are alpha-numeric codes developed by the Centers for Medicare & Medicaid Services (CMS) as a complementary coding system to the *CPT® Manual*. These codes describe physician and non-physician services not included in the *CPT® Manual*, supplies, drugs, durable medical equipment, ambulance services, etc. The correct coding edits and policy statements that follow address those HCPCS Level II codes that are reported to Medicare carriers, Fiscal Intermediaries, and A/B MACs for Part B services.

B. Evaluation and Management (E&M) Services

Medicare Global Surgery Rules define the rules for reporting evaluation and management (E&M) services with procedures covered by these rules. This section summarizes some of the rules.

All procedures on the Medicare Physician Fee Schedule are assigned a global period of 000, 010, 090, XXX, YYY, ZZZ, or MMM.

The global concept does not apply to XXX procedures. The global period for YYY procedures is defined by the Carrier (A/B MAC processing practitioner service claims). All procedures with a global period of ZZZ are related to another procedure, and the applicable global period for the ZZZ code is determined by the related procedure. Procedures with a global period of MMM are maternity procedures.

Since NCCI PTP edits are applied to same day services by the same provider to the same beneficiary, certain Global Surgery Rules are applicable to NCCI. An E&M service is separately reportable on the same date of service as a procedure with a global period of 000, 010, or 090 under limited circumstances.

If a procedure has a global period of 090 days, it is defined as a major surgical procedure. If an E&M is performed on the same date of service as a major surgical procedure for the purpose of deciding whether to perform this surgical procedure, the E&M service is separately reportable with modifier 57. Other preoperative E&M services on the same date of service as a major surgical procedure are included in the global payment for the procedure and are not separately reportable. NCCI does not contain edits based on this rule because Medicare Carriers (A/B MACs processing practitioner service claims) have separate edits.

If a procedure has a global period of 000 or 010 days, it is defined as a minor surgical procedure. In general E&M services on the same date of service as the minor surgical procedure are included in the payment for the procedure. The decision to perform a minor surgical procedure is included in the payment for the minor surgical procedure and *shall* not be reported separately as an E&M service. However, a significant and separately identifiable E&M service unrelated to the decision to perform the minor surgical procedure is separately reportable with modifier 25. The E&M service and minor surgical procedure do not require different diagnoses. If a minor surgical procedure is performed on a new patient, the same rules for reporting E&M services apply. The fact that the patient is "new" to the provider is not sufficient alone to justify reporting an E&M service on the same date of service as a minor surgical procedure. NCCI contains many, but not all, possible edits based on these principles.

Example: If a physician determines that a new patient with head trauma requires sutures, confirms the allergy and immunization status, obtains informed consent, and performs the repair, an E&M service is not separately reportable. However, if the physician also performs a medically reasonable and necessary full neurological examination, an E&M service may be separately reportable.

For major and minor surgical procedures, postoperative E&M services related to recovery from the surgical procedure during the postoperative period are included in the global surgical package as are E&M services related to complications of the surgery. Postoperative visits unrelated to the diagnosis for which the surgical procedure was performed unless related to a complication of surgery may be reported separately on the same day as a surgical procedure with modifier 24 ("Unrelated Evaluation and Management Service by the Same Physician or Other Qualified Health Care Professional During a Postoperative Period").

Procedures with a global surgery indicator of "XXX" are not covered by these rules. Many of these "XXX" procedures are performed by physicians and have inherent pre-procedure, intra-procedure, and post-procedure work usually performed each time the procedure is completed. This work *shall not* be reported as a separate E&M code. Other "XXX" procedures are not usually performed by a physician and have no physician work relative value units associated with them. A physician *shall not* report a separate E&M code with these procedures for the supervision of others performing the procedure or for the interpretation of the procedure. With most "XXX" procedures, the physician may, however, perform a significant and separately identifiable E&M service on the same date of service which may be reported by appending modifier 25 to the E&M code. This E&M service may be related to the same diagnosis necessitating performance of the "XXX" procedure but cannot include any work inherent in the "XXX" procedure, supervision of others performing the "XXX" procedure, or time for interpreting the result of the "XXX" procedure. Appending modifier 25 to a significant, separately identifiable E&M service when performed on the same date of service as an "XXX" procedure is correct coding.

C. NCCI Procedure to Procedure (PTP) Edit Specific Issues

1. HCPCS code M0064 describes a brief face-to-face office visit with a practitioner licensed to perform the service for the sole purpose of monitoring or changing drug prescriptions used in the treatment of psychiatric

disorders. HCPCS code M0064 is not separately reportable with CPT® codes 90785-90853 (psychiatric services). (HCPCS code M0064 was deleted January 1, 2015.)

2. HCPCS code Q0091 (Screening Papanicolaou smear; obtaining, preparing and conveyance of cervical or vaginal smear to laboratory) describes the services necessary to procure and transport a pap smear specimen to the laboratory. If an evaluation and management (E&M) service is performed at the same patient encounter solely for the purpose of performing a screening pap smear, the E&M service is not separately reportable. However, if a significant, separately identifiable E&M service is performed to evaluate other medical problems, both the screening pap smear and the E&M service may be reported separately. Modifier 25 should be appended to the E&M CPT® code indicating that a significant, separately identifiable E&M service was rendered.

3. HCPCS code G0101 (cervical or vaginal cancer screening; pelvic and clinical breast examination may be reported with evaluation and management (E&M) services under certain circumstances. If a Medicare covered reasonable and medically necessary E&M service requires breast and/or pelvic examination, HCPCS code G0101 *shall* not be additionally reported. However, if the Medicare covered reasonable and medically necessary E&M service and the screening service, G0101, are unrelated to one another, both HCPCS code G0101 and the E&M service may be reported appending modifier 25 to the E&M service CPT® code. Use of modifier 25 indicates that the E&M service is significant and separately identifiable from the screening service, G0101.

4. HCPCS code G0102 (Prostate cancer screening; digital rectal examination) is not separately payable with an evaluation and management code (CPT® codes 99201-99499). CMS published this policy in the *Federal Register*, November 2, 1999, Page 59414 as follows:

   "As stated in the July 1999 proposed rule, a digital rectal exam (DRE) is a very quick and simple examination taking only a few seconds. We believe it is rarely the sole reason for a physician encounter and is usually part of an E/M encounter. In those instances when it is the only service furnished or it is furnished as part of an otherwise non-covered service, we will pay separately for code G0102. In those instances when it is furnished on the same day as a covered E/M service, we believe it is appropriate to bundle it into the payment for the covered E/M encounter."

5. Positron emission tomography (PET) imaging requires use of a radiopharmaceutical diagnostic imaging agent. HCPCS codes A9555 (Rubidium Rb-82...) and A9526 (Nitrogen N-13 Ammonia...) may only be reported with PET scan CPT® codes 78491 and 78492. HCPCS code A9552 (Fluorodeoxyglucose F-18, FDG,...) may only be reported with PET scan CPT® codes 78459, 78608, and 78811-78816.

6. HCPCS code A9512 (Technetium Tc-99m pertechnetate, diagnostic...) describes a radiopharmaceutical utilized for nuclear medicine studies. Technetium Tc-99m pertechnetate is also a component of other Technetium Tc-99m radiopharmaceuticals with separate AXXXX codes. Code A9512 *shall* not be reported with other AXXXX radiopharmaceuticals containing Technetium

Tc-99m for a single nuclear medicine study. However, if two separate nuclear medicine studies are performed on the same date of service, one with the radiopharmaceutical described by HCPCS code A9512 and one with another AXXXX radiopharmaceutical labeled with Technetium Tc-99m, both codes may be reported utilizing an NCCI-associated modifier. HCPCS codes A9500, A9540, and A9541 describe radiopharmaceuticals labeled with Technetium Tc-99m that may be utilized for separate nuclear medicine studies on the same date of service as a nuclear medicine study utilizing the radiopharmaceutical described by HCPCS code A9512.

7. *NCCI contains procedure to procedure (PTP) edits that bundle some radiopharmaceutical codes into nuclear medicine procedure codes. These code pairs represent radiopharmaceuticals that should not be reported with the nuclear medicine procedure since it is inappropriate to utilize that radiopharmaceutical for that procedure. In some situations where a patient has two nuclear medicine procedures performed on the same date of service, the radiopharmaceutical utilized for one procedure may be incompatible with the second nuclear medicine procedure. In this circumstance, it may be appropriate to report the radiopharmaceutical with modifier 59.*

8. HCPCS code A4220 describes a refill kit for an implantable pump. It *shall* not be reported separately with CPT® codes 95990 (refilling and maintenance of implantable pump..., spinal... or brain...) or 95991 (refilling and maintenance of implantable pump,... spinal... or brain... requiring skill of physician or other qualified health care professional) since Medicare payment for these two CPT® codes includes the refill kit.

   Similarly, HCPCS code A4220 *shall* not be reported separately with CPT® codes 62369 (Electronic analysis of programmable, implanted pump for intrathecal or epidural drug infusion (includes evaluation of reservoir status, alarm status, drug prescription status); with reprogramming and refill) or 62370 (Electronic analysis of programmable, implanted pump for intrathecal or epidural drug infusion (includes evaluation of reservoir status, alarm status, drug prescription status); with reprogramming and refill (requiring skill of a physician or other qualified health care professional)) since Medicare payment for these two CPT® codes includes the refill kit.

9. HCPCS code E0781 describes an ambulatory infusion pump utilized by a patient for infusions outside the physician office or clinic. It is a misuse of this code to report the infusion pump typically utilized in the physician office or clinic.

10. HCPCS codes G0422 and G0423 (intensive cardiac rehabilitation;...per session) include the same services as the cardiac rehabilitation CPT® codes 93797 and 93798 but at a greater frequency. Intensive cardiac rehabilitation may be reported with as many as six hourly sessions on a single date of service. Cardiac rehabilitation services include medical nutrition services to reduce cardiac disease risk factors. Medical nutrition therapy (CPT® codes 97802-97804) *shall* not be reported separately for the same patient encounter. However, medical nutrition therapy services provided under the Medicare benefit for patients with diabetes or chronic renal failure performed at a separate patient encounter on the same date of service may be reported separately. The Medicare covered medical nutrition service cannot be provided at

the same patient encounter as the cardiac rehabilitation service.

Physical or occupational therapy services performed at the same patient encounter as cardiac rehabilitation services are included in the cardiac rehabilitation benefit and are not separately reportable. (CMS Final Rule (*Federal Register*, Vol. 74, No. 226, November 25, 2009, pages 61884-61885)). If physical therapy or occupational therapy services are performed at a separate, medically reasonable and necessary patient encounter on the same date of service as cardiac rehabilitation services, both types of services may be reported utilizing an NCCI-associated modifier.

11. Pulmonary rehabilitation (HCPCS code G0424) includes therapeutic services and all related monitoring services to improve respiratory function. It requires measurement of patient outcome which includes, but is not limited to, pulmonary function testing (e.g., pulmonary stress testing (CPT® code**s** *94618), cardiopulmonary exercise testing (CPT® code* 94621)). Pulmonary rehabilitation *shall* not be reported with HCPCS codes G0237 (therapeutic procedures to increase strength or endurance of respiratory muscles... (includes monitoring)), G0238 (therapeutic procedures to improve respiratory function... (includes monitoring)), or G0239 (therapeutic procedures to improve respiratory function or increase strength... (includes monitoring)). The services are mutually exclusive. The procedures described by HCPCS codes G0237-G0239 include therapeutic procedures as well as all related monitoring services, the latter including, but not limited to, pulmonary function testing (e.g., pulmonary stress testing (CPT® code *94618), cardiopulmonary exercise testing (CPT® code* 94621)).

Physical or occupational therapy services performed at the same patient encounter as pulmonary rehabilitation services are included in the pulmonary rehabilitation benefit and are not separately reportable. (CMS Final Rule (*Federal Register*, Vol. 74, No. 226, November 25, 2009, Pages 61884-61885)). If physical therapy or occupational therapy services are performed at a separate, medically reasonable and necessary patient encounter on the same date of service as pulmonary rehabilitation services, both types of services may be reported utilizing an NCCI-associated modifier. Similarly physical and occupational therapy services are not separately reportable with therapeutic pulmonary procedures for the same patient encounter.

Medical nutrition therapy services (CPT® codes 97802-97804) performed at the same patient encounter as a pulmonary rehabilitation or pulmonary therapeutic service are included in the pulmonary rehabilitation or pulmonary therapeutic service and are not separately reportable. The Medicare program provides a medical nutrition therapy benefit to beneficiaries for medical nutrition therapy related to diabetes mellitus or renal disease. If a physician provides a Medicare covered medical nutrition service to a beneficiary with diabetes mellitus or renal disease on the same date of service as a pulmonary rehabilitation or pulmonary therapeutic service but at a separate patient encounter, the medical nutrition therapy service may be separately reportable with an NCCI-associated modifier. The Medicare covered medical nutrition service cannot be provided at the same patient encounter as the pulmonary rehabilitation or pulmonary therapeutic service.

12. This *subsection* was revised and moved to Section D (Medically Unlikely Edits (MUEs)), *Subsection #16.*

13. HCPCS code G0434 (drug screen..., by CLIA waived test or moderate complexity test, per patient encounter) is utilized to report urine drug screening performed by a test that is CLIA waived or CLIA moderate complex. The code is reported with only one (1) unit of service regardless of the number of drugs screened. HCPCS code G0431 (drug screen... by high complexity test method..., per patient encounter) is utilized to report drug urine screening performed by a CLIA high complexity test method. This code is also reported with only one (1) unit of service regardless of the number of drugs screened. If a provider performs urine drug screening, it is generally not necessary for that provider to send an additional specimen from the patient to another laboratory for urine drug screening for the same drugs.

For a single patient encounter only G0431 or G0434 may be reported. The testing described by G0431 includes all CLIA high complexity urine drug screen testing as well as any less complex urine drug screen testing performed at the same patient encounter. HCPCS code G0431 describes a more extensive procedure than HCPCS code G0434. Physicians should not unbundle urine drug screen testing and report HCPCS codes G0431 and G0434 for the same patient encounter. (HCPCS codes G0431 and G0434 were deleted January 1, 2016.)

For Calendar Year 2016, urine drug presumptive testing should have been reported with HCPCS codes G0477-G0479. These codes differed based on the level of complexity of the testing methodology. Only one code from this code range should have been reported per date of service. These codes were deleted January 1, 2017.

Beginning January 1, 2017, urine drug presumptive testing may be reported with CPT® codes 80305-80307. These codes differ based on the level of complexity of the testing methodology. Only one code from this code range may be reported per date of service.

Beginning January 1, 2016, urine drug definitive testing may be reported with HCPCS codes G0480-G0483. These codes differ based on the number of drug classes including metabolites tested. Only one code from this code range may be reported per date of service.

14. In accordance with code descriptor changes for HCPCS codes G0416-G0419 effective January 1, 2015, CMS requires that surgical pathology, including gross and microscopic examination, of any and all submitted prostate needle biopsy specimens from a single patient be reported with one unit of service of HCPCS code G0416 rather than CPT® code 88305. (HCPCS codes G0417-G0419 were deleted January 1, 2015.)

Instructions for HCPCS codes G0416-G0419 in this Manual have undergone changes from year to year. For historical purposes, the prior instructions are reproduced.

From the calendar year 2015 Manual:

"13. HCPCS codes G0416-G0419 describe surgical pathology, including gross and microscopic examination, of separately identified and submitted prostate needle biopsy specimens from a saturation biopsy sampling procedure. CMS requires that these codes rather than CPT® code 88305 be utilized to report surgical pathology on prostate needle biopsy specimens only if the number of separately identified and submitted needle biopsy specimens is ten or more. Surgical pathology on nine or fewer separately identified and submitted prostate needle biopsy specimens should be reported with CPT® code 88305 with the unit of service corresponding to the number of separately identified and submitted biopsy specimens."

From the calendar year 2014 Manual:

"13. HCPCS codes G0416-G0419 describe surgical pathology, including gross and microscopic examination, of separately identified and submitted prostate needle biopsy specimens from a saturation biopsy sampling procedure. CMS requires that these codes rather than CPT® code 88305 be utilized to report surgical pathology on prostate needle biopsy specimens only if the number of separately identified and submitted needle biopsy specimens is ten or more. Surgical pathology on nine or fewer separately identified and submitted prostate needle biopsy specimens should be reported with CPT® code 88305 with the unit of service corresponding to the number of separately identified and submitted biopsy specimens."

From the calendar year 2013 Manual:

"13. HCPCS codes G0416-G0419 describe surgical pathology, including gross and microscopic examination, of separately identified and submitted prostate needle biopsy specimens from a saturation biopsy sampling procedure. CMS requires that these codes rather than CPT® code 88305 be utilized to report surgical pathology on prostate needle biopsy specimens only if the number of separately identified and submitted needle biopsy specimens is ten or more. Surgical pathology on nine or fewer separately identified and submitted prostate needle biopsy specimens should be reported with CPT® code 88305 with the unit of service corresponding to the number of separately identified and submitted biopsy specimens."

15. Blood products are described by HCPCS Level II P codes. If a P code describes an irradiated blood product, CPT® code 86945 (irradiation of blood product, each unit) *shall* not be reported separately since the P code includes irradiation of the blood product. If a P code describes a CMV negative blood product, CPT® codes 86644 and/or 86645 (CMV antibody) *shall* not be reported separately for that blood product since the P code includes the CMV antibody testing. If a P code describes a deglycerolized blood product, CPT® codes 86930 (frozen blood, each unit; freezing...), 86931 (frozen blood, each unit; thawing), and/or 86932 (frozen blood, each unit; freezing (includes preparation) and thawing) *shall* not be reported separately since the P code includes the freezing and thawing processes. If a P code describes a pooled blood product, CPT® code 86965 (pooling of platelets or other blood products) *shall* not be reported separately since the P code includes the pooling of the blood products. If the P code describes a "frozen" plasma product, CPT® code 86927 (fresh frozen plasma, thawing, each unit) *shall* not be reported separately since the P code includes the thawing process.

16. HCPCS codes G0396 and G0397 describe alcohol and/ or substance (other than tobacco) abuse structured assessment and intervention services. These codes *shall* not be reported separately with an evaluation and management (E&M), psychiatric diagnostic, or psychotherapy service code for the same work/time. If the E&M, psychiatric diagnostic, or psychotherapy service would normally include assessment and/or intervention of alcohol or substance abuse based on

the patient's clinical presentation, HCPCS G0396 or G0397 *shall* not be additionally reported. If a physician reports either of these G codes with an E&M, psychiatric diagnostic, or psychotherapy code utilizing an NCCI-associated modifier, the physician is certifying that the G code service is a distinct and separate service performed during a separate time period (not necessarily a separate patient encounter) than the E&M, psychiatric diagnostic, or psychotherapy service and is a service that is not included in the E&M, psychiatric diagnostic, or psychotherapy service based on the clinical reason for the E&M, psychiatric diagnostic, or psychotherapy service.

CPT® codes 99408 and 99409 describe services which are similar to those described by HCPCS codes G0396 and G0397, but are "screening" services which are not covered under the Medicare program. Where CPT® codes 99408 and 99409 are covered by State Medicaid programs, the policies explained in the previous paragraph for G0396/G0397 also apply to 99408/99409.

The same principles apply to separate reporting of E&M services with other screening, intervention, or counseling service HCPCS codes (e.g., G0442 (annual alcohol misuse screening, 15 minutes), G0443 (brief face-to-face behavioral counseling for alcohol misuse, 15 minutes), and G0444 (annual depression screening, 15 minutes). If an E&M, psychiatric diagnostic, or psychotherapy service is related to a problem which would normally require evaluation and management duplicative of the HCPCS code, the HCPCS code is not separately reportable. For example, if a patient presents with symptoms suggestive of depression, the provider *shall* not report G0444 in addition to the E&M, psychiatric diagnostic, or psychotherapy service code. The time and work effort devoted to the HCPCS code screening, intervention, or counseling service must be distinct and separate from the time and work of the E&M, psychiatric diagnostic, or psychotherapy service. Both services may occur at the same patient encounter.

17. HCPCS code G0269 describes placement of an occlusive device into a venous or arterial access site after an open or percutaneous vascular procedure. Since this code is status "B" on the Medicare Physician Fee Schedule Database, payment for this service is included in the payment for the vascular procedure. For OPPS, HCPCS code G0269 has payment status indicator "N" indicating that payment is packaged into the payment for other services paid. Providers reporting services under Medicare's hospital outpatient prospective payment system (OPPS) should report all services in accordance with appropriate Medicare *Internet-Only Manual* (*IOM*) instructions.

18. HCPCS code V2790 (amniotic membrane for surgical reconstruction, per procedure) *shall* not be reported separately with CPT® codes 65778 (Placement of amniotic membrane on the ocular surface; without sutures) or 65779 (Placement of amniotic membrane on the ocular surface; single layer, sutured) since Medicare payment for these two CPT® codes includes the amniotic membrane.

D. Medically Unlikely Edits (MUEs)

1. MUEs are described in Chapter I, Section V.

2. Providers/suppliers should be cautious about reporting services on multiple lines of a claim utilizing modifiers to bypass MUEs. MUEs were set so that such occurrences

should be uncommon. If a provider/supplier does this frequently for any HCPCS/CPT® code, the provider/supplier may be coding units of service incorrectly. The provider/supplier should consider contacting his/her national healthcare organization or the national medical/surgical society whose members commonly perform the procedure to clarify the correct reporting of units of service. A national healthcare organization, provider/supplier, or other interested third party may request a reconsideration of the MUE value of a HCPCS/CPT® code by CMS by writing the MUE contractor, Correct Coding Solutions, LLC, at the address indicated in Chapter I, Section V.

3. MUE values of HCPCS codes for discontinued drugs are zero (0).

4. The MUE value of HCPCS codes describing compounded inhalation drugs is zero (0) because compounded drugs are not FDA approved. The CMS *Internet-Only Manual, Medicare Benefit Policy Manual*, Chapter 15, Section 50.4.1 requires that claims processing contractors only pay for FDA approved drugs unless CMS issues other instructions.

5. In 2011 new HCPCS code J0171 (injection, adrenalin, epinephrine, 0.1 mg) replaced deleted HCPCS code J0170 (injection, adrenalin, epinephrine, up to 1 ml ampule). HCPCS code J0170 was often reported incorrectly. A 1 ml ampule of adrenalin/epinephrine contains 1.0 mg of adrenalin/epinephrine in a 1:1,000 solution. However, a 10 ml prefilled syringe with a 1:10,000 solution of adrenalin/epinephrine also contains only 1.0 mg of adrenalin/epinephrine. Thus a physician must recognize that ten (10) units of service for HCPCS code J0171 correspond to a 1 ml ampule or 10 ml of a prefilled syringe (1:10,000 (0.1 mg/ml) solution).

6. There are two HCPCS codes describing injectable dexamethasone. HCPCS code J1094 (injection, dexamethasone acetate, 1 mg) is no longer manufactured and has an MUE value of zero(0). HCPCS code J1100 (injection, dexamethasone sodium phosphate, 1 mg) is currently available. When billing for dexamethasone, physicians should be careful to report the correct formulation with the correct HCPCS code.

7. Based on the code descriptor, HCPCS code J3471 (injection, hyaluronidase, ovine, preservative free, per 1 USP unit (up to 999 units)) *shall* not be reported with more than 999 units of service. Per the CMS ASP (Average Sale Price) NDC (National Drug Code) HCPCS Crosswalk table, HCPCS code J3472 (injection, hyaluronidase, ovine, preservative free, per 1000 USP units) should be reported for a product that is no longer available. Therefore, if a physician utilizes more than 999 USP units of the product described by J3471, the physician may report HCPCS code J3471 on more than one line of a claim appending modifier 59 to additional claim lines and should report no more than 999 units of service on any one claim line.

8. The Medically Unlikely Edit (MUE) values for practitioner services for oral immunosuppressive, oral anti-cancer, and oral anti-emetic drugs are set at zero (0). Practitioners providing these medications to patients must bill the Durable Medical Equipment Medicare Administrative Contractors (DME MACs), rather than the Part A/Part B Medicare Administrative Contractors (A/B MACs), using the National Drug Codes(NDC). A/B MACs do not pay codes for these oral medications when submitted on practitioner claims. The MUE values for

outpatient hospital services are based on the amount of drug that might be administered to a patient on a single date of service. Facilities may not report to the A/B MAC more than a one day supply of any of these drugs for a single date of service. Outpatient hospital facilities may submit claims to DME MACs for a multiple day supply of these drugs provided on a single date of service.

9. If a HCPCS drug code descriptor defines the unit of service as "per dose", only one (1) UOS may be reported per drug administration procedure even if more than the usual amount of drug is administered. For example, HCPCS code J7321 (Hyaluronan or derivative, Hyalgan, Supartz *or VISCO-3*, for intra-articular injection, per dose) describes a drug that may be injected into the knee joint. Only one (1) UOS may be reported for injection of the drug into each knee joint even if the amount of injected drug exceeds the usual amount of drug injected.

10. The MUE values for HCPCS codes G0431 (Drug screen, qualitative; multiple drug classes by high complexity test method (e.g., immunoassay, enzyme assay), per patient encounter) and G0434 (Drug screen, other than chromatographic; any number of drug classes, by CLIA waived test or moderate complexity test, per patient encounter) are one (1) since the UOS for each code is defined as "per patient encounter" and the likelihood that a patient needs this type of testing at more than one encounter on a single date of service is very small. These codes include all drug screening at the patient encounter and should not be reported with multiple UOS at the same patient encounter. (HCPCS codes G0431 and G0434 were deleted January 1, 2016.)

For Calendar Year 2016, urine drug presumptive testing should have been reported with HCPCS codes G0477-G0479. These codes differed based on the level of complexity of the testing methodology. Only one code from this code range should have been reported per date of service. These codes were deleted January 1, 2017.

Beginning January 1, 2017, urine drug presumptive testing may be reported with CPT® codes 80305-80307. These codes differ based on the level of complexity of the testing methodology. Only one code from this code range may be reported per date of service.

Beginning January 1, 2016, urine drug definitive testing may be reported with HCPCS codes G0480-G0483. These codes are reported "per day" and *shall* not be reported with more than one UOS per day. *Urine drug definitive testing HCPCS code G0659 was implemented January 1, 2017. This code is reported "per day" and shall not be reported with more than one UOS per day.*

11. HCPCS codes Q9951 and Q9965-Q9967 describe low osmolar contrast material with different iodine concentrations. The appropriate code to report is based on the iodine concentration in the contrast material administered. The MUE value for HCPCS code Q9951 (Low osmolar contrast material, 400 or greater mg/ml iodine concentration, per ml) is zero (0). When this MUE value was established, no low osmolar contrast material products with iodine concentration of 400 mg iodine or greater per ml were identified. HCPCS code Q9951 is often incorrectly reported for low osmolar contrast material products with lower iodine concentrations. Similarly HCPCS codes Q9958-Q9964 describe high osmolar contrast material with different iodine concentrations. The appropriate code to report is based on the iodine concentration in the contrast material administered.

12. HCPCS code K0462 (Temporary replacement for patient owned equipment being repaired, any type) may be reported with one (1) unit of service (UOS) for each item of patient owned equipment that is being repaired. Component parts of a patient owned piece of equipment being repaired *shall* not be reported separately. For example, if a patient owned CPAP (continuous positive airway pressure) blower requires repair, the supplier may report one (1) UOS for K0462. The supplier *shall* not report an additional UOS for an integral humidifier even if it also requires repair. Additionally the supplier *shall* not report an additional UOS for a detachable humidifier unless it also requires repair at the same time.

13. Generally only one unit of service for an item of durable medical equipment (DME) (e.g., oxygen concentrator, wheelchair base) may be paid on a single date of service. Medicare does not allow payment for backup or duplicate durable medical equipment. More than one unit of service may be paid on a single date of service for accessories and supplies related to DME when appropriate. Prosthetics and orthotics may also be paid with more than one unit of service on a single date of service when appropriate.

14. HCPCS code P9604 describes a flat rate one way travel allowance for collection of medically necessary laboratory specimen(s) drawn from a home bound or nursing home bound patient. A round trip should be reported with modifier LR and one (1) unit of service (UOS) rather than two (2) UOS. The reported UOS *shall* be prorated for multiple patients drawn at the same address and for stops at the homes of Medicare and non-Medicare patients as described in the Medicare Internet-Only Manual, Publication 100-04 (Medicare Claims Processing Manual), Chapter 16 (Laboratory Services), Section 60.2.

15. The CMS *Internet-Only Manual* (Publication 100-04 *Medicare Claims Processing Manual*, Chapter 12 (Physicians/Nonphysician Practitioners), Section 40.7.B. and Chapter 4 (Part B Hospital (Including Inpatient Hospital Part B and OPPS)), Section 20.6.2 requires that practitioners and outpatient hospitals report bilateral surgical procedures with modifier 50 and one (1) UOS on a single claim line. MUE values for surgical procedures that may be performed bilaterally are based on this reporting requirement. Since this reporting requirement does not apply to an ambulatory surgical center (ASC), an ASC should report a bilateral surgical procedure on two claim lines, each with one (1) UOS using modifiers LT and RT on different claim lines. This reporting requirement does not apply to non-surgical diagnostic procedures.

16. HCPCS codes G0406-G0408 describe follow-up inpatient consultation services via telehealth and HCPCS codes G0425-G0427 describe emergency or initial inpatient telehealth consultation services via telehealth. These codes *shall* not be reported by a practitioner on the same date of service that the practitioner reports a face-to-face evaluation and management code. These codes are utilized to report telehealth services that, if performed with the patient physically present, would be reported with corresponding CPT® codes.

Since follow-up inpatient consultation services with a patient present are reported utilizing per diem CPT® codes 99231-99233, HCPCS codes G0406-G0408 may only be reported with a single unit of service per day.

Since initial inpatient consultation services with a patient present are reported utilizing per diem CPT® codes 99231-99233, HCPCS codes G0425-G0427 may only be reported with a single unit of service per day when reporting inpatient telehealth consultation services. However, if HCPCS codes G0425-G0427 are utilized to report emergency department services, reporting rules are comparable to CPT® codes 99281-99285.

E. General Policy Statements

1. MUE and NCCI PTP edits are based on services provided by the same physician to the same beneficiary on the same date of service. Physicians *shall* not inconvenience beneficiaries nor increase risks to beneficiaries by performing services on different dates of service to avoid MUE or NCCI PTP edits.

2. In this Manual many policies are described utilizing the term "physician". Unless indicated differently the usage of this term does not restrict the policies to physicians only but applies to all practitioners, hospitals, providers, or suppliers eligible to bill the relevant HCPCS/CPT® codes pursuant to applicable portions of the Social Security Act (SSA) of 1965, the Code of Federal Regulations (CFR), and Medicare rules. In some sections of this Manual, the term "physician" would not include some of these entities because specific rules do not apply to them. For example, Anesthesia Rules [e.g., CMS *Internet-Only Manual*, Publication 100-04 (*Medicare Claims Processing Manual*), Chapter 12 (Physician/Nonphysician Practitioners), Section 50(Payment for Anesthesiology Services)] and Global Surgery Rules [e.g., CMS *Internet-Only Manual*, Publication 100-04 (*Medicare Claims Processing Manual*), Chapter 12 (Physician/Nonphysician Practitioners), Section 40 (Surgeons and Global Surgery)] do not apply to hospitals.

3. Providers reporting services under Medicare's hospital outpatient prospective payment system (OPPS) *shall* report all services in accordance with appropriate Medicare *Internet-Only Manual* (IOM) instructions.

4. In 2010 the *CPT® Manual* modified the numbering of codes so that the sequence of codes as they appear in the *CPT® Manual* does not necessarily correspond to a sequential numbering of codes. In the *National Correct Coding Initiative Policy Manual for Medicare Services*, use of a numerical range of codes reflects all codes that numerically fall within the range regardless of their sequential order in the *CPT® Manual*.

5. With few exceptions the payment for a surgical procedure includes payment for dressings, supplies, and local anesthesia. These items are not separately reportable under their own HCPCS/CPT® codes. Wound closures utilizing adhesive strips or tape alone are not separately reportable. In the absence of an operative procedure, these types of wound closures are included in an E&M service. Under limited circumstances wound closure utilizing tissue adhesive may be reported separately. If a practitioner utilizes a tissue adhesive alone for a wound closure, it may be reported separately with HCPCS code G0168 (wound closure utilizing tissue adhesive(s) only). If a practitioner utilizes tissue adhesive in addition to staples or sutures to close a wound, HCPCS code G0168 is not separately reportable but is included in the tissue repair. Under OPPS HCPCS code G0168 is not recognized and paid. Facilities may report wound closure utilizing sutures, staples, or tissue adhesives, either singly or in combination with each other, with the appropriate CPT® code in the "Repair (Closure)" section of the *CPT® Manual*.

6. With limited exceptions Medicare Anesthesia Rules prevent separate payment for anesthesia for a medical or surgical procedure when provided by the physician performing the procedure. The physician *shall* not report CPT® codes 00100-01999, 62320-62327, or 64400-64530 for anesthesia for a procedure. Additionally, the physician *shall* not unbundle the anesthesia procedure and report component codes individually. For example, introduction of a needle or intracatheter into a vein (CPT® code 36000), venipuncture (CPT® code 36410), drug administration (CPT® codes 96360-96377) or cardiac assessment (e.g., CPT® codes 93000-93010, 93040-93042) *shall* not be reported when these procedures are related to the delivery of an anesthetic agent.

   Medicare allows separate reporting for moderate conscious sedation services (CPT® codes 99151-99153) when provided by the same physician performing a medical or surgical procedure.

   Under Medicare Global Surgery Rules, drug administration services (CPT® codes 96360-96377) are not separately reportable by the physician performing a procedure for drug administration services related to the procedure.

   Under the OPPS drug administration services related to operative procedures are included in the associated procedural HCPCS/CPT® codes. Examples of such drug administration services include, but are not limited to, anesthesia (local or other), hydration, and medications such as anxiolytics or antibiotics. Providers *shall* not report CPT® codes 96360-96377 for these services.

   Medicare Global Surgery Rules prevent separate payment for postoperative pain management when provided by the physician performing an operative procedure. CPT® codes 36000, 36410, 62320-62327, 64400-64489, and 96360-96377 describe some services that may be utilized for postoperative pain management. The services described by these codes may be reported by the physician performing the operative procedure only if provided for purposes unrelated to the postoperative pain management, the operative procedure, or anesthesia for the procedure.

   If a physician performing an operative procedure provides a drug administration service (CPT® codes 96360-96375) for a purpose unrelated to anesthesia, intra-operative care, or post-procedure pain management, the drug administration service (CPT® codes 96360-96375) may be reported with an NCCI-associated modifier if performed in a non-facility site of service.

7. The Medicare global surgery package includes insertion of urinary catheters. CPT® codes 51701-51703 (insertion of bladder catheters) *shall* not be reported with any procedure with a global period of 000, 010, or 090 days nor with some procedures with a global period of MMM.

8. Closure/repair of a surgical incision is included in the global surgical package except as noted below. Wound repair CPT® codes 12001-13153 *shall* not be reported separately to describe closure of surgical incisions for procedures with global surgery indicators of 000, 010, 090, or MMM. Simple, intermediate, and complex wound repair codes may be reported with Mohs surgery (CPT® codes 17311-17315). Intermediate and complex repair codes may be reported with excision of benign lesions (CPT® codes 11401-11406, 11421-11426, 11441-11471) and excision of malignant lesions (CPT® codes 11600-11646). Wound repair codes (CPT® codes 12001-13153) *shall* not be reported with excisions of benign lesions with an excised diameter of 0.5 cm or less (CPT® codes 11400, 11420, 11440).

9. Control of bleeding during an operative procedure is an integral component of a surgical procedure and is not separately reportable. Postoperative control of bleeding not requiring return to the operating room is included in the global surgical package and is not separately reportable. However, control of bleeding requiring return to the operating room in the postoperative period is separately reportable utilizing modifier 78.

10. A biopsy performed at the time of another more extensive procedure (e.g., excision, destruction, removal) is separately reportable under specific circumstances.

    If the biopsy is performed on a separate lesion, it is separately reportable. This situation may be reported with anatomic modifiers or modifier 59.

    If the biopsy is performed on the same lesion on which a more extensive procedure is performed, it is separately reportable only if the biopsy is utilized for immediate pathologic diagnosis prior to the more extensive procedure, and the decision to proceed with the more extensive procedure is based on the diagnosis established by the pathologic examination. The biopsy is not separately reportable if the pathologic examination at the time of surgery is for the purpose of assessing margins of resection or verifying resectability. When separately reportable modifier 58 may be reported to indicate that the biopsy and the more extensive procedure were planned or staged procedures.

    If a biopsy is performed and submitted for pathologic evaluation that will be completed after the more extensive procedure is performed, the biopsy is not separately reportable with the more extensive procedure.

11. Most NCCI PTP edits for codes describing procedures that may be performed on bilateral organs or structures (e.g., arms, eyes, kidneys, lungs) allow use of NCCI-associated modifiers (modifier indicator of "1") because the two codes of the code pair edit may be reported if the two procedures are performed on contralateral organs or structures. Most of these code pairs should not be reported with NCCI-associated modifiers when the corresponding procedures are performed on the ipsilateral organ or structure unless there is a specific coding rationale to bypass the edit. The existence of the NCCI PTP edit indicates that the two codes generally should not be reported together unless the two corresponding procedures are performed at two separate patient encounters or two separate anatomic sites. However, if the corresponding procedures are performed at the same patient encounter and in contiguous structures, NCCI-associated modifiers should generally not be utilized.

12. If fluoroscopy is performed during an endoscopic procedure, it is integral to the procedure. This principle applies to all endoscopic procedures including, but not limited to, laparoscopy, hysteroscopy, thoracoscopy, arthroscopy, esophagoscopy, colonoscopy, other GI endoscopy, laryngoscopy, bronchoscopy, and cystourethroscopy.

13. If the code descriptor for a HCPCS/CPT® code, *CPT® Manual* instruction for a code, or CMS instruction for a code indicates that the procedure includes radiologic guidance, a physician *shall* not separately report a HCPCS/CPT® code for radiologic guidance including,

but not limited to, fluoroscopy, ultrasound, computed tomography, or magnetic resonance imaging codes. If the physician performs an additional procedure on the same date of service for which a radiologic guidance or imaging code may be separately reported, the radiologic guidance or imaging code appropriate for that additional procedure may be reported separately with an NCCI-associated modifier if appropriate.

14. *CPT® code 36591 describes "collection of blood specimen from a completely implantable venous access device". CPT® code 36592 describes "collection of blood specimen using an established central or peripheral venous catheter, not otherwise specified". These codes shall not be reported with any service other than a laboratory service. That is, these codes may be reported if the only non-laboratory service performed is the collection of a blood specimen by one of these methods.*

15. *CPT® code 96523 describes "irrigation of implanted venous access device for drug delivery system". This code may be reported only if no other service is reported for the patient encounter.*

This page intentionally left blank

Appendix I: Publication 100 References

100-1, Chapter-1, 10.1

Hospital Insurance (Part A) for Inpatient Hospital, Hospice, Home Health and Skilled Nursing Facility (SNF) Services - A Brief Description

Hospital insurance is designed to help patients defray the expenses incurred by hospitalization and related care. In addition to inpatient hospital benefits, hospital insurance covers post hospital extended care in SNFs and post hospital care furnished by a home health agency in the patient's home. Blood clotting factors, for hemophilia patients competent to use such factors to control bleeding without medical or other supervision, and items related to the administration of such factors, are also a Part A benefit for beneficiaries in a covered Part A stay. The purpose of these additional benefits is to provide continued treatment after hospitalization and to encourage the appropriate use of more economical alternatives to inpatient hospital care. Program payments for services rendered to beneficiaries by providers (i.e., hospitals, SNFs, and home health agencies) are generally made to the provider. In each benefit period, payment may be made for up to 90 inpatient hospital days, and 100 days of post hospital extended care services.

Hospices also provide Part A hospital insurance services such as short-term inpatient care. In order to be eligible to elect hospice care under Medicare, an individual must be entitled to Part A of Medicare and be certified as being terminally ill. An individual is considered to be terminally ill if the individual has a medical prognosis that his or her life expectancy is 6 months or less if the illness runs its normal course.

The various Part A benefit categories (inpatient hospital services, SNF services, home health services, etc.) are subject to separate and mutually exclusive day limits, so that the use of benefit days under one of these benefits does not affect the number of benefit days that remain available under any of the other benefits. For example, the 90 days of inpatient hospital benefits (plus 60 non-renewable lifetime reserve days-- see Pub. 100-02, Medicare Benefit Policy Manual, chapter 5) that are available to a beneficiary in a hospital do not count against the 100 days of post hospital extended care benefits that are available in a SNF, and vice-versa.

100-1, Chapter-3, 20.5

Blood Deductibles (Part A and Part B)

Program payment may not be made for the first 3 pints of whole blood or equivalent units of packed red cells received under Part A and Part B combined in a calendar year. However, blood processing (e.g., administration, storage) is not subject to the deductible.

The blood deductibles are in addition to any other applicable deductible and coinsurance amounts for which the patient is responsible.

The deductible applies only to the first 3 pints of blood furnished in a calendar year, even if more than one provider furnished blood.

100-1, Chapter-3, 20.5.2

Part B Blood Deductible

Blood is furnished on an outpatient basis or is subject to the Part B blood deductible and is counted toward the combined limit. It should be noted that payment for blood may be made to the hospital under Part B only for blood furnished in an outpatient setting. Blood is not covered for inpatient Part B services.

100-1, Chapter-3, 20.5.3

Items Subject to Blood Deductibles

The blood deductibles apply only to whole blood and packed red cells. The term whole blood means human blood from which none of the liquid or cellular components have been removed. Where packed red cells are furnished, a unit of packed red cells is considered equivalent to a pint of whole blood. Other components of blood such as platelets, fibrinogen, plasma, gamma globulin, and serum albumin are not subject to the blood deductible. However, these components of blood are covered as biological.

Refer to Pub. 100-04, Medicare Claims Processing Manual, chapter 4, §231 regarding billing for blood and blood products under the Hospital Outpatient Prospective Payment System (OPPS).

100-4, Chapter 3, 20.7.3

Payment for Blood Clotting Factor Administered to Hemophilia Inpatients (2016 update)

Section 6011 of Public Law (P.L.) 101-239 amended §1886(a)(4) of the Social Security Act (the Act) to provide that prospective payment system (PPS) hospitals receive an additional payment for the costs of administering blood clotting factor to Medicare hemophiliacs who are hospital inpatients. Section 6011(b) of P.L. 101.239 specified that the payment be based on a predetermined price per unit of clotting factor multiplied by the number of units provided. This add-on payment originally was effective for blood clotting factors furnished on or after June 19, 1990, and before December 19, 1991. Section 13505 of P. L. 103-66 amended §6011 (d) of P.L. 101-239 to extend the period covered by the add-on payment for blood clotting factors administered to Medicare inpatients with hemophilia through September 30, 1994. Section 4452 of P.L. 105-33 amended §6011(d) of P.L. 101-239 to reinstate the add-on payment for the costs of administering blood-clotting factor to Medicare beneficiaries who have hemophilia and who are hospital inpatients for discharges occurring on or after October 1, 1998.

A/B MACs (B) shall process non-institutional blood clotting factor claims.

The A/B MACs (A) shall process institutional blood clotting factor claims payable under either Part A or Part B.

A. - Inpatient Bills

Under the Inpatient Prospective Payment System (IPPS), hospitals receive a special add-on payment for the costs of furnishing blood clotting factors to Medicare beneficiaries with hemophilia, admitted as inpatients of PPS hospitals.

The clotting factor add-on payment is calculated using the number of units (as defined in the HCPCS code long descriptor) billed by the provider under special instructions for units of service.

The PPS Pricer software does not calculate the payment amount. The Fiscal Intermediary Shared System (FISS) calculates the payment amount and subtracts the charges from those submitted to Pricer so that the clotting factor charges are not included in cost outlier computations.

Blood clotting factors not paid on a cost or PPS basis are priced as a drug/biological under the Medicare Part B Drug Pricing File effective for the specific date of service. As of January 1, 2005, the average sales price (ASP) plus 6 percent shall be used.

If a beneficiary is in a covered Part A stay in a PPS hospital, the clotting factors are paid in addition to the DRG/HIPPS payment (For FY 2004, this payment is based on 95 percent of average wholesale price.) For a SNF subject to SNF/PPS, the payment is bundled into the SNF/PPS rate.

For SNF inpatient Part A, there is no add-on payment for blood clotting factors.

The codes for blood-clotting factors are found on the Medicare Part B Drug Pricing File. This file is distributed on a quarterly basis.

For discharges occurring on or after October 1, 2000, and before December 31, 2005, report HCPCS Q0187 based on 1 billing unit per 1.2 mg. Effective January 1, 2006, HCPCS code J7189 replaces Q0187 and is defined as 1 billing unit per 1 microgram (mcg).

The examples below include the HCPCS code and indicate the dosage amount specified in the descriptor of that code. Facilities use the units field as a multiplier to arrive at the dosage amount.

EXAMPLE 1

HCPCS	Drug	Dosage
J7189	Factor VIIa	1 mcg

Actual dosage: 13,365 mcg

On the bill, the facility shows J7189 and 13,365 in the units field (13,365 mcg divided by 1 mcg = 13,365 units).

NOTE: The process for dealing with one international unit (IU) is the same as the process of dealing with one microgram.

EXAMPLE 2

HCPCS	Drug	Dosage
J9355	Trastuzumab	10 mg

Actual dosage: 140 mg

On the bill, the facility shows J9355 and 14 in the units field (140 mg divided by 10mg = 14 units).

When the dosage amount is greater than the amount indicated for the HCPCS code, the facility rounds up to determine units. When the dosage amount is less than the amount indicated for the HCPCS code, use 1 as the unit of measure.

EXAMPLE 3

HCPCS	Drug	Dosage
J3100	Tenecteplase	50 mg

Actual Dosage: 40 mg

The provider would bill for 1 unit, even though less than 1 full unit was furnished.

At times, the facility provides less than the amount provided in a single use vial and there is waste, i.e.; some drugs may be available only in packaged amounts that exceed the needs of an individual patient. Once the drug is reconstituted in the hospital's pharmacy, it may have a limited shelf life. Since an individual patient may receive less than the fully reconstituted amount, we encourage hospitals to schedule patients in such a way that the hospital can use the drug most efficiently. However, if the hospital must discard the remainder of a vial after administering part of it to a Medicare patient, the provider may bill for the amount of drug discarded plus the amount administered.

Example 1:

Drug X is available only in a 100-unit size. A hospital schedules three Medicare patients to receive drug X on the same day within the designated shelf life of the product. An appropriate hospital staff member administers 30 units to each patient. The remaining 10 units are billed to Medicare on the account of the last patient. Therefore, 30 units are billed on behalf of the first patient seen and 30 units are billed on behalf of the second patient seen. Forty units are billed on behalf of the last patient seen because the hospital had to discard 10 units at that point.

Example 2:

An appropriate hospital staff member must administer 30 units of drug X to a Medicare patient, and it is not practical to schedule another patient who requires the same drug. For example, the hospital has only one patient who requires drug X, or the hospital sees the patient for the first time and did not know the patient's condition. The hospital bills for 100 units on behalf of the patient, and Medicare pays for 100 units.

When the number of units of blood clotting factor administered to hemophiliac inpatients exceeds 99,999, the hospital reports the excess as a second line for revenue code 0636 and repeats the HCPCS code. One hundred thousand fifty (100,050) units are reported on one line as 99,999, and another line shows 1,051.

Revenue Code 0636 is used. It requires HCPCS. Some other inpatient drugs continue to be billed without HCPCS codes under pharmacy.

No changes in beneficiary notices are required. Coverage is applicable to hospital Part A claims only. Coverage is also applicable to inpatient Part B services in SNFs and all types of hospitals, including CAHs. Separate payment is not made to SNFs for beneficiaries in an inpatient Part A stay.

B. - A/B MAC (A) Action

The contractor is responsible for the following:

- It accepts HCPCS codes for inpatient services;
- It edits to require HCPCS codes with Revenue Code 0636. Multiple iterations of the revenue code are possible with the same or different HCPCS codes. It does not edit units except to ensure a numeric value;
- It reduces charges forwarded to Pricer by the charges for hemophilia clotting factors in revenue code 0636. It retains the charges and revenue and HCPCS codes for CWF; and
- It modifies data entry screens to accept HCPCS codes for hospital (including CAH) swing bed, and SNF inpatient claims (bill types 11X, 12X, 18x, 21x and, 22x).

100-1, Chapter-3, 30

Outpatient Mental Health Treatment Limitation

Regardless of the actual expenses a beneficiary incurs in connection with the treatment of mental, psychoneurotic, and personality disorders while the beneficiary is not an inpatient of a hospital at the time such expenses are incurred, the amount of those expenses that may be recognized for Part B deductible and payment purposes is limited to 62.5 percent of the Medicare approved amount for those services. The limitation is called the outpatient mental health treatment limitation (the limitation). The 62.5 percent limitation has been in place since the inception of the Medicare Part B program and it will remain effective at this percentage amount until January 1, 2010. However, effective January 1, 2010, through January 1, 2014, the limitation will be phased out as follows:

- January 1, 2010 –December 31, 2011, the limitation percentage is 68.75%.
  (Medicare pays 55% and the patient pays 45%).
- January 1, 2012 –December 31, 2012, the limitation percentage is 75%
  (Medicare pays 60% and the patient pays 40%).
- January 1, 2013 –December 31, 2013, the limitation percentage is 81.25%.
  (Medicare pays 65% and the patient pays 35%).
- January 1, 2014 –onward, the limitation percentage is 100%
  (Medicare pays 65% and the patient pays 35%).
- January 1, 2014 –onward, the limitation percentage is 100%
  (Medicare pays 80% and the patient pays 20%).

For additional details concerning the outpatient mental health treatment limitation, please see the Medicare Claims Processing Manual, Publication 100-04, chapter 9, section 60 and chapter 12, section 210.

100-1, Chapter-5, 90.2

Laboratory Defined

Laboratory means a facility for the biological, microbiological, serological, chemical, immuno-hematological, hematological, biophysical, cytological, pathological, or other examination of materials derived from the human body for the purpose of providing information for the diagnosis, prevention, or treatment of any disease or impairment of, or the assessment of the health of, human beings. These examinations also include procedures to determine, measure, or otherwise describe the presence or absence of various substances or organisms in the body. Facilities only collecting or preparing specimens (or both) or only serving as a mailing service and not performing testing are not considered laboratories.

100-2, Chapter-1, 10

Covered Inpatient Hospital Services Covered Under Part A

Patients covered under hospital insurance are entitled to have payment made on their behalf for inpatient hospital services. (Inpatient hospital services do not include extended care services provided by hospitals pursuant to swing bed approvals. See Pub. 100-1, Chapter 8, §10.1,"Hospital Providers of Extended Care Services."). However, both inpatient hospital and inpatient SNF benefits are provided under Part A -Hospital Insurance Benefits for the Aged and Disabled, of Title XVIII).

Additional information concerning the following topics can be found in the following manual chapters:

- Benefit periods is found in Chapter 3, "Duration of Covered Inpatient Services";
- Copayment days is found in Chapter 2, "Duration of Covered Inpatient Services";
- Lifetime reserve days is found in Chapter 5, "Lifetime Reserve Days";
- Related payment information is housed in the Provider Reimbursement Manual.

Blood must be furnished on a day which counts as a day of inpatient hospital services to be covered as a Part A service and to count toward the blood deductible. Thus, blood is not covered under Part A and does not count toward the Part A blood deductible when furnished to an inpatient after the inpatient has exhausted all benefit days in a benefit period, or where the individual has elected not to use lifetime reserve days. However, where the patient is discharged on their first day of entitlement or on the hospital's first day of participation, the hospital is permitted to submit a billing form with no accommodation charge, but with ancillary charges including blood.

The records for all Medicare hospital inpatient discharges are maintained in CMS for statistical analysis and use in determining future PPS DRG classifications and rates.

Non-PPS hospitals do not pay for non covered services generally excluded from cover age in the Medicare Program. This may result in denial of a part of the billed charges or in denial of the entire admission, depending upon circumstance. In PPS hospitals, the following are also possible:

1. In appropriately admitted cases where a non covered procedure was performed, denied services may result in payment of a different DRG (i.e., one which excludes payment for the non covered procedure); or

2. In appropriately admitted cases that become cost outlier cases, denied services may lead to denial of some or all of an outlier payment.

The following examples illustrate this principle. If care is non covered because a patient does not need to be hospitalized, the intermediary denies the admission and makes no Part A (i.e., PPS) payment unless paid under limitation on liability. Under limitation on liability, Medicare payment may be made when the provider and the beneficiary were not aware the services were not necessary and could not reasonably be expected to know that he services were not necessary. For detailed instructions, see the Medicare Claims Processing Manual, Chapter 30,"Limitation on Liability." If a patient is appropriately hospitalized but receives (beyond routine services) only non covered care, the admission is denied.

NOTE: The intermediary does not deny an admission that includes covered care, even if non covered care was also rendered. Under PPS, Medicare assumes that it is paying for only the covered care rendered whenever covered services needed to treat and/or diagnose the illness were in fact provided.

If a non covered procedure is provided along with covered non routine care, a DRG change rather than an admission denial might occur. If non covered procedures are elevating costs into the cost outlier category, outlier payment is denied in whole or in part.

When the hospital is included in PPS, most of the subsequent discussion regarding coverage of inpatient hospital services is relevant only in the context of determining the appropriateness of admissions, which DRG, if any, to pay, and the appropriateness of payment for any outlier cases.

If a patient receives items or services in excess of, or more expensive than, those for which payment can be made, payment is made only for the covered items or services or for only the appropriate prospective payment amount. This provision applies not only to inpatient services, but also to all hospital services under Parts A and B of the program. If the items or services were requested by the patient, the hospital may charge him the difference between the amount customarily charged for the services requested and the amount customarily charged for covered services.

An inpatient is a person who has been admitted to a hospital for bed occupancy for purposes of receiving inpatient hospital services. Generally, a patient is considered an inpatient if formally admitted as inpatient with the expectation that he or she will remain at least overnight and occupy a bed even though it later develops that the patient can be discharged or transferred to another hospital and not actually use a hospital bed overnight.

The physician or other practitioner responsible for a patient's care at the hospital is also responsible for deciding whether the patient should be admitted as an inpatient. Physicians should use a 24-hour period as a benchmark, i.e., they should order admission for patients who are expected to need hospital care for 24 hours or more, and treat other patients on an outpatient basis. However, the decision to admit a patient is a complex medical judgment which can be made only after the physician has considered a number of factors, including the patient's medical history and current medical needs, the types of facilities available to inpatients and to outpatients, the hospital's by-laws and admissions policies, and the relative appropriateness of treatment in each setting. Factors to be considered when making the decision to admit include such things as:

- The severity of the signs and symptoms exhibited by the patient;
- The medical predictability of something adverse happening to the patient;
- The need for diagnostic studies that appropriately are outpatient services (i.e., their performance does not ordinarily require the patient to remain at the hospital for 24 hours or more) to assist in assessing whether the patient should be admitted; and
- The availability of diagnostic procedures at the time when and at the location where the patient presents

Admissions of particular patients are not covered or non covered solely on the basis of the length of time the patient actually spends in the hospital. In certain specific situations coverage of services on an inpatient or outpatient basis is determined by the following rules:

Minor Surgery or Other Treatment - When patients with known diagnoses enter a hospital for a specific minor surgical procedure or other treatment that is expected to keep them in the hospital for only a few hours (less than 24), they are considered outpatients for coverage purposes regardless of: the hour they came to the hospital, whether they used a bed, and whether they remained in the hospital past midnight.

Renal Dialysis - Renal dialysis treatments are usually covered only as outpatient services but may under certain circumstances be covered as inpatient services depending on the patient's condition. Patients staying at home, who are ambulatory, whose conditions are stable and who come to the hospital for routine chronic dialysis treatments, and not for a diagnostic workup or a change in therapy, are considered outpatients. On the other hand, patients undergoing short-term dialysis until their kidneys recover from an acute illness (acute dialysis), or persons with borderline renal failure who develop acute renal failure every time they have an illness and require dialysis (episodic dialysis) are usually inpatients. A patient may begin dialysis as an inpatient and then progress to an outpatient status.

Under original Medicare, the Quality Improvement Organization (QIO), for each hospital is responsible for deciding, during review of inpatient admissions on a case-by-case basis, whether the admission was medically necessary. Medicare law authorizes the QIO to make these judgments, and the judgments are binding for purposes of Medicare coverage. In making these judgments, however, QIOs consider only the medical evidence which was available to the physician at the time an admission decision had to be made. They do not take into account other information (e.g., test results) which became available only after admission, except in cases where considering the post-admission information would support a finding that an admission was medically necessary.

Refer to Parts 4 and 7 of the QIO Manual with regard to initial determinations for these services. The QIO will review the swing bed services in these PPS hospitals as well.

NOTE: When patients requiring extended care services are admitted to beds in a hospital, they are considered inpatients of the hospital. In such cases, the services furnished in the hospital will not be considered extended care services, and payment may not be made under the program for such services unless the services are extended care services furnished pursuant to a swing bed agreement granted to the hospital by the Secretary of Health and Human Services.

100-2, Chapter-1, 10.1.4
Charges for Deluxe Private Room
Beneficiaries found to need a private room (either because they need isolation for medical reasons or because they need immediate admission when no other accommodations are available) may be assigned to any of the provider's private rooms. They do not have the right to insist on the private room of their choice, but their preferences should be given the same consideration as if they were paying all provider charges themselves. The program does not, under any circumstances, pay for personal comfort items. Thus, the program does not pay for deluxe accommodations and/or services. These would include a suite, or a room substantially more spacious than is required for treatment, or specially equipped or decorated, or serviced for the comfort and convenience of persons willing to pay a differential for such amenities. If the beneficiary (or representative) requests such deluxe accommodations, the provider should advise that there will be a charge, not covered by Medicare, of a specified amount per day (not exceeding the differential defined in the next sentence); and may charge the beneficiary that amount for each day he/she occupies the deluxe accommodations. The maximum amount the provider may charge the beneficiary for such accommodations is the differential between the most prevalent private room rate at the time of admission and the customary charge for the room occupied. Beneficiaries may not be charged this differential if they (or their representative) do not request the deluxe accommodations.

The beneficiary may not be charged such a differential in private room rates if that differential is based on factors other than personal comfort items. Such factors might include differences between older and newer wings, proximity to lounge, elevators or nursing stations, desirable view, etc. Such rooms are standard 1-bed units and not deluxe rooms for purposes of these instructions, even though the provider may call them deluxe and have a higher customary charge for them. No additional charge may be imposed upon the beneficiary who is assigned to a room that may be somewhat more desirable because of these factors.

100-2, Chapter-1, 40

Supplies, Appliances, and Equipment

Supplies, appliances, and equipment, which are ordinarily furnished by the hospital for the care and treatment of the beneficiary solely during the inpatient hospital stay, are covered inpatient hospital services.

Under certain circumstances, supplies, appliances, and equipment used during the beneficiary's inpatient stay are covered under Part A even though the supplies, appliances and equipment leave the hospital with the patient upon discharge. These are circumstances in which it would be unreasonable or impossible from a medical standpoint to limit the patient's use of the item to the periods during which the individual is an inpatient. Examples of items covered under this rule are:

- Items permanently installed in or attached to the patient's body while an inpatient, such as cardiac valves, cardiac pacemakers, and artificial limbs; and
- Items which are temporarily installed in or attached to the patient's body while an inpatient, and which are also necessary to permit or facilitate the patient's release from the hospital, such as tracheotomy or drainage tubes.

Hospital "admission packs" containing primarily toilet articles, such as soap, toothbrushes, toothpaste, and combs, are covered under Part A if routinely furnished by the hospital to all its inpatients. If not routinely furnished to all patients, the packs are not covered. In that situation, the hospital may charge beneficiaries for the pack, but only if they request it with knowledge of what they are requesting and what the charge to them will be.

Supplies, appliances, and equipment furnished to an inpatient for use Only outside the hospital are not, in general, covered as inpatient hospital services. However, a temporary or disposable item, which is medically necessary to permit or facilitate the patient's departure from the hospital and is required until the patient can obtain a continuing supply, is covered as an inpatient hospital service.

Oxygen furnished to hospital inpatients is covered under Part A as an inpatient supply.

100-2, Chapter-1, 70

Inpatient Services in Connection With Dental Services

When a patient is hospitalized for a dental procedure and the dentist's service is covered under Part B, the inpatient hospital services furnished are covered under Part A. For example, both the professional services of the dentist and the inpatient hospital expenses are covered when the Dentist reduces a jaw fracture of an inpatient at a participating hospital. In addition, hospital inpatient services, which are necessary because of the patient's underlying medical condition and clinical status or the severity of a non covered dental procedure, are covered.

When the hospital services are covered, all ancillary services such as x-rays, administration of anaesthesia, use of the operating room, etc., are covered.

Regardless of whether the inpatient hospital services are covered, the medical services of physicians furnished in connection with non covered dental services are not covered. The services of an anaesthesiologist, radiologist, or pathologist whose services are performed in connection with the care, treatment, filling, removal, or replacement of teeth or structures directly supporting teeth are not covered.

100-2, Chapter-6, 10

Medical and Other Health Services Furnished to Inpatients of Participating Hospitals

Payment may be made under Part B for physician services and for the nonphysician medical and other health services as provided in this section when furnished by a participating hospital (either directly or under arrangements) to an inpatient of the hospital, but only if payment for these services cannot be made under Part A. This policy applies to all hospitals and critical access hospitals (CAHs) participating in Medicare, including those paid under a prospective payment system or alternative payment methodology such as State cost control systems, and to emergency hospital services furnished by nonparticipating hospitals. In this section, the term "hospital" includes all hospitals and CAHs, regardless of payment methodology, unless otherwise specified.

For services to be covered under Part A or Part B, a hospital must furnish nonphysician services to its inpatients directly or under arrangements (see chapter 16, §170 of this manual, "Inpatient Hospital or SNF Services Not Delivered Directly or Under Arrangement by the Provider"). A nonphysician service is one which does not meet the criteria defining physicians' services specifically provided for in regulation at 42 CFR 415.102. Services "incident to" physicians' services (except for the services of nurse anesthetists employed by anesthesiologists) are nonphysician services for purposes of this provision.

100-2, Chapter 6, 20.6

Outpatient Observation Services

A. Outpatient Observation Services Defined

Observation care is a well-defined set of specific, clinically appropriate services, which include ongoing short term treatment, assessment, and reassessment before a decision can be made regarding whether patients will require further treatment as hospital inpatients or if they are able to be discharged from the hospital. Observation services are commonly ordered for patients who present to the emergency department and who then require a significant period of treatment or monitoring in order to make a decision concerning their admission or discharge.

Observation services are covered only when provided by the order of a physician or another individual authorized by State licensure law and hospital staff bylaws to admit patients to the hospital or to order outpatient tests. In the majority of cases, the decision whether to discharge a patient from the hospital following resolution of the reason for the observation care or to admit the patient as an inpatient can be made in less than 48 hours, usually in less than 24 hours. In only rare and exceptional cases do reasonable and necessary outpatient observation services span more than 48 hours.

Hospitals may bill for patients who are directly referred to the hospital for outpatient observation services. A direct referral occurs when a physician in the community refers a patient to the hospital for outpatient observation, bypassing the clinic or emergency department (ED) visit. Effective for services furnished on or after January 1, 2003, hospitals may bill for patients directly referred for observation services.

See, Pub. 100-04, Medicare Claims Processing Manual, chapter 4, section 290, at http://www.cms.hhs.gov/manuals/downloads/clm104c04.pdf for billing and payment instructions for outpatient observation services.

Future updates will be issued in a Recurring Update Notification.

B. Coverage of Outpatient Observation Services

When a physician orders that a patient receive observation care, the patient's status is that of an outpatient. The purpose of observation is to determine the need for further treatment or for inpatient admission. Thus, a patient receiving observation services may improve and be released, or be admitted as an inpatient (see Pub. 100-02, Medicare Benefit Policy Manual, Chapter 1, Section 10 "Covered Inpatient Hospital Services Covered Under Part A" at http://www.cms.hhs.gov/manuals/Downloads/bp102c01.pdf). For more information on correct reporting of observation services, see Pub. 100-04, Medicare Claims Processing Manual, chapter 4, section 290.2.2.)

All hospital observation services, regardless of the duration of the observation care, that are medically reasonable and necessary are covered by Medicare. Observation services are reported using HCPCS code G0378 (Hospital observation service, per hour). Beginning January 1, 2008, HCPCS code G0378 for hourly observation services is assigned status indicator N, signifying that its payment is always packaged. No separate payment is made for observation services reported with HCPCS code G0378. In most circumstances, observation services are supportive and ancillary to the other separately payable services provided to a patient. In certain circumstances when observation care is billed in conjunction with a high level clinic visit (Level 5), high level Type A emergency department visit (Level 4 or 5), high level Type B emergency department visit (Level5), critical care services, or direct referral for observation services as an integral part of a patient's extended encounter of care, payment may be made for the entire extended care encounter through one of two composite APCs when certain criteria are met. For information about billing and payment methodology for observation services in years prior to CY 2008, see Pub. 100-04, Medicare Claims Processing Manual, Chapter 4,§§290.3-290.4. For information about payment for extended assessment and management under composite APCs, see §290.5.

Payment for all reasonable and necessary observation services is packaged into the payments for other separately payable services provided to the patient in the same encounter. Observation services packaged through assignment of status indicator N are covered OPPS services. Since the payment for these services is included in the APC payment for other separately payable services on the claim, hospitals must not bill Medicare beneficiaries directly for the packaged services.

C. Services Not Covered by Medicare and Notification to the Beneficiary

In making the determination whether an ABN can be used to shift liability to a beneficiary for the cost of non-covered items or services related to an encounter that includes observation care, the provider should follow a two step process. First, the provider must decide whether the item or service meets either the definition of observation care or would be otherwise covered. If the item or service does not meet the definitional requirements of any Medicare-covered benefit under Part B, then the item or service is not covered by Medicare and an ABN is not required to shift the liability to the beneficiary. However, the provider may choose to provide voluntary notification for these items or services.

Second, if the item or service meets the definition of observation services or would be otherwise covered, then the provider must decide whether the item or service is "reasonable and necessary" for the beneficiary on the occasion in question, or if the item or service exceeds any frequency limitation for the particular benefit or falls outside of a timeframe for receipt of a particular benefit. In these cases, the ABN would be used to shift the liability to the beneficiary

(see Pub. 100-04, Medicare Claims Processing Manual; Chapter 30, "Financial Liability Protections," Section 20, at http://www.cms.hhs.gov/manuals/downloads/clm104c30.pdf for information regarding Limitation On Liability (LOL) Under §1879 Where Medicare Claims Are Disallowed).

If an ABN is not issued to the beneficiary, the provider may be held liable for the cost of the item or service unless the provider/supplier is able to demonstrate that they did not know and could not have reasonably been expected to know that Medicare would not pay for the item or service.

100-2, Chapter 10, 10.2.2

Reasonableness of the Ambulance Trip

Under the FS payment is made according to the level of medically necessary services actually furnished. That is, payment is based on the level of service furnished (provided they were medically necessary), not simply on the vehicle used. Even if a local government requires an ALS response for all calls, payment under the FS is made only for the level of service furnished, and then only when the service is medically necessary.

100-2, Chapter 10,10.3.3

Separately Payable Ambulance Transport Under Part B versus Patient Transportation that is Covered Under a Packaged Hospital Service

Transportation of a beneficiary from his or her home, an accident scene, or any other point of origin is covered under Part B as an ambulance service only to the nearest hospital, critical access hospital (CAH), or skilled nursing facility (SNF) that is capable of furnishing the required level and type of care for the beneficiary's illness or injury and only if medical necessity and other program coverage criteria are met.

Medicare-covered ambulance services are paid either as separately billed services, in which case the entity furnishing the ambulance service bills Part B of the program, or as a packaged service, in which case the entity furnishing the ambulance service must seek payment from the provider who is responsible for the beneficiary's care. If either the origin or the destination of the ambulance transport is the beneficiary's home, then the ambulance transport is paid separately by Medicare Part B, and the entity that furnishes the ambulance transport may bill its Medicare carrier or intermediary directly. If both the origin and destination of the ambulance transport are providers, e.g., a hospital, critical access hospital (CAH), skilled nursing facility (SNF), then responsibility for payment for the ambulance transport is determined in accordance with the following sequential criteria.

NOTE: These criteria must be applied in sequence as a flow chart and not independently of one another.

1. Provider Numbers:

   If the Medicare-assigned provider numbers of the two providers are different, then the ambulance service is separately billable to the program. If the provider number of both providers is the same, then consider criterion 2, "campus".

2. Campus:

   Following criterion 1, if the campuses of the two providers (sharing the same provider numbers) are the same, then the transport is not separately billable to the program. In this case the provider is responsible for payment. If the campuses of the two providers are different, then consider criterion 3, "patient status." "Campus" means the physical area immediately adjacent to the provider's main buildings, other areas and structures that are not strictly contiguous to the main buildings, but are located within 250 yards of the main buildings, and any of the other areas determined on an individual case basis by the CMS regional office to be part of the provider's campus.

3. Patient Status: Inpatient vs. Outpatient

    Following criteria 1 and 2, if the patient is an inpatient at both providers (i.e., inpatient status both at the origin and at the destination, providers sharing the same provider number but located on different campuses), then the transport is not separately billable. In this case the provider is responsible for payment. All other combinations (i.e., outpatient-to inpatient, inpatient-to-outpatient, outpatient-to-outpatient) are separately billable to the program.

In the case where the point of origin is not a provider, Part A coverage is not available because, at the time the beneficiary is being transported, the beneficiary is not an inpatient of any provider paid under Part A of the program and ambulance services are excluded from the 3-day preadmission payment window.

The transfer, i.e., the discharge of a beneficiary from one provider with a subsequent admission to another provider, is also payable as a Part B ambulance transport, provided all program coverage criteria are met, because, at the time that the beneficiary is in transit, the beneficiary is not a patient of either provider and not subject to either the inpatient preadmission payment window or outpatient payment packaging requirements. This includes an outpatient transfer from a remote, off- campus emergency department (ER) to becoming an inpatient or outpatient at the main campus hospital, even if the ER is owned and operated by the hospital.

Once a beneficiary is admitted to a hospital, CAH, or SNF, it may be necessary to transport the beneficiary to another hospital or other site temporarily for specialized care while the beneficiary maintains inpatient status with the original provider. This movement of the patient is considered "patient transportation" and is covered as an inpatient hospital or CAH service and as a SNF service when the SNF is furnishing it as a covered SNF service and payment is made under Part A for that service. (If the beneficiary is a resident of a SNF and must be transported by ambulance to receive dialysis or certain other high-end outpatient hospital services, the ambulance transport may be separately payable under Part B.) Because the service is covered and payable as a beneficiary transportation service under Part A, the service cannot be classified and paid for as an ambulance service under Part B. This includes intra-campus transfers between different departments of the same hospital, even where the departments are located in separate buildings. Such intra-campus transfers are not separately payable under the Part B ambulance benefit. Such costs are accounted for in the same manner as the costs of such a transfer within a single building.

100-2, Chapter 10, 20

Coverage Guidelines for Ambulance Service Claims

Payment may be made for expenses incurred by a patient for ambulance service provided conditions I, 2, and 3 in the left-hand column have been met. The right-hand column indicates the documentation needed to establish that the condition has been met.

Conditions	Review Action
1. Patient was transported by an approved supplier of ambulance services.	1. Ambulance suppliers are explained in greater detail in §10.1.3
2. The patient was suffering from an illness or injury, which contraindicated transportation by other means. (§10.2)	2. (a) The contractor presumes the requirement was met if the submitted documentation indicates that the patient: • Was transported in an emergency situation, e.g., as a result of an accident, injury or acute illness, or • Needed to be restrained to prevent injury to the beneficiary or others; or • Was unconscious or in shock; or • Required oxygen or other emergency treatment during transport to the nearest appropriate facility; or • Exhibits signs and symptoms that indicate the possibility of acute stroke; or • Had to remain immobile because of a fracture that had not been set or the possibility of a fracture; or • Was experiencing severe hemorrhage; or • Could be moved only by stretcher; or • Was bed-confined before and after the ambulance trip.

	b.
	
	In the absence of any of the conditions listed in (a) above additional documentation should be obtained to establish medical need where the evidence indicates the existence of the circumstances listed below:
	
	  i. Patient's condition would not ordinarily require movement by stretcher, or
	
	  ii. The individual was not admitted as a hospital inpatient (except in accident cases), or
	
	  iii. The ambulance was used solely because other means of transportation were unavailable, or
	
	  iv. (iv) The individual merely needed assistance in getting from his room or home to a vehicle.
	
	c. Where the information indicates a situation not listed in 2(a) or 2(b) above, refer the case to your supervisor.

Conditions	Review Action

3. The patient was transported from and to points listed below.
 	
    a. From patient's residence (or other place where need arose) to hospital or skilled nursing facility.
	3. Claims should show the ZIP Code of the point of pickup.
	
	    a.
	
	    i. Condition met if trip began within the institution's service area as shown in the carrier's locality guide.
	
	    ii. Condition met where the trip began outside the institution's service area if the institution was the nearest one with appropriate facilities.

NOTE: A patient's residence is the place where he or she makes his/her home and dwells permanently, or for an extended period of time. A skilled nursing facility is one, which is listed in the Directory of Medical Facilities as a participating SNF or as an institution which meets §1861(j)(1) of the Act.

NOTE: A claim for ambulance service to a participating hospital or skilled nursing facility should not be denied on the grounds that there is a nearer nonparticipation institution having appropriate facilities.

b. Skilled nursing facility to a hospital or hospital to a skilled nursing facility.	b.
	
	    i. Condition met if the ZIP Code of the pickup point is within the service area of the destination as shown in the carrier's locality guide.
	
	    ii. Condition met where the ZIP Code of the pickup point is outside the service area of the destination if the destination institution was the nearest appropriate facility.

c. Hospital to hospital or skilled nursing facility to skilled nursing facility.	c. Condition met if the discharging institution was not an appropriate facility and the admitting institution was the nearest appropriate facility.

d. From a hospital or skilled nursing facility to patient's residence.	d.
	
	    i. Condition met if patient's residence is within the institution's service area as shown in the carrier's locality guide.
	
	    ii. Condition met where the patient's residence is outside the institution's service area if the institution was the nearest appropriate facility.

e. Round trip for hospital or participating skilled nursing facility inpatients to the nearest hospital or nonhospital treatment facility.	e. Condition met if the reasonable and necessary diagnostic or therapeutic service required by patient's condition is not available at the institution where the beneficiary is an inpatient.

NOTE: Ambulance service to a physician's office or a physician-directed clinic is not covered. See §10.3.8 above, where a stop is made at a physician's office en route to a hospital and §10.3.3 for additional exceptions.)

4. Ambulance services involving hospital admissions in Canada or Mexico are covered (Medicare Claims Processing Manual, Chapter 1, "General Billing Requirements," §10.1.3.) if the following conditions are met :	4. (a) The foreign hospitalization has been determined to be covered; and b. The ambulance service meets the coverage requirements set forth in §§10-10.3. If the foreign hospitalization has been determined to be covered on the basis of emergency services (See the Medicare Claims Processing Manual, Chapter 1, "General Billing Requirements," §10.1.3), the necessity requirement (§10.2) and the destination requirement (§10.3) are considered met.
5. The carrier will make partial payment for otherwise covered ambulance service, which exceeded limits defined in item	5 & 6 (a) From the pickup point to the nearest appropriate facility, or 5 & 6 (b) From the nearest appropriate facility to the beneficiary's residence where he or she is being returned home from a distant institution.
6. The carrier will base the payment on the amount payable had the patient been transported:	

100-2, Chapter 10, 30.1.1

Ground Ambulance Services

Basic Life Support (BLS)

Definition: Basic life support (BLS) is transportation by ground ambulance vehicle and the provision of medically necessary supplies and services, including BLS ambulance services as defined by the State. The ambulance must be staffed by an individual who is qualified in accordance with State and local laws as an emergency medical technician-basic (EMT-Basic). These laws may vary from State to State or within a State. For example, only in some jurisdictions is an EMT-Basic permitted to operate limited equipment onboard the vehicle, assist more qualified personnel in performing assessments and interventions, and establish a peripheral intravenous (iv) line.

Basic Life Support (BLS) –Emergency

Definition: When medically necessary, the provision of BLS services, as specified above, in the context of an emergency response. An emergency response is one that, at the time the ambulance provider or supplier is called, it responds immediately. An immediate response is one in which the ambulance provider/supplier begins as quickly as possible to take the steps necessary to respond to the call.

Application: The determination to respond emergently with a BLS ambulance must be in accord with the local 911 or equivalent service dispatch protocol. If the call came in directly to the ambulance provider/supplier, then the provider's/supplier's dispatch protocol must meet, at a minimum, the standards of the dispatch protocol of the local 911 or equivalent service. In areas that do not have a local 911 or equivalent service, then the protocol must meet, at a minimum, the standards of a dispatch protocol in another similar jurisdiction within the State or, if there is no similar jurisdiction within the State, then the standards of any other dispatch protocol within the State. Where the dispatch was inconsistent with this standard of protocol, including where no protocol was used, the beneficiary's condition (for example, symptoms) at the scene determines the appropriate level of payment.

Advanced Life Support, Level 1 (ALS1)

Definition: Advanced life support, level 1 (ALS1) is the transportation by ground ambulance vehicle and the provision of medically necessary supplies and services including the provision of an ALS assessment or at least one ALS intervention.

Advanced Life Support Assessment

Definition: An advanced life support (ALS) assessment is an assessment performed by an ALS crew as part of an emergency response that was necessary because the patient's reported condition at the time of dispatch was such that only an ALS crew was qualified to perform the assessment. An ALS assessment does not necessarily result in a determination that the patient requires an ALS level of service.

Application: The determination to respond emergently with an ALS ambulance must be in accord with the local 911 or equivalent service dispatch protocol. If the call came in directly to the ambulance provider/supplier, then the provider's/supplier's dispatch protocol must meet, at a minimum, the standards of the dispatch protocol of the local 911 or equivalent service. In areas that do not have a local 911 or equivalent service, then the protocol must meet, at a minimum, the standards of a dispatch protocol in another similar jurisdiction within the State or, if there is no similar jurisdiction within the State, then the standards of any other dispatch protocol within the State. Where the dispatch was inconsistent with this standard of protocol, including where no protocol was used, the beneficiary's condition (for example, symptoms) at the scene determines the appropriate level of payment.

Advanced Life Support Intervention

Definition: An advanced life support (ALS) intervention is a procedure that is in accordance with State and local laws, required to be done by an emergency medical technician-intermediate (EMT-Intermediate) or EMT-Paramedic.

Application: An ALS intervention must be medically necessary to qualify as an intervention for payment for an ALS level of service. An ALS intervention applies only to ground transports.

Advanced Life Support, Level 1 (ALS1) –Emergency

Definition: When medically necessary, the provision of ALS1 services, as specified above, in the context of an emergency response. An emergency response is one that, at the time the ambulance provider or supplier is called, it responds immediately. An immediate response is one in which the ambulance provider/supplier begins as quickly as possible to take the steps necessary to respond to the call.

Application: The determination to respond emergently with an ALS ambulance must be in accord with the local 911 or equivalent service dispatch protocol. If the call came in directly to the ambulance provider/supplier, then the provider's/supplier's dispatch protocol must meet, at a minimum, the standards of the dispatch protocol of the local 911 or equivalent service. In areas that do not have a local 911 or equivalent service, then the protocol must meet, at a minimum, the standards of a dispatch protocol in another similar jurisdiction within the State or, if there is no similar jurisdiction

within the State, then the standards of any other dispatch protocol within the State. Where the dispatch was inconsistent with this standard of protocol, including where no protocol was used, the beneficiary's condition (for example, symptoms) at the scene determines the appropriate level of payment.

Advanced Life Support, Level 2 (ALS2)

Definition: Advanced life support, level 2 (ALS2) is the transportation by ground ambulance vehicle and the provision of medically necessary supplies and services including (1) at least three separate administrations of one or more medications by intravenous push/bolus or by continuous infusion (excluding crystalloid fluids) or (2) ground ambulance transport, medically necessary supplies and services, and the provision of at least one of theALS2 procedures listed below:

a. Manual defibrillation/cardioversion;
b. Endo tracheal intubation;
c. Central venous line;
d. Cardiac pacing;
e. Chest decompression;
f. Surgical airway; or
g. Intraosseous line.

Application: Crystalloid fluids include fluids such as 5 percent Dextrose in water, Saline and Lactated Ringer's. Medications that are administered by other means, for example: intramuscular/subcutaneous injection, oral, sublingually or nebulized, do not qualify to determine whether theALS2 level rate is payable. However, this is not an all-inclusive list. Likewise, a single dose of medication administered fractionally (i.e., one-third of a single dose quantity) on three separate occasions does not qualify for the ALS2 payment rate. The criterion of multiple administrations of the same drug requires a suitable quantity and amount of time between administrations that is in accordance with standard medical practice guidelines. The fractional administration of a single dose (for this purpose meaning a standard or protocol dose) on three separate occasions does not qualify for ALS2 payment.

In other words, the administration of 1/3of a qualifying dose 3 times does not equate to three qualifying doses for purposes of indicating ALS2 care. One-third of X given 3 times might = X (where X is a standard/protocol drug amount), but the same sequence does not equal 3 times X. Thus, if 3 administrations of the same drug are required to show that ALS2 care was given, each of those administrations must be in accord with local protocols. The run will not qualify on the basis of drug administration if that administration was not according to protocol.

An example of a single dose of medication administered fractionally on three separate occasions that would not qualify for the ALS2 payment rate would be the use of Intravenous (IV) Epinephrine in the treatment of pulse less Ventricular Tachycardia/Ventricular Fibrillation (VF/VT) in the adult patient. Administering this medication in increments of 0.25 mg, 0.25 mg, and 0.50 mg would not qualify for the ALS2 level of payment. This medication, according to the American Heart Association (AHA), Advanced Cardiac Life Support (ACLS) protocol, calls for Epinephrine to be administered in 1 mg increments every 3 to 5minutes. Therefore, in order to receive payment for an ALS2 level of service, based in part on the administration of Epinephrine, three separate administrations of Epinephrine in 1 mg increments must be administered for the treatment of pulse less VF/VT.

A second example that would not qualify for the ALS2 payment level is the use of Adenosine in increments of 2 mg, 2 mg, and

2 mg for a total of 6 mg in the treatment of an adult patient with Paroxysmal Supra ventricular Tachycardia (PSVT). According to ACLS guidelines, 6 mg of Adenosine should be given by rapid intravenous push (IVP) over 1 to 2 seconds. If the first dose does not result in the elimination of the supra ventricular tachycardia within 1 to 2 minutes, 12 mg of Adenosine should be administered IVP. If the supra ventricular tachycardia persists, a second 12 mg dose of Adenosine can be administered for a total of 30 mg of Adenosine. Three separate Administrations of the drug Adenosine in the dosage amounts outlined in the later case would qualify forALS2 payment.

Endotracheal intubation is one of the services that qualifies for the ALS2 level of payment; therefore, it is not necessary to consider medications administered by Endo tracheal intubation for the purpose of determining whether the ALS2 rate is payable. The monitoring and maintenance of an end tracheal tube that was previously inserted prior to transport also qualifies as an ALS2 procedure.

Advanced Life Support (ALS) Personnel

Definition: ALS personnel are individuals trained to the level of the emergency medical technician-intermediate (EMT-Intermediate) or paramedic.

Specialty Care Transport (SCT)

Definition: Specialty care transport (SCT) is the inter facility transportation of a critically injured or ill beneficiary by a ground ambulance vehicle, including the provision of medically necessary supplies and services, at a level of service beyond the scope of the EMT-Paramedic. SCT is necessary when a beneficiary's condition requires ongoing care that must be furnished by one or more health professionals in an appropriate specialty area, for example, emergency or critical care nursing, emergency medicine, respiratory care, cardiovascular care, or a paramedic with additional training.

Application: The EMT-Paramedic level of care is set by each State. SCT is necessary when a beneficiary's condition requires ongoing care that must be furnished by one or more health professionals in an appropriate specialty area. Care above that level that is medically necessary and that is furnished at a level of service above the EMT-Paramedic level of care is considered SCT. That is to say, if EMT-Paramedics -without specialty care certification or qualification -are permitted to furnish a given service in a State, then that service does not qualify for SCT. The phrase "EMT-Paramedic with additional training" recognizes that a State may permit a person who is not only certified as an EMT-Paramedic, but who also has successfully completed additional education as determined by the State in furnishing higher level medical services required by critically ill or critically injured patients, to furnish a level of service that otherwise would require a health professional in an appropriate specialty care area (for example, a nurse) to provide. "Additional training" means the specific additional training that a State requires a paramedic to complete in order to qualify to furnish specialty care to a critically ill or injured patient during an SCT.

Paramedic Intercept (PI)

Definition: Paramedic Intercept services are ALS services provided by an entity that does not provide the ambulance transport. This type of service is most often provided for an emergency ambulance transport in which a local volunteer ambulance that can provide only basic life support (BLS) level of service is dispatched to transport a patient. If the patient needs ALS services such as EKG monitoring, chest decompression, or I.V. therapy, another entity dispatches a paramedic to meet the BLS ambulance at the scene or once the ambulance is on the way to the hospital. The ALS paramedics then provide services to the patient.

This tiered approach to life saving is cost effective in many areas because most volunteer ambulances do not charge for their services and one paramedic service can cover many communities. Prior to March 1, 1999, Medicare payment could be made for these services, but only when the claim was submitted by the entity that actually furnished the ambulance transport. Payment could not be made directly to the intercept service provider. In those areas where State laws prohibit volunteer ambulances from billing Medicare and other health insurance, the intercept service could not receive payment for treating a Medicare beneficiary and was forced to bill the beneficiary for the entire service.

Paramedic intercept services furnished on or after March 1, 1999, may be payable separate from the ambulance transport, subject to the requirements specified below.

The intercept service(s) is:

- Furnished in a rural area;
- Furnished under a contract with one or more volunteer ambulance services; and,
- Medically necessary based on the condition of the beneficiary receiving the ambulance service.
- In addition, the volunteer ambulance service involved must:
- Meet the program's certification requirements for furnishing ambulance services;
- Furnish services only at the BLS level at the time of the intercept; and,
- Be prohibited by State law from billing anyone for any service. Finally, the entity furnishing the ALS paramedic intercept service must:
- Meet the program's certification requirements for furnishing ALS services, and,
- Bill all recipients who receive ALS paramedic intercept services from the entity, regardless of whether or not those recipients are Medicare beneficiaries.

For purposes of the paramedic intercept benefit, a rural area is an area that is designated as rural by a State law or regulation or any area outside of a Metropolitan Statistical Area or in New England, outside a New England County Metropolitan Area as defined by the Office of Management and Budget. The current list of these areas is periodically published in the Federal Register.

See the Medicare Claims Processing Manual, Chapter 15, "Ambulance," §20.1.4 for payment of paramedic intercept services.

Services in a Rural Area

Definition: Services in a rural area are services that are furnished (1) in an area outside a Metropolitan Statistical Area (MSA); or, (2) in New England, outside a New England County Metropolitan Area (NECMA); or, (3) an area identified as rural using the Goldsmith modification even though the area is within an MSA.

Emergency Response

Definition: Emergency response is a BLS or ALS1 level of service that has been provided in immediate response to a 911 call or the equivalent. An immediate response is one in which the ambulance provider/supplier begins as quickly as possible to take the steps necessary to respond to the call.

Application: The phrase "911 call or equivalent" is intended to establish the standard that the nature of the call at the time of dispatch is the determining factor. Regardless of the medium by which the call is made (e.g., a radio call could be appropriate) the call is of an emergent nature when, based on the information available to the dispatcher at the time of the call, it is reasonable for the dispatcher to issue an emergency dispatch in light of accepted, standard dispatch protocol. An emergency call need not come through 911 even in areas where a 911 call system exists. However, the determination to respond emergently must be in accord with the local 911 or equivalent service dispatch protocol. If the call came in directly to the ambulance provider/supplier, then the provider's/supplier's dispatch protocol and the dispatcher's actions must meet, at a minimum, the standards of the dispatch protocol of the local 911 or equivalent service. In areas that do not have a local 911 or equivalent service, then both the protocol and the dispatcher's actions must meet, at a minimum, the standards of the dispatch protocol in another similar jurisdiction within the State, or if there is no similar jurisdiction, then the standards of any other dispatch protocol within the State. Where the dispatch was inconsistent with this standard of protocol, including where no protocol was used, the beneficiary's condition (for example, symptoms) at the scene determines the appropriate level of payment.

EMT-Intermediate

Definition: EMT-Intermediate is an individual who is qualified, in accordance with State and local laws, as an EMT-Basic and who is also certified in accordance with State and local laws to perform essential advanced techniques and to administer a limited number of medications.

EMT-Paramedic

Definition: EMT-Paramedic possesses the qualifications of the EMT-Intermediate and, in accordance with State and local laws, has enhanced skills that include being able to administer additional interventions and medications.

Relative Value Units

Definition: Relative value units (RVUs) measure the value of ambulance services relative to the value of a base level ambulance service.

Application: The RVUs for the ambulance fee schedule are as follows:

Service Level RVUs
BLS 1.00
BLS –Emergency 1.60
ALS1 1.20
ALS1 –Emergency 1.90
ALS2 2.75
SCT 3.25
PI 1.75
RVUs are not applicable to FW and RW services.

100-4, Chapter 15, 10.4

Ambulance (2016 update)

Additional Introductory Guidelines

Since April 1, 2002 (the beginning of the transition to the full implementation of the ambulance fee schedule), payment for a medically necessary ambulance service is based on the level of service provided, not on the vehicle used.

Ambulance services are separately reimbursable only under Part B. Once a beneficiary is admitted to a hospital, Critical Access Hospitals (CAH), or Skilled Nursing Facility (SNF), it may be necessary to transport the beneficiary to another hospital or other site temporarily for specialized care while the beneficiary maintains inpatient status with the original provider. This movement of the patient is considered "patient transportation" and is covered as an inpatient hospital or CAH service under Part A and as a SNF service when the SNF is furnishing it as a covered SNF service and Part A payment is made for that service. Because the service is covered and payable as a beneficiary transportation service under Part A, the service cannot be classified and paid for as an ambulance service under Part B. This includes intra-campus transfers between different departments of the same hospital, even where the departments are located in separate buildings. Such intra-campus transfers are not separately payable under the Part B ambulance benefit. Such costs are accounted for in the same manner as the costs of such a transfer within a single building. See IOM Pub. 100-02, Medicare Benefit Policy Manual, chapter 10 - Ambulance Services, section 10.3.3 - Separately Payable Ambulance Transport Under Part B Versus Patient Transportation that is Covered Under a Packaged Institutional Service for further details. Refer to IOM Pub. 100-04, Medicare Claims Processing Manual, chapter 3 - Inpatient Hospital Billing, section 10.5 - Hospital Inpatient Bundling for additional information on hospital inpatient bundling of ambulance services. Refer to IOM Pub. 100-04, Medicare Claims Processing Manual, chapter 3 - Inpatient Hospital Billing for the definitions of an inpatient for the various inpatient facility types. All Prospective Payment Systems (PPS) have a different criteria for determining when ambulance services are payable (i.e., during an interrupted stay, on date of admission and date of discharge).

NOTE: The cost of oxygen and its administration in connection with and as part of the ambulance service is covered. Under the ambulance FS, oxygen and other items and services provided as part of the transport are included in the FS base payment rate and are NOT separately payable.

The A/B MAC (A) is responsible for the processing of claims for ambulance services furnished by a hospital based ambulance or for ambulance services provided by a supplier if provided under arrangements for an inpatient. The A/B MAC (B) is responsible for processing claims from suppliers; i.e., those entities that are not owned and operated by a provider. See section 10.2 below for further clarification of the definition of Providers and Suppliers of ambulance services.

Effective December 21, 2000, ambulance services furnished by a CAH or an entity that is owned and operated by a CAH are paid on a reasonable cost basis, but only if the CAH or entity is the only provider or supplier of ambulance services located within a 35-mile drive of such CAH or entity. Beginning February 24, 1999, ambulance transports to or from a non-hospital-based dialysis facility, origin and destination modifier "J," satisfy the program's origin and destination requirements for coverage.

Ambulance supplier services furnished under arrangements with a provider, e.g., hospital or SNF are typically not billed by the supplier to its A/B MAC (B), but are billed by the provider to its A/B MAC (A). The A/B MAC (A) is responsible for determining whether the conditions described below are met. In cases where all or part of the ambulance services are billed to the A/B MAC (B), the A/B MAC (B) has this responsibility, and the A/B MAC (A) shall contact the A/B MAC (B) to ascertain whether it has already determined if the crew and ambulance requirements are met. In such a situation, the A/B MAC (A) should accept the A/B MAC (B)'s determination without pursuing its own investigation.

Where a provider furnishes ambulance services under arrangements with a supplier of ambulance services, such services can be covered only if the supplier's vehicles and crew meet the certification requirements applicable for independent ambulance suppliers.

Effective January 1, 2006, items and services which include but are not limited to oxygen, drugs, extra attendants, supplies, EKG, and night differential are no longer paid separately for ambulance services. This occurred when CMS fully implemented the Ambulance Fee Schedule, and therefore, payment is based solely on the ambulance fee schedule.

Effective for claims on or after October 1, 2007, if ambulance claims submitted with a code(s) that is/are not separately billable the payment for the code(s) is included in the base rate.

Contractors shall use the following remittance advice messages and associated codes when rejecting/denying claims under this policy. This CARC/RARC combination is compliant with CAQH CORE Business Scenario Four.

Group Code: CO

CARC: 97

RARC: N390

MSN: 1.6

This is true whether the primary transportation service is allowed or denied. When the service is denied, the services are not separately billable to the beneficiaries as they are already part of the base rate.

Payment for ambulance services may be made only on an assignment related basis.

Prospective payment systems, including the Ambulance Fee Schedule, are exempt from Inherent Reasonableness provisions.

100-2, Chapter 12, 30.1

Rules for Payment of CORF Services

The payment basis for CORF services is 80 percent of the lesser of: (1) the actual charge for the service or (2) the physician fee schedule amount for the service when the physician fee schedule establishes a payment amount for such service. Payment for CORF services under the phnysician fee schedule is made for physical therapy, occupational therapy, speech-language pathology and respiratory therapy services, as well as the nursing and social and/or psychological services, which are a part of, or directly relate to, the rehabilitation plan of treatment.

Payment for covered durable medical equipment, orthotic and prosthetic (DMEPOS) devices and supplies provided by a CORF is based upon: the lesser of 80 percent of actual charges or the payment amount established under the DMEPOS fee schedule; or, the single payment amount established under the DMEPOS competitive bidding program, provided that payment for such an item is not included in the payment amount for other CORF services.

If there is no fee schedule amount for a covered CORF item or service, payment should be based on the lesser of 80 percent of the actual charge for the service provided or an amount determined by the local Medicare contractor.

The following conditions apply to CORF physical therapy, occupational therapy, and speech-language pathology services;

- Claims must contain the required functional reporting. (Reference: Sections 42 CFR 410.105.) Refer to Pub. 100-04, Medicare Claims Processing Manual, chapter 5, section 10.6.

- The functional reporting on claims must be consistent with the functional limitations identified as part of the patient's therapy plan of care and expressed as part of the patient's therapy goals; effective for claims with dates of service on and after January, 1, 2013. (Reference: 42 CFR 410.105.) See Pub. 100-04, Medicare Claims Processing Manual, chapter 5, section 10.6.

- The National Provider Identifier (NPI) of the certifying physician identified for a CORF physical therapy, occupational therapy, and speech-language pathology plan of treatment must be included on the therapy claim. This requirement is effective for claims with dates of service on or after October 1, 2012. (See Pub. 100-04, Medicare Claims Processing Manual, chapter 5, section 10.3.)

Payment for CORF social and/or psychological services is made under the physician fee schedule only for HCPCS code G0409, as appropriate, and only when billed using revenue codes 0560, 0569, 0910, 0911, 0914 and 0919.

Payment for CORF respiratory therapy services is made under the physician fee schedule when provided by a respiratory therapist as defined at 42CFR485.70(j) and, only to the extent that these services support or are an adjunct to the rehabilitation plan of treatment, when billed using revenue codes 0410, 0412 and 0419. Separate payment is not made for diagnostic tests or for services related to physiologic monitoring services which are bundled into other respiratory therapy services appropriately performed by a respiratory therapist, such as HCPCS codes G0237, G0238 and G0239.

Payment for CORF nursing services is made under the physician fee schedule only when provided by a registered nurse as defined at 42CFR485.70 (h) for nursing services only to the extent that these services support or are an adjunct to the rehabilitation plan of treatment. In addition, payment for CORF nursing services is made only when provided by a registered nurse. HCPCS code G0128 is used to bill for these services and only with revenue codes 0550 and 0559.

For specific payment requirements for CORF items and services see Pub. 100-04, Medicare Claims Processing Manual, Chapter 5, Part B Outpatient Rehabilitation and CORF/OPT Services.

100-2, Chapter 12, 40.5

Respiratory Therapy Services

A respiratory therapy plan of treatment is wholly established and signed by the referring physician before the respiratory therapist initiates the actual treatment.

A. Definition

Respiratory therapy services include only those services that can be appropriately provided to CORF patients by a qualified respiratory therapist, as defined at 42CFR485.70 (j), under a physician-established respiratory therapy plan of treatment. The facility physician must be present in the facility for a sufficient time to provide, in accordance with accepted principles of medical practice, medical direction, medical care services and consultation. Respiratory therapy services include the physiological monitoring necessary to furnish these services. Payment for these services is bundled into the payment for respiratory therapy services and is not payable separately. Diagnostic and other medical services provided in the CORF setting are not considered CORF services, and therefore may not be included in a respiratory therapy plan of treatment because these are covered under separate benefit categories.

The respiratory therapist assesses the patient to determine the appropriateness of pursed lip breathing activity and may check the patient's oxygen saturation level (via pulse oximetry). If appropriate, the respiratory therapist then provides the initial training in order to ensure that the patient can accurately perform the activity. The respiratory therapist may again check the patient's oxygen saturation level, or perform peak respiratory flow, or check other respiratory parameters. These types of services are considered "physiological monitoring" and are bundled into the payment for HCPCS codes G0237, G0238 and G0239. Physiological monitoring also includes the provision of a 6-minute walk test that is typically conducted before the start of the patient's respiratory therapy activities. The time to provide this walk "test" assessment is included as part of the HCPCS code G0238. When provided as part of a CORF respiratory therapy plan of treatment, payment for these monitoring activities is bundled into the payment for other services provided by the respiratory therapist, such as the three respiratory therapy specific G-codes.

B. Guidelines for Applying Coverage Criteria

There are some conditions for which respiratory therapy services may be indicated. However, respiratory therapy performed as part of a standard protocol without regard to the individual patient's actual condition, capacity for improving, and the need for such services as established, is not reasonable and medically necessary. All respiratory therapy services must meet the test of being "reasonable and medically necessary" pursuant to §1862(a)(1)(A) of the Act. Determinations of medical necessity are made based on local contractor decisions on a claim-by-claim basis.

The three HCPCS codes G0237, G0238, and G0239 are specific to services provided under the respiratory therapy plan of treatment and, as such, are not designated as subject to the therapy caps.

C. Patient Education Programs

Instructing a patient in the use of equipment, breathing exercises, etc. may be considered reasonable and necessary to the patient's respiratory therapy plan of treatment and can usually be given to a patient during the course of treatment by the respiratory therapist.

These educational instructions are bundled into the covered service and separate payment is not made.

100-2, Chapter 12, 40.8

Nursing Services

CORF nursing services may only be provided by an individual meeting the qualifications of a registered nurse, as defined at 42CFR485.70 (h). They must relate to, or be a part of, the rehabilitation plan of treatment.

CORF nursing services must be reasonable and medically necessary and are provided as an adjunct to the rehabilitation plan of treatment. For example, a registered nurse may perform or instruct a patient, as appropriate, in the proper procedure of "in and out" urethral catheterization, tracheostomy tube suctioning, or the cleaning for ileostomy or colostomy bags.

Nursing services may not substitute for or supplant the services of physical therapists, occupational therapists, speech-language pathologists and respiratory therapists,

but instead must support or further the services and goals provided in the rehabilitation plan of treatment.

CORF nursing services must be provided by a registered nurse and may only be coded as HCPCS code G0128 indicating that CORF "nursing services" were provided.

100-2, Chapter 12, 40.11

Vaccines

A CORF may provide pneumococcal pneumonia, influenza virus, and hepatitis B vaccines to its patients. While not included as a service under the CORF benefit, Medicare will make payment to the CORF for certain vaccines and their administration provided to CORF patients (CY 2008 PFS Rule 72 FR 66293).

The following three vaccinations are covered in a CORF if a physician who is a doctor of medicine or osteopathy orders it for a CORF patient:

- Pneumococcal pneumonia vaccine and its administration;
- Hepatitis B vaccine and its administration furnished to a beneficiary who is at high or intermediate risk of contracting hepatitis B; and
- Influenza virus vaccine and its administration

Payment for covered pneumococcal pneumonia, influenza virus, and hepatitis B vaccines provided in the CORF setting is based on 95 percent of the average wholesale price. The CORF registered nurse provides administration of any of these vaccines using HCPCS codes G0008, G0009 or G0010 with payment based on CPT® code 90471.

100-2, Chapter 15, 50

Drugs and Biologicals

The Medicare program provides limited benefits for outpatient drugs. The program covers drugs that are furnished "incident to" a physician's service provided that the drugs are not usually self-administered by the patients who take them.

Generally, drugs and biologicals are covered only if all of the following requirements are met:

- They meet the definition of drugs or biologicals (see §50.1);
- They are of the type that are not usually self-administered. (see §50.2);
- They meet all the general requirements for coverage of items as incident to a physician's services (see §§50.1 and 50.3);
- They are reasonable and necessary for the diagnosis or treatment of the illness or injury for which they are administered according to accepted standards of medical practice (see §50.4);
- They are not excluded as non covered immunizations (see §50.4.4.2); and
- They have not been determined by the FDA to be less than effective. (See §§50.4.4)

Medicare Part B does generally not cover drugs that can be self-administered, such as those in pill form, or are used for self-injection. However, the statute provides for the coverage of some self-administered drugs. Examples of self-administered drugs that are covered include blood-clotting factors, drugs used in immunosuppressive therapy, erythropoietin for dialysis patients, osteoporosis drugs for certain homebound patients, and certain oral cancer drugs. (See §110.3for coverage of drugs, which are necessary to the effective use of Durable Medical Equipment (DME) or prosthetic devices.)

100-2, Chapter 15, 50.2

Determining Self-Administration of Drug or Biological

The Medicare program provides limited benefits for outpatient prescription drugs. The program covers drugs that are furnished "incident to" a physician's service provided that the drugs are not usually self-administered by the patients who take them. Section 112 of the Benefits, Improvements & Protection Act of 2000 (BIPA) amended sections 1861(s)(2)(A) and 1861(s)(2)(B) of the Act to redefine this exclusion. The prior statutory language referred to those drugs "which cannot be self-administered." Implementation of the BIPA provision requires interpretation of the phrase "not usually self-administered by the patient"

A. Policy

Fiscal intermediaries, carriers and Medicare Administrative Contractors (MACs) are instructed to follow the instructions below when applying the exclusion for drugs that are usually self administered by the patient. Each individual contractor must make its own individual determination on each drug. Contractors must continue to apply the policy that not only the drug is medically reasonable and necessary for any individual claim, but also that the route of administration is medically reasonable and necessary. That is, if a drug is available in both oral and injectable forms, the injectable form of the drug must be medically reasonable and necessary as compared to using the oral form.

For certain injectable drugs, it will be apparent due to the nature of the condition(s) for which they are administered or the usual course of treatment for those conditions, they are, or are not, usually self-administered. For example, an injectable drug used to treat migraine headaches is usually self-administered. On the other hand, an injectable drug, administered at the same time as chemotherapy, used to treat anemia secondary to chemotherapy is not usually self-administered.

B. Administered

The term "administered" refers only to the physical process by which the drug enters the patient's body. It does not refer to whether the process is supervised by a medical professional (for example, to observe proper technique or side-effects of the drug). Injectable drugs, including intravenously administered drugs, are typically eligible for inclusion under the "incident to" benefit. With limited exceptions, other routes of administration including, but not limited to, oral drugs, suppositories, topical medications are considered to be usually self-administered by the patient.

C. Usually

For the purposes of applying this exclusion, the term "usually" means more than 50 percent of the time for all Medicare beneficiaries who use the drug. Therefore, if a drug is self-administered by more than 50 percent of Medicare beneficiaries, the drug is excluded from coverage and the contractor may not make any Medicare payment for it. In arriving at a single determination as to whether a drug is usually self-administered, contractors should make a separate determination for each indication for a drug as to whether that drug is usually self-administered.

After determining whether a drug is usually self-administered for each indication, contractors should determine the relative contribution of each indication to total use of the drug (i.e., weighted average) in order to make an overall determination as to whether the drug is usually self-administered. For example, if a drug has three indications, is not self-administered for the first indication, but is self administered for the second and third indications, and the first indication makes up 40 percent of total usage, the second indication makes up 30 percent of total usage,

and the third indication makes up 30 percent of total usage, then the drug would be considered usually self-administered.

Reliable statistical information on the extent of self-administration by the patient may not always be available. Consequently, CMS offers the following guidance for each contractor's consideration in making this determination in the absence of such data:

1. Absent evidence to the contrary, presume that drugs delivered intravenously are not usually self- administered by the patient.

2. Absent evidence to the contrary, presume that drugs delivered by intramuscular injection are not usually self-administered by the patient. (Avonex, for example, is delivered by intramuscular injection, not usually self-administered by the patient.) The contractor may consider the depth and nature of the particular intramuscular injection in applying this presumption. In applying this presumption, contractors should examine the use of the particular drug and consider the following factors:

3. Absent evidence to the contrary, presume that drugs delivered by subcutaneous injection are self-administered by the patient. However, contractors should examine the use of the particular drug and consider the following factors:

    A. **Acute Condition** -Is the condition for which the drug is used an acute condition? If so, it is less likely that a patient would self-administer the drug. If the condition were longer term, it would be more likely that the patient would self-administer the drug.

    B. **Frequency of Administration** -How often is the injection given? For example, if the drug is administered once per month, it is less likely to be self-administered by the patient. However, if it is administered once or more per week, it is likely that the drug is self-administered by the patient.

In some instances, carriers may have provided payment for one or perhaps several doses of a drug that would otherwise not be paid for because the drug is usually self-administered. Carriers may have exercised this discretion for limited coverage, for example, during a brief time when the patient is being trained under the supervision of a physician in the proper technique for self-administration. Medicare will no longer pay for such doses. In addition, contractors may no longer pay for any drug when it is administered on an outpatient emergency basis, if the drug is excluded because it is usually self-administered by the patient.

D. Definition of Acute Condition

For the purposes of determining whether a drug is usually self-administered, an acute condition means a condition that begins over a short time period, is likely to be of short duration and/or the expected course of treatment is for a short, finite interval. A course of treatment consisting of scheduled injections lasting less than 2 weeks, regardless of frequency or route of administration, is considered acute. Evidence to support this may include Food and Drug Administration (FDA) approval language, package inserts, drug compendia, and other information.

E. By the Patient

The term "by the patient" means Medicare beneficiaries as a collective whole. The carrier includes only the patients themselves and not other individuals (that is, spouses, friends, or other care- givers are not considered the patient). The determination is based on whether the drug is self-administered by the patient a majority of the time that the drug is used on an outpatient basis by Medicare beneficiaries for medically necessary indications. The carrier ignores all instances when the drug is administered on an inpatient basis.

The carrier makes this determination on a drug-by-drug basis, not on a beneficiary-by-beneficiary basis. In evaluating whether beneficiaries as a collective whole self-administer, individual beneficiaries who do not have the capacity to self-administer any drug due to a condition other than the condition for which they are taking the drug in question are not considered. For example, an individual afflicted with paraplegia or advanced dementia would not have the capacity to self-administer any injectable drug, so such individuals would not be included in the population upon which the determination for self-administration by the patient was based. Note that some individuals afflicted with a less severe stage of an otherwise debilitating condition would be included in the population upon which the determination for "self-administered by the patient" was based; for example, an early onset of dementia.

F. Evidentiary Criteria

Contractors are only required to consider the following types of evidence: peer reviewed medical literature, standards of medical practice, evidence-based practice guidelines, FDA approved label, and package inserts. Contractors may also consider other evidence submitted by interested individuals or groups subject to their judgment.

Contractors should also use these evidentiary criteria when reviewing requests for making a determination as to whether a drug is usually self-administered, and requests for reconsideration of a pending or published determination.

Note that prior to August 1, 2002, one of the principal factors used to determine whether a drug was subject to the self-administered exclusion was whether the FDA label contained instructions for self-administration. However, CMS notes that under the new standard, the fact that the FDA label includes instructions for self-administration is not, by itself, a determining factor that a drug is subject to this exclusion.

G. Provider Notice of Noncovered Drugs

Contractors must describe on their Web site the process they will use to determine whether a drug is usually self-administered and thus does not meet the "incident to" benefit category. Contractors must publish a list of the injectable drugs that are subject to the self-administered exclusion on their Web site, including the data and rationale that led to the determination. Contractors will report the workload associated with developing new coverage statements in CAFM 21208.

Contractors must provide notice 45 days prior to the date that these drugs will not be covered. During the 45-day time period, contractors will maintain existing medical review and payment procedures. After the 45-day notice, contractors may deny payment for the drugs subject to the notice.

Contractors must not develop local coverage determinations (LCDs) for this purpose because further elaboration to describe drugs that do not meet the 'incident to' and the 'not usually self-administered' provisions of the statute are unnecessary. Current LCDs based solely on these provisions must be withdrawn. LCDs that address the self-administered exclusion and other information may be reissued absent the self-administered drug exclusion material. Contractors will report this workload in CAFM 21206. However, contractors may continue to use and write LCDs to describe reasonable and necessary uses of drugs that are not usually self-administered.

H. Conferences Between Contractor

Contractors' Medical Directors may meet and discuss whether a drug is usually self-administered without reaching a formal consensus. Each contractor uses its discretion as to whether or not it will participate in such discussions. Each contractor must make its own individual determinations, except that fiscal intermediaries may, at their discretion, follow the determinations of the local carrier with respect to the self-administered exclusion.

I. Beneficiary Appeals

If a beneficiary's claim for a particular drug is denied because the drug is subject to the "Self-administered drug" exclusion, the beneficiary may appeal the denial. Because it is a "benefit category" denial and not a denial based on medical necessity, an Advance Beneficiary Notice (ABN) is not required. A "benefit category" denial (i.e., a denial based on the fact that there is no benefit category under which the drug may be covered) does not trigger the financial liability protection provisions of Limitation On Liability (under §1879 of the Act). Therefore, physicians or providers may charge the beneficiary for an excluded drug.

J. Provider and Physician Appeals

A physician accepting assignment may appeal a denial under the provisions found in Pub. 100-04, Medicare Claims Processing Manual, chapter 29.

K. Reasonable and Necessary

Contractors will make the determination of reasonable and necessary with respect to the medical appropriateness of a drug to treat the patient's condition. Contractors will continue to make the determination of whether the intravenous or injection form of a drug is appropriate as opposed to the oral form. Contractors will also continue to make the determination as to whether a physician's office visit was reasonable and necessary. However, contractors should not make a determination of whether it was reasonable and necessary for the patient to choose to have his or her drug administered in the physician's office or outpatient hospital setting. That is, while a physician's office visit may not be reasonable and necessary in a specific situation, in such a case an injection service would be payable.

L. Reporting Requirements

Each carrier, intermediary and Medicare Administrative Contractor (MAC) must report to CMS its complete list of injectable drugs that the contractor has determined are excluded when furnished incident to a physician's service on the basis that the drug is usually self-administered. The CMS expects that contractors will review injectable drugs on a rolling basis and update their list of excluded drugs as it is developed and no less frequently than annually. For example, contractors should not wait to publish this list until every drug has been reviewed. Contractors must enter their self-administered drug exclusion list to the Medicare Coverage Database (MCD). This database can be accessed at www.cms.hhs.gov/mcd. See Pub.100-08, Medicare Program Integrity Manual, Chapter 3, Section 3.3, "Policies and Guidelines Applied During Review", for instructions on submitting these lists to the MCD.

M. Drugs Treated as Hospital Outpatient Supplies

In certain circumstances, Medicare pays for drugs that may be considered usually self-administered by the patient when such drugs function as supplies. This is the case when the drugs provided are an integral component of a procedure or are directly related to it, i.e., when they facilitate the performance of or recovery from a particular procedure. Except for the applicable copayment, hospitals may not bill beneficiaries for these types of drugs because their costs, as supplies, are packaged into the payment for the procedure with which they are used. Listed below are examples of when drugs are treated as supplies and hospitals should bill Medicare for the drug as a supply and should not separately bill the beneficiary.

- Sedatives administered to a patient while he or she is in the preoperative area being prepared for a procedure.
- Mydriatic drops instilled into the eye to dilate the pupils, anti-inflammatory drops, antibiotic drops/ointments, and ocular hypotensives that are administered to a patient immediately before, during, or immediately following an ophthalmic procedure. This does not refer to the patient's eye drops that the patient uses pre-and postoperatively.
- Barium or low osmolar contrast media provided integral to a diagnostic imaging procedure.
- Topical solution used with photodynamic therapy furnished at the hospital to treat nonhyperkeratotic actinic keratosis lesions of the face or scalp.
- Antibiotic ointments such as bacitracin, placed on a wound or surgical incision at the completion of a procedure.

The following are examples of when a drug is not directly related or integral to a procedure, and does not facilitate the performance of or recovery from a procedure. Therefore the drug is not considered a packaged supply. In many of these cases the drug itself is the treatment instead of being integral or directly related to the procedure, or facilitating the performance of or recovery from a particular procedure.

- Drugs given to a patient for his or her continued use at home after leaving the hospital.
- Oral pain medication given to an outpatient who develops a headache while receiving chemotherapy administration treatment.
- Daily routine insulin or hypertension medication given preoperatively to a patient.
- A fentanyl patch or oral pain medication such as hydrocodone, given to an outpatient presenting with pain.
- A laxative suppository for constipation while the patient waits to receive an unrelated X-ray.

These two lists of examples may serve to guide hospitals in deciding which drugs are supplies packaged as a part of a procedure, and thus may be billed under Part B. Hospitals should follow CMS' guidance for billing drugs that are packaged and paid as supplies, reporting coded and uncoded drugs with their charges under the revenue code associated with the cost center under which the hospital accumulates the costs for the drugs.

100-2, Chapter 15, 50.4.2

Unlabeled Use of Drug

An unlabeled use of a drug is a use that is not included as an indication on the drugs label as approved by the FDA. FDA approved drugs used for indications other than what is indicated on the official label may be covered under Medicare if the carrier determines the use to be medically accepted, taking into consideration the major drug compendia, authoritative medical literature and/or accepted standards of medical practice. In the case of drugs used in an anti-cancer chemotherapeutic regimen, unlabeled uses are covered for a medically accepted indication as defined in §50.5.

These decisions are made by the contractor on a case-by-case basis.

100-2, Chapter 15, 50.4.4.2

Immunizations

Vaccinations or inoculations are excluded as immunizations unless they are directly related to the treatment of an injury or direct exposure to a disease or condition, such as anti-rabies treatment, tetanus antitoxin or booster vaccine, botulin antitoxin, antivenin sera, or immune globulin. In the absence of injury or direct exposure, preventive immunization (vaccination or inoculation) against such diseases as smallpox, polio, diphtheria, etc., is not covered. However, pneumococcal, hepatitis B, and influenza virus vaccines are exceptions to this rule. (See items A, B, and C below.) In cases where a vaccination or inoculation is excluded from coverage, related charges are also not covered.

A. Pneumococcal Pneumonia Vaccinations

1. **Background and History of Coverage:**

   Section 1861(s)(10)(A) of the Social Security Act and regulations at 42 CFR 410.57 authorize Medicare coverage under Part B for pneumococcal vaccine and its administration.

   For services furnished on or after May 1, 1981 through September 18, 2014, the Medicare Part B program covered pneumococcal pneumonia vaccine and its administration when furnished in compliance with any applicable State law by any provider of services or any entity or individual with a supplier number. Coverage included an initial vaccine administered only to persons at high risk of serious pneumococcal disease (including all people 65 and older; immunocompetent adults at increased risk of pneumococcal disease or its complications because of chronic illness; and individuals with compromised immune systems), with revaccination administered only to persons at highest risk of serious pneumococcal infection and those likely to have a rapid decline in pneumococcal antibody levels, provided that at least 5 years had passed since the previous dose of pneumococcal vaccine.

   Those administering the vaccine did not require the patient to present an immunization record prior to administering the pneumococcal vaccine, nor were they compelled to review the patient's complete medical record if it was not available, relying on the patient's verbal history to determine prior vaccination status.

   Effective July 1, 2000, Medicare no longer required for coverage purposes that a doctor of medicine or osteopathy order the vaccine. Therefore, a beneficiary could receive the vaccine upon request without a physician's order and without physician supervision.

2. **Coverage Requirements:**

   Effective for claims with dates of service on and after September 19, 2014, an initial pneumococcal vaccine may be administered to all Medicare beneficiaries who have never received a pneumococcal vaccination under Medicare Part B. A different, second pneumococcal vaccine may be administered 1 year after the first vaccine was administered (i.e., 11 full months have passed following the month in which the last pneumococcal vaccine was administered).

   Those administering the vaccine should not require

the patient to present an immunization record prior to administering the pneumococcal vaccine, nor should they feel compelled to review the patient's complete medical record if it is not available. Instead, provided that the patient is competent, it is acceptable to rely on the patient's verbal history to determine prior vaccination status.

Medicare does not require for coverage purposes that a doctor of medicine or osteopathy order the vaccine. Therefore, the beneficiary may receive the vaccine upon request without a physician's order and without physician supervision. B. Hepatitis B Vaccine Effective for services furnished on or after September 1, 1984, P.L. 98-369 provides coverage under Part B for hepatitis B vaccine and its administration, furnished to a Medicare beneficiary who is at high or intermediate risk of contracting hepatitis B. High-risk groups currently identified include (see exception below):

- ESRD patients;
- Hemophiliacs who receive Factor VIII or IX concentrates;
- Clients of institutions for the mentally retarded;
- Persons who live in the same household as a Hepatitis B Virus (HBV) carrier;
- Homosexual men;
- Illicit injectable drug abusers; and

Persons diagnosed with diabetes mellitus. Intermediate risk groups currently identified include:

- Staff in institutions for the mentally retarded; and
- Workers in health care professions who have frequent contact with blood or blood-derived body fluids during routine work.

EXCEPTION: Persons in both of the above-listed groups in paragraph B, would not be considered at high or intermediate risk of contracting hepatitis B, however, if there were laboratory evidence positive for antibodies to hepatitis B. (ESRD patients are routinely tested for hepatitis B antibodies as part of their continuing monitoring and therapy.)

For Medicare program purposes, the vaccine may be administered upon the order of a doctor of medicine or osteopathy, by a doctor of medicine or osteopathy, or by home health agencies, skilled nursing facilities, ESRD facilities, hospital outpatient departments, and persons recognized under the incident to physicians' services provision of law.

A charge separate from the ESRD composite rate will be recognized and paid for administration of the vaccine to ESRD patients.

B. Hepatitis B Vaccine

Effective for services furnished on or after September 1, 1984, P.L. 98-369 provides coverage under Part B for hepatitis B vaccine and its administration, furnished to a Medicare beneficiary who is at high or intermediate risk of contracting hepatitis B. This coverage is effective for services furnished on or after September 1, 1984. High-risk groups currently identified include (see exception below):

- ESRD patients;
- Hemophiliacs who receive Factor VIII or IX concentrates;
- Clients of institutions for the mentally retarded;
- Persons who live in the same household as a Hepatitis B Virus (HBV) carrier;

- Homosexual men;
- Illicit injectable drug abusers; and
- Persons diagnosed with diabetes mellitus.

Intermediate risk groups currently identified include:

- Staff in institutions for the mentally retarded; and
- Workers in health care professions who have frequent contact with blood or blood-derived body fluids during routine work.

EXCEPTION: Persons in both of the above-listed groups in paragraph B, would not be considered at high or intermediate risk of contracting hepatitis B, however, if there were laboratory evidence positive for antibodies to hepatitis B. (ESRD patients are routinely tested for hepatitis B antibodies as part of their continuing monitoring and therapy.)

For Medicare program purposes, the vaccine may be administered upon the order of a doctor of medicine or osteopathy, by a doctor of medicine or osteopathy, or by home health agencies, skilled nursing facilities, ESRD facilities, hospital outpatient departments, and persons recognized under the incident to physicians' services provision of law.

A charge separate from the ESRD composite rate will be recognized and paid for administration of the vaccine to ESRD patients.

C. Influenza Virus Vaccine

Effective for services furnished on or after May 1, 1993, the Medicare Part B program covers influenza virus vaccine and its administration when furnished in compliance with any applicable State law by any provider of services or any entity or individual with a supplier number. Typically, these vaccines are administered once a flu season. Medicare does not require, for coverage purposes, that a doctor of medicine or osteopathy order the vaccine. Therefore, the beneficiary may receive the vaccine upon request without a physician's order and without physician supervision.

100-2, Chapter 15, 100

Surgical Dressings, Splints, Casts, and Other Devices Used for Reductions of Fractures and Dislocations

Surgical dressings are limited to primary and secondary dressings required for the treatment of a wound caused by, or treated by, a surgical procedure that has been performed by a physician or other health care professional to the extent permissible under State law. In addition, surgical dressings required after debridement of a wound are also covered, irrespective of the type of debridement, as long as the debridement was reasonable and necessary and was performed by a health care professional acting within the scope of his/her legal authority when performing this function. Surgical dressings are covered for as long as they are medically necessary.

Primary dressings are therapeutic or protective coverings applied directly to wounds or lesions either on the skin or caused by an opening to the skin. Secondary dressing materials that serve a therapeutic or protective function and that are needed to secure a primary dressing are also covered. Items such as adhesive tape, roll gauze, bandages, and disposable compression material are examples of secondary dressings. Elastic stockings, support hose, foot coverings, leotards, knee supports, surgical leggings, gauntlets, and pressure garments for the arms and hands are examples of items that are not ordinarily covered as surgical dressings. Some items, such as transparent film, may be used as a primary or secondary dressing.

If a physician, certified nurse midwife, physician assistant, nurse practitioner, or clinical nurse specialist applies surgical dressings as part of a professional service that is billed to Medicare, the surgical dressings are considered incident to the professional services of the health care practitioner. (See §§60.1, 180, 190, 200, and 210.) When surgical dressings are not covered incident to the services of a health care practitioner and are obtained by the patient from a supplier (e.g., a drugstore, physician, or other health care practitioner that qualifies as a supplier) on an order from a physician or other health care professional authorized under State law or regulation to make such an order, the surgical dressings are covered separately under Part B.

Splints and casts, and other devices used for reductions of fractures and dislocations are covered under Part B of Medicare. This includes dental splints.

100-2, Chapter 15, 110

Durable Medical Equipment -General

Expenses incurred by a beneficiary for the rental or purchases of durable medical equipment (DME) are reimbursable if the following three requirements are met:

- The equipment meets the definition of DME (§110.1);
- The equipment is necessary and reasonable for the treatment of the patient's illness or injury or to improve the functioning of his or her malformed body member (§110.1); and
- The equipment is used in the patient's home.

The decision whether to rent or purchase an item of equipment generally resides with the beneficiary, but the decision on how to pay rests with CMS. For some DME, program payment policy calls for lump sum payments and in others for periodic payment. Where covered DME is furnished to a beneficiary by a supplier of services other than a provider of services, the DMERC makes the reimbursement. If a provider of services furnishes the equipment, the intermediary makes the reimbursement. The payment method is identified in the annual fee schedule update furnished by CMS.

The CMS issues quarterly updates to a fee schedule file that contains rates by HCPCS code and also identifies the classification of the HCPCS code within the following categories.

Category Code	Definition
IN	Inexpensive and Other Routinely Purchased Items
FS	Frequently Serviced Items
CR	Capped Rental Items
OX	Oxygen and Oxygen Equipment
OS	Ostomy, Tracheostomy & Urological Items
SD	Surgical Dressings
PO	Prosthetics & Orthotics
SU	Supplies
TE	Transcutaneous Electrical Nerve Stimulators

The DMERCs, carriers, and intermediaries, where appropriate, use the CMS files to determine payment rules. See the Medicare Claims Processing Manual, Chapter 20, "Durable Medical Equipment, Surgical Dressings and Casts, Orthotics and Artificial Limbs, and Prosthetic Devices," for a detailed description of payment rules for each classification.

Payment may also be made for repairs, maintenance, and delivery of equipment and for expendable and nonreusable items essential to the effective use of the equipment subject to the conditions in §110.2 .

See the Medicare Benefit Policy Manual, Chapter 11, "End Stage Renal Disease," for hemodialysis equipment and supplies.

100-2, Chapter 15, 110.1

Definition of Durable Medical Equipment

Durable medical equipment is equipment which:

- Can withstand repeated use;
- Is primarily and customarily used to serve a medical purpose;
- Generally is not useful to a person in the absence of an illness or injury; and
- Is appropriate for use in the home.

All requirements of the definition must be met before an item can be considered to be durable medical equipment.

The following describes the underlying policies for determining whether an item meets the definition of DME and may be covered.

A. Durability

An item is considered durable if it can withstand repeated use, i.e., the type of item that could normally be rented. Medical supplies of an expendable nature, such as incontinent pads, lambs wool pads, catheters, ace bandages, elastic stockings, surgical facemasks, irrigating kits, sheets, and bags are not considered "durable" within the meaning of the definition. There are other items that, although durable in nature, may fall into other coverage categories such as supplies, braces, prosthetic devices, artificial arms, legs, and eyes.

B. Medical Equipment

Medical equipment is equipment primarily and customarily used for medical purposes and is not generally useful in the absence of illness or injury. In most instances, no development will be needed to determine whether a specific item of equipment is medical in nature. However, some cases will require development to determine whether the item constitutes medical equipment. This development would include the advice of local medical organizations (hospitals, medical schools, medical societies) and specialists in the field of physical medicine and rehabilitation. If the equipment is new on the market, it may be necessary, prior to seeking professional advice, to obtain information from the supplier or manufacturer explaining the design, purpose, effectiveness and method of using the equipment in the home as well as the results of any tests or clinical studies that have been conducted.

1. Equipment Presumptively Medical

Items such as hospital beds, wheelchairs, hemodialysis equipment, iron lungs, respirators, intermittent positive pressure breathing machines, medical regulators, oxygen tents, crutches, canes, trapeze bars, walkers, inhalators, nebulizers, commodes, suction machines, and traction equipment presumptively constitute medical equipment. (Although hemodialysis equipment is covered as a prosthetic device (§120), it also meets the definition of DME, and reimbursement for the rental or purchase of such equipment for use in the beneficiary's home will be made only under the provisions for payment applicable to DME. See the Medicare Benefit Policy Manual, Chapter 11, "End Stage Renal Disease" §30.1, for coverage of home use of hemodialysis.)

NOTE: There is a wide variety in types of respirators and suction machines. The DMERC's medical staff should determine whether the apparatus specified in the claim is appropriate for home use.

2. Equipment Presumptively Nonmedical

Equipment which is primarily and customarily used for a nonmedical purpose may not be considered "medical" equipment for which payment can be made under the medical insurance program. This is true even though the item has some remote medically related use. For example, in the case of a cardiac patient, an air conditioner might possibly be used to lower room temperature to reduce fluid loss in the patient and to restore an environment conducive to maintenance of the proper fluid balance. Nevertheless, because the primary and customary use of an air conditioner is a nonmedical one, the air conditioner cannot be deemed to be medical equipment for which payment can be made.

Other devices and equipment used for environmental control or to enhance the environmental setting in which the beneficiary is placed are not considered covered DME. These include, for example, room heaters, humidifiers, dehumidifiers, and electric air cleaners. Equipment which basically serves comfort or convenience functions or is primarily for the convenience of a person caring for the patient, such as elevators, stairway elevators, and posture chairs, do not constitute medical equipment. Similarly, physical fitness equipment (such as an exercycle), first-aid or precautionary-type equipment (such as preset portable oxygen units), self-help devices (such as safety grab bars), and training equipment (such as Braille training texts) are considered nonmedical in nature.

3. Special Exception Items

Specified items of equipment may be covered under certain conditions even though they do not meet the definition of DME because they are not primarily and customarily used to serve a medical purpose and/or are generally useful in the absence of illness or injury. These items would be covered when it is clearly established that they serve a therapeutic purpose in an individual case and would include:

a. Gel pads and pressure and water mattresses (which generally serve a preventive purpose) when prescribed for a patient who had bed sores or there is medical evidence indicating that they are highly susceptible to such ulceration; and

b. Heat lamps for a medical rather than a soothing or cosmetic purpose, e.g., where the need for heat therapy has been established.

In establishing medical necessity for the above items, the evidence must show that the item is included in the physician's course of treatment and a physician is supervising its use.

NOTE: The above items represent special exceptions and no extension of coverage to other items should be inferred

C. Necessary and Reasonable

Although an item may be classified as DME, it may not be covered in every instance. Coverage in a particular case is subject to the requirement that the equipment be necessary and reasonable for treatment of an illness or injury, or to improve the functioning of a malformed body member. These considerations will bar payment for equipment which cannot reasonably be expected to perform a therapeutic function in an individual case or will permit only partial therapeutic function in an individual case or will permit only partial payment when the type of equipment furnished substantially exceeds that required for the treatment of the illness or injury involved.

See the Medicare Claims Processing Manual, Chapter 1, "General Billing Requirements;" §60, regarding the rules for providing advance beneficiary notices (ABNs) that advise beneficiaries, before items or services actually are furnished, when Medicare is likely to deny payment for them. ABNs allow beneficiaries to make an informed consumer decision about receiving items or services for which they may have to pay out-of-pocket and to be more active participants in their own health care treatment decisions.

1. Necessity for the Equipment

Equipment is necessary when it can be expected to make a meaningful contribution to the treatment of the patient's illness or injury or to the improvement of his or her malformed body member. In most cases the physician's prescription for the equipment and other medical information available to the DMERC will be sufficient to establish that the equipment serves this purpose.

2. Reasonableness of the Equipment

Even though an item of DME may serve a useful medical purpose, the DMERC or intermediary must also consider to what extent, if any, it would be reasonable for the Medicare program to pay for the item prescribed. The following considerations should enter into the determination of reasonableness:

1. Would the expense of the item to the program be clearly disproportionate to the therapeutic benefits which could ordinarily be derived from use of the equipment?

2. Is the item substantially more costly than a medically appropriate and realistically feasible alternative pattern of care?

3. Does the item serve essentially the same purpose as equipment already available to the beneficiary?

3. Payment Consistent With What is Necessary and Reasonable

Where a claim is filed for equipment containing features of an aesthetic nature or features of a medical nature which are not required by the patient's condition or where there exists a reasonably feasible and medically appropriate alternative pattern of care which is less costly than the equipment furnished, the amount payable is based on the rate for the equipment or alternative treatment which meets the patient's medical needs.

The acceptance of an assignment binds the supplier-assignee to accept the payment for the medically required equipment or service as the full charge and the supplier-assignee cannot charge the beneficiary the differential attributable to the equipment actually furnished.

4. Establishing the Period of Medical Necessity

Generally, the period of time an item of durable medical equipment will be considered to be medically necessary is based on the physician's estimate of the time that his or her patient will need the equipment. See the Medicare Program Integrity Manual, Chapters 5 and 6, for medical review guidelines.

D. Definition of a Beneficiary's Home

For purposes of rental and purchase of DME a beneficiary's home may be his/her own dwelling, an apartment, a relative's home, a home for the aged, or some other type of institution (such as an assisted living facility, or an intermediate care facility for the mentally retarded (ICF/MR)). However, an institution may not be considered a beneficiary's home if it:

• Meets at least the basic requirement in the definition of a hospital, i.e., it is primarily engaged in providing by or under the supervision of physicians, to inpatients, diagnostic and therapeutic services for medical diagnosis, treatment, and care of injured, disabled, and sick persons, or rehabilitation services for the rehabilitation of injured, disabled, or sick persons; or

- Meets at least the basic requirement in the definition of a skilled nursing facility, i.e., it is primarily engaged in providing to inpatients skilled nursing care and related services for patients who require medical or nursing care, or rehabilitation services for the rehabilitation of injured, disabled, or sick persons.

Thus, if an individual is a patient in an institution or distinct part of an institution which provides the services described in the bullets above, the individual is not entitled to have separate Part B payment made for rental or purchase of DME. This is because such an institution may not be considered the individual's home. The same concept applies even if the patient resides in a bed or portion of the institution not certified for Medicare.

If the patient is at home for part of a month and, for part of the same month is in an institution that cannot qualify as his or her home, or is outside the U.S., monthly payments may be made for the entire month. Similarly, if DME is returned to the provider before the end of a payment month because the beneficiary died in that month or because the equipment became unnecessary in that month, payment may be made for the entire month.

100-2, Chapter 15, 110.2

Repairs, Maintenance, Replacement, and Delivery

Under the circumstances specified below, payment may be made for repair, maintenance, and replacement of medically required DME, including equipment which had been in use before the user enrolled in Part B of the program. However, do not pay for repair, maintenance, or replacement of equipment in the frequent and substantial servicing or oxygen equipment payment categories. In addition, payments for repair and maintenance may not include payment for parts and labor covered under a manufacturer's or supplier's warranty.

A. Repairs

To repair means to fix or mend and to put the equipment back in good condition after damage or wear. Repairs to equipment which a beneficiary owns are covered when necessary to make the equipment serviceable. However, do not pay for repair of previously denied equipment or equipment in the frequent and substantial servicing or oxygen equipment payment categories. If the expense for repairs exceeds the estimated expense of purchasing or renting another item of equipment for the remaining period of medical need, no payment can be made for the amount of the excess. (See subsection C where claims for repairs suggest malicious damage or culpable neglect.)

Since renters of equipment recover from the rental charge the expenses they incur in maintaining in working order the equipment they rent out, separately itemized charges for repair of rented equipment are not covered. This includes items in the frequent and substantial servicing, oxygen equipment, capped rental, and inexpensive or routinely purchased payment categories which are being rented.

A new Certificate of Medical Necessity (CMN) and/or physician's order is not needed for repairs.

For replacement items, see Subsection C below.

B. Maintenance

Routine periodic servicing, such as testing, cleaning, regulating, and checking of the beneficiary's equipment, is not covered.

The owner is expected to perform such routine maintenance rather than a retailer or some other person who charges the beneficiary. Normally, purchasers of DME are given operating manuals which describe the type of servicing an owner may perform to properly maintain the equipment. It is reasonable to expect that beneficiaries will perform this maintenance. Thus, hiring a third party to do such work is for the convenience of the beneficiary and is not covered. However, more extensive maintenance which, based on the manufacturers' recommendations, is to be performed by authorized technicians, is covered as repairs for medically necessary equipment which a beneficiary owns. This might include, for example, breaking down sealed components and performing tests which require specialized testing equipment not available to the beneficiary. Do not pay for maintenance of purchased items that require frequent and substantial servicing or oxygen equipment.

Since renters of equipment recover from the rental charge the expenses they incur in maintaining in working order the equipment they rent out, separately itemized charges for maintenance of rented equipment are generally not covered. Payment may not be made for maintenance of rented equipment other than the maintenance and servicing fee established for capped rental items. For capped rental items which have reached the 13-month rental cap, contractors pay claims for maintenance and servicing fees after 6 months have passed from the end of the final paid rental month or from the end of the period the item is no longer covered under the supplier's or manufacturer's warranty, whichever is later. See the Medicare Claims Processing Manual, Chapter 20, "Durable Medical Equipment, Prosthetics and Orthotics, and Supplies (DMEPOS)," for additional instruction and an example.

A new CMN and/or physician's order is not needed for covered maintenance.

In cases where one or more monthly rental payments have been made in accordance with 42 CFR 414.229 for a capped rental DME item, medical necessity for the equipment has been established. In cases where one or more rental payments have been made for an item classified as capped rental DME, and the supplier transfers title to the equipment prior to the end of a 13 month period of continuous use per 42 CFR 414.230, Medicare payment can be made for reasonable and necessary maintenance and servicing of the beneficiary-owned DME. Under the regulations at 42 CFR 414.210(e)(1), reasonable and necessary charges for maintenance and servicing are those made for parts and labor not otherwise covered under a manufacturer's or supplier's warranty. Charges for routine maintenance and servicing would not be covered. Charges for maintenance and servicing that exceed the purchase price of the equipment (i.e., the capped rental monthly fee multiplied by 10) would not be reasonable and necessary and should be denied.

C. Replacement

Replacement refers to the provision of an identical or nearly identical item. Situations involving the provision of a different item because of a change in medical condition are not addressed in this section.

Equipment which the beneficiary owns or is a capped rental item may be replaced in cases of loss or irreparable damage. Irreparable damage refers to a specific accident or to a natural disaster (e.g., fire, flood). A physician's order and/or new Certificate of Medical Necessity (CMN), when required, is needed to reaffirm the medical necessity of the item.

Irreparable wear refers to deterioration sustained from day-to-day usage over time and a specific event cannot be identified. Replacement of equipment due to irreparable wear takes into consideration the reasonable useful lifetime of the equipment. If the item of equipment has been in continuous use by the patient on either a rental or purchase basis for the equipment's useful lifetime, the beneficiary may elect to obtain a new piece of equipment. Replacement may be reimbursed when a new physician order and/or new CMN, when required, is needed to reaffirm the medical necessity of the item.

The reasonable useful lifetime of durable medical equipment is determined through program instructions. In the absence of program instructions, A/B MACS (B) may determine the reasonable useful lifetime of equipment, but in no case can it be less than 5 years. Computation of the useful lifetime is based on when the equipment is delivered to the beneficiary, not the age of the equipment. Replacement due to wear is not covered during the reasonable useful lifetime of the equipment. During the reasonable useful lifetime, Medicare does cover repair up to the cost of replacement (but not actual replacement) for medically necessary equipment owned by the beneficiary. (See subsection A.)

Charges for the replacement of oxygen equipment, items that require frequent and substantial servicing or inexpensive or routinely purchased items which are being rented are not covered.

Cases suggesting malicious damage, culpable neglect, or wrongful disposition of equipment should be investigated and denied where the DME MACs determines that it is unreasonable to make program payment under the circumstances. DME MACs refer such cases to the program integrity specialist in the RO.

D. Delivery

Payment for delivery of DME whether rented or purchased is generally included in the fee schedule allowance for the item. See Pub. 100-04, Medicare Claims Processing Manual, Chapter 20, "Durable Medical Equipment, Prosthetics and Orthotics, and Supplies (DMEPOS)," for the rules that apply to making reimbursement for exceptional cases.

100-2, Chapter 15, 110.3

Coverage of Supplies and Accessories

Payment may be made for supplies, e.g., oxygen, that are necessary for the effective use of durable medical equipment. Such supplies include those drugs and biologicals which must be put directly into the equipment in order to achieve the therapeutic benefit of the durable medical equipment or to assure the proper functioning of the equipment, e.g., tumor chemotherapy agents used with an infusion pump or heparin used with a home dialysis system. However, the coverage of such drugs or biologicals does not preclude the need for a determination that the drug or biological itself is reasonable and necessary for treatment of the illness or injury or to improve the functioning of a malformed body member.

In the case of prescription drugs, other than oxygen, used in conjunction with durable medical equipment, prosthetic, orthotics, and supplies (DMEPOS) or prosthetic devices, the entity that dispenses the drug must furnish it directly to the patient for whom a prescription is written. The entity that dispenses the drugs must have a Medicare supplier number, must possess a current license to dispense prescription drugs in the State in which the drug is dispensed, and must bill and receive payment in its own name. A supplier that is not the entity that dispenses the drugs cannot purchase the drugs used in conjunction with DME for resale to the beneficiary. Reimbursement may be made for replacement of essential accessories such as hoses, tubes, mouthpieces, etc., for necessary DME, only if the beneficiary owns or is purchasing the equipment.

100-8, Chapter 4, 4.26.1

Proof of Delivery Requirements (2016 update)

The Medicare Administrative Contractor is hereby advised that this constitutes technical direction as defined in your contract. CMS does not construe this as a change to the MAC Statement of Work. The contractor is not obligated to incur costs in excess of the amounts allotted in your contract unless and until specifically authorized by the Contracting Officer. If the contractor considers anything provided, as described above, to be outside the current scope of work, the contractor shall withhold performance on the part(s) in question and immediately notify the Contracting Officer, in writing or by e-mail, and request formal directions regarding continued performance requirements.

A. Background

One of the requirements for suppliers of Durable Medical Equipment Prosthetics, Orthotics and Supplies (DMEPOS), as described below, requires suppliers to maintain a proof of delivery for DMEPOS items provided to Medicare beneficiaries. Chapter 4, section 4.26.1 of Pub. 100-08 details this requirement for the purpose of medical review. Recently, DMEPOS suppliers have notified the Centers for Medicare & Medicaid Services (CMS) of their concern that the proof of delivery instruction related to DMEPOS provided to beneficiaries residing in SNFs is subject to interpretation and variation in application. CMS is also further clarifying the proof of delivery section in chapter 4, section 4.26.1 of Pub. 100-08 to address this concern.

B. Policy

Set forth in 42 CFR 424.57, this regulation requires that suppliers of DMEPOS must maintain proof of delivery for items they provide to Medicare beneficiaries.

Section A: For Medicare Administrative Contractors (MACs):

The Medicare Administrative Contractor is hereby advised that this constitutes technical direction as defined in your contract. CMS does not construe this as a change to the MAC Statement of Work. The contractor is not obligated to incur costs in excess of the amounts allotted in your contract unless and until specifically authorized by the Contracting Officer. If the contractor considers anything provided, as described above, to be outside the current scope of work, the contractor shall withhold performance on the part(s) in question and immediately notify the Contracting Officer, in writing or by e-mail, and request formal directions regarding continued performance requirements.

Proof of Delivery and Delivery Methods

For the purpose of the delivery methods noted below, **designee** is defined as:

"Any person who can sign and accept the delivery of durable medical equipment on behalf of the beneficiary."

Suppliers, their employees, or anyone else having a financial interest in the delivery of the item are prohibited from signing and accepting an item on behalf of a beneficiary (i.e., acting as a designee on behalf of the beneficiary). The relationship of the designee to the beneficiary should be noted on the delivery slip obtained by the supplier (i.e., spouse, neighbor). The signature of the designee should be legible. If the signature of the designee is not legible, the supplier/shipping service should note the name of the designee on the delivery slip.

Suppliers may deliver directly to the beneficiary or the designee. An example of proof of delivery to a beneficiary is having a signed delivery slip, and it is recommended that the delivery slip include: 1) The patient's name; 2) The quantity delivered; 3) A detailed description of the item being delivered; 4) The brand name; and 5) The serial number. The long description of the HCPCS code, for example, may be used as a means to provide a detailed description of the item being delivered; though suppliers are encouraged to include as much information as necessary to adequately describe the delivered item. The date of signature on the delivery slip must be the date that the DMEPOS item was received by the beneficiary or designee. In instances where the supplies are delivered directly by the supplier, the date the beneficiary received the DMEPOS supply shall be the date of service on the claim.

If the supplier utilizes a shipping service or mail order, an example of proof of delivery would include the service's tracking slip, and the supplier's own shipping invoice. If possible, the supplier's records should also include the delivery service's package identification number for that package sent to the beneficiary. The shipping service's tracking slip should reference each individual package, the delivery address, the corresponding package identification number given by the shipping service, and if possible, the date delivered. If a supplier utilizes a shipping service or mail order, suppliers shall use the shipping date as the date of service on the claim.

Suppliers may also utilize a return postage-paid delivery invoice from the beneficiary or designee as a form of proof of delivery. The descriptive information concerning the DMEPOS item (i.e., the patient's name, the quantity, detailed description, brand name, and serial number) as well as the required signatures from either the beneficiary or the beneficiary's designee should be included on this invoice as well.

For DMEPOS products that are supplied as refills to the original order, suppliers must contact the beneficiary prior to dispensing the refill. This shall be done to ensure that the refilled item is necessary and to confirm any changes/modifications to the order. Contact with the beneficiary or designee regarding refills shall take place no sooner than 14 calendar days prior to the delivery/shipping date. For subsequent deliveries of refills, the supplier shall deliver the DMEPOS product no sooner than 10 calendar days prior to the end of usage for the current product. This is regardless of which delivery method is utilized. DME MACs shall allow for the processing of claims for refills delivered/shipped prior to the beneficiary exhausting his/her supply.

For those patients that are residents of a nursing facility, upon request from the DME MAC, suppliers should obtain copies of the necessary documentation from the nursing facility to document proof of delivery or usage by the beneficiary (e.g., nurse's notes).

100-2, Chapter 15, 120

Prosthetic Devices

A. General

Prosthetic devices (other than dental) which replace all or part of an internal body organ (including contiguous tissue), or replace all or part of the function of a permanently inoperative or malfunctioning internal body organ are covered when furnished on a physician's order. This does not require a determination that there is no possibility that the patient's condition may improve sometime in the future. If the medical record, including the judgment of the attending physician, indicates the condition is of long and indefinite duration, the test of permanence is considered met. (Such a device may also be covered under §60.1 as a supply when furnished incident to a physician's service.)

Examples of prosthetic devices include artificial limbs, parenteral and enteral (PEN) nutrition, cardiac pacemakers, prosthetic lenses (see subsection B), breast prostheses (including a surgical brassiere) for post mastectomy patients, maxillofacial devices, and devices which replace all or part of the ear or nose. A urinary collection and retention system with or without a tube is a prosthetic device replacing bladder function in case of permanent urinary incontinence. The Foley catheter is also considered a prosthetic device when ordered for a patient with permanent urinary incontinence. However, chucks, diapers, rubber sheets, etc., are supplies that are not covered under this provision. Although hemodialysis equipment is a prosthetic device, payment for the rental or purchase of such equipment in the home is made only for use under the provisions for payment applicable to durable medical equipment.

An exception is that if payment cannot be made on an inpatient's behalf under Part A, hemodialysis equipment, supplies, and services required by such patient could be covered under Part B as a prosthetic device, which replaces the function of a kidney. See the Medicare Benefit Policy Manual, Chapter 11, "End Stage Renal Disease," for payment for hemodialysis equipment used in the home. See the Medicare Benefit Policy Manual, Chapter 1, "Inpatient Hospital Services," §10, for additional instructions on hospitalization for renal dialysis.

NOTE: Medicare does not cover a prosthetic device dispensed to a patient prior to the time at which the patient undergoes the procedure that makes necessary the use of the device. For example, the carrier does not make a separate Part B payment for an intraocular lens (IOL) or pacemaker that a physician, during an office visit prior to the actual surgery, dispenses to the patient for his or her use. Dispensing a prosthetic device in this manner raises health and safety issues. Moreover, the need for the device cannot be clearly established until the procedure that makes its use possible is successfully performed. Therefore, dispensing a prosthetic device in this manner is not considered reasonable and necessary for the treatment of the patient's condition.

Colostomy (and other ostomy) bags and necessary accouterments required for attachment are covered as prosthetic devices. This coverage also includes irrigation and flushing equipment and other items and supplies directly related to ostomy care, whether the attachment of a bag is required.

Accessories and/or supplies which are used directly with an enteral or parenteral device to achieve the therapeutic benefit of the prosthesis or to assure the proper functioning of the device may also be covered under the prosthetic device benefit subject to the additional guidelines in the Medicare National Coverage Determinations Manual.

Covered items include catheters, filters, extension tubing, infusion bottles, pumps (either food or infusion), intravenous (I.V.) pole, needles, syringes, dressings, tape, Heparin Sodium (parenteral only), volumetric monitors (parenteral only), and parenteral and enteral nutrient solutions. Baby food and other regular grocery products that can be blenderized and used with the enteral system are not covered. Note that some of these items, e.g., a food pump and an I.V. pole, qualify as DME. Although coverage of the enteral and parenteral nutritional therapy systems is provided on the basis of the prosthetic device benefit, the payment rules relating to lump sum or monthly payment for DME apply to such items.

The coverage of prosthetic devices includes replacement of and repairs to such devices as explained in subsection D.

Finally, the Benefits Improvement and Protection Act of 2000 amended §1834(h)(1) of the Act by adding a provision (1834 (h)(1)(G)(i)) that requires Medicare payment to be made for the replacement of prosthetic devices which are artificial limbs, or for the replacement of any part of such devices, without regard to continuous use or useful lifetime restrictions if an ordering physician determines that the replacement device, or replacement part of such a device, is necessary.

Payment may be made for the replacement of a prosthetic device that is an artificial limb, or replacement part of a device if the ordering physician determines that the replacement device or part is necessary because of any of the following:

1. A change in the physiological condition of the patient;

2. An irreparable change in the condition of the device, or in a part of the device; or

3. The condition of the device, or the part of the device, requires repairs and the cost of such repairs would be more than 60 percent of the cost of a replacement device, or, as the case may be, of the part being replaced.

This provision is effective for items replaced on or after April 1, 2001. It supersedes any rule that that provided a 5-year or other replacement rule with regard to prosthetic devices.

B. Prosthetic Lenses

The term "internal body organ" includes the lens of an eye. Prostheses replacing the lens of an eye include post-surgical lenses customarily used during convalescence from eye surgery in which the lens of the eye was removed. In addition, permanent lenses are also covered when required by an individual lacking the organic lens of the eye because of surgical removal or congenital absence. Prosthetic lenses obtained on or after the beneficiary's date of entitlement to supplementary medical insurance benefits may be covered even though the surgical removal of the crystalline lens occurred before entitlement.

1. Prosthetic Cataract Lenses

One of the following prosthetic lenses or combinations of prosthetic lenses furnished by a physician (see §30.4 for coverage of prosthetic lenses prescribed by a doctor of optometry) may be covered when determined to be reasonable and necessary to restore essentially the vision provided by the crystalline lens of the eye:

- Prosthetic bifocal lenses in frames;

- Prosthetic lenses in frames for far vision, and prosthetic lenses in frames for near vision; or

- When a prosthetic contact lens(es) for far vision is prescribed (including cases of binocular and monocular aphakia), make payment for the contact lens(es) and prosthetic lenses in frames for near vision to be worn at the same time as the contact lens(es), and prosthetic lenses in frames to be worn when the contacts have been removed.

Lenses which have ultraviolet absorbing or reflecting properties may be covered, in lieu of payment for regular (untinted) lenses, if it has been determined that such lenses are medically reasonable and necessary for the individual patient.

Medicare does not cover cataract sunglasses obtained in addition to the regular (untinted) prosthetic lenses since the sunglasses duplicate the restoration of vision function performed by the regular prosthetic lenses.

2. Payment for Intraocular Lenses (IOLs) Furnished in Ambulatory Surgical Centers (ASCs)

Effective for services furnished on or after March 12, 1990, payment for intraocular lenses (IOLs) inserted during or subsequent to cataract surgery in a Medicare certified ASC is included with the payment for facility services that are furnished in connection with the covered surgery.

Refer to the Medicare Claims Processing Manual, Chapter 14, "Ambulatory Surgical Centers," for more information.

3. Limitation on Coverage of Conventional Lenses

One pair of conventional eyeglasses or conventional contact lenses furnished after each cataract surgery with insertion of an IOL is covered.

C. Dentures

Dentures are excluded from coverage. However, when a denture or a portion of the denture is an integral part (built-in) of a covered prosthesis (e.g., an obturatorto fill an opening in the palate), it is covered as part of that prosthesis.

D. Supplies, Repairs, Adjustments, and Replacement

Supplies are covered that are necessary for the effective use of a prosthetic device (e.g., the batteries needed to operate an artificial larynx). Adjustment of prosthetic devices required by wear or by a change in the patient's condition is covered when ordered by a physician. General provisions relating to the repair and replacement of durable medical equipment in §110.2 for the repair and replacement of prosthetic devices are applicable. (See the Medicare Benefit Policy Manual, Chapter 16, "General Exclusions from Coverage," §40.4, for payment for devices replaced under a warranty.) Replacement of conventional eyeglasses or contact lenses furnished in accordance with §120.B.3 is not covered.

Necessary supplies, adjustments, repairs, and replacements are covered even when the device had been in use before the user enrolled in Part B ofthe program, so long as the device continues to be medically required.

100-2, Chapter 15, 130

Leg, Arm, Back, and Neck Braces, Trusses, and Artificial Legs, Arms, and Eyes

These appliances are covered under Part B when furnished incident to physicians' services or on a physician's order. A brace includes rigid and semi-rigid devices which are used for the purpose of supporting a weak or deformed body member or restricting or eliminating motion in a diseased or injured part of the body. Elastic stockings, garter belts, and similar devices do not come within the scope of the definition of a brace. Back braces include, but are not limited to, special corsets, e.g., sacroiliac, sacrolumbar, dorsolumbar corsets, and belts. A terminal device (e.g., hand or hook) is covered under this provision whether an artificial limb is required by the patient. Stump stockings and harnesses (including replacements) are also covered when these appliances are essential to the effective use of the artificial limb.

Adjustments to an artificial limb or other appliance required by wear or by a change in the patient's condition are covered when ordered by a physician.

Adjustments, repairs and replacements are covered even when the item had been in use before the user enrolled in Part B of the program so long as the device continues to be medically required.

100-2, Chapter 15, 140

Therapeutic Shoes for Individuals with Diabetes

Coverage of therapeutic shoes (depth or custom-molded) along with inserts for individuals with diabetes is available as of May 1, 1993. These diabetic shoes are covered if the requirements as specified in this section concerning certification and prescription are fulfilled. In addition, this benefit provides for a pair of diabetic shoes even if only one foot suffers from diabetic foot disease. Each shoe is equally equipped so that the affected limb, as well as the remaining limb, is protected. Claims for therapeutic shoes for diabetics are processed by the Durable Medical Equipment Regional Carriers (DMERCs).

Therapeutic shoes for diabetics are not DME and are not considered DME nor orthotics, but a separate category of coverage under Medicare Part B. (See §1861(s)(12)and §1833(o) of the Act.)

A. Definitions

The following items may be covered under the diabetic shoe benefit:

1. Custom-Molded Shoes

Custom-molded shoes are shoes that:

- Are constructed over a positive model of the patient's foot;
- Are made from leather or other suitable material of equal quality;
- Have removable inserts that can be altered or replaced as the patient's condition warrants; and
- Have some form of shoe closure.

2. Depth Shoes

Depth shoes are shoes that:

- Have a full length, heel-to-toe filler that, when removed, provides a minimum of 3/16 inch of additional depth used to accommodate custom-molded or customized inserts;
- Are made from leather or other suitable material of equal quality;
- Have some form of shoe closure; and
- Are available in full and half sizes with a minimum of three widths so that the sole is graded to the size and width of the upper portions of the shoes according to the American standard last sizing schedule or its equivalent. (The American standard last sizing schedule is the numerical shoe sizing system used for shoes sold in the United States.)

3. Inserts

Inserts are total contact, multiple density, removable inlays that are directly molded to the patient's foot or a model of the patient's foot and that are made of a suitable material with regard to the patient's condition.

B. Coverage

1. Limitations

For each individual, coverage of the footwear and inserts is limited to one of the following within one calendar year:

- No more than one pair of custom-molded shoes (including inserts provided with such shoes) and two additional pairs of inserts; or
- No more than one pair of depth shoes and three pairs of inserts (not including the non customized removable inserts provided with such shoes).

2. Coverage of Diabetic Shoes and Brace

Orthopedic shoes, as stated in the Medicare Claims Processing Manual, Chapter 20, "Durable Medical Equipment, Surgical Dressings and Casts, Orthotics and Artificial Limbs, and Prosthetic Devices," generally are not covered. This exclusion does not apply to orthopedic shoes that are an integral part of a leg brace. In situations in which an individual qualifies for both diabetic shoes and a leg brace, these items are covered separately. Thus, the diabetic shoes may be covered if the requirements for this section are met, while the brace may be covered if the requirements of §130 are met.

3. Substitution of Modifications for Inserts

An individual may substitute modification(s) of custom-molded or depth shoes instead of obtaining a pair(s) of inserts in any combination. Payment for the modification(s) may not exceed the limit set for the inserts for which the individual is entitled. The following is a list of the most common shoe modifications available, but it is not meant as an exhaustive list of the modifications available for diabetic shoes:

- **Rigid Rocker Bottoms** - These are exterior elevations with apex positions for 51 percent to 75 percent distance measured from the back end of the heel. The apex is a narrowed or pointed end of an anatomical structure. The apex must be positioned behind the metatarsal heads and tapered off sharply to the front tip of the sole. Apex height helps to eliminate pressure at the metatarsal heads. Rigidity is ensured by the steel in the shoe. The heel of the shoe tapers off in the back in order to cause the heel to strike in the middle of the heel;
- **Roller Bottoms (Sole or Bar)**-These are the same as rocker bottoms, but the heel is tapered from the apex to the front tip of the sole;
- **Metatarsal Bars**-An exterior bar is placed behind the metatarsal heads in order to remove pressure from the metatarsal heads. The bars are of various shapes, heights, and construction depending on the exact purpose;
- **Wedges (Posting)**-Wedges are either of hind foot, fore foot, or both and may be in the middle or to the side. The function is to shift or transfer weight bearing upon standing or during ambulation to the opposite side for added support, stabilization, equalized weight distribution, or balance; and
- **Offset Heels**-This is a heel flanged at its base either in the middle, to the side, or a combination, that is then extended upward to the shoe in order to stabilize extreme positions of the hind foot.

Other modifications to diabetic shoes include, but are not limited to flared heels, Velcro closures, and inserts for missing toes.

4. Separate Inserts

Inserts may be covered and dispensed independently of diabetic shoes if the supplier of the shoes verifies in writing that the patient has appropriate footwear into which the insert can be placed. This footwear must meet the definitions found above for depth shoes and custom-molded shoes.

C. Certification

The need for diabetic shoes must be certified by a physician who is a doctor of medicine or a doctor of osteopathy and who is responsible for diagnosing and treating the patient's diabetic systemic condition through a comprehensive plan of care. This managing physician must:

- Document in the patient's medical record that the patient has diabetes;
- Certify that the patient is being treated under a comprehensive plan of care for diabetes, and that the patient needs diabetic shoes; and

- Document in the patient's record that the patient has one or more of the following conditions

  - Peripheral neuropathy with evidence of callus formation;
  - History of pre-ulcerative calluses;
  - History of previous ulceration;
  - Foot deformity;
  - Previous amputation of the foot or part of the foot; or
  - Poor circulation.

D. Prescription

Following certification by the physician managing the patient's systemic diabetic condition, a podiatrist or other qualified physician who is knowledgeable in the fitting of diabetic shoes and inserts may prescribe the particular type of footwear necessary.

E. Furnishing Footwear

The footwear must be fitted and furnished by a podiatrist or other qualified individual such as a pedorthist, an orthotist, or a prosthetist. The certifying physician may not furnish the diabetic shoes unless the certifying physician is the only qualified individual in the area. It is left to the discretion of each carrier to determine the meaning of "in the area."

100-2, Chapter 15, 150

Dental Services

As indicated under the general exclusions from coverage, items and services in connection with the care, treatment, filling, removal, or replacement of teeth or structures directly supporting the teeth are not covered. "Structures directly supporting the teeth" means the periodontium, which includes the gingivae, dentogingival junction, periodontal membrane, cementum of the teeth, and alveolar process.

In addition to the following, see Pub 100-01, the Medicare General Information, Eligibility, and Entitlement Manual, Chapter 5, Definitions and Pub 3, the Medicare National Coverage Determinations Manual for specific services which may be covered when furnished by a dentist. If an otherwise non covered procedure or service is performed by a dentist as incident to and as an integral part of a covered procedure or service performed by the dentist, the total service performed by the dentist on such an occasion is covered.

EXAMPLE 1:

The reconstruction of a ridge performed primarily to prepare the mouth for dentures is a noncovered procedure. However, when the reconstruction of a ridge is performed as a result of and at the same time as the surgical removal of a tumor (for other than dental purposes), the totality of surgical procedures is a covered service.

EXAMPLE 2:

Medicare makes payment for the wiring of teeth when this is done in connection with the reduction of a jaw fracture.

The extraction of teeth to prepare the jaw for radiation treatment of neoplastic disease is also covered. This is an exception to the requirement that to be covered, a noncovered procedure or service performed by a dentist must be an incident to and an integral part of a covered procedure or service performed by the dentist. Ordinarily, the dentist extracts the patient's teeth, but another physician, e.g., a radiologist, administers the radiation treatments.

When an excluded service is the primary procedure involved, it is not covered, regardless of its complexity or difficulty. For example, the extraction of an impacted tooth is not covered. Similarly, an alveoplasty (the surgical improvement of the shape and condition of the alveolar process) and a frenectomy are excluded from coverage when either of these procedures is performed in connection with an excluded service, e.g., the preparation of the mouth for dentures. In a like manner, the removal of a torus palatinus (a bony protuberance of the hard palate) may be a covered service. However, with rare exception, this surgery is performed in connection with an excluded service, i.e., the preparation of the mouth for dentures. Under such circumstances, Medicare does not pay for this procedure.

Dental splints used to treat a dental condition are excluded from coverage under 1862(a)(12) of the Act. On the other hand, if the treatment is determined to be a covered medical condition (i.e., dislocated upper/lower jaw joints), then the splint can be covered. Whether such services as the administration of anesthesia, diagnostic x-rays, and other related procedures are covered depends upon whether the primary procedure being performed by the dentist is itself covered. Thus, an x-ray taken in connection with the reduction of a fracture of the jaw or facial bone is covered. However, a single x-ray or x-ray survey taken in connection with the care or treatment of teeth or the periodontium is not covered.

Medicare makes payment for a covered dental procedure no matter where the service is performed. The hospitalization or non hospitalization of a patient has no direct bearing on the coverage or exclusion of a given dental procedure.

Payment may also be made for services and supplies furnished incident to covered dental services. For example, the services of a dental technician or nurse who is under the direct supervision of the dentist or physician are covered if the services are included in the dentist's or physician's bill.

100-2, Chapter 15, 150.1

Treatment of Temporomandibular Joint (TMJ) Syndrome

There are a wide variety of conditions that can be characterized as TMJ, and an equally wide variety of methods for treating these conditions. Many of the procedures fall within the Medicare program's statutory exclusion that prohibits payment for items and services that have not been demonstrated to be reasonable and necessary for the diagnosis and treatment of illness or injury (§1862(a)(1) of the Act). Other services and appliances used to treat TMJ fall within the Medicare program's statutory exclusion at 1862(a)(12), which prohibits payment "for services in connection with the care, treatment, filling, removal, or replacement of teeth or structures directly supporting teeth...." For these reasons, a diagnosis of TMJ on a claim is insufficient. The actual condition or symptom must be determined.

100-2, Chapter 15, 230

Practice of Physical Therapy, Occupational Therapy, and Speech-Language Pathology

A. Group Therapy Services. Contractors pay for outpatient physical therapy services (which includes outpatient speech-language pathology services) and outpatient occupational therapy services provided simultaneously to two or more individuals by a practitioner as group therapy services (97150). The individuals can be, but need not be performing the same activity. The physician or therapist involved in group therapy services must be in constant attendance, but one-on-one patient contact is not required.

B. Therapy Students

1. General

Only the services of the therapist can be billed and paid under Medicare Part B. The services performed by a student are not reimbursed even if provided under "line of sight" supervision of the therapist; however, the presence of the student "in the room" does not make the service unbillable. Pay for the direct (one-to-one) patient contact services of the physician or therapist provided to Medicare Part B patients. Group therapy services performed by a therapist or physician may be billed when a student is also present "in the room".

EXAMPLES

Therapists may bill and be paid for the provision of services in the following scenarios:

- The qualified practitioner is present and in the room for the entire session. The student participates in the delivery of services when the qualified practitioner is directing the service, making the skilled judgment, and is responsible for the assessment and treatment.

- The qualified practitioner is present in the room guiding the student in service delivery when the therapy student and the therapy assistant student are participating in the provision of services, and the practitioner is not engaged in treating another patient or doing other tasks at the same time.

- The qualified practitioner is responsible for the services and as such, signs all documentation. (A student may, of course, also sign but it is not necessary since the Part B payment is for the clinician's service, not for the student's services).

2. Therapy Assistants as Clinical Instructors

Physical therapist assistants and occupational therapy assistants are not precluded from serving as clinical instructors for therapy students, while providing services within their scope of work and performed under the direction and supervision of a licensed physical or occupational therapist to a Medicare beneficiary.

3. Services Provided Under Part A and Part B

The payment methodologies for Part A and B therapy services rendered by a student are different. Under the MPFS (Medicare Part B), Medicare pays for services provided by physicians and practitioners that are specifically authorized by statute. Students do not meet the definition of practitioners under Medicare Part B. Under SNF PPS, payments are based upon the case mix or Resource Utilization Group (RUG) category that describes the patient. In the rehabilitation groups, the number of therapy minutes delivered to the patient determines the RUG category. Payment levels for each category are based upon the costs of caring for patients in each group rather than providing specific payment for each therapy service as is done in Medicare Part B.

100-2, Chapter 15, 231

Pulmonary Rehabilitation (PR) Program Services Furnished On or After January 1, 2010

A pulmonary rehabilitation (PR) program is typically a physician-supervised, multidisciplinary program individually tailored and designed to optimize physical and social performance and autonomy of care for patients with chronic respiratory impairment. The main goal is to empower the individuals' ability to exercise independently. Exercise is combined with other training and support mechanisms to encourage long-term adherence to the treatment plan.

Effective January 1, 2010, Medicare Part B pays for PR programs and related items and services if specific criteria is met by the Medicare beneficiary, the PR program itself, the setting in which it is administered, and the physician administering the program, as outlined below:

PR Program Beneficiary Requirements:

As specified in 42 CFR 410.47, Medicare covers PR items and services for patients with moderate to very severe chronic obstructive pulmonary disease (COPD) (defined as GOLD classification II, III, and IV), when referred by the physician treating the chronic respiratory disease. Additional medical indications for coverage for PR program services may be established through the national coverage determination process.

PR Program Component Requirements:

- Physician-prescribed exercise. This physical activity includes techniques such as exercise conditioning, breathing retraining, and step and strengthening exercises. Some aerobic exercise must be included in each PR session. Both low-and high-intensity exercise is recommended to produce clinical benefits and a combination of endurance and strength training should be conducted at least twice per week.

- Education or training. This should be closely and clearly related to the individual's care and treatment and tailored to the individual's needs, including information on respiratory problem management and, if appropriate, brief smoking cessation counseling. Any education or training must assist in achievement of individual goals towards independence in activities of daily living, adaptation to limitations, and improved quality of life (QoL).

- Psychosocial assessment. This assessment means a written evaluation of an individual's mental and emotional functioning as it relates to the individual's rehabilitation or respiratory condition. It should include: (1) an assessment of those aspects of the individual's family and home situation that affects the individual's rehabilitation treatment, and, (2) a psychological evaluation of the individual's response to, and rate of progress under, the treatment plan. Periodic re-evaluations are necessary to ensure the individual's psychosocial needs are being met.

- Outcomes assessment. These should include: (1) beginning and end evaluations based on patient-centered outcomes, which are conducted by the physician at the start and end of the program, and, (2) objective clinical measures of the effectiveness of the PR program for the individual patient, including exercise performance and self-reported measures of shortness of breath, and behavior. The assessments should include clinical measures such as the 6-minute walk, weight, exercise performance, self-reported dyspnea, behavioral measures(supplemental oxygen use, smoking status,) and a QoL assessment.

- An individualized treatment plan describing the individual's diagnosis and detailing how components are utilized for each patient. The plan must be established, reviewed, and signed by a physician every 30 days. The plan may initially be developed by the referring physician or the PR physician. If the plan is developed by the referring physician who is not the PR physician, the PR physician must also review and sign the plan prior to imitation of the PR program. It is expected that the supervising physician would have initial, direct contact with the individual prior to subsequent treatment by ancillary personnel, and also have at least one direct contact in each 30-day period. The plan must have written specificity with regards to the type, amount, frequency, and duration of PR items and services furnished to the individual, and specify the appropriate mix of services for the patient's needs. It must include measurable and expected outcomes and estimated timetables to achieve these outcomes.

As specified at 42 CFR 410.47(f), PR program sessions are limited to a maximum of 2 1-hour sessions per day for up to 36 sessions, with the option for an additional 36 sessions if medically necessary.

PR Program Setting Requirements:

PR items and services must be furnished in a physician's office or a hospital outpatient setting. The setting must have the necessary cardio-pulmonary, emergency, diagnostic, and therapeutic life-saving equipment accepted by the medical community as medically necessary (for example, oxygen, cardiopulmonary resuscitation equipment, and a defibrillator) to treat chronic respiratory disease. All settings must have a physician immediately available and accessible for medical consultations and emergencies at all times that the PR items and services are being furnished under the program. This provision is satisfied if the physician meets the requirements for direct supervision of physician office services as specified at 42 CFR 410.26, and for hospital outpatient therapeutic services as specified at 42 CFR 410.27.

PR Program Physician Requirements:

Medicare Part B pays for PR services supervised by a physician only if the physician meets all of the following requirements: (1) expertise in the management of individuals with respiratory pathophysiology, (2) licensed to practice medicine in the state in which the PR program is offered, (3) responsible and accountable for the PR program, and, (4) involved substantially, in consultation with staff, in directing the progress of the individual in the PR program.

(See Publication 100-04, Claims Processing Manual, chapter 32, section 140.4, for specific claims processing, coding, and billing requirements for PR program services.)

100-2, Chapter 15, 232

Cardiac Rehabilitation (CR) and Intensive Cardiac Rehabilitation (ICR) Services Furnished On or After January 1, 2010

Cardiac rehabilitation (CR) services mean a physician-supervised program that furnishes physician prescribed exercise, cardiac risk factor modification, including education, counseling, and behavioral intervention; psychosocial assessment, outcomes assessment, and other items/services as determined by the Secretary under certain conditions. Intensive cardiac rehabilitation (ICR) services mean a physician-supervised program that furnishes the same items/services under the same conditions as a CR program but must also demonstrate, as shown in peer-reviewed published research, that it improves patients' cardiovascular disease through specific outcome measurements described in 42 CFR 410.49(c). Effective January 1, 2010, Medicare Part B pays for CR/ICR programs and related items/services if specific criteria is met by the Medicare beneficiary, the CR/ICR program itself, the setting in which is it administered, and the physician administering the program, as outlined below:

CR/ICR Program Beneficiary Requirements:

Medicare covers CR/ICR program services for beneficiaries who have experienced one or more of the following:

- Acute myocardial infarction within the preceding 12 months;
- Coronary artery bypass surgery;
- Current stable angina pectoris;
- Heart valve repair or replacement;
- Percutaneous transluminal coronary angioplasty (PTCA) or coronary stenting;
- Heart or heart-lung transplant;

For cardiac rehabilitation only: Stable, chronic heart failure defined as patients with left ventricular ejection fraction of 35% or less and New York Heart Association (NYHA) class II to IV symptoms despite being on optimal heart failure therapy for at least 6 weeks. (Effective February 18, 2014.)

CR/ICR Program Component Requirements:

Physician-prescribed exercise. This physical activity includes aerobic exercise combined with other types of exercise (i.e., strengthening, stretching) as determined to be appropriate for individual patients by a physician each day CR/ICR items/services are furnished.

Cardiac risk factor modification. This includes education, counseling, and behavioral intervention, tailored to the patients' individual needs.

Psychosocial assessment. This assessment means an evaluation of an individual's mental and emotional functioning as it relates to the individual's rehabilitation. It should include: (1) an assessment of those aspects of the individual's family and home situation that affects the individual's rehabilitation treatment, and, (2) a psychosocial evaluation of the individual's response to, and rate of progress under, the treatment plan.

Outcomes assessment. These should include: (i) minimally, assessments from the commencement and conclusion of CR/ICR, based on patient-centered outcomes which must be measured by the physician immediately at the beginning and end of the program, and, (ii) objective clinical measures of the effectiveness of the CR/ICR program for the individual patient, including exercise performance and self-reported measures of exertion and behavior.

Individualized treatment plan. This plan should be written and tailored to each individual patient and include (i) a description of the individual's diagnosis; (ii) the type, amount, frequency, and duration of the CR/ICR items/services furnished; and (iii) the goals set for the individual under the plan. The individualized treatment plan must be established, reviewed, and signed by a physician every 30 days.

As specified at 42 CFR 410.49(f)(1), CR sessions are limited to a maximum of 2 1-hour sessions per day for up to 36 sessions over up to 36 weeks with the option for an additional 36 sessions over an extended period of time if approved by the contractor under section 1862(a)(1)(A) of the Act. ICR sessions are limited to 72 1-hour sessions (as defined in section 1848(b)(5) of the Act), up to 6 sessions per day, over a period of up to 18 weeks.

CR/ICR Program Setting Requirements:

CR/ICR services must be furnished in a physician's office or a hospital outpatient setting (for ICR, the hospital outpatient setting must provide ICR using an approved ICR program). All settings must have a physician immediately available and accessible for medical consultations and emergencies at all times when items/services are being furnished under the program. This provision is satisfied if the physician meets the requirements for direct supervision of physician office services as specified at 42 CFR 410.26, and for hospital outpatient services as specified at 42 CFR 410.27.

ICR Program Approval Requirements:

All prospective ICR programs must be approved through the national coverage determination (NCD) process. To be approved as an ICR program, it must demonstrate through peer-reviewed, published research that it has accomplished one or more of the following for its patients: (i) positively affected the progression of coronary heart disease, (ii) reduced the need for coronary bypass surgery, or, (iii) reduced the need for percutaneous coronary interventions.

An ICR program must also demonstrate through peer-reviewed, published research that it accomplished a statistically significant reduction in five or more of the following measures for patients from their levels before CR services to after CR services: (i) low density lipoprotein, (ii) triglycerides, (iii) body mass index, (iv) systolic blood pressure, (v) diastolic blood pressure, and (vi) the need for cholesterol, blood pressure, and diabetes medications.

A list of approved ICR programs, identified through the NCD process, will be posted to the CMS Web site and listed in the Federal Register.

Once an ICR program is approved through the NCD process, all prospective ICR sites wishing to furnish ICR items/services via an approved ICR program may enroll with their local contractor to become an ICR program supplier using the designated forms as specified at 42 CFR 424.510, and report specialty code 31 to be identified as an enrolled ICR supplier. For purposes of appealing an adverse determination concerning site approval, an ICR site is considered a supplier (or prospective supplier) as defined in 42 CFR 498.2.

CR/ICR Program Physician Requirements:

Physicians responsible for CR/ICR programs are identified as medical directors who oversee or supervise the CR/ICR program at a particular site. The medical director, in consultation with staff, is involved in directing the progress of individuals in the program. The medical director, as well as physicians acting as the supervising physician, must possess all of the following: (1) expertise in the management of individuals with cardiac pathophysiology, (2) cardiopulmonary training in basic life support or advanced cardiac life support, and (3) licensed to practice medicine in the state in which the CR/ICR program is offered. Direct physician supervision may be provided by a supervising physician or the medical director.

(See Pub. 100-03, Medicare National Coverage Determinations Manual, Chapter 1, Part 1, section 20.10.1, Pub. 100-04, Medicare Claims Processing Manual, Chapter 32, section 140, Pub. 100-08, Medicare Program Integrity Manual, Chapter 15, section 15.4.2.8, for specific claims processing, coding, and billing requirements for CR/ICR program services).

100-2, Chapter 15, 270

Telehealth Services

Background

Section 223 of the Medicare, Medicaid and SCHIP Benefits Improvement and Protection Act of 2000 (BIPA) -Revision of Medicare Reimbursement for Telehealth Services amended §1834 of the Act to provide for an expansion of Medicare payment for telehealth services.

Effective October 1, 2001, coverage and payment for Medicare telehealth includes consultation, office visits, individual psychotherapy, and pharmacologic management delivered via a telecommunications system. Eligible geographic areas include rural health professional shortage areas (HPSA) and counties not classified as a metropolitan statistical area (MSA). Additionally, Federal telemedicine demonstration projects as of December 31, 2000, may serve as the originating site regardless of geographic location.

An interactive telecommunications system is required as a condition of payment; however, BIPA does allow the use of asynchronous "store and forward" technology in delivering these services when the originating site is a Federal telemedicine demonstration program in Alaska or Hawaii. BIPA does not require that a practitioner present the patient for interactive telehealth services.

With regard to payment amount, BIPA specified that payment for the professional service performed by the distant site practitioner (i.e., where the expert physician or practitioner is physically located at time of telemedicine encounter) is equal to what would have been paid without the use of telemedicine. Distant site practitioners include only a physician as described in §1861(r) of the Act and a medical practitioner as described in §1842(b)(18)(C) of the Act. BIPA also expanded payment under Medicare to include a $20 originating site facility fee (location of beneficiary).

Previously, the Balanced Budget Act of 1997 (BBA) limited the scope of Medicare telehealth coverage to consultation services and the implementing regulation prohibited the use of an asynchronous 'store and forward' telecommunications system. The BBA of 1997 also required the professional fee to be shared between the referring and consulting practitioners, and prohibited Medicare payment for facility fees and line charges associated with the telemedicine encounter.

The BIPA required that Medicare Part B (Supplementary Medical Insurance) pay for this expansion of telehealth services beginning with services furnished on October 1, 2001.

Section 149 of the Medicare Improvements for Patients and Providers Act of 2008 (MIPPA) amended §1834(m) of the Act to add certain entities as originating sites for payment of telehealth services. Effective for services furnished on or after January 1, 2009, eligible originating sites include a hospital-based or critical access hospital-based renal dialysis center (including satellites); a skilled nursing facility (as defined in §1819(a) of the Act); and a community mental health center (as defined in §1861(ff)(3)(B) of the Act). MIPPA also amended§1888(e)(2)(A)(ii) of the Act to exclude telehealth services furnished under §1834(m)(4)(C)(ii)(VII) from the consolidated billing provisions of the skilled nursing facility prospective payment system (SNF PPS).

NOTE: MIPPA did not add independent renal dialysis facilities as originating sites for payment of telehealth services.

The telehealth provisions authorized by §1834(m) of the Act are implemented in 42 CFR 410.78 and 414.65.

100-2, Chapter 15, 270.2

List of Medicare Telehealth Services

The use of a telecommunications system may substitute for an in-person encounter for professional consultations, office visits, office psychiatry services, and a limited number of other physician fee schedule (PFS) services. These services are listed below.

Consultations (Effective October 1, 2001-December 31, 2009)

Telehealth consultations, emergency department or initial inpatient (Effective January 1, 2010)

Follow-up inpatient telehealth consultations (Effective January 1, 2009)

Office or other outpatient visits

Subsequent hospital care services (with the limitation of one telehealth visit every 3 days) (Effective January 1, 2011)

Subsequent nursing facility care services (with the limitation of one telehealth visit every 30 days) (Effective January 1, 2011)

Individual psychotherapy

Pharmacologic management (Effective March 1, 2003)

Psychiatric diagnostic interview examination (Effective March 1, 2003)

End stage renal disease related services (Effective January 1, 2005)

Individual and group medical nutrition therapy (Individual effective January 1, 2006; group effective January 1, 2011)

Neurobehavioral status exam (Effective January 1, 2008)

Individual and group health and behavior assessment and intervention (Individual effective January 1, 2010; group effective January 1, 2011)

Individual and group kidney disease education (KDE) services (Effective January 1, 2011)

Individual and group diabetes self-management training (DSMT) services (with a minimum of 1 hour of in-person instruction to be furnished in the initial year training period to ensure effective injection training) (Effective January 1, 2011).

Smoking Cessation Services (Effective January 1, 2012)

Alcohol and/or substance (other than tobacco) abuse structured assessment and intervention services (Effective January 1, 2013)

Annual alcohol misuse screening (Effective January 1, 2013)

Brief face-to-face behavioral counseling for alcohol misuse (Effective January 1, 2013)

Annual Depression Screening (Effective January 1, 2013)

High-intensity behavioral counseling to prevent sexually transmitted infections (Effective January 1, 2013)

Annual, face-to-face Intensive behavioral therapy for cardiovascular disease (Effective January 1, 2013)

Face-to-face behavioral counseling for obesity (Effective January 1, 2013)

Transitional Care Management Services (Effective January 1, 2014)

NOTE: Beginning January 1, 2010, CMS eliminated the use of all consultation codes, except for inpatient telehealth consultation G-codes. CMS no longer recognizes office/outpatient or inpatient consultation CPT® codes for payment of office/outpatient or inpatient visits. Instead, physicians and practitioners are instructed to bill a new or established patient office/outpatient visit CPT® code or appropriate hospital or nursing facility care code, as appropriate to the particular patient, for all office/outpatient or inpatient visits. For detailed instructions regarding reporting these and other telehealth services, see Pub. 100-04, Medicare Claims Processing Manual, chapter 12, section 190.3.

The conditions of payment for Medicare telehealth services, including qualifying originating sites and the types of telecommunications systems recognized by Medicare, are subject to the provisions of 42 CFR 410.78. Payment for these services is subject to the provisions of 42 CFR 414.65.

100-2, Chapter 15, 270.4.3

Payment for Diabetes Self-Management Training (DSMT) as a Telehealth Service

Individual and group DSMT services may be paid as a Medicare telehealth service; however, at least 1 hour of the 10 hour benefit in the year following the initial DSMT service must be furnished in-person to allow for effective injection training. The injection training may be furnished through either individual or group DSMT services. By reporting the –GT or –GQ modifier with HCPCS code GO108 (Diabetes outpatient self-management training services, individual, per 30 minutes) or G0109 Diabetes outpatient self-management training services, group session (2 or more), per 30 minutes), the distant site practitioner certifies that the beneficiary has received or will receive 1 hour of in-person DSMT services for purposes of injection training during the year following the initial DSMT service.

As specified in 42 CFR 410.141(e) and stated in section 300.2 of this chapter, individual DSMT services may be furnished by a physician, individual, or entity that furnishes other services for which direct Medicare payment may be made and that submits necessary documentation to, and is accredited by, an accreditation organization approved by CMS. However, consistent with the statutory requirements of section 1834(m)(1) of the Act, as provided in 42 CFR 410.78(b)(1) and (b)(2) and stated in section 270.4 of this chapter, Medicare telehealth services, including individual DSMT services furnished as a telehealth service, could only be furnished by a licensed physician assistant (PA), nurse practitioner (NP), clinical nurse specialist (CNS), certified nurse-midwife (CNM), clinical psychologist, clinical social worker, or registered die titian or nutrition professional.

100-2, Chapter 15, 280.1

Glaucoma Screening

A. Conditions of Coverage

The regulations implementing the Benefits Improvements and Protection Act of 2000, §102, provide for annual coverage for glaucoma screening for beneficiaries in the following high risk categories:

- Individuals with diabetes mellitus;
- Individuals with a family history of glaucoma; or
- African-Americans age 50 and over.

In addition, beginning with dates of service on or after January 1, 2006, 42 CFR 410.23(a)(2), revised, the definition of an eligible beneficiary in a high-risk category is expanded to include:

- Hispanic-Americans age 65 and over.

Medicare will pay for glaucoma screening examinations where they are furnished by or under the direct supervision in the office setting of an ophthalmologist or optometrist, who is legally authorized to perform the services under State law.

Screening for glaucoma is defined to include:

- A dilated eye examination with an intraocular pressure measurement; and
- A direct ophthalmoscopy examination, or a slit-lamp biomicroscopic examination.

Payment may be made for a glaucoma screening examination that is performed on an eligible beneficiary after at least 11 months have passed following the month in which the last covered glaucoma screening examination was performed.

The following HCPCS codes apply for glaucoma screening:

G0117-Glaucoma screening for high-risk patients furnished by an optometrist or ophthalmologist; and

G0118 -Glaucoma screening for high-risk patients furnished under the direct supervision of an optometrist or ophthalmologist.

The type of service for the above G codes is: TOS Q.

For providers who bill A/B MACs, applicable types of bill for screening glaucoma services are 13X, 22X, 23X, 71X, 73X, 75X, and 85X. The following revenue codes should be reported when billing for screening glaucoma services:

- Comprehensive outpatient rehabilitation facilities (CORFs), critical access hospitals (CAHs), skilled nursing facilities (SNFs), independent and provider-based RHCs and free standing and provider-based FQHCs bill for this service under revenue code 770. CAHs electing the optional method of payment for outpatient services report this service under revenue codes 96X, 97X,or 98X.

- Hospital outpatient departments bill for this service under any valid/appropriate revenue code. They are not required to report revenue code 770.

Calculating the Frequency

- Once a beneficiary has received a covered glaucoma screening procedure, the beneficiary may receive another procedure after 11 full months have passed. To determine the 11-month period, start the count beginning with the month after the month in which the previous covered screening procedure was performed.

Diagnosis Coding Requirements

- Providers bill glaucoma screening using diagnosis codes for screening services. Claims submitted without a screening diagnosis code may be returned to the provider as unprocessable.

Payment Methodology

A/B MACs (B)

- Contractors pay for glaucoma screening based on the Medicare physician fee schedule. Deductible and coinsurance apply. Claims from physicians or other providers where assignment was not taken are subject to the Medicare limiting charge (refer to the Medicare Claims Processing Manual, Chapter 12, "Physician/Non-physician Practitioners," for more information about the Medicare limiting charge).

A/B MACs (A)

- Payment is made for the facility expense as follows:
- Independent and provider-based RHC/free standing and provider-based FQHC -payment is made under the all inclusive rate for the screening glaucoma service based on the visit furnished to the RHC/FQHC patient;
- CAH -payment is made on a reasonable cost basis unless the CAH has elected the optional method of payment for outpatient services in which case, procedures outlined in the Medicare Claims Processing Manual, Chapter 3, §30.1.1, should be followed;
- CORF -payment is made under the Medicare physician fee schedule;
- Hospital outpatient department -payment is made under outpatient prospective payment system (OPPS);
- Hospital inpatient Part B -payment is made under OPPS;

- SNF outpatient -payment is made under the Medicare physician fee schedule (MPFS); and
- SNF inpatient Part B -payment is made under MPFS

Deductible and coinsurance apply.

E. Special Billing Instructions for RHCs and FQHCs

Screening glaucoma services are considered RHC/FQHC services. RHCs and FQHCs bill the contractor under bill type 71X or 73X along with revenue code 770 and HCPCS codes G0117 or G0118 and RHC/FQHC revenue code 520 or 521 to report the related visit. Reporting of revenue code 770 and HCPCS codes G0117 and G0118 in addition to revenue code 520 or 521 is required for this service in order for CWF to perform frequency editing.

Payment should not be made for a screening glaucoma service unless the claim also contains a visit code for the service. Therefore, the contractor installs an edit in its system to assure payment is not made for revenue code 770 unless the claim also contains a visit revenue code (520 or 521).

100-2, Chapter 15, 280.5

Annual Wellness Visit (AWV) Providing Personalized Prevention Plan Services (PPPS)

A. General

Pursuant to section 4103 of the Affordable Care Act of 2010 (the ACA), the; Centers for Medicare & Medicaid Services (CMS) amended section 42 CFR 411.15(a)(1) and 42 CFR 411.15(k)(15) (list of examples of routine physical examinations excluded from coverage), effective for services furnished on or after January 1, 2011. This expanded coverage, as established at 42 CFR 410.15, is subject to certain eligibility and other limitations that allow payment for an annual wellness visit (AWV) providing personalized prevention plan services (PPPS), when performed by a health professional (as defined in this section), for an individual who is no longer within 12 months after the effective date of his/her first Medicare Part B coverage period, and has not received either an initial preventive physical examination (IPPE) or an AWV within the past 12 months. Medicare coinsurance and Part B deductibles do not apply.

The AWV will include the establishment of, or update to, the individual's medical/family history, measurement of his/her height, weight, body-mass index (BMI) or waist circumference, and blood pressure (BP), with the goal of health promotion and disease detection and encouraging patients to obtain the screening and preventive services that may already be covered and paid for under Medicare Part B. Definitions relative to the AWV are included below.

Coverage is available for an AWV that meets the following requirements:

1. It is performed by a health professional; and,
2. It is furnished to an eligible beneficiary who is no longer within 12 months after the effective date of his/her first Medicare Part B coverage period, and he/she has not received either an IPPE or an AWV providing PPPS within the past 12 months.

Sections 4103 and 4104 of the ACA also provide for a waiver of the Medicare coinsurance and Part B deductible requirements for an AWV effective for services furnished on or after January 1, 2011.

B. Definitions Relative to the AWV:

Detection of any cognitive impairment: The assessment of an individual's cognitive function by direct observation, with due consideration of information obtained by way of patient reorts, concerns raised by family members, friends, caretakers, or others.

Eligible beneficiary: An individual who is no longer within 12 months after the effective date of his/her first Medicare Part B coverage period and who has not received either an IPPE or an AWV providing PPPS within the past 12 months.

Establishment of, or an update to, the individual's medical/family history:

At a minimum, the collection and documentation of the following:

a. Past medical and surgical history, including experiences with illnesses, hospital stays, operations, allergies, injuries, and treatments.

b. Use or exposure to medications and supplements, including calcium and vitamins.

c. Medical events in the beneficiary's parents and any siblings and children, including diseases that may be hereditary or place the individual at increased risk.

First AWV providing PPPS: The provision of the following services to an eligible beneficiary by a health professional that include, and take into account the results of, a health risk assessment as those terms are defined in this section:

a. Review (and administration if needed) of a health risk assessment (as defined in this section).

b. Establishment of an individual's medical/family history.

c. Establishment of a list of current providers and suppliers that are regularly involved in providing medical care to the individual.

d. Measurement of an individual's height, weight, BMI (or waist circumference, if appropriate), BP, and other routine measurements as deemed appropriate, based on the beneficiary's medical/family history.

e. Detection of any cognitive impairment that the individual may have as defined in this section.

f. Review of the individual's potential (risk factors) for depression, including current or past experiences with depression or other mood disorders, based on the use of an appropriate screening instrument for persons without a current diagnosis of depression, which the health professional may select from various available standardized screening tests designed for this purpose and recognized by national medical professional organizations.

g. Review of the individual's functional ability and level of safety based on direct observation, or the use of appropriate screening questions or a screening questionnaire, which the health professional may select from various available screening questions or standardized questionnaires designed for this purpose and recognized by national professional medical organizations.

h. Establishment of the following:

1. A written screening schedule for the individual, such as a checklist for the next 5 to 10 years, as appropriate, based on recommendations of the United States Preventive Services Task Force (USPSTF) and the Advisory Committee on Immunization Practices (ACIP), and the individual's health risk assessment (as that term is defined in this section), the individual's health status, screening history, and age-appropriate preventive services covered by Medicare.

2. A list of risk factors and conditions for which primary, secondary, or tertiary interventions are recommended or are underway for the individual, including any mental health conditions or any such risk factors or conditions that have been identified through an IPPE, and a list of treatment options and their associated risks and benefits.

i. Furnishing of personalized health advice to the individual and a referral, as appropriate, to health education or preventive counseling services or programs aimed at reducing identified risk factors and improving self-management, or community-based lifestyle interventions to reduce health risks and promote self-management and wellness, including weight loss, physical activity, smoking cessation, fall prevention, and nutrition.

j. Any other element determined appropriate through the National Coverage Determination (NCD) process.

Health professional:

a. A physician who is a doctor of medicine or osteopathy (as defined in section 1861(r)(1) of the Social Security Act (the Act); or,

b. A physician assistant, nurse practitioner, or clinical nurse specialist (as defined in section 1861(aa)(5) of the Act); or,

c. A medical professional (including a health educator, registered dietitian, or nutrition professional or other licensed practitioner) or a team of such medical professionals, working under the direct supervision (as defined in 42CFR 410.32(b)(3)(ii)) of a physician as defined in this section.

Health Risk Assessment means, for the purposes of the annual wellness visit, an evaluation tool that meets the following criteria:

a. collects self-reported information about the beneficiary.

b. can be administered independently by the beneficiary or administered by a health professional prior to or as part of the AWV encounter.

c. is appropriately tailored to and takes into account the communication needs of underserved populations, persons with limited English proficiency, and persons with health literacy needs.

d. takes no more than 20 minutes to complete.

e. addresses, at a minimum, the following topics:

1. demographic data, including but not limited to age, gender, race, and ethnicity.

2. self assessment of health status, frailty, and physical functioning.

3. psychosocial risks, including but not limited to, depression/life satisfaction, stress, anger, loneliness/social isolation, pain, and fatigue.

4. Behavioral risks, including but not limited to, tobacco use, physical activity, nutrition and oral health, alcohol consumption, sexual health, motor vehicle safety (seat belt use), and home safety.

5. Activities of daily living (ADLs), including but not limited to, dressing, feeding, toileting, grooming, physical ambulation (including balance/risk of falls), and bathing.

6. Instrumental activities of daily living (IADLs), including but not limited to, shopping, food preparation, using the telephone, housekeeping, laundry, mode of transportation, responsibility for own medications, and ability to handle finances.

Review of the individual's functional ability and level of safety: At a minimum, includes assessment of the following topics:

    a. Hearing impairment,

    b. Ability to successfully perform activities of daily living,

    c. Fall risk, and,

    d. Home safety.

Subsequent AWV providing PPPS: The provision of the following services to an eligible beneficiary by a health professional that include, and take into account the results of an updated health risk assessment, as those terms are defined in this section:

    a. Review (and administration if needed) of an updated health risk assessment (as defined in this section).

    b. An update of the individual's medical/family history.

    c. An update of the list of current providers and suppliers that are regularly involved in providing medical care to the individual, as that list was developed for the first AWV providing PPPS or the previous subsequent AWV providing PPPS.

    d. Measurement of an individual's weight (or waist circumference), BP, and other routine measurements as deemed appropriate, based on the individual's medical/family history.

    e. Detection of any cognitive impairment that the individual may have as defined in this section.

    f. An update to the following:

        1. The written screening schedule for the individual as that schedule is defined in this section, that was developed at the first AWV providing PPPS, and,

        2. The list of risk factors and conditions for which primary, secondary, or tertiary interventions are recommended or are under way for the individual, as that list was developed at the first AWV providing PPPS or the previous subsequent AWV providing PPPS.

    g. Furnishing of personalized health advice to the individual and a referral, as appropriate, to health education or preventive counseling services or programs as that advice and related services are defined for the first AWV providing PPPS.

    h. Any other element determined appropriate by the Secretary through the NCD process.

See Pub. 100-04, Medicare Claims Processing Manual, chapter 18, section 140, for detailed claims processing and billing instructions.

100-2, Chapter 15, 290

Foot Care

A. Treatment of Subluxation of Foot

Subluxations of the foot are defined as partial dislocations or displacements of joint surfaces, tendons ligaments, or muscles of the foot. Surgical or nonsurgical treatments undertaken for the sole purpose of correcting a subluxated structure in the foot as an isolated entity are not covered.

However, medical or surgical treatment of subluxation of the ankle joint (talo-crural joint) is covered. In addition, reasonable and necessary medical or surgical services, diagnosis, or treatment for medical conditions that have resulted from or are associated with partial displacement of structures is covered. For example, if a patient has osteoarthritis that has resulted

in a partial displacement of joints in the foot, and the primary treatment is for the osteoarthritis, coverage is provided.

B. Exclusions from Coverage

The following foot care services are generally excluded from coverage under both Part A and Part B. (See §290.Fand §290. Gfor instructions on applying foot care exclusions.)

1. Treatment of Flat Foot

The term "flat foot" is defined as a condition in which one or more arches of the foot have flattened out. Services or devices directed toward the care or correction of such conditions, including the prescription of supportive devices, are not covered.

2. Routine Foot Care

Except as provided above, routine foot care is excluded from coverage. Services that normally are considered routine and not covered by Medicare include the following:

- The cutting or removal of corns and calluses;
- The trimming, cutting, clipping, or debriding of nails; and
- Other hygienic and preventive maintenance care, such as cleaning and soaking the feet, the use of skin creams to maintain skin tone of either ambulatory or bedfast patients, and any other service performed in the absence of localized illness, injury, or symptoms involving the foot.

3. Supportive Devices for Feet

Orthopedic shoes and other supportive devices for the feet generally are not covered. However, this exclusion does not apply to such a shoe if it is an integral part of a leg brace, and its expense is included as part of the cost of the brace. Also, this exclusion does not apply to therapeutic shoes furnished to diabetics.

C. Exceptions to Routine Foot Care Exclusion

1. Necessary and Integral Part of Otherwise Covered Services

In certain circumstances, services ordinarily considered to be routine may be covered if they are performed as a necessary and integral part of otherwise covered services, such as diagnosis and treatment of ulcers, wounds, or infections.

2. Treatment of Warts on Foot

The treatment of warts (including plantar warts) on the foot is covered to the same extent as services provided for the treatment of warts located elsewhere on the body.

3. Presence of Systemic Condition

The presence of a systemic condition such as metabolic, neurologic, or peripheral vascular disease may require scrupulous foot care by a professional that in the absence of such condition(s) would be considered routine (and, therefore, excluded from coverage). Accordingly, foot care that would otherwise be considered routine may be covered when systemic condition(s) result in severe circulatory embarrassment or areas of diminished sensation in the individual's legs or feet. (See subsection A.)

In these instances, certain foot care procedures that otherwise are considered routine (e.g., cutting or removing corns and calluses, or trimming, cutting, clipping, or debriding nails) may pose a hazard when performed by a nonprofessional person on patients with such systemic conditions. (See§290.G for procedural instructions.)

4. Mycotic Nails

In the absence of a systemic condition, treatment of mycotic nails may be covered.

The treatment of mycotic nails for an ambulatory patient is covered only when the physician attending the patient's mycotic condition documents that (1) there is clinical evidence of mycosis of the toenail, and (2) the patient has marked limitation of ambulation, pain, or secondary infection resulting from the thickening and dystrophy of the infected toenail plate.

The treatment of mycotic nails for a nonambulatory patient is covered only when the physician attending the patient's mycotic condition documents that (1) there is clinical evidence of mycosis of the toenail, and (2) the patient suffers from pain or secondary infection resulting from the thickening and dystrophy of the infected toenail plate.

For the purpose of these requirements, documentation means any written information that is required by the carrier in order for services to be covered. Thus, the information submitted with claims must be substantiated by information found in the patient's medical record. Any information, including that contained in a form letter, used for documentation purposes is subject to carrier verification in order to ensure that the information adequately justifies coverage of the treatment of mycotic nails.

D. Systemic Conditions That Might Justify Coverage

Although not intended as a comprehensive list, the following metabolic, neurologic, and peripheral vascular diseases (with synonyms in parentheses) most commonly represent the underlying conditions that might justify coverage for routine foot care.

Diabetes mellitus *

Arteriosclerosis obliterans (A.S.O., arteriosclerosis of the extremities, occlusive peripheral arteriosclerosis)

Buerger's disease (thromboangiitis obliterans)

Chronic thrombophlebitis *

Peripheral neuropathies involving the feet-

Associated with malnutrition and vitamin deficiency *

- Malnutrition (general, pellagra)
- Alcoholism
- Malabsorption (celiac disease, tropical sprue)
- Pernicious anemia

Associated with carcinoma *

Associated with diabetes mellitus *

Associated with drugs and toxins *

Associated with multiple sclerosis *

Associated with uremia (chronic renal disease) *

Associated with traumatic injury

Associated with leprosy or neurosyphilis

Associated with hereditary disorders

- Hereditary sensory radicular neuropathy
- Angiokeratoma corporis diffusum (Fabry's)
- Amyloid neuropathy

When the patient's condition is one of those designated by an asterisk (*), routine procedure s are covered only if the patient is under the active care of a doctor of medicine or osteopathy who documents the condition.

E. Supportive Devices for Feet

Orthopedic shoes and other supportive devices for the feet generally are not covered. However, this exclusion does not apply to such a shoe if it is an integral part of a leg brace, and its expense is included as part of the cost of the brace. Also, this exclusion does not apply to therapeutic shoes furnished to diabetics.

F. Presumption of Coverage

In evaluating whether the routine services can be reimbursed, a presumption of coverage may be made where the evidence available discloses certain physical and/or clinical findings consistent with the diagnosis and indicative of severe peripheral involvement. For purposes of applying this presumption the following findings are pertinent:

Class A Findings

Nontraumatic amputation of foot or integral skeletal portion thereof.

Class B Findings

Absent posterior tibial pulse;

Advanced trophic changes as: hair growth (decrease or absence) nail changes (thickening) pigmentary changes (discoloration) skin texture (thin, shiny) skin color (rubor or redness) (Three required); and

Absent dorsalis pedis pulse.

Class C Findings

Claudication;

Temperature changes (e.g., cold feet);

Edema;

Paresthesias (abnormal spontaneous sensations in the feet); and

Burning.

The presumption of coverage may be applied when the physician rendering the routine foot care has identified:

1. A Class A finding;
2. Two of the Class B findings; or
3. One Class B and two Class C findings

Cases evidencing findings falling short of these alternatives may involve podiatric treatment that may constitute covered care and should be reviewed by the intermediary's medical staff and developed as necessary.

For purposes of applying the coverage presumption where the routine services have been rendered by a podiatrist, the contractor may deem the active care requirement met if the claim or other evidence available discloses that the patient has seen an M.D. or D.O. for treatment and/or evaluation of the complicating disease process during the 6-month period prior to the rendition of the routine-type services. The intermediary may also accept the podiatrist's statement that the diagnosing and treating M.D. or D.O. also concurs with the podiatrist's findings as to the severity of the peripheral involvement indicated.

Services ordinarily considered routine might also be covered if they are performed as a necessary and integral part of otherwise covered services, such as diagnosis and treatment of diabetic ulcers, wounds, and infections.

G. Application of Foot Care Exclusions to Physician's Services

The exclusion of foot care is determined by the nature of the service. Thus, payment for an excluded service should be denied whether performed by a podiatrist, osteopath, or a doctor of medicine, and without regard to the difficulty or complexity of the procedure.

When an itemized bill shows both covered services and noncovered services not integrally related to the covered service, the portion of charges attributable to the noncovered services should be denied. (For example, if an itemized bill shows surgery for an ingrown toenail and also removal of calluses not necessary for the performance of toe surgery, any additional charge attributable to removal of the calluses should be denied.)

In reviewing claims involving foot care, the carrier should be alert to the following exceptional situations:

1. Payment may be made for incidental noncovered services performed as a necessary and integral part of, and secondary to, a covered procedure. For example, if trimming of toenails is required for application of a cast to a fractured foot, the carrier need not allocate and deny a portion of the charge for the trimming of the nails. However, a separately itemized charge for such excluded service should be disallowed. When the primary procedure is covered the administration of anesthesia necessary for the performance of such procedure is also covered.

2. Payment may be made for initial diagnostic services performed in connection with a specific symptom or complaint if it seems likely that its treatment would be covered even though the resulting diagnosis may be one requiring only noncovered care.

The name of the M.D. or D.O. who diagnosed the complicating condition must be submitted with the claim. In those cases, where active care is required, the approximate date the beneficiary was last seen by such physician must also be indicated.

NOTE: Section 939 of P.L. 96-499 removed "warts" from the routine foot care exclusion effective July 1, 1981.

Relatively few claims for routine-type care are anticipated considering the severity of conditions contemplated as the basis for this exception. Claims for this type of foot care should not be paid in the absence of convincing evidence that nonprofessional performance of the service would have been hazardous for the beneficiary because of an underlying systemic disease. The mere statement of a diagnosis such as those mentioned in §D above does not of itself indicate the severity of the condition. Where development is indicated to verify diagnosis and/or severity the carrier should follow existing claims processing practices, which may include review of carrier's history and medical consultation as well as physician contacts.

The rules in §290.F concerning presumption of coverage also apply.

Codes and policies for routine foot care and supportive devices for the feet are not exclusively for the use of podiatrists. These codes must be used to report foot care services regardless of the specialty of the physician who furnishes the services. Carriers must instruct physicians to use the most appropriate code available when billing for routine foot care.

100-2, Chapter 15, 300

Diabetes Self-Management Training Services

Section 4105 of the Balanced Budget Act of 1997 permits Medicare coverage of diabetes self- management training (DSMT) services when these services are furnished by a certified provider who meets certain quality standards. This program is intended to educate beneficiaries in the successful self-management of diabetes. The program includes instructions in self-monitoring of blood glucose; education about diet and exercise; an insulin treatment plan developed specifically for the patient who is insulin-dependent; and motivation for patients to use the skills for self-management.

Diabetes self-management training services may be covered by Medicare only if the treating physician or treating qualified non-physician practitioner who is managing the beneficiary's diabetic condition certifies that such services are needed. The referring physician or qualified non-physician practitioner must maintain the plan of care in the beneficiary's medical record and documentation substantiating the need for training on an individual basis when group training is typically covered, if so ordered. The order must also include a statement signed by the physician that the service is needed as well as the following:

*   The number of initial or follow-up hours ordered (the physician can order less than 10 hours of training);
*   The topics to be covered in training (initial training hours can be used for the full initial training program or specific areas such as nutrition or insulin training); and
*   A determination that the beneficiary should receive individual or group training.

The provider of the service must maintain documentation in a file that includes the original order from the physician and any special conditions noted by the physician.

When the training under the order is changed, the training order/referral must be signed by the physician or qualified non-physician practitioner treating the beneficiary and maintained in the beneficiary's file in the DSMT's program records.

NOTE: All entities billing for DSMT under the fee-for-service payment system or other payment systems must meet all national coverage requirements.

100-2, Chapter 15, 300.2

Certified Providers

A designated certified provider bills for DSMT provided by an accredited DSMT program. Certified providers must submit a copy of their accreditation certificate to the contractor. The statute states that a "certified provider" is a physician or other individual or entity designated by the Secretary that, in addition to providing outpatient self management training services, provides other items and services for which payment may be made under title XVIII, and meets certain quality standards. The CMS is designating all providers and suppliers that bill Medicare for other individual services such as hospital outpatient departments, renal dialysis facilities, physicians and durable medical equipment suppliers as certified. All suppliers/providers who may bill for other Medicare services or items and who represent a DSMT program that is accredited as meeting quality standards can bill and receive payment for the entire DSMT program. Registered dietitians are eligible to bill on behalf of an entire DSMT program on or after January 1, 2002, as long as the provider has obtained a Medicare provider number. A dietitian may not be the sole provider of the DSMT service. There is an exception for rural areas. In a rural area, an individual who is qualified as a registered dietitian and as a certified diabetic educator who is currently certified by an organization approved by CMS may furnish training and is deemed to meet the multidisciplinary team requirement.

The CMS will not reimburse services on a fee-for-service basis rendered to a beneficiary under Part A.

NOTE: While separate payment is not made for this service to Rural Health Clinics (RHCs), the service is covered but is considered included in the all-inclusive encounter rate.

Effective January 1, 2006, payment for DSMT provided in a Federally Qualified Health Clinic (FQHC) that meets all of the requirements identified in Pub. 100-04, chapter 18, section 120 may be made in addition to one other visit the beneficiary had during the same day.

All DSMT programs must be accredited as meeting quality standards by a CMS approved national accreditation organization. Currently, CMS recognizes the American Diabetes Association, American Association of Diabetes Educators and the Indian Health Service as approved national accreditation organizations. Programs without accreditation by a CMS-approved national accreditation organization are not covered. Certified providers may be asked to submit updated accreditation documents at any time or to submit outcome data to an organization designated by CMS.

Enrollment of DMEPOS Suppliers

The DMEPOS suppliers are reimbursed for diabetes training through local carriers. In order to file claims for DSMT, a DMEPOS supplier must be enrolled in the Medicare program with the National Supplier Clearinghouse (NSC). The supplier must also meet the quality standards of a CMS-approved national accreditation organization as stated above. DMEPOS suppliers must obtain a provider number from the local carrier in order to bill for DSMT.

The carrier requires a completed Form CMS-855, along with an accreditation certificate as part of the provider application process. After it has been determined that the quality standards are met, a billing number is assigned to the supplier. Once a supplier has received a National Provider Identification (NPI) number, the supplier can begin receiving reimbursement for this service.

Carriers should contact the National Supplier Clearinghouse (NSC) according to the instruction in Pub 100-08, the Medicare Program Integrity Manual, Chapter 10, "Healthcare Provider/ Supplier Enrollment," to verify an applicant is currently enrolled and eligible to receive direct payment from the Medicare program.

The applicant is assigned specialty 87.

Any DMEPOS supplier that has its billing privileges deactivated or revoked by the NSC will also have the billing number deactivated by the carrier.

100-2, Chapter 15, 300.3

Frequency of Training

A -Initial Training

The initial year for DSMT is the 12 month period following the initial date.

Medicare will cover initial training that meets the following conditions:

- Is furnished to a beneficiary who has not previously received initial or follow-up training under HCPCS codes G0108 or G0109;
- Is furnished within a continuous 12-month period;
- Does not exceed a total of 10 hours* (the 10 hours of training can be done in any combination of 1/2 hour increments);
- With the exception of 1 hour of individual training, training is usually furnished in a group setting, which can contain other patients besides Medicare beneficiaries, and;
- One hour of individual training may be used for any part of the training including insulin training.

* When a claim contains a DSMT HCPCS code and the associated units cause the total time for the DSMT initial year to exceed '10' hours, a CWF error will set.

B -Follow-Up Training

Medicare covers follow-up training under the following conditions:

- No more than 2 hours individual or group training per beneficiary per year;
- Group training consists of 2 to 20 individuals who need not all be Medicare beneficiaries;
- Follow-up training for subsequent years is based on a 12 month calendar after completion of the full 10 hours of initial training;
- Follow-up training is furnished in increments of no less than one-half hour*; and
- The physician (or qualified non-physician practitioner) treating the beneficiary must document in the beneficiary's medical record that the beneficiary is a diabetic.

*When a claim contains a DSMT HCPCS code and the associated units cause the total time for any follow-up year to exceed 2 hours, a CWF error will set.

100-2, Chapter 15, 300.4

Coverage Requirements for Individual Training

Medicare covers training on an individual basis for a Medicare beneficiary under any of the following conditions.

- No group session is available within 2 months of the date the training is ordered;
- The beneficiary's physician (or qualified non-physician practitioner) documents in the beneficiary's medical record that the beneficiary has special needs resulting from conditions, such as severe vision, hearing or language limitations or other such special conditions as identified by the treating physician or non-physician practitioner, that will hinder effective participation in a group training session; or
- The physician orders additional insulin training.
- The need for individual training must be identified by the physician or non-physician practitioner in the referral.

NOTE: If individual training has been provided to a Medicare beneficiary and subsequently the carrier or intermediary determines that training should have been provided in a group, carriers and intermediaries down-code the reimbursement from individual to the group level and provider education would be the appropriate actions instead of denying the service as billed.

100-2, Chapter 15, 310

Kidney Disease Patient Education Services

By definition, chronic kidney disease (CKD) is kidney damage for 3 months or longer, regardless of the cause of kidney damage. CKD typically evolves over a long period of time and patients may not have symptoms until significant, possibly irreversible, damage has been done. Complications can develop from kidneys that do not function properly, such as high blood pressure, anemia, and weak bones. When CKD progresses, it may lead to kidney failure, which requires artificial means to perform kidney functions (dialysis) or a kidney transplant to maintain life.

Patients can be classified into 5 stages based on their glomerular filtration rate (GFR, how quickly blood is filtered through the kidneys), with stage I having kidney damage with normal or increased GFR to stage V with kidney failure, also called end-stage renal disease (ESRD). Once patients with CKD are identified, treatment is available to help prevent complications of decreased kidney function, slow the progression of kidney disease, and reduce the risk of other diseases such as heart disease.

Beneficiaries with CKD may benefit from kidney disease education (KDE) interventions due to the large amount of medical information that could affect patient outcomes, including the increasing emphasis on self-care and patients' desire for informed, autonomous decision-making. Pre-dialysis education can help patients achieve better understanding of their illness, dialysis modality options, and may help delay the need for dialysis. Education interventions should be patient-centered, encourage collaboration, offer support to the patient, and be delivered consistently.

Effective for claims with dates of service on and after January 1, 2010, Section 152(b) of the Medicare Improvements for Patients and Providers Act of 2008 (MIPPA) covers KDE services under Medicare Part B. KDE services are designed to provide beneficiaries with Stage IV CKD comprehensive information regarding: the management of comorbidities, including delaying the need for dialysis; prevention of uremic complications; all therapeutic options (each option for renal replacement therapy, dialysis access options, and transplantation); ensuring that the beneficiary has opportunities to actively participate in his/her choice of therapy; and that the services be tailored to meet the beneficiary's needs.

Regulations for KDE services were established at 42 CFR 410.48. Claims processing instructions and billing requirements can be found in Pub. 100-04, Medicare Claims Processing Manual, Chapter 32 –Billing Requirements for Special Services, Section 20.

100-2, Chapter 15, 310.1

Beneficiaries Eligible for Coverage

Medicare Part B covers outpatient, face-to-face KDE services for a beneficiary that:

- is diagnosed with Stage IV CKD, using the Modification of Diet in Renal Disease (MDRD) Study formula (severe decrease in GFR, GFR value of 15-29 mL/min/1.73 m2), and
- obtains a referral from the physician managing the beneficiary's kidney condition. The referral should be documented in the beneficiary's medical records.

100-2, Chapter 15, 310.2

Qualified Person

Medicare Part B covers KDE services provided by a 'qualified person,' meaning a:

- physician (as defined in section 30 of this chapter),
- physician assistant, nurse practitioner, or clinical nurse specialist (as defined in sections 190, 200, and 210 of this chapter),
- hospital, critical access hospital (CAH), skilled nursing facility (SNF), comprehensive outpatient rehabilitation facility (CORF), home health agency (HHA), or hospice,if the KDE services are provided in a rural area (using the actual geographic location core based statistical area (CBSA) to identify facilities located in rural areas), or

- hospital or CAH that is treated as being rural (was reclassified from urban to rural status per 42 CFR 412.103).

NOTE: The "incident to" requirements at section 1861(s)(2)(A) of the Social Security Act (the Act) do not apply to KDE services.

The following providers are not 'qualified persons' and are excluded from furnishing KDE services:

- A hospital, CAH, SNF, CORF, HHA, or hospice located outside of a rural area (using the actual geographic location CBSA to identify facilities located outside of a rural area), unless the services are furnished by a hospital or CAH that is treated as being in a rural area; and
- Renal dialysis facilities.

100-2, Chapter 15, 310.3

Limitations for Coverage

Medicare Part B covers KDE services:

- Up to six (6) sessions as a beneficiary lifetime maximum. A session is 1 hour. In order to bill for a session, a session must be at least 31 minutes in duration. A session that lasts at least 31 minutes, but less than 1 hour still constitutes 1 session.
- On an individual basis or in group settings; if the services are provided in a group setting, a group consists of 2 to 20 individuals who need not all be Medicare beneficiaries.

NOTE: Two HCPCS codes were created for this benefit and one or the other must be present, along with the appropriate ICD diagnosis codes.

The diagnosis codes are:

- ICD-9-CM - code 585.4 (chronic kidney disease, Stage IV (severe)), or
- ICD-10-CM - code N18.4 (chronic kidney disease, Stage IV).

The HCPCS codes are:

- G0420: Face-to-face educational services related to the care of chronic kidney disease; individual, per session, per one hour
- G0421: Face-to-face educational services related to the care of chronic kidney disease; group, per session, per one hour

100-2, Chapter 15, 310.4

Standards for Content

Medicare Part B covers KDE services, provided by a qualified person, which provide comprehensive information regarding:

A. The management of comorbidities, including delaying the need for dialysis, which includes, but is not limited to, the following topics:

- Prevention and treatment of cardiovascular disease,
- Prevention and treatment of diabetes,
- Hypertension management,
- Anemia management,
- Bone disease and disorders of calcium and phosphorus metabolism management,
- Symptomatic neuropathy management, and
- Impairments in functioning and well-being.

B. Prevention of uremic complications, which includes, but is not limited to, the following topics

- Information on how the kidneys work and what happens when the kidneys fail,

- Understanding if remaining kidney function can be protected, preventing disease progression, and realistic chances of survival,

- Diet and fluid restrictions, and

- Medication review, including how each medication works, possible side effects and minimization of side effects, the importance of compliance, and informed decision making if the patient decides not to take a specific drug.

C. Therapeutic options, treatment modalities and settings, advantages and disadvantages of each treatment option, and how the treatments replace the kidney, including, but not limited to, the following topics:

- Hemodialysis, both at home and in-facility;

- Peritoneal dialysis (PD), including intermittent PD, continuous ambulatory PD, and continuous cycling PD, both at home and in-facility;

- All dialysis access options for hemodialysis and peritoneal dialysis; and

- Transplantation.

D. Opportunities for beneficiaries to actively participate in the choice of therapy and be tailored to meet the needs of the individual beneficiary involved, which includes, but is not limited to, the following topics:

- Physical symptoms,

- Impact on family and social life,

- Exercise,

- The right to refuse treatment,

- Impact on work and finances,

- The meaning of test results, and

- Psychological impact.

100-2, Chapter 15, 310.5

Outcomes Assessment

Qualified persons that provide KDE services must develop outcomes assessments that are designed to measure beneficiary knowledge about CKD and its treatment. The assessment must be administered to the beneficiary during a KDE session, and be made available to the Centers for Medicare & Medicaid Services (CMS) upon request. The outcomes assessments serve to assist KDE educators and CMS in improving subsequent KDE programs, patient understanding, and assess program effectiveness of:

- Preparing the beneficiary to make informed decisions about their healthcare options related to CKD, and

- Meeting the communication needs of underserved populations, including persons with disabilities, persons with limited English proficiency, and persons with health literacy needs.

100-2, Chapter 16, 10

General Exclusions From Coverage

No payment can be made under either the hospital insurance or supplementary medical insurance program for certain items and services, when the following conditions exist:

- Not reasonable and necessary (§20);

- No legal obligation to pay for or provide (§40);

- Paid for by a governmental entity (§50);

- Not provided within United States (§60);

- Resulting from war (§70);

- Personal comfort (§80);

- Routine services and appliances (§90);

- Custodial care (§110);

- Cosmetic surgery (§120);

- Charges by immediate relatives or members of household (§130);

- Dental services (§140);

- Paid or expected to be paid under workers' compensation (§150);

- Non-physician services provided to a hospital inpatient that were not provided directly or arranged for by the hospital (§170);

- Services Related to and Required as a Result of Services Which are not Covered Under Medicare (§180);

- Excluded foot care services and supportive devices for feet (§30); or,

- Excluded investigational devices (See Chapter 14).

100-2, Chapter 16, 20

Services Not Reasonable and Necessary

Items and services which are not reasonable and necessary for the diagnosis or treatment of illness or injury or to improve the functioning of a malformed body member are not covered, e.g., payment cannot be made for the rental of a special hospital bed to be used by the patient in their home unless it was a reasonable and necessary part of the patient's treatment. See also §80.

A health care item or service for the purpose of causing, or assisting to cause, the death of any individual (assisted suicide) is not covered. This prohibition does not apply to the provision of an item or service for the purpose of alleviating pain or discomfort, even if such use may increase the risk of death, so long as the item or service is not furnished for the specific purpose of causing death.

100-2, Chapter 16, 90

Routine Services and Appliances

Routine physical checkups; eyeglasses, contact lenses, and eye examinations for the purpose of prescribing, fitting, or changing eyeglasses; eye refractions by whatever practitioner and for whatever purpose performed; hearing aids and examinations for hearing aids; and immunizations are not covered.

The routine physical checkup exclusion applies to (a) examinations performed without relationship to treatment or diagnosis for a specific illness, symptom, complaint, or injury; and (b) examinations required by third parties such as insurance companies, business establishments, or Government agencies.

The routine physical checkup exclusion does not apply to the following services (as noted in section 42 CFR 411.15(a)(1)):

- Screening mammography,
- Colorectal cancer screening tests,
- Screening pelvic exams,
- Prostate cancer screening tests,
- Glaucoma screening exams,
- Ultrasound screening for abdominal aortic aneurysms (AAA),
- cardiovascular disease screening tests,
- diabetes screening tests,
- screening electrocardiogram,
- Initial preventive physical examinations,
- Annual wellness visits providing personalized prevention plan services, and
- Additional preventive services that meet the criteria specified in 42 CFR 410.64.

If the claim is for a diagnostic test or examination performed solely for the purpose of establishing a claim under title IV of Public Law 91-173, "Black Lung Benefits," the service is not covered under Medicare and the claimant should be advised to contact their Social Security office regarding the filing of a claim for reimbursement under the "Black Lung" program.

The exclusions apply to eyeglasses or contact lenses, and eye examinations for the purpose of prescribing, fitting, or changing eyeglasses or contact lenses for refractive errors. The exclusions do not apply to physicians' services (and services incident to a physicians' service) performed in conjunction with an eye disease, as for example, glaucoma or cataracts, or to post-surgical prosthetic lenses which are customarily used during convalescence from eye surgery in which the lens of the eye was removed, or to permanent prosthetic lenses required by an individual lacking the organic lens of the eye, whether by surgical removal or congenital disease. Such prosthetic lens is a replacement for an internal body organ -the lens of the eye. (See the Medicare Benefit Policy Manual, Chapter 15, "Covered Medical and Other Health Services," §120).

Expenses for all refractive procedures, whether performed by an ophthalmologist (or any other physician) or an optometrist and without regard to the reason for performance of the

refraction, are excluded from coverage.

A. Immunizations

Vaccinations or inoculations are excluded as immunizations unless they are either:

- Directly related to the treatment of an injury or direct exposure to a disease or condition, such as antirabies treatment, tetanus antitoxin or booster vaccine, botulin antitoxin, antivenin sera, or immune globulin. (In the absence of injury or direct exposure, preventive immunization (vaccination or inoculation) against such diseases as smallpox, polio, diphtheria, etc., is not covered.); or
- Specifically covered by statute, as described in the Medicare Benefit Policy Manual, Chapter 15, "Covered Medical and Other Health Services," §50.4.4.2.

B. Antigens

Prior to the Omnibus Reconciliation Act of 1980, a physician who prepared an antigen for a patient could not be reimbursed for that service unless the physician also administered the antigen to the patient. Effective January 1, 1981, payment may be made for a reasonable supply of antigens that have been prepared for a particular patient even though they have not been administered to the patient by the same physician who prepared them if:

- The antigens are prepared by a physician who is a doctor of medicine or osteopathy, and
- The physician who prepared the antigens has examined the patient and has determined a plan of treatment and a dosage regimen.

A reasonable supply of antigens is considered to be not more than a 12-month supply of antigens that has been prepared for a particular patient at any one time. The purpose of the reasonable supply limitation is to assure that the antigens retain their potency and effectiveness over the period in which they are to be administered to the patient. (See the Medicare Benefit Policy Manual, Chapter 15, "Covered Medical and Other Health Services," §50.4.4.1)

100-2, Chapter 16, 140

Dental Services Exclusion

Items and services in connection with the care, treatment, filling, removal, or replacement of teeth, or structures directly supporting the teeth are not covered. Structures directly supporting the teeth mean the periodontium, which includes the gingivae, dentogingival junction, periodontal membrane, cementum, and alveolar process. However, payment may be made for certain other services of a dentist. (See the Medicare Benefit Policy Manual, Chapter 15, "Covered Medical and Other Health Services," §150.)

The hospitalization or nonhospitalization of a patient has no direct bearing on the coverage or exclusion of a given dental procedure.

When an excluded service is the primary procedure involved, it is not covered regardless of its complexity or difficulty. For example, the extraction of an impacted tooth is not covered. Similarly, an alveoplasty (the surgical improvement of the shape and condition of the alveolar process) and a frenectomy are excluded from coverage when either of these procedures is performed in connection with an excluded service, e.g., the preparation of the mouth for dentures. In like manner , the removal of the torus palatinus (a bony protuberance of the hard palate) could be a covered service. However, with rare exception, this surgery is performed in connection with an excluded service, i.e., the preparation of the mouth for dentures. Under such circumstances, reimbursement is not made for this purpose.

The extraction of teeth to prepare the jaw for radiation treatments of neoplastic disease is also covered. This is an exception to the requirement that to be covered, a noncovered procedure or service performed by a dentist must be an incident to and an integral part of a covered procedure or service performed by the dentist. Ordinarily, the dentist extracts the patient's teeth, but another physician, e.g., a radiologist, administers the radiation treatments.

Whether such services as the administration of anesthesia, diagnostic x-rays, and other related procedures are covered depends upon whether the primary procedure being performed by the dentist is covered. Thus, an x-ray taken in connection with the reduction of a fracture of the jaw or facial bone is covered. However, a single x-ray or x-ray survey taken in connection with the care or treatment of teeth or the periodontium is not covered.

See also the Medicare Benefit Policy Manual, Chapter 1, "Inpatient Hospital Services," §70, and Chapter 15, "Covered Medical and Other Health Services," §150 for additional information on dental services

100-3, Chapter 1, Part 1, 10.2

Transcutaneous Electrical Nerve Stimulation (TENS) for Acute Post-Operative Pain

The use of transcutaneous electrical nerve stimulation (TENS) for the relief of acute post-operative pain is covered under Medicare. TENS may be covered whether used as an adjunct to the use of drugs, or as an alternative to drugs, in the treatment of acute pain resulting from surgery.

The TENS devices, whether durable or disposable, may be used in furnishing this service. When used for the purpose of treating acute post-operative pain, TENS devices are considered supplies. As such they may be hospital supplies furnished inpatients covered under Part A, or supplies incident to a physician's service when furnished in connection with surgery done on an outpatient basis, and covered under Part B.

It is expected that TENS, when used for acute post-operative pain, will be necessary for relatively short periods of time, usually 30 days or less. In cases when TENS is used for longer periods, contractors should attempt to ascertain whether TENS is no longer being used for acute pain but rather for chronic pain, in which case the TENS device may be covered as durable medical equipment as described in §160.27.

Cross-references:

 Medicare Benefit Policy Manual, Chapter 1, "Inpatient Hospital Services," §40;
Medicare Benefit Policy Manual, Chapter 2, "Hospital Services Covered Under Part B," §§20, 20.4, and 80; Medicare Benefit Policy Manual, Chapter 15, "Covered Medical and other Health Services, §110."

100-3, Chapter 1, Part 1, 20.21

Chelation Therapy for Treatment of Atherosclerosis

Chelation therapy is the application of chelation techniques for the therapeutic or preventive effects of removing unwanted metal ions from the body. The application of chelation therapy using ethylenediamine-tetra-acetic acid (EDTA) for the treatment and prevention of atherosclerosis is controversial. There is no widely accepted rationale to explain the beneficial effects attributed to this therapy. Its safety is questioned and its clinical effectiveness has never been established by well-designed, controlled clinical trials. It is not widely accepted and practiced by American physicians. EDTA chelation therapy for atherosclerosis is considered experimental. For these reasons, EDTA chelation therapy for the treatment or prevention of atherosclerosis is not covered. Some practitioners refer to this therapy as chemoendarterectomy and may also show a diagnosis other than atherosclerosis, such as arteriosclerosis or calcinosis. Claims employing such variant terms should also be denied under this section.

Cross-reference: §20.22

100-3, Chapter 1, Part 1, 20.22

Ethylenediamine-Tetra-Acetic (EDTA) Chelation Therapy for Treatment of Atherosclerosis

The use of EDTA as a chelating agent to treat atherosclerosis, arteriosclerosis, calcinosis, or similar generalized condition not listed by the FDA as an approved use is not covered. Any such use of EDTA is considered experimental. See §20.21 for an explanation of this conclusion.

100-3, Chapter 1, Part 1, 40.7

Outpatient Intravenous Insulin Treatment (Effective December 23, 2009)

A. General

The term outpatient intravenous (IV) insulin therapy (OIVIT) refers to an outpatient regimen that integrates pulsatile or continuous intravenous infusion of insulin via any means, guided by the results of measurement of:

- respiratory quotient; and/or
- urine urea nitrogen (UUN); and/or
- arterial, venous, or capillary glucose; and/or
- potassium concentration; and

performed in scheduled recurring periodic intermittent episodes.

This regimen is also sometimes termed Cellular Activation Therapy (CAT), Chronic Intermittent Intravenous Insulin Therapy (CIIT), Hepatic Activation Therapy (HAT), Intercellular Activation Therapy (iCAT), Metabolic Activation Therapy (MAT), Pulsatile Intravenous Insulin Treatment (PIVIT), Pulse Insulin Therapy (PIT), and Pulsatile Therapy (PT).

In OIVIT, insulin is intravenously administered in the outpatient setting for a variety of indications. Most commonly, it is delivered in pulses, but it may be delivered as a more conventional drip solution. The insulin administration is adjunctive to the patient's routine diabetic management regimen (oral agent or insulin-based) or other disease management regimen, typically performed on an intermittent basis (often weekly), and frequently performed chronically without duration limits. Glucose or other carbohydrate is available ad libitum (in accordance with patient desire).

B. Nationally Covered Indications

N/A

C. Nationally Non-Covered Indications

Effective for claims with dates of service on and after December 23, 2009, the Centers for Medicare and Medicaid Services (CMS) determines that the evidence does not support a conclusion that OIVIT improves health outcomes in Medicare beneficiaries. Therefore, CMS has determined that OIVIT is not reasonable and necessary for any indication under section 1862(a)(1)(A) of the Social Security Act. Services comprising an OIVIT regimen are nationally non-covered under Medicare when furnished pursuant to an OIVIT regimen (see subsection A. above).

D. Other

Individual components of OIVIT may have medical uses in conventional treatment regimens for diabetes and other conditions. Coverage for such other uses may be determined by other local or national Medicare determinations, and do not pertain to OIVIT. For example, see Pub. 100-03, NCD Manual, Section 40.2, Home Blood Glucose Monitors, Section 40.3,

Closed-loop Blood Glucose Control Devices (CBGCD), Section 190.20, Blood Glucose Testing, and Section 280.14, Infusion Pumps, as well as Pub. 100-04, Claims Processing Manual, Chapter 18, Section 90, Diabetics Screening.

100-3, Chapter 1, Part 1, 80.2

Photodynamic Therapy

Photodynamic therapy is a medical procedure which involves the infusion of a photosensitive (light-activated) drug with a very specific absorption peak. This drug is chemically designed to have a unique affinity for the diseased tissue intended for treatment. Once introduced to the body, the drug accumulates and is retained in diseased tissue to a greater degree than in normal tissue. Infusion is followed by the targeted irradiation of this tissue with a non-thermal laser, calibrated to emit light at a wavelength that corresponds to the drug's absorption peak. The drug then becomes active and locally treats the diseased tissue.

Ocular Photodynamic Therapy (OPT)

Ocular Photodynamic Therapy (OPT) is used in the treatment of ophthalmologic diseases. OPT is only covered when used in conjunction with verteporfin (see section 80.3, "Photosensitive Drugs").

- Classic Subfoveal Choroidal Neovascular (CNV) Lesions -OPT is covered with a diagnosis of neovascular age-related macular degeneration (AMD) with predominately classic subfoveal choroidal neovascular (CNV) lesions (where the area of classic CNV occupies ≥ 50 percent of the area of the entire lesion) at the initial visit as determined by a fluorescein angiogram. Subsequent follow-up visits will require either an optical coherence tomography (OCT) or a fluorescein angiogram (FA) to access treatment response. There are no requirements regarding visual acuity, lesion size, and number of re-treatments.
- Occult Subfoveal Choroidal Neovascular (CNV) Lesions -OPT is noncovered for patients with a diagnosis of age-related macular degeneration (AMD) with occult and no classic CNV lesions.

Other Conditions -Use of OPT with verteporfin for other types of AMD (e.g.,patients with minimally classic CNV lesions, atrophic, or dry AMD) is noncovered. OPT with verteporfin for other ocular indications such as pathologic myopia or presumed ocular histoplasmosis syndrome, is eligible for coverage through individual contractor discretion.

100-3, Chapter 1, Part 1, 80.2.1

A. General

Ocular Photodynamic Therapy (OPT) is used in the treatment of ophthalmologic diseases; specifically, for age-related macular degeneration (AMD), a common eye disease among the elderly. OPT involves the infusion of an intravenous photosensitizing drug called verteporfin followed by exposure to a laser. OPT is only covered when used in conjunction with verteporfin.

Effective July 1, 2001, OPT with verteporfin was approved for a diagnosis of neovascular AMD with predominately classic subfoveal choroidal neovascularization (CNV) lesions (where the area of classic CNV occupies ≥ 50% of the area of the entire lesion) at the initial visit as determined by a fluorescein angiogram (FA).

On October 17, 2001, the Centers for Medicare & Medicaid Services (CMS) announced its "intent to cover" OPT with verteporfin for AMD patients with occult and no classic subfoveal CNV as determined by an FA. The October 17, 2001, decision was never implemented.

On March 28, 2002, after thorough review and reconsideration of the October 17, 2001, intent to cover policy, CMS determined that the current non-coverage policy for OPT for verteporfin for AMD patients with occult and no classic subfoveal CNV as determined by an FA should remain in effect.

Effective August 20, 2002, CMS issued a non-covered instruction for OPT with verteporfin for AMD patients with occult and no classic subfoveal CNVas determined by an FA.

B. Nationally Covered Indications

Effective April 1, 2004, OPT with verteporfin continues to be approved for a diagnosis of neovascular AMD with predominately classic subfoveal CNV lesions (where the area of classic CNV occupies ≥ 50% of the area of the entire lesion) at the initial visit as determined by an FA. (CNV lesions are comprised of classic and/or occult components.) Subsequent follow-up visits require either an optical coherence tomography (OCT) (effective April 3. 2013) or an FA (effective April 1, 2004) to access treatment response. There are no requirements regarding visual acuity, lesion size, and number of re-treatments when treating predominantly classic lesions.

In addition, after thorough review and reconsideration of the August 20, 2002, non-coverage policy, CMS determines that the evidence is adequate to conclude that OPT with verteporfin is reasonable and necessary for treating:

1. Subfoveal occult with no classic CNV associated with AMD; and,
2. Subfoveal minimally classic CNV (where the area of classic CNV occupies <50% of the area of the entire lesion) associated with AMD.

The above 2 indications are considered reasonable and necessary only when:

1. The lesions are small (4 disk areas or less in size)at the time of initial treatment or within the 3 months prior to initial treatment; and,
2. The lesions have shown evidence of progression within the 3 months prior to initial treatment. Evidence of progression must be documented by deterioration of visual acuity (at least 5 letters on a standard eye examination chart), lesion growth (an increase in at least 1 disk area), or the appearance of blood associated with the lesion.

C. Nationally Non-Covered Indications

Other uses of OPT with verteporfin to treat AMD not already addressed by CMS will continue to be non-covered. These include, but are not limited to, the following AMD indications:

- Juxtafoveal or extrafoveal CNV lesions (lesions outside the fovea),
- Inability to obtain a fluorescein angiogram,
- Atrophic or "dry" AMD.

D. Other

The OPT with verteporfin for other ocular indications, such as pathologic myopia or presumed ocular histoplasmosis syndrome, continue to be eligible for local coverage determinations through individual contractor discretion.

100-3, Chapter 1, Part 1, 80.3

Photosensitive Drugs

Photosensitive drugs are the light-sensitive agents used in photodynamic therapy. Once introduced into the body, these drugs selectively identify and adhere to diseased tissue. The drugs remain inactive until they are exposed to a specific wavelength of light, by means of a laser, that corresponds to their absorption peak. The activation of a photosensitive drug results in a photochemical reaction which treats the diseased tissue without affecting surrounding normal tissue.

Verteporfin

Verteporfin, a benzoporphyrin derivative, is an intravenous lipophilic photosensitive drug with an absorption peak of 690 nm. This drug was first approved by the Food and Drug Administration (FDA) on April 12, 2000, and subsequently, approved for inclusion in the United States Pharmacopoeia on July 18, 2000, meeting Medicare's definition of a drug when used in conjunction with ocular photodynamic therapy (OPT) (see section 80.2, "Photodynamic Therapy") when furnished intravenously incident to a physician's service. For patients with age-related macular degeneration (AMD), Verteporfin is only covered with a diagnosis of neovascular age-related macular degeneration with predominately classic subfoveal choroidal neovascular (CNV) lesions (where the area of classic CNV occupies ≥ 50 percent of the area of the entire lesion) at the initial visit as determined by a fluorescein angiogram (FA). Subsequent follow-up visits will require either an optical coherence tomography (OCT) or an FA to access treatment response. OPT with verteporfin is covered for the above indication and will remain non-covered for all other indications related to AMD (see section 80.2). OPT with Verteporfin for use in non-AMD conditions is eligible for coverage through individual contractor discretion.

100-3, Chapter 1, Part 1, 80.3.1

Verteporfin -Effective April 3, 2013

A. General

Verteporfin, a benzoporphyrin derivative, is an intravenous lipophilic photosensitive drug with an absorption peak of 690 nm. Verteporfin was first approved by the Food and Drug Administration on April 12, 2000, and subsequently approved for inclusion in the United States Pharmacopoeia on July 18, 2000, meeting Medicare's definition of a drug as defined under §1861(t)(1) of the Social Security Act. Verteporfin is only covered when used in conjunction with ocular photodynamic therapy OPT) when furnished intravenously incident to a physician's service.

B. Nationally Covered Indications

Effective April 1, 2004, OPT with verteporfin is covered for patients with a diagnosis of neovascular age-related macular degeneration (AMD) with:

- Predominately classic subfoveal choroidal neovascularization (CNV) lesions (where the area of classic CNV occupies ≥ 50% of the area of the entire lesion) at the initial visit as determined by a fluorescein angiogram. (CNV lesions are comprised of classic and/or occult components.) Subsequent follow-up visits require either an optical coherence tomography (OCT) (effective April 3, 2013) or a fluorescein angiogram (FA) (effective April 1, 2004) to access treatment response.

  There are no requirements regarding visual acuity, lesion size,and number of retreatments when treating predominantly classic lesions.

- Subfoveal occult with no classic associated with AMD.
- Subfoveal minimally classic CNV CNV (where the area of classic CNV occupies <50% of the area of the entire lesion) associated with AMD.
- The above 2 indications are considered reasonable and necessary only when:

1. The lesions are small (4 disk areas or less in size) at the time of initial treatment or within the 3 months prior to initial treatment; and,
2. The lesions have shown evidence of progression within the 3 months prior to initial treatment. Evidence of progression must be documented by deterioration of visual acuity (at least 5 letters on a standard eye examination chart), lesion growth (an increase in at least 1 disk area), or the appearance of blood associated with the lesion.

C. Nationally Non-Covered Indications

Other uses of OPT with verteporfin to treat AMD not already addressed by the Centers for Medicare & Medicaid Services will continue to be non-covered. These include, but are not limited to, the following AMD indications: juxtafoveal or extrafoveal CNV lesions (lesions outside the fovea), inability to obtain an FA, or atrophic or "dry" AMD.

D. Other

The OPT with verteporfin for other ocular indications, such as pathologic myopia or presumed ocular histoplasmosis syndrome, continue to be eligible for local coverage determinations through individual contractor discretion.

100-3, Chapter 1, Part 2, 90.1

Pharmacogenomic Testing to Predict Warfarin Responsiveness (Effective August 3, 2009)

A. General

Warfarin sodium is an orally administered anticoagulant drug that is marketed most commonly as Coumadin®. (The Food and Drug Administration (FDA) approved labeling for Coumadin® includes a Black Box Warning dating back to 2007.) Anticoagulant drugs are sometimes referred to as blood thinners by the lay public. Warfarin affects the vitamin K-dependent clotting factors II, VII, IX, and X. Warfarin is thought to interfere with clotting factor synthesis by inhibition of the C1 subunit of the vitamin K epoxide reductase (VKORC1) enzyme complex, thereby reducing the regeneration of vitamin K1 epoxide. The elimination of warfarin is almost entirely by metabolic conversion to inactive metabolites by cytochrome P450 (CYP) enzymes in liver cells. CYP2C9 is the principal cytochrome P450 enzyme that modulates the anticoagulant activity of warfarin. From results of clinical studies, genetic variation in the CYP2C9 and/or VKORC1 genes can, in concert with clinical factors, predict how each individual responds to warfarin.

Pharmacogenomics denotes the study of how an individual's genetic makeup, or genotype, affects the body's response to drugs. Pharmacogenomics as a science examines associations among variations in genes with individual responses to a drug or medication. In application, pharmacogenomic results (i.e., information on the patient's genetic variations) can contribute to predicting a patient's response to a given drug: good, bad, or none at all. Pharmacogenomic testing of CYP2C9 or VKORC1 alleles to predict a patient's response to warfarin occurs ideally prior to initiation of the drug. This would be an once-in-a-lifetime test, absent any reason to believe that the patient's personal genetic characteristics would change over time. Although such pharmacogenomic testing would be used to attempt to better approximate the best starting dose of warfarin, it would not eliminate the need for periodic PT/INR testing, a standard diagnostic test for coagulation activity and for assessing how a patient is reacting to a warfarin dose.

Nationally Covered Indications

Effective August 3, 2009, the Centers for Medicare & Medicaid Services (CMS) believes that the available evidence supports that coverage with evidence development (CED) under §1862(a)(1)(E) of the Social Security Act (the Act) is appropriate for pharmacogenomic testing of CYP2C9 or VKORC1 alleles to predict warfarin responsiveness by any method, and is therefore covered only when provided to Medicare beneficiaries who are candidates for anticoagulation therapy with warfarin who:

1. Have not been previously tested for CYP2C9 or VKORC1 alleles; and

2. Have received fewer than five days of warfarin in the anticoagulation regimen for which the testing is ordered; and

3. Are enrolled in a prospective, randomized, controlled clinical study when that study meets the following standards.

A clinical study seeking Medicare payment for pharmacogenomic testing of CYP2C9 or VKORC1 alleles to predict warfarin responsiveness provided to the Medicare beneficiary who is a candidate for anticoagulation therapy with warfarin pursuant to CED must address one or more aspects of the following question:

Prospectively, in Medicare-aged subjects whose warfarin therapy management includes pharmacogenomic testing of CYP2C9 or VKORC1 alleles to predict warfarin response, what is the frequency and severity of the following outcomes, compared to subjects whose warfarin therapy management does not include pharmacogenomic testing?

- Major hemorrhage
- Minor hemorrhage
- Thromboembolism related to the primary indication for anticoagulation
- Other thromboembolic event
- Mortality

The study must adhere to the following standards of scientific integrity and relevance to the Medicare population:

a. The principal purpose of the research study is to test whether a particular intervention potentially improves the participants' health outcomes.

b. The research study is well-supported by available scientific and medical information or it is intended to clarify or establish the health outcomes of interventions already in common clinical use.

c. The research study does not unjustifiably duplicate existing studies.

d. The research study design is appropriate to answer the research question being asked in the study.

e. The research study is sponsored by an organization or individual capable of executing the proposed study successfully.

f. The research study is in compliance with all applicable Federal regulations concerning the protection of human subjects found in the Code of Federal Regulations (CFR) at 45 CFR Part 46. If a study is regulated by the FDA, it also must be in compliance with 21 CFR Parts 50 and 56.

g. All aspects of the research study are conducted according to the appropriate standards of scientific integrity.

h. The research study has a written protocol that clearly addresses, or incorporates by reference, the Medicare standards.

i. The clinical research study is not designed to exclusively test toxicity or disease pathophysiology in healthy individuals. Trials of all medical technologies measuring therapeutic outcomes as one of the objectives meet this standard only if the disease or condition being studied is life-threatening as defined in 21 CFR § 312.81(a) and the patient has no other viable treatment options.

j. The clinical research study is registered on the www. ClinicalTrials.gov website by the principal sponsor/ investigator prior to the enrollment of the first study subject.

k. The research study protocol specifies the method and timing of public release of all pre-specified outcomes to be measured including release of outcomes if outcomes are negative or study is terminated early. The results must be made public within 24 months of the end of data collection. If a report is planned to be published in a peer-reviewed journal, then that initial release may be an abstract that meets the requirements of the International Committee of Medical Journal Editors. However, a full report of the outcomes must be made public no later than 3 years after the end of data collection.

l. The research study protocol must explicitly discuss subpopulations affected by the treatment under investigation, particularly traditionally underrepresented groups in clinical studies, how the inclusion and exclusion criteria affect enrollment of these populations, and a plan for the retention and reporting of said populations on the trial. If the inclusion and exclusion criteria are expected to have a negative effect on the recruitment or retention of underrepresented populations, the protocol must discuss why these criteria are necessary.

m. The research study protocol explicitly discusses how the results are or are not expected to be generalizable to the Medicare population to infer whether Medicare patients may benefit from the intervention. Separate discussions in the protocol may be necessary for populations eligible for Medicare due to age, disability or Medicaid eligibility.

B. Nationally Non-Covered Indications

The CMS believes that the available evidence does not demonstrate that pharmacogenomic testing of CYP2C9 or VKORC1 alleles to predict warfarin responsiveness improves health outcomes in Medicare beneficiaries outside the context of CED, and is therefore not reasonable and necessary under §1862(a)(1)(A) of the Act.

C.Other

This NCD does not determine coverage to identify CYP2C9 or VKORC1 alleles for other purposes, nor does it determine national coverage to identify other alleles to predict warfarin responsiveness.

100-3, Chapter 1, Part 2, 110.22

Autologous Cellular Immunotherapy Treatment (Effective June 30, 2011)

A. General

Prostate cancer is the most common non-cutaneous cancer in men in the United States. In 2009, an estimated 192,280 new cases of prostate cancer were diagnosed and an estimated 27,360 deaths were reported. The National Cancer Institute states that prostate cancer is predominantly a cancer of older men; the median age at diagnosis is 72 years. Once the patient has castration-resistant, metastatic prostate cancer the median survival is generally less than two years.

In 2010 the Food and Drug Administration (FDA) approved sipuleucel-T (PROVENGE®; APC8015), for patients with castration-resistant, metastatic prostate cancer. The posited mechanism of action, immunotherapy, is different from that of anti-cancer chemotherapy such as docetaxel. This is the first immunotherapy for prostate cancer to receive FDA approval.

The goal of immunotherapy is to stimulate the body's natural defenses (such as the white blood cells called dendritic cells, T-lymphocytes and mononuclear cells) in a specific manner so that they attack and destroy, or at least prevent, the proliferation of cancer cells. Specificity is attained by intentionally exposing a patient's white blood cells to a particular protein (called an antigen) associated with the prostate cancer. This exposure "trains" the white blood cells to target and attack the prostate cancer cells. Clinically, this is expected to result in a decrease in the size and/or number of cancer sites, an increase in the time to cancer progression, and/or an increase in survival of the patient.

Sipuleucel-T differs from other infused anti-cancer therapies. Most such anti-cancer therapies are manufactured and sold by a biopharmaceutical company and then purchased by and dispensed from a pharmacy. In contrast, once the decision is made to treat with sipuleucel-T, a multi-step process is used to produce sipuleucel-T. Sipuleucel-T is made individually for each patient with his own white blood cells. The patient's white blood cells are removed via a procedure called leukapheresis. In a laboratory the white blood cells are exposed to PA2024, which is a molecule created by linking prostatic acid phosphatase (PAP) with granulocyte/macrophage-colony stimulating factor (GM-CSF). PAP is an antigen specifically associated with prostate cancer cells; GM-CSF is a protein that targets a receptor on the surface of white blood cells. Hence, PAP serves to externally manipulate the immunological functioning of the patient's white blood cells while GM-CSF serves to stimulate the white blood cells into action. As noted in the FDA's clinical review, each dose of sipuleucel-T contains a minimum of 40 million treated white blood cells, however there is "high inherent variability" in the yield of sipuleucel-T from leukapheresis to leukapheresis in the same patient as well as from patient to patient. The treated white blood cells are then infused back into the same patient. The FDA-approved dosing regimen is three doses with each dose administered two weeks apart.

Indications and Limitations of Coverage

B. Nationally Covered Indications

Effective for services performed on or after June 30, 2011, The Centers for Medicare and Medicaid Services (CMS) proposes that the evidence is adequate to conclude that the use of autologous cellular immunotherapy treatment -sipuleucel-T; PROVENGE® improves health outcomes for Medicare beneficiaries with asymptomatic or minimally symptomatic metastatic castrate-resistant (hormone refractory) prostate cancer, and thus is reasonable and necessary for this on-label indication under 1862(a)(1)(A) of the Social Security Act.

C. Nationally Non-Covered Indications

N/A

D. Other

Effective for services performed on or after June 30, 2011, coverage of all off-label uses of autologous cellular immunotherapy treatment –sipuleucel-T; PROVENGE® for the treatment of pro state cancer is left to the discretion of the local Medicare Administrative Contractors.

(NCD last reviewed June 2011.)

100-3, Chapter 1, Part 2, 150.11

Thermal Intradiscal Procedures (TIPs) (Effective September 29, 2008)

A. General

Percutaneous thermal intradiscal procedures (TIPs) involve the insertion of a catheter(s)/probe(s) in the spinal disc under fluoroscopic guidance for the purpose of producing or applying heat and/or disruption within the disc to relieve low back pain.

The scope of this national coverage determination on TIPs includes percutaneous intradiscal techniques that employ the use of a radiofrequency energy source or electrothermal energy to apply or create heat and/or disruption within the disc for coagulation and/or decompression of disc material to treat symptomatic patients with annular disruption of a contained herniated disc, to seal annular tears or fissures, or destroy nociceptors for the purpose of relieving pain. This includes techniques that use single or multiple probe(s)/catheter(s), which utilize a resistance coil or other delivery system technology, are flexible or rigid, and are placed within the nucleus, the nuclear-annular junction, or the annulus.

Although not intended to be an all inclusive list, TIPs are commonly identified as intradiscal electrothermal therapy (IDET), intradiscal thermal annuloplasty (IDTA), percutaneous intradiscal radiofrequency thermocoagulation (PIRFT), radiofrequency annuloplasty (RA), intradiscal biacuplasty (IDB), percutaneous (or plasma) disc decompression (PDD) or coblation, or targeted disc decompression (TDD). At times, TIPs are identified or labeled based on the name of the catheter/probe that is used (e.g., SpineCath, discTRODE, SpineWand, Accutherm, or TransDiscal electrodes). Each technique or device has it own protocol for application of the therapy. Percutaneous disc decompression or nucleoplasty procedures that do not utilize a radiofrequency energy procedure) are not within the scope of this NCD.

B. Nationally Covered Indications

N/A

C. Nationally Non-Covered Indications

Effective for services performed on or after September 29, 2008, the Centers for Medicare and Medicaid Services has determined that TIPs are not reasonable and necessary for the treatment of low back pain. Therefore, TIPs, which include procedures that employ the use of a radiofrequency energy source or electrothermal energy to apply or create heat and/or disruption within the disc for the treatment of low back pain, are noncovered.

D. Other

N/A

(This NCD last reviewed September 2008.)

100-3, Chapter 1, Part 2, 150.12

Collagen Meniscus Implant (Effective May 25, 2010)

A. General

The knee menisci are wedge-shaped, semi-lunar discs of fibrous tissue located in the knee joint between the ends of the femur and the tibia and fibula. There is a lateral and medial meniscus in each knee. It is known now that the menisci provide mechanical support, localized pressure distribution, and lubrication of the knee joint. Initially, meniscal tears were treated with total meniscectomy; however, as knowledge of the function of the menisci and the potential long term effects of total meniscectomy on the knee joint evolved, treatment of symptomatic meniscal tears gravitated to repair of the tear, when possible, or partial meniscectomy.

The collagen meniscus implant (also referred to as collagen scaffold (CS), CMI or Menaflex ™ meniscus implant throughout the published literature) is used to fill meniscal defects that result from partial meniscectomy. The collagenmeniscus implant is not intended to replace the entire meniscus at it requires a meniscal rim for attachment. The literature describes the placement of the collagen meniscus implant through an arthroscopic procedure with an additional incision for capture of the repair needles and tying of the sutures. After debridement of the damaged meniscus, the implant is trimmed to the size of meniscal defect and sutured into place. The collagen meniscus implant is described as a tissue engineered scaffold to support the generation of new meniscus-like tissue. The collagen meniscus implant is manufactured from bovine collagen and should not be confused with the meniscus transplant which involves the replacement of the meniscus with a transplant meniscus from a cadaver donor. The meniscus transplant is not addressed under this national coverage determination.

B. Nationally Covered Indications

N/A

C. Nationally Non-Covered Indications

Effective for claims with dates of service performed on or after May 25, 2010, the Centers for Medicare & Medicaid Services has determined that the evidence is adequate to conclude that the collagen meniscus implant does not improve health outcomes and, therefore, is not reasonable and necessary for the treatment of meniscal injury/tear under section 1862(a)(1)(A) of the Social Security Act. Thus, the collagen meniscus implant is non-covered by Medicare.

D. Other

N/A

(This NCD last reviewed May 2010.)

100-3, Chapter 1, Part 2, 160.13

Supplies Used in the Delivery of Transcutaneous Electrical Nerve Stimulation (TENS) and Neuromuscular Electrical Stimulation (NMES)

Transcutaneous Electrical Nerve Stimulation (TENS) and/or Neuromuscular Electrical Stimulation (NMES) can ordinarily be delivered to patients through the use of conventional electrodes, adhesive tapes and lead wires. There may be times, however, where it might be medically necessary for certain patients receiving TENS or NMES treatment to use, as an alternative to conventional electrodes, adhesive tapes and lead wires, a form-fitting conductive garment (i.e., a garment with conductive fibers which are separated from the patients' skin by layers of fabric).

A form-fitting conductive garment (and medically necessary related supplies) may be covered under the program only when:

1. It has received permission or approval for marketing by the Food and Drug Administration;
2. It has been prescribed by a physician for use in delivering covered TENS or NMES treatment; and
3. One of the medical indications outlined below is met:
   - The patient cannot manage without the conductive garment because there is such a large area or so many sites to be stimulated and the stimulation would have to be delivered so frequently that it is not feasible to use conventional electrodes, adhesive tapes and lead wires;
   - The patient cannot manage without the conductive garment for the treatment of chronic intractable pain because the areas or sites to be stimulated are inaccessible with the use of conventional electrodes, adhesive tapes and lead wires;
   - The patient has a documented medical condition such as skin problems that preclude the application of conventional electrodes, adhesive tapes and lead wires;
   - The patient requires electrical stimulation beneath a cast either to treat disuse atrophy, where the nerve supply to the muscle is intact, or to treat chronic intractable pain; or
   - The patient has a medical need for rehabilitation strengthening (pursuant to a written plan of rehabilitation) following an injury where the nerve supply to the muscle is intact.

A conductive garment is not covered for use with a TENS device during the trial period specified in §160.3 unless:

4. The patient has a documented skin problem prior to the start of the trial period; and
5. The A/B MAC (B)'s medical consultants are satisfied that use of such an item is medically necessary for the patient.

(See conditions for coverage of the use of TENS in the diagnosis and treatment of chronic intractable pain in §§160.3, 160.13, and 160.27, and the use of NMES in the treatment of disuse atrophy in §150.4.)

100-3, Chapter 1, Part 2, 160.27

Transcutaneous Electrical Nerve Stimulation (TENS) for Chronic Low Back Pain (CLBP)

The TENS is a type of electrical nerve stimulator that is employed to treat chronic intractable pain. This stimulator is attached to the surface of the patient's skin over the peripheral nerve to be stimulated. It may be applied in a variety of settings (in the patient's home, a physician's office, or in an outpatient clinic). Payment for TENS may be made under the durable medical equipment benefit.

A. General

For the purposes of this decision chronic low back pain (CLBP) is defined as:

1. an episode of low back pain that has persisted for three months or longer; and
2. is not a manifestation of a clearly defined and generally recognizable primary disease entity. For example, there are cancers that, through metastatic spread to the spine or pelvis, may elicit pain in the lower back as a symptom;

and certain systemic diseases such as rheumatoid arthritis and multiple sclerosis manifest many debilitating symptoms of which low back pain is not the primary focus.

B. Nationally Covered Indications

Effective June 8, 2012, the Centers for Medicare & Medicaid Services (CMS) will allow coverage for Transcutaneous Electrical Nerve Stimulation (TENS) for CLBP only when all of the following conditions are met.

In order to support additional research on the use of TENS for CLBP, we will cover this item under section 1862(a)(1)(E) of the Social Security Act (the Act) subject to all of the following conditions:

1. Coverage under this section expires three years after the publication of this decision on the CMS website.

2. The beneficiary is enrolled in an approved clinical study meeting all of the requirements below. The study must address one or more aspects of the following questions in a randomized, controlled design using validated and reliable instruments. This can include randomized crossover designs when the impact of prior TENS use is appropriately accounted for in the study protocol.

    i. Does the use of TENS provide clinically meaningful reduction in pain in Medicare beneficiaries with CLBP?

    ii. Does the use of TENS provide a clinically meaningful improvement of function in Medicare beneficiaries with CLBP?

    iii. Does the use of TENS impact the utilization of other medical treatments or services used in the medical management of CLBP?

These studies must be designed so that the patients inthe control and comparison groups receive the same concurrent treatments and either sham (placebo) TENS or active TENS intervention.

The study must adhere to the following standards of scientific integrity and relevance to the Medicare population:

a. The principal purpose of the research study is to test whether a particular intervention potentially improves the participants' health outcomes.

b. The research study is well supported by available scientific and medical information or it is intended to clarify or establish the health outcomes of interventions already in common clinical use.

c. The research study does not unjustifiably duplicate existing studies.

d. The research study design is appropriate to answer the research question being asked in the study.

e. The research study is sponsored by an organization or individual capable of executing the proposed study successfully.

f. The research study is in compliance with all applicable Federal regulations concerning the protection of human subjects found at 45 CFR Part 46. If a study is regulated by the Food and Drug Administration (FDA), it must be in compliance with 21 CFR parts 50 and 56.

g. All aspects of the research study are conducted according to appropriate standards of scientific integrity (see http://www.icmje.org).

h. The research study has a written protocol that clearly addresses, or incorporates by reference, the standards listed here as Medicare requirements for CED coverage.

i. The clinical research study is not designed to exclusively test toxicity or disease pathophysiology in healthy individuals. Trials of all medical technologies measuring therapeutic outcomes as one of the objectives meet this standard only if the disease or condition being studied is life threatening as defined in 21 CFR §312.81(a) and the patient has no other viable treatment options.

j. The clinical research study is registered on the ClinicalTrials.gov website by the principal sponsor/investigator prior to the enrollment of the first study subject.

k. The research study protocol specifies the method and timing of public release of all prespecified outcomes to be measured including release of outcomes if outcomes are negative or study is terminated early. The results must be made public within 24 months of the end of data collection. If a report is planned to be published in a peer reviewed journal, then that initial release may be an abstract that meets the requirements of the International Committee of Medical Journal Editors (http://www.icmje.org).

l. The research study protocol must explicitly discuss subpopulations affected by the treatment under investigation, particularly traditionally underrepresented groups in clinical studies, how the inclusion and exclusion criteria effect enrollment of these populations, and a plan for the retention and reporting of said populations on the trial. If the inclusion and exclusion criteria are expected to have a negative effect on the recruitment or retention of underrepresented populations, the protocol must discuss why these criteria are necessary.

m. The research study protocol explicitly discusses how the results are or are not expected to be generalizable to the Medicare population to infer whether Medicare patients may benefit from the intervention. Separate discussions in the protocol may be necessary for populations eligible for Medicare due to age, disability or Medicaid eligibility.

C. Nationally Non-Covered Indications

TENS is not reasonable and necessary for the treatment of CLBP under section 1862(a)(1)(A) of the Act.

D. Other

See§160.13 for an explanation of coverage of medically necessary supplies for the effective use of TENS. See §160.7.1 for an explanation of coverage for assessing patients suitability for electrical nerve stimulation therapy. See §10.2 for an explanation of coverage of transcutaneous electrical nerve stimulation (TENS) for acute post-operative pain. Please note, §280.13 Transcutaneous Electrical Nerve Stimulators (TENS) NCD has been removed from the NCD manual and incorporated into NCD 160.27

(This NCD last reviewed June 2012.)

100-3, Chapter 1, Part 2, 160.7.1

Assessing Patients Suitability for Electrical Nerve Stimulation Therapy

Electrical nerve stimulation is an accepted modality for assessing a patient's suitability for ongoing treatment with a transcutaneous or an implanted nerve stimulator.

Accordingly, program payment may be made for the following techniques when used to determine the potential therapeutic usefulness of an electrical nerve stimulator:

A. Transcutaneous Electrical Nerve Stimulation (TENS)

This technique involves attachment of a transcutaneous nerve stimulator to the surface of the skin over the peripheral nerve to be stimulated. It is used by the patient on a trial basis and its effectiveness in modulating pain is monitored by the physician, or physical therapist. Generally, the physician or physical therapist is able to determine whether the patient is likely to derive a significant therapeutic benefit from continuous use of a transcutaneous stimulator within a trial period of one month; in a few cases this determination may take longer to make. Document the medical necessity for such services which are furnished beyond the first month.(See §160.13 for an explanation of coverage of medically necessary supplies for the effective use of TENS.)

If TENS significantly alleviates pain, it may be considered as primary treatment; if it produces no relief or greater discomfort than the original pain electrical nerve stimulation therapy is ruled out. However, where TENS produces incomplete relief, further evaluation with percutaneous electrical nerve stimulation may be considered to determine whether an implanted peripheral nerve stimulator would provide significant relief from pain.

Usually, the physician or physical therapist providing the services will furnish the equipment necessary for assessment. Where the physician or physical therapist advises the patient to rent the TENS from a supplier during the trial period rather than supplying it himself/herself, program payment may be made for rental of the TENS as well as for the services of the physician or physical therapist who is evaluating its use. However, the combined program payment which is made for the physician's or physical therapist's services and the rental of the stimulator from a supplier should not exceed the amount which would be payable for the total service, including the stimulator, furnished by the physician or physical therapist alone.

B. Percutaneous Electrical Nerve Stimulation (PENS)

This diagnostic procedure which involves stimulation of peripheral nerves by a needle electrode inserted through the skin is performed only in a physician's office, clinic, or hospital outpatient department. Therefore, it is covered only when performed by a physician or incident to physician's service. If pain is effectively controlled by percutaneous stimulation, implantation of electrodes is warranted.

As in the case of TENS (described in subsection A), generally the physician should be able to determine whether the patient is likely to derive a significant therapeutic benefit from continuing use of an implanted nerve stimulator within a trial period of 1 month. In a few cases, this determination may take longer to make. The medical necessity for such diagnostic services which are furnished beyond the first month must be documented.

NOTE: Electrical nerve stimulators do not prevent pain but only alleviate pain as it occurs. A patient can be taught how to employ the stimulator, and once this is done, can use it safely and effectively without direct physician supervision. Consequently, it is inappropriate for a patient to visit his/her physician, physical therapist, or an outpatient clinic on a continuing basis for treatment of pain with electrical nerve stimulation. Once it is determined that electrical nerve stimulation should be continued as therapy and the patient has been trained to use the stimulator, it is expected that a stimulator will be implanted or the patient will employ the TENS on a continual basis in his/her home. Electrical nerve stimulation treatments furnished by a physician in his/her office, by a physical therapist or outpatient clinic are excluded from coverage by §1862(a)(1) of the Act. (See §160.7 for an explanation of coverage of the therapeutic use of implanted peripheral nerve stimulators under the prosthetic devices benefit.) See §160.27 for an explanation of coverage of the therapeutic use of TENS under the durable medical equipment benefit.

100-3, Chapter 1, Part 3, 190.11

Home Prothrombin Time/International Normalized Ratio (PT/INR) Monitoring for Anticoagulation Management –Effective March 19, 2008

A. General

Use of the International Normalized Ratio (INR) or prothrombin time (PT) -standard measurement for reporting the blood's clotting time) -allows physicians to determine the level of anticoagulation in a patient independent of the laboratory reagents used. The INR is the ratio of the patient's PT (extrinsic or tissue-factor dependent coagulation pathway) compared to the mean PT for a group of normal individuals. Maintaining patients within his/her prescribed therapeutic range minimizes adverse events associated with inadequate or excessive anticoagulation such as serious bleeding or thromboembolic events. Patient self-testing and self-management through the use of a home INR monitor may be used to improve the time in therapeutic rate (TTR) for select groups of patients. increased TTR leads to improved clinical outcomes and reductions in thromboembolic and hemorrhagic events.

Warfarin (also prescribed under other trade names, e.g., Coumadin®) is a self-administered, oral anticoagulant (blood thinner) medication that affects the vitamin K-dependent clotting factors II, VII, IX and X. It is widely used for various medical conditions, and has a narrow therapeutic index, meaning it is a drug with less than a 2-fold difference between median lethal dose and median effective dose. For this reason, since October 4, 2006, it falls under the category of a Food and Drug Administration (FDA) "black-box" drug whose dosage must be closely monitored to avoid serious complications. A PT/INR monitoring system is a portable testing device that includes a finger-stick and an FDA-cleared meter that measures the time it takes for a person's blood plasma to clot

B. Nationally Covered Indications

For services furnished on or after March 19, 2008, Medicare will cover the use of home PT/INR monitoring for chronic, oral anticoagulation management for patients with mechanical heart valves, chronic atrial fibrillation, or venous thromboembolism (inclusive of deep venous thrombosis and pulmonary embolism) on warfarin. The monitor and the home testing must be prescribed by a treating physician as provided at 42 CFR 410.32(a), and all of the following requirements must be met:

1. The patient must have been anticoagulated for at least 3 months prior to use of the home INR device; and,
2. The patient must undergo a face-to-face educational program on anticoagulation management and must have demonstrated the correct use of the device prior to its use in the home; and,
3. The patient continues to correctly use the device in the context of the management of the anticoagulation therapy following the initiation of home monitoring; and,
4. Self-testing with the device should not occur more frequently than once a week.

C. Nationally Non-Covered Indications

N/A

D. Other

1. All other indications for home PT/INR monitoring not indicated as nationally covered above remain at local Medicare contractor discretion.

2. This national coverage determination (NCD) is distinct from, and makes no changes to, the PT clinical laboratory NCD at section 190.17 of Publication 100-03 of the NCD Manual.

(This NCD last reviewed March 2008.)

100-3, Chapter 1, Part 3, 190.14

Human Immunodeficiency Virus (HIV) Testing (Diagnosis)

Diagnosis of HIV infection is primarily made through the use of serologic assays. These assays take one of two forms: antibody detection assays and specific HIV antigen (p24) procedures. The antibody assays are usually enzyme immunoassays (EIA), which are used to confirm exposure of an individual's immune system to specific viral antigens. These assays may be formatted to detect HIV-1, HIV-2, or HIV-1 and 2 simultaneously, and to detect both IgM and IgG. When the initial EIA test is repeatedly positive or indeterminant, an alternative test is used to confirm the specificity of the antibodies to individual viral components. The most commonly used method is the Western Blot.

The HIV-1 core antigen (p24) test detects circulating viral antigen which may be found prior to the development of antibodies and may also be present in later stages of illness in the form of recurrent or persistent antigenemia. Its prognostic utility in HIV infection has been diminished as a result of development of sensitive viral RNA assays, and its primary use today is as a routine screening tool in potential blood donors.

In several unique situations, serologic testing alone may not reliably establish an HIV infection. This may occur because the antibody response (particularly the IgG response detected by Western Blot) has not yet developed (that is, acute retroviral syndrome) or is persistently equivocal because of inherent viral antigen variability. It is also an issue in perinatal HIV infection due to transplacental passage of maternal HIV antibody. In these situations, laboratory evidence of HIV in blood by culture, antigen assays, or proviral DNA or viral RNA assays, is required to establish a definitive determination of HIV infection.

Indications

Diagnostic testing to establish HIV infection may be indicated when there is a strong clinical suspicion supported by one or more of the following clinical findings:

1. The patient has a documented, otherwise unexplained, AIDS-defining or AIDS-associated opportunistic infection.

2. The patient has another documented sexually transmitted disease, which identifies significant risk of exposure to HIV and the potential for an early or subclinical infection.

3. The patient has documented acute or chronic hepatitis B or C infection that identifies a significant risk of exposure to HIV and the potential for an early or subclinical infection.

4. The patient has a documented AIDS-defining or AIDS-associated neoplasm.

5. The patient has a documented AIDS-associated neurologic disorder or otherwise unexplained dementia.

6. The patient has another documented AIDS-defining clinical condition, or a history of other severe, recurrent, or persistent conditions which suggest an underlying immune deficiency (for example, cutaneous or mucosal disorders).

7. The patient has otherwise unexplained generalized signs and symptoms suggestive of a chronic process with an underlying immune deficiency (for example, fever, weight loss, malaise, fatigue, chronic diarrhea, failure to thrive, chronic cough,hemoptysis, shortness of breath, or lymphadenopathy).

8. The patient has otherwise unexplained laboratory evidence of a chronic disease process with an underlying immune deficiency (for example, anemia, leukopenia, pancytopenia, lymphopenia,or low CD4+ lymphocyte count).

9. The patient has signs and symptoms of acute retroviral syndrome with fever, malaise, lymphadenopathy, and skin rash.

10. The patient has documented exposure to blood or body fluids known to be capable of transmitting HIV (for example, needle sticks and other significant blood exposures) and antiviral therapy is initiated or anticipated to be initiated.

11. The patient is undergoing treatment for rape. (HIV testing is part of the rape treatment protocol.)

Limitations

1. 1.HIV antibody testing in the United States is usually performed using HIV-1 or HIV-1/2 combination tests. HIV-2 testing is indicated if clinical circumstances suggest HIV-2 is likely (that is, compatible clinical finding and HIV-1 test negative). HIV-2 testing may also be indicated in areas of the country where there is greater prevalence of HIV-2 infections.

2. The Western Blot test should be performed only after documentation that the initial EIA tests are repeatedly positive or equivocal on a single sample.

3. The HIV antigen tests currently have no defined diagnostic usage.

4. Direct viral RNA detection may be performed in those situations where serologic testing does not establish a diagnosis but strong clinical suspicion persists (for example, acute retroviral syndrome, nonspecific serologic evidence of HIV, or perinatal HIV infection).

5. If initial serologic tests confirm an HIV infection, repeat testing is not indicated.

6. If initial serologic tests are HIV EIA negative and there is no indication for confirmation of infection by viral RNA detection, the interval prior to retesting is 3-6 months.

7. Testing for evidence of HIV infection using serologic methods may be medically appropriate in situations where there is a risk of exposure to HIV.

8. The CPT® Editorial Panel has issued a number of codes for infectious agent detection by direct antigen or nucleic acid probe techniques that have not yet been developed or are only being used on an investigational basis. Laboratory providers are advised to remain current on FDA-approved status for these tests.

100-3, Chapter 1, Part 4, 210.3

Colorectal Cancer Screening Tests

A. General

Sections 1861(s)(2)(R) and 1861(pp) of the Social Security Act (the Act) and regulations at 42 CFR 410.37 authorize Medicare coverage for screening colorectal cancer tests under Medicare Part B. The statute and regulations authorize the Secretary to add other tests and procedures (and modifications to tests and procedures for colorectal cancer screening) as the Secretary finds appropriate based on consultation with appropriate experts and organizations.

B. Nationally Covered Indications

1. Fecal Occult Blood Tests (FOBT) (effective January 1, 2004)

Fecal occult blood tests (FOBTs) are generally divided into two types: immunoassay and guaiac types. Immunoassay (or immunochemical) fecal occult blood tests (iFOBT) use "antibodies directed against human globin epitopes. While most iFOBTs use spatulas to collect stool samples, some use a brush to collect toilet water surrounding the stool. Most iFOBTs require laboratory processing.

Guaiac fecal occult blood tests (gFOBT) use a peroxidase reaction to indicate presence of the heme portion of hemoglobin. Guaiac turns blue after oxidation by oxidants or peroxidases in the presence of an oxygen donor such as hydrogen peroxide. Most FOBTs use sticks to collect stool samples and may be developed in a physician's office or a laboratory. In 1998, Medicare began reimbursement for guaiac FOBTs, but not immunoassay type tests for colorectal cancer screening. Since the undamental process is similar for other iFOBTs, the Centers for Medicare & Medicaid Services evaluated colorectal cancer screening using immunoassay FOBTs in general.

Effective for dates of service on and after January 1, 2004, Medicare covers one screening FOBT per annum for the early detection of colorectal cancer. This means that Medicare will cover one guaiac-based (gFOBT) or one immunoassay-based (iFOBT) at a frequency of every 12 months; i.e., at least 11 months have passed following the month in which the last covered screening FOBT was performed, for beneficiaries aged 50 years and older. The beneficiary completes the existing gFOBT by taking samples from two different sites of three consecutive stools; the beneficiary completes the iFOBT by taking the appropriate number of stool samples according to the specific manufacturer's instructions. This screening requires a written order from the beneficiary's attending physician. ("Attending physician" means a doctor of medicine or osteopathy (as defined in §1861(r)(1) of the Act) who is fully knowledgeable about the beneficiary's medical condition, and who would be responsible for using the results of any examination performed in the overall management of the beneficiary's specific medical problem.)

2. The CologuardTM - Multitarget Stool DNA (sDNA) Test (effective October 9, 2014)

Screening stool or fecal DNA (deoxyribonucleic acid, sDNA) testing detects molecular markers of altered DNA that are contained in the cells shed by colorectal cancer and pre-malignant colorectal epithelial neoplasia into the lumen of the large bowel. Through the use of selective enrichment and amplification techniques, sDNA tests are designed to detect very small amounts of DNA markers to identify colorectal cancer or pre-malignant colorectal neoplasia. The CologuardTM - multitarget sDNA test is a proprietary in vitro diagnostic device that incorporates both sDNA and fecal immunochemical test techniques and is designed to analyze patients' stool samples for markers associated with the presence of colorectal cancer and pre-malignant colorectal neoplasia.

Effective for dates of service on or after October 9, 2014, The CologuardTM test is covered once every three years for Medicare beneficiaries that meet all of the following criteria:

- Age 50 to 85 years, and,
- Asymptomatic (no signs or symptoms of colorectal disease including but not limited to lower gastrointestinal pain, blood in stool, positive guaiac fecal occult blood test (gFOBT) or fecal immunochemical test (iFOBT)), and,
- At average risk of developing colorectal cancer (no personal history of adenomatous polyps, colorectal cancer, or inflammatory bowel disease, including Crohn's Disease and ulcerative colitis; no family history of colorectal cancers or adenomatous polyps, familial adenomatous polyposis, or hereditary nonpolyposis colorectal cancer).

C. Nationally Non-Covered Indications

All other indications for colorectal cancer screening not otherwise specified in the Act and regulations, or otherwise specified above remain nationally non-covered. Noncoverage specifically includes:

1. All screening sDNA tests, effective April 28, 2008, through October 8, 2014. Effective for dates of service on or after October 9, 2014, all other screening sDNA tests not otherwise specified above remain nationally non-covered.

2. Screening computed tomographic colonography (CTC), effective May 12, 2009.

D. Other

N/A

(This NCD last reviewed October 2014.)

100-3, Chapter 1, Part 4, 210.4

210.4 - Smoking and Tobacco-Use Cessation Counseling

(Rev.202, Issued: 08- 25-17, Effective: 09-26-17, Implementation: 09- 26-17)Effective September 30, 2015 this section is deleted and the remaining NCD entitled Counseling to Prevent Tobacco Use (210.4.1) remains effective.

100-3, Chapter-1, Part-4, 210.7

Screening for the Human Immunodeficiency Virus (HIV)

A. General

Infection with the human immunodeficiency virus (HIV) is a continuing, worldwide pandemic described by the World Health Organization as "the most serious infectious disease challenge to global public health". Acquired immunodeficiency syndrome (AIDS) is diagnosed when a HIV-infected person's immune system becomes severely compromised and/or a person becomes ill with a HIV-related opportunistic infection. Without treatment, AIDS usually develops within 8-10 years after a person's initial HIV infection. While there is presently no cure for HIV, an infected individual can be recognized by screening, and subsequent access to skilled care plus vigilant monitoring and adherence to continuous antiretroviral therapy may delay the onset of AIDS and increase quality of life for many years.

Significantly, more than half of new HIV infections are estimated to be sexually transmitted from infected individuals who are unaware of their HIV status. Consequently, improved secondary disease prevention and wider availability of screening linked to HIV care and treatment would not only delay disease progression and complications in untested or unaware older individuals, but could also decrease the spread of disease to those living with or partnered with HIV-infected individuals.

HIV antibody testing first became available in 1985. These commonly used, Food and Drug Administration (FDA)-approved HIV antibody screening tests –using serum or plasma from a venipuncture or blood draw –are known as EIA (enzyme immunoassay) or ELISA (enzyme-linked immunosorbent assay) tests.

Developed for point-of-care testing using alternative samples, six rapid HIV-1 and/or HIV-2 antibody tests –using fluid obtained from the oral cavity or using whole blood, serum, or plasma from a blood draw or fingerstick –were approved by the FDA from 2002-2006.

Effective January 1, 2009, the Centers for Medicare & Medicaid Services (CMS) is allowed to add coverage of "additional preventive services" through the national coverage determination (NCD) process if certain statutory requirements are met, as provided under section 101(a) of the Medicare Improvements for Patients and Providers Act. One of those requirements is that the service(s) be categorized as a grade A (strongly recommends) or grade B (recommends) rating by the US Preventive Services Task Force (USPSTF). The USPSTF strongly recommends screening for all adolescents and adults at risk for HIV infection, as well as all pregnant women.

B. Nationally Covered Indications

Effective for claims with dates of service on and after December 8, 2009, CMS determines that the evidence is adequate to conclude that screening for HIV infection is reasonable and necessary for early detection of HIV and is appropriate for individuals entitled to benefits under Part A or enrolled under Part B. Therefore, CMS proposes to cover both standard and FDA-approved HIV rapid screening tests for:

1. A maximum of one, annual voluntary HIV screening of Medicare beneficiaries at increased risk for HIV infection per USPSTF guidelines as follows:

   - Men who have had sex with men after 1975

   - Men and women having unprotected sex with multiple [more than one] partners

   - Past or present injection drug users

   - Men and women who exchange sex for money or drugs, or have sex partners who do

   - Individuals whose past or present sex partners were HIV-infected, bisexual or injection drug users

   - Persons being treated for sexually transmitted diseases

   - Persons with a history of blood transfusion between 1978 and 1985

   - Persons who request an HIV test despite reporting no individual risk factors, since this group is likely to include individuals not willing to disclose high-risk behaviors; and,

2. A maximum of three, voluntary HIV screenings of pregnant Medicare beneficiaries: (1) when the diagnosis of pregnancy is known, (2) during the third trimester, and (3) at labor, if ordered by the woman's clinician.

C. Nationally Non-Covered Indications

Effective for claims with dates of service on and after December 8, 2009, Medicare beneficiaries with any known diagnosis of a HIV-related illness are not eligible for this screening test.

Medicare beneficiaries (other than those who are pregnant) who have had a prior HIV screening test within one year are not eligible (11 full months must have elapsed following the month in which the previous test was performed in order for the subsequent test to be covered).

Pregnant Medicare beneficiaries who have had three screening tests within their respective term of pregnancy are not eligible (beginning with the date of the first test).

D. Other

N/A

(This NCD last reviewed November 2009.)

100-3, Chapter-1, Part-4, 210.8

Screening and Behavioral Counseling Interventions in Primary Care to Reduce Alcohol Misuse(Effective October 14, 2011)

A. General

Based upon authority to cover "additional preventive services" for Medicare beneficiaries if certain statutory requirements are met, the Centers for Medicare & Medicaid Services (CMS) initiated a new national coverage analysis on annual screening and brief behavioral counseling in primary care to reduce alcohol misuse in adults, including pregnant women. Annual screening and behavioural counseling for alcohol misuse in adults is recommended with a grade of B by the U.S. Preventive Services Task Force (USPSTF) and is appropriate for individuals entitled to benefits under Part A and Part B.

CMS will cover annual alcohol screening and up to four, brief face-to-face behavioral counseling in primary care settings to reduce alcohol misuse. CMS does not identify specific alcohol misuse screening tools. Rather, the decision to use a specific tool is at the discretion of the clinician in the primary care setting. Various screening tools are available for screening for alcohol misuse.

B. Nationally Covered Indications

Effective for claims with dates of service on or after October 14, 2011, CMS will cover annual alcohol screening, and for those that screen positive, up to four brief, face-to-face, behavioral counseling interventions per year for Medicare beneficiaries, including pregnant women:

- Who misuse alcohol, but whose levels or patterns of alcohol consumption do not meet criteria for alcohol dependence (defined as at least three of the following: tolerance, withdrawal symptoms, impaired control, preoccupation with acquisition and/or use, persistent desire or unsuccessful efforts to quit, sustains social, occupational, or recreational disability, use continues despite adverse consequences); and

- Who are competent and alert at the time that counseling is provided; and,

- Whose counseling is furnished by qualified primary care physicians or other primary care practitioners in a primary care setting.

Each of the behavioral counseling interventions should be consistent with the 5A's approach that has been adopted by the USPSTF to describe such services. They are:

1. Assess: Ask about/assess behavioral health risk(s) and factors affecting choice of behavior change goals/methods.

2. Advise: Give clear, specific, and personalized behavior change advice, including information about personal health harms and benefits.

3. Agree: Collaboratively select appropriate treatment goals and methods based on the patient's interest in and willingness to change the behavior.

4. Assist: Using behavior change techniques (self-help and/or counseling), aid the patient in achieving agreed upon goals by acquiring the skills, confidence, and social/environmental supports for behavior change, supplemented with adjunctive medical treatments when appropriate.

5. Arrange: Schedule follow-up contacts (in person or by telephone) to provide ongoing assistance/support and to adjust the treatment plan as needed, including referral to more intensive or specialized treatment.

For the purposes of this policy, a primary care setting is defined as one in which there is provision of integrated, accessible health care services by clinicians who are accountable for addressing a large majority of personal health care needs, developing a sustained partnership with patients, and practicing in the context of family and community. Emergency departments, inpatient hospital settings, ambulatory surgical centers, independent diagnostic testing facilities, skilled nursing facilities, inpatient rehabilitation facilities and hospices are not considered primary care settings under this definition.

For the purposes of this policy a "primary care physician" and "primary care practitioner" are to be defined based on two existing sections of the Social Security Act, §1833(u)(6), §1833(x)(2)(A)(i)(I) and §1833(x)(2)(A)(i)(II):

§1833(u)

6. Physician Defined.—For purposes of this paragraph, the term"physician" means a physician described in section 1861(r)(1) and the term "primary care physician" means a physician who is identified in the available data as a general practitioner, family practice practitioner, general internist, or obstetrician or gynecologist.

§1833(x)(2)(A)(i)

i. is a physician (as described in section 1861(r)(1)) who has a primary specialty designation of family medicine, internal medicine, geriatric medicine, or pediatric medicine; or

ii. is a nurse practitioner, clinical nurse specialist, or physician assistant (as those terms are defined in section 1861(aa)(5)).

C. Nationally Non-Covered Indications

1. Alcohol screening is non-covered when performed more than one time in a 12-month period.

2. Brief face-to-face behavioral counseling interventions are non-covered when performed more than once a day; that is, two counseling interventions on the same day are non-covered.

3. Brief face-to-face behavioral counseling interventions are non-covered when performed more than four times in a 12-month period

D. Other

Medicare coinsurance and Part B deductible are waived for this preventive service

(This NCD last reviewed October 2011.)

100-3, Chapter-1, Part-4, 210.10

Screening for Sexually Transmitted Infections (STIs) and High Intensity Behavioral Counseling (HIBC) to Prevent STIs

A. General

Sexually transmitted infections (STIs) are infections that are passed from one person to another through sexual contact. STIs remain an important cause of morbidity in the United States and have both health and economic consequences. Many of the complications of STIs are borne by women and children Often, STIs do not present any symptoms so can go untreated for long periods of time The presence of an STI during pregnancy may result in significant health complications for the woman and infant. In fact, any person who has an STI may develop health complications. Screening tests for the STIs in this national coverage determination (NCD) are laboratory tests.

Under §1861(ddd) of the Social Security Act (the Act), the Centers for Medicare & Medicaid Services (CMS) has the authority to add coverage of additional preventive services if certain statutory requirements are met. The regulations provide:

§410.64 Additional preventive services

a. Medicare Part B pays for additional preventive services not described in paragraph (1) or (3) of the definition of "preventive services" under §410.2, that identify medical conditions or risk factors for individuals if the Secretary determines through the national coverage determination process (as defined in section 1869(f)(1)(B) of the Act) that these services are all of the following: (1) reasonable and necessary for the prevention or early detection of illness or disability.(2)recommended with a grade of A or B by the United States Preventive Services Task Force, (3) appropriate for individuals entitled to benefits under Part A or enrolled under Part B.

b. In making determinations under paragraph (a) of this section regarding the coverage of a new preventive service, the Secretary may conduct an assessment of the relation between predicted outcomes and the expenditures for such services and may take into account the results of such an assessment in making such national coverage determinations.

The scope of the national coverage analysis for this NCD evaluated the evidence for the following STIs and high intensity behavioral counseling (HIBC) to prevent STIs for which the United States Preventive Services Task Force (USPSTF) has issued either an A or B recommendation:

- Screening for chlamydial infection for all sexually active non-pregnant young women aged 24 and younger and for older non-pregnant women who are at increased risk,

- Screening for chlamydial infection for all pregnant women aged 24 and younger and for older pregnant women who are at increased risk,

- Screening for gonorrhea infection in all sexually active women, including those who are pregnant, if they are at increased risk,

- Screening for syphilis infection for all pregnant women and for all persons at increased risk,
- Screening for hepatitis B virus (HBV) infection in pregnant women at their first prenatal visit,
- HIBC for the prevention of STIs for all sexually active adolescents, and for adults at increased risk for STIs

B. Nationally Covered Indications

CMS has determined that the evidence is adequate to conclude that screening for chlamydia, gonorrhea, syphilis, and hepatitis B, as well as HIBC to prevent STIs, consistent with the grade A and B recommendations by the USPSTF, is reasonable and necessary for the early detection or prevention of an illness or disability and is appropriate for individuals entitled to benefits under Part A or enrolled under Part B.

Therefore, effective for claims with dates of services on or after November 8, 2011, CMS will cover screening for these USPSTF-indicated STIs with the appropriate Food and Drug Administration (FDA) -approved/cleared laboratory tests, used consistent with FDA-approved labeling, and in compliance with the Clinical Laboratory Improvement Act (CLIA) regulations, when ordered by the primary care physician or practitioner, and performed by an eligible Medicare provider for these services.

Screening for chlamydia and gonorrhea:

- Pregnant women who are 24 years old or younger when the diagnosis of pregnancy is known, and then repeat screening during the third trimester if high-risk sexual behavior has occurred since the initial screening test.
- Pregnant women who are at increased risk for STIs when the diagnosis of pregnancy is known, and then repeat screening during the third trimester if high-risk sexual behavior has occurred since the initial screening test.
- Women at increased risk for STIs annually.

Screening for syphilis:

- Pregnant women when the diagnosis of pregnancy is known, and then repeat screening during the third trimester and at delivery if high-risk sexual behaviour has occurred since the previous screening test.
- Men and women at increased risk for STIs annually.

Screening for hepatitis B:

- Pregnant women at the first prenatal visit when the diagnosis of pregnancy is known, and then rescreening at time of delivery for those with new or continuing risk factors.

In addition, effective for claims with dates of service on or after November 8, 2011, CMS will cover up to two individual 20-to 30-minute, face-to-face counseling sessions annually for Medicare beneficiaries for HIBC to prevent STIs, for all sexually active adolescents, and for adults at increased risk for STIs, if referred for this service by a primary care physician or practitioner, and provided by a Medicare eligible primary care provider in a primary care setting. Coverage of HIBC to prevent STIs is consistent with the USPSTF recommendation. HIBC is defined as a program intended to promote sexual risk reduction or risk avoidance, which includes each of these broad topics, allowing flexibility for appropriate patient-focused elements:

- education,
- skills training,
- guidance on how to change sexual behavior.

The high/increased risk individual sexual behaviors, based on the USPSTF guidelines, include any of the following:

- Multiple sex partners
- Using barrier protection inconsistently
- Having sex under the influence of alcohol or drugs
- Having sex in exchange for money or drugs
- Age (24 years of age or younger and sexually active for women for chlamydia and gonorrhea)
- Having an STI within the past year
- IV drug use (for hepatitis B only)
- In addition for men - men having sex with men (MSM) and engaged in high risk sexual behavior, but no regard to age

In addition to individual risk factors, in concurrence with the USPSTF recommendations, community social factors such as high prevalence of STIs in the community populations should be considered in determining high/increased risk for chlamydia, gonorrhea, syphilis, and for recommending HIBC.

High/increased risk sexual behavior for STIs is determined by the primary care provider by assessing the patient's sexual history which is part of any complete medical history, typically part of an annual wellness visit or prenatal visit and considered in the development of a comprehensive prevention plan. The medical record should be a reflection of the service provided.

For the purposes of this NCD, a primary care setting defined as the provision of integrated, accessible health care services by clinicians who are accountable for addressing a large majority of personal health care needs, developing a sustained partnership with patients, and practicing in the context of family and community. Emergency departments, inpatient hospital settings, ambulatory surgical centers, independent diagnostic testing facilities, skilled nursing facilities, inpatient rehabilitation facilities, clinics providing a limited focus of health care services, and hospice are examples of settings not considered primary care settings under this definition.

For the purposes of this NCD, a "primary care physician" and "primary care practitioner" will be defined based on existing sections of the Social Security Act (§1833(u)(6), §1833(x)(2)(A)(i)(I) and §1833(x)(2)(A)(i)(II)).

§1833(u)

(6) Physician Defined.—For purposes of this paragraph, the term "physician" means a

physician described in section 1861(r)(1)and the term "primary care physician" means a physician who is identified in the available data as a general practitioner, family practice practitioner, general internist, or obstetrician or gynecologist.

§1833(x)(2)(A)(i)

i. is a physician (as described in section 1861(r)(1)) who has a primary specialty designation of family medicine, internal medicine, geriatric medicine, or pediatric medicine; or

ii. is a nurse practitioner, clinical nurse specialist, or physician assistant (as those terms are defined in section 1861(aa)(5));

C. Nationally Non-Covered Indications

Unless specifically covered in this NCD, any other NCD, or in statute, preventive services are non-covered by Medicare.

D. Other

Medicare coinsurance and Part B deductible are waived for these preventive services.

HIBC to prevent STIs may be provided on the same date of services as an annual wellness visit, evaluation and management (E&M) service, or during the global billing period for obstetrical car, but only one HIBC may be provided on any one date of service. See the claims processing manual for further instructions on claims processing.

For services provided on an annual basis, this is defined as a 12-Month period.

(This NCD last reviewed November 2011.)

100-3, Chapter-1, Part-4, 210.11

Intensive Behavioral Therapy for Cardiovascular Disease (CVD) (Effective November 8, 2011)

A. General

Cardiovascular disease (CVD) is the leading cause of mortality in the United States. CVD, which is comprised of hypertension, coronary heart disease (such as myocardial infarction and angina pectoris), heart failure and stroke, is also the leading cause of hospitalizations. Although the overall adjusted mortality rate from heart disease has declined over the past decade, opportunities for improvement still exist. Risk factors for CVD include being overweight, obesity, physical inactivity, diabetes, cigarette smoking, high blood pressure, high blood cholesterol, family history of myocardial infarction, and older age.

Under §1861(ddd) of the Social Security Act (the Act), the Centers for Medicare & Medicaid Services (CMS) has the authority to add coverage of additional preventive services through the National Coverage Determination (NCD) process if certain statutory requirements are met. Following its review, CMS has determined that the evidence is adequate to conclude that intensive behavioral therapy for CVD is reasonable and necessary for the prevention or early detection of illness or disability, is appropriate for individuals entitled to benefits under Part A or enrolled under Part B, and is comprised of components that are recommended with a grade of A or B by the U.S. Preventive Services Task Force (USPSTF).

B. Nationally Covered Indications

Effective for claims with dates of service on or after November 8, 2011, CMS covers intensive behavioral therapy for CVD (referred to below as a CVD risk reduction visit), which consists of the following three components:

- encouraging aspirin use for the primary prevention of CVD when the benefits outweigh the risks for men age 45-79 years and women 55-79 years;
- screening for high blood pressure in adults age 18 years and older; and
- intensive behavioral counseling to promote a healthy diet for adults with hyperlipidemia, hypertension, advancing age, and other known risk factors for cardiovascular-and diet-related chronic disease.

We note that only a small proportion (about 4%) of the Medicare population is under 45 years (men) or 55 years (women), therefore the vast majority of beneficiaries should receive all three components. Intensive behavioral counseling to promote a healthy diet is broadly recommended to cover close to 100% of the population due to the prevalence of known risk factors.

Therefore, CMS covers one, face-to-face CVD risk reduction visit per year for Medicare beneficiaries who are competent and alert at the time that counseling is provided, and whose counseling is furnished by a qualified primary care physician or other primary care practitioner in a primary care setting.

The behavioral counseling intervention for aspirin use and healthy diet should be consistent with the Five As approach that has been adopted by the USPSTF to describe such services:

- **Assess:** Ask about/assess behavioral health risk(s) and factors affecting choice of behavior change goals/methods.
- **Advise:** Give clear, specific, and personalized behavior change advice, including information about personal health harms and benefits.
- **Agree:** Collaboratively select appropriate treatment goals and methods based on the patient's interest in and willingness to change the behavior.
- **Assist:** Using behavior change techniques (self-help and/or counseling), aid the patient in achieving agreed-upon goals by acquiring the skills, confidence, and social/environmental supports for behavior change, supplemented with adjunctive medical treatments when appropriate.
- **Arrange:** Schedule follow-up contacts (in person or by telephone) to provide ongoing assistance/support and to adjust the treatment plan as needed, including referral to more intensive or specialized treatment.

For the purpose of this NCD, a primary care setting is defined as the provision of integrated, accessible health care services by clinicians who are accountable for addressing a large majority of personal health care needs, developing a sustained partnership with patients, and practicing in the context of family and community. Emergency departments, inpatient hospital settings, ambulatory surgical centers, independent diagnostic testing facilities, skilled nursing facilities, inpatient rehabilitation facilities, and hospices are not considered primary care settings under this definition.

For the purpose of this NCD, a "primary care physician" and "primary care practitioner" are defined consistent with existing sections of the Act (§1833(u)(6), §1833(x)(2)(A)(i)(I) and §1833(x)(2)(A)(i)(II)).

§1833(u)

(6) Physician Defined.—For purposes of this paragraph, the term "physician" means a physician described in section 1861(r)(1)and the term "primary care physician" means a physician who is identified in the available data as a general practitioner, family practice practitioner, general internist, or obstetrician or gynecologist.

physician who is identified in the available data as a general practitioner, family practice practitioner, general internist, or obstetrician or gynecologist.

§1833(x)(2) (A) Primary care practitioner.—The term "primary care practitioner" means an individual—

(i) who—

 I. is a physician (as described in section 1861(r)(1)) who has a primary specialty designation of family medicine, internal medicine, geriatric medicine, or pediatric medicine; or

 II. is a nurse practitioner, clinical nurse specialist, or physician assistant (as those terms are defined in section 1861(aa)(5)).

C. Nationally Non-Covered Indications

Unless specifically covered in this NCD, any other NCD, or in statute, preventive services are non-covered by Medicare.

D. Other

Medicare coinsurance and Part B deductible are waived for this preventive service.

(This NCD last reviewed November 2011.)

100-3, Chapter-1, Part-4, 210.12

Intensive Behavioral Therapy for Obesity (Effective November 29, 2011)

A. General

Based upon authority to cover "additional preventive services" for Medicare beneficiaries if certain statutory requirements are met, the Centers for Medicare & Medicaid Services (CMS) initiated a new national coverage analysis on intensive behavioral therapy for obesity. Screening for obesity in adults is recommended with a grade of B by the U.S. Preventive Services Task Force (USPSTF) and is appropriate for individuals entitled to benefits under Part A and Part B.

The Centers for Disease Control (CDC) reported that "obesity rates in the U.S. have increased dramatically over the last 30 years, and obesity is now epidemic in the United States." In the Medicare population over 30% of men and women are obese. Obesity is directly or indirectly associated with many chronic diseases including cardiovascular disease, musculoskeletal conditions and diabetes.

B. Nationally Covered Indications

Effective for claims with dates of service on or after November 29, 2011, CMS covers intensive behavioral therapy for obesity, defined as a body mass index (BMI) ≥ 30 kg/m2, for the prevention or early detection of illness or disability.

Intensive behavioral therapy for obesity consists of the following:

1. Screening for obesity in adults using measurement of BMI calculated by dividing weight in kilograms by the square of height in meters (expressed kg/m2);
2. Dietary (nutritional) assessment; and Intensive behavioral counseling and behavioral therapy to promote sustained
3. weight loss through high intensity interventions on diet and exercise.

The intensive behavioral intervention for obesity should be consistent with the 5-A

framework that has been highlighted by the USPSTF:

1. **Assess:** Ask about/assess behavioral health risk(s) and factors affecting choice of behavior change goals/ methods.
2. **Advise:** Give clear, specific, and personalized behavior change advice, including information about personal health harms and benefits.
3. **Agree:** Collaboratively select appropriate treatment goals and methods based on the patient's interest in and willingness to change the behavior.
4. **Assist:** Using behavior change techniques (self-help and/ or counseling), aid the patient in achieving agreed-upon goals by acquiring the skills, confidence, and social/ environmental supports for behavior change, supplemented with adjunctive medical treatments when appropriate.

5. **Arrange:** Schedule follow-up contacts (in person or by telephone) to provide ongoing assistance/support and to adjust the treatment plan as needed, including referral to more intensive or specialized treatment.

For Medicare beneficiaries with obesity, who are competent and alert at the time that counseling is provided and whose counseling is furnished by a qualified primary care physician or other primary care practitioner and in a primary care setting, CMS covers:

- One face-to-face visit every week for the first month;
- One face-to-face visit every other week for months 2-6;
- One face-to-face visit every month for months 7-12, if the beneficiary meets the 3kg weight loss requirement during the first six months as discussed below.

At the six month visit, a reassessment of obesity and a determination of the amount of weight loss must be performed. To be eligible for additional face-to-face visits occurring once a month for an additional six months, beneficiaries must have achieved a reduction in weight of at least 3kg over the course of the first six months of intensive therapy. This determination must be documented in the physician office records for applicable beneficiaries consistent with usual practice. For beneficiaries who do not achieve a weight loss of at least 3kg during the first six months of intensive therapy, a reassessment of their readiness to change and BMI is appropriate after an additional six month period.

For the purposes of this decision memorandum, a primary care setting is defined as one in which there is provision of integrated, accessible health care services by clinicians who are accountable for addressing a large majority of personal health care needs, developing a sustained partnership with patients, and practicing in the context of family and community. Emergency departments, inpatient hospital settings, ambulatory surgical centers, independent diagnostic testing facilities, skilled nursing facilities, inpatient rehabilitation facilities and hospices are not considered primary care settings under this definition.

For the purposes of this decision memorandum a "primary care physician" and "primary care practitioner" will be defined consistent with existing sections of the Social Security Act (§1833(u)(6), §1833(x)(2)(A)(i)(I) and §1833(x)(2)(A)(i)(II)).

§1833(u)

(6) Physician Defined.—For purposes of this paragraph, the term "physician" means a physician described in section 1861(r)(1) and the term "primary care physician" means a physician who is identified in the available data as a general practitioner, family practice practitioner, general internist, or obstetrician or gynecologist.

§1833(x)(2)(A)

Primary care practitioner—The term "primary care practitioner" means an individual—

(i) who—

I. is a physician (as described in section 1861(r)(1)) who has a primary specialty designation of family medicine, internal medicine, geriatric medicine, or pediatric medicine; or

II. is a nurse practitioner, clinical nurse specialist, or physician assistant (as those terms are defined in section 1861(aa)(5))

C. Nationally Non-Covered Indications

All other indications remain non-covered.

D. Other

Medicare coinsurance and Part B deductible are waived for this service

(This NCD last reviewed November 2011)

100-3, Chapter-1, Part-4, 220.6

Positron Emission Tomography (PET) Scans

Positron Emission Tomography (PET) is a minimally invasive diagnostic imaging procedure used to evaluate metabolism in normal tissues as well as in diseased tissues in conditions such as cancer, ischemic heart disease, and some neurologic disorders. A radiopharmaceutical is injected into the patient that gives off sub-atomic particles, known as positrons, as it decays. PET uses a positron camera (tomograph) to measure the decay of the radiopharmaceutical. The rate of decay provides biochemical information to on the metabolism of the tissue being studied.

NOTE: This manual section, 220.6 lists all Medicare–covered uses of PET scans. Except as set forth below in cancer indications listed as "Coverage with Evidence Development," a particular use of PET scans is not covered unless this manual specifically provides that such use is covered. Although this section, 220.6 lists some non-covered uses of PET scans, it does not non-covered uses of PET scans, it does not constitute an exhaustive list of all non- covered uses.

Effective for dates of service on or after March 7, 2013, local Medicare Administrative Contractors (MACs) may determine coverage within their respective jurisdictions for positron emission tomography (PET) using radiopharmaceuticals for their Food and Drug Administration (FDA) approved labeled indications for oncologic imaging.

We emphasize each of the following points:

1. Changing the 'restrictive' language of prior PET decisions will not by itself suffice to expand Medicare coverage to new PET radiopharmaceuticals.
2. The scope of this change extends only to FDA-approved indications for oncologic uses of PET tracers.
3. This change does not include screening uses of PET scanning.

The Centers for Medicare & Medicaid Services (CMS) acknowledges the advances relating to the assessment of diagnostic performance and patient safety, as pioneered by the FDA in its regulatory policies and guidelines for diagnostic PET imaging agents and systems during the past decade. We note for completeness that local coverage cannot be in conflict with NCDs or other national policies. Finally, we note that future CMS NCDs, if any, regarding diagnostic PET imaging would not be precluded by this NCD.

100-3, Chapter-1, Part-4, 220.6.1

PET for Perfusion of the Heart (220.6.1) (Various Effective Dates)

1. Rubidium 82 (Effective March 14, 1995)

Effective for services performed on or after March 14, 1995, PET scans performed at rest or with pharmacological stress used for noninvasive imaging of the perfusion of the heart for the diagnosis and management of patients with known or suspected coronary artery disease using the FDA approved radiopharmaceutical Rubidium 82 (Rb 82) are covered, provided the requirements below are met:

- The PET scan, whether at rest alone, or rest with stress, is performed in place of, but not in addition to, a single photon emission computed tomography (SPECT); or

- The PET scan, whether at rest alone or rest with stress, is used following a SPECT that was found to be inconclusive. In these cases, the PET scan must have been considered necessary in order to determine what medical or surgical intervention is required to treat the patient. (For purposes of this requirement, an inconclusive test is a test(s) whose results are equivocal, technically uninterpretable, or discordant with a patient's other clinical data and must be documented in the beneficiary's file.)

- For any PET scan for which Medicare payment is claimed for dates of services prior to July 1, 2001, the claimant must submit additional specified information on the claim form (including proper codes and/or modifiers), to indicate the results of the PET scan. The claimant must also include information on whether the PET scan was performed after an inconclusive non-invasive cardiac test. The information submitted with respect to the previous noninvasive cardiac test must specify the type of test performed prior to the PET scan and whether it was inconclusive or unsatisfactory. These explanations are in the form of special G codes used for billing PET scans using Rb 82. Beginning July 1, 2001, claims should be submitted with the appropriate codes.

2. Ammonia N-13 (Effective October 1, 2003)

Effective for services performed on or after October 1, 2003, PET scans performed at rest or with pharmacological stress used for noninvasive imaging of the perfusion of the heart for the diagnosis and management of patients with known or suspected coronary artery disease using the FDA approved radiopharmaceutical ammonia N-13 are covered, provided the requirements below are met:

- The PET scan, whether at rest alone, or rest with stress, is performed in place of, but not in addition to, a SPECT; or

- The PET scan, whether at rest alone or rest with stress, is used following a SPECT that was found to be inconclusive. In these cases, the PET scan must have been considered necessary in order to determine what medical or surgical intervention is required to treat the patient. (For purposes of this requirement, an inconclusive test is a test whose results are equivocal, technically uninterpretable, or discordant with a patient's other clinical data and must be documented in the beneficiary's file.)

(This NCD last reviewed March 2005.)

100-3, Chapter-1, Part-4, 220.6.17

Positron Emission Tomography (FDG PET) for Oncologic Conditions (Effective June 11, 2013)

A. General

FDG (2-[F18] fluoro-2-deoxy-D-glucose) Positron Emission Tomography (PET) is a minimally-invasive diagnostic imaging procedure used to evaluate glucose metabolism in normal tissue as well as in diseased tissues in conditions such as cancer, ischemic heart disease, and some neurologic disorders. FDG is an injected radionuclide (orradiopharmaceutical) that emits sub-atomic particles, known as positrons, as it decays. FDG PET uses a positron camera (tomograph) to measure the decay of FDG. The rate of FDG decay provides biochemical information on glucose metabolism in the tissue being studied. As malignancies can cause abnormalities of metabolism and blood flow, FDG PET evaluation may indicate the probable presence or absence of a malignancy based upon observed differences in biologic activity compared to adjacent tissues.

The Centers for Medicare and Medicaid Services (CMS) was asked by the National Oncologic PET Registry (NOPR) to reconsider section 220.6 of the National Coverage Determinations (NCD) Manual to end the prospective data collection requirements under Coverage with Evidence Development (CED) across all oncologic indications ofFDG PET imaging. The CMS received public input indicating that the current coverage framework of prospective data collection under CED be ended for all oncologic uses of FDG PET imaging.

1. Framework

Effective for claims with dates of service on and after June 11, 2013, CMS is adopting a coverage framework that ends the prospective data collection requirements by NOPR under CED for all oncologic uses of FDG PET imaging. CMS is making this change for all NCDs that address coverage of FDG PET for oncologic uses addressed in this decision. This decision does not change coverage for any use of PET imaging using radiopharmaceuticals NaF-18 (fluorine-18 labeled sodium fluoride), ammonia N-13, or rubidium-82 (Rb-82).

4. Initial Anti-Tumor Treatment Strategy

CMS continues to believe that the evidence is adequate to determine that the results of FDG PET imaging are useful in determining the appropriate initial anti-tumor treatment strategy for beneficiaries with suspected cancer and improve health outcomes and thus are reasonable and necessary under §1862(a)(1)(A) of the Social Security Act (the Act).

Therefore, CMS continues to nationally cover one FDG PET study for beneficiaries who have cancers that are biopsy proven or strongly suspected based on other diagnostic testing when the beneficiary's treating physician determines that the FDG PET study is needed to determine the location and/or extent of the tumor for the following therapeutic purposes related to the initial anti-tumor treatment strategy:

- To determine whether or not the beneficiary is an appropriate candidate for an invasive diagnostic or therapeutic procedure; or
- To determine the optimal anatomic location for an invasive procedure; or
- To determine the anatomic extent of tumor when the recommended anti-tumor treatment reasonably depends on the extent of the tumor.

See the table at the end of this section for a synopsis of all nationally covered and non-covered oncologic uses of FDG PET imaging.

B.1. Initial Anti-Tumor Treatment Strategy Nationally Covered Indications

a. CMS continues to nationally cover FDG PET imaging for the initial anti-tumor treatment strategy for male and female breast cancer only when used in staging distant metastasis.

b. CMS continues to nationally cover FDG PET to determine initial anti-tumor treatment strategy for melanoma other than for the evaluation of regional lymph Nodes

c. CMS continues to nationally cover FDG PET to determine initial anti-tumor treatment strategy for melanoma other than for the evaluation of regional lymph nodes

d. C.1 Initial Anti-Tumor Treatment Strategy Nationally Non-Covered Indications

a. CMS continues to nationally non-cover initial anti-tumor treatment strategy in Medicare beneficiaries who have adenocarcinoma of the prostate.

b. CMS continues to nationally non-cover FDG PET imaging for diagnosis of breast cancer and initial staging of axillary nodes.

c. CMS continues to nationally non-cover FDG PET imaging for initial anti-tumor treatment strategy for the evaluation of regional lymph nodes in melanoma.

d. CMS continues to nationally non-cover FDG PET imaging for the diagnosis of cervical cancer related to initial anti-tumor treatment strategy.

3. Subsequent Anti-Tumor Treatment Strategy

B.2. Subsequent Anti-Tumor Treatment Strategy Nationally Covered Indications

Three FDG PET scans are nationally covered when used to guide subsequent management of anti-tumor treatment strategy after completion of initial anti-cancer therapy. Coverage of more than three FDG PET scans to guide subsequent management of anti-tumor treatment strategy after completion of initial anti-cancer therapy shall be determined by the local Medicare Administrative Contractors.

4. Synopsis of Coverage of FDG PET for Oncologic Conditions

Effective for claims with dates of service on and after June 11, 2013, the chart below summarizes national FDG PET coverage for oncologic conditions:

FDG PET for Cancers Tumor Type	Initial Treatment Strategy (formerly "diagnosis" & "staging")	Subsequent Treatment Strategy (formerly "restaging" & "monitoring response to treatment")
Colorectal	Cover	Cover
Esophagus	Cover	Cover
Head and Neck (not thyroid, CNS)	Cover	Cover
Lymphoma	Cover	Cover
Non-small cell lung	Cover	Cover
Ovary	Cover	Cover
Brain	Cover	Cover
Cervix	Cover with exceptions *	Cover
Small cell lung	Cover	Cover
Soft tissue sarcoma	Cover	Cover
Pancreas	Cover	Cover
Testes	Cover	Cover
Prostate	Non-cover	Cover
Thyroid	Cover	Cover
Breast (male and female)	Cover with exceptions *	Cover
Melanoma	Cover with exceptions *	Cover

FDG PET for Cancers Tumor Type	Initial Treatment Strategy (formerly "diagnosis" & "staging"	Subsequent Treatment Strategy (formerly "restaging" & "monitoring response to treatment"
All other solid tumors	Cover	Cover
Myeloma	Cover	Cover
All other cancers not listed	Cover	Cover

*Cervix: Nationally non-covered for the initial diagnosis of cervical cancer related to initial anti-tumor treatment strategy. All other indications for initial anti-tumor treatment strategy for cervical cancer are nationally covered.

*Breast: Nationally non-covered for initial diagnosis and/or staging of axillary lymph nodes. Nationally covered for initial staging of metastatic disease. All other indications for initial anti-tumor treatment strategy for breast cancer are nationally covered.

*Melanoma: Nationally non-covered for initial staging of regional lymph nodes. All other indications for initial anti-tumor treatment strategy for melanoma are nationally covered.

D. Other

N/A

100-3, Chapter-1, Part-4, 220.6.19

Positron Emission Tomography NaF-18 (NaF-18 PET) to Identify Bone Metastasis of Cancer (Effective February 26, 2010)

A. General

Positron Emission Tomography (PET) is a non-invasive, diagnostic imaging procedure that assesses the level of metabolic activity and perfusion in various organ systems of the body. A positron camera (tomograph) is used to produce cross-sectional tomographic images, which are obtained from positron-emitting radioactive tracer substances (radiopharmaceuticals) such as F-18 sodium fluoride. NaF-18 PET has been recognized as an excellent technique for imaging areas of altered osteogenic activity in bone. The clinical value of detecting and assessing the initial extent of metastatic cancer in bone is attested by a number of professional guidelines for oncology. Imaging to detect bone metastases is also recommended when a patient, following completion of initial treatment, is symptomatic with bone pain suspicious for metastases from a known primary tumor.

B. Nationally Covered Indications

Effective February 26, 2010, the Centers for Medicare & Medicaid Services (CMS) will cover NaF-18 PET imaging when the beneficiary's treating physician determines that the NaF-18 PET study is needed to inform to inform the initial antitumor treatment strategy or to guide subsequent antitumor treatment strategy after the completion of initial treatment, and when the beneficiary is enrolled in, and the NaF-18 PET provider is participating in, the following type of prospective clinical study:

A NaF-18 PET clinical study that is designed to collect additional information at the time of the scan to assist in initial antitumor treatment planning or to guide subsequent treatment strategy by the identification, location and quantification of bone metastases in beneficiaries in whom bone metastases are strongly suspected based on clinical symptoms or the results of other diagnostic studies. Qualifying clinical studies must ensure that specific hypotheses are addressed; appropriate data elements are collected; hospitals and providers are qualified to provide the PET scan and interpret the results; participating hospitals and providers accurately report data on all enrolled patients not included in other qualifying trials through adequate auditing mechanisms; and all patient confidentiality, privacy, and other Federal laws must be followed.

The clinical studies for which Medicare will provide coverage must answer one or more of the following questions:

Prospectively, in Medicare beneficiaries whose treating physician determines that the NaF-18 PET study results are needed to inform the initial antitumor treatment strategy or to guide subsequent antitumor treatment strategy after the completion of initial treatment, does the addition of NaF-18 PET imaging lead to:

- A change in patient management to more appropriate palliative care; or
- A change in patient management to more appropriate curative care; or
- Improved quality of life; or
- Improved survival?

The study must adhere to the following standards of scientific integrity and relevance to the Medicare population:

a. The principal purpose of the research study is to test whether a particular intervention potentially improves the participants' health outcomes.

b. The research study is well-supported by available scientific and medical information or it is intended to clarify or establish the health outcomes of interventions already in common clinical use.

c. The research study does not unjustifiably duplicate existing studies.

d. The research study design is appropriate to answer the research question being asked in the study

e. The research study is sponsored by an organization or individual capable of executing the proposed study successfully.

f. The research study is in compliance with all applicable Federal regulations concerning the protection of human subjects found in the Code of Federal Regulations (CFR) at 45 CFR Part 46. If a study is regulated by the Food and Drug Administration (FDA), it also must be in compliance with 21 CFR Parts 50 and 56.

g. All aspects of the research study are conducted according to the appropriate standards of scientific integrity.

h. The research study has a written protocol that clearly addresses, or incorporates by reference, the Medicare standards.

i. The clinical research study is not designed to exclusively test toxicity or disease pathophysiology in healthy individuals. Trials of all medical technologies measuring therapeutic outcomes as one of the objectives meet this standard only if the disease or condition being studied is life-threatening as defined in 21 CFR §312.81(a) and the patient has no other viable treatment options.

j. The clinical research study is registered on the www.ClinicalTrials.gov Web site by the principal sponsor/investigator prior to the enrollment of the first study subject.

k. The research study protocol specifies the method and timing of public release of all pre-specified outcomes to be measured including release of outcomes if outcomes are negative or study is terminated early. The results must be made public within 24 months of the end of data collection. If a report is planned to be published in a peer-reviewed journal, then that initial release may be an abstract that meets the requirements of the International Committee of Medical Journal Editors. However, a full report of the outcomes must be made public no later than three (3) years after the end of data collection.

l. The research study protocol must explicitly discuss subpopulations affected by the treatment under investigation, particularly traditionally underrepresented groups in clinical studies, how the inclusion and exclusion criteria affect enrollment of these populations, and a plan for the retention and reporting of said populations on the trial. If the inclusion an exclusion criteria are expected to have a negative effect on the recruitment or retention of underrepresented populations, the protocol must discuss why these criteria are necessary.

m. The research study protocol explicitly discusses how the results are or are not expected to be generalizable to the Medicare population to infer whether Medicare patients may benefit from the intervention. Separate discussions in the protocol may be necessary for populations eligible for Medicare due to age, disability or Medicaid eligibility.

Consistent with section 1142 of the Social Security Act (the Act), the Agency for Healthcare Research and Quality (AHRQ) supports clinical research studies that the Centers for Medicare and Medicaid Services (CMS) determines meet the above-listed standards and address the above-listed research questions.

C. Nationally Non-Covered Indications

Effective February 26, 2010, CMS determines that the evidence is not sufficient to determine that the results of NaF-18 PET imaging to identify bone metastases improve health outcomes of beneficiaries with cancer and is not reasonable and necessary under §1862(a)(1)(A) of the Act unless it is to inform initial antitumor treatment strategy or to guide subsequent antitumor treatment strategy after completion of initial treatment, and then only under CED. All other uses and clinical indications of NaF-18 PET are nationally non-covered.

D. Other

The only radiopharmaceutical diagnostic imaging agents covered by Medicare for PET cancer imaging are 2-[F-18] Fluoro-D-Glucose (FDG) and NaF-18 (sodium fluoride-18). All other PET radiopharmaceutical diagnostic imaging agents are non-covered for this indication.

(This NCD was last reviewed in February 2010.)

100-3, Chapter-1, Part-4, 240.4

Continuous Positive Airway Pressure (CPAP) Therapy For Obstructive Sleep Apnea (OSA) (Effective April 4, 2005) (Effective March 13, 2008)

A. General

Continuous Positive Airway Pressure (CPAP) is a non-invasive technique for providing single levels of air pressure from a flow generator, via a nose mask, through the nares. The purpose is to prevent the collapse of the oropharyngeal walls and the obstruction of airflow during sleep, which occurs in obstructive sleep apnea (OSA).

The apnea hypopnea index (AHI) is equal to the average number of episodes of apnea and hypopnea per hour. The respiratory disturbance index (RDI) is equal to the average number of respiratory disturbances per hour.

Apnea is defined as a cessation of airflow for at least 10 seconds. Hypopnea is defined as an abnormal respiratory event lasting at least 10 seconds with at least a 30% reduction in thoracoabdominal movement or airflow as compared to baseline, and with at least a 4% oxygen desaturation.

The AHI and/or RDI may be measured by polysomnography (PSG) in a facility-based sleep study laboratory, or by a Type II home sleep test (HST) monitor, a Type III HST monitor, or a Type IV HST monitor measuring at least 3 channels.

B. Nationally Covered Indications

Effective for claims with dates of service on and after March 13, 2008, the Centers for Medicare & Medicaid Services (CMS) determines that CPAP therapy when used in adult patients with OSA is considered reasonable and necessary under the following situations:

1. The use of CPAP is covered under Medicare when used in adult patients with OSA. Coverage of CPAP is initially limited to a 12-week period to identify beneficiaries diagnosed with OSA as subsequently described who benefit from CPAP. CPAP is subsequently covered only for those beneficiaries diagnosed with OSA who benefit from CPAP during this 12-week period.

2. The provider of CPAP must conduct education of the beneficiary prior to the use of the CPAP device to ensure that the beneficiary has been educated in the proper use of the device. A caregiver, for example a family member, may be compensatory, if consistently available in the beneficiary's home and willing and able to safely operate the CPAP device.

3. A positive diagnosis of OSA for the coverage of CPAP must include a clinical evaluation and a positive:

    a. attended PSG performed in a sleep laboratory; or

    b. unattended HST with a Type II home sleep monitoring device; or

    c. unattended HST with a Type III home sleep monitoring device; or

    d. unattended HST with a Type IV home sleep monitoring device that measures at least 3 channels.

4. The sleep test must have been previously ordered by the beneficiary's treating physician and furnished under appropriate physician supervision.

5. An initial 12-week period of CPAP is covered in adult patients with OSA if either of the following criterion using the AHI or RDI are met:

    a. AHI or RDI greater than or equal to 15 events per hour, or

    b. AHI or RDI greater than or equal to 5 events and less than or equal to 14 events per hour with documented symptoms of excessive daytime sleepiness, impaired cognition, mood disorders or insomnia, or documented hypertension, ischemic heart disease, or history of stroke.

6. The AHI or RDI is calculated on the average number of events of per hour. If the AHI or RDI is calculated based on less than 2 hours of continuous recorded sleep, the total number of recorded events to calculate the AHI or RDI during sleep testing must be at a minimum the number of events that would have been required in a 2-hour period.

7. Apnea is defined as a cessation of airflow for at least 10 seconds. Hypopnea is defined as an abnormal respiratory event lasting at least 10 seconds with at least a 30% reduction in thoracoabdominal movement or airflow as compared to baseline, and with at least a 4% oxygen desaturation.

8. Coverage with Evidence Development (CED): Medicare provides the following limited coverage for CPAP in adult beneficiaries who do not qualify for CPAP coverage based on criteria 1-7 above. A clinical study seeking Medicare payment for CPAP provided to a beneficiary who is an enrolled subject in that study must address one or more of the following questions:

    a. In Medicare-aged subjects with clinically identified risk factors for OSA, how does the diagnostic accuracy of a clinical trial of CPAP compare with PSG and Type II, III & IV HST in identifying subjects with OSA who will respond to CPAP?

    b. In Medicare-aged subjects with clinically identified risk factors for OSA who have not undergone confirmatory testing with PSG or Type II, III & IV HST, does CPAP cause clinically meaningful harm?

    c. The study must meet the following additional standards:

    d. The principal purpose of the research study is to test whether a particular intervention potentially improves the participants' health outcomes.

    e. The research study is well-supported by available scientific and medical information or it is intended to clarify or establish the health outcomes of interventions already in common clinical use.

    f. The research study does not unjustifiably duplicate existing studies.

    g. The research study design is appropriate to answer the research question being asked in the study.

    h. The research study is sponsored by an organization or individual capable of executing the proposed study successfully.

    i. The research study is in compliance with all applicable Federal regulations concerning the protection of human subjects found at 45 CFR Part 46. If a study is Food and Drug Administration-regulated, it also must be in compliance with 21 CFR Parts 50 and 56.

    j. All aspects of the research study are conducted according to the appropriate standards of scientific integrity.

    k. The research study has a written protocol that clearly addresses, or incorporates by reference, the Medicare standards.

    l. The clinical research study is not designed to exclusively test toxicity or disease pathophysiology in healthy individuals. Trials of all medical technologies measuring therapeutic outcomes as one of the objectives meet this standard only if the disease or condition being studied is life-threatening as defined in 21 CFR §312.81(a) and the patient has no other viable treatment options.

    m. The clinical research study is registered on the ClinicalTrials.gov Web site by the principal sponsor/investigator prior to the enrollment of the first study subject.

    n. The research study protocol specifies the method and timing of public release of all pre-specified outcomes to be measured, including release of outcomes if outcomes are negative or study is terminated early. The results must be made public within 24 months of the end of data collection. If a report is planned for publication in a peer-reviewed journal, then that initial release may be an abstract that meets the requirements of the International Committee of Medical Journal Editors. However, a full report of the outcomes must be made public no later than 3 years after the end of data collection.

    o. The research study protocol must explicitly discuss subpopulations affected by the treatment under investigation, particularly traditionally underrepresented groups in clinical studies, how the inclusion and exclusion criteria affect enrollment of these populations, and a plan for the retention and reporting of said populations in the trial. If the inclusion and exclusion criteria are expected to have a negative effect on the recruitment or retention of underrepresented populations, the protocol must discuss why these criteria are necessary.

    p. The research study protocol explicitly discusses how the results are or are not expected to be generalizable to the Medicare population to infer whether Medicare patients may benefit from the intervention. Separate discussions in the protocol may be necessary for populations eligible for Medicare due to age, disability, or Medicaid eligibility.

C. Nationally Non-covered Indications

Effective for claims with dates of services on and after March 13, 2008, other diagnostic tests for the diagnosis of OSA, other than those noted above for prescribing CPAP, are not sufficient for the coverage of CPAP.

D. Other

N/A

(This NCD last reviewed March 2008.)

100-3, Chapter-1, Part-4, 240.4.1

Sleep Testing for Obstructive Sleep Apnea (OSA) (Effective March 3, 2009)

A. General

Obstructive sleep apnea (OSA) is the collapse of the oropharyngeal walls and the obstruction of airflow occurring during sleep. Diagnostic tests for OSA have historically been classified into four types. The most comprehensive is designated Type I attended facility based polysomnography (PSG), which is considered the reference standard for diagnosing OSA. Attended facility based polysomnogram is a comprehensive diagnostic sleep test including at least electroencephalography (EEG), electro-oculography (EOG), electromyography (EMG), heart rate or electrocardiography (ECG), airflow, breathing/respiratory effort, and arterial oxygen saturation (SaO2) furnished in a sleep laboratory facility in which a technologist supervises the recording during sleep time and has the ability to intervene if needed. Overnight PSG is the conventional diagnostic test for OSA. The American Thoracic Society and the American Academy of Sleep Medicine have recommended supervised PSG in the sleep laboratory over 2 nights for the diagnosis of OSA and the initiation of continuous positive airway pressure (CPAP).

Three categories of portable monitors (used both in attended and unattended settings) have been developed for the diagnosis of OSA. Type II monitors have a minimum of 7 channels (e.g., EEG, EOG, EMG, ECG-heart rate, airflow, breathing/respiratory effort, SaO2)-this type of device monitors sleep staging, so AHI can be calculated). Type III monitors have a minimum of 4 monitored channels including ventilation or airflow (at least two channels of respiratory movement or respiratory movement and airflow), heart rate or ECG, and oxygen saturation. Type IV devices may measure one, two, three or more parameters but do not meet all the criteria of a higher category device. Some monitors use an actigraphy algorithm to identify periods of sleep and wakefulness.

B. Nationally Covered Indications

Effective for claims with dates of service on and after March 3, 2009, the Centers for Medicare & Medicaid Services finds that the evidence is sufficient to determine that the results of the sleep tests identified below can be used by a beneficiary's treating physician to diagnose OSA, that the use of such sleep testing technologies demonstrates improved health outcomes in Medicare beneficiaries who have OSA and receive the appropriate treatment, and that these tests are thus reasonable and necessary under section 1862(a)(1)(A) of the Social Security Act.

1. Type I PSG is covered when used to aid the diagnosis of OSA in beneficiaries who have clinical signs and symptoms indicative of OSA if performed attended in a sleep lab facility.

2. Type II or Type III sleep testing devices are covered when used to aid the diagnosis of OSA in beneficiaries who have clinical signs and symptoms indicative of OSA if performed unattended in or out of a sleep lab facility or attended in a sleep lab facility.

3. Type IV sleep testing devices measuring three or more channels, one of which is airflow, are covered when used to aid the diagnosis of OSA in beneficiaries who have signs and symptoms indicative of OSA if performed unattended in or out of a sleep lab facility or attended in a sleep lab facility.

4. Sleep testing devices measuring three or more channels that include actigraphy, oximetry, and peripheral arterial tone, are covered when used to aid the diagnosis of OSA in beneficiaries who have signs and symptoms indicative of OSA if performed unattended in or out of a sleep lab facility or attended in a sleep lab facility.

C. Nationally Non-Covered Indications

Effective for claims with dates of services on and after March 3, 2009, other diagnostic sleep tests for the diagnosis of OSA, other than those noted above for prescribing CPAP, are not sufficient for the coverage of CPAP and are not covered.

D. Other

N/A

(This NCD last reviewed March 2009.)

100-3, Chapter-1, Part-4, 250.5

Dermal Injections for the Treatment of Facial Lipodystrophy Syndrome (LDS) - Effective March 23, 2010

A. General

Treatment of persons infected with the human immunodeficiency virus (HIV) or persons who have Acquired Immune Deficiency Syndrome (AIDS) may include highly active antiretroviral therapy (HAART). Drug reactions commonly associated with long-term use of HAART include metabolic complications such as, lipid abnormalities, e.g., hyperlipidemia, hyperglycemia, diabetes, lipodystrophy, and heart disease. Lipodystrophy is characterized by abnormal fat distribution in the body.

The LDS is often characterized by a loss of fat that results in a facial abnormality such as severely sunken cheeks. The patient's physical appearance may contribute to psychological conditions (e.g., depression) or adversely impact a patient's adherence to antiretroviral regimens (therefore jeopardizing their health) and both of these are important health-related outcomes of interest in this population. Therefore, improving a patient's physical appearance through the use of dermal injections could improve these health-related outcomes.

B. Nationally Covered Indications

Effective for claims with dates of service on and after March 23, 2010, dermal injections for LDS are only reasonable and necessary using dermal fillers approved by the Food and Drug Administration (FDA) for this purpose, and then only in HIV-infected beneficiaries when LDS caused by antiretroviral HIV treatment is a significant contributor to their depression.

C. Nationally Non-Covered Indications

1. Dermal fillers that are not approved by the FDA for the treatment of LDS.

2. Dermal fillers that are used for any indication other than LDS in HIV-infected individuals who manifest depression as a result of their antiretroviral HIV treatments.

D. Other

N/A

(This NCD last reviewed March 2010.)

100-3, Chapter-1, Part-4, 260.6

Dental Examination Prior to Kidney Transplantation

Despite the "dental services exclusion" in §1862(a)(12) of the Act (see the Medicare Benefit Policy Manual, Chapter 16, "General Exclusions From Coverage," §140;), an oral or dental examination performed on an inpatient basis as part of a comprehensive workup prior to renal transplant surgery is a covered service. This is because the purpose of the examination is not for the care of the teeth or structures directly supporting the teeth. Rather, the examination is for the identification, prior to a complex surgical procedure, of existing medical problems where the increased possibility of infection would not only reduce the chances for successful surgery but would also expose the patient to additional risks in undergoing such surgery.

Such a dental or oral examination would be covered under Part A of the program if performed by a dentist on the hospital's staff, or under Part B if performed by a physician. (When performing a dental or oral examination, a dentist is not recognized as a physician under §1861(r) of the Act.) (See the Medicare General Information, Eligibility, and Entitlement Manual, Chapter 5, "Definitions," §70.2, and the Medicare Benefit Policy Manual, Chapter 15, "Covered Medical and Other Health Services," §150.)

100-3, Chapter-1, Part-4, 270.3

Blood-Derived Products for Chronic Non-Healing Wounds

A. General

Wound healing is a dynamic, interactive process that involves multiple cells and proteins. There are three progressive stages of normal wound healing, and the typical wound healing duration is about 4 weeks. While cutaneous wounds are a disruption of the normal, anatomic structure and function of the skin, subcutaneous wounds involve tissue below the skin's surface. Wounds are categorized as either acute, in where the normal wound healing stages are not yet completed but it is presumed they will be, resulting in orderly and timely wound repair, or chronic, in where a wound has failed to progress through the normal wound healing stages and repair itself within a sufficient time period.

Platelet-rich plasma (PRP) is produced in an autologous or homologous manner. Autologous PRP is comprised of blood from the patient who will ultimately receive the PRP. Alternatively, homologous PRP is derived from blood from multiple donors.

Blood is donated by the patient and centrifuged to produce an autologous gel for treatment of chronic, non-healing cutaneous wounds that persists for 30 days or longer and fail to properly complete the healing process. Autologous blood derived products for chronic, non-healing wounds includes both: (1) platelet derived growth factor (PDGF) products (such as Procuren), and (2) PRP (such as AutoloGel).

The PRP is different from previous products in that it contains whole cells including white cells, red cells, plasma, platelets, fibrinogen, stem cells, macrophages, and fibroblasts.

The PRP is used by physicians in clinical settings in treating chronic, non-healing wounds, open, cutaneous wounds, soft tissue, and bone. Alternatively, PDGF does not contain cells and was previously marketed as a product to be used by patients at home.

B. Nationally Covered Indications

Effective August 2, 2012, upon reconsideration, The Centers for Medicare and Medicaid Services (CMS) has determined that platelet-rich plasma (PRP) – an autologous blood-derived product, will be covered only for the treatment of chronic non-healing diabetic, venous and/or pressure wounds and only when the following conditions are met:

The patient is enrolled in a clinical trial that addresses the following questions using validated and reliable methods of evaluation. Clinical study applications for coverage pursuant to this National coverage Determination (NCD) must be received by August 2, 2014.

The clinical research study must meet the requirements specified below to assess the effect of PRP for the treatment of chronic non-healing diabetic, venous and/or pressure wounds. The clinical study must address:

Prospectively, do Medicare beneficiaries that have chronic non-healing diabetic, venous and/or pressure wounds who receive well-defined optimal usual care along with PRP therapy, experience clinically significant health outcomes compared to patients who receive well-defined optimal usual care for chronic non-healing diabetic, venous and/or pressure wounds as indicated by addressing at least one of the following:

a. Complete wound healing?

b. Ability to return to previous function and resumption of normal activities?

c. Reduction of wound size or healing trajectory which results in the patient's ability to return to previous function and resumption of normal activities?

The required clinical trial of PRP must adhere to the following standards of scientific integrity and relevance to the Medicare population:

a. The principal purpose of the CLINICAL STUDY is to test whether PRP improves the participants' health outcomes.

b. The CLINICAL STUDY is well supported by available scientific and medical information or it is intended to clarify or establish the health outcomes of interventions already in common clinical use.

c. The CLINICAL STUDY does not unjustifiably duplicate existing studies.

d. The CLINICAL STUDY design is appropriate to answer the research question being asked in the study.

e. The CLINICAL STUDY is sponsored by an organization or individual capable of executing the proposed study successfully.

f. The CLINICAL STUDY is in compliance with all applicable Federal regulations concerning the protection of human subjects found at 45 CFR Part 46.

g. All aspects of the CLINICAL STUDY are conducted according to appropriate standards of scientific integrity set by the International Committee of Medical Journal Editors (http://www.icmje.org).

h. The CLINICAL STUDY has a written protocol that clearly addresses, or incorporates by reference, the standards listed here as Medicare requirements for coverage with evidence development (CED).

i. The CLINICAL STUDY is not designed to exclusively test toxicity or disease pathophysiology in healthy individuals. Trials of all medical technologies measuring therapeutic outcomes as one of the objectives meet this standard only if the disease or condition being studied is life threatening as defined in 21 CFR §312.81(a) and the patient has no other viable treatment options.

j. The CLINICAL STUDY is registered on the ClinicalTrials. gov website by the principal sponsor/investigator prior to the enrollment of the first study subject.

k. The CLINICAL STUDY protocol specifies the method and timing of public release of all pre-specified outcomes to be measured including release of outcomes if outcomes are negative or study is terminated early. The results must be made public within 24 months of the end of data collection. If a report is planned to be published in a peer reviewed journal, then that initial release may be an abstract that meets the requirements of the International Committee of Medical Journal Editors (http://www.icmje.org). However a full report of the outcomes must be made public no later than three (3) years after the end of data collection.

l. The CLINICAL STUDY protocol must explicitly discuss subpopulations affected by the treatment under investigation, particularly traditionally underrepresented groups in clinical studies, how the inclusion and exclusion criteria effect enrollment of these populations, and a plan for the retention and reporting of said populations on the trial. If the inclusion and exclusion criteria are expected to have a negative effect on the recruitment or retention of underrepresented populations, the protocol must discuss why these criteria are necessary.

m. The CLINICAL STUDY protocol explicitly discusses how the results are or are not expected to be generalizable to the Medicare population to infer whether Medicare patients may benefit from the intervention. Separate discussions in the protocol may be necessary for populations eligible for Medicare due to age, disability or Medicaid eligibility.

Consistent with §1142 of the Social Security Act (the Act), the Agency for Healthcare Research and Quality (AHRQ) supports clinical research studies that CMS determines meet the above-listed standards and address the above-listed research questions.

Any clinical study undertaken pursuant to this NCD must be approved no later than August 2, 2014. If there are no approved clinical studies on or before August 2, 2014, this CED will expire. Any clinical study approved will adhere to the timeframe designated in the approved clinical study protocol.

C. Nationally Non-Covered Indications

1. Effective December 28, 1992, the Centers for Medicare & Medicaid Services (CMS) issued a national non-coverage determination for platelet-derived wound-healing formulas intended to treat patients with chronic, non-healing wounds. This decision was based on a lack of sufficient published data to determine safety and efficacy, and a public health service technology assessment.

2. Effective July 23, 2004, upon reconsideration, the clinical effectiveness of autologous PDGF products continues to not be adequately proven in scientific literature. As the evidence is insufficient to conclude that autologous PDGF in a platelet-poor plasma is reasonable and necessary, it remains non-covered for treatment of chronic, non-healing cutaneous wounds. Also, the clinical evidence does not support a benefit in the application of autologous PRP for the treatment of chronic, non-healing, cutaneous wounds. Therefore, CMS determines it is not reasonable and necessary and is nationally non-covered.

3. Effective April 27, 2006, coverage for treatments utilizing coverage for treatments utilizing becaplermin, a non-autologous growth factor for chronic, non-healing subcutaneous wounds, remains nationally non-covered under Part B based on section 1861(s)(2)(A) and (B) of the Social Security Act because this product is usually administered by the patient.

4. Effective March 19, 2008, upon reconsideration, the evidence is not adequate to conclude that autologous PRP is reasonable and necessary and remains non-covered for the treatment of chronic non-healing, cutaneous wounds. Additionally, upon reconsideration, the evidence is not adequate to conclude that autologous PRP is reasonable and necessary for the treatment of acute surgical wounds when the autologous PRP is applied directly to the closed incision, or for dehiscent wounds.

D. Other

In accordance with section 310.1 of the National Coverage Determinations Manual, the routine costs in Federally sponsored or approved clinical trials assessing the efficacy of autologous PRP in treating chronic, non-healing cutaneous wounds are covered by Medicare.

100-4, Chapter-1, 30.3.1

Mandatory Assignment on Carrier Claims

The following practitioners who provide services under the Medicare program are required to accept assignment for all Medicare claims for their services. This means that they must accept the Medicare allowed amount as payment in full for their practitioner services. The beneficiary's liability is limited to any applicable deductible plus the 20 percent coinsurance.

Assignment is mandated for the following claims:

- Clinical diagnostic laboratory services and physician lab services;
- Physician services to individuals dually entitled to Medicare and Medicaid;

Services of physician assistants, nurse practitioners, clinical nurse specialists, nurse midwives, certified registered nurse anesthetists, clinical psychologists, clinical social workers, registered dietitians/nutritionists, anesthesiologist assistants, and mass immunization roster billers.

NOTE: The provider type Mass Immunization Roster Biller can only bill for influenza and pneumococcal vaccinations and administrations. These services are not subject to the deductible or the 20 percent coinsurance.

- Ambulatory surgical center services; (No deductible and 25% coinsurance for colorectal cancer screening colonoscopies {G0105 and G0121) and effective for dates of service on or after January 1, 2008 G0104 also applies);
- Home dialysis supplies and equipment paid under Method II for dates of service prior to January 1, 2011. Refer to Section 30.3.8 for information regarding the elimination of Method II home dialysis for dates of service on and after January 1, 2011;
- Drugs and biologicals; and,
- Ambulance services

When these claims are inadvertently submitted as unassigned, carriers process them as assigned.

Note that, unlike physicians, practitioners, or suppliers bound by a participation agreement, practitioners/entities providing the services/supplies identified above are required to accept assignment only with respect to these services/supplies (unless they have signed participation agreements which blanket the full range of their services).

The carrier system must be able to identify (and update) the codes for those services subject to the assignment mandate.

For the practitioner services of physicians and independently practicing physical and occupational therapists, the acceptance of assignment is not mandatory. Nor is the acceptance of assignment mandatory for the suppliers of radiology services or diagnostic tests. However, these practitioners and suppliers may nevertheless voluntarily agree to participate to take advantage of the higher payment rate, in which case the participation status makes assignment mandatory for the term of the agreement. Such an agreement is known as the Medicare Participating Physician or Supplier Agreement. (See §30.3.12.2 Carrier Participation Agreement.) Physicians, practitioners, and suppliers who sign this agreement to participate are agreeing to accept assignment on all Medicare claims. The Medicare Participation Agreement and general instructions are on the CMS Web site.

Future updates to this section will be communicated in a Recurring Update Notification.

100-4, Chapter-1, 30.3.5

Effect of Assignment Upon Purchase of Cataract Glasses From Participating Physician or Supplier on Claims Submitted to Carriers

A pair of cataract glasses is comprised of two distinct products: a professional product (the prescribed lenses) and a retail commercial product (the frames). The frames serve not only as a holder of lenses but also as an article of personal apparel. As such, they are usually selected on the basis of personal taste and style. Although Medicare will pay only for standard frames, most patients want deluxe frames. Participating physicians and suppliers cannot profitably furnish such deluxe frames unless they can make an extra (noncovered) charge for the frames even though they accept assignment.

Therefore, a participating physician or supplier (whether an ophthalmologist, optometrist, or optician) who accepts assignment on cataract glasses with deluxe frames may charge the Medicare patient the difference between his/her usual charge to private pay patients for glasses with standard frames and his/her usual charge to such patients for glasses with deluxe frames, in addition to the applicable deductible and coinsurance on glasses with standard frames, if all of the following requirements are met:

A. The participating physician or supplier has standard frames available, offers them for sale to the patient, and issues and ABN to the patient that explains the price and other differences between standard and deluxe frames. Refer to Chapter 30.

B. The participating physician or supplier obtains from the patient (or his/her representative) and keeps on file the following signed and dated statement:

Name of Patient   Medicare Claim Number

Having been informed that an extra charge is being made by the physician or supplier for deluxe frames, that this extra charge is not covered by Medicare, and that standard frames are available for purchase from the physician or supplier at no extra charge, I have chosen to purchase deluxe frames.

Signature Date

C. The participating physician or supplier itemizes on his/her claim his/her actual charge for the lenses, his/her actual charge for the standard frames, and his/her actual extra charge for the deluxe frames (charge differential).

Once the assigned claim for deluxe frames has been processed, the carrier will follow the ABN instructions as described in §60.

100-4, Chapter-1, 50.3.2

Policy and Billing Instructions for Condition Code 44

In cases where a hospital or a CAH's UR committee determines that an inpatient admission does not meet the hospital's inpatient criteria, the hospital or CAH may change the beneficiary's status from inpatient to outpatient and submit an outpatient claim (bill type 13x or 85x) for medically necessary Medicare Part B services that were furnished to the beneficiary, provided all of the following conditions are met:

1. The change in patient status from inpatient to outpatient is made prior to discharge or release, while the beneficiary is still a patient of the hospital;

2. The hospital has not submitted a claim to Medicare for the inpatient admission;

3. The practitioner responsible for the care of the patient and the UR committee concur with the decision; and

4. The concurrence of the practitioner responsible for the care of the patient and the UR committee is documented in the patient's medical record.

While typically the full UR committee makes the decision for the committee that a change in patient status under Condition Code 44 is warranted, in accordance with *§482.30(d)(1)* one physician member of the UR committee may make the decision for the committee, provided he or she is a different person from the concurring practitioner who is responsible for the care of the patient.

When the hospital has determined that it may submit an outpatient claim according to the conditions described above, the entire episode of care should be billed as an outpatient episode of care on a 13x or 85x bill type and outpatient services that were ordered and furnished should be billed as appropriate.

Refer to Pub. 100-04, Medicare Claims Processing Manual; Chapter 30, Financial Liability Protections; Section 20, Limitation On Liability (LOL) Under §1879 Where Medicare Claims Are Disallowed, for information regarding financial liability protections.

When the hospital submits a 13x or 85x bill for services furnished to a beneficiary whose status was changed from inpatient to outpatient, the hospital is required to report Condition Code 44 on the outpatient claim in one of Form Locators 24-30, or in the ASC X12N 837 institutional claim in loop 2300, HI segment, with qualifier BG, on the outpatient claim. Additional information may be found in Chapter 25 of this manual, (Completing and Processing the Form CMS-1450 Data Set). Condition Code 44 is used by CMS and QIOs to track and monitor these occurrences. The reporting of Condition Code 44 on a claim does not affect the amount of hospital outpatient payment that would otherwise be made for a hospital outpatient claim that did not require the reporting Condition Code 44.

One of the requirements for the use of Condition Code 44 is concurrence by the practitioner who is responsible for the care of the patient with the determination that an inpatient admission does not meet the hospital's admission criteria and that the patient should have been registered as an outpatient. This prerequisite for use of Condition Code 44 is consistent with the requirements in the CoP in §482.30 (d) of the regulations. This paragraph provides that the practitioner or practitioners responsible for the care of the patient must be consulted and allowed to present their views before the UR committee or QIO makes its determination that an admission is not medically necessary. It may also be appropriate to include the practitioner who admitted the patient if this is a different person than the practitioner responsible for the care of the patient.

If the conditions for use of Condition Code 44 are not met, the hospital may submit a 12x bill type for covered "Part B Only" services that were furnished to the inpatient. Medicare may still make payment for certain Part B services furnished to an inpatient of a hospital when payment cannot be made under Part A because an inpatient admission is determined not to be medically necessary. Information about "Part B Only" services is located in Pub. 100-02, Medicare Benefit Policy Manual, chapter 6, section 10. Examples of such services include, but are not limited to, diagnostic x-ray tests, diagnostic laboratory tests, surgical dressings and splints, prosthetic devices, and certain other services. The Medicare Benefit Policy Manual includes a complete list of the payable "Part B Only" services. See Pub. 100-04, Medicare Claims Processing Manual, chapter 4, section 10.12 for a discussion of the billing and payment rules regarding services furnished within the payment window for outpatient services treated as inpatient services.

Entries in the medical record cannot be expunged or deleted and must be retained in their original form. Therefore, all orders and all entries related to the inpatient admission must be retained in the record in their original form. If a patient's status changes in accordance with the requirements for use of Condition Code 44, the change must be fully documented in the medical record, complete with orders and notes that indicate why the change was made, the care that was furnished to the beneficiary, and the participants in making the decision to change the patient's status.

When Condition Code 44 is appropriately used, the hospital reports on the outpatient bill the services that were ordered and provided to the patient for the entire patient encounter. However, in accordance with the general Medicare requirements for services furnished to beneficiaries and billed to Medicare, even in Condition Code 44 situations, hospitals may not report observation services using HCPCS code G0378 (Hospital observation service, per hour) for observation services furnished during a hospital encounter prior to a physician's order for observation services. Medicare does not permit retroactive orders or the inference of physician orders. Like all hospital outpatient services, observation services must be ordered by a physician. The clock time begins at the time that observation services are initiated in accordance with a physician's order.

While hospitals may not report observation services under HCPCS code G0378 for the time period during the hospital encounter prior to a physician's order for observation services, in Condition Code 44 situations, as for all other hospital outpatient encounters, hospitals may include charges on the outpatient claim for the costs of all hospital resources utilized in the care of the patient during the entire encounter. For example, a beneficiary is admitted as an inpatient and receives 12 hours of monitoring and nursing care, at which point the hospital changes the status of the beneficiary from inpatient to outpatient and the physician orders observation services, with all criteria for billing under Condition Code 44 being met. On the outpatient claim on an uncoded line with revenue code 0762, the hospital could bill for the 12 hours of monitoring and nursing care that were provided prior to the change in status and the physician order for observation services, in addition to billing HCPCS code G0378 for the observation services that followed the change in status and physician order for observation services. For other rules related to billing and payment of observation services, see chapter 4, section 290 of this manual, and Pub.100-02, Medicare Benefit Policy Manual, chapter 6, Section 20.6.

100-4, Chapter-3, 10.4

Payment of Nonphysician Services for Inpatients

All items and nonphysician services furnished to inpatients must be furnished directly by the hospital or billed through the hospital under arrangements. This provision applies to all hospitals, regardless of whether they are subject to PPS.

A. Other Medical Items, Supplies, and Services

The following medical items, supplies, and services furnished to inpatients are covered under Part A. Consequently, they are covered by the prospective payment rate or reimbursed as reasonable costs under Part A to hospitals excluded from PPS.

- Laboratory services (excluding anatomic pathology services and certain clinical pathology services);
- Pacemakers and other prosthetic devices including lenses, and artificial limbs,knees, and hips;
- Radiology services including computed tomography (CT) scans furnished to inpatients by a physician's office, other hospital, or radiology clinic;
- Total parenteral nutrition (TPN) services; and
- Transportation, including transportation by ambulance, to and from another hospital or freestanding facility to receive specialized diagnostic or therapeutic services not available at the facility where the patient is an inpatient.

•

The hospital must include the cost of these services in the appropriate ancillary service cost center, i.e., in the cost of the diagnostic or therapeutic service. It must not show them separately under revenue code 0540.

EXCEPTIONS:

- **Pneumococcal Vaccine** - is payable under Part B only and is billed by the hospital on the Form CMS-1450.
- **Ambulance Service** - For purposes of this section "hospital inpatient" means a beneficiary who has been formally admitted it does not include a beneficiary who is in the process of being transferred from one hospital to another. Where the patient is transferred from one hospital to another, and is admitted as an inpatient to the second, the ambulance service is payable under only Part B. If transportation is by a hospital owned and operated ambulance, the hospital bills separately on Form CMS-1450 as appropriate. Similarly, if the hospital arranges for the ambulance transportation with an ambulance operator, including paying the ambulance operator, it bills separately. However, if the hospital does not assume any financial responsibility, the billing is to the carrier by the ambulance operator or beneficiary, as appropriate, if an ambulance is used for the transportation of a hospital inpatient to another facility for diagnostic tests or special treatment the ambulance trip is considered part of the DRG, and not separately billable, if the resident hospital is under PPS.
- **Part B Inpatient Services** - Where Part A benefits are not payable, payment may be made to the hospital under Part B for certain medical and other health services. See Chapter 4 for a description of Part B inpatient services.
- **Anesthetist Services "Incident to" Physician Services** - If a physician's practice was to employ anesthetists and to bill on a reasonable charge basis for these services and that practice was in effect as of the last day of the hospital's most recent 12-month cost reporting period ending before September 30, 1983, the physician may continue that practice through cost reporting periods beginning October 1, 1984. However, if the physician chooses to continue this practice, the hospital may not add costs of the anesthetist's service to its base period costs for purposes of its transition payment rates. If it is the existing or new practice of the physician to employ certified registered nurse anesthetists (CRNAs) and other qualified anesthetists and include charges for their services in the physician bills for anesthesiology services for the hospital's cost report periods beginning on or after October 1, 1984, and before October 1, 1987, the physician may continue to do so.

B. Exceptions/Waivers

These provisions were waived before cost reporting periods beginning on or after October 1, 1986, under certain circumstances. The basic criteria for waiver was that services furnished by outside suppliers are so extensive that a sudden change in billing practices would threaten the stability of patient care. Specific criteria for waiver and processing procedures are in §2804 of the Provider Reimbursement Manual (CMS Pub. 15-1).

100-4, Chapter-3, 20.7.3

Payment for Blood Clotting Factor Administered to Hemophilia Inpatients

Section 6011 of Public Law (P.L.) 101-239 amended §1886(a)(4) of the Social Security Act (the Act) to provide that prospective payment system (PPS) hospitals receive an additional payment for the costs of administering blood clotting factor to Medicare hemophiliacs who are hospital inpatients. Section 6011(b) of P.L. 101.239 specified that the payment be based on a predetermined price per unit of clotting factor multiplied by the number of units provided. This add-on payment originally was effective for blood clotting factors furnished on or after June 19, 1990, and before December 19, 1991. Section 13505 of P. L. 103-66 amended §6011 (d) of P.L. 101-239 to extend the period covered by the add-on payment for blood clotting factors administered to Medicare inpatients with hemophilia through September 30, 1994 Section 4452 of P.L. 105-33 amended §6011(d) of P.L. 101-239 to reinstate the add-on payment for the costs of administering blood-clotting factor to Medicare beneficiaries who have hemophilia and who are hospital inpatients for discharges occurring on or after October 1, 1998.

A/B MACs (B) shall process non-institutional blood clotting factor claims.

The A/B MACs (A) shall process institutional blood clotting factor claims payable under either Part A or Part B.

A. Inpatient Bills

Under the Inpatient Prospective Payment System (IPPS), hospitals receive a special add-on payment for the costs of furnishing blood clotting factors to Medicare beneficiaries with hemophilia, admitted as inpatients of PPS hospitals. The clotting factor add-on payment is calculated using the number of units (as defined in the HCPCS code long descriptor) billed by the provider under special instructions for units of service.

The PPS Pricer software does not calculate the payment amount. The Fiscal Intermediary Shared System (FISS) calculates the payment amount and subtracts the charges from those submitted to Pricer so that the clotting factor charges are not included in cost outlier computations.

Blood clotting factors not paid on a cost or PPS basis are priced as a drug/biological under the Medicare Part B Drug Pricing File effective for the specific date of service. As of January 1, 2005, the average sales price (ASP) plus 6 percent shall be used.

If a beneficiary is in a covered Part A stay in a PPS hospital, the clotting factors are paid in addition to the DRG/HIPPS payment (For FY 2004, this payment is based on 95 percent of average wholesale price.) For a SNF subject to SNF/PPS, the payment is bundled into the SNF/PPS rate.

For SNF inpatient Part A, there is no add-on payment for blood clotting factors.

The codes for blood-clotting factors are found on the Medicare Part B Drug Pricing File. This file is distributed on a quarterly basis.

For discharges occurring on or after October 1, 2000, and before December 31, 2005, report HCPCS Q0187 based on 1 billing unit per 1.2 mg. Effective January 1, 2006, HCPCS code J7189 replaces Q0187 and is defined as 1 billing unit per 1 microgram (mcg).

The examples below include the HCPCS code and indicate the dosage amount specified in the descriptor of that code. Facilities use the units field as a multiplier to arrive at the dosage amount.

EXAMPLE 1

HCPCS	Drug	Dosage
J7189	Factor VIIa	1 mcg

Actual dosage: 13,365 mcg

On the bill, the facility shows J7189 and 13,365 in the units field (13,365 mcg divided by 1 mcg = 13,365 units).

NOTE: The process for dealing with one international unit (IU) is the same as the process of dealing with one microgram.

EXAMPLE 2

HCPCS	Drug	Dosage
J9355	Trastuzumab	10 mg

Actual dosage: 140 mg

On the bill, the facility shows J9355 and 14 in the units field (140 mg divided by 10mg = 14 units).

When the dosage amount is greater than the amount indicated for the HCPCS code, the facility rounds up to determine units. When the dosage amount is less than the amount indicated for the HCPCS code, use 1 as the unit of measure.

EXAMPLE 3

HCPCS	Drug	Dosage
J9355	Tenecteplase	50 mg

Actual Dosage: 40 mg

The provider would bill for 1 unit, even though less than 1 full unit was furnished.

At times, the facility provides less than the amount provided in a single use vial and there is waste, i.e.; some drugs may be available only in packaged amounts that exceed the needs of an individual patient. Once the drug is reconstituted in the hospital's pharmacy, it may have a limited shelf life. Since an individual patient may receive less than the fully reconstituted amount, we encourage hospitals to schedule patients in such a way that the hospital can use the drug most efficiently. However, if the hospital must discard the remainder of a vial after administering part of it to a Medicare patient, the provider may bill for the amount of drug discarded plus the amount administered.

Example 1:

Drug X is available only in a 100-unit size. A hospital schedules three Medicare patients to receive drug X on the same day within the designated shelf life of the product. An appropriate hospital staff member administers 30 units to each patient. The remaining 10 units are billed to Medicare on the account of the last patient. Therefore, 30 units are billed on behalf of the first patient seen and 30 units are billed on behalf of the second patient seen. Forty units are billed on behalf of the last patient seen because the hospital had to discard 10 units at that point.

Example 2:

An appropriate hospital staff member must administer 30 units of drug X to a Medicare patient, and it is not practical to schedule another patient who requires the same drug. For example, the hospital has only one patient who requires drug X, or the hospital sees the patient for the first time and did not know the patient's condition. The hospital bills for 100 units on behalf of the patient, and Medicare pays for 100 units.

When the number of units of blood clotting factor administered to hemophiliac inpatients exceeds 99,999, the hospital reports the excess as a second line for revenue code 0636 and repeats the HCPCS code. One hundred thousand fifty (100,050) units are reported on one line as 99,999, and another line shows 1,051.

Revenue Code 0636 is used. It requires HCPCS. Some other inpatient drugs continue to be billed without HCPCS codes under pharmacy.

No changes in beneficiary notices are required. Coverage is applicable to hospital Part A claims only. Coverage is also applicable to inpatient Part B services in SNFs and all types of hospitals, including CAHs. Separate payment is not made to SNFs for beneficiaries in an inpatient Part A stay.

B. -A/B MAC (A) Action

The contractor is responsible for the following:

- It accepts HCPCS codes for inpatient services;
- It edits to require HCPCS codes with Revenue Code 0636. Multiple iterations of the revenue code are possible with the same or different HCPCS codes. It does not edit units except to ensure a numeric value;
- It reduces charges forwarded to Pricer by the charges for hemophilia clotting factors in revenue code 0636. It retains the charges and revenue and HCPCS codes for CWF; and
- It modifies data entry screens to accept HCPCS codes for hospital (including CAH) swing bed, and SNF inpatient claims (bill types 11X, 12X, 18x, 21x and, 22x).

The September 1, 1993, IPPS final rule (58 FR 46304) states that payment will be made for the blood clotting factor only if an ICD-9-CM diagnosis code for hemophilia is included on the bill.

Inpatient blood-clotting factors are covered only for beneficiaries with hemophilia. One of the following hemophilia diagnosis codes must be reported on the claim for payment to be made for blood clotting factors.

100-4, Chapter-3, 40.2.2

Charges to Beneficiaries for Part A Services

The hospital submits a bill even where the patient is responsible for a deductible which covers the entire amount of the charges for non-PPS hospitals, or in PPS hospitals, where the DRG payment amount will be less than the deductible.

A hospital receiving payment for a covered hospital stay (or PPS hospital that includes at least one covered day, or one treated as covered under guarantee of payment or limitation on liability) may charge the beneficiary, or other person, for items and services furnished during the stay only as described in subsections A through H. If limitation of liability applies, a beneficiary's liability for payment is governed by the limitation on liability notification rules in Chapter 30 of this manual. For related notices for inpatient hospitals, see CMS Transmittal 594, Change Request 3903, dated June 24, 2005.

A. Deductible and Coinsurance

The hospital may charge the beneficiary or other person for applicable deductible and coinsurance amounts. The deductible is satisfied only by charges for covered services. The FI deducts the deductible and coinsurance first from the PPS payment. Where the deductible exceeds the PPS amount, the excess will be applied to a subsequent payment to the hospital. (See Chapter 3 of the Medicare General Information, Eligibility, and Entitlement Manual for specific policies.)

B. Blood Deductible

The Part A blood deductible provision applies to whole blood and red blood cells, and reporting of the number of pints is applicable to both PPS and non-PPS hospitals. (See Chapter 3 of the Medicare General Information, Eligibility, and Entitlement Manual for specific policies.) Hospitals shall report charges for red blood cells using revenue code 381, and charges for whole blood using revenue code 382.

C. Inpatient Care No Longer Required

The hospital may charge for services that are not reasonable and necessary or that constitute custodial care. Notification may be required under limitation of liability. See CMS Transmittal 594, Change Request 3903, dated June 24, 2005, section V. of the attachment, for specific notification requirements. Note this transmittal will be placed in Chapter 30 of this manual at a future point. Chapter 1, section 150 of this manual also contains related billing information in addition to that provided below.

In general, after proper notification has occurred, and assuming an expedited decision is received from a Quality Improvement Organization (QIO), the following entries are required on the bill the hospital prepares:

- Occurrence code 31 (and date) to indicate the date the hospital notified the patient in accordance with the first bullet above;
- Occurrence span code 76 (and dates) to indicate the period of noncovered care for which it is charging the beneficiary;
- Occurrence span code 77 (and dates) to indicate the period of noncovered care for which the provider is liable, when it is aware of this prior to billing; and
- Value code 31 (and amount) to indicate the amount of charges it may bill the beneficiary for days for which inpatient care was no longer required. They are included as noncovered charges on the bill.

D. Change in the Beneficiary's Condition

If the beneficiary remains in the hospital after receiving notice as described in subsection C, and the hospital, the physician who concurred in the hospital's determination, or the QIO, subsequently determines that the beneficiary again requires inpatient hospital care, the hospital may not charge the beneficiary or other person for services furnished after the beneficiary again required inpatient hospital care until proper notification occurs (see subsection C).

If a patient who needs only a SNF level of care remains in the hospital after the SNF bed becomes available, and the bed ceases to be available, the hospital may continue to charge the beneficiary. It need not provide the beneficiary with another notice when the patient chose not to be discharged to the SNF bed.

E. Admission Denied

If the entire hospital admission is determined to be not reasonable or necessary, limitation of liability may apply. See 2005 CMS transmittal 594, section V. of the attachment, for specific notification requirements.

NOTE: This transmittal will be placed in Chapter 30 of this manual at a future point.

In such cases the following entries are required on the bill:

- Occurrence code 31 (and date) to indicate the date the hospital notified the beneficiary.

- Occurrence span code 76 (and dates) to indicate the period of noncovered care for which the hospital is charging the beneficiary.
- Occurrence span code 77 (and dates) to indicate any period of noncovered care for which the provider is liable (e.g., the period between issuing the notice and the time it may charge the beneficiary) when the provider is aware of this prior to billing.
- Value code 3l (and amount) to indicate the amount of charges the hospital may bill the beneficiary for hospitalization that was not necessary or reasonable. They are included as noncovered charges on the bill.

F. Procedures, Studies and Courses of Treatment That Are Not Reasonable or Necessary

If diagnostic procedures, studies, therapeutic studies and courses of treatment are excluded from coverage as not reasonable and necessary (even though the beneficiary requires inpatient hospital care) the hospital may charge the beneficiary or other person for the services or care according the procedures given in CMS Transmittal 594, Change Request 3903, dated June 24, 2005.

The following bill entries apply to these circumstances:

- Occurrence code 32 (and date) to indicate the date the hospital provided the notice to the beneficiary.
- Value code 3l (and amount) to indicate the amount of such charges to be billed to the beneficiary. They are included as noncovered charges on the bill.

G. Nonentitlement Days and Days after Benefits Exhausted

If a hospital stay exceeds the day outlier threshold, the hospital may charge for some, or all, of the days on which the patient is not entitled to Medicare Part A, or after the Part A benefits are exhausted (i.e., the hospital may charge its customary charges for services furnished on those days). It may charge the beneficiary for the lesser of:

- The number of days on which the patient was not entitled to benefits or after the benefits were exhausted; or
- The number of outlier days. (Day outliers were discontinued at the end of FY 1997.)

If the number of outlier days exceeds the number of days on which the patient was not entitled to benefits, or after benefits were exhausted, the hospital may charge for all days on which the patient was not entitled to benefits or after benefits were exhausted. If the number of days on which the beneficiary was not entitled to benefits, or after benefits were exhausted, exceeds the number of outlier days, the hospital determines the days for which it may charge by starting with the last day of the stay (i.e., the day before the day of discharge) and identifying and counting off in reverse order, days on which the patient was not entitled to benefits or after the benefits were exhausted, until the number of days counted off equals the number of outlier days. The days counted off are the days for which the hospital may charge.

H. Contractual Exclusions

In addition to receiving the basic prospective payment, the hospital may charge the beneficiary for any services that are excluded from coverage for reasons other than, or in addition to, absence of medical necessity, provision of custodial care, non-entitlement to Part A, or exhaustion of benefits. For example, it may charge for most cosmetic and dental surgery.

I. Private Room Care

Payment for medically necessary private room care is included in the prospective payment. Where the beneficiary requests private room accommodations, the hospital must inform the beneficiary of the additional charge. (See the Medicare Benefit Policy Manual, Chapter 1.) When the beneficiary accepts the liability, the hospital will supply the service, and bill the beneficiary directly. If the beneficiary believes the private room was medically necessary, the beneficiary has a right to a determination and may initiate a Part A appeal.

J. Deluxe Item or Service

Where a beneficiary requests a deluxe item or service, i.e., an item or service which is more expensive than is medically required for the beneficiary's condition, the hospital may collect the additional charge if it informs the beneficiary of the additional charge. That charge is the difference between the customary charge for the item or service most commonly furnished by the hospital to private pay patients with the beneficiary's condition, and the charge for the more expensive item or service requested. If the beneficiary believes that the more expensive item or service was medically necessary, the beneficiary has a right to a determination and may initiate a Part A appeal.

K – Inpatient Acute Care Hospital Admission Followed By a Death or Discharge Prior To Room Assignment

A patient of an acute care hospital is considered an inpatient upon issuance of written doctor's orders to that effect. If a patient either dies or is discharged prior to being assigned and/or occupying a room, a hospital may enter an appropriate room and board charge on the claim. If a patient leaves of their own volition prior to being assigned and/or occupying a room, a hospital may enter an appropriate room and board charge on the claim as well as a patient status code 07 which indicates they left against medical advice. A hospital is not required to enter a room and board charge, but failure to do so may have a minimal impact on future DRG weight calculations.

100-4, Chapter-4, 10.4

Packaging

Under the OPPS, packaged services are items and services that are considered to be an integral part of another service that is paid under the OPPS. No separate payment is made for packaged services, because the cost of these items and services is included in the APC payment for the service of which they are an integral part. For example, routine supplies, anesthesia, recovery room use, and most drugs are considered to be an integral part of a surgical procedure so payment for these items is packaged into the APC payment for the surgical procedure.

A. Packaging for Claims Resulting in APC Payments

If a claim contains services that result in an APC payment but also contains packaged services, separate payment for the packaged services is not made since payment is included in the APC. However, charges related to the packaged services are used for outlier and Transitional Corridor Payments (TOPs) as well as for future rate setting.

Therefore, it is extremely important that hospitals report all HCPCS codes consistent with their descriptors; CPT® and/or CMS instructions and correct coding principles, and all charges for all services they furnish, whether payment for the services is made separately paid or is packaged.

B. Packaging for Claims Resulting in No APC Payments

If the claim contains only services payable under cost reimbursement, such as corneal tissue, and services that would be packaged services if an APC were payable, then the packaged services are not separately payable. In addition, these charges for the packaged services are not used to calculate TOPs. If the claim contains only services payable under a fee schedule, such as clinical diagnostic laboratory tests, and also contains services that would be packaged services if an APC were payable, the packaged services are not separately payable. In addition, the charges are not used to calculate TOPs.

If a claim contains services payable under cost reimbursement, services payable under a fee schedule, and services that would be packaged services if an APC were payable, the packaged services are not separately payable. In addition, the charges are not used to calculate TOPs payments.

C. Packaging Types Under the OPPS

1. Unconditionally packaged services are services for which separate payment is never made because the payment for the service is always packaged into the payment for other services. Unconditionally packaged services are identified in the OPPS Addendum B with status indicator of N. See the OPPS Web site at http://www.cms.hhs.gov/HospitalOutpatientPPS/ for the most recent Addendum B (HCPCS codes with status indicators). In general, the charges for unconditionally packaged services are used to calculate outlier and TOPS payments when they appear on a claim with a service that is separately paid under the OPPS because the packaged service is considered to be part of the package of services for which payment is being made through the APC payment for the separately paid service.

2. STV-packaged services are services for which separate payment is made only if there is no service with status indicator S, T, V or reported with the same date of service on the same claim. If a claim includes a service that is assigned status indicator S, T, V reported on the same date of service as the STV- packaged service, the payment for the STV-packaged service is packaged into the payment for the service(s) with status indicator S, T, V and no separate payment is made for the STV-packaged service. STV-packaged services are assigned status indicator Q1. See the OPPS Webpage at http://www.cms.hhs.gov/HospitalOutpatientPPS/ for identification of STV-packaged codes.

3. T-packaged services are services for which separate payment is made only if there is no service with status indicator T reported with the same date of service on the same claim. When there is a claim that includes a service that is assigned status indicator T reported on the same date of service as the T-packaged service, the payment for the T-packaged service is packaged into the payment for the service(s) with status indicator T and no separate payment is made for the T-packaged service. T-packaged services are assigned status indicator Q2. See the OPPS Web site at http://www.cms.hhs.gov/HospitalOutpatientPPS/ for identification of T-packaged codes.

4. A service that is assigned to a composite APC is a major component of a single episode of care. The hospital receives one payment through a composite APC for multiple major separately identifiable services. Services mapped to composite APCs are assigned status indicator

Q3. See the discussion of composite APCs in section 10.2.1.

5. J1 services are assigned to comprehensive APCs. Payment for all adjunctive services reported on the same claim as a J1 service is packaged into payment for the primary J1 service. See the discussion of comprehensive APCs in section 10.2.2.

100-4, Chapter-4, 160

Clinic and Emergency Visits

CMS has acknowledged from the beginning of the OPPS that CMS believes that CPT® Evaluation and Management (E/M) codes were designed to reflect the activities of physicians and do not describe well the range and mix of services provided by hospitals during visits of clinic and emergency department patients. While awaiting the development of a national set of facility-specific codes and guidelines, providers should continue to apply their current internal guidelines to the existing CPT® codes. Each hospital's internal guidelines should follow the intent of the CPT® code descriptors, in that the guidelines should be designed to reasonably relate the intensity of hospital resources to the different levels of effort represented by the codes. Hospitals should ensure that their guidelines accurately reflect resource distinctions between the five levels of codes.

Effective January 1, 2007, CMS is distinguishing between two types of emergency departments: Type A emergency departments and Type B emergency departments.

A Type A emergency department is defined as an emergency department that is available 24 hours a day, 7 days a week and is either licensed by the State in which it is located under applicable State law as an emergency room or emergency department or it is held out to the public (by name, posted signs, advertising, or other means) as a place that provides care for emergency medical conditions on an urgent basis without requiring a previously scheduled appointment.

A Type B emergency department is defined as an emergency department that meets the definition of a "dedicated emergency department" as defined in 42 CFR 489.24 under the EMTALA regulations. It must meet at least one of the following requirements:

(1) It is licensed by the State in which it is located under applicable State law as an emergency room or emergency department;

(2) It is held out to the public (by name, posted signs, advertising, or other means) as a place that provides care for emergency medical conditions on an urgent basis without requiring a previously scheduled appointment; or

(3) During the calendar year immediately preceding the calendar year in which a determination under 42 CFR 489.24 is being made, based on a representative sample of patient visits that occurred during that calendar year, it provides at least one-third of all of its outpatient visits for the treatment of emergency medical conditions on an urgent basis without requiring a previously scheduled appointment.

Hospitals must bill for visits provided in Type A emergency departments using CPT® emergency department E/M codes. Hospitals must bill for visits provided in Type B emergency departments using the G-codes that describe visits provided in Type B emergency departments.

Hospitals that will be billing the new Type B ED visit codes may need to update their internal guidelines to report these codes.

Emergency department and clinic visits are paid in some cases separately and in other cases as part of a composite APC payment.

100-4, Chapter-4, 160.1

Critical Care Services

Hospitals should separately report all HCPCS codes in accordance with correct coding principles, CPT® code descriptions, and any additional CMS guidance, when available. Specifically with respect to CPT® code 99291 (Critical care, evaluation and management of the critically ill or critically injured patient; first 30-74 minutes), hospitals must follow the CPT® instructions related to reporting that CPT® code. Prior to January 1, 2011, any services that CPT® indicates are included in the reporting of CPT® code 99291 (including those services that would otherwise be reported by and paid to hospitals using any of the CPT® codes specified by CPT®) should not be billed separately by the hospital. Instead, hospitals should report charges for any services provided as part of the critical care services. In establishing payment rates for critical care services, and other services, CMS packages the costs of certain items and services separately reported by HCPCS codes into payment for critical care services and other services, according to the standard OPPS methodology for packaging costs.

Beginning January 1, 2011, in accordance with revised CPT® guidance, hospitals that report in accordance with the CPT® guidelines will begin reporting all of the ancillary services and their associated charges separately when they are provided in conjunction with critical care. CMS will continue to recognize the existing CPT® codes for critical care services and will establish payment rates based on historical data, into which the cost of the ancillary services is intrinsically packaged. The I/OCE conditionally packages payment for the ancillary services that are reported on the same date of service as critical care services in order to avoid overpayment. The payment status of the ancillary services does not change when they are not provided in conjunction with critical care services. Hospitals may use HCPCS modifier -59 to indicate when an ancillary procedure or service is distinct or independent from critical care when performed on the same day but in a different encounter.

Beginning January 1, 2007, critical care services will be paid at two levels, depending on the presence or absence of trauma activation. Providers will receive one payment rate for critical care without trauma activation and will receive additional payment when critical care is associated with trauma activation.

To determine whether trauma activation occurs, follow the National Uniform Billing Committee (NUBC) guidelines in the Claims Processing Manual, Pub 100-04, Chapter 25, §75.4 related to the reporting of the trauma revenue codes in the 68x series. The revenue code series 68x can be used only by trauma centers/hospitals as licensed or designated by the state or local government authority authorized to do so, or as verified by the American College of Surgeons. Different subcategory revenue codes are reported by designated Level 1-4 hospital trauma centers. Only patients for whom there has been prehospital notification based on triage information from prehospital caregivers, who meet either local, state or American College of Surgeons field triage criteria, or are delivered by inter-hospital transfers, and are given the appropriate team response can be billed a trauma activation charge.

When critical care services are provided without trauma activation, the hospital may bill CPT® code 99291, Critical care, evaluation and management of the critically ill or critically injured patient; first 30-74 minutes (and 99292, if appropriate). If trauma activation occurs under the circumstances described by the NUBC guidelines that would permit reporting a charge under 68x, the hospital may also bill one unit of code G0390, which describes trauma activation associated with hospital critical care services. Revenue code 68x must be reported on the same date of service. The OCE will edit to ensure that G0390 appears with revenue code 68x on the same date of service and that only one unit of G0390 is billed. CMS believes that trauma activation is a one-time occurrence in association with critical care services, and therefore, CMS will only pay for one unit of G0390 per day.

The CPT® code 99291 is defined by CPT® as the first 30-74 minutes of critical care. This 30 minute minimum has always applied under the OPPS. The CPT® code 99292, Critical care, evaluation and management of the critically ill or critically injured patient; each additional 30 minutes, remains a packaged service under the OPPS, so that hospitals do not have the ongoing administrative burden of reporting precisely the time for each critical service provided. As the CPT® guidelines indicate, hospitals that provide less than 30 minutes of critical care should bill for a visit, typically an emergency department visit, at a level consistent with their own internal guidelines.

Under the OPPS, the time that can be reported as critical care is the time spent by a physician and/or hospital staff engaged in active face-to-face critical care of a critically ill or critically injured patient. If the physician and hospital staff or multiple hospital staff members are simultaneously engaged in this active face-to-face care, the time involved can only be counted once.

- Beginning in CY 2007 hospitals may continue to report a charge with RC 68x without any HCPCS code when trauma team activation occurs. In order to receive additional payment when critical care services are associated with trauma activation, the hospital must report G0390 on the same date of service as RC 68x, in addition to CPT® code 99291 (or 99292, if appropriate.)
- Beginning in CY 2007 hospitals should continue to report 99291 (and 99292 as appropriate) for critical care services furnished without trauma team activation. CPT® 99291 maps to APC 0617 (Critical Care). (CPT® 99292 is packaged and not paid separately, but should be reported if provided.)

Critical care services are paid in some cases separately and in other cases as part of a composite APC payment.

Future updates will be issued in a Recurring Update Notification.

100-4, Chapter-4, 200.1

Billing for Corneal Tissue

Corneal tissue will be paid on a cost basis, not under OPPS. To receive cost based reimbursement hospitals must bill charges for corneal tissue using HCPCS code V2785.

100-4, Chapter-4, 200.2

Hospital Dialysis Services For Patients With and Without End Stage Renal Disease (ESRD)

Effective with claims with dates of service on or after August 1, 2000, hospital-based End Stage Renal Disease (ESRD) facilities must submit services covered under the ESRD benefit in 42 CFR 413.174 (maintenance dialysis and those items and services directly related to dialysis such as drugs, supplies) on a separate claim from services not covered under the ESRD benefit. Items and services not covered under the ESRD benefit must be billed by the hospital using the hospital bill type and be paid under the Outpatient Prospective Payment System (OPPS) (or to a CAH at reasonable cost). Services covered under the ESRD benefit in 42 CFR 413.174 must be billed on the ESRD bill type and must be paid under the ESRD PPS. This requirement is necessary to properly pay only unrelated ESRD services (those not covered under the ESRD benefit) under OPPS (or to a CAH at reasonable cost).

Medicare does not allow payment for routine or related dialysis treatments, which are covered and paid under the ESRD PPS, when furnished to ESRD patients in the outpatient department of a hospital. However, in certain medical situations in which the ESRD outpatient cannot obtain her or his regularly scheduled dialysis treatment at a certified ESRD facility, the OPPS rule for 2003 allows payment for non-routine dialysis treatments (which are not covered under the ESRD benefit) furnished to ESRD outpatients in the outpatient department of a hospital. Payment for unscheduled dialysis furnished to ESRD outpatients and paid under the OPPS is limited to the following circumstances:

- Dialysis performed following or in connection with a dialysis-related procedure such as vascular access procedure or blood transfusions;
- Dialysis performed following treatment for an unrelated medical emergency; e.g., if a patient goes to the emergency room for chest pains and misses a regularly scheduled dialysis treatment that cannot be rescheduled, CMS allows the hospital to provide and bill Medicare for the dialysis treatment; or
- Emergency dialysis for ESRD patients who would otherwise have to be admitted as inpatients in order for the hospital to receive payment.

In these situations, non-ESRD certified hospital outpatient facilities are to bill Medicare using the Healthcare Common Procedure Coding System (HCPCS) code G0257 (Unscheduled or emergency dialysis treatment for an ESRD patient in a hospital outpatient department that is not certified as an ESRD facility).

HCPCS code G0257 may only be reported on type of bill 13X (hospital outpatient service) or type of bill 85X (critical access hospital) because HCPCS code G0257 only reports services for hospital outpatients with ESRD and only these bill types are used to report services to hospital outpatients. Effective for services on and after October 1, 2012, claims containing HCPCS code G0257 will be returned to the provider for correction if G0257 is reported with a type of bill other than 13X or 85X (such as a 12x inpatient claim).

HCPCS code 90935 (Hemodialysis procedure with single physician evaluation) may be reported and paid only if one of the following two conditions is met:

1. The patient is a hospital inpatient with or without ESRD and has no coverage under Part A, but has Part B coverage. The charge for hemodialysis is a charge for the use of a prosthetic device. See Benefits Policy Manual 100-02 Chapter 15 section 120. A. The service must be reported on a type of bill 12X or type of bill 85X. See the Benefits Policy Manual 100-02 Chapter 6 section 10 (Medical and Other Health Services Furnished to Inpatients of Participating Hospitals) for the criteria that must be met for services to be paid when a

hospital inpatient has Part B coverage but does not have coverage under Part A; or

2. A hospital outpatient does not have ESRD and is receiving hemodialysis in the hospital outpatient department. The service is reported on a type of bill 13X or type of bill 85X.

CPT® code 90945 (Dialysis procedure other than hemodialysis (e.g. peritoneal dialysis, hemofiltration, or other continuous replacement therapies)), with single physician evaluation, may be reported by a hospital paid under the OPPS or CAH method I or method II on type of bill 12X, 13X or 85X.

100-4, Chapter-4, 200.4

Billing for Amniotic Membrane

Hospitals should report HCPCS code V2790 (Amniotic membrane for surgical reconstruction, per procedure) to report amniotic membrane tissue when the tissue is used. A specific procedure code associated with use of amniotic membrane tissue is CPT® code 65780 (Ocular surface reconstruction; amniotic membrane transplantation). Payment for the amniotic membrane tissue is packaged into payment for CPT® code 65780 or other procedures with which the amniotic membrane is used.

100-4, Chapter-4, 200.6

Billing and Payment for Alcohol and/or Substance Abuse Assessment and Intervention Services

For CY 2008, the CPT® Editorial Panel has created two new Category I CPT® codes for reporting alcohol and/or substance abuse screening and intervention services. They are CPT® code 99408 (Alcohol and/or substance (other than tobacco) abuse structured screening (e.g., AUDIT, DAST), and brief intervention (SBI) services; 15 to 30 minutes); and CPT® code 99409 (Alcohol and/or substance (other than tobacco) abuse structured screening (e.g., AUDIT, DAST), and brief intervention (SBI) services; greater than 30 minutes). However, screening services are not covered by Medicare without specific statutory authority, such as has been provided for mammography, diabetes, and colorectal cancer screening. Therefore, beginning January 1, 2008, the OPPS recognizes two parallel G-codes (HCPCS codes G0396 and G0397) to allow for appropriate reporting and payment of alcohol and substance abuse structured assessment and intervention services that are not provided as screening services, but that are performed in the context of the diagnosis or treatment of illness or injury.

Contractors shall make payment under the OPPS for HCPCS code G0396 (Alcohol and/or substance (other than tobacco) abuse structured assessment (e.g., AUDIT, DAST) and brief intervention, 15 to 30 minutes) and HCPCS code G0397, (Alcohol and/or substance (other than tobacco) abuse structured assessment (e.g., AUDIT, DAST) and intervention greater than 30 minutes), only when reasonable and necessary (i.e., when the service is provided to evaluate patients with signs/symptoms of illness or injury) as per section 1862(a)(1)(A) of the Act.

HCPCS codes G0396 and G0397 are to be used for structured alcohol and/or substance (other than tobacco) abuse assessment and intervention services that are distinct from other clinic and emergency department visit services performed during the same encounter. Hospital resources expended performing services described by HCPCS codes G0396 and G0397 may not be counted as resources for determining the level of a visit service and vice versa (i.e., hospitals may not double count the same facility resources in order to reach a higher level clinic or emergency department visit). However, alcohol and/or substance structured assessment or intervention services lasting less than 15 minutes should not be reported using these HCPCS codes, but the hospital resources expended should be included in determining the level of the visit service reported.

100-4, Chapter-4, 200.7.2

Cardiac Echocardiography With Contrast

Hospitals are instructed to bill for echocardiograms with contrast using the applicable HCPCS code(s) included in Table 200.7.2 below. Hospitals should also report the appropriate units of the HCPCS codes for the contrast agents used in the performance of the echocardiograms.

Table 200.7.2 – HCPCS Codes For Echocardiograms With Contrast

HCPCS	Long Descriptor
C8921	Transthoracic echocardiography with contrast, or without contrast followed by with contrast, for congenital cardiac anomalies; complete
C8922	Transthoracic echocardiography with contrast, or without contrast followed by with contrast, for congenital cardiac anomalies; follow-up or limited study
C8923	Transthoracic echocardiography with contrast, or without contrast followed by with contrast, real-Time with image documentation (2D), includes M-mode recording, when performed, complete, without spectral or color Doppler echocardiography
C8924	Transthoracic echocardiography with contrast, or without contrast followed by with contrast, real-time with image documentation (2D), includes M-mode recording, when performed, follow-up or limited study
C8925	Transesophageal echocardiography (TEE) with contrast, or without contrast followed by with contrast, real time with image documentation (2D) (with or without M-mode recording); including probe placement, image acquisition, interpretation and report
C8926	Transesophageal echocardiography (TEE) with contrast, or without contrast followed by with contrast, for congenital cardiac anomalies; including probe placement, image acquisition, interpretation and report
C8927	Transesophageal echocardiography (TEE) with contrast, or without contrast followed by with contrast, for monitoring purposes, including probe placement, real time 2-dimensional image acquisition and interpretation leading to ongoing (continuous) assessment of (dynamically changing) cardiac pumping function and to therapeutic measures on an immediate time basis
C8928	Transthoracic echocardiography with contrast, or without contrast followed by with contrast, real-time with image documentation (2D), includes M-mode recording, when performed, during rest and cardiovascular stress test using treadmill, bicycle exercise and/or pharmacologically induced stress, with interpretation and report
C8929	Transthoracic echocardiography with contrast, or without contrast followed by with contrast, real-time with image documentation (2D), includes M-mode recording, when performed, complete, with spectral

Doppler echocardiography, and with color flow Doppler echocardiography

C8930	Transthoracic echocardiography, with contrast, or without contrast followed by with contrast, real-time with image documentation (2D), includes M-mode recording, when performed, during rest and cardiovascular stress test using treadmill, bicycle exercise and/or pharmacologically induced stress, with interpretation and report; including performance of continuous electrocardiographic monitoring, with physician supervision

100-4, Chapter-4, 230.2

Coding and Payment for Drug Administration

A. Overview

Drug administration services furnished under the Hospital Outpatient Prospective Payment System (OPPS) during CY 2005 were reported using CPT® codes 90780, 90781, and 96400-96459.

Effective January 1, 2006, some of these CPT® codes were replaced with more detailed CPT® codes incorporating specific procedural concepts, as defined and described by the CPT® manual, such as initial, concurrent, and sequential.

Hospitals are instructed to use the full set of CPT® codes, including those codes referencing concepts of initial, concurrent, and sequential, to bill for drug administration services furnished in the hospital outpatient department beginning January 1, 2007. In addition, hospitals are instructed to continue billing the HCPCS codes that most accurately describe the service(s) provided.

Hospitals are reminded to bill a separate Evaluation and Management code (with modifier 25) only if a significant, separately identifiable E/M service is performed in the same encounter with OPPS drug administration services.

B. Billing for Infusions and Injections

Beginning in CY 2007, hospitals were instructed to use the full set of drug administration CPT® codes (90760-90779; 96401-96549), (96413-96523 beginning in CY 2008) (96360-96549 beginning in CY 2009) when billing for drug administration services provided in the hospital outpatient department. In addition, hospitals are to continue to bill HCPCS code C8957 (Intravenous infusion for therapy/diagnosis; initiation of prolonged infusion (more than 8 hours), requiring use of portable or implantable pump) when appropriate. Hospitals are expected to report all drug administration CPT® codes in a manner consistent with their descriptors, CPT® instructions, and correct coding principles. Hospitals should note the conceptual changes between CY 2006 drug administration codes effective under the OPPS and the CPT® codes in effect beginning January 1, 2007, in order to ensure accurate billing under the OPPS. Hospitals should report all HCPCS codes that describe the drug administration services provided, regardless of whether or not those services are separately paid or their payment is packaged.

Medicare's general policy regarding physician supervision within hospital outpatient departments meets the physician supervision requirements for use of CPT® codes 90760-90779, 96401-96549, (96413-96523 beginning in CY 2008). (Reference: Pub.100-02, Medicare Benefit Policy Manual, Chapter 6, §20.4.)

Drug administration services are to be reported with a line item date of service on the day they are provided. In addition, only one initial drug administration service is to be reported per vascular access site per encounter, including during an encounter where observation services span more than 1 calendar day.

C. Payments For Drug Administration Services

For CY 2007, OPPS drug administration APCs were restructured, resulting in a six-level hierarchy where active HCPCS codes have been assigned according to their clinical coherence and resource use. Contrary to the CY 2006 payment structure that bundled payment for several instances of a type of service (non-chemotherapy, chemotherapy by infusion, non-infusion chemotherapy) into a per-encounter APC payment, structure introduced in CY 2007 provides a separate APC payment for each reported unit of a separately payable HCPCS code.

Hospitals should note that the transition to the full set of CPT® drug administration codes provides for conceptual differences when reporting, such as those noted below.

- In CY 2006, hospitals were instructed to bill for the first hour (and any additional hours) by each type of infusion service (non-chemotherapy, chemotherapy by infusion, non-infusion chemotherapy). Beginning in CY 2007, the first hour concept no longer exists. CPT® codes in CY 2007 and beyond allow for only one initial service per encounter, for each vascular access site, no matter how many types of infusion services are provided; however, hospitals will receive an APC payment for the initial service and separate APC payment(s) for additional hours of infusion or other drug administration services provided that are separately payable.

- In CY 2006, hospitals were instructed to bill for the first hour (and any additional hours) by each type of infusion service (non-chemotherapy, chemotherapy by infusion, non-infusion chemotherapy). Beginning in CY 2007, the first hour concept no longer exists. CPT® codes in CY 2007 and beyond allow for only one initial service per encounter, for each vascular access site, no matter how many types of infusion services are provided; however, hospitals will receive an APC payment for the initial service and separate APC payment(s) for additional hours of infusion or other drug administration services provided that are separately payable.

  (NOTE: This list above provides a brief overview of a limited number of the conceptual changes between CY 2006 OPPS drug administration codes and CY 2007 OPPS drug administration codes - this list is not comprehensive and does not include all items hospitals will need to consider during this transition)

For APC payment rates, refer to the most current quarterly version of Addendum B on the CMS Web site at http://www.cms.hhs.gov/HospitalOutpatientPPS/.

D. Infusions Started Outside the Hospital

Hospitals may receive Medicare beneficiaries for outpatient services who are in the process of receiving an infusion at their time of arrival at the hospital (e.g., a patient who arrives via ambulance with an ongoing intravenous infusion initiated by paramedics during transport). Hospitals are reminded to bill for all services provided using the HCPCS code(s) that most accurately describe the service(s) they provided. This includes hospitals reporting an initial hour of infusion, even if the hospital did not initiate the infusion, and additional HCPCS codes for additional or sequential infusion services if needed.

1100-4, Chapter-4, 231.4

Billing for Split Unit of Blood

HCPCS code P9011 was created to identify situations where one unit of blood or a blood product is split and some portion of the unit is transfused to one patient and the other portions are transfused to other patients or to the same patient at other times. When a patient receives a transfusion of a split unit of blood or blood product, OPPS providers should bill P9011 for the blood product transfused, as well as CPT® 86985 (Splitting, blood products) for each splitting procedure performed to prepare the blood product for a specific patient.

Providers should bill split units of packed red cells and whole blood using Revenue Code 389 (Other blood), and should not use Revenue Codes 381 (Packed red cells) or 382 (Whole blood). Providers should bill split units of other blood products using the applicable revenue codes for the blood product type, such as 383 (Plasma) or 384 (Platelets), rather than 389. Reporting revenue codes according to these specifications will ensure the Medicare beneficiary's blood deductible is applied correctly

EXAMPLE: OPPS provider splits off a 100cc aliquot from a 250 cc unit of leukocyte-reduced red blood cells for a transfusion to Patient X. The hospital then splits off an 80cc aliquot of the remaining unit for a transfusion to Patient Y. At a later time, the remaining 70cc from the unit is transfused to Patient Z.

In billing for the services for Patient X and Patient Y, the OPPS provider should report the charges by billing P9011 and 86985 in addition to the CPT® code for the transfusion service, because a specific splitting service was required to prepare a split unit for transfusion to each of those patients. However, the OPPS provider should report only P9011 and the CPT® code for the transfusion service for Patient Z because no additional splitting was necessary to prepare the split unit for transfusion to Patient Z. The OPPS provider should bill Revenue Code 0389 for each split unit of the leukocyte-reduced red blood cells that was transfused.

100-4, Chapter-4, 240

Inpatient Part B Hospital Services

Medicare pays for hospital (including CAH) inpatient Part B services in the circumstances provided in Pub. 100-02, Medicare Benefit Policy Manual, Chapter 6, § 10 ("Medical and Other Health Services Furnished to Inpatients of Participating Hospitals"). Hospitals must bill Part B inpatient services on a 12x Type of Bill. This Part B inpatient claim is subject to the statutory time limit for filing Part B claims described in chapter 1, §70 of this manual.

Inpatient Part B services include inpatient ancillary services that do not require an outpatient status and are not strictly provided in an outpatient setting. Services that require an outpatient status and are provided only in an outpatient setting are not payable inpatient Part B services, including Clinic Visits, Emergency Department Visits, and Observation Services (this is not a complete listing).

Inpatient routine services in a hospital generally are those services included by the provider in a daily service charge--sometimes referred to as the "Room and Board" charge. They include the regular room, dietary and nursing services, minor medical and surgical supplies, medical social services, psychiatric social services, and the use of certain equipment and facilities for which a separate charge is not customarily made to Medicare Part A. Many nursing services provided by the floor nurse (such as IV infusions and injections, blood administration, and nebulizer treatments, etc.) may or may not have a separate charge established depending upon the classification of an item or service as routine or ancillary among providers of the same class in the same State. Some provider's customary charging practice has established separate charges for these services following the PRM–1 instructions, however, in order for a provider's customary charging practice to be recognized it must be consistently followed for all patients and this must not result in an inequitable apportionment of cost to the program. If the PRM–1 instructions have not been followed, a provider cannot bill these services as separate charges. Additionally, it is important that the charges for service rendered and documentation meet the definition of the HCPCS in order to separately bill.

100-4, Chapter-4, 290.1

Observation Services Overview

Observation care is a well-defined set of specific, clinically appropriate services, which include ongoing short term treatment, assessment, and reassessment, that are furnished while a decision is being made regarding whether patients will require further treatment as hospital inpatients or if they are able to be discharged from the hospital. Observation services are commonly ordered for patients who present to the emergency department and who then require a significant period of treatment or monitoring in order to make a decision concerning their admission or discharge. Observation services are covered only when provided by the order of a physician or another individual authorized by State licensure law and hospital staff bylaws to admit patients to the hospital or to order outpatient services.

Observation services must also be reasonable and necessary to be covered by Medicare. In only rare and exceptional cases do reasonable and necessary outpatient observation services span more than 48 hours. In the majority of cases, the decision whether to discharge a patient from the hospital following resolution of the reason for the observation care or to admit the patient as an inpatient can be made in less than 48 hours, usually in less than 24 hours.

100-4, Chapter-4, 290.2.2

Reporting Hours of Observation

Observation time begins at the clock time documented in the patient's medical record, which coincides with the time that observation care is initiated in accordance with a physician's order. Hospitals should round to the nearest hour. For example, a patient who began receiving observation services at 3:03 p.m. according to the nurses' notes and was discharged to home at 9:45 p.m. when observation care and other outpatient services were completed, should have a "7" placed in the units field of the reported observation HCPCS code.

General standing orders for observation services following all outpatient surgery are not recognized. Hospitals should not report as observation care, services that are part of another Part B service, such as postoperative monitoring during a standard recovery period (e.g., 4-6 hours), which should be billed as recovery room services. Similarly, in the case of patients who undergo diagnostic testing in a hospital outpatient department, routine preparation services furnished prior to the testing and recovery afterwards are included in the payments for those diagnostic services.

Observation services should not be billed concurrently with diagnostic or therapeutic services for which active monitoring is a part of the procedure (e.g., colonoscopy, chemotherapy). In situations where such a procedure interrupts observation services, hospitals may determine the most appropriate way to account for this time. For example, a hospital may record for each period of observation services the beginning and ending times during the hospital outpatient encounter and add the length of time for the periods of observation services together to reach the total number of units reported on the claim for the hourly observation services HCPCS code G0378 (Hospital observation service, per hour). A hospital may also deduct the average length of time of the interrupting procedure, from the total duration of time that the patient receives observation services.

Observation time ends when all medically necessary services related to observation care are completed. For example, this could be before discharge when the need for observation has ended, but other medically necessary services not meeting the definition of observation care are provided (in which case, the additional medically necessary services would be billed separately or included as part of the emergency department or clinic visit). Alternatively, the end time of observation services may coincide with the time the patient is actually discharged from the hospital or admitted as an inpatient. Observation time may include medically necessary services and follow-up care provided after the time that the physician writes the discharge order, but before the patient is discharged. However, reported observation time would not include the time patients remain in the hospital after treatment is finished for reasons such as waiting for transportation home.

If a period of observation spans more than 1 calendar day, all of the hours for the entire period of observation must be included on a single line and the date of service for that line is the date that observation care begins.

100-4, Chapter-4, 290.4.1

Billing and Payment for All Hospital Observation Services Furnished Between January 1, 2006 and December 31, 2007

Since January 1, 2006, two G-codes have been used to report observation services and direct referral for observation care. For claims for dates of service January 1, 2006 through December 31, 2007, the Integrated Outpatient Code Editor (I/OCE) determines whether the observation care or direct referral services are packaged or separately payable. Thus, hospitals provide consistent coding and billing under all circumstances in which they deliver observation care.

Beginning January 1, 2006, hospitals should not report CPT® codes 99217-99220 or 99234-99236 for observation services. In addition, the following HCPCS codes were discontinued as of January 1, 2006: G0244 (Observation care by facility to patient), G0263 (Direct Admission with congestive heart failure, chest pain or asthma), and G0264 (Assessment other than congestive heart failure, chest pain, or asthma).

The three discontinued G-codes and the CPT® codes that were no longer recognized were replaced by two new G-codes to be used by hospitals to report all observation services, whether separately payable or packaged, and direct referral for observation care, whether separately payable or packaged:

- G0378- Hospital observation service, per hour; and
- G0379- Direct admission of patient for hospital observation care.

The I/OCE determines whether observation services billed as units of G0378 are separately payable under APC 0339 (Observation) or whether payment for observation services will be packaged into the payment for other services provided by the hospital in the same encounter. Therefore, hospitals should bill HCPCS code G0378 when observation services are ordered and provided to any patient regardless of the patient's condition. The units of service should equal the number of hours the patient receives observation services.

Hospitals should report G0379 when observation services are the result of a direct referral for observation care without an associated emergency room visit, hospital outpatient clinic visit, critical care service, or hospital outpatient surgical procedure (status indicator T procedure) on the day of initiation of observation services. Hospitals should only report HCPCS code G0379 when a patient is referred directly for observation care after being seen by a physician in the community (see §290.4.2 below)

Some non-repetitive OPPS services provided on the same day by a hospital may be billed on different claims, provided that all charges associated with each procedure or service being reported are billed on the same claim with the HCPCS code which describes that service. See chapter 1, section 50.2.2 of this manual. It is vitally important that all of the charges that pertain to a non-repetitive, separately paid procedure or service be reported on the same claim with that procedure or service. It should also be emphasized that this relaxation of same day billing requirements for some non-repetitive services does not apply to non-repetitive services provided on the same day as either direct referral to observation care or observation services because the OCE claim-by-claim logic cannot function properly unless all services related to the episode of observation care, including diagnostic tests, lab services, hospital clinic visits, emergency department visits, critical care services, and status indicator T procedures, are reported on the same claim. Additional guidance can be found in chapter 1, section 50.2.2 of this manual.

100-4, Chapter-4, 290.4.2

Separate and Packaged Payment for Direct Referral for Observation Services Furnished Between January 1, 2006 and December 31, 2007

In order to receive separate payment for a direct referral for observation care (APC 0604), the claim must show:

1. Both HCPCS codes G0378 (Hourly Observation) and G0379 (Direct Admit to Observation) with the same date of service;

2. That no services with a status indicator T or V or Critical care (APC 0617) were provided on the same day of service as HCPCS code G0379; and

3. The observation care does not qualify for separate payment under APC 0339.

Only a direct referral for observation services billed on a 13X bill type may be considered for a separate APC payment.

Separate payment is not allowed for HCPCS code G0379, direct admission to observation care, when billed with the same date of service as a hospital clinic visit, emergency room visit, critical care service, or "T" status procedure.

If a bill for the direct referral for observation services does not meet the three requirements listed above, then payment for the direct referral service will be packaged into payments for other separately payable services provided to the beneficiary in the same encounter.

100-4, Chapter-4, 290.4.3

Separate and Packaged Payment for Observation Services Furnished Between January 1, 2006 and December 31, 2007

Separate payment may be made for observation services provided to a patient with congestive heart failure, chest pain, or asthma. The list of ICD-9-CM diagnosis codes eligible for separate payment is reviewed annually. Any changes in applicable ICD-9-CM diagnosis codes are included in the October quarterly update of the OPPS and also published in the annual OPPS Final Rule. The list of qualifying ICD-9-CM diagnosis codes is also published on the OPPS Web page.

All of the following requirements must be met in order for a hospital to receive a separate APC payment for observation services through APC 0339:

1. Diagnosis Requirements

   a. The beneficiary must have one of three medical conditions: congestive heart failure, chest pain, or asthma.

   b. Qualifying ICD-9-CM diagnosis codes must be reported in Form Locator (FL) 76, Patient Reason for Visit, or FL 67, principal diagnosis, or both in order for the hospital to receive separate payment for APC 0339. If a qualifying ICD-9-CM diagnosis code(s) is reported in the secondary diagnosis field, but is not reported in either the Patient Reason for Visit field (FL 76) or in the principal diagnosis field (FL 67), separate payment for APC 0339 is not allowed.

2. Observation Time

   a. Observation time must be documented in the medical record.

   b. Hospital billing for observation services begins at the clock time documented in the patient's medical record, which coincides with the time that observation services are initiated in accordance with a physician's order for observation services.

   c. A beneficiary's time receiving observation services (and hospital billing) ends when all clinical or medical interventions have been completed, including follow-up care furnished by hospital staff and physicians that may take place after a physician has ordered the patient be released or admitted as an inpatient.

   d. The number of units reported with HCPCS code G0378 must equal or exceed 8 hours.

3. Additional Hospital Services

   a. The claim for observation services must include one of the following services in addition to the reported observation services. The additional services listed below must have a line item date of service on the same day or the day before the date reported for observation:

   - An emergency department visit (APC 0609, 0613, 0614, 0615, 0616) or

   - A clinic visit (APC 0604, 0605, 0606, 0607, 0608); or

   - Critical care (APC 0617); or

   - Direct referral for observation care reported with HCPCS code G0379 (APC 0604); must be reported on the same date of service as the date reported for observation services.

   b. No procedure with a T status indicator can be reported on the same day or day before observation care is provided.

4. Physician Evaluation

   a. The beneficiary must be in the care of a physician during the period of observation, as documented in the medical record by outpatient registration, discharge, and other appropriate progress notes that are timed, written, and signed by the physician.

   b. The medical record must include documentation that the physician explicitly assessed patient risk to determine that the beneficiary would benefit from observation care.

Only observation services that are billed on a 13X bill type may be considered for a separate APC payment.

Hospitals should bill all of the other services associated with the observation care, including direct referral for observation, hospital clinic visits, emergency room visits, critical care services, and T status procedures, on the same claim so that the claims processing logic may appropriately determine the payment status (either packaged or separately payable) of HCPCS codes G0378 and G0379.

If a bill for observation care does not meet all of the requirements listed above, then payment for the observation care will be packaged into payments for other separately payable services provided to the beneficiary in the same encounter.

100-4, Chapter-4, 290.5.1

Billing and Payment for Observation Services Beginning January 1, 2008

Observation services are reported using HCPCS code G0378 (Hospital observation service, per hour). Beginning January 1, 2008, HCPCS code G0378 for hourly observation services is assigned status indicator N, signifying that its payment is always packaged. No separate payment is made for observation services reported with HCPCS code G0378, and APC 0339 is deleted as of January 1, 2008. In most circumstances, observation services are supportive and ancillary to the other services provided to a patient. Beginning January 1, 2014, in certain circumstances when observation care is billed in conjunction with a clinic visit, high level Type A emergency department visit (Level 4 or 5), high level Type B emergency department visit (Level 5), critical care services, or a direct referral as an integral part of a patient's extended encounter of care, payment may be made for the entire extended care encounter through APC 8009 (Extended Assessment and Management Composite) when certain criteria are met. Prior to January 1, 2014, in certain circumstances when observation care was billed in conjunction with a high level clinic visit (Level 5), high level Type A emergency department visit (Level 4 or 5), high level Type B emergency department visit (Level 5), critical care services, or a direct referral as an integral part of a patient's extended encounter of care, payment could be made for the entire extended care encounter through one of two composite APCs (APCs 8002 and 8003) when certain criteria were met. APCs 8002 and 8003 are deleted as of January 1, 2014. For information about payment for extended assessment and management composite APC, see §10.2.1 (Composite APCs) of this chapter.

There is no limitation on diagnosis for payment of APC 8009; however, composite APC payment will not be made when observation services are reported in association with a surgical procedure (T status procedure) or the hours of observation care reported are less than 8. The I/OCE evaluates every claim received to determine if payment through a composite APC is appropriate. If payment through a composite APC is inappropriate, the I/OCE, in conjunction with the Pricer, determines the appropriate status indicator, APC, and payment for every code on a claim.

All of the following requirements must be met in order for a hospital to receive an APC payment for an extended assessment and management composite APC:

1. Observation Time

   a. Observation time must be documented in the medical record.

   b. Hospital billing for observation services begins at the clock time documented in the patient's medical record, which coincides with the time that observation services are initiated in accordance with a physician's order for observation services.

   c. A beneficiary's time receiving observation services (and hospital billing) ends when all clinical or medical interventions have been completed, including follow-up care furnished by hospital staff and physicians that may take place after a physician has ordered the patient be released or admitted as an inpatient.

   d. The number of units reported with HCPCS code G0378 must equal or exceed 8 hours.

2. Additional Hospital Services

   a. The claim for observation services must include one of the following services in addition to the reported observation services. The additional services listed below must have a line item date of service on the same day or the day before the date reported for observation:

      • A Type A or B emergency department visit (CPT® codes 99284 or 99285 or HCPCS code G0384); or

      • A clinic visit (HCPCS code G0463 beginning January 1, 2014; CPT® code 99205 or 99215 prior to January 1, 2014); or

      • Critical care (CPT® code 99291); or

      • Direct referral for observation care reported with HCPCS code G0379 (APC 0633) must be reported on the same date of service as the date reported for observation services.

   b. No procedure with a T status indicator can be reported on the same day or day before observation care is provided.

3. Physician Evaluation.

   a. The beneficiary must be in the care of a physician during the period of observation, as documented in the medical record by outpatient registration, discharge, and other appropriate progress notes that are timed, written, and signed by the physician.

   b. The medical record must include documentation that the physician explicitly assessed patient risk to determine that the beneficiary would benefit from observation care.

Criteria 1 and 3 related to observation care beginning and ending time and physician evaluation apply regardless of whether the hospital believes that the criteria will be met for payment of the extended encounter through extended assessment and management composite payment.

Only visits, critical care and observation services that are billed on a 13X bill type may be considered for a composite APC payment.

Non-repetitive services provided on the same day as either direct referral for observation care or observation services must be reported on the same claim because the OCE claim-by-claim logic cannot function properly unless all services related to the episode of observation care, including hospital clinic visits, emergency department visits, critical care services, and T status procedures, are reported on the same claim. Additional guidance can be found in chapter 1, section 50.2.2 of this manual.

If a claim for services provided during an extended assessment and management encounter including observation care does not meet all of the requirements listed above, then the usual APC logic will apply to separately payable items and services on the claim; the special logic for direct admission will apply, and payment for the observation care will be packaged into payments for other separately payable services provided to the beneficiary in the same encounter.

100-4, Chapter-4, 290.5.2

Billing and Payment for Direct Referral for Observation Care Furnished Beginning January 1, 2008

Direct referral for observation is reported using HCPCS code G0379 (Direct referral for hospital observation care). : Prior to January 1, 2010, the code descriptor for HCPCS code G0379 was (Direct admission of patient for hospital observation care). Hospitals should report G0379 when observation services are the result of a direct referral for observation care without an associated emergency room visit, hospital outpatient clinic visit, or critical care service on the day of initiation of observation services. Hospitals should only report HCPCS code G0379 when a patient is referred directly to observation care after being seen by a physician in the community.

Payment for direct referral for observation care will be made either separately as a low level hospital clinic visit under APC 0633 (Level 3 Examinations & Related Services) or packaged into payment for composite APC 8009 (Extended Assessment and Management Composite) or packaged into the payment for other separately payable services provided in the same encounter. For information about payment for extended assessment and management composite APCs, see, §10.2.1 (Composite APCs) of this chapter.

The criteria for payment of HCPCS code G0379 under either APC 0633 or APC 8009 include:

1. Both HCPCS codes G0378 (Hospital observation services, per hr.) and G0379 (Direct referral for hospital observation care) are reported with the same date of service.
2. No service with a status indicator of T or V or Critical Care (APC 0617) is provided on the same day of service as HCPCS code G0379.

If either of the above criteria is not met, HCPCS code G0379 will be assigned status indicator N and will be packaged into payment for other separately payable services provided in the same encounter.

Only a direct referral for observation services billed on a 13X bill type may be considered for a composite APC payment.

100-4, Chapter-4, 300.6

Common Working File (CWF) Edits

The CWF edit will allow 3 hours of therapy for MNT in the initial calendar year. The edit will allow more than 3 hours of therapy if there is a change in the beneficiary's medical condition, diagnosis, or treatment regimen and this change must be documented in the beneficiary's medical record. Two new G codes have been created for use when a beneficiary receives a

second referral in a calendar year that allows the beneficiary to receive more than 3 hours of therapy. Another edit will allow 2 hours of follow-up MNT with another referral in subsequent years.

Advance Beneficiary Notice (ABN)

The beneficiary is liable for services denied over the limited number of hours with referrals for MNT. An ABN should be issued in these situations. In absence of evidence of a valid ABN, the provider will be held liable.

An ABN should not be issued for Medicare-covered services such as those provided by hospital dietitians or nutrition professionals who are qualified to render the service in their state but who have not obtained Medicare provider numbers.

Duplicate Edits

Although beneficiaries are allowed to receive training and therapy during the same time period Diabetes Self-Management and Training (DSMT) and Medical Nutrition Therapy (MNT) services may not be provided on the same day to the same beneficiary. Effective April 1, 2010 CWF shall implement a new duplicate crossover edit to identify and prevent claims for DSMT/MNT services from being billed with the same dates of services for the same beneficiaries submitted from institutional providers and from a professional provider.

100-4, Chapter-4, 320

Outpatient Intravenous Insulin Treatment (OIVIT)

Effective for claims with dates of service on and after December 23, 2009, the Centers for Medicare and Medicaid Services (CMS) determines that the evidence does not support a conclusion that OIVIT improves health outcomes in Medicare beneficiaries. Therefore, CMS has determined that OIVIT is not reasonable and necessary for any indication under section 1862(a)(1)(A) of the Social Security Act. Services comprising an OIVIT regimen are nationally non-covered under Medicare when furnished pursuant to an OIVIT regimen.

See Pub. 100-03, Medicare National Coverage Determinations Manual, Section 40.7, Outpatient Intravenous Insulin Treatment (Effective December 23, 2009), for general information and coverage indications.

100-4, Chapter-4, 320.1

HCPCS Coding for OIVIT

HCPCS code G9147, effective with the April IOCE and MPFSDB updates, is to be used on claims with dates of service on and after December 23, 2009, billing for non-covered OIVIT and any services comprising an OIVIT regimen.

NOTE: HCPCS codes 99199 or 94681(with or without diabetes related conditions 250.00-250.93) are not to be used on claims billing for non-covered OIVIT and any services comprising an OIVIT regimen when furnished pursuant to an OIVIT regimen. Claims billing for HCPCS codes 99199 and 94681 for non-covered OIVIT are to be returned to provider/returned as unprocessable.

100-4, Chapter-4, 320.2

Medicare Summary Notices (MSN), Reason Codes, and Remark Codes

When returning non-covered OIVIT claims billed with HCPCS 99199 to provider/returning as unprocessable, contractors shall use:

Claims Adjustment Reason Code (CARC) 189: NOS or unlisted procedure code (CPT®/HCPCS) was billed when there is a specific procedure code for this procedure/service,

Remittance Advice Remark Code (RARC) N56: The procedure code billed is not correct/valid for the services billed or the date of service billed, and,

RARC MA66: Missing/incomplete/invalid principal procedure code.

When returning non-covered OIVIT claims billed with HCPCS 94681 with or without diabetes-related conditions 250-00-250.93 to provider/returning as unprocessable, contractors shall use:

CARC 11: The diagnosis is inconsistent with the procedure,

RARC N56: The procedure code billed is not correct/valid for the services billed or the date of service billed, and,

RARC MA66: Missing/incomplete/invalid principal procedure code.

When denying claims for non-covered OIVIT and any services comprising an OIVIT regimen billed with HCPCS code G9147, contractors shall use:

MSN 16.10 - Medicare does not pay for these item(s) or service(s),

CARC 96: Non-covered charge(s),

CARC M51: Missing/Incomplete /Invalid Procedure Code(s), and,

RARC N386: This decision was based on an NCD. An NCD provides a coverage determination as to whether a particular item or service is covered. A copy of this policy is available at http://www.cms.hhs.gov/mcd/search.asp. If you do not have Web access, you may contact the contractor to request a copy of the NCD.

100-4, Chapter-5, 10.2

The Financial Limitation Legislation

A. Legislation on Limitations

The dollar amount of the limitations (caps) on outpatient therapy services is established by statute. The updated amount of the caps is released annually via Recurring Update Notifications and posted on the CMS Website www.cms.gov/TherapyServices, on contractor Websites, and on each beneficiary's Medicare Summary Notice. Medicare contractors shall publish the financial limitation amount in educational articles. It is also available at 1-800-Medicare.

Section 4541(a)(2) of the Balanced Budget Act (BBA) (P.L. 105-33) of 1997, which added §1834(k)(5) to the Act, required payment under a prospective payment system (PPS) for outpatient rehabilitation services (except those furnished by or under arrangements with a hospital). Outpatient rehabilitation services include the following services:

- Physical therapy
- Speech-language pathology; and
- Occupational therapy.

Section 4541(c) of the BBA required application of financial limitations to all outpatient rehabilitation services (except those furnished by or under arrangements with a hospital). In 1999, an annual per beneficiary limit of $1,500 was applied, including all outpatient physical therapy services and speech-language pathology services. A separate limit applied to all occupational therapy services. The limits were based on incurred expenses and included applicable deductible and coinsurance. The BBA provided that the limits be indexed by the Medicare Economic Index (MEI) each year beginning in 2002.

Since the limitations apply to outpatient services, they do not apply to skilled nursing facility (SNF) residents in a covered Part A stay, including patients occupying swing beds. Rehabilitation services are included within the global Part A per diem payment that the SNF receives under the prospective payment system (PPS) for the covered stay. Also, limitations do not apply to any therapy services covered under prospective payment systems for home health or inpatient hospitals, including critical access hospitals.

The limitation is based on therapy services the Medicare beneficiary receives, not the type of practitioner who provides the service. Physical therapists, speech-language pathologists, and occupational therapists, as well as physicians and certain nonphysician practitioners, could render a therapy service.

B. Moratoria and Exceptions for Therapy Claims

Since the creation of therapy caps, Congress has enacted several moratoria. The Deficit Reduction Act of 2005 directed CMS to develop exceptions to therapy caps for calendar year 2006 and the exceptions have been extended periodically. The cap exception for therapy services billed by outpatient hospitals was part of the original legislation and applies as long as caps are in effect. Exceptions to caps based on the medical necessity of the service are in effect only when Congress legislates the exceptions.

100-4, Chapter-5, 10.6

Functional Reporting

A. General

Section 3005(g) of the Middle Class Tax Relief and Jobs Creation Act (MCTRJCA) amended Section 1833(g) of the Act to require a claims-based data collection system for outpatient therapy services, including physical therapy (PT), occupational therapy (OT) and speech-language pathology (SLP) services. 42 CFR 410.59, 410.60, 410.61, 410.62 and 410.105 implement this requirement. The system will collect data on beneficiary function during the course of therapy services in order to better understand beneficiary conditions, outcomes, and expenditures.

Beneficiary unction information is reported using 42 nonpayable functional G-codes and seven severity/complexity modifiers on claims for PT, OT, and SLP services. Functional reporting on one functional limitation at a time is required periodically throughout an entire PT, OT, or SLP therapy episode of care.

The nonpayable G-codes and severity modifiers provide information about the beneficiary's functional status at the outset of the therapy episode of care, including projected goal status, at specified points during treatment, and at the time of discharge. These G-codes, along with the associated modifiers, are required at specified intervals on all claims for outpatient therapy services – not just those over the cap.

B. Application of New Coding Requirements

This functional data reporting and collection system is effective for therapy services with dates of service on and after January 1, 2013. A testing period will be in effect from January 1, 2013, until July 1, 2013, to allow providers and practitioners to use the new coding requirements to assure that systems work. Claims for therapy services furnished on and after July

1, 2013, that do not contain the required functional G-code/modifier information will be returned or rejected, as applicable.

C. Services Affected

These requirements apply to all claims for services furnished under the Medicare Part B outpatient therapy benefit and the PT, OT, and SLP services furnished under the CORF benefit. They also apply to the therapy services furnished personally by and incident to the service of a physician or a nonphysician practitioner (NPP), including a nurse practitioner (NP), a certified nurse specialist (CNS), or a physician assistant (PA), as applicable.

D. Providers and Practitioners Affected.

The functional reporting requirements apply to the therapy services furnished by the following providers: hospitals, CAHs, SNFs, CORFs, rehabilitation agencies, and HHAs (when the beneficiary is not under a home health plan of care). It applies to the following practitioners: physical therapists, occupational therapists, and speech-language pathologists in private practice (TPPs), physicians, and NPPs as noted above. The term "clinician" is applied to these practitioners throughout this manual section. (See definition section of Pub. 100-02, Chapter 15, section 220.)

E. Function-related G-codes

There are 42 functional G-codes, 14 sets of three codes each. Six of the G-code sets are generally for PT and OT functional limitations and eight sets of G-codes are for SLP functional limitations.

The following G-codes are for functional limitations typically seen in beneficiaries receiving PT or OT services. The first four of these sets describe categories of functional limitations and the final two sets describe "other" functional limitations, which are to be used for functional limitations not described by one of the four categories.

NONPAYABLE G-CODES FOR FUNCTIONAL LIMITATIONS		
Code	Long Descriptor	Short Descriptor
Mobility G-code Set		
G8978	Mobility: walking & moving around functional limitation, current status, at therapy episode outset and at reporting intervals	Mobility current status
G8979	Mobility: walking & moving around functional limitation, projected goal status, at therapy episode outset, at reporting intervals, and at discharge or to end reporting	Mobility goal status
G8980	Mobility: walking & moving around functional limitation, discharge status, at discharge from therapy or to end reporting	Mobility D/C status
Changing & Maintaining Body Position G-code Set		
G8981	Changing & maintaining body position functional limitation, current status, at therapy episode outset and at reporting intervals	Body pos current status
G8982	Changing & maintaining body position functional limitation, projected goal status, at therapy episode outset, at reporting intervals, and at discharge or to end reporting	Body pos goal status
G8983	Changing & maintaining body position functional limitation, discharge status, at discharge from therapy or to end reporting	Body pos D/C status

Carrying, Moving & Handling Objects G-code Set		
G8984	Carrying, moving & handling objects functional limitation, current status, at therapy episode outset and at reporting intervals	Carry current status
G8985	Carrying, moving & handling objects functional limitation, projected goal status, at therapy episode outset, at reporting intervals, and at discharge or to end reporting	Carry goal status
G8986	Carrying, moving & handling objects functional limitation, discharge status, at discharge from therapy or to end reporting	Carry D/C status
Self-Care G-code Set		
G8987	Self-care functional limitation, current status, at therapy episode outset and at reporting intervals	Self-care current status
G8988	Self-care functional limitation, projected goal status, at therapy episode outset, at reporting intervals, and at discharge or to end reporting	Self-care goal status
G8989	Self-care functional limitation, discharge status, at discharge from therapy or to end reporting	Self-care D/C status

The following "other PT/OT" functional G-codes are used to report:

- a beneficiary's functional limitation that is not defined by one of the above four categories;

- a beneficiary whose therapy services are not intended to treat a functional limitation;

- or a beneficiary's functional limitation when an overall, composite or other score from a functional assessment too is used and it does not clearly represent a functional limitation defined by one of the above four code sets.

Code	Long Descriptor	Short Descriptor
Other PT/OT Primary G-code Set		
G8990	Other physical or occupational therapy primary functional limitation, current status, at therapy episode outset and at reporting intervals	Other PT/OT current status
G8991	Other physical or occupational therapy primary functional limitation, projected goal status, at therapy episode outset, at reporting intervals, and at discharge or to end reporting	Other PT/OT goal status
G8992	Other physical or occupational therapy primary functional limitation, discharge status, at discharge from therapy or to end reporting	Other PT/OT D/C status
Other PT/OT Subsequent G-code Set		
G8993	Other physical or occupational therapy subsequent functional limitation, current status, at therapy episode outset and at reporting intervals	Sub PT/OT current status
G8994	Other physical or occupational therapy subsequent functional limitation, projected goal status, at therapy episode outset, at reporting intervals, and at discharge or to end reporting	Sub PT/OT goal status

The following G-codes are for functional limitations typically seen in beneficiaries receiving SLP services. Seven are for specific functional communication measures, which are modeled after the National Outcomes Measurement System (NOMS), and one is for any "other" measure not described by one of the other seven.

Code	Long Descriptor	Short Descriptor
Swallowing G-code Set		
G8996	Swallowing functional limitation, current status, at therapy episode outset and at reporting intervals	Swallow current status
G8997	Swallowing functional limitation, projected goal status, at therapy episode outset, at reporting intervals, and at discharge or to end reporting	Swallow goal status
G8998	Swallowing functional limitation, discharge status, at discharge from therapy or to end reporting	Swallow D/C status
Motor Speech G-code Set **(Note: These codes are not sequentially numbered)**		
G8999	Motor speech functional limitation, current status, at therapy episode outset and at reporting intervals	Motor speech current status
G9186	Motor speech functional limitation, projected goal status at therapy episode outset, at reporting intervals, and at discharge or to end reporting	Motor speech goal status
G9158	Motor speech functional limitation, discharge status, at discharge from therapy or to end reporting	Motor speech D/C status
Spoken Language Comprehension G-code Set		
G9159	Spoken language comprehension functional limitation, current status, at therapy episode outset and at reporting intervals	Lang comp current status
G9160	Spoken language comprehension functional limitation, projected goal status, at therapy episode outset, at reporting intervals, and at discharge or to end reporting	Lang comp goal status
G9161	Spoken language comprehension functional limitation, discharge status, at discharge from therapy or to end reporting	Lang comp D/C status
Spoken Language Expressive G-code Set		
G9162	Spoken language expression functional limitation, current status, at therapy episode outset and at reporting intervals	Lang express current status
G9163	Spoken language expression functional limitation, projected goal status, at therapy episode outset, at reporting intervals, and at discharge or to end reporting	Lang press goal status
G9164	Spoken language expression functional limitation, discharge status, at discharge from therapy or to end reporting	Lang express D/C status
Attention G-code Set		
G9165	Attention functional limitation, current status, at therapy episode outset and at reporting intervals	Atten current status
G9166	Attention functional limitation, projected goal status, at therapy episode outset, at reporting intervals, and at discharge or to end reporting	Atten goal status
G9167	Attention functional limitation, discharge status, at discharge from therapy or to end reporting	Atten D/C status

Code	Long Descriptor	Short Descriptor
Memory G-code Set		
G9168	Memory functional limitation, current status, at therapy episode outset and at reporting intervals	Memory current status
G9169	Memory functional limitation, projected goal status, at therapy episode outset, at reporting intervals, and at discharge or to end reporting	Memory goal status
G9170	Memory functional limitation, discharge status, at discharge from therapy or to end reporting	Memory D/C status
Voice G-code Set		
G9171	Voice functional limitation, current status, at therapy episode outset and at reporting intervals	Voice current status
G9172	Voice functional limitation, projected goal status, at therapy episode outset, at reporting intervals, and at discharge or to end reporting	Voice goal status
G9173	Voice functional limitation, discharge status, at discharge from therapy or to end reporting	Voice D/C status

The following "other SLP" G-code set is used to report:

- on one of the other eight NOMS-defined functional measures not described by the above code sets; or

- to report an overall, composite or other score from assessment tool that does not clearly represent one of the above seven categorical SLP functional measures.

Code	Long Descriptor	Short Descriptor
Other Speech Language Pathology G-code Set		
G9174	Other speech language pathology functional limitation, current status, at therapy episode outset and at reporting intervals	Speech lang current status
G9175	Other speech language pathology functional limitation, projected goal status, at therapy episode outset, at reporting intervals, and at discharge or to end reporting	Speech lang goal status
G9176	Other speech language pathology functional limitation, discharge status, at discharge from therapy or to end reporting	Speech lang D/C status

F. Severity/Complexity Modifiers

For each nonpayable functional G-code, one of the modifiers listed below must be used to report the severity/complexity for that functional limitation.

Modifier	Impairment Limitation Restriction
CH	0 percent impaired, limited or restricted
CI	At least 1 percent but less than 20 percent impaired, limited or restricted
CJ	At least 20 percent but less than 40 percent impaired, limited or restricted
CK	At least 40 percent but less than 60 percent impaired, limited or restricted
CL	At least 60 percent but less than 80 percent impaired, limited or restricted
CM	At least 80 percent but less than 100 percent impaired, limited or restricted
CN	100 percent impaired, limited or restricted

The severity modifiers reflect the beneficiary's percentage of functional impairment as determined by the clinician furnishing the therapy services.

G. Required Reporting of Functional G-codes and Severity Modifiers

The functional G-codes and severity modifiers listed above are used in the required reporting on therapy claims at certain specified points during therapy episodes of care. Claims containing these functional G-codes must also contain another billable and separately payable (non-bundled) service. Only one functional limitation shall be reported at a given time for each related therapy plan of care (POC).

Functional reporting using the G-codes and corresponding severity modifiers is required reporting on specified therapy claims. Specifically, they are required on claims:

- At the outset of a therapy episode of care (i.e., on the claim for the date of service (DOS) of the initial therapy service);

- At least once every 10 treatment days, which corresponds with the progress reporting period;

- When an evaluative procedure, including a re-evaluative one, (HCPCS/CPT® codes 92521, 92522, 92523, 92524, 92597, 92607, 92608, 92610, 92611, 92612, 92614, 92616, 96105, 96125, 97001, 97002, 97003, 97004) is furnished and billed;

- At the time of discharge from the therapy episode of care– (i.e., on the date services related to the discharge [progress] report are furnished); and

- At the time reporting of a particular functional limitation is ended in cases where the need for further therapy is necessary.

- At the time reporting is begun for a new or different functional limitation within the same episode of care (i.e., after the reporting of the prior functional limitation is ended)

Functional reporting is required on claims throughout the entire episode of care. When the beneficiary has reached his or her goal or progress has been maximized on the initially selected functional limitation, but the need for treatment continues, reporting is required for a second functional limitation using another set of G-codes. In these situations two or more functional limitations will be reported for a beneficiary during the therapy episode of care. Thus, reporting on more than one functional limitation may be required for some beneficiaries but not simultaneously.

When the beneficiary stops coming to therapy prior to discharge, the clinician should report the functional information on the last claim. If the clinician is unaware that the beneficiary is not returning for therapy until after the last claim is submitted, the clinician cannot report the discharge status.

When functional reporting is required on a claim for therapy services, two G-codes will generally be required.

Two exceptions exist:

1. Therapy services under more than one therapy POC-- Claims may contain more than two nonpayable functional G-codes when in cases where a beneficiary receives therapy services under multiple POCs (PT, OT, and/or SLP) from the same therapy provider.

2. One-Time Therapy Visit-- When a beneficiary is seen and future therapy services are either not medically indicated or are going to be furnished by another provider, the clinician reports on the claim for the DOS of the visit, all three G-codes in the appropriate code set (current status, goal status and discharge status), along with corresponding severity modifiers.

Each reported functional G-code must also contain the following line of service information:

- Functional severity modifier

- Therapy modifier indicating the related discipline/ POC -- GP, GO or GN -- for PT, OT, and SLP services, respectively

- Date of the related therapy service

- Nominal charge, e.g., a penny, for institutional claims submitted to the A/B MACs (A). For professional claims, a zero charge is acceptable for the service line. If provider billing software requires an amount for professional claims, a nominal charge, e.g., a penny, may be included.

NOTE: The KX modifier is not required on the claim line for nonpayable G-codes, but would be required with the procedure code for medically necessary therapy services furnished once the beneficiary's annual cap has been reached.

The following example demonstrates how the G-codes and modifiers are used. In this example, the clinician determines that the beneficiary's mobility restriction is the most clinically relevant functional limitation and selects the Mobility G-code set (G8978 – G8980) to represent the beneficiary's functional limitation. The clinician also determines the severity/complexity of the beneficiary's functional limitation and selects the appropriate modifier. In this example, the clinician determines that the beneficiary has a 75 percent mobility restriction for which the CL modifier is applicable. The clinician expects that at the end of therapy the beneficiaries will have only a 15 percent mobility restriction for which the CI modifier is applicable. When the beneficiary attains the mobility goal, therapy continues to be medically necessary to address a functional limitation for which there is no categorical G-code. The clinician reports this using (G8990 – G8992).

At the outset of therapy-- On the DOS for which the initial evaluative procedure is furnished or the initial treatment day of a therapy POC, the claim for the service will also include two G-codes as shown below.

- G8978-CL to report the functional limitation (Mobility with current mobility limitation of "at least 60 percent but less than 80 percent impaired, limited or restricted")

- G8979-CI to report the projected goal for a mobility restriction of "at least 1 percent but less than 20 percent impaired, limited or restricted."

At the end of each progress reporting period-- On the claim for the DOS when the services related to the progress report (which must be done at least once each 10 treatment days) are furnished, the clinician will report the same two G-codes but the modifier for the current status may be different.

- G8978 with the appropriate modifier are reported to show the beneficiary's current status as of this DOS. So if the beneficiary has made no progress, this claim will include G8978-CL. If the beneficiary made progress and now has a mobility restriction of 65 percent CL would still be the appropriate modifier for 65 percent, and G8978-CL would be reported in this case. If the beneficiary now has a mobility restriction of 45 percent, G8978-CK would be reported.

- G8979-CI would be reported to show the projected goal. This severity modifier would not change unless the clinician adjusts the beneficiary's goal.

This step is repeated as necessary and clinically appropriate, adjusting the current status modifier used as the beneficiary progresses through therapy.

At the time the beneficiary is discharged from the therapy episode. The final claim for therapy episode will include two G-codes.

- G8979-CI would be reported to show the projected goal. G8980-CI would be reported if the beneficiary attained the 15 percent mobility goal. Alternatively, if the beneficiary's mobility restriction only reached 25 percent; G8980-CJ would be reported.

To end reporting of one functional limitation-- As noted above, functional reporting is required to continue throughout the entire episode of care. Accordingly, when further therapy is medically necessary after the beneficiary attains the goal for the first reported functional limitation, the clinician would end reporting of the first functional limitation by using the same G-codes and modifiers that would be used at the time of discharge. Using the mobility example, to end reporting of the mobility functional limitation, G8979-CI and G8980-CI would be reported on the same DOS that coincides with end of that progress reporting period.

To begin reporting of a second functional limitation. At the time reporting is begun for a new and different functional limitation, within the same episode of care (i.e., after the reporting of the prior functional limitation is ended). Reporting on the second functional limitation, however, is not begun until the DOS of the next treatment day -- which is day one of the new progress reporting period. When the next functional limitation to be reported is NOT defined by one of the other three PT/OT categorical codes, the G-code set (G8990 - G8992) for the "other PT/OT primary" functional limitation is used, rather than the G-code set for the "other PT/OT subsequent" because it is the first reported "other PT/OT" functional limitation. This reporting begins on the DOS of the first treatment day following the mobility "discharge" reporting, which is counted as the initial service for the "other PT/OT primary" functional limitation and the first treatment day of the new progress reporting period. In this case, G8990 and G8991, along with the corresponding modifiers, are reported on the claim for therapy services.

The table below illustrates when reporting is required using this example and what G-codes would be used.

Example of Required Reporting

Key: Reporting Period (RP)	Begin RP #1 for Mobility at Episode Outset	End RP#1 for Mobility at Progress Report	Mobility RP #2 Begins Next Treatment Day	End RP #2 for Mobility at Progress Report	Mobility RP #3 Begins Next Treatment Day	D/C or End Reporting for Mobility	Begin RP #1 for Other PT/OT Primary
Mobility: Walking & Moving Around							
G8978 – Current Status	X	X	X				
G 8979– Goal Status	X	X	X			X	
G8980 – Discharge Status						X	
Other PT/OT Primary							

Key: Reporting Period (RP)	Begin RP #1 for Mobility at Episode Outset	End RP#1 for Mobility at Progress Report	Mobility RP #2 Begins Next Treatment Day	End RP #2 for Mobility at Progress Report	Mobility RP #3 Begins Next Treatment Day	D/C or End Reporting for Mobility	Begin RP #1 for Other PT/OT Primary
G8990 – Current Status							X
G8991 – Goal Status							X
G8992 – Discharge Status							
No Functional Reporting Required		X		X			

H. Required Tracking and Documentation of Functional G-codes and Severity Modifiers

The clinician who furnishes the services must not only report the functional information on the therapy claim, but, he/she must track and document the G-codes and severity modifiers used for this reporting in the beneficiary's medical record of therapy services.

For details related to the documentation requirements, refer to, Medicare Benefit Policy Manual, Pub. 100-02, Chapter 15, section 220.4 - Functional Reporting. For coverage rules related to MCTRJCA and therapy goals, refer to Pub. 100-02: a) for outpatient therapy services, see Chapter 15, section 220.1.2 B and b) for instructions specific to PT, OT, and SLP services in the CORF, see Chapter 12, section 10.

100-4, Chapter-5, 20

HCPCS Coding Requirement

A. Uniform Coding

Section 1834(k)(5) of the Act requires that all claims for outpatient rehabilitation therapy services and all comprehensive outpatient rehabilitation facility (CORF) services be reported using a uniform coding system. The current Healthcare Common Procedure Coding System/Current Procedural Terminology is used for the reporting of these services. The uniform coding requirement in the Act is specific to payment for all CORF services and outpatient rehabilitation therapy services - including physical therapy, occupational therapy, and speech-language pathology - that is provided and billed to Medicare contractors. The Medicare physician fee schedule (MPFS) is used to make payment for these therapy services at the non facility rate.

Effective for claims submitted on or after April 1, 1998, providers that had not previously reported HCPCS/CPT® for outpatient rehabilitation and CORF services began using HCPCS to report these services. This requirement does not apply to outpatient rehabilitation services provided by:

- Critical access hospitals, which are paid on a cost basis, not MPFS;

- RHCs, and FQHCs for which therapy is included in the all-inclusive rate; or

- Providers that do not furnish therapy services.

The following "providers of services" must bill the A/B MAC (A) for outpatient rehabilitation services using HCPCS codes:

- Hospitals (to outpatients and inpatients who are not in a covered Part A stay);
- Skilled nursing facilities (SNFs) (to residents not in a covered Part A stay and to nonresidents who receive outpatient rehabilitation services from the SNF);
- Home health agencies (HHAs) (to individuals who are not homebound or otherwise are not receiving services under a home health plan of care (POC).
- Comprehensive outpatient rehabilitation facilities (CORFs); and
- Providers of outpatient physical therapy and speech-language pathology services (OPTs), also known as rehabilitation agencies (previously termed outpatient physical therapy facilities in this instruction).

Note 1. The requirements for hospitals and SNFs apply to inpatient Part B and outpatient services only. Inpatient Part A services are bundled into the respective prospective payment system payment; no separate payment is made.

Note 2. For HHAs, HCPCS/CPT® coding for outpatient rehabilitation services is required only when the HHA provides such service to individuals that are not homebound and, therefore, not under a home health plan of care.

The following practitioners must bill the A/B MAC (B) for outpatient rehabilitation therapy services using HCPCS/CPT® codes:

- Physical therapists in private practice (PTPPs),
- Occupational therapists in private practice (OTPPs),
- Speech-language pathologists in private practice (SLPPs),
- Physicians, including MDs, DOs, podiatrists and optometrists, and
- Certain nonphysician practitioners (NPPs), acting within their State scope of practice, e.g., nurse practitioners and clinical nurse specialists.

Providers billing to intermediaries shall report:

- The date the therapy plan of care was either established or last reviewed (see §220.1.3B) in Occurrence Code 17, 29, or 30.
- The first day of treatment in Occurrence Code 35, 44, or 45.

B. Applicable Outpatient Rehabilitation HCPCS Codes

The CMS identifies the codes listed at:

http://www.cms.hhs.gov/TherapyServices/05_Annual_Therapy_Update.asp#TopOfPage as therapy services, regardless of the presence of a financial limitation. Therapy services include only physical therapy, occupational therapy and speech-language pathology services. Therapist means only a physical therapist, occupational therapist or speech language pathologist. Therapy modifiers are GP for physical therapy, GO for occupational therapy, and GN for speech-language pathology.

When in effect, any financial limitation will also apply to services represented unless otherwise noted on the therapy page on the CMS Web site.

C. Additional HCPCS Codes

Some HCPCS/CPT® codes that are not on the list of therapy services should not be billed with a modifier. For example, outpatient non-rehabilitation HCPCS codes G0237, G0238, and G0239 should be billed without therapy modifiers. These HCPCS codes describe services for the improvement of respiratory function and may represent

either "incident to" services or respiratory therapy services that may be appropriately billed in the CORF setting. When the services described by these G-codes are provided by physical therapists (PTs) or occupational therapists (OTs) treating respiratory conditions, they are considered therapy services and must meet the other conditions for physical and occupational therapy. The PT or OT would use the appropriate HCPCS/CPT® code(s) in the 97000 - 97799 series and the corresponding therapy modifier, GP or GO, must be used.

Another example of codes that are not on the list of therapy services and should not be billed with a therapy modifier includes the following HCPCS codes: 95860, 95861, 95863, 95864, 95867, 95869, 95870, 95900, 95903, 95904, and 95934. These services represent diagnostic services - not therapy services; they must be appropriately billed and shall not include therapy modifiers.

Other codes not on the therapy code list, and not paid under another fee schedule, are appropriately billed with therapy modifiers when the services are furnished by therapists or provided under a therapy plan of care and where the services are covered and appropriately delivered (e.g., the therapist is qualified to provide the service). One example of non-listed codes where a therapy modifier is indicated regards the provision of services described in the CPT® code series, 29000 through 29590, for the application of casts and strapping. Some of these codes previously appeared on the therapy code list, but were deleted because we determined that they represented services that are most often performed outside a therapy plan of care. However, when these services are provided by therapists or as an integral part of a therapy plan of care, the CPT® code must be accompanied with the appropriate therapy modifier.

NOTE: The above lists of HCPCS/CPT® codes are intended to facilitate the contractor's ability to pay claims under the MPFS. It is not intended to be an exhaustive list of covered services, imply applicability to provider settings, and does not assure coverage of these services.

100-4, Chapter-5, 20.4

Coding Guidance for Certain CPT® Codes - All Claims

The following provides guidance about the use of codes 96105, 97026, 97150, 97545, 97546, and G0128.

- CPT® Codes 96105, 97545, and 97546.

Providers report code 96105, assessment of aphasia with interpretation and report in 1- hour units. This code represents formal evaluation of aphasia with an instrument such as the Boston Diagnostic Aphasia Examination. If this formal assessment is performed during treatment, it is typically performed only once during treatment and its medical necessity should be documented. If the test is repeated during treatment, the medical necessity of the repeat administration of the test must also be documented. It is common practice for regular assessment of a patient's progress in therapy to be documented in the chart, and this may be done using test items taken from the formal examinations. This is considered to be part of the treatment and should not be billed as 96105 unless a full, formal assessment is completed. Other timed physical medicine codes are 97545 and 97546. The interval for code 97545 is 2 hours and for code 97546, 1 hour. These are specialized codes to be used in the context of rehabilitating a worker to return to a job. The expectation is that the entire time period specified in the codes 97545 or 97546 would be the treatment period, since a shorter period of treatment could be coded with another code such as codes 97110, 97112, or 97537. (Codes 97545 and 97546 were developed for reporting services to persons in the worker's compensation program, thus CMS does not expect to see them reported for Medicare patients except under very unusual circumstances. Further, CMS would not expect to see code 97546 without also seeing code 97545 on the same claim. Code 97546, when used, is used in conjunction with 97545.)

- CPT® Code 97026

Effective for services performed on or after October 24, 2006, the Centers for Medicare & Medicaid Services announce a NCD stating the use of infrared and/or near-infrared light and/or heat, including monochromatic infrared energy (MIRE), is non-covered for the treatment, including symptoms such as pain arising from these conditions, of diabetic and/or non-diabetic peripheral sensory neuropathy, wounds and/or ulcers of the skin and/or subcutaneous tissues in Medicare beneficiaries. Further coverage guidelines can be found in the National Coverage Determination Manual (Pub. 100-03), section 270.6.

Contractors shall deny claims with CPT® 97026 (infrared therapy incident to or as a PT/OT benefit) and HCPCS E0221 or A4639, if the claim contains any of the following diagnosis codes:

ICD-9-CM

250.60 - 250.63

354.4, 354.5, 354.9

355.1 - 355.4

355.6 - 355.9

356.0, 356.2-356.4, 356.8-356.9

357.0 - 357.7

674.10, 674.12, 674.14, 674.20, 674.22, 674.24

707.00 -707.07, 707.09-707.15, 707.19

870.0 - 879.9

880.00 - 887.7

890.0 - 897.7

998.31 - 998.32

ICD-10-CM

See Addendum A Chapter 5, Section 20.4 (at end of this chapter) for the list of ICD 10-CM diagnosis codes that require denial with the above HCPCD codes.

Contractors can use the following messages when denying the service:

- Medicare Summary Notice # 21.11 "This service was not covered by Medicare at the time you received it."

- Reason Claim Adjustment Code #50 "These are non covered services because this is not deemed a medical necessity by the payer."

Advanced Beneficiary Notice (ABN):

Physicians, physical therapists, occupational therapists, outpatient rehabilitation facilities (ORFs), comprehensive outpatient rehabilitation facilities (CORFs), home health agencies (HHA), and hospital outpatient departments are liable if the service is performed, unless the beneficiary signs an ABN.

Similarly, DME suppliers and HHA are liable for the devices when they are supplied, unless the beneficiary signs an ABN.

100-4, Chapter-5, 100.4

Outpatient Mental Health Treatment Limitation

The Outpatient Mental Health Treatment Limitation (the limitation) is not applicable to CORF services because CORFs do not provide services to treat mental, psychoneurotic and personality disorders that are subject to the limitation in section 1833(c) of the Act. For dates of service on or after October 1, 2012, HCPCS code G0409 is the only code allowed for social work and psychological services furnished in a CORF. This service is not subject to the limitation because it is not a sychiatric mental health treatment service.

For additional information on the limitation, see Publication 100-01, Chapter 3, section 30 and Publication 100-02, Chapter 12, sections 50-50.5.

100-4, Chapter-5, 100.11

Billing for Social Work and Psychological Services in a CORF

The CORF providers shall only bill social work and psychological services with the following HCPCS code:

G0409 –Social work and psychological services, directly relating to and/or the patient's rehabilitation goals, each 15 minutes, face-to-face; individual (services provided by a CORF-qualified social worker or psychologist in a CORF)

In addition, HCPCS code G0409 shall only be billed with revenue code 0569 or 0911.

100-4, Chapter-8, 60.2.1.1

Separately Billable ESRD Drugs

The following categories of drugs (including but not limited to) are separately billable when used to treat the patient's renal condition:

- Antibiotics;
- Analgesics;
- Anabolics;
- Hematinics;
- Muscle relaxants;
- Sedatives;
- Tranquilizers; and
- Thrombolytics: used to declot central venous catheters. Note: Thrombolytics were removed from the separately billable drugs for claims with dates of service on or after January 1, 2013.

For claims with dates of service on or after July 1, 2013, when these drugs are administered through the dialysate the provider must append the modifier JE (Administered via Dialysate).

These separately billable drugs may only be billed by an ESRD facility if they are actually administered in the facility by the facility staff. Staff time used to administer separately billable drugs is covered under the composite rate and may not be billed separately. However, the supplies used to administer these drugs may be billed in addition to the composite rate.

Effective January 1, 2011, section 153b of the MIPPA requires that all ESRD-related drugs and biologicals be billed by the renal dialysis facility. When a drug or biological is billed by providers other than the ESRD facility and the drug or biological furnished is designated as a drug or biological that is included in the ESRD PPS (ESRD-related), the claim will be rejected or denied. In the event that an ESRD-related drug or biological was furnished to an ESRD beneficiary for reasons other than for the treatment of ESRD, the provider may submit a claim for separate payment using modifier AY.

All drugs reported on the renal dialysis facility claim are considered included in the ESRD PPS. The list of drugs and biologicals for consolidated billing are designated as always ESRD-related and therefore not allowing separate payment to be made to ESRD facilities. However, CMS has determined that some of these drugs may warrant separate payment.

Exceptions to "Always ESRD Related" Drugs:

The following drugs have been approved for separate payment consideration when billed with the AY modifier attesting to the drug not being used for the treatment of ESRD. The ESRD facility is required to indicate (in accordance with ICD-coding guidelines) the diagnosis code for which the drug is indicated.

- Vancomycin, effective January 1, 2012
- Daptomycin, effective January 1, 2013

Items and services subject to the consolidated billing requirements for the ESRD PPS can be found on the CMS website at:

http://www.cms.gov/ESRDPayment/50_Consolidated_Billing. asp# TopOfPage.

Other drugs and biologicals may be considered separately payable to the dialysis facility if the drug was not for the treatment of ESRD. The facility must include the modifier AY to indicate it was not for the treatment of ESRD.

Drugs are assigned HCPCS codes. If no HCPCS code is listed for a drug (e.g., a new drug) the facility bills using HCPCS code J3490, "Unclassified Drugs," and submits documentation identifying the drug. To establish a code for the drug, the FI checks HCPCS to verify that there is no acceptable HCPCS code for billing and if a code is not found checks with the local carrier, which may have a code and price that is appropriate.

If no code is found the drug is processed under HCPCS code J3490. See Chapter 17 for a complete description of drug pricing.

100-4, Chapter-8, 60.4

Erythropoietin Stimulating Agents (ESAs)

Coverage rules for ESAs are explained in the Medicare Benefit Policy Manual, Publication 100-02, chapter 11.

Fiscal intermediaries (FIs) pay for ESAs, to end-stage renal disease (ESRD) facilities as separately billable drugs to the composite rate. No additional payment is made to administer an ESA, whether in a facility or a home. Effective January 1, 2005, the cost of supplies to administer EPO may be billed to the FI. HCPCS A4657 and Revenue Code 270 should be used to capture the charges for syringes used in the administration of EPO.

ESAs and their administration supplies are included in the payment for the ESRD Prospective Payment System effective January 1, 2011. Providers must continue to report ESAs on the claim as ESAs are subject to a national claims monitoring program and are entitled to outlier payment consideration. The Medicare allowed payment (MAP) amount for outlier includes the ESA rate provided on the Average Sale Price (ASP) list, subject to reduction based on the ESA monitoring policy.

Medicare has an established national claims monitoring policy for erythropoietin stimulating agents for the in-facility dialysis population as outlined in the sections below.

100-4, Chapter-8, 60.4.1

ESA Claims Monitoring Policy

Effective for services provided on or after April 1, 2006, Medicare has implemented a national claims monitoring policy for ESAs administered in Medicare renal dialysis facilities. This policy does not apply to claims for ESAs for patients who receive their dialysis at home and self-administer their ESA.

While Medicare is not changing its coverage policy on erythropoietin use to maintain a target hematocrit level between 30% and 36%, we believe the variability in response to ESAs warrants postponing requiring monitoring until the hematocrit reaches higher levels. For dates of services April 1, 2006, and later, the Centers for Medicare & Medicaid Services (CMS) claims monitoring policy applies when the hematocrit level exceeds 39.0% or the hemoglobin level exceeds 13.0g/dL. This does not preclude the contractors from performing medical review at lower levels.

Effective for services provided on or after April 1, 2006, for claims reporting hematocrit or hemoglobin levels exceeding the monitoring threshold, the dose shall be reduced by 25% over the preceding month. Providers may report that a dose reduction did occur in response to the reported elevated hematocrit or hemoglobin level by adding a GS modifier on the claim. The definition of the GS modifier is defined as: "Dosage of ESA has been reduced and maintained in response to hematocrit or hemoglobin level." Thus, for claims reporting a hematocrit level or hemoglobin level exceeding the monitoring threshold without the GS modifier, CMS will reduce the covered dosage reported on the claim by 25%. The excess dosage is considered to be not reasonable and necessary. Providers are reminded that the patient's medical records should reflect hematocrit/hemoglobin levels and any dosage reduction reported on the claim during the same time period for which the claim is submitted.

Effective for dates of service provided on and after January 1, 2008, requests for payments or claims for ESAs for ESRD patients receiving dialysis in renal dialysis facilities reporting a hematocrit level exceeding 39.0% (or hemoglobin exceeding 13.0g/dL) shall also include modifier ED or EE. Claims reporting neither modifier or both modifiers will be returned to the provider for correction.

The definition of modifier ED is "The hematocrit level has exceeded 39.0% (or hemoglobin level has exceeded 13.0g/dL) 3 or more consecutive billing cycles immediately prior to and including the current billing cycle." The definition of modifier EE is "The hematocrit level has exceeded 39.0% (or hemoglobin level has exceeded 13.0g/dL) less than 3 consecutive billing cycles immediately prior to and including the current billing cycle." The GS modifier continues to be defined as stated above.

Providers may continue to report the GS modifier when the reported hematocrit or hemoglobin levels exceed the monitoring threshold for less than 3 months and a dose reduction has occurred. When both modifiers GS and EE are included, no reduction in the covered dose will occur. Claims reporting a hematocrit or hemoglobin level exceeding the monitoring threshold and the ED modifier shall have an automatic 50% reduction in the covered dose applied, even if the claim also reports the GS modifier.

Below is a chart illustrating the resultant claim actions under all possible reporting scenarios:

Hct Exceeds 39.0% or Hgb Exceeds 13.0g/dL	ED Modifier? (Hct >39% or Hgb >13g/dL ≥3 cycles)	EE Modifier? (Hct >39% or Hgb >13g/dL <3 cycles)	GS Modifier? (Dosage reduced and maintained)	Claim Action
No	N/A	N/A	N/A	Do not reduce reported dose.
Yes	No	No	No	Return to provider for correction. Claim must report either modifier ED or EE.
Yes	No	No	Yes	Return to provider for correction. Claim must report either modifier ED or EE.
Yes	No	Yes	Yes	Do not reduce reported dose.
Yes	No	Yes	No	Reduce reported dose 25%.
Yes	Yes	No	Yes	Reduce reported dose 50%.
Yes	Yes	No	No	Reduce reported dose 50%.

In some cases, physicians may believe there is medical justification to maintain a hematocrit above 39.0% or hemoglobin above 13.0g/dL. Beneficiaries, physicians, and/or renal facilities may submit additional medical documentation to justify this belief under the routine appeal process. You may reinstate any covered dosage reduction amounts under this first level appeal process when you believe the documentation supports a higher hematocrit/hemoglobin level.

Providers are reminded that, in accordance with FDA labeling, CMS expects that as the hematocrit approaches 36.0% (hemoglobin 12.0g/dL), a dosage reduction occurs. Providers are expected to maintain hematocrit levels between 30.0 to 36.0% (hemoglobin 10.0-12.0g/dL). Hematocrit levels that remain below 30.0% (hemoglobin levels below 10.0g/dL)) despite dosage increases, should have causative factors evaluated. The patient's medical record should reflect the clinical reason for dose changes and hematocrit levels outside the range of 30.0-36.0% (hemoglobin levels 10.0-12.0g/dL). Medicare contractors may review medical records to assure appropriate dose reductions are applied and maintained and hematological target ranges are maintained.

These hematocrit requirements apply only to ESAs furnished as an ESRD benefit under §1881(b) of the Social Security Act.

Medically Unlikely Edits (MUE)

For dates of service on and after January 1, 2008, the MUE for claims billing for Epogen® is reduced to 400,000 units from 500,000. The MUE for claims for Aranesp® is reduced to 1200 mcg from 1500 mcg.

For dates of service on and after April 1, 2013, the MUE for claims billing for peginesatide is applicable when units billed are equal to or greater than 26 mg.

It is likely that claims reporting doses exceeding the threshold reflect typographical errors and will be returned to providers for correction.

100-4, Chapter-8, 60.4.4.1

Payment for Epoetin Alfa (EPO) in Other Settings

With the implementation of the ESRD PPS, ESRD-related EPO is included in ESRD PPS payment amount and is not separately payable on Part B claims with dates of service on or after January 1, 2011 for other providers with the exception of a hospital billing for an emergency or unscheduled dialysis session.

In the hospital inpatient setting, payment under Part A is included in the DRG.

In the hospital inpatient setting, payment under Part B is made on bill type 12x. Hospitals report the drug units based on the units defined in the HCPCS description. Hospitals do not report value code 68 for units of EPO. For dates of service prior to April 1, 2006, report EPO under revenue code 0636. For dates of service from April 1, 2006 report EPO under the respective revenue code 0634 for EPO less than 10,000 units and revenue code 0635 for EPO over 10,000 units. Payment will be based on the ASP Pricing File.

In a skilled nursing facility (SNF), payment for EPO covered under the Part B EPO benefit is not included in the prospective payment rate for the resident's Medicare-covered SNF stay.

In a hospice, payment is included in the hospice per diem rate.

For a service furnished by a physician or incident to a physician's service, payment is made to the physician by the carrier in accordance with the rules for 'incident to" services. When EPO is administered in the renal facility, the service is not an "incident to" service and not under the "incident to" provision.

100-4, Chapter-8, 60.4.4.2

Epoetin Alfa (EPO) Provided in the Hospital Outpatient Departments

When ESRD patients come to the hospital for an unscheduled or emergency dialysis treatment they may also require the administration of EPO. Effective January 1, 2005, EPO will be paid based on the ASP Pricing File.

Hospitals use type of bill 13X (or 85X for Critical Access Hospitals) and report charges under the respective revenue code 0634 for EPO less than 10,000 units and revenue code 0635 for EPO over 10,000 units. Hospitals report the drug units based on the units defined in the HCPCS description. Hospitals do not report value code 68 for units of EPO. Value code 49 must be reported with the hematocrit value for the hospital outpatient visits prior to January 1, 2006, and for all claims with dates of service on or after January 1, 2008.

100-4, Chapter-8, 60.4.5.1

Self Administered ESA Supply

Initially, facilities may bill for up to a 2-month supply of an ESA for Method I beneficiaries who meet the criteria for selection for self-administration. After the initial two months' supply, the facility will bill for one month's supply at a time. Condition code 70 is used to indicate payment requested for a supply of an ESA furnished a beneficiary. Usually, revenue code 0635 would apply to EPO since the supply would be over 10,000 units. Facilities leave FL 46, Units of Service, blank since they are not administering the drug.

For claims with dates of service on or after January 1, 2008, supplies of an ESA for self administration should be billed according to the pre-determined plan of care schedule provided to the beneficiary. Submit a separate line item for each date an administration is expected to be performed with the expected dosage. In the event that the schedule was changed, the provider should note the changes in the medical record and bill according to the revised schedule. For patients beginning to self administer an ESA at home receiving an extra month supply of the drug, bill the one month reserve supply on one claim line and include modifier EM defined as "Emergency Reserve Supply (for ESRD benefit only)".

When billing for drug wastage in accordance with the policy in chapter 17 of this manual, section 40.1 the provider must show the wastage on a separate line item with the modifier JW. The line item date of service should be the date of the last covered administration according to the plan of care or if the patient dies use the date of death.

Condition code 70 should be reported on claims billing for home dialysis patients that self administer anemia management drugs including ESAs.

100-4, Chapter-8, 60.4.6.3

Payment Amount for Darbepoetin Alfa (Aranesp)

For Method I patients, the FI pays the facility per one mcg of Aranesp administered, in accordance with the MMA Drug Payment Limits Pricing File rounded up to the next highest whole mcg. Effective January 1, 2005, Aranesp will be paid based on the ASP Pricing File. Effective January 1, 2005, the cost of supplies to administer Aranesp may be billed to the FI. HCPCS A4657 and Revenue Code 270 should be used to capture the charges for syringes used in the administration of Aranesp.

Physician payment is calculated through the drug payment methodology described in Chapter 17, of the Claims Processing Manual.

The coinsurance and deductible are based on the Medicare allowance payable, not on the provider's charges. The provider may not charge the beneficiary more than 20 percent of the Medicare Aranesp allowance. This rule applies to independent and hospital based renal facilities.

Payment for ESRD-related Aranesp is included in the ESRD PPS for claims with dates of service on or after January 1, 2011.

100-4, Chapter-8, 60.4.6.4

Payment for Darbepoetin Alfa (Aranesp) in Other Settings

In the hospital inpatient setting, payment under Part A for Aranesp is included in the DRG.

In the hospital inpatient setting, payment under Part B is made on bill type 12x when billed with revenue code 0636. The total number of units as a multiple of 1mcg is placed in the unit field. Reimbursement is based on the payment allowance limit for Medicare Part B drugs as found in the ASP pricing file.

In a skilled nursing facility (SNF), payment for Aranesp covered under the Part B EPO benefit is not included in the prospective payment rate for the resident's Medicare-covered SNF stay.

In a hospice, payment is included in the hospice per diem rate.

For a service furnished by a physician or incident to a physician's service, payment is made to the physician by the carrier in accordance with the rules for 'incident to" services. When Aranesp is administered in the renal facility, the service is not an "incident to" service and not under the "incident to" provision.

With the implementation of the ESRD PPS, ESRD-related Aranesp is included in the ESRD PPS payment amount and is not separately payable on Part B claims with dates of service on or after January 1,2011 for other providers, with the exception of a hospital billing for an emergency or unscheduled dialysis session.

100-4, Chapter-8, 60.4.6.5

Payment for Darbepoetin Alfa (Aranesp) in the Hospital Outpatient Department

When ESRD patients come to the hospital for an unscheduled or emergency dialysis treatment they may also require the administration of Aranesp. For patients with ESRD who are on a regular course of dialysis, Aranesp administered in a hospital outpatient department is paid the MMA Drug Pricing File rate. Effective January 1, 2005, Aranesp will be paid based on the ASP Pricing File.

Hospitals use bill type 13X (or 85X for Critical Access Hospitals) and report charges under revenue code 0636. The total number of units as a multiple of 1mcg is placed in the unit field. Value code 49 must be reported with the hematocrit value for the hospital outpatient visits prior to January 1, 2006, and for all claims with dates of service on or after January 1, 2008.

100-4, Chapter-8, 60.4.7

Payment for Peginesatide in the Hospital Outpatient Department

When ESRD patients come to the hospital for an unscheduled or emergency dialysis treatment they may also require the administration of an ESA, such as peginesatide. When hospitals bill for an unscheduled or emergency outpatient dialysis session (G0257) they may include the administration of an ESA.

100-4, Chapter-8, 60.6

Vaccines Furnished to ESRD Patients

The Medicare program covers hepatitis B, influenza virus and Pneumococcal pneumonia virus (PPV) vaccines and their administration when furnished to eligible beneficiaries in accordance with coverage rules. Payment may be made for both the vaccine and the administration. The costs associated with the syringe and supplies are included in the administration fee: HCPCS code A4657 should not be billed for these vaccines.

Vaccines and their administration are reported using separate codes. See Chapter 18 of this manual for the codes required for billing vaccines and the administration of the vaccine.

Payment for vaccine administration (PPV, Influenza Virus, and Hepatitis B Virus) to freestanding RDFs is based on the Medicare Physician Fee Schedule (MPFS) according to the rate in the MPFS associated with code 90782 for services provided prior to March 1, 2003 and code 90471 for services provided March 1, 2005 and later and on reasonable cost for provider-based RDFs.

Vaccines remain separately payable under the ESRD PPS.

100-4, Chapter-9, 150

Initial Preventive Physical Examination (IPPE)

Effective for services furnished on or after January 1, 2005, Section 611 of the Medicare Prescription Drug Improvement and Modernization Act of 2003 (MMA) provides for coverage under Part B of one initial preventive physical examination (IPPE) for new beneficiaries only, subject to certain eligibility and other limitations. For RHCs the Part B deductible for IPPE is waived for services provided on or after January 1, 2009. FQHC services are always exempt from the Part B deductible. Coinsurance is applicable. For RHCs and FQHCs coinsurance is waived for services provided on or after January 1, 2011.

Payment for the professional services will be made under the all-inclusive rate. Encounters with more than one health professional and multiple encounters with the same health professionals that take place on the same day and at a single location generally constitute a single visit. However, in rare circumstances an RHC/FQHC can receive a separate payment for an encounter in addition to the payment for the IPPE when they are performed on the same day.

RHCs and FQHCs must HCPCS code for IPPE for the following reasons:

- To avoid application of deductible (on RHC claims);
- To assure payment for this service in addition to another encounter on the same day if they are both separate, unrelated, and appropriate; and
- To update the CWF record to track this once in a lifetime benefit.

Beginning with dates of service on or after January 1, 2009 if an IPPE is provided in an RHC or FQHC, the professional portion of the service is billed to the FI or Part A MAC using TOBs 71X and 73X/77X, respectively, and the appropriate site of service revenue code in the 052X revenue code series, and must include HCPCS code G0402. Additional information on IPPE can be found in Chapter 18, section 80 of this manual.

NOTE: The technical component of an EKG performed at a clinic/center is not a Medicare-covered RHC/FQHC service and is not billed by the independent RHC/FQHC. Rather, it is billed to Medicare carriers or Part B MACs on professional claims (Form CMS-1500 or 837P) under the practitioner's ID following instructions for submitting practitioner claims. Likewise, the technical component of the EKG performed at a provider-based clinic/center is not a Medicare-covered RHC\FQHC service and is not billed by the provider-based RHC\FQHC. Instead, it is billed on the applicable TOB and submitted to the FI or Part A MAC using the base provider's ID following instructions for submitting claims to the FI/Part A MAC from the base provider. For the professional component of the EKG, there is no separate payment and no separate billing of it. The IPPE is the only HCPCS code for which the deductible is waived under this benefit. For more information on billing for a screening EKG see chapter 18 section 80 of this manual.

100-4, Chapter-9, 160

Ultrasound Screening for Abdominal Aortic Aneurysm (AAA)

Section 5112 of the Deficit Reduction Act of 2005 amended the Social Security Act to provide coverage under Part B of the Medicare program for a one-time ultrasound screening for abdominal aortic aneurysms (AAA). Payment for the professional services that meet all of the program requirements will be made under the all-inclusive rate. For RHCs the Part B deductible for screening AAA is waived for dates of service on or after January 1, 2007. FQHC services are always exempt from the Part B deductible. Coinsurance is applicable. For RHCs and FQHCs, coinsurance for screening AAA is waived for dates of service on or after January 1, 2011. Additional information on AAA can be found in Chapter 18, section 110 of this manual.

If the screening is provided in an RHC or FQHC, the professional portion of the service is billed to the FI or Part A MAC using TOBs 71X and 73X/77X, respectively, and the appropriate site of service revenue code in the 052X revenue code series and must include HCPCS code G0389 (this code has been deleted or 2017).

If the AAA screening is provided in an independent RHC or freestanding FQHC, the technical component of the service can be billed by the practitioner to the carrier or Part B MAC under the practitioner's ID following instructions for submitting practitioner claims.

If the screening is provided in a provider-based RHC/FQHC, the technical component of the service can be billed by the base provider to the FI or Part A MAC under the base provider's ID, following instructions for submitting claims to the FI/Part A MAC from the base provider.

100-4, Chapter-9, 181

Diabetes Self-Management Training (DSMT) Services Provided by RHCs and FQHCs

A – FQHCs

Previously, DSMT type services rendered by qualified registered dietitians or nutrition professionals were considered incident to services under the FQHC benefit, if all relevant program requirements were met. Therefore, separate all-inclusive encounter rate payment could not be made for the provision of DSMT services. With passage of DRA, effective January 1, 2006, FQHCs are eligible for a separate payment under Part B for these services provided they meet all program requirements. See Pub. 100-04, chapter 18, section 120. Payment is made at the all-inclusive encounter rate to the FQHC. This payment can be in addition to payment for any other qualifying visit on the same date of service as the beneficiary received qualifying DSMT services.

For FQHCs to qualify for a separate visit payment for DSMT services, the services must be a one-on-one face-to-face encounter. Group sessions don't constitute a billable visit for any FQHC services. Rather, the cost of group sessions is included in the calculation of the all-inclusive FQHC visit rate. To receive separate payment for DSMT services, the DSMT services must be billed on TOB 73x/77x with HCPCS code G0108 and the appropriate site of service revenue code in the 052X revenue code series. This payment can be in addition to payment for any other qualifying visit on the same date of service that the beneficiary received qualifying DSMT services as long as the claim for DSMT services contains the appropriate coding specified above. Additional information on DSMT can be found in Chapter 18, section 120 of this manual.

NOTE: DSMT is not a qualifying visit on the same day that MNT is provided.

Group services (G0109) do not meet the criteria for a separate qualifying encounter. All line items billed on TOBs 73x/77x with HCPCS codes for DSMT services will be denied.

B – RHCs

Separate payment to RHCs for these practitioners/services continues to be precluded as these services are not within the scope of Medicare-covered RHC benefits. Note that the provision of the services by registered dietitians or nutritional professionals, might be considered incident to services in the RHC setting, provided all applicable conditions are met. However, they do not constitute an RHC visit, in and of themselves. All line items billed on TOB 71x with HCPCS code 0108 or G0109 will be denied.

100-4, Chapter-9, 182

Medical Nutrition Therapy (MNT) Services

A – FQHCs

Previously, MNT type services were considered incident to services under the FQHC benefit, if all relevant program requirements were met. Therefore, separate all-inclusive encounter rate payment could not be made for the provision of MNT services. With passage of DRA, effective January 1, 2006, FQHCs are eligible for a separate payment under Part B for these services provided they meet all program requirements. Payment is made at the all-inclusive encounter rate to the FQHC. This payment can be in addition to payment for any other qualifying visit on the same date of service as the beneficiary received qualifying MNT services.

For FQHCs to qualify for a separate visit payment for MNT services, the services must be a one-on-one face-to-face encounter. Group sessions don't constitute a billable visit for any FQHC services. Rather, the cost of group sessions is included in the calculation of the all-inclusive FQHC visit rate. To receive payment for MNT services, the MNT services must be billed on TOB 73/x77x with the appropriate individual MNT HCPCS code (97802, 97803, or G0270) and with the appropriate site of service revenue code in the 052X revenue code series. This payment can be in addition to payment for any other qualifying visit on the same date of service as the beneficiary received qualifying MNT services as long as the claim for MNT services contain the appropriate coding specified above.

NOTE: MNT is not a qualifying visit on the same day that DSMT is provided.

Additional information on MNT can be found in Chapter 4, section 300 of this manual.Group services (HCPCS code 97804 or G0271) do not meet the criteria for a separate qualifying encounter. All line items billed on TOB 73x/77x with HCPCS code 97804 or G0271 will be denied.

B – RHCs

Separate payment to RHCs for these practitioners/services continues to be precluded as these services are not within the scope of Medicare-covered RHC benefits. All line items billed on TOB 71x with HCPCS codes for MNT services will be denied.

100-4, Chapter 10, 40.2

HH PPS Claims

The following data elements are required to submit a claim under home health PPS. For billing of home health claims not under an HH plan of care (not under HH PPS), see §90. Home health services under a plan of care are paid based on a 60-day episode of care. Payment for this episode will usually be made in two parts. After a RAP has been paid and a 60-day episode has been completed, or the patient has been discharged, the HHA submits a claim to receive the balance of payment due for the episode.

HH PPS claims will be processed in Medicare claims processing systems as debit/credit adjustments against the record created by the RAP, except in the case of "No-RAP" LUPA claims (see §40.3). As the claim is processed the payment on the RAP will be reversed in full and the full payment due for the episode will be made on the claim. Both the debit and credit actions will be reflected on the RA so the net payment on the claim can be easily understood. Detailed RA information is contained in chapter 22 of this manual.

Billing Provider Name, Address, and Telephone Number

Required – The HHA's minimum entry is the agency's name, city, State, and ZIP Code. The post office box number or street name and number may be included. The State may be abbreviated using standard post office abbreviations. Five or nine-digit ZIP Codes are acceptable. Medicare contractors use this information in connection with the provider identifier to verify provider identity.

Patient Control Number and Medical/Health Record Number

Required - The patient's control number may be shown if the patient is assigned one and the number is needed for association and reference purposes.

The HHA may enter the number assigned to the patient's medical/health record. If this number is entered, the Medicare contractor must carry it through their system and return it on the remittance record.

Type of Bill

Required - This 4-digit alphanumeric code gives two pieces of information. The first three digits indicate the base type of bill. The fourth digit indicates the sequence of this bill in this particular episode of care. The types of bill accepted for HH PPS requests for anticipated payment are:

032x - Home Health Services under a Plan of Treatment

4th Digit - Definition

7 - Replacement of Prior Claim - HHAs use to correct a previously submitted bill. Apply this code for the corrected or "new" bill. These adjustment claims must be accepted at any point within the timely filing period after the payment of the original claim.

8 - Void/Cancel of a Prior Claim - HHAs use this code to indicate this bill is an exact duplicate of an incorrect bill previously submitted. A replacement RAP or claim must be submitted for the episode to be paid.

9 - Final Claim for an HH PPS Episode - This code indicates the HH bill should be processed as a debit/credit adjustment to the RAP. This code is specific to home health and does not replace codes 7, or 8.

HHAs must submit HH PPS claims with the 4th digit of "9." These claims may be adjusted with code "7" or cancelled with code "8." Medicare contractors do not accept late charge bills, submitted with code "5," on HH PPS claims. To add services within the period of a paid HH claim, the HHA must submit an adjustment.

NOTE: Type of bill 033x is no longer valid, effective October 1, 2013.

Statement Covers Period

Required - The beginning and ending dates of the period covered by this claim. The "from" date must match the date submitted on the RAP for the episode. For continuous care episodes, the "through" date must be 59 days after the "from" date. The patient status code must be 30 in these cases.

In cases where the beneficiary has been discharged or transferred within the 60-day episode period, HHAs will report the date of discharge in accordance with internal discharge procedures as the "through" date. If the beneficiary has died, the HHA reports the date of death in the "through date."

Any NUBC approved patient status code may be used in these cases. The HHA may submit claims for payment immediately after the claim "through" date. It is not required to hold claims until the end of the 60-day episode unless the beneficiary continues under care.

Patient Name/Identifier

Required - The HHA enters the patient's last name, first name, and middle initial.

Patient Address

Required - The HHA enters the patient's full mailing address, including street number and name, post office box number or RFD, City, State, and ZIP Code.

Patient Birth Date

Required - The HHA enters the month, day, and year of birth of patient. If the full correct date is not known, leave blank.

Patient Sex

Required - "M" for male or "F" for female must be present. This item is used in conjunction with diagnoses and surgical procedures to identify inconsistencies.

Admission/Start of Care Date

Required - The HHA enters the same date of admission that was submitted on the RAP for the episode.

Point of Origin for Admission or Visit

Required - The HHA enters the same point of origin code that was submitted on the RAP for the episode.

Patient Discharge Status

Required - The HHA enters the code that most accurately describes the patient's status as of the "Through" date of the billing period. Any applicable NUBC approved code may be used.

Patient status code 06 should be reported in all cases where the HHA is aware that the episode will be paid as a PEP adjustment. These are cases in which the agency is aware that the beneficiary has transferred to another HHA within the 60-day episode, or the agency is aware that the beneficiary was discharged with the goals of the original plan of care met and has been readmitted within the 60-day episode. Situations may occur in which the HHA is unaware at the time of billing the discharge that these circumstances exist. In these situations, Medicare claims processing systems will adjust the discharge claim automatically to reflect the PEP adjustment, changing the patient status code on the paid claims record to 06.

In cases where an HHA is changing the Medicare contractor to which they submit claims, the service dates on the claims must fall within the provider's effective dates at each contractor. To ensure this, RAPs for all episodes with "from" dates before the provider's termination date must be submitted to the contractor the provider is leaving. The resulting episode must be resolved by the provider submitting claims for shortened periods, with "through" dates on or before the termination date. The provider must indicate that these claims will be PEP adjustments by using patient status code 06.

Billing for the beneficiary is being "transferred" to the new contractor. In cases where the ownership of an HHA is changing and the CMS certification number (CCN) also changes, the service dates on the claims must fall within the effective dates of the terminating CCN. To ensure this, RAPs for all episodes with "from" dates before the termination date of the CCN must be resolved by the provider submitting claims for shortened periods, with "through" dates on or before the termination date. The provider must indicate that these claims will be PEP adjustments by using patient status 06. Billing for the beneficiary is being "transferred" to the new agency ownership. In changes of ownership which do not affect the CCN, billing for episodes is also unaffected.

In cases where an HHA is aware in advance that a beneficiary will become enrolled in a Medicare Advantage (MA) Organization as of a certain date, the provider should submit a claim for the shortened period prior to the MA Organization enrollment date. The claim should be coded with patient status 06. Payment responsibility for the beneficiary is being "transferred" from Medicare fee-for-service to MA Organization, since HH PPS applies only to Medicare fee-for-service.

If HHAs require guidance on OASIS assessment procedures in these cases, they should contact the appropriate state OASIS education coordinator.

Condition Codes

Conditional – The HHA enters any NUBC approved code to describe conditions that apply to the claim.

If the RAP is for an episode in which the patient has transferred from another HHA, the HHA enters condition code 47.

HHAs that are adjusting previously paid claims enter one of the condition codes representing Claim Change Reasons (code values D0 through E0). If adjusting the claim to correct a HIPPS code, HHAs use condition code D2 and enter "Remarks" indicating the reason for the HIPPS code change. HHAs use D9 if multiple changes are necessary.

When submitting an HH PPS claim as a demand bill, HHAs use condition code 20. See §50 for more detailed instructions regarding demand billing.

When submitting an HH PPS claim for a denial notice, HHAs use condition code 21. See §60 for more detailed instructions regarding no-payment billing.

Required - If canceling the claim (TOB 0328), HHAs report the condition codes D5 or D6 and enter "Remarks" indicating the reason for cancellation of the claim.

Occurrence Codes and Dates

Conditional - The HHA enters any NUBC approved code to describe occurrences that apply to the claim.

Occurrence Span Code and Dates

Conditional - The HHA enters any NUBC approved Occurrence Span code to describe occurrences that apply to the claim. Reporting of occurrence span code 74 is not required to show the dates of an inpatient admission during an episode.

Value Codes and Amounts

Required - Home health episode payments must be based upon the site at which the beneficiary is served. For episodes in which the beneficiary's site of service changes from one CBSA to another within the episode period, HHAs should submit the CBSA code corresponding to the site of service at the end of the episode on the claim.

NOTE: Contractor-entered value codes. The Medicare contractor enters codes 17 and 62 - 65 on the claim in processing. They may be visible in the Medicare contractor's online claim history and on remittances.

Code	Title	Definition
17	Outlier Amount	The amount of any outlier payment returned by the Pricer with this code. (Contractors always place condition code 61 on the claim along with this value code.)
61	Location Where Service is Furnished (HHA and Hospice)	HHAs report the MSA number or Core Based Statistical Area (CBSA) number (or rural state code) of the location where the home health or hospice service is delivered. The HHA reports the number in dollar portion of the form locator right justified to the left of the dollar/cents delimiter, add two zeros to the cents field if no cents.
62	HH Visits - Part A	The number of visits determined by Medicare to be payable from the Part A trust fund to reflect the shift of payments from the Part A to the Part B trust fund as mandated by §1812 (a)(3) of the Social Security Act.
63	HH Visits - Part B	The number of visits determined by Medicare to be payable from the Part B trust fund to reflect the shift of payments from the Part A to the Part B trust fund as mandated by §1812 (a)(3) of the Social Security Act.
64	HH Reimbursement - Part A	The dollar amounts determined to be associated with the HH visits identified in a value code 62 amount. This Part A payment reflects the shift of payments from the Part A to the Part B trust fund as mandated by §1812 (a)(3) of the Social Security Act.
65	HH Reimbursement - Part B	The dollar amounts determined to be associated with the HH visits identified in a value code 63 amount. This Part B payment reflects the shift of payments from the Part A to the Part B trust fund as mandated by §1812 (a)(3) of the Social Security Act.

If information returned from the CWF indicates all visits on the claim are Part A, the shared system must place value codes 62 and 64 on the claim record, showing the total visits and total PPS payment amount as the values, and send the claim to CWF with RIC code V.

If information returned from CWF indicates all visits on the claim are Part B, the shared system must place value codes 63 and 65 on the claim record, showing the total visits and total PPS payment amount as the values, and send the claim to CWF with RIC code W.

If information returned from CWF indicates certain visits on the claim are payable from both Part A and Part B, the shared system must place value codes 62, 63, 64, and 65 on the claim record. The shared system also must populate the values for code 62 and 63 based on the numbers of visits returned from CWF and prorate the total PPS reimbursement amount based on the numbers of visits to determine the dollars amounts to be associated with value codes 64 and 65. The shared system will return the claim to CWF with RIC code U.

Revenue Code and Revenue Description
Required

HH PPS claims must report a 0023 revenue code line on which the first four positions of the HIPPS code match the code submitted on the RAP. The fifth position of the code represents the NRS severity level. This fifth position may differ to allow the HHA to change a code that represents that supplies were provided to a code that represents that supplies were not provided, or vice versa. However, the fifth position may only change between the two values that represent the same NRS severity level. Section 10.1.9 of this chapter contains the pairs of corresponding values. If these criteria are not met, Medicare claims processing systems will return the claim.

HHAs enter only one 0023 revenue code per claim in all cases.

Unlike RAPs, claims must also report all services provided to the beneficiary within the episode. Each service must be reported in line item detail. Each service visit (revenue codes 042x, 043x, 044x, 055x, 056x and 057x) must be reported as a separate line. Any of the following revenue codes may be used:

027x	Medical/Surgical Supplies (Also see 062x, an extension of 027x) Required detail: With the exception of revenue code 0274 (prosthetic and orthotic devices), only service units and a charge must be reported with this revenue code. If also reporting revenue code 0623 to separately identify specific wound care supplies, not just supplies for wound care patients, ensure that the charge amounts for revenue code 0623 lines are mutually exclusive from other lines for supply revenue codes reported on the claim. Report only nonroutine supply items in this revenue code or in 0623. Revenue code 0274 requires an HCPCS code, the date of service units and a charge amount. **NOTE:** Revenue Codes 0275 through 0278 are not used for Medicare billing on HH PPS types of bills
042x	Physical Therapy Required detail: One of the physical therapy HCPCS codes defined below in the instructions for the HCPCS code field, the date of service, service units which represent the number of 15 minute increments that comprised the visit, and a charge amount.
043x	Occupational Therapy Required detail: One of the occupational therapy HCPCS codes defined below in the instructions for the HCPCS code field, the date of service, service units which represent the number of 15 minute increments that comprised the visit, and a charge amount.
044x	Speech-Language Pathology Required detail: One of the speech-language pathology HCPCS codes defined below in the instructions for the HCPCS code field, the date of service, service units which represent the number of 15 minute increments that comprised the visit, and a charge amount.
055x	Skilled Nursing Required detail: One of the skilled nursing HCPCS codes defined below in the instructions for the HCPCS code field, the date of service, service units which represent the number of 15 minute increments that comprised the visit, and a charge amount.
056x	Medical Social Services Required detail: The medical social services HCPCS code defined below in the instructions for the HCPCS code field, the date of service, service units which represent the number of 15 minute increments that comprised the visit, and a charge amount.
057x	Home Health Aide (Home Health) Required detail: The home health aide HCPCS code defined below in the instructions for the HCPCS code field, the date of service, service units which represent the number of 15 minute increments that comprised the visit, and a charge amount.

NOTE: Contractors do not accept revenue codes 058x or 059x when submitted with covered charges on Medicare home health claims under HH PPS. They also do not accept revenue code 0624, investigational devices, on HH claims under HH PPS.

Revenue Codes for Optional Billing of DME

Billing of DME provided in the episode is not required on the HH PPS claim. Home health agencies retain the option to bill these services to their Medicare contractor processing home health claims or to have the services provided under arrangement with a supplier that bills these services to the DME MAC. Agencies that choose to bill DME services on their HH PPS claims must use the revenue codes below. These services will be paid separately in addition to the HH PPS amount, based on the applicable Medicare fee schedule. For additional instructions for billing DME services see chapter 20 of this manual.

0274	Prosthetic/Orthotic Devices Required detail: The applicable HCPCS code for the item, a date of service, a number of service units, and a charge amount.
029x	Durable Medical Equipment (DME) (Other Than Renal) Required detail: The applicable HCPCS code for the item, a date of service indicating the purchase date or the beginning date of a monthly rental, a number of service units, and a charge amount. Monthly rental items should be reported with a separate line for each month's rental and service units of one. Revenue code 0294 is used to bill drugs/supplies for the effective use of DME.
060x	Oxygen (Home Health) Required detail: The applicable HCPCS code for the item, a date of service, a number of service units, and a charge amount.

Revenue Code for Optional Reporting of Wound Care Supplies

0623	Medical/Surgical Supplies - Extension of 027x Required detail: Only service units and a charge must be reported with this revenue code. If also reporting revenue code 027x to identify nonroutine supplies other than those used for wound care, the HHA must ensure that the charge amounts for the two revenue code lines are mutually exclusive.

HHAs may voluntarily report a separate revenue code line for charges for nonroutine wound care supplies, using revenue code 0623. Notwithstanding the standard abbreviation "surg dressings," HHAs use this code to report charges for ALL nonroutine wound care supplies, including but not limited to surgical dressings.

Pub. 100-02, Medicare Benefit Policy Manual, chapter 7, defines routine vs. nonroutine supplies. HHAs use that definition to determine whether any wound care supply item should be reported in this line because it is nonroutine.

HHAs can assist Medicare's future refinement of payment rates if they consistently and accurately report their charges for nonroutine wound care supplies under revenue center code 0623. HHAs should ensure that charges reported under revenue code 027x for nonroutine supplies are also complete and accurate.

Validating Required Reporting of Supply Revenue Code

The HH PPS includes a separate case-mix adjustment for non-routine supplies. Nonroutine supply severity levels are indicated on HH PPS claims through a code value in the 5th position of the HIPPS code. The 5th position of the HIPPS code can contain two sets of values. One set of codes (the letters S through X) indicate that supplies were provided. The second set of codes (the numbers 1 through 6) indicate the HHA is intentionally reporting that they did not provide supplies during the episode. See section 10.1.9 for the complete composition of HIPPS under the HH PPS.

HHAs must ensure that if they are submitting a HIPPS code with a 5th position containing the letters S through X, the claim must also report a non-routine supply revenue code with covered charges. This revenue code may be either revenue code 27x, excluding 274, or revenue code 623, consistent with the instructions for optional separate reporting of wound care supplies.

Medicare systems will return the claim to the HHA if the HIPPS code indicates nonroutine supplies were provided and supply charges are not reported on the claim. When the HHA receives a claim returned for this reason, the HHA must review their records regarding the supplies provided to the beneficiary. The HHA may take one of the following actions, based on the review of their records:

- If non-routine supplies were provided, the supply charges must be added to the claim using the appropriate supply revenue code.
- If non-routine supplies were not provided, the HHA must indicate that on the claim by changing the 5th position of the HIPPS code to the appropriate numeric value in the range 1 through 6.

After completing one of these actions, the HHA may return the claim to the Medicare contractor for continued adjudication.

HCPCS/Accommodation Rates/HIPPS Rate Codes

Required - On the 0023 revenue code line, the HHA must report the HIPPS code that was reported on the RAP. The first four positions of the code must be identical to the value reported on the RAP. The fifth position may vary from the letter value reported on the RAP to the corresponding number which represents the same non-routine supply severity level but which reports that non-routine supplies were not provided.

HHAs enter only one HIPPS code per claim in all cases. Claims submitted with additional HIPPS codes will be returned to the provider.

Medicare may change the HIPPS used for payment of the claim in the course of claims processing, but the HIPPS code submitted by the provider in this field is never changed or replaced. If the HIPPS code is changed, the code used for payment is recorded in the APC-HIPPS field of the electronic claim record.

For revenue code lines other than 0023, the HHA reports HCPCS codes as appropriate to that revenue code.

To report HH visits on episodes beginning before January 1, 2011, the HHA reports a single HCPCS code to represent a visit by each HH care discipline. These codes are:

G0151 Services of physical therapist in home health or hospice setting, each 15 minutes.

G0152 Services of an occupational therapist in home health or hospice setting, each 15 minutes.

G0153 Services of a speech language pathologist in home health or hospice setting, each 15 minutes.

G0154 (this code has been deleted or 2017) Services of skilled nurse in the home health or hospice settings, each 15 minutes.

G0155 Services of a clinical social worker under a home health plan of care, each 15 minutes.

G0156 Services of a home health aide under a home health plan of care, each 15 minutes.

To report HH visits on episodes beginning on or after January 1, 2011, the HHA reports one of the following HCPCS codes to represent a visit by each HH care discipline:

Physical Therapy (revenue code 042x)

G0151 Services performed by a qualified physical therapist in the home health or hospice setting, each 15 minutes.

G0157 Services performed by a qualified physical therapist assistant in the home health or hospice setting, each 15 minutes.

G0159 Services performed by a qualified physical therapist, in the home health setting, in the establishment or delivery of a safe and effective physical therapy maintenance program, each 15 minutes.

Occupational Therapy (revenue code 043x)

G0152 Services performed by a qualified occupational therapist in the home health or hospice setting, each 15 minutes.

G0158 Services performed by a qualified occupational therapist assistant in the home health or hospice setting, each 15 minutes.

G0160 Services performed by a qualified occupational therapist, in the home health setting, in the establishment or delivery of a safe and effective occupational therapy maintenance program, each 15 minutes.

Speech-Language Pathology (revenue code 044x)

G0153 Services performed by a qualified speech-language pathologist in the home health or hospice setting, each 15 minutes.

G0161 Services performed by a qualified speech-language pathologist, in the home health setting, in the establishment or delivery of a safe and effective speech-language pathology maintenance program, each 15 minutes.

Note that modifiers indicating services delivered under a therapy plan of care (modifiers GN, GO or GP) are not required on HH PPS claims.

Skilled Nursing (revenue code 055x)

G0154 (this code has been deleted or 2017) Direct skilled services of a licensed nurse (LPN or RN) in the home health or hospice setting, each 15 minutes.

G0162 Skilled services by a licensed nurse (RN only) for management and evaluation of the plan of care, each 15 minutes (the patient's underlying condition or complication requires an RN to ensure that essential non-skilled care achieves its purpose in the home health or hospice setting).

G0163 (this code has been deleted or 2017) Skilled services of a licensed nurse (LPN or RN) for the observation and assessment of the patient's condition, each 15 minutes (the change in the patient's condition requires skilled nursing personnel to identify and evaluate the patient's need for possible modification of treatment in the home health or hospice setting).

G0164 (this code has been deleted or 2017) Skilled services of a licensed nurse (LPN or RN), in the training and/or education of a patient or family member, in the home health or hospice setting, each 15 minutes.

Medical Social Services (revenue code 056x)

G0155 Services of a clinical social worker under a home health plan of care, each 15 minutes.

Home Health Aide (revenue code 057x)

G0156 Services of a home health aide under a home health plan of care, each 15 minutes.

Regarding all skilled nursing and skilled therapy visits

In the course of a single visit, a nurse or qualified therapist may provide more than one of the nursing or therapy services reflected in the codes above. HHAs must not report more than one G-code for each visit regardless of the variety of services provided during the visit. In cases where more than one nursing or therapy service is provided in a visit, the HHA must report the G-code which reflects the service for which the clinician spent most of his/her time.

For instance, if direct skilled nursing services are provided, and the nurse also provides training/education of a patient or family member during that same visit, Medicare would expect the HHA to report the G-code which reflects the service for which most of the time was spent during that visit. Similarly, if a qualified therapist is performing a therapy service and also establishes a maintenance program during the same visit, the HHA should report the G-code that reflects the service for which most of the time was spent during that visit. In all cases, however, the number of 15-minute increments reported for the visit should reflect the total time of the visit.

For episodes beginning on or after July 1, 2013, HHAs must report where home health services were provided. The following codes are used for this reporting:

Q5001: Hospice or home health care provided in patient's home/residence

Q5002: Hospice or home health care provided in assisted living facility

Q5009: Hospice or home health care provided in place not otherwise specified

The location where services were provided must always be reported along with the first visit reported on the claim. In addition to reporting a visit line using the G codes as described above, HHAs must report an additional line item with the same revenue code and date of service, reporting one of the three Q codes (Q5001, Q5002, and Q5009), one unit and a nominal covered charge (e.g., a penny). If the location where services were provided changes during the episode, the new location should be reported with an additional line corresponding to the first visit provided in the new location.

Service Date

Required - For initial episodes, the HHA reports on the 0023 revenue code line the date of the first covered visit provided during the episode. For subsequent episodes, the HHA reports on the 0023 revenue code the date of the first visit provided during the episode line, regardless of whether the visit was covered or non-covered.

For other line items detailing all services within the episode period, it reports service dates as appropriate to that revenue code. For service visits that begin in 1 calendar day and span into the next calendar day, report one visit using the date the visit ended as the service date.

When the claim Admission Date matches the Statement Covers "From" Date, Medicare systems ensure that the Service Date on the 0023 revenue code line also matches these dates.

Service Units

Required - Transaction standards require the reporting of a number greater than zero as the units on the 0023 revenue code line. However, Medicare systems will disregard the submitted units in processing the claim. For line items detailing all services within the episode period, the HHA reports units of service as appropriate to that revenue code. Coding detail for each revenue code under HH PPS is defined above under Revenue Codes.

For the revenue codes that represent home health visits (042x, 043x, 044x, 055x, 056x, and 057x), the HHA reports as service units a number of 15 minute increments that comprise the time spent treating the beneficiary. Time spent completing the OASIS assessment in the home as part of an otherwise covered and billable visit and time spent updating medical records in the home as part of such a visit may also be reported. Visits of any length are to be reported, rounding the time to the nearest 15-minute increment. Visits cannot be split into multiple lines. Report covered and noncovered increments of the same visit on the same line.

Total Charges

Required - The HHA must report zero charges on the 0023 revenue code line (the field must contain zero).

For line items detailing all services within the episode period, the HHA reports charges as appropriate to that revenue code. Coding detail for each revenue code under HH PPS is defined above under Revenue Codes. Charges may be reported in dollars and cents (i.e., charges are not required to be rounded to dollars and zero cents). Medicare claims processing systems will not make any payments based upon submitted charge amounts.

Non-covered Charges

Required – The HHA reports the total non-covered charges pertaining to the related revenue code here. Examples of non-covered charges on HH PPS claims may include:

- Visits provided exclusively to perform OASIS assessments
- Visits provided exclusively for supervisory or administrative purposes
- Therapy visits provided prior to the required re-assessments

Payer Name

Required - See chapter 25.

Release of Information Certification Indicator

Required - See chapter 25.

National Provider Identifier – Billing Provider

Required - The HHA enters their provider identifier.

Insured's Name

Required only if MSP involved. See Pub. 100-05, Medicare Secondary Payer Manual.

Patient's Relationship To Insured

Required only if MSP involved. See Pub. 100-05, Medicare Secondary Payer Manual.

Insured's Unique Identifier

Required only if MSP involved. See Pub. 100-05, Medicare Secondary Payer Manual.

Insured's Group Name

Required only if MSP involved. See Pub. 100-05, Medicare Secondary Payer Manual.

Insured's Group Number

Required only if MSP involved. See Pub. 100-05, Medicare Secondary Payer Manual.

Treatment Authorization Code

Required - The HHA enters the claim-OASIS matching key output by the Grouper software. This data element enables historical claims data to be linked to individual OASIS assessments supporting the payment of individual claims for research purposes. It is also used in recalculating payment group codes in the HH Pricer (see section 70).

The format of the treatment authorization code is shown here:

Position	Definition	Format
1-2	M0030 (Start-of-care date) – 2 digit year	99
3-4	M0030 (Start-of-care date) – alpha code for date	XX
5-6	M0090 (Date assessment completed) – 2 digit year	99
7-8	M0090 (Date assessment completed) – alpha code for date	XX
9	M0100 (Reason for assessment)	9
10	M0110 (Episode Timing) – Early = 1, Late = 2	9
11	Alpha code for Clinical severity points – under Equation 1	X
12	Alpha code for Functional severity points – under Equation 1	X
13	Alpha code for Clinical severity points – under Equation 2	X
14	Alpha code for Functional severity points – under Equation 2	X
15	Alpha code for Clinical severity points – under Equation 3	X
16	Alpha code for Functional severity points – under Equation 3	X
17	Alpha code for Clinical severity points – under Equation 4	X
18	Alpha code for Functional severity points – under Equation 4	X

NOTE: The dates in positions 3-4 and 7-8 are converted to 2 position alphabetic values using a hexavigesimal coding system. The 2 position numeric point scores in positions 11 –

18 are converted to a single alphabetic code using the same system. Tables defining these conversions are included in the documentation for the Grouper software that is available on the CMS Web site. The conversion scheme may vary slightly from year to year to reflect changes in how the point scores are assigned to severity levels in the HH PPS case mix system.

Position	Definition	Actual Value	Resulting Code
1-2	M0030 (Start-of-care date) – 2 digit year	2007	07
3-4	M0030 (Start-of-care date) – code for date	09/01	JK
5-6	M0090 (Date assessment completed) – 2 digit year	2008	08
7-8	M0090 (Date assessment completed) – code for date	01/01	AA
9	M0100 (Reason for assessment)	04	4
10	M0110 (Episode Timing)	01	1
11	Clinical severity points – under Equation 1	7	G
12	Functional severity points – under Equation 1	2	B
13	Clinical severity points – under Equation 2	13	M
14	Functional severity points – under Equation 2	4	D
15	Clinical severity points – under Equation 3	3	C
16	Functional severity points – under Equation 3	4	D
17	Clinical severity points – under Equation 4	12	L
18	Functional severity points – under Equation 4	7	G

This is an example of a treatment authorization code created using this format:

The treatment authorization code that would appear on the claim would be, in this example: 07JK08AA41GBMDCDLG.

In cases of billing for denial notice, using condition code 21, this code may be filled with a placeholder value as defined in section 60.

The investigational device (IDE) revenue code, 0624, is not allowed on HH PPS claims.

Therefore, treatment authorization codes associated with IDE items must never be submitted in this field.

The claims-OASIS matching key on the claim will match that submitted on the RAP.

Medicare systems validate the length of the treatment authorization code and ensure that each position is in the correct format.

Document Control Number (DCN)

Required - If submitting an adjustment (TOB 0327) to a previously paid HH PPS claim, the HHA enters the control number assigned to the original HH PPS claim here.

Since HH PPS claims are processed as adjustments to the RAP, Medicare claims processing systems will match all HH PPS claims to their corresponding RAP and populate this field on the electronic claim record automatically. Providers do not need to submit a DCN on all HH PPS claims, only on adjustments to paid claims.

Employer Name

Required only if MSP involved. See Pub. 100-05, Medicare Secondary Payer Manual.

Principal Diagnosis Code

Required - The HHA enters the ICD code for the principal diagnosis. The code must be reported according to Official ICD Guidelines for Coding and Reporting, as required by the HIPAA. The code must be the full diagnosis code, including all five digits for ICD-9- CM or all seven digits for ICD-10 CM where applicable. Where the proper code has fewer than the maximum number of digits, the HHA does not fill it with zeros.

The ICD code and principle diagnosis reported must match the primary diagnosis code reported on the OASIS form item M1020 (Primary Diagnosis).

The principal diagnosis code on the claim will match that submitted on the RAP.

Other Diagnosis Codes

Required - The HHA enters the full diagnosis codes for additional conditions if they coexisted at the time of the establishment of the plan of care. These codes may not duplicate the principal diagnosis as an additional or secondary diagnosis.

For other diagnoses, the diagnoses and ICD codes reported on the claim must match the additional diagnoses reported on the OASIS, form item M1022 (Other Diagnoses). In listing the diagnoses, the HHA places them in order to best reflect the seriousness of the patient's condition and to justify the disciplines and services provided in accordance with the Official ICD Guidelines for Coding and Reporting. The sequence of codes should follow ICD guidelines for reporting manifestation codes. Therefore, if a manifestation code is part of the primary diagnosis, the first two diagnoses should match and appear in the same sequence on both forms. Medicare does not have any additional requirements regarding the reporting or sequence of the codes beyond those contained in ICD guidelines.

Diagnosis codes in OASIS form item M1024, which reports Payment Diagnoses, are not directly reported in any field of the claim form. If under ICD coding guidelines the codes reported in these OASIS items must be reported as Other Diagnoses, the codes may be repeated in OASIS form item M1022 and will be reported on the claim. In other circumstances, the codes reported in payment diagnosis fields in OASIS may not appear on the claim form at all.

Attending Provider Name and Identifiers

Required - The HHA enters the name and provider identifier of the attending physician who has signed the plan of care.

Remarks

Conditional - Remarks are required only in cases where the claim is cancelled or adjusted.

100-4, Chapter 10, 90.1

Osteoporosis Injections as HHA Benefit

A -Billing Requirements

The administration of the drug is included in the charge for the skilled nursing visit billed using type of bill 32X. The cost of the drug is billed using type of bill 34X, using revenue code 0636. Drugs that have the ingredient calcitonin are billed using HCPCS code J0630. Drugs that have the ingredient teriparatide may be billed using HCPCS code J3110, if all existing guidelines for coverage under the home health benefit are met. All other osteoporosis drugs that are FDA approved and are awaiting an HCPCS code must use the miscellaneous code of J3490 until a specific HCPCS code is approved for use.

HCPCS code J0630 is defined as up to 400 units. Therefore, the provider must calculate units for the bill as follows:

Units Furnished During Billing Period	Units of Service Entry on Bill
100-400	1
401-800	2
801-1200	3
1201-1600	4
1601-2000	5
2001-2400	6

HCPCS code J3110 is defined as 10 mcg. Providers should report 1 unit for each 10 mcg dose provided during the billing period. These codes are paid on a reasonable cost basis, using the provider's submitted charges to make initial payments, which are subject to annual cost settlement. Coverage requirements for osteoporosis drugs are found in Pub. 100-02, Medicare Benefit Policy Manual, chapter 7, section 50.4.3. Coverage requirements for the home health benefit in general are found in Pub. 100-02, Medicare Benefit Policy Manual, chapter 7, section 30.

B -Edits

Medicare system edits require that the date of service on a 34Xclaim for covered osteoporosis drugs falls within the start and end dates of an existing home health PPS episode. Once the system ensures the service dates on the 34X claim fall within an HH PPS episode that is open for the beneficiary on CWF, CWF edits to assure that the provider number on the 34X claim matches the provider number on the episode file. This is to reflect that although the osteoporosis drug is paid separately from the HH PPS episode rate it is included in consolidated billing requirements(see §10.1.25 regarding consolidated billing).

Claims are also edited to assure that the claim is an HH claim (type of bill 34X), the beneficiary is female and that the diagnosis code 733.01 (post-menopausal osteoporosis) is present.

100-4, Chapter 11, 10.1

Hospice Pre-Election Evaluation and Counseling Services

Effective January 1, 2005, Medicare allows payment to a hospice for specified hospice pre-election evaluation and counseling services when furnished by a physician who is either the medical director of or employee of the hospice.

Medicare covers a one-time only payment on behalf of a beneficiary who is terminally ill, (defined as having a prognosis of 6 months or less if the disease follows its normal course), has no previous hospice elections, and has not previously received hospice pre-election evaluation and counseling services.

HCPCS code G0337 "Hospice Pre-Election Evaluation and Counseling Services" is used to designate that these services have been provided by the medical director or a physician employed by the ho spice. Hospice agencies bill their Medicare contractor with home health and hospice jurisdiction directly using HCPCS G0337 with Revenue Code 0657. No other revenue codes may appear on the claim.

Claims for "Hospice Pre-Election and Counseling Services", HCPCS code G0337, are not subject to the editing usually required on hospice claims to match the claim to an established hospice period. Further, contractors do not apply payments for hospice pre-election evaluation and counseling consultation services to the overall hospice cap amount.

Medicare must ensure that this counseling service occurs only one time per beneficiary by imposing safeguards to detect and prevent duplicate billing for similar services. If "new patient" physician services (HCPCS codes 99201-99205) are submitted by a Medicare contractor to CWF for payment authorization but HCPCS code G0337 (Hospice Pre-Election Evaluation and Counseling Services) has already been approved for a hospice claim for the same beneficiary, for the same date of service, by the same physician, the physician service will be rejected by CWF and the service shall be denied as a duplicate. Medicare contractors use the following messages in this case:

HCPCS code G0337 is only payable when billed on a hospice claim. Contractors shall not make payment for HCPCS code G0337 on professional claims. Contractors shall deny line items on professional claims for HCPCS code G0337 and use the following messages:

MSN message 17.9: "Medicare (Part A/Part B) pays for this service. The provider must bill the correct Medicare contractor."

CARC 109: "Claim not covered by this payer/contractor. You must send the claim to the correct payer/contractor ."

100-4, Chapter 11, 30.3

Data Required on the Institutional Claim to Medicare Contractor

See Pub. 100-02, Medicare Benefit Policy Manual, chapter 9, §§10 & 20.2 for coverage requirements for Hospice benefits. This section addresses only the submittal of claims. Before submitting claims, the hospice must submit a Notice of Election (NOE) to the Medicare contractor. See section 20, of this chapter for information on NOE transaction types.

The Social Security Act at §1862 (a)(22) requires that all claims for Medicare payment must be submitted in an electronic form specified by the Secretary of Health and Human Services, unless an exception described at §1862 (h) applies. The electronic format required for billing hospice services is the ASC X12 837 institutional claim transaction. Since the data structure of this transaction is difficult to express in narrative form and to provide assistance to small providers excepted from the electronic claim requirement, the instructions below are given relative to the data element names on the Form CMS-1450 hardcopy form. Each data element name is shown in bold type. Information regarding the form locator numbers that correspond to these data element names is found in Chapter 25.

Because claim formats serve the needs of many payers, some data elements may not be needed by a particular payer. Detailed information is given only for items required for Medicare hospice claims. Items not listed need not be completed although hospices may complete them when billing multiple payers.

Provider Name, Address, and Telephone Number

The hospice enters this information for their agency.

Type of Bill

This three-digit alphanumeric code gives three specific pieces of information. The first digit identifies the type of facility. The second classifies the type of care. The third indicates the sequence of this bill in this particular benefit period. It is referred to as a "frequency" code.

Code Structure

1st Digit -Type of Facility
8- Specialfacility (Hospice)

2nd Digit -Classification (Special Facility Only)
1- Hospice(Nonhospital based)
2- Hospice(Hospital based)

3rd Digit –Frequency	Definition
0- Nonpayment/Zero Claims	Used when no payment from Medicare is anticipated.
1 - Admit Through Discharge Claim	This code is used for a bill encompassing an entire course of hospice treatment for which the provider expects payment from the payer, i.e., no further bills will be submitted for this patient.
2 - Interim – First Claim	This code is used for the first of an expected series of payment bills for a hospice course of treatment.
3 - Interim - Continuing Claim	This code is used when a payment bill for a hospice course of treatment has already been submitted and further bills are expected to be submitted.
4 - Interim - Last Claim	This code is used for a payment bill that is the last of a series for a hospice course of treatment. The "Through" date of this bill is the discharge date, transfer date, or date of death.
5 - Late Charges	Use this code for late charges that need to be billed. Late charges can be submitted only for revenue codes not on the original bill. Effective April 1, 2012, hospice late charge claims are no longer accepted by Medicare. Providers should use type of bill frequency 7. See below.
7 - Replacement of Prior Claim	This code is used by the provider when it wants to correct a previously submitted bill. This is the code used on the corrected or "new" bill. For additional information on replacement bills see Chapter 3.
8 - Void/Cancel of a Prior Claim	This code is used to cancel a previously processed claim. For additional information on void/cancel bills see Chapter 3.

Statement Covers Period (From-Through)

The hospice shows the beginning and ending dates of the period covered by this bill in numeric fields (MM-DD-YY). The hospice does not show days before the patient's entitlement began. Since the 12-month hospice "cap period" (see §80.2) ends each year on October 31, hospices must submit separate bills for October and November.

Patient Name/Identifier

The hospice enters the beneficiary's name exactly as it appears on the Medicare card.

Patient Address
Patient Birth date
Patient Sex

The hospice enters the appropriate address, date of birth and gender information describing the beneficiary.

Admission/Start of Care Date

The hospice enters the admission date, which must be the same date as the effective date of the hospice election or change of election. The date of admission may not precede the physician's certification by more than 2 calendar days.

The admission date stays the same on all continuing claims for the same hospice election.

Patient Discharge Status

This code indicates the patient's status as of the "Through" date of the billing period. The hospice enters the most appropriate National Uniform Billing Committee (NUBC) approved code.

NOTE: that patient discharge status code 20 is not used on hospice claims. If the patient has died during the billing period, use codes 40, 41 or 42 as appropriate.

Medicare regulations at 42 CFR 418.26 define three reasons for discharge from hospice care:

1. The beneficiary moves out of the hospice's service area or transfers to another hospice,
2. The hospice determines that the beneficiary is no longer terminally ill or
3. The hospice determines the beneficiary meets their internal policy regarding discharge for cause.

Each of these discharge situations requires different coding on Medicare claims.

Reason 1: A beneficiary may move out of the hospice's service area either with, or without, a transfer to another hospice. In the case of a discharge when the beneficiary moves out of the hospice's service area without a transfer, the hospice uses the NUBC approved discharge status code that best describes the beneficiary's situation and appends condition code 52. The hospice does not report occurrence code 42 on their claim. This discharge claim will terminate the beneficiary's current hospice benefit period as of the "Through" date on the claim. The beneficiary may re-elect the hospice benefit at any time as long they remain eligible for the benefit.

In the case of a discharge when the beneficiary moves out of the hospice's service area and transfers to another hospice, the hospice uses discharge status code 50 or 51, depending on whether the beneficiary is transferring to home hospice or hospice in a medical facility. The hospice does not report occurrence code 42 on their claim. This discharge claim does not terminate the beneficiary's current hospice benefit period. The admitting hospice submits a transfer Notice of Election (type of bill 8xC) after the transfer has occurred and the beneficiary's hospice benefit is not affected.

Reason 2: In the case of a discharge when the hospice determines the beneficiary is no longer terminally ill, the hospice uses the NUBC approved discharge status code that best describes the beneficiary's situation. The hospice does not report occurrence code 42 on their claim. This discharge claim will terminate the beneficiary's current hospice benefit period as of the "Through" date on the claim.

Reason 3: In the case of a discharge for cause, the hospice uses the NUBC approved discharge status code that best describes the beneficiary's situation. The hospice does not report occurrence code 42 on their claim. Instead, the hospice reports condition code H2 to indicate a discharge for cause. The effect of this discharge claim on the beneficiary's current hospice benefit period depends on the discharge status.

If the beneficiary is transferred to another hospice (discharge status codes 50 or 51) the claim does not terminate the beneficiary's current hospice benefit period. The admitting hospice submits a transfer Notice of Election (type of bill 8xC) after the transfer has occurred and the beneficiary's hospice benefit is not affected. If any other appropriate discharge status code is used, this discharge claim will terminate the beneficiary's current hospice benefit period as of the "Through" date on the claim. The beneficiary may re-elect the hospice benefit if they are certified as terminally ill and eligible for the benefit again in the future.

If the beneficiary has chosen to revoke their hospice election, the provider uses the NUBC approved discharge patient status code and the occurrence code 42 indicating the date the beneficiary revoked the benefit. The beneficiary may re-elect the hospice benefit if they are certified as terminally ill and eligible for the benefit again in the future.

Discharge Reason	Coding Required in Addition to Patient Status Code
Beneficiary Revokes	Occurrence Code 42
Beneficiary Transfers Hospices	Patient Status Code 50 or 51; no other indicator
Beneficiary No Longer Terminally Ill	No other indicator
Beneficiary Discharged for Cause	Condition code H2
Beneficiary Moves Out of Service Area	Condition code 52

If a hospice beneficiary is discharged alive or if a hospice beneficiary revokes the election of hospice care, the hospice shall file a timely-filed Notice of Election Termination / Revocation (NOTR) using type of bill 8xB, unless it has already filed a final claim. A timely-filed NOTR is a NOTR that is submitted to the Medicare contractor and accepted by the Medicare contractor within 5 calendar days after the effective date of discharge or revocation. While a timely-filed NOTR is one that is submitted to and accepted by the Medicare contractor within 5 calendar days after the hospice election, posting to the CWF may not occur within that same timeframe. The date of posting to the CWF is not a reflection of whether the NOTR is considered timely-filed. A NOTR (type of bill 8xB) is entered via Direct Data Entry in the same way as an NOE (type of bill 8xA). Hospices continue to have 12 months from the date of service in which to file their claims timely.

Untimely Face-to-Face Encounters and Discharge

When a required face-to-face encounter occurs prior to, but no more than 30 calendar days prior to, the third benefit period recertification and every benefit period recertification thereafter, it is considered timely. A timely face-to-face encounter would be evident when examining the face-to-face attestation, which is part of the recertification, as that attestation includes the date of the encounter. If the required face-to-face encounter is not timely, the hospice would be unable to recertify the patient as being terminally ill, and the patient would cease to be eligible for the Medicare hospice benefit. In such instances, the hospice must discharge the patient from the Medicare hospice benefit because he or she is not considered terminally ill for Medicare purposes.

When a discharge from the Medicare hospice benefit occurs due to failure to perform a required face-to-face encounter timely, the claim should include the most appropriate patient discharge status code. The hospice can re-admit the patient

to the Medicare hospice benefit once the required encounter occurs, provided the patient continues to meet all of the eligibility requirements and the patient (or representative) files an election statement in accordance with CMS regulations. Where the only reason the patient ceases to be eligible for the Medicare hospice benefit is the hospice's failure to meet the face-to-face requirement, CMS would expect the hospice to continue to care for the patient at its own expense until the required encounter occurs, enabling the hospice to re-establish Medicare eligibility.

Occurrence span code 77 does not apply to the above described situations when the face-to-face encounter has not occurred timely.

While the face-to-face encounter itself must occur no more than 30 calendar days prior to the start of the third benefit period recertification and each subsequent recertification, its accompanying attestation must be completed before the claim is submitted.

Condition Codes

The hospice enters any appropriate NUBC approved code(s) identifying conditions related to this bill that may affect processing.

Codes listed below are only those most frequently applicable to hospice claims. For a complete list of codes, see the NUBC manual.

07	Treatment of Non-terminal Condition for Hospice	Code indicates the patient has elected hospice care but the provider is not treating the terminal condition, and is, therefore, requesting regular Medicare payment.
20	Beneficiary Requested Billing	Code indicates the provider realizes the services on this bill are at a noncovered level of care or otherwise excluded from coverage, but the beneficiary has requested a formal determination.
21	Billing for Denial Notice	Code indicates the provider realizes services are at a noncovered level of care or excluded, but requests a denial notice from Medicare in order to bill Medicaid or other insurers.
H2	Discharge by a Hospice Provider for Cause	Discharge by a Hospice Provider for Cause. NOTE: Used by the provider to indicate the patient meets the hospice's documented policy addressing discharges for cause.
52	Out of Hospice Service Area	Code indicates the patient is discharged for moving out of the hospice service area. This can include patients who relocate or who go on vacation outside of the hospice's service area, or patients who are admitted to a hospital or SNF that does not have contractual arrangements with the hospice.

Occurrence Codes and Dates

The hospice enters any appropriate NUBC approved code(s) and associated date(s) defining specific event(s) relating to this billing period. Event codes are two numeric digits, and dates are six numeric digits (MM-DD-YY). If there are more occurrences than there are spaces on the form, use the occurrence span code fields to record additional occurrences and dates.

Codes listed below are only those most frequently applicable to hospice claims. For a complete list of codes, see the NUBC manual.

Code	Title	Definition
23	Cancellation of Hospice Election Period (Medicare contractor USE ONLY)	Code indicates date on which a hospice period of election is cancelled by a Medicare contractor as opposed to revocation by the beneficiary.
24	Date Insurance Denied	Code indicates the date of receipt of a denial of coverage by a higher priority payer.
27	Date of Hospice Certification or Re-Certification	Code indicates the date of certification or re-certification of the hospice benefit period, beginning with the first 2 initial benefit periods of 90 days each and the subsequent 60-day benefit periods. NOTE: regarding transfers from one hospice to another hospice: If a patient is in the first certification period when they transfer to another hospice, the receiving hospice would use the same certification date as the previous hospice until the next certification period. However, if they were in the next certification at the time of transfer, then they would enter that date in the Occurrence Code 27 and date.
42	Date of Termination of Hospice Benefit	Enter code to indicate the date on which beneficiary terminated his/her election to receive hospice benefits. This code can be used only when the beneficiary has revoked the benefit. It is not used in transfer situations.

Occurrence code 27 is reported on the claim for the billing period in which the certification or re-certification was obtained. When the re-certification is late and not obtained during the month it was due, the occurrence span code 77 should be reported with the through date of the span code equal to the through date of the claim.

Occurrence Span Code and Dates

The hospice enters any appropriate NUBC approved code(s) and associated beginning and ending date(s) defining a specific event relating to this billing period are shown. Event codes are two alphanumeric digits and dates are shown numerically as MM-DD-YY.

Codes listed below are only those most frequently applicable to hospice claims. For a complete list of codes, see the NUBC manual.

Code	Title	Definition
M2	Dates of Inpatient Respite Care	Code indicates From/Through dates of a period of inpatient respite care for hospice patients to differentiate separate respite periods of less than 5 days each. M2 is used when respite care is provided more than once during a benefit period.
77	Provider Liability – Utilization Charged	Code indicates From/Through dates for a period of non-covered hospice care for which the provider accepts payment liability (other than for medical necessity or custodial care).

Respite care is payable only for periods of respite up to 5 consecutive days. Claims reporting respite periods greater than 5 consecutive days will be returned to the provider. Days of respite care beyond 5 days must be billed at the appropriate home care rate for payment consideration.

For example: If the patient enters a respite period on July 1 and is returned to routine home care on July 6, the units of respite reported on the line item would be 5 representing July 1 through July 5, July 6 is reported as a day of routine home care regardless of the time of day entering respite or returning to routine home care.

When there is more than one respite period in the billing period, the provider must include the M2 occurrence span code for all periods of respite. The individual respite periods reported shall not exceed 5 days, including consecutive respite periods.

For example: If the patient enters a respite period on July 1 and is returned to routine home care on July 6 and later returns to respite care from July 15 to July 18, and completes the month on routine home care, the provider must report two separate line items for the respite periods and two occurrence span code M2, as follows:

Revenue Line items:

- Revenue code 0655 with line item date of service 07/01/XX (for respite period July 1 through July 5) and line item units reported as 5
- Revenue code 0651 with line item date of service 07/06/XX (for routine home care July 6 through July 14) and line item units reported as 9
- Revenue code 0655 with line item date of service 07/15/XX (for respite period July 15 through 17th) and line item units reported as 3
- Revenue code 0651 with line item date of service 07/18/XX (for routine home care on date of discharge from respite through July 31 and line item units reported as 14.

Occurrence Span Codes:

- M2 0701XX – 0705XX
- M2 0715XX – 0717XX

Provider Liability Periods Using Occurrence Span Code 77: Hospices must use occurrence span code 77 to identify days of care that are not covered by Medicare due to:

Untimely physician recertification. This is particularly important when the non-covered days fall at the beginning of a billing period other than the initial certification period.

Late-filing of a Notice of Election (NOE). A timely-filed NOE is a NOE that is submitted to the Medicare contractor and accepted by the Medicare contractor within 5 calendar days after the hospice admission date. When the hospice files a NOE late, Medicare shall not cover and pay for the days of hospice care from the hospice admission date to the date the NOE is submitted to and accepted by the Medicare contractor. The date the NOE is submitted to and accepted by the Medicare contractor is an allowable day for payment.

Example:

Admission date is 10/10/2014 (Fri).

Day 1 = Sat. 10/11/2014

Day 2 = Sun. 10/12/2014

Day 3 = Mon. 10/13/2014

Day 4 = Tues. 10/14/2014

Day 5 = Weds. 10/15/2014 10/15/2014 is the NOE Due Date.

IF NOE Receipt date is 10/16/2014, the hospice reports 10/10-10/15 as non-covered days using occurrence span code 77 or CWF rejects the claim back to FISS. The contractor returns the claim to the provider for correction.

Value Codes and Amounts

The hospice enters any appropriate NUBC approved code(s) and the associated value amounts identifying numeric information related to this bill that may affect processing.

The most commonly used value codes on hospice claims are value codes 61 and G8, which are used to report the location of the site of hospice services. Otherwise, value codes are commonly used only to indicate Medicare is secondary to another payer. For detailed information on reporting Medicare secondary payer information, see the Medicare Secondary Payer Manual.

Code	Title	Definition
61	Place of Residence where Service is Furnished (Routine Home Care and Continuous Home Care)	MSA or Core-Based Statistical Area (CBSA) number (or rural State code) of the location where the hospice service is delivered. A residence can be an inpatient facility if an individual uses that facility as a place of residence. It is the level of care that is required and not the location where hospice services are provided that determines payment. In other words, if an individual resides in a freestanding hospice facility and requires routine home care, then claims are submitted for routine home care. Hospices must report value code 61 when billing revenue codes 0651 and 0652.
G8	Facility where Inpatient Hospice Service is Delivered (General Inpatient and Inpatient Respite Care).	MSA or Core Based Statistical Area (CBSA) number (or rural State code) of the facility where inpatient hospice services are delivered. Hospices must report value code G8 when billing revenue codes 0655 and 0656.

If hospice services are provided to the beneficiary in more than one CBSA area during the billing period, the hospice reports the CBSA that applies at the end of the billing period. For routine home care and continuous home care (e.g., the beneficiary's residence changes between locations in different CBSAs), report the CBSA of the beneficiary's residence at the end of the billing period. For general inpatient and inpatient respite care (e.g., the beneficiary is served in inpatient facilities in different CBSAs), report the CBSA of the latest facility that served the beneficiary. If the beneficiary receives both home and inpatient care during the billing period, the latest home CBSA is reported with value code 61 and the latest facility CBSA is reported with value code G8.

Revenue Codes

The hospice assigns a revenue code for each type of service provided and enters the appropriate four-digit numeric revenue code to explain each charge.

For claims with dates of service before July 1, 2008, hospices only reported the revenue codes in the table below. Effective on claims with dates of service on or after January 1, 2008, additional revenue codes will be reported describing the visits provided under each level of care. However, Medicare payment will continue to be reflected only on claim lines with the revenue codes in this table.

Hospice claims are required to report separate line items for the level of care each time the level of care changes. This includes revenue codes 0651, 0655 and 0656. For example, if a patient begins the month receiving routine home care followed by a period of general inpatient care and then later returns to routine home care all in the same month, in addition to the one line reporting the general inpatient care days,

there should be two separate line items for routine home care. Each routine home care line reports a line item date of service to indicate the first date that level of care began for that consecutive period. This will ensure visits and calls reported on the claim will be associated with the level of care being billed.

Code	Description	Standard Abbreviation
0651*	Routine Home Care	RTN Home
0652*	Continuous Home Care	CTNS Home A minimum of 8 hours of primarily nursing care within a 24-hour period. The 8-hours of care do not need to be continuous within the 24-hour period, but a need for an aggregate of 8 hours of primarily nursing care is required. Nursing care must be provided by a registered nurse or a licensed practical nurse. If skilled intervention is required for less than 8 aggregate hours (or less than 32 units) within a 24 hour period, then the care rendered would be covered as a routine home care day. Services provided by a nurse practitioner as the attending physician are not included in the CHC computation nor is care that is not directly related to the crisis included in the computation. CHC billing should reflect direct patient care during a period of crisis and should not reflect time related to staff working hours, time taken for meal breaks, time used for educating staff, time used to report etc.
0655***	Inpatient Respite Care	IP Respite
0656***	General Inpatient Care	GNL IP
0657**	Physician Services	PHY SER (must be accompanied by a physician procedure code)

* Reporting of value code 61 is required with these revenue codes.
**Reporting of modifier GV is required with this revenue code when billing physician services performed by a nurse practitioner.
***Reporting of value code G8 is required with these revenue codes.
*** The date of discharge from general or respite inpatient care is paid at the appropriate home care rate and must be billed with the appropriate home care revenue code unless the patient is deceased at time of discharge in which case, the appropriate inpatient respite or general care revenue code should be used.

NOTE: Hospices use revenue code 0657 to identify hospice charges for services furnished to patients by physician or nurse practitioner employees, or physicians or nurse practitioners receiving compensation from the hospice. Physician services performed by a nurse practitioner require the addition of the modifier GV in conjunction with revenue code 0657. Procedure codes are required in order for the Medicare contractor to determine the reimbursement rate for the physician services. Appropriate procedure codes are available from the Medicare contractor.

Effective on claims with dates of service on or after July 1, 2008, hospices must report the number of visits that were provided to the beneficiary in the course of delivering the hospice levels of care billed with the codes above. Charges for these codes will be reported on the appropriate level of care line. Total number of patient care visits is to be reported by the discipline (registered nurse, nurse practitioner, licensed nurse, home health aide (also known as a hospice aide), social worker, physician or nurse practitioner serving as the beneficiary's attending physician) for each week at each location of service. If visits are provided in multiple sites, a separate line for each site and for each discipline will be required. The total number of visits does not imply the total number of activities or interventions provided. If patient care visits in a particular discipline are not provided under a given level of care or service location, do not report a line for the corresponding revenue code.

To constitute a visit, the discipline, (as defined above) must have provided care to the beneficiary. Services provided by a social worker to the beneficiary's family also constitute a visit. For example, phone calls, documentation in the medical/clinical record, interdisciplinary group meetings, obtaining physician orders, rounds in a facility or any other activity that is not related to the provision of items or services to a beneficiary, do not count towards a visit to be placed on the claim. In addition, the visit must be reasonable and necessary for the palliation and management of the terminal illness and related conditions as described in the patient's plan of care.

Example 1: Week 1: A visit by the RN was made to the beneficiary's home on Monday and Wednesday where the nurse assessed the patient, verified effect of pain medications, provided patient teaching, obtained vital signs and documented in the medical record. A home health aide assisted the patient with a bath on Tuesday and Thursday. There were no social work or physician visits. Thus for that week there were 2 visits provided by the nurse and 2 by the home health aide. Since there were no visits by the social worker or by the physician, there would not be any line items for each of those disciplines.

Example 2: If a hospice patient is receiving routine home care while residing in a nursing home, the hospice would record visits for all of its physicians, nurses, social workers, and home health aides who visit the patient to provide care for the palliation and management of the terminal illness and related conditions, as described in the patient's plan of care. In this example the nursing home is acting as the patient's home. Only the patient care provided by the hospice staff constitutes a visit.

Hospices must enter the following visit revenue codes, when applicable as of July 1, 2008:

055x Skilled Nursing	Required detail: The earliest date of service this discipline was provided during the delivery of each level of care in each service location, service units which represent the number of visits provided in that location, and a charge amount.
056x Medical Social Services	Required detail: The earliest date of service this discipline was provided during the delivery of each level of care in each service location, service units which represent the number of visits provided in that location, and a charge amount.
057x Home Health Aide	Required detail: The earliest date of service this discipline was provided during the delivery of each level of care in each service location, service units which represent the number of visits provided in that location, and a charge amount.

For services provided on or after January 1, 2010, hospices report social worker phone calls and visits performed by hospice staff for other than General Inpatient (GIP) care in 15 minute increments using the following revenue codes and associated HCPCS. Hospices shall report line-item visit data for hospice staff providing general inpatient care (GIP) to hospice patients in skilled nursing facilities or in hospitals

for claims with dates of service on or after April 1, 2014. Hospices may voluntarily begin this reporting as of January 1, 2014. This includes visits by hospice nurses, aides, social workers, physical therapists, occupational therapists, and speech-language pathologists, on a line-item basis, with visit and visit length reported as is done for routine home care and continuous home care. This also includes certain calls by hospice social workers (as described further below).

Revenue Code	Required HCPCS	Required Detail
042x Physical Therapy	G0151	Required detail: Each visit is identified on a separate line item with the appropriate line item date of service and a charge amount. The units reported on the claim are the multiplier for the total time of the visit defined in the HCPCS description.
043x Occupational Therapy	G0152	Required detail: Each visit is identified on a separate line item with the appropriate line item date of service and a charge amount. The units reported on the claim are the multiplier for the total time of the visit defined in the HCPCS description.
044x Speech Therapy – Language Pathology	G0153	Required detail: Each visit is identified on a separate line item with the appropriate line item date of service and a charge amount. The units reported on the claim are the multiplier for the total time of the visit defined in the HCPCS description.
055x Skilled Nursing	G0154 (this code has been deleted or 2017)	Required detail: Each visit is identified on a separate line item with the appropriate line item date of service and a charge amount. The units reported on the claim are the multiplier for the total time of the visit defined in the HCPCS description.
056x Medical Social Services	G0155	Required detail: Each visit is identified on a separate line item with the appropriate line item date of service and a charge amount. The units reported on the claim are the multiplier for the total time of the visit defined in the HCPCS description.
0569 Other Medical Social Services	G0155	Required detail: Each social service phone call is identified on a separate line item with the appropriate line item date of service and a charge amount. The units reported on the claim are the multiplier for the total time of the call defined in the HCPCS description.
057x Aide	G0156	Required detail: Each visit is identified on a separate line item with the appropriate line item date of service and a charge amount. The units reported on the claim are the multiplier the total time of the visit defined in the HCPCS description.

Visits by registered nurses, licensed vocational nurses and nurse practitioners (unless the nurse practitioner is acting as the beneficiary's attending physician) are reported under revenue code 055x.

All visits to provide care related to the palliation and management of the terminal illness or related conditions, whether provided by hospice employees or provided under arrangement, must be reported. The two exceptions are related to General Inpatient Care and Respite care. CMS is not requiring hospices to report visit data at this time for visits made by non-hospice staff providing General Inpatient Care or respite care in contract facilities. However, General Inpatient Care or respite care visits related to the palliation and management of the terminal illness or related conditions provided by hospice staff in contract facilities must be reported, and all General Inpatient Care and respite care visits related to the palliation and management of the terminal illness or related conditions provided in hospice-owned facilities must be reported.

Charges associated with the reported visits are covered under the hospice bundled payment and reflected in the payment for the level of care billed on the claim. No additional payment is made on the visit revenue lines. The visit charges will be identified on the provider remittance advice notice with remittance code 97 "Payment adjusted because the benefit for this service is included in the payment / allowance for another service/procedure that has already been adjudicated."

Effective January 1, 2010, Medicare will require hospices to report additional detail for visits on their claims. For all Routine Home Care (RHC), Continuous Home Care (CHC) and Respite care billing, Medicare hospice claims should report each visit performed by nurses, aides, and social workers who are employed by the hospice, and their associated time per visit in the number of 15 minute increments, on a separate line. The visits should be reported using revenue codes 055x (nursing services), 057x (aide services), or 056x (medical social services), with the time reported using the associated HCPCS G-code in the range G0154 (this code has been deleted or 2017) to G0156. Hospices should report in the unit field on the line level the units as a multiplier of the visit time defined in the HCPCS description.

Additionally, providers should begin reporting each RHC, CHC, and Respite visit performed by physical therapists, occupational therapists, and speech-language therapists and their associated time per visit in the number of 15 minute increments on a separate line. Providers should use existing revenue codes 042x for physical therapy, 043x for occupational therapy, and 044x for speech language therapy, in addition to the appropriate HCPCS G-code for recording of visit length in 15 minute increments. HCPCS G-codes G0151 to G0153 will be used to describe the therapy discipline and visit time reported on a particular line item. Hospices should report in the unit field on the line level the units as a multiplier of the visit time defined in the HCPCS description. If a hospice patient is receiving Respite care in a contract facility, visit and time data by non-hospice staff should not be reported.

Social worker phone calls made to the patient or the patient's family should be reported using revenue code 0569, and HCPCS G-code G0155 for the length of the call, with each call being a separate line item. Hospices should report in the unit field on the line level the units as a multiplier of the visit time defined in the HCPCS description. Only phone calls that are necessary for the palliation and management of the terminal illness and related conditions as described in the patient's plan of care (such as counseling or speaking with a patient's family or arranging for a placement) should be reported. Report only social worker phone calls related to providing and or coordinating care to the patient and family and documented as such in the clinical records.

When recording any visit or social worker phone call time, providers should sum the time for each visit or call, rounding to the nearest 15 minute increment. Providers should not include travel time or documentation time in the time recorded for any visit or call. Additionally, hospices may not include interdisciplinary group time in time and visit reporting.

Hospice agencies shall report injectable and non-injectable prescription drugs for the palliation and management of the terminal illness and related conditions on their claims. Both injectable and non-injectable prescription drugs shall be reported on claims on a line-item basis per fill, based on the amount dispensed by the pharmacy.

When a facility (hospital, SNF, NF, or hospice inpatient facility) uses a medication management system where each administration of a hospice medication is considered a fill for hospice patients receiving care, the hospice shall report a monthly total for each drug (i.e., report a total for the period covered by the claim), along with the total dispensed.

Hospices shall report multi-ingredient compound prescription drugs (non-injectable) using revenue code 0250. The hospice shall specify the same prescription number for each ingredient of a compound drug according to the 837i guidelines in loop 2410. In addition, the hospice shall provide the NDC for each ingredient in the compound; the NDC qualifier represents the quantity of the drug filled (meaning the amount dispensed) and shall be reported as the unit measure.

When reporting prescription drugs in a comfort kit/pack, the hospice shall report the NDC of each prescription drug within the package, in accordance with the procedures for non-injectable prescriptions.

Hospice agencies shall report infusion pumps (a type of DME) on a line-item basis for each pump and for each medication fill and refill. The hospice claim shall reflect the total charge for the infusion pump for the period covered by the claim, whether the hospice is billed for it daily, weekly, biweekly, with each medication refill, or in some other fashion. The hospice shall include on the claim the infusion pump charges on whatever basis is easiest for its billing systems, so long as in total, the claim reflects the charges for the pump for the time period of that claim.

Revenue code reporting required for claims with dates of service on or after April 1, 2014:

0250 Non-injectable Prescription Drugs	N/A	Required detail: Report on a line-item basis per fill, using revenue code 0250 and the National Drug Code (NDC). The NDC qualifier represents the quantity of the drug filled, and should be reported as the unit measure.
029X Infusion pumps	Applicable HCPCS	Required detail: Report on the claim on a line-item basis per pump order and per medication refill, using revenue code 029X for the equipment and 0294 for the drugs along with the appropriate HCPCS.
0636 Injectable Drugs	Applicable HCPCS	Required detail: Report on a line item basis per fill with units representing the amount filled. (i.e., Q1234 Drug 100mg and the fill was for 200 mg, units reported = 2).

HCPCS/Accommodation Rates/HIPPS Rate Codes

For services provided on or before December 31, 2006, HCPCS codes are required only to report procedures on service lines for attending physician services (revenue 657). Level of care revenue codes (651, 652, 655 or 656) do not require HCPCS coding.

For services provided on or after January 1, 2007, hospices must also report a HCPCS code along with each level of care revenue code (651, 652, 655 and 656) to identify the type of service location where that level of care was provided.

The following HCPCS codes will be used to report the type of service location for hospice services:

HCPCS Code	Definition
Q5001	HOSPICE CARE PROVIDED IN PATIENT'S HOME/RESIDENCE
Q5002	HOSPICE CARE PROVIDED IN ASSISTED LIVING FACILITY
Q5003	HOSPICE CARE PROVIDED IN NURSING LONG TERM CARE FACILITY (LTC) OR NON-SKILLED NURSING FACILITY (NF)
Q5004	HOSPICE CARE PROVIDED IN SKILLED NURSING FACILITY (SNF)
Q5005	HOSPICE CARE PROVIDED IN INPATIENT HOSPITAL
Q5006	HOSPICE CARE PROVIDED IN INPATIENT HOSPICE FACILITY
Q5007	HOSPICE CARE PROVIDED IN LONG TERM CARE HOSPITAL (LTCH)
Q5008	HOSPICE CARE PROVIDED IN INPATIENT PSYCHIATRIC FACILITY
Q5009	HOSPICE CARE PROVIDED IN PLACE NOT OTHERWISE SPECIFIED (NOS)
Q5010	Hospice home care provided in a hospice facility

If care is rendered at multiple locations, each location is to be identified on the claim with a corresponding HCPCS code. For example, routine home care may be provided for a portion of the billing period in the patient's residence and another portion in an assisted living facility. In this case, report one revenue code 651 line with HCPCS code Q5001 and the number of days of routine home care provided in the residence and another revenue code 651 line with HCPCS code Q5002 and the number of days of routine home care provided in the assisted living facility.

Q5004 shall be used for hospice patients in a skilled nursing facility (SNF), or hospice patients in the SNF portion of a dually-certified nursing facility. There are 4 situations where this would occur:

1. If the beneficiary is receiving hospice care in a solely-certified SNF.
2. If the beneficiary is receiving general inpatient care in the SNF.
3. If the beneficiary is in a SNF receiving SNF care under the Medicare SNF benefit for a condition unrelated to the terminal illness and related conditions, and is receiving hospice routine home care; this is uncommon.
4. If the beneficiary is receiving inpatient respite care in a SNF.

If a beneficiary is in a nursing facility but doesn't meet the criteria above for Q5004, the site shall be coded as Q5003, for a long term care nursing facility.

These service location HCPCS codes are not required on revenue code lines describing the visits provided under each level of care (e.g. 055X, 056X, 057X).

General inpatient care provided by hospice staff requires line item visit reporting in units of 15 minute increments when provided in the following sites of service: Skilled Nursing Facility (Q5004), Inpatient Hospital (Q5005), Long Term Care Hospital (Q5007), Inpatient Psychiatric Facility (Q5008).

Modifiers

The following modifier is required reporting for claims with dates of service on or after April 1, 2014:

PM – Post-mortem visits. Hospices shall report visits and length of visits (rounded to the nearest 15 minute increment), for nurses, aides, social workers, and therapists who are employed by the hospice, that occur on the date of death, after the patient has passed away. Post mortem visits occurring on a date subsequent to the date of death are not to be reported. The reporting of post-mortem visits, on the date of death, should occur regardless of the patient's level of care or site of service. Date of death is defined as the date of death reported on the death certificate. Hospices shall report hospice visits that occur before death on a separate line from those which occur after death.

For example, assume that a nurse arrives at the home at 9 pm to provide routine home care (RHC) to a dying patient, and that the patient passes away at 11 pm. The nurse stays with the family until 1:30 am. The hospice should report a nursing visit with eight 15-minute time units for the visit from 9 pm to 11 pm. On a separate line, the hospice should report a nursing visit with a PM modifier with four 15-minute time units for the portion of the visit from 11 pm to midnight to account for the 1 hour post mortem visit. If the patient passes away suddenly, and the hospice nurse does not arrive until after his death at 11:00 pm, and remains with the family until 1:30 am, then the hospice should report a line item nursing visit with a PM modifier and four 15-minute increments of time as the units to account for the 1 hour post mortem visit from 11:00 pm to midnight.

The following modifier may be used to identify requests for an exception to the consequences of not filing the NOE timely for claims with dates of service on or after October 1, 2014:

KX - Requirements specified in the medical policy have been met. This modifier is used to indicate that the hospice has documentation indicating an exception condition applies. The hospice reports the KX modifier with the Q HCPCS code on the earliest dated level of care revenue code line on the claim (revenue code 0651, 0652, 0655 or 0656). When this modifier is present, the Medicare contractor will request the documentation from the hospice (see section 20.1.1).

Service Date

The HIPAA standard 837 Institutional claim format requires line item dates of service for all outpatient claims. Medicare classifies hospice claims as outpatient claims (see Chapter 1, §60.4). For services provided on or before December 31, 2006, CMS allows hospices to satisfy the line item date of service requirement by placing any valid date within the Statement Covers Period dates on line items on hospice claims.

For services provided on or after January 1, 2007, service date reporting requirements will vary between continuous home care lines (revenue code 652) and other revenue code lines.

Revenue code 652 – report a separately dated line item for each day that continuous home care is provided, reporting the number of hours, or parts of hours rounded to 15-minute increments, of continuous home care that was provided on that date.

Other payment revenue codes – report a separate line for each level of care provided at each service location type, as described in the instructions for HCPCS coding reported above. Hospices report the earliest date that each level of care was provided at each service location. Attending physician services should be individually dated, reporting the date that each HCPCS code billed was delivered.

Non-payment service revenue codes – report dates as described in the table above under Revenue Codes.

For services provided on or after January 1, 2010, hospices report social worker phone calls and visits performed by hospice staff for other than GIP care as separate line items for each with the appropriate line item date of service. GIP visit reporting has not changed with the January 2010 update. GIP visits will continue to be reported as the number of visits per week.

For service visits that begin in one calendar day and span into the next calendar day, report one visit using the date the visit ended as the service date.

Any service dates that fall within an occurrence span code 77 period must be reported with non-covered charges.

Service Units

The hospice enters the number of units for each type of service. Units are measured in days for revenue codes 651, 655, and 656, in hours for revenue code 652, and in procedures for revenue code 657. For services provided on or after January 1, 2007, hours for revenue code 652 are reported in 15-minute increments. For services provided on or after January 1, 2008, units for visit discipline revenue codes are measured by the number of visits.

When days are non-covered due to not filing a timely NOE, the hospice reports two lines for the affected level of care. For example, if a billing period contains 31 days of routine home care and the first 5 days are non-covered due to not filing a timely NOE:

- *The hospice reports one revenue code 0651 line containing the earliest non-covered date of service, 5 units and all non-covered charges*
- *The hospice reports a second revenue code 0651 line containing the first covered date of service, 26 units and all covered charges.*

For services provided on or after January 1, 2010, hospices report social worker phone calls and visits performed by hospice staff for other than GIP care as a separate line item with the appropriate line item date of service and the units as an increment of 15 minutes. GIP visit reporting has not changed with the January 2010 update. The units for visits under GIP level of care continue to reflect the number of visits per week.

Report in the unit field on the line level the units as a multiplier of the visit time defined in the HCPCS description.

Total Charges

The hospice enters the total charge for the service described on each revenue code line. This information is being collected for purposes of research and will not affect the amount of reimbursement.

Non-Covered Charges

The hospice enters a charge amount equal to the Total Charges for any revenue code line with a Service Date within a non-covered period (e.g., an occurrence span code 77 period).

Payer Name

The hospice identifies the appropriate payer(s) for the claim.

National Provider Identifier – Billing Provider

The hospice enters its own National Provider Identifier (NPI).

Principal Diagnosis Code

The hospice enters diagnosis coding as required by ICD-9-CM / ICD-10-CM Coding Guidelines.

CMS accepts only HIPAA approved ICD-9-CM or ICD-10-CM/ICD-10-PCS codes, depending on the date of service. The official ICD-9-CM codes, which were updated annually through October 1, 2013, are posted at http://www.cms.gov/Medicare/Coding/ICD9ProviderDiagnosticCodes/codes.html

The official annual updates to ICD-10-CM and ICD-10-PCS codes are posted at http://www.cms.gov/Medicare/Coding/ICD10/index.html .

Use full diagnosis codes including all applicable digits, up to five digits for ICD-9-CM and up to seven digits for ICD-10-CM.

The principal diagnosis listed is the diagnosis most contributory to the terminal prognosis.

Non-reportable Principal Diagnosis Codes to be returned to the provider for correction:

- Hospices may not report ICD-9CM v-codes and ICD-10-CM z-codes as the principal diagnosis on hospice claims.
- Hospices may not report debility, failure to thrive, or dementia codes classified as unspecified as principal hospice diagnoses on the hospice claim.
- Hospices may not report diagnosis codes that cannot be used as the principal diagnosis according to ICD-9-CM or ICD-10-CM Coding Guidelines or require further compliance with various ICD-9-CM or ICD-10-CM coding conventions, such as those that have principal diagnosis code sequencing guidelines.

Other Diagnosis Codes

The hospice enters diagnosis coding as required by ICD-9-CM and ICD-10-CM Coding Guidelines. All of a patient's coexisting or additional diagnoses that are related to the terminal illness and related conditions should be reported on the hospice claim.

Attending Provider Name and Identifiers

For claims with dates of service before January 1, 2010, the hospice enters the National Provider Identifier (NPI) and name of the physician currently responsible for certifying the terminal illness, and signing the individual's plan of care for medical care and treatment.

For claims with dates of service on or after January 1, 2010, the hospice shall enter the NPI and name of the attending physician designated by the patient as having the most significant role in the determination and delivery of the patient's medical care.

Other Provider Name and Identifiers

For claims with dates of service before January 1, 2010, if the attending physician is a nurse practitioner, the hospice enters the NPI and name of the nurse practitioner.

For claims with dates of service on or after January 1, 2010, the hospice enters the NPI and name of the hospice physician responsible for certifying that the patient is terminally ill, with a life expectancy of 6 months or less if the disease runs its normal course. Note: Both the attending physician and other physician fields should be completed unless the patient's designated attending physician is the same as the physician certifying the terminal illness. When the attending physician is also the physician certifying the terminal illness, only the attending physician is required to be reported.

NOTE: for electronic claims using version 5010 or later, this information is reported in Loop ID 2310F – Referring Provider Name.

Hospices shall report the NPI of any nursing facility, hospital, or hospice inpatient facility where the patient is receiving hospice services, regardless of the level of care provided when the site of service is not the billing hospice. The billing hospice shall obtain the NPI for the facility where the patient is receiving care and report the facility's name, address and NPI on the 837 Institutional claim format in loop 2310 E Service Facility Location. When the patient has received care in more than one facility during the billing month, the hospice shall report the NPI of the facility where the patient was last treated. Failure to report this information for claims reporting place of service HCPCS Q5003 (long term care nursing facility), Q5004 (skilled nursing facility), Q5005 (inpatient hospital), Q5007 (long term care hospital) and Q5008 (inpatient psychiatric facility) with dates of service on or after April 1, 2014, will result in the claim being returned to the provider.

100-4, Chapter 11, 40.1.3.1

Care Plan Oversight

Care plan oversight (CPO) exists where there is physician supervision of patients under care of hospices that require complex and multidisciplinary care modalities involving regular physician development and/or revision of care plans. Implicit in the concept of CPO is the expectation that the physician has coordinated an aspect of the patient's care with the hospice during the month for which CPO services were billed.

For a physician or NP employed by or under arrangement with a hospice agency, CPO functions are incorporated and are part of the hospice per diem payment and as such may not be separately billed.

For information on separately billable CPO services by the attending physician or nurse practitioner see Chapter 12, §180 of this manual.

100-4, Chapter 11, 100.1

Billing for Denial of Hospice Room and Board Charges

Hospice providers wishing to receive a line item denial for room and board charges may submit the charges as non-covered using revenue code 0659 with HCPCS A9270 and modifier GY on an otherwise covered hospice claim.

100-4, Chapter 12, 30.4

Cardiovascular System (Codes 92950-93799)

A. Echocardiography Contrast Agents

Effective October 1, 2000, physicians may separately bill for contrast agents used in echocardiography. Physicians should use HCPCS Code A9700 (Supply of Injectable Contrast Material for Use in Echocardiography, per study). The type of service code is 9. This code will be carrier-priced.

B. Electronic Analyses of Implantable Cardioverter-defibrillators and Pacemakers

The CPT® codes 93731, 93734, 93741 and 93743 are used to report electronic analyses of single or dual chamber pacemakers and single or dual chamber implantable cardioverter-defibrillators. In the office, a physician uses a device called a programmer to obtain information about the status and performance of the device and to evaluate the patient's cardiac rhythm and response to the implanted device.

Advances in information technology now enable physicians to evaluate patients with implanted cardiac devices without requiring the patient to be present in the physician's office. Using a manufacturer's specific monitor/transmitter, a patient can send complete device data and specific cardiac data to a distant receiving station or secure Internet server. The electronic analysis of cardiac device data that is remotely obtained provides immediate and long-term data on the device and clinical data on the patient's cardiac functioning equivalent to that obtained during an in-office evaluation. Physicians should report the electronic analysis of an implanted cardiac device using remotely obtained data as described above with CPT® code 93731, 93734, 93741 or 93743, depending on the type of cardiac device implanted in the patient.

100-4, Chapter 12, 30.6.15.4

Power Mobility Devices (PMDs) (Code G0372)

Section 302(a)(2)(E)(iv) of the Medicare Prescription Drug, Improvement, and Modernization Act of 2003 (MMA) sets forth revised conditions for Medicare payment of Power Mobility Devices (PMDs). This section of the MMA states that payment for motorized or power wheelchairs may not be made unless a physician (as defined in §1861(r)(1) of the Act), a physician assistant, nurse practitioner, or a clinical nurse specialist (as those terms are defined in §1861(aa)(5)) has conducted a face-to-face examination of the beneficiary and written a prescription for the PMD.

Payment for the history and physical examination will be made through the appropriate evaluation and management (E&M) code corresponding to the history and physical examination of the patient. Due to the MMA requirement that the physician or treating practitioner create a written prescription and a regulatory requirement that the physician or treating practitioner prepare pertinent parts of the medical record for submission to the durable medical equipment supplier, code G0372 (physician service required to establish and document the need for a power mobility device)has been established to recognize additional physician services and resources required to establish and document the need for the PMD.

The G code indicates that all of the information necessary to document the PMD prescription is included in the medical record, and the prescription and supporting documentation is delivered to the PMD supplier within 30 days after the face-to-face examination.

Effective October 25, 2005, G0372 will be used to recognize additional physician services and resources required to establish and document the need for the PMD and will be added to the Medicare physician fee schedule.

100-4, Chapter 12,80.1

Coverage of Physicians' Services Provided in Comprehensive Outpatient Rehabilitation Facility
B3-2220

Rehabilitation services furnished by comprehensive outpatient rehabilitation facilities (CORFs) are covered by Medicare Part B.

Under §1832(a)(2)(E), §1861(cc)(2), and related provisions of the Act, a CORF is recognized as a provider of services on the basis of its reasonable costs. Except for diagnostic and therapeutic services provided by physicians to individual patients, payment is made to the CORF by intermediaries (acting in the role of the Part B carrier.)

Physicians' diagnostic and therapeutic services furnished to a CORF patient are not considered CORF physician's services. Instead they are services that the physician must bill to the Part B carrier. If covered services, payment is made according to the Medicare Physician Fee Schedule. When physician's diagnostic and therapeutic services are furnished in a CORF, the claim must be annotated to show the CORF as the place of treatment.

Services considered administrative services provided by the physician associated with the CORF are considered CORF services reimbursable to the CORF by the FI. Administrative services include consultation with and medical supervision of nonphysician staff, establishing and reviewing the plan of treatment, and other medical and facility administration activities.

100-4, Chapter 12, 100.1.1

Evaluation and Management (E/M) Services

A .General Documentation Instructions and Common Scenarios

Evaluation and Management (E/M) Services --For a given encounter, the selection of the appropriate level of E/M service should be determined according to the code definitions in the American Medical Association's Current Procedural Terminology (CPT®) and any applicable documentation guidelines.

For purposes of payment, E/M services billed by teaching physicians require that they personally document at least the following;

- That they performed the service or were physically present during the key or critical portions of the service when performed by the resident; and
- The participation of the teaching physician in the management of the patient.

When assigning codes to services billed by teaching physicians, reviewers will combine the documentation of both the resident and the teaching physician.

Documentation by the resident of the presence and participation of the teaching physician is not sufficient to establish the presence and participation of the teaching physician.

On medical review, the combined entries into the medical record by the teaching physician and the resident constitute the documentation for the service and together must support the medical necessity of the service.

Following are four common scenarios for teaching physicians providing E/M services:

Scenario 1:

The teaching physician personally performs all the required elements of an E/M service without a resident. In this scenario the resident may or may not have performed the E/M service independently.

In the absence of a note by a resident, the teaching physician must document as he/she would document an E/M service in a nonteaching setting.

Where a resident has written notes, the teaching physician's note may reference the resident's note. The teaching physician must document that he/she performed the critical or key portion(s) of the service, and that he/she was directly involved in the management of the patient. For payment, the composite of the teaching physician's entry and the resident's entry together must support the medical necessity of the billed service and the level of the service billed by the teaching physician.

Scenario 2:

The resident performs the elements required for an E/M service in the presence of, or jointly with, the teaching physician and the resident documents the service. In this case, the teaching physician must document that he/she was present during the performance of the critical or key portion(s) of the service and that he/she was directly involved in the management of the patient. The teaching physician's note should reference the resident's note. For payment, the composite of the teaching physician's entry and the resident's entry together must support the medical necessity and the level of the service billed by the teaching physician.

Scenario 3:

The resident performs some or all of the required elements of the service in the absence of the teaching physician and documents his/her service. The teaching physician independently performs the critical or key portion(s) of the service with or without the resident present and, as appropriate, discusses the case with the resident. In this instance, the teaching physician must document that he/she personally saw the patient, personally performed critical or key portions of the service, and participated in the management of the patient. The teaching physician's note should reference the resident's note. For payment, the composite of the teaching physician's entry and the resident's entry together must support the medical necessity of the billed service and the level of the service billed by the teaching physician.

Scenario 4

When a medical resident admits a patient to a hospital late at night and the teaching physician does not see the patient until later, including the next calendar day.

- The teaching physician must document that he/she personally saw the patient and participated in the management of the patient. The teaching physician may reference the resident's note in lieu of re-documenting the history of present illness, exam, medical decision-making, review of systems and/or past family/social history provided that the patient's condition has not changed, and the teaching physician agrees with the resident's note.
- The teaching physician's note must reflect changes in the patient's condition and clinical course that require that the resident's note be amended with further information to address the patient's condition and course at the time the patient is seen personally by the teaching physician.
- The teaching physician's bill must reflect the date of service he/she saw the patient and his/her personal work of obtaining a history, performing a physical, and participating in medical decision-making regardless of whether the combination of the teaching physician's and resident's documentation satisfies criteria for a higher level of service. For payment, the composite of the teaching physician's entry and the resident's entry together must support the medical necessity of the billed service and the level of the service billed by the teaching Physician.

Following are examples of minimally acceptable documentation for each of these scenarios:

Scenario 1:

Admitting **Note:** "I performed a history and physical examination of the patient and discussed his management with the resident. I reviewed the resident's note and agree with the documented findings and plan of care".

Follow-up Visit: "Hospital Day #3. I saw and evaluated the patient. I agree with the findings and the plan of care as documented in the resident's note".

Follow-up Visit: "Hospital Day #5. I saw and examined the patient. I agree with the resident's note except the heart murmur is louder, so I will obtain an echo to evaluate".

(NOTE: In this scenario if there are no resident notes, the teaching physician must document as he/she would document an E/M service in a non-teaching setting.)

Scenario 2:

Initial or Follow-up Visit: "I was present with the resident during the history and exam. I discussed the case with the resident and agree with the findings and plan as documented in the resident's note."

Follow-up Visit: "I saw the patient with the resident and agree with the resident's findings and plan."

Scenarios 3 and 4:

Initial Visit: "I saw and evaluated the patient. I reviewed the resident's note and agree, except that picture is more consistent with pericarditis than myocardial ischemia. Will begin NSAIDs."

Initial or Follow-up Visit: "I saw and evaluated the patient. Discussed with resident and agree with resident's findings and plan as documented in the resident's note."

Follow-up Visit: "See resident's note for details. I saw and evaluated the patient and agree with the resident's finding and plans as written."

Follow-up Visit: "I saw and evaluated the patient. Agree with resident's note but lower extremities are weaker, now 3/5; MRI of L/S Spine today."

Following are examples of unacceptable documentation:

"Agree with above.", followed by legible countersignature or identity;"Rounded, Reviewed, Agree.", followed by legible countersignature or identity;

"Discussed with resident. Agree.", followed by legible countersignature or identity;"Seen and agree.", followed by legible countersignature or identity;

"Patient seen and evaluated.", followed by legible countersignature or identity; and

A legible countersignature or identity alone.

Such documentation is not acceptable, because the documentation does not make it possible to determine whether the teaching physician was present, evaluated the patient, and/or had any involvement with the plan of care.

B. E/M Service Documentation Provided By Students

Any contribution and participation of a student to the performance of a billable service (other than the review of systems and/or past family/social history which are not separately billable, but are taken as part of an E/M service) must be performed in the physical presence of a teaching physician or physical presence of a resident in a service meeting the requirements set forth in this section for teaching physician billing.

Students may document services in the medical record. However, the documentation of an E/M service by a student that may be referred to by the teaching physician is limited to documentation related to the review of systems and/or past family/social history. The teaching physician may not refer to a student's documentation of physical exam findings or medical decision making in his or her personal note. If the medical student documents E/M services, the teaching physician must verify and redocument the history of present illness as well as perform and redocument the physical exam and medical decision making activities of the service.

C. Exception for E/M Services Furnished in Certain Primary Care Centers

Teaching physicians providing E/M services with a GME program granted a primary care exception may bill Medicare for lower and mid-level E/M services provided by residents. For the E/M codes listed below, teaching physicians may submit claims for services furnished by residents in the absence of a teaching physician:

New Patient	Established Patient
99201	99211
99202	99212
99203	99213

Effective January 1, 2005, the following code is included under the primary care exception: HCPCS code G0402 (Initial preventive physical examination; face-to-face visit services limited to new beneficiary during the first 12 months of Medicare enrollment).

Effective January 1, 2011, the following codes are included under the primary care exception: HCPCS codes G0438 (Annual wellness visit, including personal preventive plan service, first visit) and G0439 (Annual wellness visit, including personal preventive plan service, subsequent visit).

If a service other than those listed above needs to be furnished, then the general teaching physician policy set forth in §100.1 applies. For this exception to apply, a center must attest in writing that all the following conditions are met for a particular residency program. Prior approval is not necessary, but centers exercising the primary care exception must maintain records demonstrating that they qualify for the exception.

The services must be furnished in a center located in the outpatient department of a hospital or another ambulatory care entity in which the time spent by residents in patient care activities is included in determining direct GME payments to a teaching hospital by the hospital's FI. This requirement is not met when the resident is assigned to a physician's office away from the center or makes home visits. In the case of a nonhospital entity, verify with the FI that the entity meets the requirements of a written agreement between the hospital and the entity set forth at 42 CFR 413.78(e)(3)(ii).

Under this exception, residents providing the billable patient care service without the physical presence of a teaching physician must have completed at least 6 months of a GME approved residency program. Centers must maintain information under the provisions at 42 CFR 413.79(a)(6).

Teaching physicians submitting claims under this exception may not supervise more than four residents at any given time and must direct the care from such proximity as to constitute immediate availability. Teaching physicians may include residents with less than 6 months in a GME approved residency program in the mix of four residents under the teaching physician's supervision. However, the teaching physician must be physically present for the critical or key portions of services furnished by the residents with less than 6 months in a GME approved residency program. That is,the primary care exception does not apply in the case of residents with less than 6 months in a GME approved residency program.

Teaching physicians submitting claims under this exception must:

- Not have other responsibilities (including the supervision of other personnel) at the time the service was provided by the resident;
- Have the primary medical responsibility for patients cared for by the residents;
- Ensure that the care provided was reasonable and necessary;
- Review the care provided by the resident during or immediately after each visit. This must include a review of the patient's medical history, the resident's findings on physical examination, the patient's diagnosis, and treatment plan (i.e., record of tests and therapies); and
- Document the extent of his/her own participation in the review and direction of the services furnished to each patient.

Patients under this exception should consider the center to be their primary location for health care services. The residents must be expected to generally provide care to the same group of established patients during their residency training. The types of services furnished by residents under this exception include:

- Acute care for undifferentiated problems or chronic care for ongoing conditions including chronic mental illness;
- Coordination of care furnished by other physicians and providers; and,
- Comprehensive care not limited by organ system or diagnosis.

Residency programs most likely qualifying for this exception include family practice, general internal medicine, geriatric medicine, pediatrics, and obstetrics/gynecology.

Certain GME programs in psychiatry may qualify in special situations such as when the program furnishes comprehensive care for chronically mentally ill patients. These would be centers in which the range of services the residents are trained to furnish, and actually do furnish, include comprehensive medical care as well as psychiatric care. For example, antibiotics are being prescribed as well as psychotropic drugs.

100-4, Chapter 12, 180

Care Plan Oversight Services

The Medicare Benefit Policy Manual, Chapter 15, contains requirements for coverage for medical and other health services including those of physicians and non-physician practitioners.

Care plan oversight (CPO)is the physician supervision of a patient receiving complex and/or multidisciplinary care as part of Medicare-covered services provided by a participating home health agency or Medicare approved hospice. CPO services require complex or multidisciplinary care modalities involving:

- Regular physician development and/or revision of care plans;
- Review of subsequent reports of patient status;
- Review of related laboratory and other studies;

- Communication with other health professionals not employed in the same practice who are involved in the patient's care;
- Integration of new information into the medical treatment plan; and/or
- Adjustment of medical therapy.

The CPO services require recurrent physician supervision of a patient involving 30 or more minutes of the physician's time per month. Services not countable toward the 30 minutes threshold that must be provided in order to bill for CPO include, but are not limited to:

- Time associated with discussions with the patient, his or her family or friends to adjust medication or treatment;
- Time spent by staff getting or filing charts;
- Travel time; and/or
- Physician's time spent telephoning prescriptions into the pharmacist unless the telephone conversation involves discussions of pharmaceutical therapies .

Implicit in the concept of CPO is the expectation that the physician has coordinated an aspect of the patient's care with the home health agency or hospice during the month for which CPO services were billed. The physician who bills for CPO must be the same physician who signs the plan of care.

Nurse practitioners, physician assistants, and clinical nurse specialists, practicing within the scope of State law, may bill for care plan oversight. These non-physician practitioners must have been providing ongoing care for the beneficiary through evaluation and management services. These non-physician practitioners may not bill for CPO if they have been involved only with the delivery of the Medicare-covered home health or hospice service.

A. Home Health CPO

Non-physician practitioners can perform CPO only if the physician signing the plan of care provides regular ongoing care under the same plan of care as does the NPP billing for CPO and either:

- The physician and NPP are part of the same group practice; or
- If the NPP is a nurse practitioner or clinical nurse specialist, the physician signing the plan of care also has a collaborative agreement with the NPP; or
- If the NPP is a physician assistant, the physician signing the plan of care is also the physician who provides general supervision of physician assistant services for the practice. Billing may be made for care plan oversight services furnished by an NPP when:
- The NPP providing the care plan oversight has seen and examined the patient;
- The NPP providing care plan oversight is not functioning as a consultant whose participation is limited to a single medical condition rather than multidisciplinary coordination of care; and
- The NPP providing care plan oversight integrates his or her care with that of the physician who signed the plan of care. NPPs may not certify the beneficiary for home health care.

NPPs may not certify the beneficiary for home health care.

B. Hospice CPO

The attending physician or nurse practitioner (who has been designated as the attending physician) may bill for hospice CPO when they are acting as an "attending physician". An "attending physician" is one who has been identified by the individual, at the time he/she elects hospice coverage, as having the most significant role in the determination and delivery of their medical care. They are not employed nor paid by the hospice. The care plan oversight services are billed using Form CMS-1500 or electronic equivalent. For additional information on hospice CPO, see Chapter 11, §40.1.3.1 of this manual.

100-4, Chapter 12, 180.1

Care Plan Oversight Billing Requirements

A. Codes for Which Separate Payment May Be Made

Effective January 1, 1995, separate payment may be made for CPO oversight services for 30 minutes or more if the requirements specified in the Medicare Benefits Policy Manual, Chapter 15 are met.

Providers billing for CPO must submit the claim with no other services billed on that claim and may bill only after the end of the month in which the CPO services were rendered. CPO services may not be billed across calendar months and should be submitted (and paid) only for one unit of service.

Physicians may bill and be paid separately for CPO services only if all the criteria in the Medicare Benefit Policy Manual, Chapter 15 are met.

B. Physician Certification and Recertification of Home Health Plans of Care

Effective 2001, two new HCPCS codes for the certification and recertification and development of plans of care for Medicare-covered home health services were created.

See the Medicare General Information, Eligibility, and Entitlement Manual, Pub. 100-01, Chapter 4, "Physician Certification and Recertification of Services," §10-60, and the Medicare Benefit Policy Manual, Pub. 100-02, Chapter 7, "Home Health Services", §30.

The home health agency certification code can be billed only when the patient has not received Medicare-covered home health services for at least 60 days. The home health agency recertification code is used after a patient has received services for at least 60 days (or one certification period) when the physician signs the certification after the initial certification period. The home health agency recertification code will be reported only once every 60 days, except in the rare situation when the patient starts a new episode before 60 days elapses and requires a new plan of care to start a new episode.

C. Provider Number of Home Health Agency (HHA) or Hospice

For claims for CPO submitted on or after January 1, 1997, physicians must enter on the Medicare claim form the 6-character Medicare provider number of the HHA or hospice providing Medicare-covered services to the beneficiary for the period during which CPO services was furnished and for which the physician signed the plan of care. Physicians are responsible for obtaining the HHA or hospice Medicare provider numbers.

Additionally, physicians should provide their UPIN to the HHA or hospice furnishing services to their patient.

NOTE: There is currently no place on the HIPAA standard ASC X12N 837 professional format to specifically include the HHA or hospice provider number required for a care plan oversight claim. For this reason, the requirement to include the HHA or hospice provider number on a care plan oversight claim is temporarily waived until a new version of this electronic standard format is adopted under HIPAA and includes a place

to provide the HHA and hospice provider numbers for care plan oversight claims.

100-4, Chapter 12, 190.3

List of Medicare Telehealth Services

The use of a telecommunications system may substitute for an in-person encounter for professional consultations, office visits, office psychiatry services, and a limited number of other physician fee schedule (PFS) services. The various services and corresponding current procedure terminology (CPT®) or Healthcare Common Procedure Coding System (HCPCS) codes are listed below.

- Consultations (CPT® codes 99241 -99275) -Effective October 1, 2001 –December 31, 2005;
- Consultations (CPT® codes 99241 -99255) -Effective January 1, 2006 –December 31, 2009;
- Telehealth consultations, emergency department or initial inpatient (HCPCS codes G0425 –G0427) -Effective January 1, 2010;
- Follow-up inpatient telehealth consultations (HCPCS codes G0406, G0407, and G0408) -Effective January 1, 2009;
- Office or other outpatient visits (CPT® codes 99201 -99215);
- Subsequent hospital care services, with the limitation of one telehealth visit every 3 days (CPT® codes 99231, 99232, and 99233) –Effective January 1, 2011;
- Subsequent nursing facility care services, with the limitation of one telehealth visit every 30 days (CPT® codes 99307, 99308,99309, and 99310) –Effective January 1, 2011;
- Pharmacologic management (CPT® code 90862) – Effective March 1, 2003 –December 31, 2012; (HCPCS code G0459) –Effective January 1, 2013;
- Individual psychotherapy (CPT® codes 90804 -90809); Psychiatric diagnostic interview examination (CPT® code 90801) –Effective March 1, 2003 –December 31, 2012;
- Individual psychotherapy (CPT® codes 90832 –90834, 90836 –90838); Psychiatric diagnostic interview examination (CPT® codes 90791 --90792) –Effective January 1, 2013.
- Neurobehavioral status exam (CPT® code 96116) -Effective January 1, 2008;
- End Stage Renal Disease (ESRD) related services (HCPCS codes G0308, G0309, G0311, G0312, G0314, G0315, G0317, and G0318) –Effective January 1, 2005 –December 31, 2008;
- End Stage Renal Disease (ESRD) related services (CPT® codes 90951, 90952, 90954, 90955, 90957, 90958, 90960, and 90961) –Effective January 1, 2009;
- Individual and group medical nutrition therapy (HCPCS codes G0270, 97802, 97803, and 97804) –Individual effective January 1, 2006; group effective January 1, 2011;
- Individual and group health and behavior assessment and intervention (CPT® codes 96150 –96154) –Individual effective January 1, 2010; group effective January 1, 2011.
- Individual and group kidney disease education (KDE) services (HCPCS codes G0420 and G0421) –Effective January 1, 2011; and
- Individual and group diabetes self-management training (DSMT) services, with a minimum of 1 hour of in-person

instruction to be furnished in the initial year training period to ensure effective injection training (HCPCS codes G0108 and G0109) -Effective January 1, 2011.

- Smoking Cessation Services (CPT® codes 99406 and 99407 and HCPCS codes G0436 (this code has been deleted or 2017) and G0437 (this code has been deleted or 2017)) –Effective January 1, 2012.

- Alcohol and/or substance (other than tobacco) abuse structured assessment and intervention services (HCPCS codes G0396 and G0397) –Effective January 1, 2013.

- Annual alcohol misuse screening (HCPCS code G0442) –Effective January 1, 2013.

- Brief face-to-face behavioral counseling for alcohol misuse (HCPCS code G0443)–Effective January 1, 2013.

- Annual Depression Screening (HCPCS code G0444) – Effective January 1, 2013.

- High-intensity behavioral counseling to prevent sexually transmitted infections (HCPCS code G0445) –Effective January 1, 2013.

- Annual, face-to-face Intensive behavioral therapy for cardiovascular disease (HCPCS code G0446) –Effective January 1, 2013.

- Face-to-face behavioural counseling for obesity (HCPCS code G0447)–Effective January 1, 2013.

- Transitional Care Management Services (CPT® codes 99495 -99496) – Effective January 1, 2014.

NOTE: Beginning January 1, 2010, CMS eliminated the use of all consultation codes, except for inpatient telehealth consultation G-codes. CMS no longer recognizes office/outpatient or inpatient consultation CPT® codes for payment of office/outpatient or inpatient visits. Instead, physicians and practitioners are instructed to bill a new or established patient office/outpatient visit CPT® code or appropriate hospital or nursing facility care code, as appropriate to the particular patient, for all office/outpatient or inpatient visits.

100-4, Chapter 12, 190.3.1

Telehealth Consultation Services, Emergency Department or Initial Inpatient versus Inpatient Evaluation and Management (E/M) Visits

A consultation service is an evaluation and management (E/M) service furnished to evaluate and possibly treat a patient's problem(s). It can involve an opinion, advice, recommendation, suggestion, direction, or counsel from a physician or qualified nonphysician practitioner (NPP) at the request of another physician or appropriate source.

Section 1834(m) of the Social Security Act includes "professional consultations" in the definition of telehealth services. Inpatient or emergency department consultations furnished via telehealth can facilitate the provision of certain services and/or medical expertise that might not otherwise be available to a patient located at an originating site.

The use of a telecommunications system may substitute for an in-person encounter for emergency department or initial and follow-up inpatient consultations.

Medicare contractors pay for reasonable and medically necessary inpatient or emergency department telehealth consultation services furnished to beneficiaries in hospitals or SNFs when all of the following criteria for the use of a consultation code are met:

- An inpatient or emergency department consultation service is distinguished from other inpatient or

emergency department evaluation and management (E/M) visits because it is provided by a physician or qualified nonphysician practitioner (NPP) whose opinion or advice regarding evaluation and/or management of a specific problem is requested by another physician or other appropriate source. The qualified NPP may perform consultation services within the scope of practice and licensure requirements for NPPs in the State in which he/she practices;

- A request for an inpatient or emergency department telehealth consultation from an appropriate source and the need for an inpatient or emergency department telehealth consultation (i.e., the reason for a consultation service) shall be documented by the consultant in the patient's medical record and included in the requesting physician or qualified NPP's plan of care in the patient's medical record; and

- After the inpatient or emergency department telehealth consultation is provided, the consultant shall prepare a written report of his/her findings and recommendations, which shall be provided to the referring physician.

The intent of an inpatient or emergency department telehealth consultation service is that a physician or qualified NPP or other appropriate source is asking another physician or qualified NPP for advice, opinion, a recommendation, suggestion, direction, or counsel, etc. in evaluating or treating a patient because that individual has expertise in a specific medical area beyond the requesting professional's knowledge.

Unlike inpatient or emergency department telehealth consultations, the majority of subsequent inpatient hospital, emergency department and nursing facility care services require in-person visits to facilitate the comprehensive, coordinated, and personal care that medically volatile, acutely ill patients require on an ongoing basis.

Subsequent hospital care services are limited to one telehealth visit every 3 days. Subsequent nursing facility care services are limited to one telehealth visit every 30 days.

100-4, Chapter 12, 190.3.2

Telehealth Consultation Services, Emergency Departmentor Initial Inpatient Defined

Emergency department or initial inpatient telehealth consultations are furnished to beneficiaries in hospitals or SNFs via telehealth at the request of the physician of record, the attending physician, or another appropriate source. The physician or practitioner who furnishes the emergency department or initial inpatient consultation via telehealth cannot be the physician of record or the attending physician, and the emergency department or initial inpatient telehealth consultation would be distinct from the care provided by the physician of record or the attending physician. Counseling and coordination of care with other providers or agencies is included as well, consistent with the nature of the problem(s) and the patient's needs. Emergency department or initial inpatient telehealth consultations are subject to the criteria for emergency department or initial inpatient telehealth consultation services, as described in section 190.3.1 of this chapter.

Payment for emergency department or initial inpatient telehealth consultations includes all consultation related services furnished before, during, and after communicating with the patient via telehealth. Pre-service activities would include, but would not be limited to, reviewing patient data (for example, diagnostic and imaging studies, interim labwork) and communicating with other professionals or family members. Intra-service activities must include the three key elements described below for each procedure code. Post-service activities would include, but would not be limited to, completing medical records or other documentation and communicating results of the consultation and further care plans to other health care professionals. No additional E/M service could be billed for work related to an emergency department or initial inpatient telehealth consultation.

Emergency department or initial inpatient telehealth consultations could be provided at various levels of complexity:

- Practitioners taking a problem focused history, conducting a problem focused examination, and engaging in medical decision making that is straightforward, would bill HCPCS code G0425 (Telehealth consultation, emergency department or initial inpatient, typically 30 minutes communicating with the patient via telehealth).
- Practitioners taking a detailed history, conducting a detailed examination, and engaging in medical decision making that is of moderate complexity, would bill HCPCS code G0426 (Telehealth consultation, emergency department or initial inpatient, typically 50 minutes communicating with the patient via telehealth).
- Practitioners taking a comprehensive history, conducting a comprehensive examination, and engaging in medical decision making that is of high complexity, would bill HCPCS code G0427 (Telehealth consultation, emergency department or initial inpatient, typically 70 minutes or more communicating with the patient via telehealth).

Although emergency department or initial inpatient telehealth consultations are specific to telehealth, these services must be billed with either the -GT or -GQ modifier to identify the telehealth technology used to provide the service.

100-4, Chapter 12, 190.3.3

Follow-Up Inpatient Telehealth Consultations Defined

Follow-up inpatient telehealth consultations are furnished to beneficiaries in hospitals or SNFs via telehealth to follow-up on an initial consultation, or subsequent consultative visits requested by the attending physician. The initial inpatient consultation may have been provided in-person or via telehealth.

Follow-up inpatient telehealth consultations include monitoring progress, recommending management modifications, or advising on a new plan of care in response to changes in the patient's status or no changes on the consulted health issue. Counseling and coordination of care with other providers or agencies is included as well, consistent with the nature of the problem(s) and the patient's needs.

The physician or practitioner who furnishes the inpatient follow-up consultation via telehealth cannot be the physician of record or the attending physician, and the follow-up inpatient consultation would be distinct from the follow-up care provided by the physician of record or the attending physician. If a physician consultant has initiated treatment at an initial consultation and participates thereafter in the patient's ongoing care management, such care would not be included in the definition of a follow-up inpatient consultation. Follow-up inpatient telehealth consultations are subject to the criteria for inpatient telehealth consultation services, as described in section 190.3.1 of this chapter.

Payment for follow-up inpatient telehealth consultations includes all consultation related services furnished before, during, and after communicating with the patient via telehealth. Pre-service activities would include, but would not be limited to, reviewing patient data (for example, diagnostic and imaging studies, interim labwork) and communicating with other professionals or family members. Intra-service activities must include at least two of the three key elements described below for each procedure code. Post-service activities would include, but would not be limited to, completing medical records or other documentation and communicating results of the consultation and further care plans to other health care professionals. No additional evaluation and management service could be billed for work related to a follow-up inpatient telehealth consultation.

Follow-up inpatient telehealth consultations could be provided at various levels of complexity:

- Practitioners taking a problem focused interval history, conducting a problem focused examination, and engaging in medical decision making that is straightforward or of low complexity, would bill a limited service, using HCPCS code G0406 (Follow-up inpatient telehealth consultation, limited, physicians typically spend 15 minutes communicating with the patient via telehealth).
- Practitioners taking an expanded focused interval history, conducting an expanded problem focused examination, and engaging in medical decision making that is of moderate complexity, would bill an intermediate service using HCPCS code G0407(Follow-up inpatient telehealth consultation, intermediate, physicians typically spend 25 minutes communicating with the patient via telehealth).
- Practitioners taking a detailed interval history, conducting a detailed examination, and engaging in medical decision making that is of high complexity, would bill a complex service, using HCPCS code G0408 (Follow-up inpatient telehealth consultation, complex, physicians typically spend 35 minutes or more communicating with the patient via telehealth).Although follow-up inpatient telehealth consultations are specific to telehealth, these services must be billed with either the -GT or –GQ modifier to identify the telehealth technology used to provide the service.

100-4, Chapter 12, 190.6

Originating Site Facility Fee Payment Methodology

1. Originating site defined

The term originating site means the location of an eligible Medicare beneficiary at the time the service being furnished via a telecommunications system occurs. For asynchronous, store and forward telecommunications technologies, an originating site is only a Federal telemedicine demonstration program conducted in Alaska or Hawaii.

2. Facility fee for originating site

The originating site facility fee is a separately billable Part B payment. The contractor pays it outside of other payment methodologies. This fee is subject to post payment verification.

For telehealth services furnished from October 1, 2001, through December 31, 2002, the originating site facility fee is the lesser of $20 or the actual charge. For services furnished on or after January 1 of each subsequent year, the originating site facility fee is updated by the Medicare Economic Index.

The updated fee is included in the Medicare Physician Fee Schedule (MPFS) Final Rule, which is published by November 1 prior to the start of the calendar year for which it is effective. The updated fee for each calendar year is also issued annually in a Recurring Update Notification instruction for January of each year.

3. Payment amount:

The originating site facility fee is a separately billable Part B payment. The payment amount to the originating site is the lesser of 80 percent of the actual charge or 80 percent of the originating site facility fee, except CAHs. The beneficiary is responsible for any unmet deductible amount and Medicare coinsurance.

The originating site facility fee payment methodology for each type of facility is clarified below.

Hospital outpatient department. When the originating site is a hospital outpatient department, payment for the originating site facility fee must be made as described above and not under the outpatient prospective payment system (OPPS). Payment is not based on the OPPS payment methodology.

Hospital inpatient. For hospital inpatients, payment for the originating site facility fee must be made outside the diagnostic related group (DRG) payment, since this is a Part B benefit, similar to other services paid separately from the DRG payment, (e.g., hemophilia blood clotting factor).

Critical access hospitals. When the originating site is a critical access hospital, make payment separately from the cost-based reimbursement methodology. For CAH's, the payment amount is 80 percent of the originating site facility fee.

Federally qualified health centers (FQHCs) and rural health clinics (RHCs). The originating site facility fee for telehealth services is not an FQHC or RHC service. When an FQHC or RHC serves as the originating site, the originating site facility fee must be paid separately from the center or clinic all-inclusive rate.

Physicians' and practitioners' offices. When the originating site is a physician's or practitioner's office, the payment amount, in accordance with the law, is the lesser of 80 percent of the actual charge or 80 percent of the originating site facility fee, regardless of geographic location. The carrier shall not apply the geographic practice cost index (GPCI) to the originating site facility fee. This fee is statutorily set and is not subject to the geographic payment adjustments authorized under the MPFS.

Hospital-based or critical access-hospital based renal dialysis center (or their satellites). When a hospital-based or critical access hospital-based renal dialysis center (or their satellites) serves as the originating site, the originating site facility fee is covered in addition to any composite rate or MCP amount.

Skilled nursing facility (SNF). The originating site facility fee is outside the SNF prospective payment system bundle and, as such, is not subject to SNF consolidated billing. The originating site facility fee is a separately billable Part B payment.

Community Mental Health Center (CMHC). The originating site facility fee is not a partial hospitalization service. The originating site facility fee does not count towards the number of services used to determine payment for partial hospitalization services. The originating site facility fee is not bundled in the per diem payment for partial hospitalization. The originating site facility fee is a separately billable Part B payment.

To receive the originating facility site fee, the provider submits claims with HCPCS code "Q3014, telehealth originating site facility fee"; short description "telehealth facility fee." The type of service for the telehealth originating site facility fee is "9, other items and services." For carrier-processed claims, the "office" place of service (code 11) is the only payable setting for code Q3014. There is no participation payment differential for code Q3014. Deductible and coinsurance rules apply to Q3014. By submitting Q3014 HCPCS code, the originating site authenticates they are located in either a rural HPSA or non-MSA county.

This benefit may be billed on bill types 12X, 13X, 22X, 23X, 71X, 72X, 73X, 76X, and 85X. Unless otherwise applicable, report the originating site facility fee under revenue code 078X and include HCPCS code "Q3014, telehealth originating site facility fee."

Hospitals and critical access hospitals bill their intermediary for the originating site facility fee. Telehealth bills originating in inpatient hospitals must be submitted on a 12X TOB using the date of discharge as the line item date of service.

Independent and provider-based RHCs and FQHCs bill the appropriate intermediary using the RHC or FQHC bill type and billing number. HCPCS code Q3014 is the only non-RHC/FQHC service that is billed using the clinic/center bill type and provider number. All RHCs and FQHCs must use revenue code 078X when billing for the originating site facility fee. For all other non-RHC/FQHC services, provider based RHCs and FQHCs must bill using the base provider's bill type and billing number. Independent RHCs and FQHCs must bill the carrier for all other non-RHC/FQHC services. If an RHC/FQHC visit occurs on the same day as a telehealth service, the RHC/FQHC serving as an originating site must bill for HCPCS code Q3014 telehealth originating site facility fee on a separate revenue line from the RHC/FQHC visit using revenue code 078X.

Hospital-based or CAH-based renal dialysis centers (including satellites) bill their local FIs and/or Part A MACs for the originating site facility fee. Telehealth bills originating in renal dialysis centers must be submitted on a 72X TOB. All hospital-based or CAH-based renal dialysis centers (including satellites) must use revenue code 078X when billing for the originating site facility fee. The renal dialysis center serving as an originating site must bill for HCPCS code Q3014, telehealth originating site facility fee, on a separate revenue line from any other services provided to the beneficiary.

Skilled nursing facilities (SNFs) bill their local FIs and/or Part A MACs for the originating site facility fee. Telehealth bills originating in SNFs must be submitted on TOB 22X or 23X. For SNF inpatients in a covered Part A stay, the originating site facility fee must be submitted on a 22X TOB. All SNFs must use revenue code 078X when billing for the originating site facility fee. The SNF serving as an originating site must bill for HCPCS code Q3014, telehealth originating site facility fee, on a separate revenue line from any other services provided to the beneficiary.

Community mental health centers (CMHCs) bill their local FIs and/or Part A MACs for the originating site facility fee. Telehealth bills originating in CMHCs must be submitted on a 76X TOB. All CMHCs must use revenue code 078X when billing for the originating site facility fee. The CMHC serving as an originating site must bill for HCPCS code Q3014, telehealth originating site facility fee, on a separate revenue line from any other services provided to the beneficiary. Note that Q3014 does not count towards the number of services used to determine per diem payments for partial hospitalization services.

The beneficiary is responsible for any unmet deductible amount and Medicare coinsurance.

100-4, Chapter 12, 190.7

Contractor Editing of Telehealth Claims

Medicare telehealth services (as listed in section 190.3) are billed with either the "GT" or "GQ" modifier. The contractor shall approve covered telehealth services if the physician or practitioner is licensed under State law to provide the service. Contractors must familiarize themselves with licensure provisions of States for which they process claims and disallow telehealth services furnished by physicians or practitioners who are not authorized to furnish the applicable telehealth service under State law. For example, if a nurse practitioner is not licensed to provide individual psychotherapy under State law, he or she would not be permitted to receive payment for individual psychotherapy under Medicare. The contractor shall install edits to ensure that only properly licensed physicians and practitioners are paid for covered telehealth services.

If a contractor receives claims for professional telehealth services coded with the "GQ" modifier (representing "via asynchronous telecommunications system"), it shall approve/pay for these services only if the physician or practitioner is affiliated with a Federal telemedicine demonstration conducted in Alaska or Hawaii. The contractor may require the physician or practitioner at the distant site to document his or her participation in a Federal telemedicine demonstration program conducted in Alaska or Hawaii prior to paying for telehealth services provided via asynchronous, store and forward technologies.

If a contractor denies telehealth services because the physician or practitioner may not bill for them, the contractor uses MSN message 21.18: "This item or service is not covered when performed or ordered by this practitioner." The contractor uses remittance advice message 52 when denying the claim based upon MSN message 21.18.

If a service is billed with one of the telehealth modifiers and the procedure code is not designated as a covered telehealth service, the contractor denies the service using MSN message 9.4: "This item or service was denied because information required to make payment was incorrect." The remittance advice message depends on what is incorrect, e.g., B18 if procedure code or modifier is incorrect, 125 for submission billing errors, 4-12 for difference inconsistencies. The contractor uses B18 as the explanation for the denial of the claim.

The only claims from institutional facilities that FIs shall pay for telehealth services at the distant site, except for MNT services, are for physician or practitioner services when the distant site is located in a CAH that has elected Method II, and the physician or practitioner has reassigned his/her benefits to the CAH. The CAH bills its regular FI for the professional services provided at the distant site via a telecommunications system, in any of the revenue codes 096x, 097x or 098x. All requirements for billing distant site telehealth services apply.

Claims from hospitals or CAHs for MNT services are submitted to the hospital's or CAH's regular FI. Payment is based on the non-facility amount on the Medicare Physician Fee Schedule for the particular HCPCS codes.

100-4, Chapter 12, 210

Outpatient Mental Health Treatment Limitation

Regardless of the actual expenses a beneficiary incurs in connection with the treatment of mental, psychoneurotic, and personality disorders while the beneficiary is not an inpatient of a hospital at the time such expenses are incurred, the amount of those expenses that may be recognized for Part B deductible and payment purposes is limited to 62.5 percent of the Medicare approved amount for those services. This limitation is called the outpatient mental health treatment limitation (the limitation). The 62.5 percent limitation has been in place since the inception of the Medicare Part B program and it will remain effective at this percentage amount until January 1, 2010. However, effective January 1, 2010, through January 1, 2014, the limitation will be phased out as follows:

- January 1, 2010 –December 31, 2011, the limitation percentage is 68.75%.
  (Medicare pays 55% and the patient pays 45%).

- January 1, 2012 –December 31, 2012, the limitation percentage is 75%.
  (Medicare pays 60% and the patient pays 40%).

- January 1, 2013 –December 31, 2013, the limitation percentage is 81.25%.
  (Medicare pays 65% and the patient pays 35%).

- January 1, 2014 –onward, the limitation percentage is 100%.
  (Medicare pays 80% and the patient pays 20%).

For additional details concerning computation of the limitation, please see the examples under section 210.1 E.

100-4, Chapter 12, 210.1

Application of the Limitation

A. Status of Patient

The limitation is applicable to expenses incurred in connection with the treatment of an individual who is not an inpatient of a hospital. Thus, the limitation applies to mental health services furnished to a person in a physician's office, in the patient's home, in a skilled nursing facility, as an outpatient, and so forth. The term "hospital" in this context means an institution, which is primarily engaged in providing to inpatients, by or under the supervision of a physician(s):

- Diagnostic and therapeutic services for medical diagnosis, treatment and care of injured, disabled, or sick persons;
- Rehabilitation services for injured, disabled, or sick persons; or
- Psychiatric services for the diagnosis and treatment of mentally ill patients.

B. Disorders Subject to the Limitation

The term "mental, psychoneurotic, and personality disorders" is defined as the specific psychiatric diagnoses described in the International Classification of Diseases, 9th Revision (ICD-9), under the code range 290-319.When the treatment services rendered are both for a psychiatric diagnosis as defined in the ICD-9 and one or more nonpsychiatric conditions, separate the expenses for the psychiatric aspects of treatment from the expenses for the nonpsychiatric aspects of treatment. However, in any case in which the psychiatric treatment component is not readily distinguishable from the nonpsychiatric treatment component, all of the expenses are allocated to whichever component constitutes the primary diagnosis.

1. Diagnosis Clearly Meets Definition –If the primary diagnosis reported for a particular service is the same as or equivalent to a condition described in the ICD-9 under the code range 290-319 that represents mental,

psychoneurotic and personality disorders, the expense for the service is subject to the limitation except as described in subsection

2. Diagnosis Does Not Clearly Meet Definition -When it is not clear whether the primary diagnosis reported meets the definition of mental, psychoneurotic, and personality disorders, it may be necessary to contact the practitioner to clarify the diagnosis. In deciding whether contact is necessary in a given case, give consideration to such factors as the type of services rendered, the diagnosis, and the individual's previous utilization history.

C. Services Subject to the Limitation

Medicare Contractors must apply the limitation to claims for professional services that represent mental health treatment furnished to individuals who are not hospital inpatients by physicians, clinical psychologists, clinical social workers, nurse practitioners, clinical nurse specialists and physician assistants. Items and supplies furnished by physicians or other mental health practitioners in connection with treatment are also subject to the limitation.

Generally, Medicare Contractors must apply the limitation only to treatment services. However, diagnostic psychological and neuropsychological testing services performed to evaluate a patient's progress during treatment are considered part of treatment and are subject to the limitation.

D. Services Not Subject to the Limitation

1. Diagnosis of Alzheimer's Disease or Related Disorder -When the primary diagnosis reported for a particular service is Alzheimer's Disease or an Alzheimer's related disorder, Medicare Contractors must look to the nature of the service that has been rendered in determining whether it is subject to the limitation. Alzheimer's disease is coded 331.0 in the "International Classification of Diseases, 9th Revision", which is outside the code range 290-319 that represents mental, psychoneurotic and personality disorders. Additionally, Alzheimer's related disorders are identified by contractors under ICD-9 codes that are within the 290-319 code range (290.XX or others as contractors determine appropriate) or outside the 290-319 code range as determined appropriate by contractors. When the primary treatment rendered to a patient with a diagnosis of Alzheimer's disease or a related disorder is psychotherapy, it is subject to the limitation. However, typically, treatment provided to a patient with a diagnosis of Alzheimer's Disease or a related disorder represents medical management of the patient's condition (such as described under CPT® code 90862 or any successor code) and is not subject to the limitation. CPT® code 90862 describes pharmacologic management, including prescription, use, and review of medication with no more than minimal medical psychotherapy.

2. Brief Office Visits for Monitoring or Changing Drug Prescriptions -Brief office visits for the sole purpose of monitoring or changing drug prescriptions used in the treatment of mental, psychoneurotic and personality disorders are not subject to the limitation. These visits are reported using HCPCS code M0064 or any successor code (brief office visit for the sole purpose of monitoring or changing drug prescriptions used in the treatment of mental, psychoneurotic, and personality disorders). Claims where the diagnosis reported is a mental, psychoneurotic, or personality disorder (other than a diagnosis specified in subsection A) are subject to the limitation except for the procedure identified by HCPCS code M0064 or any successor code.

3. Diagnostic Services -Medicare Contractors do not apply the limitation to psychiatric diagnostic evaluations and diagnostic psychological and neuropsychological tests performed to establish or confirm the patient's diagnosis. Diagnostic services include psychiatric diagnostic evaluations billed under CPT® codes 90801 or 90802 (or any successor codes) and, psychological and neuropsychological tests billed under CPT® code range 96101-96118 (or any successor code range).

An initial visit to a practitioner for professional services often combines diagnostic evaluation and the start of therapy. Such a visit is neither solely diagnostic nor solely therapeutic. Therefore, contractors must deem the initial visit to be diagnostic so that the limitation does not apply. Separating diagnostic and therapeutic components of a visit is not administratively feasible, unless the practitioner already has separately identified them on the bill. Determining the entire visit to be therapeutic is not justifiable since some diagnostic work must be done before even a tentative diagnosis can be made and certainly before therapy can be instituted. Moreover, the patient should not be disadvantaged because therapeutic as well as diagnostic services were provided in the initial visit. In the rare cases where a practitioner's diagnostic services take more than one visit, Medicare contractors must not apply the limitation to the additional visits. However, it is expected such cases are few. Therefore, when a practitioner bills for more than one visit for professional diagnostic services, Medicare contractors may find it necessary to request documentation to justify the reason for more than one diagnostic visit.

4. Partial Hospitalization Services Not Directly Provided by a Physician or a Practitioner -The limitation does not apply to partial hospitalization services that are not directly provided by a physician, clinical psychologist, nurse practitioner, clinical nurse specialist or a physician assistant. Partial hospitalization services are billed by hospital outpatient departments and community mental health centers (CMHCs) to Medicare Contractors. However, services furnished by physicians, clinical psychologists, nurse practitioners, clinical nurse specialists, and physician assistants to partial hospitalization patients are billed separately from the partial hospitalization program of services. Accordingly, these professional's mental health services to partial hospitalization patients are paid under the physician fee schedule by Medicare Contractors and may be subject to the limitation. (See chapter 4, section 260.1C).

E. Computation of Limitation

Medicare Contractors determine the Medicare approved payment amount for services subject to the limitation. They:

- Multiply the approved amount by the limitation percentage amount;
- Subtract any unsatisfied deductible; and,
- Multiply the remainder by 0.8 to obtain the amount of Medicare payment.

The beneficiary is responsible for the difference between the amount paid by Medicare and the full Medicare approved amount.

The following examples illustrate the application of the limitation in various circumstances as it is gradually reduced under section 102 of the Medicare Improvements for Patients and Providers Act (MIPPA). Please note that although the calendar year 2009 Part B deductible of $135 is used under these examples, the actual deductible amount for calendar year 2010 and future years is unknown and will be subject to change.

Example #1: In 2010, a clinical psychologist submits a claim for $200 for outpatient treatment of a patient's mental disorder. The Medicare-approved amount is $180. Since clinical psychologists must accept assignment, the patient is not liable for the $20 in excess charges. The patient previously satisfied the $135 annual Part B deductible. The limitation reduces the amount of incurred expenses to 68 ¾ percent of the approved amount. Medicare pays 80 percent of the remaining incurred expenses. The Medicare payment and patient liability are computed as follows:

1. Actual charges..$200.00
2. Medicare-approved amount.............................$180.00
3. Medicare incurred expenses (0.6875 x line 2..........$123.75
4. Unmet deductible..$0.00
5. Remainder after subtracting deductible
   (line 3 minus line 4)......................................$123.75
6. Medicare payment (0.80 x line 5)......................$99.00
7. Patient liability (line 2 minus line 6)..................$81.00

Example #2: In 2012, a clinical social worker submits a claim for $135 for outpatient treatment of a patient's mental disorder. The Medicare-approved amount is $120. Since clinical social workers must accept assignment, the patient is not liable for the $15 in excess charges. The limitation reduces the amount of incurred expenses to 75 percent of the approved amount. The patient previously satisfied $70 of the $135 annual Part B deductible, leaving $65 unmet. The Medicare payment and patient liability are computed as follows:

1. Actual charges..$135.00
2. Medicare-approved amount.............................$120.00
3. Medicare incurred expenses (0.75 x line 2)...............$90.00
4. Unmet deductible..$65.00
5. Remainder after subtracting deductible
   (line 3 minus line 4)......................................$25.00
6. Medicare payment (0.80 x line 5).......................$20.00
7. Patient liability (line 2 minus line 6)..................$100.00

Example #3: In calendar year 2013, a physician who does not accept assignment submits a claim for $780 for services in connection with the treatment of a mental disorder that did not require inpatient hospitalization. The Medicare-approved amount is $750. Because the physician does not accept assignment, the patient is liable for the $30 in excess charges. The patient has not satisfied any of the $135 Part B annual deductible. The Medicare payment and patient liability are computed as follows:

1. Actual charges..$780.00
2. Medicare-approved amount.............................$750.00
3. Medicare incurred expenses (0.8125 x line 2)...........$609.38
4. Unmet deductible..$135.00
5. Remainder after subtracting deductible
   (line 3 minus line 4)......................................$474.38
6. Medicare payment (0.80 x line 5).......................$379.50
7. Patient liability (line 1 minus line 6)..................$400.50

Example #4: A patient's Part B expenses during calendar year 2014 are for a physician's services in connection with the treatment of a mental disorder that initially required inpatient hospitalization, with subsequent physician services furnished on an outpatient basis. The patient has not satisfied any of the $135 Part B deductible. The physician accepts assignment and submits a claim for $780. The Medicare-approved amount is $750. Since the limitation will be completely phased out as of January 1, 2014, the entire $750 Medicare-approved amount is recognized as the total incurred expenses because such expenses are no longer reduced. Also, there is no longer any distinction between mental health services the patient receives

as an inpatient or outpatient. The Medicare payment and patient liability are computed as follows:

1. Actual charges..$780.00
2. Medicare-approved amount.............................$750.00
3. Medicare incurred expenses (1.00 x line 2)...............$750.00
4. Unmet deductible..$135.00
5. Remainder after subtracting deductible
   (line 3 minus line 4)......................................$615.00
6. Medicare payment (0.80 x line 5).......................$492.00
   Beneficiary liability (line 2 minus line 6)..................$258.00

100-4, Chapter 13, 40

Magnetic Resonance Imaging (MRI) Procedures

Effective September 28, 2009

The Centers for Medicare & Medicaid Services (CMS) finds that the non-coverage of magnetic resonance imaging (MRI) for blood flow determination is no longer supported by the available evidence. CMS is removing the phrase "blood flow measurement" and local Medicare contractors will have the discretion to cover (or not cover).

Consult Publication (Pub.) 100-03, National Coverage Determinations (NCD) Manual, chapter 1, section 220.2, for specific coverage and non-coverage indications associated with MRI and MRA (Magnetic Resonance Angiography).

Prior to January 1, 2007

Carriers do not make additional payments for three or more MRI sequences. The relative value units (RVUs) reflect payment levels for two sequences.

The technical component (TC) RVUs for MRI procedures that specify "with contrast" include payment for paramagnetic contrast media. Carriers do not make separate payment under code A4647.

A diagnostic technique has been developed under which an MRI of the brain or spine is first performed without contrast material, then another MRI is performed with a standard (0.1mmol/kg) dose of contrast material and, based on the need to achieve a better image, a third MRI is performed with an additional double dosage (0.2mmol/kg) of contrast material. When the high-dose contrast technique is utilized, carriers:

- Do not pay separately for the contrast material used in the second MRI procedure;
- Pay for the contrast material given for the third MRI procedure through supply code Q9952, the replacement code for A4643, when billed with Current Procedural Terminology (CPT®) codes 70553, 72156, 72157, and 72158;
- Do not pay for the third MRI procedure. For example, in the case of an MRI of the brain, if CPT® code 70553 (without contrast material, followed by with contrast material(s) and further sequences) is billed, make no payment for CPT® code 70551 (without contrast material(s)), the additional procedure given for the purpose of administering the double dosage, furnished during the same session. Medicare does not pay for the third procedure (as distinguished from the contrast material) because the CPT® definition of code 70553 includes all further sequences; and
- Do not apply the payment criteria for low osmolar contrast media in §30.1.2 to billings for code Q9952, the replacement code for A4643.

Effective January 1, 2007

With the implementation for calendar year 2007 of a bottom-up methodology, which utilizes the direct inputs to determine the practice expense (PE) relative value units (RVUs), the cost of the contrast media is not included in the PE RVUs. Therefore, a separate payment for the contrast media used in various imaging procedures is paid. In addition to the CPT® code representing the imaging procedure, separately bill the appropriate HCPCS "Q" code (Q9945 –Q9954; Q9958-Q9964) for the contrast medium utilized in performing the service.

Effective February 24, 2011

Medicare will allow for coverage of MRI for beneficiaries with implanted PMs or cardioverter defibrillators (ICDs) for use in an MRI environment in a Medicare-approved clinical study as described in section 220.C.1 of the NCD manual.

Effective July 7, 2011

Medicare will allow for coverage of MRI for beneficiaries with implanted pacemakers (PMs) when the PMs are used according to the Food and Drug Administration (FDA)-approved labeling for use in an MRI environment as described in section 220.2.C.1 of the NCD Manual.

100-4, Chapter 13, 40.1.2

HCPCS Coding Requirements

Providers must report HCPCS codes when submitting claims for MRA of the chest, abdomen, head, neck or peripheral vessels of lower extremities. The following HCPCS codes should be used to report these services:

MRA of head	70544, 70544-26, 70544-TC
MRA of head	70545, 70545-26, 70545-TC
MRA of head	70546, 70546-26, 70546-TC
MRA of neck	70547, 70547-26, 70547-TC
MRA of neck	70548, 70548-26, 70548-TC
MRA of neck	70549, 70549-26, 70549-TC
MRA of chest	71555, 71555-26, 71555-TC
MRA of pelvis	72198, 72198-26, 72198-TC
MRA of abdomen (dates of service on or after July 1, 2003) –see below.	74185, 74185-26, 74185-TC
MRA of peripheral vessels of lower extremities	73725, 73725-26, 73725-TC

100-4, Chapter 13, 60

Positron Emission Tomography (PET) Scans – General Information

Positron emission tomography (PET) is a noninvasive imaging procedure that assesses perfusion and the level of metabolic activity in various organ systems of the human body. A positron camera (tomograph) is used to produce cross-sectional tomographic images which are obtained by detecting radioactivity from a radioactive tracer substance (radiopharmaceutical) that emits a radioactive tracer substance (radiopharmaceutical FDG) such as 2 –[F-18] flouro-D-glucose FDG, that is administered intravenously to the patient.

The Medicare National Coverage Determinations (NCD) Manual, chapter 1, §220.6, contains additional coverage instructions to indicate the conditions under which a PET scan is performed.

A. Definitions

For all uses of PET, excluding Rubidium 82 for perfusion of the heart, myocardial viability and refractory seizures, the following definitions apply:

Diagnosis: PET is covered only in clinical situations in which the PET results may assist in avoiding an invasive diagnostic procedure, or in which the PET results may assist in determining the optimal anatomical location to perform an invasive diagnostic procedure. In general, for most solid tumors, a tissue diagnosis is made prior to the performance of PET scanning. PET scans following a tissue diagnosis are generally performed for the purpose of staging, rather than diagnosis. Therefore, the use of PET in the diagnosis of lymphoma, esophageal and colorectal cancers, as well as in melanoma, should be rare. PET is not covered for other diagnostic uses, and is not covered for screening (testing of patients without specific signs and symptoms of disease).

Staging: PET is covered in clinical situations in which (1) (a) the stage of the cancer remains in doubt after completion of a standard diagnostic workup, including conventional imaging (computed tomography, magnetic resonance imaging, or ultrasound) or, (b) the use of PET would also be considered reasonable and necessary if it could potentially replace one or more conventional imaging studies when it is expected that conventional study information is insufficient for the clinical management of the patient and, (2) clinical management of the patient would differ depending on the stage of the cancer identified.

NOTE: Effective for services on or after April 3, 2009, the terms "diagnosis" and "staging" will be replaced with "Initial Treatment Strategy." For further information on this new term, refer to Pub. 100-03, NCD Manual, section 220.6.17.

Restaging: PET will be covered for restaging: (1) after the completion of treatment for the purpose of detecting residual disease, (2) for detecting suspected recurrence ,or metastasis, (3) to determine the extent of a known recurrence, or (4) if it could potentially replace one or more conventional imaging studies when it is expected that conventional study information is to determine the extent of a known recurrence, or if study information is insufficient for the clinical management of the patient. Restaging applies to testing after a course of treatment is completed and is covered subject to the conditions above.

Monitoring: Use of PET to monitor tumor response to treatment during the planned course of therapy (i.e., when a change in therapy is anticipated).

NOTE: Effective for services on or after April 3, 2009, the terms "restaging" and "monitoring" will be replaced with "Subsequent Treatment Strategy." For further information on this new term, refer to Pub. 100-03, NCD Manual, section 220.6.17.

B. Limitations

For staging and restaging: PET is covered in either/or both of the following circumstances:

- The stage of the cancer remains in doubt after completion of a standard diagnostic workup, including conventional imaging (computed tomography, magnetic resonance imaging, or ultrasound); and/or
- The clinical management of the patient would differ depending on the stage of the cancer identified. PET will be covered for restaging after the completion of treatment

for the purpose of detecting residual disease, for detecting suspected recurrence, or to determine the extent of a known recurrence. Use of PET would also be considered reasonable and necessary if it could potentially replace one or more conventional imaging studies when it is expected that conventional study information is insufficient for the clinical management of the patient.

The PET is not covered for other diagnostic uses, and is not covered for screening (testing of patients without specific symptoms). Use of PET to monitor tumor response during the planned course of therapy (i.e., when no change in therapy is being contemplated) is not covered.

100-4, Chapter 13, 60.3

PET Scan Qualifying Conditions and HCPCS Code Chart

Below is a summary of all covered PET scan conditions, with effective dates.

NOTE: The G codes below except those a # can be used to bill for PET Scan services through January 27, 2005. Effective for dates of service on or after January 28, 2005, providers must bill for PET Scan services using the appropriate CPT® codes. See section 60.3.1. The G codes with a # can continue to be used for billing after January 28, 2005 and these remain non-covered by Medicare. (**NOTE:** PET Scanners must be FDA-approved.)

Conditions	Coverage Effective Date	****HCPCS/ CPT®
*Myocardial perfusion imaging (following previous PET G0030-G0047) single study, rest or stress (exercise and/or pharmacologic)	3/14/95	G0030
*Myocardial perfusion imaging (following previous PET G0030-G0047) multiple studies, rest or stress (exercise and/or pharmacologic)	3/14/95	G0031
*Myocardial perfusion imaging (following rest SPECT, 78464); single study, rest or stress (exercise and/or pharmacologic)	3/14/95	G0032
*Myocardial perfusion imaging (following rest SPECT 78464); multiple studies, rest or stress (exercise and/or pharmacologic)	3/14/95	G0033
*Myocardial perfusion (following stress SPECT 78465); single study, rest or stress (exercise and/or pharmacologic)	3/14/95	G0034
*Myocardial Perfusion Imaging (following stress SPECT 78465); multiple studies, rest or stress (exercise and/or pharmacologic)	3/14/95	G0035
*Myocardial Perfusion Imaging (following coronary angiography 93510-93529); single study, rest or stress (exercise and/or pharmacologic)	3/14/95	G0036
*Myocardial Perfusion Imaging, (following coronary angiography), 93510-93529); multiple studies, rest or stress (exercise and/or pharmacologic)	3/14/95	G0037
*Myocardial Perfusion Imaging (following stress planar myocardial perfusion, 78460); single study, rest or stress (exercise and/or pharmacologic)	3/14/95	G0038

Conditions	Coverage Effective Date	****HCPCS/ CPT®
*Myocardial Perfusion Imaging (following stress planar myocardial perfusion, 78460); multiple studies, rest or stress (exercise and/or pharmacologic)	3/14/95	G0039
*Myocardial Perfusion Imaging (following stress echocardiogram 93350); single study, rest or stress (exercise and/or pharmacologic)	3/14/95	G0040
*Myocardial Perfusion Imaging (following stress echocardiogram, 93350); multiple studies, rest or stress (exercise and/or pharmacologic)	3/14/95	G0041
*Myocardial Perfusion Imaging (following stress nuclear ventriculogram 78481 or 78483); single study, rest or stress (exercise and/or pharmacologic)	3/14/95	G0042
*Myocardial Perfusion Imaging (following stress nuclear ventriculogram 78481 or 78483); multiple studies, rest or stress (exercise and/or pharmacologic)	3/14/95	G0043
*Myocardial Perfusion Imaging (following stress ECG, 93000); single study, rest or stress (exercise and/or pharmacologic)	3/14/95	G0044
*Myocardial perfusion (following stress ECG, 93000), multiple studies; rest or stress (exercise and/or pharmacologic)	3/14/95	G0045
*Myocardial perfusion (following stress ECG, 93015), single study; rest or stress (exercise and/or pharmacologic)	3/14/95	G0046
*Myocardial perfusion (following stress ECG, 93015); multiple studies, rest or stress (exercise and/or pharmacologic)	3/14/95	G0047
PET imaging regional or whole body; single pulmonary nodule	1/1/98	G0125
Lung cancer, non-small cell (PET imaging whole body) Diagnosis, Initial Staging, Restaging	7/1/01	G0210 G0211 G0212
Colorectal cancer (PET imaging whole body) Diagnosis, Initial Staging, Restaging	7/1/01	G0213 G0214 G0215
Melanoma (PET imaging whole body) Diagnosis, Initial Staging, Restaging	7/1/01	G0216 G0217 G0218
Melanoma for non-covered indications	7/1/01	#G0219
Lymphoma (PET imaging whole body) Diagnosis, Initial Staging, Restaging	7/1/01	G0220 G0221 G0222
Head and neck cancer; excluding thyroid and CNS cancers (PET imaging whole body or regional) Diagnosis, Initial Staging, Restaging	7/1/01	G0223 G0224 G0225
Esophageal cancer (PET imaging whole body) Diagnosis, Initial Staging, Restaging	7/1/01	G0226 G0227 G0228
Metabolic brain imaging for pre-surgical evaluation of refractory seizures	7/1/01	G0229
Metabolic assessment for myocardial viability following inconclusive SPECT study	7/1/01	G0230

Conditions	Coverage Effective Date	****HCPCS/ CPT®
Recurrence of colorectal or colorectal metastatic cancer (PET whole body, gamma cameras only)	1/1/02	G0231
Staging and characterization of lymphoma (PET whole body, gamma cameras only)	1/1/02	G0232
Recurrence of melanoma or melanoma metastatic cancer (PET whole body, gamma cameras only)	1/1/02	G0233
Regional or whole body, for solitary pulmonary nodule following CT, or for initial staging of non-small cell lung cancer (gamma cameras only)	1/1/02	G0234
Non-Covered Service PET imaging, any site not otherwise specified	1/28/05	#G0235
Non-Covered Service Initial diagnosis of breast cancer and/or surgical planning for breast cancer (e.g., initial staging of axillary lymph nodes), not covered (full- and partial-ring PET scanners only)	10/1/02	#G0252
Breast cancer, staging/restaging of local regional recurrence or distant metastases, i.e., staging/restaging after or prior to course of treatment (full- and partial-ring PET scanners only)	10/1/02	G0253
Breast cancer, evaluation of responses to treatment, performed during course of treatment (full- and partial-ring PET scanners only)	10/1/02	G0254
Myocardial imaging, positron emission tomography (PET), metabolic evaluation)	10/1/02	78459
Restaging or previously treated thyroid cancer of follicular cell origin following negative I-131 whole body scan (full- and partial-ring PET scanner only)	10/1/03	G0296
Tracer Rubidium**82 (Supply of Radiopharmaceutical Diagnostic Imaging Agent) (This is only billed through Outpatient Perspective Payment System, OPPS.) (Carriers must use HCPCS Code A4641).	10/1/03	Q3000
Supply of Radiopharmaceutical Diagnostic Imaging Agent, Ammonia N-13	01/1/04	A9526
PET imaging, brain imaging for the differential diagnosis of Alzheimer's disease with aberrant features vs. fronto-temporal dementia	09/15/04	Appropriate CPT® Code from section 60.3.1
PET Cervical Cancer Staging as adjunct to conventional imaging, other staging, diagnosis, restaging, monitoring	1/28/05	Appropriate CPT® Code from section 60.3.1

*NOTE: Carriers must report A4641 for the tracer Rubidium 82 when used with PET scan codes G0030 through G0047 for services performed on or before January 27, 2005.

**NOTE: Not FDG PET

***NOTE: For dates of service October 1, 2003, through December 31, 2003, use temporary code Q4078 for billing this radiopharmaceutical.

100-4, Chapter 13, 60.3.1

Appropriate CPT® Codes Effective for PET Scans for Services Performed on or After January 28, 2005

NOTE: All PET scan services require the use of a radiopharmaceutical diagnostic imaging agent (tracer). The applicable tracer code should be billed when billing for a PET scan service. See section 60.3.2 below for applicable tracer codes.

CPT® Code	Description
78459	Myocardial imaging, positron emission tomography (PET), metabolic evaluation
78491	Myocardial imaging, positron emission tomography (PET), perfusion, single study at rest or stress
78492	Myocardial imaging, positron emission tomography (PET), perfusion, multiple studies at rest and/or stress
78608	Brain imaging, positron emission tomography (PET); metabolic evaluation
78811	Tumor imaging, positron emission tomography (PET); limited area (eg, chest, head/neck)
78812	Tumor imaging, positron emission tomography (PET); skull base to mid-thigh
78813	Tumor imaging, positron emission tomography (PET); whole body
78814	Tumor imaging, positron emission tomography (PET) with concurrently acquired computed tomography (CT) for attenuation correction and anatomical localization; limited area (e.g., chest, head/neck)
78815	Tumor imaging, positron emission tomography (PET) with concurrently acquired computed tomography (CT) for attenuation correction and anatomical localization; skull base to mid-thigh
78816	Tumor imaging, positron emission tomography (PET) with concurrently acquired computed tomography (CT) for attenuation correction and anatomical localization; whole body

100-4, Chapter 13, 60.3.2

Tracer Codes Required for PET Scans

The following tracer codes are applicable only to CPT® 78491 and 78492. They can not be reported with any other code.

Institutional providers billing the fiscal intermediary

HCPCS	Description
*A9555	Rubidium Rb-82, Diagnostic, Per study dose, Up To 60 Millicuries
* Q3000 (Deleted effective 12/31/05)	Supply of Radiopharmaceutical Diagnostic Imaging Agent, Rubidium Rb-82, per dose
A9526	Nitrogen N-13 Ammonia, Diagnostic, Per study dose, Up To 40 Millicuries

NOTE: For claims with dates of service prior to 1/01/06, providers report Q3000 for supply of radiopharmaceutical diagnostic imaging agent, Rubidium Rb-82. For claims with dates of service 1/01/06 and later, providers report A9555 for radiopharmaceutical diagnostic imaging agent, Rubidium Rb-82 in place of Q3000.

Physicians / practitioners billing the carrier:

*A4641	Supply of Radiopharmaceutical Diagnostic Imaging Agent, Not Otherwise Classified
A9526	Nitrogen N-13 Ammonia, Diagnostic, Per study dose, Up To 40 Millicuries
A9555	Rubidium Rb-82, Diagnostic, Per study dose, Up To 60 Millicuries

*__NOTE:__ Effective January 1, 2008, tracer code A4641 is not applicable for PET Scans.

The following tracer codes are applicable only to CPT® 78459, 78608, 78811-78816. They can not be reported with any other code:

Institutional providers billing the fiscal intermediary:

* A9552	Fluorodeoxyglucose F18, FDG, Diagnostic, Per study dose, Up to 45 Millicuries
* C1775 (Deleted effective 12/31/05)	Supply of Radiopharmaceutical Diagnostic Imaging Agent, Fluorodeoxyglucose F18, (2-Deoxy-2-18F Fluoro-D-Glucose), Per dose (4-40 Mci/Ml)
**A4641	Supply of Radiopharmaceutical Diagnostic Imaging Agent, Not Otherwise Classified

The following tracer codes are applicable only to CPT® 78811-78816. They can not be reported with any other code:

A9580	Sodium Fluoride F-18, Diagnostic, per study dose, up to 30 Millicuries

__NOTE:__ For claims with dates of service prior to 1/01/06, OPPS hospitals report C1775 for supply of radiopharmaceutical diagnostic imaging agent, Fluorodeoxyglucose F18. For claims with dates of service 1/01/06 and later, providers report A9552 for radiopharmaceutical diagnostic imaging agent, Fluorodeoxyglucose F18 in place of C1775.

**__NOTE:__ Effective January 1, 2008, tracer code A4641 is not applicable for PET Scans.

***__NOTE:__ Effective for claims with dates of service February 26, 2010 and later, tracer code A9580 is applicable for PET Scans.

Physicians / practitioners billing the carrier:

A9552	Fluorodeoxyglucose F18, FDG, Diagnostic, Per study dose, Up to 45 Millicuries
*A4641	Supply of Radiopharmaceutical Diagnostic Imaging Agent, Not Otherwise Classified

The following tracer code is applicable only to 78811-78816. They can not be reported with any other code:

A9580	Sodium Fluoride F-18, Diagnostic, per study dose, up to 30 Millicuries

*__NOTE:__ Effective January 1, 2008, tracer code A4641 is not applicable for PET Scans.

***__NOTE:__ Effective for claims with dates of service February 26, 2010 and later, tracer code A9580 is applicable for PET Scans.

CPT®	Short Descriptor	Tracer/ Code	or	Tracer/ Code	Comment
78459	Myocardial imaging, positron emission tomography (PET), metabolic imaging	FDG A9552	--	--	N/A

CPT®	Short Descriptor	Tracer/ Code	or	Tracer/ Code	Comment
78491	Myocardial imaging, positron emission tomography (PET), perfusion; single study at rest or stress	N-13 A9526	or	Rb-82 A9555	N/A
78492	Myocardial imaging, positron emission tomography (PET), perfusion; multiple studies at rest and/ or stress	N-13 A9526	or	Rb-82 A9555	N/A
78608	Brain imaging, positron emission tomography (PET); metabolic evaluation	FDG A9552	--	--	Covered indications: Alzheimer's disease/ dementias, intractable seizures Note: This code is also covered for dedicated PET brain tumor imaging.
78609	Brain imaging, positron emission tomography (PET); perfusion evaluation	--	--	--	Nationally noncovered
78811	Positron emission tomography (PET) imaging; limited area (e.g, chest, head/ neck)	FDG A9552	or	NaF-18 A9580	NaF-18 PET is covered only to identify bone metastasis of cancer.
78812	Positron emission tomography (PET) imaging, skull base to mid-thigh	FDG A9552	or	NaF-18 A9580	NaF-18 PET is covered only to identify bone metastasis of cancer.
78813	Positron emission tomography (PET) imaging, whole body	FDG A9552	or	NaF-18 A9580	NaF-18 PET s covered only to identify bone metastasis of cancer.
78814	PET/CT imaging, limited area (e.g., chest, head/neck)	FDG A9552	or	NaF-18 A9580	NaF-18 PET is covered only to identify bone metastasis of cancer.
78815	PET/CT imaging, skull base to mid-thigh	FDG A9552	or	NaF-18 A9580	NaF-18 PET is covered only to identify bone metastasis of cancer.
78816	PET/CT imaging, whole body	FDG A9552	or	NaF-18 A9580	NaF-18 PET is covered only to identify bone metastasis of cancer.

Format 100-4, Chapter 13, 60.13

Billing Requirements for PET Scans for Specific Indications of Cervical Cancer for Services Performed on or After January 28, 2005

Contractors shall accept claims for these services with the appropriate CPT® code listed in section 60.3.1. Refer to Pub. 100-03, section 220.6.17, for complete coverage guidelines for this new PET oncology indication. The implementation date for these CPT® codes will be April 18, 2005. Also see section 60.17, of this chapter for further claims processing instructions for cervical cancer indications.

100-4, Chapter 13, 60.14

Billing Requirements for PET Scans for Non-Covered Indications

For services performed on or after January 28, 2005, contractors shall accept claims with the following HCPCS code for non-covered PET indications:

-G0235: PET imaging, any site not otherwise specified Short Descriptor: PET not otherwise specified Type of Service:4

NOTE: This code is for a non-covered service.

100-4, Chapter 13, 60.15

Billing Requirements for CMS - Approved Clinical Trials and Coverage With Evidence Development Claims for PET Scans for Neurodegenerative Diseases, Previously Specified Cancer Indications, and All Other Cancer Indications Not Previously Specified

A/B MACs (A and B)

Effective for services on or after January 28, 2005, contractors shall accept and pay for claims for Positron Emission Tomography (PET) scans for lung cancer, esophageal cancer, colorectal cancer, lymphoma, melanoma, head & neck cancer, breast cancer, thyroid cancer, soft tissue sarcoma, brain cancer, ovarian cancer, pancreatic cancer, small cell lung cancer, and testicular cancer, as well as for neurodegenerative diseases and all other cancer indications not previously mentioned in this chapter, if these scans were performed as part of a Centers for Medicare & Medicaid (CMS)-approved clinical trial. (See Pub. 100-03, National Coverage Determinations (NCD) Manual, sections 220.6.13 and 220.6.17.)

Contractors shall also be aware that PET scans for all cancers not previously specified at Pub. 100-03, NCD Manual, section 220.6.17, remain nationally non-covered unless performed in conjunction with a CMS-approved clinical trial.

Effective for dates of service on or after June 11, 2013, Medicare has ended the coverage with evidence development (CED) requirement for FDG (2-[F18] fluoro-2-deoxy-Dglucose) PET and PET/computed tomography (CT) and PET/magnetic resonance imaging (MRI) for all oncologic indications contained in section 220.6.17 of the NCD Manual. Modifier -Q0 (Investigational clinical service provided in a clinical research study that is in an approved clinical research study) or -Q1 (routine clinical service provided in a clinical research study that is in an approved clinical research study) is no longer mandatory for these services when performed on or after June 11, 2013.

A/B MACs (B) Only

A/B MACs (B) shall pay claims for PET scans for beneficiaries participating in a CMS approved clinical trial submitted with an appropriate current procedural terminology (CPT®) code from section 60.3.1 of this chapter and modifier Q0/Q1 for services performed on or after January 1, 2008, through June 10, 2013. (NOTE: Modifier QR (Item or service provided in a Medicare specified study) and QA (FDA investigational device exemption) were replaced by modifier Q0 effective January 1, 2008.) Modifier QV (item or service provided as routine care in a Medicare qualifying clinical trial) was replaced by modifier Q1 effective January 1, 2008.) Beginning with services performed on or after June 11, 2013, modifier Q0/Q1 is no longer required for PET FDG services.

A/B MACs (A) Only

In order to pay claims for PET scans on behalf of beneficiaries participating in a CMS approved clinical trial, A/B MACs (A) require providers to submit claims with, if ICD-9- CM is applicable, ICD-9 code V70.7; if ICD-10-CM is applicable, ICD-10 code Z00.6 in the primary/secondary diagnosis position using the ASC X12 837 institutional claim format or on Form CMS-1450, with the appropriate principal diagnosis code and an appropriate CPT® code from section 60.3.1. Effective for PET scan claims for dates of service on or after January 28, 2005, through December 31, 2007, A/B MACs (A) shall accept claims with the QR, QV, or QA modifier on other than inpatient claims. Effective for services on or after January 1, 2008, through June 10, 2013, modifier Q0 replaced the QR and QA modifier, modifier Q1 replaced the QV modifier. Modifier Q0/Q1 is no longer required for services performed on or after June 11, 2013

100-4, Chapter 13, 60.16

Billing and Coverage Changes for PET Scans Effective for Services on or After April 3, 2009

A. Summary of Changes

Effective for services on or after April 3, 2009, Medicare will not cover the use of FDG PET imaging to determine initial treatment strategy in patients with adenocarcinoma of the prostate.

Medicare will also not cover FDG PET imaging for subsequent treatment strategy for tumor types other than breast, cervical, colorectal, esophagus, head and neck (nonCNS/thyroid), lymphoma, melanoma, myeloma, non-small cell lung, and ovarian, unless the FDG PET is provided under the coverage with evidence development (CED) paradigm (billed with modifier -Q0/-Q1, see section 60.15 of this chapter).

Medicare will cover FDG PET imaging for initial treatment strategy for myeloma.

Effective for services performed on or after June 11, 2013, Medicare has ended the CED requirement for FDG PET and PET/CT and PET/MRI for all oncologic indications contained in section 220.6.17 of the NCD Manual. Effective for services on or after June 11, 2013, the Q0/Q1 modifier is no longer required.

Beginning with services performed on or after June 11, 2013, contractors shall pay for up to three (3) FDG PET scans when used to guide subsequent management of anti-tumor treatment strategy (modifier PS) after completion of initial anti-cancer therapy (modifier PI) for the exact same cancer diagnosis.

Coverage of any additional FDG PET scans (that is, beyond 3) used to guide subsequent management of anti-tumor treatment strategy after completion of initial anti-tumor therapy for the same cancer diagnosis will be determined by the A/B MACs (A or B). Claims will include the KX modifier indicating the coverage criteria is met for coverage of four or more FDG PET scans for subsequent treatment strategy for the same cancer diagnosis under this NCD.

A different cancer diagnosis whether submitted with a PI or a PS modifier will begin the count of one initial and three subsequent FDG PET scans not requiring the KX modifier and four or more FDG PET scans for subsequent treatment strategy for the same cancer diagnosis requiring the KX modifier.

NOTE: The presence or absence of an initial treatment strategy claim in a beneficiary's record does not impact the frequency criteria for subsequent treatment strategy claims for the same cancer diagnosis.

NOTE: Providers please refer to the following link for a list of appropriate diagnosis codes, http://cms.gov/medicare/coverage/determinationprocess/downloads/petforsolidtumorsonc ologicdxcodesattachment_NCD220_6_17.pdf

For further information regarding the changes in coverage, refer to Pub.100-03, NCD Manual, section 220.6.17.

B. Modifiers for PET Scans

Effective for claims with dates of service on or after April 3, 2009, the following modifiers have been created for use to inform for the initial treatment strategy of biopsy-proven or strongly suspected tumors or subsequent treatment strategy of cancerous tumors:

PI Positron Emission Tomography (PET) or PET/Computed Tomography (CT) to inform the initial treatment strategy of tumors that are biopsy proven or strongly suspected of being cancerous based on other diagnostic testing.

Short descriptor: PET tumor init tx strat

PS Positron Emission Tomography (PET) or PET/Computed Tomography (CT) to inform the subsequent treatment strategy of cancerous tumors when the beneficiary's treatment

physician determines that the PET study is needed to inform subsequent anti-tumor strategy.

Short descriptor: PS - PET tumor subsq tx strategy

C. Billing for A/B MACs

Effective for claims with dates of service on or after April 3, 2009, contractors shall accept FDG PET claims billed to inform initial treatment strategy with the following CPT® codes AND modifier PI: 78608, 78811, 78812, 78813, 78814, 78815, 78816.

Effective for claims with dates of service on or after April 3, 2009, contractors shall accept FDG PET claims with modifier PS for the subsequent treatment strategy for solid tumors using a CPT® code above AND a cancer diagnosis code.

Contractors shall also accept FDG PET claims billed to inform initial treatment strategy or subsequent treatment strategy when performed under CED with one of the PET or PET/CT CPT® codes above AND modifier PI OR modifier PS AND a cancer diagnosis code AND modifier Q0/Q1. Effective for services performed on or after June 11, 2013, the CED requirement has ended and modifier Q0/Q1, along with condition code 30 (institutional claims only), or ICD-9 code

V70.7, (both institutional and practitioner claims) are no longer required.

D. Medicare Summary Notices, Remittance Advice Remark Codes, and Claim Adjustment Reason Codes

Effective for dates of service on or after April 3, 2009, contractors shall return as unprocessable/return to provider claims that do not include the PI modifier with one of the PET/PET/CT CPT® codes listed in subsection C. above when billing for the initial treatment strategy for solid tumors in accordance with Pub.100-03, NCD Manual, section 220.6.17.

In addition, contractors shall return as unprocessable/return to provider claims that do not include the PS modifier with one of the CPT® codes listed in subsection C. above when billing for the subsequent treatment strategy for solid tumors in accordance with Pub.100-03, NCD Manual, section 220.6.17.

The following messages apply:

- Claim Adjustment Reason Code (CARC) 4 - The procedure code is inconsistent with the modifier used or a required modifier is missing.
- Remittance Advice Remark Code (RARC) MA-130 - Your claim contains incomplete and/or invalid information, and no appeal rights are afforded because the claim is unprocessable. Submit a new claim with the complete/correct information.
- RARC M16 - Alert: See our Web site, mailings, or bulletins for more details concerning this policy/procedure/decision.

Effective for claims with dates of service on or after April 3, 2009, through June 10, 2013, contractors shall return as unprocessable/return to provider FDG PET claims billed to inform initial treatment strategy or subsequent treatment strategy when performed under CED without one of the PET/PET/CT CPT® codes listed in subsection C. above AND modifier PI OR modifier PS AND a cancer diagnosis code AND modifier Q0/Q1.

The following messages apply to return as unprocessable claims:

- CARC 4 - The procedure code is inconsistent with the modifier used or a required modifier is missing.
- RARC MA-130 - Your claim contains incomplete and/or invalid information, and no appeal rights are afforded because the claim is unprocessable. Submit a new claim with the complete/correct information.
- RARC M16 - Alert: See our Web site, mailings, or bulletins for more details concerning this policy/procedure/decision.

Effective April 3, 2009, contractors shall deny claims with ICD-9/ICD-10 diagnosis code 185/C61 for FDG PET imaging for the initial treatment strategy of patients with adenocarcinoma of the prostate.

For dates of service prior to June 11, 2013, contractors shall also deny claims for FDG PET imaging for subsequent treatment strategy for tumor types other than breast, cervical, colorectal, esophagus, head and neck (non-CNS/thyroid), lymphoma, melanoma, myeloma, non-small cell lung, and ovarian, unless the FDG PET is provided under CED (submitted with the Q0/Q1 modifier) and use the following messages:

- Medicare Summary Notice 15.4 - Medicare does not support the need for this service or item
- CARC 50 - These are non-covered services because this is not deemed a 'medical necessity' by the payer.

- Contractors shall use Group Code CO (Contractual Obligation)

If the service is submitted with a GA modifier indicating there is a signed Advance Beneficiary Notice (ABN) on file, the liability falls to the beneficiary. However, if the service is submitted with a GZ modifier indicating no ABN was provided, the liability falls to the provider.

Effective for dates of service on or after June 11, 2013, contractors shall use the following messages when denying claims in excess of three for PET FDG scans for subsequent treatment strategy when the KX modifier is not included, identified by CPT® codes 78608, 78811, 78812, 78813, 78814, 78815, or 78816, modifier PS, HCPCS A9552, and the same cancer diagnosis code.

- CARC 96: "Non-Covered Charge(s). Note: Refer to the 835 Healthcare Policy Identification Segment (loop 2110 Service Payment Information REF), if present."
- RARC N435: "Exceeds number/frequency approved/ allowed within time period without support documentation."
- MSN 23.17: "Medicare won't cover these services because they are not considered medically necessary."

Spanish Version: "Medicare no cubrirá estos servicios porque no son considerados necesarios por razones médicas."

Contractors shall use Group Code PR assigning financial liability to the beneficiary, if a claim is received with a GA modifier indicating a signed ABN is on file.

Contractors shall use Group Code CO assigning financial liability to the provider, if a claim is received with a GZ modifier indicating no signed ABN is on file.

100-4, Chapter 13, 60.17

Billing and Coverage Changes for PET Scans for Cervical

A. Billing Changes for A/B MACs (A and B)

Effective for claims with dates of service on or after November 10, 2009, contractors shall accept FDG PET oncologic claims billed to inform initial treatment strategy; specifically for staging in beneficiaries who have biopsy-proven cervical cancer when the beneficiary's treating physician determines the FDG PET study is needed to determine the location and/or extent of the tumor as specified in Pub. 100-03, section 220.6.17.

EXCEPTION: CMS continues to non-cover FDG PET for initial diagnosis of cervical cancer related to initial treatment strategy.

NOTE: Effective for claims with dates of service on and after November 10, 2009, the – Q0 modifier is no longer necessary for FDG PET for cervical cancer.

B. Medicare Summary Notices, Remittance Advice Remark Codes, and Claim

Adjustment Reason Codes

Additionally, contractors shall return as unprocessable /return to provider for FDG PET for cervical cancer for initial treatment strategy billed without the following: one of the PET/PET/ CT CPT® codes listed in 60.16 C above AND modifier PI AND a cervical cancer diagnosis code.

Use the following messages:

- Claim Adjustment Reason Code 4 - The procedure code is inconsistent with the modifier used or a required modifier is missing.

- Remittance Advice Remark Code MA-130 - Your claim contains incomplete and/or invalid information, and no appeal rights are afforded because the claim is unprocessable. Submit a new claim with the complete/ correct information.
- Remittance Advice Remark Code M16 - Alert: See our Web site, mailings, or bulletins for more details concerning this policy/procedure/decision.

100-4, Chapter 13, 60.18

Billing and Coverage Changes for PET (NaF-18) Scans to Identify Bone Metastasis of Cancer Effective for Claims With Dates of Services on or After February 26, 2010

A. Billing Changes for A/B MACs (A and B)

Effective for claims with dates of service on and after February 26, 2010, contractors shall pay for NaF-18 PET oncologic claims to inform of initial treatment strategy (PI) or subsequent treatment strategy (PS) for suspected or biopsy proven bone metastasis ONLY in the context of a clinical study and as specified in Pub. 100-03, section 220.6. All other claims for NaF-18 PET oncology claims remain non-covered.

B. Medicare Summary Notices, Remittance Advice Remark Codes, and Claim Adjustment Reason Codes

Effective for claims with dates of service on or after February 26, 2010, contractors shall return as unprocessable NaF-18 PET oncologic claims billed with modifier TC or globally (for A/B MACs (A) modifier TC or globally does not apply) and HCPCS A9580 to inform the initial treatment strategy or subsequent treatment strategy for bone metastasis that do not include ALL of the following:

- PI or PS modifier AND
- PET or PET/CT CPT® code (78811, 78812, 78813, 78814, 78815, 78816) AND
- Cancer diagnosis code AND
- Q0 modifier - Investigational clinical service provided in a clinical research study, are present on the claim.

NOTE: For institutional claims, continue to include ICD-9 diagnosis code V70.7 or ICD-10 diagnosis code Z00.6 and condition code 30 to denote a clinical study.

Use the following messages:

- Claim Adjustment Reason Code 4 - The procedure code is inconsistent with the modifier used or a required modifier is missing. Note: Refer to the 835 Healthcare Policy Identification Segment (loop 2110 Service Payment Information REF), if present.
- Remittance Advice Remark Code MA-130 - Your claim contains incomplete and/or invalid information, and no appeal rights are afforded because the claim is unprocessable. Submit a new claim with the complete/ correct information.
- Remittance Advice Remark Code M16 - Alert: See our Web site, mailings, or bulletins for more details concerning this policy/procedure/decision.
- Claim Adjustment Reason Code 167 - This (these) diagnosis(es) is (are) not covered.

Effective for claims with dates of service on or after February 26, 2010, contractors shall accept PET oncologic claims billed with modifier 26 and modifier KX to inform the initial treatment strategy or subsequent treatment strategy for bone metastasis that include the following:

- PI or PS modifier AND
- PET or PET/CT CPT® code (78811, 78812, 78813, 78814, 78815, 78816) AND
- Cancer diagnosis code AND
- Q0 modifier - Investigational clinical service provided in a clinical research study, are present on the claim.

NOTE: If modifier KX is present on the professional component service, Contractors shall process the service as PET NaF-18 rather than PET with FDG.

Contractors shall also return as unprocessable NaF-18 PET oncologic professional component claims (i.e., claims billed with modifiers 26 and KX) to inform the initial treatment strategy or subsequent treatment strategy for bone metastasis billed with HCPCS A9580 and use the following message:

Claim Adjustment Reason Code 97 - The benefit for this service is included in the payment/allowance for another service/procedure that has already been adjudicated.

NOTE: Refer to the 835 Healthcare Policy identification Segment (loop 2110 Service Payment Information REF), if present.

100-4, Chapter 13, 140

Bone Mass Measurements (BMMs)

Sections 1861(s)(15)and (rr)(1)of the Social Security Act (the Act) (as added by §4106 of the Balanced Budget Act (BBA) of 1997) standardize Medicare coverage of medically necessary bone mass measurements by providing for uniform coverage under Medicare Part B. This coverage is effective for claims with dates of service furnished on or after July 1, l998.

Effective for dates of service on and after January 1, 2007, the CY 2007 Physician Fee Schedule final rule expanded the number of beneficiaries qualifying for BMM by reducing the dosage requirement for glucocorticoid (steroid) therapy from 7.5 mg of prednisone per day to 5.0 mg. It also changed the definition of BMM by removing coverage for a single-photon absorptiometry as it is not considered reasonable and necessary under section 1862 (a)(1)(A) of the Act. Finally, it required that in the case of monitoring and confirmatory baseline BMMs, they be performed with a dual-energy x-ray absorptiometry (axial) test.

Conditions of Coverage for BMMs are located in Pub.100-02, Medicare Benefit Policy Manual, chapter 15.

100-4, Chapter 14, 40.3

Payment for Intraocular Lens (IOL)

Prior to January 1, 2008, payment for facility services furnished by an ASC for IOL insertion during or subsequent to cataract surgery includes an allowance for the lens. The procedures that include insertion of an IOL are:

Payment Group 6: CPT®-4 Codes 66985 and 66986

Payment Group 8: CPT®-4 Codes 66982, 66983 and 66984

Physicians or suppliers are not paid for an IOL furnished to a beneficiary in an ASC after July 1, 1988. Separate claims for IOLs furnished to ASC patients beginning March 12, 1990 are denied. Also, effective March 12, 1990, procedures 66983 and 66984 are treated as single procedures for payment purposes.

Beginning January 1, 2008, the Medicare payment for the IOL is included in the Medicare ASC payment for the associated surgical procedure. Consequently, no separate payment

for the IOL is made, except for a payment adjustment for NTIOLs established according to the process outlined in 42 CFR 416.185. ASCs should not report separate charges for conventional IOLs because their payment is included in the Medicare payment for the associated surgical procedure. The ASC payment system logic that excluded $150 for IOLs for purposes of the multiple surgery reduction in cases of cataract surgery prior to January 1, 2008 no longer applies, effective for dates of service on or after January 1, 2008.

Effective for dates of service on and after February 27, 2006, through February 26, 2011, Medicare pays an additional $50 for specified Category 3 NTIOLs that are provided in association with a covered ASC surgical procedure. The list of Category 3 NTIOLS is available at:http://www.cms.hhs.gov/ASCPayment/08_NTIOLs.asp#TopOfPage.

ASCs should use HCPCS code Q1003 to bill for a Category 3 NTIOL. HCPCS code Q1003, along with one of the approved surgical procedure codes (CPT® codes 66982, 66983, 66984, 66985, 66986) are to be used on all NTIOL Category 3 claims associated with reduced spherical aberration from February 27, 2006, through February 26, 2011. The payment adjustment for the NTIOL is subject to beneficiary coinsurance but is not wage-adjusted.

Any subsequent IOL recognized by CMS as having the same characteristics as the first NTIOL recognized by CMS for a payment adjustment as a Category III NTIOL (those of reduced spherical aberration) will receive the same adjustment for the remainder of the 5-year period established by the first recognized IOL.

100-4, Chapter 14, 40.8

Payment When a Device is Furnished With No Cost or With Full or Partial Credit Beginning January 1, 2008

Contractors pay ASCs a reduced amount for certain specified procedures when a specified device is furnished without cost or for which either a partial or full credit is received (e.g., device recall). For specified procedure codes that include payment for a device, ASCs are required to include modifier –FB on the procedure code when a specified device is furnished without cost or for which full credit is received. If the ASC receives a partial credit of 50 percent or more of the cost of a specified device, the ASC is required to include modifier –FC on the procedure code if the procedure is on the list of specified procedures to which the -FC reduction applies. A single procedure code should not be submitted with both modifiers –FB and -FC. The pricing determination related to modifiers –FB and -FC is made prior to the application of multiple procedure payment reductions. Contractors adjust beneficiary coinsurance to reflect the reduced payment amount. Tables listing the procedures and devices to which the payment adjustments apply, and the full and partial adjustment amounts, are available on the CMS Web site.

In order to report that the receipt of a partial credit of 50 percent or more of the cost of a device, ASCs have the option of either: 1) Submitting the claim for the procedure to their Medicare contractor after the procedure's performance but prior to manufacturer acknowledgement of credit for a specified device, and subsequently contacting the contractor regarding a claims adjustment once the credit determination is made; or 2) holding the claim for the procedure until a determination is made by the manufacturer on the partial credit and submitting the claim with modifier –FC appended to the implantation procedure HCPCS code if the partial credit is 50 percent or more of the cost of the device. If choosing the first billing option, to request a claims adjustment once the credit determination is made, ASCs should keep in mind that the initial Medicare payment for the procedure involving the device is conditional and subject to adjustment.

100-4, Chapter 14, 40.9

Payment and Coding for Presbyopia Correcting IOLs (P-C IOLs) and Astigmatism Correcting IOLs (A-C IOLs)

CMS payment policies and recognition of P-C IOLs and A-C IOLs are contained in Transmittal 636 (CR3927) and Transmittal 1228 (CR5527) respectively.

Effective for dates of service on and after January 1, 2008, when inserting an approved A-C IOL in an ASC concurrent with cataract extraction, HCPCS code V2787 (Astigmatism-correcting function of intraocular lens) should be billed to report the non-covered charges for the A-C IOL functionality of the inserted intraocular lens. Additionally, note that HCPCS code V2788 (Presbyopia-correcting function of intraocular lens) is no longer valid to report non-covered charges associated with the A-C IOL. However, this code continues to be valid toreport non-covered charges for a P-C IOL. The payment for the conventional lens portion of the A-C IOL and P-C IOL continues to be bundled with the ASC procedure payment.

Effective for services on and after January 1, 2010, ASCs are to bill for insertion of a Category 3 new technology intraocular lens (NTIOL) that is also an approved A-C IOL or P-C IOL, concurrent with cataract extraction, using three separate codes. ASCs shall use HCPCS code V2787 or V2788, as appropriate, to report charges associated with the non-covered functionality of the A-C IOL or P-C IOL, the appropriate HCPCS code 66982 (Extracapsular cataract removal with insertion of intraocular lens prosthesis (one stage procedure), manual or mechanical technique (e.g., irrigation and aspiration or phacoemulsification), complex, requiring devices or techniques not generally used in routine cataract surgery (e.g., iris expansion device, suture support for intraocular lens, or primary posterior capsulorrhexis) or performed on patients in the amblyogenic developmental stage); 66983 (Intracapsular cataract extraction with insertion of intraocular lens prosthesis (1 stage procedure)); or 66984 (Extracapsular cataract removal with insertion of intraocular lens prosthesis (1 stage procedure), manual or mechanical technique (e.g., irrigation and aspiration or phacoemulsification)), to report the covered cataract extraction and insertion procedure; and Q1003 (New technology, intraocular lens, category 3 (reduced spherical aberration) as defined in Federal Register notice, Vol. 65, dated May 3, 2000) to report the covered NTIOL aspect of the lens on claims for insertion of an A-C IOL or P-C IOL that is also designated as an NTIOL. Listings of the CMS-approved Category 3 NTIOLs, A-C IOLs, and P-C IOLs are available on the CMS Web site.

100-4, Chapter 14, 60.1

Applicable Messages for NTIOLs

Contractors shall return as unprocessable any claims for NTIOLs containing Q1003 alone or with a code other than one of the procedure codes listed in 40.3. Use the following messages for these returned claims:

- Claim Adjustment Reason Code 16 -Claim/service lacks information which is needed for adjudication. Additional information is supplied using remittance advice remark codes whenever appropriate.

- RA Remark Code M67 -Missing/Incomplete/Invalid other procedure codes.
- RA Remark Code MA130 -Your claim contains incomplete and/or invalid information, and no appeal rights are afforded because the claim is unprocessable. Please submit a new claim with the complete/correct information.

Contractors shall deny payment for Q1003 if services are furnished in a facility other than a Medicare-approved ASC. Use the following messages when denying these claims:

- MSN 16.2 -This service cannot be paid when provided in this location/facility.
- Claims Adjustment Reason Code 58 -Payment adjusted because treatment was deemed by the payer to have been rendered in an inappropriate or invalid place of service.

Contractors shall deny payment for Q1003 if billed by an entity other than a Medicare-approved ASC. Use the following messages when denying these claims:

- MSN 33.1 -The ambulatory surgical center must bill for this service.
- Claim Adjustment Reason Code 170 -Payment is denied when performed/billed by this type of provider.

Contractors shall deny payment for Q1003 if submitted for payment past the discontinued date (after the 5-year period, or after February 26, 2011). Use the following messages when denying these claims:

- MSN 21.11 -This service was not covered by Medicare at the time you received it.
- Claim Adjustment Reason Code 27 Expenses incurred after coverage terminated.

Contractors shall deny payment for Q1003 if submitted for payment past the discontinued date (after the 5-year period, or after February 26, 2011). Use the following messages when denying these claims:

- MSN 21.11 -This service was not covered by Medicare at the time you received it.
- Claim Adjustment Reason Code 27 -Expenses incurred after coverage terminated.

Carriers shall deny payment for Q1003 if services are furnished in a facility other than a Medicare-approved ASC. Use the following messages when denying these claims:

- MSN 16.2 -This service cannot be paid when provided in this location/facility.
- Claims Adjustment Reason Code 58 -Payment adjusted because treatment was deemed by the payer to have been rendered in an inappropriate or invalid place of service.

Carriers shall deny payment for Q1003 if billed by an entity other than a Medicare -approved ASC. Use the following messages when denying these claims:

- MSN 33.1 -The ambulatory surgical center must bill for this service.
- Claim Adjustment Reason Code 170 -Payment is denied when performed/billed by this type of provider.

Carriers shall deny payment for Q1003 if submitted for payment past the discontinued date (after the 5-year period, or after February 26, 2011). Use the following messages when denying these claims:

- MSN 21.11 -This service was not covered by Medicare at the time you received it.
- Claim Adjustment Reason Code 27 -Expenses incurred after coverage terminated.

100-4, Chapter 15, 20.1.4

Components of the Ambulance Fee Schedule

The mileage rates provided in this section are the base rates that are adjusted by the yearly ambulance inflation factor (AIF). The payment amount under the fee schedule is determined as follows:

- **For ground ambulance services,** the fee schedule amount includes:
  1. A money amount that serves as a nationally uniform base rate, called a "conversion factor" (CF), for all ground ambulance services;
  2. A relative value unit (RVU) assigned to each type of ground ambulance service;
  3. A geographic adjustment factor (GAF) for each ambulance fee schedule locality area (geographic practice cost index (GPCI));
  4. A nationally uniform loaded mileage rate;
  5. An additional amount for certain mileage for a rural point-of-pickup; and
  6. For specified temporary periods, certain additional payment amounts as described in section 20.1.4A, below.
- **For air ambulance services**, the fee schedule amount includes:
  1. A nationally uniform base rate for fixed wing and a nationally uniform base rate for rotary wing;
  2. A geographic adjustment factor (GAF) for each ambulance fee schedule locality area (GPCI);
  3. A nationally uniform loaded mileage rate for each type of air service; and
  4. A rural adjustment to the base rate and mileage for services furnished for a rural point-of-pickup

A. Ground Ambulance Services
1. Conversion Factor

The conversion factor (CF) is a money amount used to develop a base rate for each category of ground ambulance service. The CF is updated annually by the ambulance inflation factor and for other reasons as necessary.

2. Relative Value Units

Relative value units (RVUs) set a numeric value for ambulance services relative to the value of a base level ambulance service. Since there are marked differences in resources necessary to furnish the various levels of ground ambulance services, different levels of payment are appropriate for the various levels of service. The different payment amounts are based on level of service. An RVU expresses the constant multiplier for a particular type of service (including, where appropriate, an emergency response). An RVU of 1.00 is assigned to the BLS of ground service, e.g., BLS has an RVU of 1; higher RVU values are assigned to the other types of ground ambulance services, which require more service than BLS.

The RVUs are as follows:

Service Level	RVU
BLS	1.00
BLS - Emergency	1.60
ALS1	1.20
ALS1- Emergency	1.90
ALS2	2.75
SCT	3.25
PI	1.75

3. Geographic Adjustment Factor (GAF)

The GAF is one of two factors intended to address regional differences in the cost of furnishing ambulance services. The GAF for the ambulance FS uses the non-facility practice expense (PE) of the geographic practice cost index (GPCI) of the Medicare physician fee schedule to adjust payment to account for regional differences. Thus, the geographic areas applicable to the ambulance FS are the same as those used for the physician fee schedule.

The location where the beneficiary was put into the ambulance (POP) establishes which GPCI applies. For multiple vehicle transports, each leg of the transport is separately evaluated for the applicable GPCI. Thus, for the second (or any subsequent) leg of a transport, the POP establishes the applicable GPCI for that portion of the ambulance transport.

For ground ambulance services, the applicable GPCI is multiplied by 70 percent of the base rate. Again, the base rate for each category of ground ambulance services is the CF multiplied by the applicable RVU. The GPCI is not applied to the ground mileage rate.

4. Mileage

In the context of all payment instructions, the term "mileage" refers to loaded mileage. The ambulance FS provides a separate payment amount for mileage. The mileage rate per statute mile applies for all types of ground ambulance services, except Paramedic Intercept, and is provided to all Medicare contractors electronically by CMS as part of the ambulance FS. Providers and suppliers must report all medically necessary mileage, including the mileage subject to a rural adjustment, in a single line item.

5. Adjustment for Certain Ground Mileage for Rural Points of Pickup (POP)

The payment rate is greater for certain mileage where the POP is in a rural area to account for the higher costs per ambulance trip that are typical of rural operations where fewer trips are made in any given period.

If the POP is a rural ZIP Code, the following calculations should be used to determine the rural adjustment portion of the payment allowance. For loaded miles 1-17, the rural adjustment for ground mileage is 1.5 times the rural mileage allowance.

For services furnished during the period July 1, 2004 through December 31, 2008, a 25 percent increase is applied to the appropriate ambulance FS mileage rate to each mile of a transport (both urban and rural POP) that exceeds 50 miles (i.e., mile 51 and greater).

The following chart summarizes the above information:

Service	Dates of Service	Bonus	Calculation
Loaded miles 1-17, Rural POP	Beginning 4/1/02	50%	FS Rural mileage * 1.5
Loaded miles 18-50, Rural POP	4/1/02 – 12/31/03	25%	FS Rural mileage * 1.25
All loaded miles (Urban or Rural POP) 51+	7/1/04 – 12/31/08	25%	FS Urban or Rural mileage * 1.25

The POP, as identified by ZIP Code, establishes whether a rural adjustment applies to a particular service. Each leg of a multi-leg transport is separately evaluated for a rural adjustment application. Thus, for the second (or any subsequent) leg of a transport, the ZIP Code of the POP establishes whether a rural adjustment applies to such second (or subsequent) transport.

For the purpose of all categories of ground ambulance services except paramedic intercept, a rural area is defined as a U.S. Postal Service (USPS) ZIP Code that is located, in whole or in part, outside of either a Metropolitan Statistical Area (MSA) or in New England, a New England County Metropolitan Area (NECMA), or is an area wholly within an MSA or NECMA that has been identified as rural under the "Goldsmith modification." (The Goldsmith modification establishes an operational definition of rural areas within large counties that contain one or more metropolitan areas. The Goldsmith areas are so isolated by distance or physical features that they are more rural than urban in character and lack easy geographic access to health services.)

For Paramedic Intercept, an area is a rural area if:

- It is designated as a rural area by any law or regulation of a State;
- It is located outside of an MSA or NECMA; or
- It is located in a rural census tract of an MSA as determined under the most recent Goldsmith modification.

See IOM Pub. 100-02, Medicare Benefit Policy Manual, chapter 10 –Ambulance Services, section 30.1.1 –Ground Ambulance Services for coverage requirements for the Paramedic Intercept benefit. Presently, only the State of New York meets these requirements.

Although a transport with a POP located in a rural area is subject to a rural adjustment for mileage, Medicare still pays the lesser of the billed charge or the applicable FS amount for mileage. Thus, when rural mileage is involved, the contractor compares the calculated FS rural mileage payment rate to the provider's/supplier's actual charge for mileage and pays the lesser amount.

The CMS furnishes the ambulance FS files to claims processing contractors electronically. A version of the Ambulance Fee Schedule is also posted to the CMS website (http://www.cms.hhs.gov/AmbulanceFeeSchedule/02_afspuf.asp) for public consumption. To clarify whether a particular ZIP Code is rural or urban, please refer to the most recent version of the Medicare supplied ZIP Code file.

6. Regional Ambulance FS Payment Rate Floor for Ground Ambulance Transports

For services furnished during the period July 1, 2004 through December 31, 2009, the base rate portion of the payment under the ambulance FS for ground ambulance transports is subject to a minimum amount. This minimum amount depends upon the area of the country in which the service is furnished. The country is divided into 9 census divisions and each of the census divisions has a regional FS that is constructed using the same methodology as the national FS. Where the regional FS is greater than the national FS, the base rates for ground ambulance transports are determined by a blend of the national rate and the regional rate in accordance with the following schedule:

Year	National FS Percentage	Regional FS Percentage
7/1/04 - 12/31/04	20%	80%
CY 2005	40%	60%
CY 2006	60%	40%
CY 2007 – CY 2009	80%	20%
CY 2010 and thereafter	100%	0%

Where the regional FS is not greater than the national FS, there is no blending and only the national FS applies. Note that this provision affects only the FS portion of the blended transition payment rate. This floor amount is calculated by CMS centrally and is incorporated into the FS amount that appears in the FS file maintained by CMS and downloaded by CMS contractors. There is no calculation to be done by the Medicare B/MAC or A/MAC in order to implement this provision.

7. Adjustments for FS Payment Rate for Certain Rural Ground Ambulance Transports

For services furnished during the period July 1, 2004 through December 31, 2010, the base rate portion of the payment under the FS for ground ambulance transports furnished in certain rural areas is increased by a percentage amount determined by CMS . Section 3105 (c) and 10311 (c) of the Affordable Care Act amended section 1834 (1) (13) (A) of the Act to extend this rural bonus for an additional year through December 31, 2010. This increase applies if the POP is in a rural county (or Goldsmith area) that is comprised by the lowest quartile by population of all such rural areas arrayed by population density. CMS will determine this bonus amount and the designated POP rural ZIP Codes in which the bonus applies. Beginning on July 1, 2004, rural areas qualifying for the additional bonus amount will be identified with a "B" indicator on the national ZIP Code file. Contractors must apply the additional rural bonus amount as a multiplier to the base rate portion of the FS payment for all ground transports originating in the designated POP ZIP Codes.

Subsequently, section of 106 (c) of the MMEA again amended section 1843 (l) (13) (A) of the Act to extend the rural bonus an additional year, through December 31, 2011

8. Adjustments for FS Payment Rates for Ground Ambulance Transports

The payment rates under the FS for ground ambulance transports (both the fee schedule base rates and the mileage amounts) are increased for services furnished during the period July 1, 2004 through December 31, 2006 as well as July 1, 2008 through December 31, 2010. For ground ambulance transport services furnished where the POP is urban, the rates are increased by 1 percent for claims with dates of service July 1, 2004 through December 31, 2006 in accordance with Section 414 of the Medicare Modernization Act (MMA) of 2004 and by 2 percent for claims with dates of service July 1, 2008 through December 31, 2010 in accordance with Section 146(a) of the Medicare Improvements for Patients and Providers Act of 2008 and Sections 3105(a) and 10311(a) of the Patient Protection and Affordable Care Act (ACA) of 2010. For ground ambulance transport services furnished where the POP is rural, the rates are increased by 2 percent for claims with dates of service July 1, 2004 through December 31, 2006 in accordance with Section 414 of the Medicare Modernization Act (MMA) of 2004 and by 3 percent for claims with dates of service July 1, 2008 through December 31, 2010 in accordance with Section 146(a) of the Medicare Improvements for Patients and Providers Act of 2008 and Sections 3105(a) and 10311(a) of the Patient Protection and Affordable Care Act (ACA) of 2010. Subsequently, section 106 (a) of the Medicare and Medicaid Extenders Act of 2010 (MMEA) again amended section 1834 (1) (12) (A) of the Act to extend the payment increases for an additional year, through December 31, 2011. These amounts are incorporated into the fee schedule amounts that appear in the Ambulance FS file maintained by CMS and downloaded by CMS contractors. There is no calculation to be done by the Medicare carrier or intermediary in order to implement this provision.

The following chart summarizes the Medicare Prescription Drug, Improvement, and Modernization Act (MMA) of 2003 payment changes for ground ambulance services that became effective on July 1, 2004 as well as the Medicare Improvement for Patients and Providers Act (MIPPA) of 2008 changes that became effective July 1, 2008 and were extended by the Patient Protection and Affordable Care Act of 2010 and the Medicare and Medicaid Extenders Act of 2010 (MMEA).

Summary Chart of Additional Payments for Ground Ambulance Services Provided by MMA, MIPPA and MMEA

Service	Effective Dates	Payment Increase*
All rural miles	7/1/04 - 12/31/06	2%
All rural miles	7/1/08 – 12/31/11	3%
Rural miles 51+	7/1/04 - 12/31/08	25% **
All urban miles	7/1/04 - 12/31/06	1%
All urban miles	7/1/08 – 12/31/11	2%
Urban miles 51+	7/1/04 - 12/31/08	25% **
All rural base rates	7/1/04 - 12/31/06	2%
All rural base rates	7/1/08 – 12/31/11	3%
Rural base rates (lowest quartile)	7/1/04 - 12/31/11	22.6 %**
All urban base rates	7/1/04 - 12/31/06	1%
All urban base rates	7/1/08 – 12/31/11	2%
All base rates (regional fee schedule blend)	7/1/04 - 12/31/09	Floor

NOTES: *All payments are percentage increases and all are cumulative.

**Contractor systems perform this calculation. All other increases are incorporated into the CMS Medicare Ambulance FS file.

B. Air Ambulance Services

1. Base Rates

Each type of air ambulance service has a base rate. There is no conversion factor (CF) applicable to air ambulance services.

2. Geographic Adjustment Factor (GAF)

The GAF, as described above for ground ambulance services, is also used for air ambulance services. However, for air ambulance services, the applicable GPCI is applied to 50 percent of each of the base rates (fixed and rotary wing).

3. Mileage

The FS for air ambulance services provides a separate payment for mileage.

4. Adjustment for Services Furnished in Rural Areas

The payment rates for air ambulance services where the POP is in a rural area are greater than in an urban area. For air ambulance services (fixed or rotary wing), the rural adjustment is an increase of 50 percent to the unadjusted FS amount,

e.g., the applicable air service base rate multiplied by the GAF plus the mileage amount or, in other words, 1.5 times both the applicable air service base rate and the total mileage amount.

The basis for a rural adjustment for air ambulance services is determined in the same manner as for ground services. That is, whether the POP is within a rural ZIP Code as described above for ground services.

100-4, Chapter 15, 20.2

Payment for Mileage Charges

Charges for mileage must be based on loaded mileage only, e.g., from the pickup of a patient to his/her arrival at destination. It is presumed that all unloaded mileage costs are taken into account when a supplier establishes his basic charge for ambulance services and his rate for loaded mileage. Suppliers should be notified that separate charges for unloaded mileage will be denied.

Instructions on billing mileage are found in §30.

100-4, Chapter 15, 20.3

Air Ambulance

Refer to IOM Pub. 100-02, Medicare Benefit Policy Manual, chapter 10 -Ambulance Services, section 10.4 –Air Ambulance Services, for additional information on the coverage of air ambulance services. Under certain circumstances, transportation by airplane or helicopter may qualify as covered ambulance services. If the conditions of coverage are met, payment may be made for the air ambulance services.

Air ambulance services are paid at different rates according to two air ambulance categories:

- AIR ambulance service, conventional air services, transport, one way, fixed wing (FW) (HCPCS code A0430)
- AIR ambulance service, conventional air services, transport, one way, rotary wing(RW) (HCPCS code A0431)

Covered air ambulance mileage services are paid when the appropriate HCPCS code is reported on the claim:

- HCPCS code A0435 identifies FIXED WING AIR MILEAGE
- HCPCS code A0436 identifies ROTARY WING AIR MILEAGE

Air mileage must be reported in whole numbers of loaded statute miles flown. Contractors must ensure that the appropriate air transport code is used with the appropriate mileage code.

Air ambulance services may be paid only for ambulance services to a hospital. Other destinations e.g., skilled nursing facility, a physician's office, or a patient's home may not be paid air ambulance. The destination is identified by the use of an appropriate modifier As defined in Section 30(A) of this chapter.

Claims for air transports may account for all mileage from the point of pickup, including where applicable: ramp to taxiway, taxiway to runway, takeoff run, air miles, roll out upon landing, and taxiing after landing. Additional air mileage may be allowed by the contractor in situations where additional mileage is incurred, due to circumstances beyond the pilot's control. These circumstances include, but are not limited to, the following:

- Military base and other restricted zones, air-defense zones, and similar FAA restrictions and prohibitions;
- Hazardous weather; or
- Variances in departure patterns and clearance routes required by an air traffic controller.

If the air transport meets the criteria for medical necessity, Medicare pays the actual miles flown for legitimate reasons as determined by the Medicare contractor, once the Medicare beneficiary is loaded onto the air ambulance.

IOM Pub. 100-08, Medicare Program Integrity Manual, chapter 6 –Intermediary MR Guidelines for Specific Services contains instructions for Medical Review of Air Ambulance Services.

100-4, Chapter 15, 20.6

Payment for Non-Emergency Trips to/from ESRD Facilities

Section 637 of the American Taxpayer Relief Act of 2012 requires that, effective for transports occurring on and after October 1, 2013, fee schedule payments for non-emergency basic life support (BLS) transports of individuals with end-stage renal disease (ESRD) to and from renal dialysis treatment be reduced by 10%. The payment reduction affects transports (base rate and mileage) to and from hospital-based and freestanding renal dialysis treatment facilities for dialysis services provided on a non-emergency basis. Non-emergency BLS ground transports are identified by Healthcare Common Procedure Code System (HCPCS) code A0428. Ambulance transports to and from renal dialysis treatment are identified by modifier codes "G" (hospital-based ESRD) and "J" (freestanding ESRD facility) in either the first position (origin code) or second position (destination code) within the two-digit ambulance modifier. (See Section 30 (A) for information regarding modifiers specific to ambulance.)

Effective for claims with dates of service on and after October 1, 2013, the 10% reduction will be calculated and applied to HCPCS code A0428 when billed with modifier code "G" or "J". The reduction will also be applied to any mileage billed in association with a non-emergency transport of a beneficiary with ESRD to and from renal dialysis treatment. BLS mileage is identified by HCPCS code A0425.

The 10% reduction will be taken after calculation of the normal fee schedule payment amount, including any add-on or bonus payments , and will apply to transports in rural and urban areas as well as areas designated as "super rural".

Payment for emergency transports is not affected by this reduction. Payment for non-emergency BLS transports to other destinations is also not affected. This reduction does not affect or change the Ambulance Fee Schedule.

Note: The 10% reduction applies to beneficiaries with ESRD that are receiving non-emergency BLS transport to and from renal dialysis treatment. While it is possible that a beneficiary who is not diagnosed with ESRD will require routine transport to and from renal dialysis treatment, it is highly unlikely. However, contractors have discretion to override or reverse the reduction on appeal if they deem it appropriate based on supporting documentation.

100-4, Chapter 15, 30.1.2

Coding Instructions for Paper and Electronic Claim Forms

Except as otherwise noted, beginning with dates of service on or after January 1, 2001, the following coding instructions must be used.

Origin

Electronic billers should refer to the Implementation Guide to determine how to report the origin information (e.g., the ZIP Code of the point of pickup). Beginning with the early implementation of version 5010 of the ASC X12 837 professional claim format on January 1, 2011, electronic billers are required to submit, in addition to the loaded ambulance trip's origin information (e.g., the ZIP Code of the point of pickup), the loaded ambulance trip's destination information (e.g., the ZIP code of the point of drop-off). Refer to the appropriate Implementation Guide to determine how to report the destination information. Only the ZIP Code of the point of pickup will be used to adjudicate and price the ambulance claim, not the point of drop-off. However, the point of drop-off is an additional reporting requirement on version 5010 of the ASC X12 837 professional claim format.

Where the CMS-1500 Form is used the ZIP code is reported in item 23. Since the ZIP Code is used for pricing, more than one ambulance service may be reported on the same paper claim for a beneficiary if all points of pickup have the same ZIP Code. Suppliers must prepare a separate paper claim for each trip if the points of pickup are located in different ZIP Codes.

Claims without a ZIP Code in item 23 on the CMS-1500 Form item 23, or with multiple ZIP Codes in item 23, must be returned as unprocessable. A/B MACs (B) use message N53 on the remittance advice in conjunction with reason code 16.

ZIP Codes must be edited for validity.

The format for a ZIP Code is five numerics. If a nine-digit ZIP Code is submitted, the last four digits are ignored. If the data submitted in the required field does not match that format, the claim is rejected.

Mileage

Generally, each ambulance trip will require two lines of coding, e.g., one line for the service and one line for the mileage. Suppliers who do not bill mileage would have one line of code for the service.

Beginning with dates of service on or after January 1, 2011, mileage billed must be reported as fractional units in the following situations:

- Where billing is by ASC X12 claims transaction (professional or institutional), and
- Where billing is by CMS-1500 paper form.

Electronic billers should see the appropriate Implementation Guide to determine where to report the fractional units. Item 24G of the Form CMS-1500 paper claim is used.

Fractional units are not required on Form CMS-1450

For trips totaling up to 100 covered miles suppliers must round the total miles up to the nearest tenth of a mile and report the resulting number with the appropriate HCPCS code for ambulance mileage. The decimal must be used in the appropriate place (e.g., 99.9).

For trips totaling 100 covered miles and greater, suppliers must report mileage rounded up to the next whole number mile without the use of a decimal (e.g., 998.5 miles should be reported as 999).

For trips totaling less than 1 mile, enter a "0" before the decimal (e.g., 0.9).

For mileage HCPCS billed on a the ASC X12 837 professional transaction or the CMS-1500 paper form only, contractors shall automatically default to "0.1" units when the total mileage units are missing.

Multiple Patients on One Trip

Ambulance suppliers submitting a claim using the ASC X12 professional format or the CMS-1500 paper form for an ambulance transport with more than one patient onboard must use the "GM" modifier ("Multiple Patients on One Ambulance Trip") for each service line item. In addition, suppliers are required to submit documentation to A/B MACs (Part B) to specify the particulars of a multiple patient transport. The documentation must include the total number of patients transported in the vehicle at the same time and the Health Insurance Claim Numbers (HICN) for each Medicare beneficiary. A/B/MACs (Part B) shall calculate payment amounts based on policy instructions found in Pub.100-02, Medicare Benefit Policy Manual, Chapter 10 – Ambulance Services, Section 10.3.10 – Multiple Patient Ambulance Transport.

Ambulance claims submitted on or after January 1, 2011, in version 5010 of the ASC X12 837 professional claim format require the presence of a diagnosis code and the absence of diagnosis code will cause the ambulance claim to not be accepted into the claims processing system. The presence of a diagnosis code on an ambulance claim is not required as a condition of ambulance payment policy. The adjudicative process does not take into account the presence (or absence) of a diagnosis code, but a diagnosis code is required on the ASC X12 837 professional claim format.

100-4, Chapter 15, 30.2

Fiscal Intermediary Shared System (FISS) Guidelines

For SNF Part A, the cost of medically necessary ambulance transportation to receive most services included in the RUG rate is included in the cost for the service. Payment for the SNF claim is based on the RUGs, which takes into account the cost of such transportation to receive the ancillary services.

Refer to Pub. 100-04, Medicare Claims Processing Manual, chapter 6 – SNF Inpatient Part A Billing, Section 20.3.1 – Ambulance Services, for additional information on SNF consolidated billing and ambulance transportation.

Refer to Pub. 100-04, Medicare Claims Processing Manual, chapter 3 – Inpatient Hospital Billing, section 10.5 – Hospital Inpatient Bundling, for additional information on hospital inpatient bundling of ambulance services.

In general, the A/B MAC (A) processes claims for Part B ambulance services provided by an ambulance supplier under arrangements with hospitals or SNFs. These providers bill A/B MACs (A) using only Method 2.

The provider must furnish the following data in accordance with A/B MAC (A) instructions. The A/B MAC (A) will make arrangements for the method and media for submitting the data:

- A detailed statement of the condition necessitating the ambulance service;
- A statement indicating whether the patient was admitted as an inpatient. If yes the name and address of the facility must be shown;
- Name and address of certifying physician;
- Name and address of physician ordering service if other than certifying physician;
- Point of pickup (identify place and completed address);
- Destination (identify place and complete address);
- Number of loaded miles (the number of miles traveled when the beneficiary was in the ambulance);

- Cost per mile;
- Mileage charge;
- Minimum or base charge; and
- Charge for special items or services. Explain.

A. General

The reasonable cost per trip of ambulance services furnished by a provider of services may not exceed the prior year's reasonable cost per trip updated by the ambulance inflation factor. This determination is effective with services furnished during Federal Fiscal Year (FFY) 1998 (between October 1, 1997, and September 30, 1998). Providers are to bill for Part B ambulance services using the billing method of base rate including supplies, with mileage billed separately as described below.

The following instructions provide billing procedures implementing the above provisions.

B. Applicable Bill Types

The appropriate type of bill (13X, 22X, 23X, 83X, and 85X) must be reported. For SNFs, ambulance cannot be reported on a 21X type of bill.

C. Value Code Reporting

For claims with dates of service on or after January 1, 2001, providers must report on every Part B ambulance claim value code A0 (zero) and the related ZIP Code of the geographic location from which the beneficiary was placed on board the ambulance in the Value Code field. The value code is defined as "ZIP Code of the location from which the beneficiary is initially placed on board the ambulance." Providers report the number in dollar portion of the form location right justified to the left of the dollar/cents delimiter.

More than one ambulance trip may be reported on the same claim if the ZIP Codes of all points of pickup are the same. However, since billing requirements do not allow for value codes (ZIP Codes) to be line item specific and only one ZIP Code may be reported per claim, providers must prepare a separate claim for a beneficiary for each trip if the points of pickup are located in different ZIP Codes.

For claims with dates of service on or after April 1, 2002, providers must report value code 32 (multiple patient ambulance transport) when an ambulance transports more than one patient at a time to the same destination. Providers must report value code 32 and the number of patients transported in the amount field as a whole number to the left of the delimiter.

NOTE: Information regarding the claim form locator that corresponds to the Value Code field is found in Pub.100-04, Medicare Claims Processing Manual, chapter 25 – Completing and Processing the Form CMS-1450 Data Set.

D. Revenue Code/HCPCS Code Reporting

Providers must report revenue code 054X and, for services provided before January 1, 2001, one of the following CMS HCPCS codes for each ambulance trip provided during the billing period:

A0030 (discontinued 12/31/2000); A0040 (discontinued 12/31/2000); A0050 (discontinued 12/31/2000); A0320 (discontinued 12/31/2000); A0322 (discontinued 12/31/2000); A0324 (discontinued 12/31/2000); A0326 (discontinued 12/31/2000); A0328, (discontinued 12/31/2000); or A0330 (discontinued 12/31/2000).

In addition, providers report one of A0380 or A0390 for mileage HCPCS codes. No other HCPCS codes are acceptable for reporting ambulance services and mileage. Providers report one of the following revenue codes:

0540;

0542;

0543;

0545;

0546; or

0548.

Do not report revenue codes 0541, 0544, or 0547.

For claims with dates of service on or after January 1, 2001, providers must report revenue code 540 and one of the following HCPCS codes for each ambulance trip provided during the billing period:

A0426; A0427;

A0428; A0429; A0430; A0431; A0432; A0433; or

A0434.

Providers using an ALS vehicle to furnish a BLS level of service report HCPCS code, A0426 (ALS1) or A0427 (ALS1 emergency), and are paid accordingly. In addition, all providers report one of the following mileage HCPCS codes: A0380; A0390; A0435; or A0436.

Since billing requirements do not allow for more than one HCPCS code to be reported for per revenue code line, providers must report revenue code 0540 (ambulance) on two separate and consecutive lines to accommodate both the Part B ambulance service and the mileage HCPCS codes for each ambulance trip provided during the billing period. Each loaded (e.g., a patient is onboard) 1-way ambulance trip must be reported with a unique pair of revenue code lines on the claim. Unloaded trips and mileage are NOT reported.

However, in the case where the beneficiary was pronounced dead after the ambulance is called but before the ambulance arrives at the scene: Payment may be made for a BLS service if a ground vehicle is dispatched or at the fixed wing or rotary wing base rate, as applicable, if an air ambulance is dispatched. Neither mileage nor a rural adjustment would be paid. The blended rate amount will otherwise apply. Providers report the A0428 (BLS) HCPCS code. Providers report modifier QL (Patient pronounced dead after ambulance called) in Form Locator (FL) 44 "HCPCS/Rates" instead of the origin and destination modifier. In addition to the QL modifier, providers report modifier QM or QN.

NOTE: Information regarding the claim form locator that corresponds to the HCPCS code is found in Pub. 100-04, Medicare Claims Processing Manual, Chapter 25 – Completing and Processing the Form CMS-1450 Data Set.

E. Modifier Reporting

See the above Section 30 (A) (Modifiers Specific to Ambulance Service Claims) for instructions regarding the usage of modifiers.

F. Line-Item Dates of Service Reporting

Providers are required to report line-item dates of service per revenue code line. This means that they must report two separate revenue code lines for every ambulance trip provided during the billing period along with the date of each trip. This includes situations in which more than one ambulance service is provided to the same beneficiary on the same day. Line-item dates of service are reported in the Service Date field.

NOTE: Information regarding the claim form locator that corresponds to the Service Date is found in Pub. 100-04, Medicare Claims Processing Manual, Chapter 25 – Completing and Processing the Form CMS-1450 Data Set.

G. Service Units Reporting

For line items reflecting HCPCS code A0030, A0040, A0050, A0320, A0322, A0324, A0326, A0328, or A0330 (services before January 1, 2001) or code A0426, A0427, A0428, A0429, A0430, A0431, A0432, A0433, or A0434 (services on and after January 1, 2001), providers are required to report in Service Units each ambulance trip provided during the billing period. Therefore, the service units for each occurrence of these HCPCS codes are always equal to one. In addition, for line items reflecting HCPCS code A0380 or A0390, the number of loaded miles must be reported. (See examples below.)

Therefore, the service units for each occurrence of these HCPCS codes are always equal to one. In addition, for line items reflecting HCPCS code A0380, A0390, A0435, or A0436, the number of loaded miles must be reported.

H. Total Charges Reporting

For line items reflecting HCPCS codes A0426, A0427, A0428, A0429, A0430, A0431, A0432, A0433, or A0434;

Providers are required to report in Total Charges the actual charge for the ambulance service including all supplies used for the ambulance trip but excluding the charge for mileage. For line items reflecting HCPCS code A0380, A0390, A0435, or A0436, report the actual charge for mileage.

NOTE: There are instances where the provider does not incur any cost for mileage, e.g., if the beneficiary is pronounced dead after the ambulance is called but before the ambulance arrives at the scene. In these situations, providers report the base rate ambulance trip and mileage as separate revenue code lines. Providers report the base rate ambulance trip in accordance with current billing requirements. For purposes of reporting mileage, they must report the appropriate HCPCS code, modifiers, and units as a separate line item. For the related charges, providers report $1.00 in FL48 for non-covered charges. A/B MACs (A) should assign remittance adjustment Group Code OA to the $1.00 non- covered mileage line, which in turn informs the beneficiaries and providers that they each have no liability.

Prior to submitting the claim to CWF, the A/B MAC (A) will remove the entire revenue code line containing the mileage amount reported in Non-covered Charges to avoid non-acceptance of the claim.

NOTE: Information regarding the claim form locator that corresponds to the Charges fields is found in Pub. 100-04, Medicare Claims Processing Manual, Chapter 25 – Completing and Processing the Form CMS-1450 Data Set.

EXAMPLES: The following provides examples of how bills for Part B ambulance services should be completed based on the reporting requirements above. These examples reflect ambulance services furnished directly by providers. Ambulance services provided under arrangement between the provider and an ambulance company are reported in the same manner except providers report a QM modifier instead of a QN modifier.

EXAMPLE 1: Claim containing only one ambulance trip:

Revenue Code	HCPCS/ Modifiers	Date of Service	Units	Total Charges
0540	A0428RHQN	082701	1 (trip)	100.00
0540	A0380RHQN	082701	4 (mileage)	8.00

EXAMPLE 2: Claim containing multiple ambulance trips:

For the hard copy Form CMS-1450, providers report as follows:

Revenue Code	HCPCS	Modifiers #1	#2	Date of Service	Units	Total Charges
0540	A0429	RH	QN	082801	1 (trip)	100.00
0540	A0380	RH	QN	082801	2 (mileage)	4.00
0540	A0330	RH	QN	082901	1 (trip)	400.00
0540	A0390	RH	QN	082901	3 (mileage)	6.00

EXAMPLE 3: Claim containing more than one ambulance trip provided on the same day:

For the hard copy CMS-1450, providers report as follows:

Revenue Code	HCPCS	Modifiers		Date of Service	Units	Total Charges
0540	A0429	RH	QN	090201	1 (trip)	100.00
0540	A0380	RH	QN	090201	2 (mileage)	4.00
0540	A0429	HR	QN	090201	1 (trip)	100.00
0540	A0380	HR	QN	090201	2 (mileage)	4.00

I. Edits

FISS edits to assure proper reporting as follows:

For claims with dates of service on or after January 1, 2001, each pair of revenue codes 0540 must have one of the following ambulance HCPCS codes - A0426, A0427, A0428, A0429, A0430, A0431, A0432, A0433, or A0434; and one of the following mileage HCPCS codes – A0435, A0436 or for claims with dates of service on or after April 1, 2002, A0425;

- For claims with dates of service on or after January 1, 2001, the presence of an origin and destination modifier and a QM or QN modifier for every line item containing revenue code 0540;
- The units field is completed for every line item containing revenue code 0540;
- For claims with dates of service on or after January 1, 2001, the units field is completed for every line item containing revenue code 0540;
- Service units for line items containing HCPCS codes A0426, A0427, A0428, A0429, A0430, A0431, A0432, A0433, or A0434 always equal "1"

For claims with dates of service on or after July 1, 2001, each 1-way ambulance trip, line- item dates of service for the ambulance service, and corresponding mileage are equal.

100-4, Chapter 15, 30.2.1

A/B MAC (A) Bill Processing Guidelines Effective April 1, 2002, as a Result of Fee Schedule Implementation

For SNF Part A, the cost of medically necessary ambulance transportation to receive most services included in the RUG rate is included in the cost for the service. Payment for the SNF claim is based on the RUGs, which takes into account the cost of such transportation to receive the ancillary services.

Refer to IOM Pub. 100-04, Medicare Claims Processing Manual, chapter 6 – SNF Inpatient Part A Billing, Section 20.3.1 – Ambulance Services for additional information on SNF consolidated billing and ambulance transportation.

Refer to IOM Pub. 100-04, Medicare Claims Processing Manual, chapter 3 – Inpatient Hospital Billing, section 10.5 – Hospital Inpatient Bundling, for additional information on hospital inpatient bundling of ambulance services.

In general, the A/B MAC (A) processes claims for Part B ambulance services provided by an ambulance supplier under arrangements with hospitals or SNFs. These providers bill A/B MACs (A) using only Method 2.

The provider must furnish the following data in accordance with A/B MAC (A) instructions. The A/B MAC (A) will make arrangements for the method and media for submitting the data:

A detailed statement of the condition necessitating the ambulance service;

- A statement indicating whether the patient was admitted as an inpatient. If yes the name and address of the facility must be shown;
- Name and address of certifying physician;
- Name and address of physician ordering service if other than certifying physician;
- Point of pickup (identify place and completed address);
- Destination (identify place and complete address);
- Number of loaded miles (the number of miles traveled when the beneficiary was in the ambulance);
- Cost per mile;
- Mileage charge;
- Minimum or base charge; and
- Charge for special items or services. Explain.

A. Revenue Code Reporting on Form CMS-1450

Providers report ambulance services under revenue code 540 in FL 42 "Revenue Code."

B. HCPCS Codes Reporting on Form CMS-1450

Providers report the HCPCS codes established for the ambulance fee schedule. No other HCPCS codes are acceptable for the reporting of ambulance services and mileage. The HCPCS code must be used to reflect the type of service the beneficiary received, not the type of vehicle used.

Providers must report one of the following HCPCS codes in FL 44 "HCPCS/Rates" for each base rate ambulance trip provided during the billing period:

A0426;

A0427;

A0428;

A0429;

A0430;

A0431;

A0432;

A0433; or

A0434.

These are the same codes required effective for services January 1, 2001.

In addition, providers must report one of HCPCS mileage codes:

A0425;

A0435; or

A0436.

Since billing requirements do not allow for more than one HCPCS code to be reported per revenue code line, providers must report revenue code 540 (ambulance) on two separate and consecutive line items to accommodate both the ambulance service and the mileage HCPCS codes for each ambulance trip provided during the billing period. Each loaded (e.g., a patient is onboard) 1-way ambulance trip must be reported with a unique pair of revenue code lines on the claim. Unloaded trips and mileage are NOT reported.

For Form CMS-1450 claims submission prior to August 1, 2011, providers code one mile for trips less than a mile. Miles must be entered as whole numbers. If a trip has a fraction of a mile, round up to the nearest whole number.

Beginning with dates of service on or after January 1, 2011, for Form CMS-1450 hard copy claims submissions August 1, 2011 and after, mileage must be reported as fractional units. When reporting fractional mileage, providers must round the total miles up to the nearest tenth of a mile and the decimal must be used in the appropriate place (e.g., 99.9).

For trips totaling less than 1 mile, enter a "0" before the decimal (e.g., 0.9).

100-4, Chapter 15, 30.2.4

Non-covered Charges on Institutional Ambulance Claims

Medicare law contains a restriction that miles beyond the closest available facility cannot be billed to Medicare. Non-covered miles beyond the closest facility are billed with HCPCS procedure code A0888 ("non-covered ambulance mileage per mile, e.g., for miles traveled beyond the closest appropriate facility"). These non-covered line items can be billed on claims also containing covered charges. Ambulance claims may use the –GY modifier on line items for such non-covered mileage, and liability for the service will be assigned correctly to the beneficiary.

The method of billing all miles for the same trip, with covered and non-covered portions, on the same claim is preferable in this scenario. However, billing the non-covered mileage using condition code 21 claims is also permitted, if desired, as long as all line items on the claims are non-covered and the beneficiary is liable. Additionally, unless requested by the beneficiary or required by specific Medicare policy, services excluded by statute do not have to be billed to Medicare.

When the scenario is point of pick up outside the United States, including U.S. territories but excepting some points in Canada and Mexico in some cases, mileage is also statutorily excluded from Medicare coverage. Such billings are more likely to be submitted on entirely non-covered claims using condition code 21. This scenario requires the use of a different message on the Medicare Summary Notice (MSN) sent to beneficiaries.

Another scenario in which billing non-covered mileage to Medicare may occur is when the beneficiary dies after the ambulance has been called but before the ambulance arrives. The –QL modifier should be used on the base rate line in this scenario, in place of origin and destination modifiers, and the line is submitted with covered charges. The –QL modifier should also be used on the accompanying mileage line, if submitted, with non-covered charges. Submitting this non-covered mileage line is optional for providers.

Non-covered charges may also apply is if there is a subsidy of mileage charges that are never charged to Medicare. Because there are no charges for Medicare to share in, the only billing option is to submit non-covered charges, if the provider bills Medicare at all (it is not required in such cases). These non-covered charges are unallowable, and should not be considered in settlement of cost reports. However, there is a difference in billing if such charges are subsidized, but otherwise would normally be charged to Medicare as the primary payer. In this latter case, CMS examination of existing rules relating to grants policy since October 1983, supported by Federal regulations (42CFR 405.423), generally requires providers to reduce their costs by the amount of grants and gifts restricted to pay for such costs. Thereafter, section 405.423 was deleted from the regulations.

Thus, providers were no longer required to reduce their costs for restricted grants and gifts, and charges tied to such grants/gifts/subsidies should be submitted as covered charges. This is in keeping with Congress's intent to encourage hospital philanthropy, allowing the provider receiving the subsidy to use it, and also requiring Medicare to share in the unreduced cost. Treatment of subsidized charges as non-covered Medicare charges serves to reduce Medicare payment on the Medicare cost report contrary to the 1983 change in policy.

Medicare requires the use of the –TQ modifier so that CMS can track the instances of the subsidy scenario for non-covered charges. The –TQ should be used whether the subsidizing entity is governmental or voluntary. The -TQ modifier is not required in the case of covered charges submitted when a subsidy has been made, but charges are still normally made to Medicare as the primary payer.

If providers believe they have been significantly or materially penalized in the past by the failure of their cost reports to consider covered charges occurring in the subsidy case, since Medicare had previous billing instructions that stated all charges in the case of a subsidy, not just charges when the entity providing the subsidy never charges another entity/primary payer, should be submitted as non-covered charges, they may contact their FI about reopening the reports in question for which the time period in 42 CFR 405.1885 has not expired. FIs have the discretion to determine if the amount in question warrants reopening. The CMS does not expect many such cases to occur.

Billing requirements for all these situations, including the use of modifiers, are presented in the chart below:

Mileage Scenario	HCPCS	Modifiers*	Liability	Billing	Remit. Requirements	MSN Message
STATUTE: Miles beyond closest facility, OR **Pick up point outside of U.S.	A0888 on line item for the non-covered mileage	-QM or –QN, origin/destination modifier, and –GY unless condition code 21 claim used	Beneficiary	Bill mileage line item with A0888 –GY and other modifiers as needed to establish liability, line item will be denied; OR bill service on condition code 21 claim, no –GY required, claim will be denied	Group code PR, reason code 96	16.10 "Medicare does not pay for this item or service"; OR, "Medicare no paga por este artículo o servicio"
Beneficiary dies after ambulance is called	Most appropriate ambulance HCPCS mileage code (i.e., ground, air)	–QL unless condition code –21 claim	Provider	Bill mileage line item with –QL as non-covered, line item will be denied	Group Code CO, reason code 96	16.58 "The provider billed this charge as non-covered. You do not have to pay this amount."; OR, "El proveedor facuró este cargo como no cubierto. Usted no tiene que pagar ests cantidad."
Subsidy or government owned Ambulance, Medicare NEVER billed***	A0888 on line item for the non-covered mileage	-QM or –QN, origin/destination modifier, and -TQ must be used for policy purposes	Provider	Bill mileage line item with A0888, and modifiers as non-covered, line item will be denied	Group Code CO, reason code 96	16.58 "The provider billed this charge as non-covered. You do not have to pay this amount."; OR, "El proveedor facuró este cargo como no cubierto. Usted no tiene que pagar ests cantidad."

*Current ambulance billing requirements state that either the –QM or –QN modifier must be used on services. The –QM is used when the "ambulance service is provided under arrangement by a provider of services," and the –QN when the "ambulance service is provided directly by a provider of services." Line items using either the –QM or–QN modifiers are not subject to the FISS edit associated with FISS reason code 31322 so that these lines items will process to completion. Origin/destination modifiers, also required by current instruction, combine two alpha characters: one for origin, one for destination, and are not non-covered by definition.

** This is the one scenario where the base rate is not paid in addition to mileage, and there are certain exceptions in Canada and Mexico where mileage is covered as described in existing ambulance instructions.

***If Medicare would normally have been billed, submit mileage charges as covered charges despite subsidies.

Medicare systems may return claims to the provider if they do not comply with the requirements in the table.

100-4, Chapter 15, 40

Medical Conditions List and Instructions

See http://www.cms.gov/Center/Provider-Type/Ambulances-Services-Center.html for a medical conditions list and instructions to assist ambulance providers and suppliers to communicate the patient's condition to Medicare contractors, as reported by the dispatch center and as observed by the ambulance crew. Use of the medical conditions list does not guarantee payment of the claim or payment for a certain level of service.

In addition to reporting one of the medical conditions on the claim, one of the transportation indicators may be included on the claim to indicate why it was necessary for the patient to be transported in a particular way or circumstance. The provider or supplier will place the transportation indicator in the "narrative" field on the claim. Information on the appropriate use of transportation indicators is also available at http://www.cms.gov/Center/ProviderType/Ambulances-Services-Center.html.

100-4, Chapter 16, 60.1.4

Coding Requirements for Specimen Collection

The following HCPCS codes and terminology must be used:

- 36415 –Collection of venous blood by venipuncture.
- P9615 –Catheterization for collection of specimen(s).

The allowed amount for specimen collection in each of the above circumstances is included in the laboratory fee schedule distributed annually by CMS.

100-4, Chapter 16, 60.2

Travel Allowance

In addition to a specimen collection fee allowed under §60.1, Medicare, under Part B, covers a specimen collection fee and travel allowance for a laboratory technician to draw a specimen from either a nursing home patient or homebound patient under §1833(h)(3) of the Act and payment is made based on the clinical laboratory fee schedule. The travel allowance is intended to cover the estimated travel costs of collecting a specimen and to reflect the technician's salary and travel costs.

The additional allowance can be made only where a specimen collection fee is also payable, i.e., no travel allowance is made where the technician merely performs a messenger service to pick up a specimen drawn by a physician or nursing home personnel. The travel allowance may not be paid to a physician unless the trip to the home, or to the nursing home was solely for the purpose of drawing a specimen. Otherwise travel costs are considered to be associated with the other purposes of the trip.

The travel allowance is not distributed by CMS. Instead, the carrier must calculate the travel allowance for each claim using the following rules for the particular Code. The following HCPCS codes are used for travel allowances:

Per Mile Travel Allowance (P9603)

- The minimum "per mile travel allowance" is $1.03. The per mile travel allowance is to be used in situations where the average trip to patients' homes is longer than 20 miles round trip, and is to be pro-rated in situations where specimens are drawn or picked up from non-Medicare patients in the same trip. - one way, in connection with medically necessary laboratory specimen collection drawn from homebound or nursing home bound patient; prorated miles actually traveled (carrier allowance on per mile basis); or

- The per mile allowance was computed using the Federal mileage rate plus an additional 45 cents a mile to cover the technician's time and travel costs. Contractors have the option of establishing a higher per mile rate in excess of the minimum ($1.03 a mile in CY 2015) if local conditions warrant it. The minimum mileage rate will be reviewed and updated in conjunction with the clinical lab fee schedule as needed. At no time will the laboratory be allowed to bill for more miles than are reasonable or for miles not actually traveled by the laboratory technician.

Example 1: In CY 2015, a laboratory technician travels 60 miles round trip from a lab in a city to a remote rural location, and back to the lab to draw a single Medicare patient's blood. The total reimbursement would be $61.80 (60 miles x $1.03 cents a mile), plus the specimen collection fee.

Example 2: In CY 2015, a laboratory technician travels 40 miles from the lab to a Medicare patient's home to draw blood, and then travels an additional 10 miles to a non-Medicare patient's home and then travels 30 miles to return to the lab. The total miles traveled would be 80 miles. The claim submitted would be for one half of the miles traveled or $41.20 (40 x $1.03), plus the specimen collection fee.

Flat Rate (P9604)

The CMS will pay a minimum of $10.30 (based on CY 2015) one way flat rate travel allowance. The flat rate travel allowance is to be used in areas where average trips are less than 20 miles round trip. The flat rate travel fee is to be pro-rated for more than one blood drawn at the same address, and for stops at the homes of Medicare and non-Medicare patients. The laboratory does the pro-ration when the claim is submitted based on the number of patients seen on that trip. The specimen collection fee will be paid for each patient encounter.

This rate is based on an assumption that a trip is an average of 15 minutes and up to 10 miles one way. It uses the Federal mileage rate and a laboratory technician's time of $17.66 an hour, including overhead. Contractors have the option of establishing a flat rate in excess of the minimum of $10.30, if local conditions warrant it. The minimum national flat rate will be reviewed and updated in conjunction with the clinical laboratory fee schedule, as necessitated by adjustments in the Federal travel allowance and salaries.

The claimant identifies round trip travel by use of the LR modifier

Example 3: A laboratory technician travels from the laboratory to a single Medicare patient's home and returns to the laboratory without making any other stops. The flat rate would be calculated as follows: 2 x $10.30 for a total trip reimbursement of $20.60, plus the specimen collection fee.

Example 4: A laboratory technician travels from the laboratory to the homes of five patients to draw blood, four of the patients are Medicare patients and one is not. An additional flat rate would be charged to cover the 5 stops and the return trip to the lab (6 x $10.30 = $61.80). Each of the claims submitted would be for $12.36 ($61.80/5 = $12.36). Since one of the patients is non-Medicare, four claims would be submitted for $12.36 each, plus the specimen collection fee for each.

Example 5: A laboratory technician travels from a laboratory to a nursing home and draws blood from 5 patients and returns to the laboratory. Four of the patients are on Medicare and one is not. The $10.30 flat rate is multiplied by two to cover the return trip to the laboratory (2 x $10.30 = $20.60) and then divided by five (1/5 of $20.60 = $4.12). Since one of the patients is non-Medicare, four claims would be submitted for $4.12 each, plus the specimen collection fee.

If a carrier determines that it results in equitable payment, the carrier may extend the former payment allowances for additional travel (such as to a distant rural nursing home) to all circumstances where travel is required. This might be appropriate, for example, if the carrier's former payment allowance was on a per mile basis. Otherwise, it should establish an appropriate allowance and inform the suppliers in its service area. If a carrier decides to establish a new allowance, one method is to consider developing a travel allowance consisting of:

- The current Federal mileage allowance for operating personal automobiles, plus a personnel allowance per mile to cover personnel costs based upon an estimate of average hourly wages and average driving speed.

Carriers must prorate travel allowance amounts claimed by suppliers by the number of patients (including Medicare and non-Medicare patients) from whom specimens were drawn on a given trip.

The carrier may determine that payment in addition to the routine travel allowance determined under this section is appropriate if:

- The patient from whom the specimen must be collected is in a nursing home or is homebound; and

- The clinical laboratory tests are needed on an emergency basis outside the general business hours of the laboratory making the collection.

- Subsequent updated travel allowance amounts will be issued by CMS via Recurring Update Notification (RUN) on an annual basis.

For electronic claims submissions prior to January 1, 2011, providers code one mile for trips less than a mile. Miles must be entered as whole numbers. If a trip has a fraction of a mile, round up to the nearest whole number.

Beginning with dates of service on or after January 1, 2011, for electronic claim submissions only, mileage must be reported as fractional units for trips totaling up to 100 covered miles. When reporting fractional mileage, providers must round the total miles up to the nearest tenth of a mile and the decimal must be used in the appropriate place (e.g., 99.9).

For trips totaling 100 covered miles and greater, providers must report mileage rounded up to the nearest whole number mile (e.g., 999) and not use a decimal when reporting whole number miles over 100 miles.

For trips totaling less than 1 mile, enter a "0" before the decimal (e.g., 0.9).

C. Modifier Reporting

Providers must report an origin and destination modifier for each ambulance trip provided and either a QM (Ambulance service provided under arrangement by a provider of services) or QN (Ambulance service furnished directly by a provider of services) modifier in FL 44 "HCPCS/Rates".

D. Service Units Reporting

For line items reflecting HCPCS codes A0426, A0427, A0428, A0429, A0430, A0431, A0432, A0433, or A0434, providers are required to report in "Service Units" for each ambulance trip provided. Therefore, the service units for each occurrence of these HCPCS codes are always equal to one. In addition, for line items reflecting HCPCS code A0425, A0435, or A0436, providers must also report the number of loaded miles.

E. Total Charges Reporting

For line items reflecting HCPCS codes A0426, A0427, A0428, A0429, A0430, A0431, A0432, A0433, or A0434, providers are required to report in Total Charges the actual charge for the ambulance service including all supplies used for the ambulance trip, but excluding the charge for mileage.

For line items reflecting HCPCS codes A0425, A0435, or A0436, providers are to report the actual charge for mileage.

NOTE: There are instances where the provider does not incur any cost for mileage, e.g., if the beneficiary is pronounced dead after the ambulance is called but before the ambulance arrives at the scene. In these situations, providers report the base rate ambulance trip and mileage as separate revenue code lines. Providers report the base rate ambulance trip in accordance with current billing requirements. For purposes of reporting mileage, they must report the appropriate HCPCS code, modifiers, and units. For the related charges, providers report $1.00 in non-covered charges. A/B MACs (A) should assign remittance adjustment Group Code OA to the $1.00 non-covered mileage line, which in turn informs the beneficiaries and providers that they each have no liability.

F. Edits (A/B MAC (A) Claims with Dates of Service On or After 4/1/02)

For claims with dates of service on or after April 1, 2002, FISS performs the following edits to assure proper reporting:

- Edit to assure each pair of revenue codes 540 have one of the following ambulance HCPCS codes - A0426, A0427, A0428, A0429, A0430, A0431, A0432, A0433, or A0434; and one of the following mileage HCPCS codes - A0425, A0435, or A0436.
- Edit to assure the presence of an origin, destination modifier, and a QM or QN modifier for every line item containing revenue code 540;
- Edit to assure that the unit's field is completed for every line item containing revenue code 540;
- Edit to assure that service units for line items containing HCPCS codes A0426, A0427, A0428, A0429, A0430, A0431, A0432, A0433, or A0434 always equal "1"; and
- Edit to assure on every claim that revenue code 540, a value code of A0 (zero), and a corresponding ZIP Code are reported. If the ZIP Code is not a valid ZIP Code

in accordance with the USPS assigned ZIP Codes, intermediaries verify the ZIP Code to determine if the ZIP Code is a coding error on the claim or a new ZIP Code from the USPS not on the CMS supplied ZIP Code File.

- Beginning with dates of service on or after April 1, 2012, edit to assure that only non-emergency trips (i.e., HCPCS A0426, A0428 [when A0428 is billed without modifier QL]) require an NPI in the Attending Physician field. Emergency trips do not require an NPI in the Attending Physician field (i.e., A0427, A0429, A0430, A0431, A0432, A0433, A0434 and A0428 [when A0428 is billed with modifier QL])

G. CWF (A/B MACs (A))

A/B MACs (A) report the procedure codes in the financial data section. They include revenue code, HCPCS code, units, and covered charges in the record. Where more than one HCPCS code procedure is applicable to a single revenue code, the provider reports each HCPCS code and related charge on a separate line, and the A/B MAC (A) reports this to CWF. Report the payment amount before adjustment for beneficiary liability in "Rate" and the actual charge in "Covered Charges."

100-4, Chapter 16, 70.8

Certificate of Waiver

Effective September 1, 1992, all laboratory testing sites (except as provided in 42CFR 493.3(b)) must have either a CLIA certificate of waiver, certificate for provider-performed microscopy procedures, certificate of registration, certificate of compliance, or certificate of accreditation to legally perform clinical laboratory testing on specimens from individuals in the United States.

The Food and Drug Administration approves CLIA waived tests on a flow basis. The CMS identifies CLIA waived tests by providing an updated list of waived tests to the Medicare contractors on a quarterly basis via a Recurring Update Notification. To be recognized as a waived test, some CLIA waived tests have unique HCPCS procedure codes and some must have a QW modifier included with the HCPCS code.

For a list of specific HCPCS codes subject to CLIA see

http://www.cms.hhs.gov/CLIA/downloads/waivetbl.pdf

100-4, Chapter 17, 80.4.1

Clotting Factor Furnishing Fee

The Medicare Modernization Act section 303(e)(1) added section 1842(o)(5)(C) of the Social Security Act which requires that, beginning January 1, 2005, a furnishing fee will be paid for items and services associated with clotting factor.

Beginning January 1, 2005, a clotting factor furnishing fee is separately payable to entities that furnish clotting factor unless the costs associated with furnishing the clotting factor is paid through another payment system.

The clotting factor furnishing fee is updated each calendar year based on the percentage increase in the consumer price index (CPI) for medical care for the 12-month period ending with June of the previous year. The clotting factor furnishing fees applicable for dates of service in each calendar year (CY) are listed below:

CY 2005 - 0.140 per unit

CY 2006 - 0.146 per unit

CY 2007 - 0.152 per unit

CY 2008 - 0.158 per unit

CY 2009 - 0.164 per unit

CY 2010 - 0.170 per unit

CY 2011 - 0.176 per unit

CY 2012 - 0.181 per unit

CY 2013 - 0.188 per unit

CY 2014 - 0.192 per unit

CY 2015 - 0.197 per unit

Annual updates to the clotting factor furnishing fee are subsequently communicated by a Recurring Update Notification.

CMS includes this clotting factor furnishing fee in the nationally published payment limit for clotting factor billing codes. When the clotting factor is not included on the Average Sales Price (ASP) Medicare Part B Drug Pricing File or Not Otherwise Classified (NOC) Pricing File, the contractor must make payment for the clotting factor as well as make payment for the furnishing fee.

100-4, Chapter 17, 90.3

Hospital Outpatient Payment Under OPPS for New, Unclassified Drugs and Biologicals After FDA Approval But Before Assignment of a Product-Specific Drug or Biological HCPCS Code

Section 621(a) of the MMA amends Section 1833(t) of the Social Security Act by adding paragraph (15), Payment for New Drugs and Biologicals Until HCPCS Code Assigned. Under this provision, payment for an outpatient drug or biological that is furnished as part of covered outpatient department services for which a product-specific HCPCS code has not been assigned shall be paid an amount equal to 95 percent of average wholesale price (AWP). This provision applies only to payments under the hospital outpatient prospective payment system (OPPS).

Beginning January 1, 2004, hospital outpatient departments may bill for new drugs and biologicals that are approved by the FDA on or after January 1, 2004, for which a product-specific HCPCS code has not been assigned. Beginning on or after the date of FDA approval, hospitals may bill for the drug or biological using HCPCS code C9399, Unclassified drug or biological.

Hospitals report in the ASC X12 837 institutional claim format in specific locations, or in the "Remarks" section of Form CMS-1450):

- the National Drug Code (NDC),
- the quantity of the drug that was administered, expressed in the unit of measure applicable to the drug or biological, and
- the date the drug was furnished to the beneficiary.

Contractors shall manually price the drug or biological at 95 percent of AWP. They shall pay hospitals 80 percent of the calculated price and shall bill beneficiaries 20 percent of the calculated price, after the deductible is met. Drugs and biologicals that are manually priced at 95 percent of AWP are not eligible for outlier payment.

HCPCS code C9399 is only to be reported for new drugs and biologicals that are approved by FDA on or after January 1, 2004, for which there is no HCPCS code that describes the drug.

100-4, Chapter 18, 10.1.2

Influenza Virus Vaccine

Effective for services furnished on or after May 1, 1993, the influenza virus vaccine and its administration is covered when furnished in compliance with any applicable State law. Typically, this vaccine is administered once a flu season. Medicare does not require for coverage purposes that a doctor of medicine or osteopathy order the vaccine. Therefore, the beneficiary may receive the vaccine upon request without a physician's order and without physician supervision. Since there is no yearly limit, contractors determine whether such services are reasonable and allow payment if appropriate.

See Pub. 100-02, Medicare Benefit Policy Manual, Chapter 15, Section 50.4.4.2 for additional coverage requirements for influenza virus vaccine.

100-4, Chapter 18, 10.2.1

Healthcare Common Procedure Coding System (HCPCS) and Diagnosis Codes

Vaccines and their administration are reported using separate codes. The following codes are for reporting the vaccines only

HCPCS	Definition
90653	Influenza virus vaccine, inactivated, subunit, adjuvanted, for intramuscular use
90654	Influenza virus vaccine, split virus, preservative-free, for intradermal use, for adults ages 18 – 64;
90655	Influenza virus vaccine, split virus, preservative free, for children 6-35 months of age, for intramuscular use;
90656	Influenza virus vaccine, split virus, preservative free, for use in individuals 3 years and above, for intramuscular use;
90657	Influenza virus vaccine, split virus, for children 6-35 months of age, for intramuscular use;
90660	Influenza virus vaccine, live, for intranasal use;
90661	Influenza virus vaccine, derived from cell cultures, subunit, preservative and antibiotic free, for intramuscular use
90662	Influenza virus vaccine, split virus, preservative free, enhanced immunogenicity via increased antigen content, for intramuscular use
90669	Pneumococcal conjugate vaccine, polyvalent, for children under 5 years, for intramuscular use
90670	Pneumococcal conjugate vaccine, 13 valent, for intramuscular use
90672	Influenza virus vaccine, live, quadrivalent, for intranasal use
90673	Influenza virus vaccine, trivalent, derived from recombinant DNA (RIV3), hemagglutinin (HA) protein only, preservative and antibiotic free, for intramuscular use
90685	Influenza virus vaccine, quadrivalent, split virus, preservative free, when administered to children 6-35 months of age, for intramuscular use
90686	Influenza virus vaccine, quadrivalent, split virus, preservative free, when administered to individuals 3 years of age and older, for intramuscular use

90687   Influenza virus vaccine, quadrivalent, split virus, when administered to children 6-35 months of age, for intramuscular use

90688   Influenza virus vaccine, quadrivalent, split virus, when administered to individuals 3 years of age and older, for intramuscular use

90732   Pneumococcal polysaccharide vaccine, 23-valent, adult or immunosuppressed patient dosage, for use in individuals 2 years or older, for subcutaneous or intramuscular use;

90739   Hepatitis B vaccine, adult dosage (2 dose schedule), for intramuscular use

90740   Hepatitis B vaccine, dialysis or immunosuppressed patient dosage (3 dose schedule), for intramuscular use;

90743   Hepatitis B vaccine, adolescent (2 dose schedule), for intramuscular use;

90744   Hepatitis B vaccine, pediatric/adolescent dosage (3 dose schedule), for intramuscular use;

90746   Hepatitis B vaccine, adult dosage, for intramuscular use; and

90747   Hepatitis B vaccine, dialysis or immunosuppressed patient dosage (4 dose schedule), for intramuscular use.

The following codes are for reporting administration of the vaccines only. The administration of the vaccines is billed using:

HCPCS   Definition

G0008   Administration of influenza virus vaccine;

G0009   Administration of pneumococcal vaccine; and

*G0010   Administration of hepatitis B vaccine.

*90471   Immunization administration. (For OPPS hospitals billing for the hepatitis B vaccine administration)

*90472   Each additional vaccine. (For OPPS hospitals billing for the hepatitis B vaccine administration)

NOTE: For claims with dates of service prior to January 1, 2006, OPPS and non-OPPS hospitals report G0010 for hepatitis B vaccine administration. For claims with dates of service January 1, 2006 until December 31, 2010, OPPS hospitals report 90471 or 90472 for hepatitis B vaccine administration as appropriate in place of G0010. Beginning January 1, 2011, providers should report G0010 for billing under the OPPS rather than 90471 or 90472 to ensure correct waiver of coinsurance and deductible for the administration of hepatitis B vaccine.

One of the following diagnosis codes must be reported as appropriate. If the sole purpose for the visit is to receive a vaccine or if a vaccine is the only service billed on a claim the applicable following diagnosis code may be used.

Diagnosis Code	Description
V03.82	Pneumococcus
V04.81**	Influenza
V06.6***	Pneumococcus and Influenza
V05.3	Hepatitis B

**Effective for influenza virus claims with dates of service October 1, 2003 and later.

***Effective October 1, 2006, providers may report diagnosis code V06.6 on claims for pneumococcus and/or influenza virus vaccines when the purpose of the visit was to receive both vaccines.

If a diagnosis code for pneumococcus, hepatitis B, or influenza virus vaccination is not reported on a claim, contractors may not enter the diagnosis on the claim. Contractors must follow current resolution processes for claims with missing diagnosis codes.

If the diagnosis code and the narrative description are correct, but the HCPCS code is incorrect, the carrier or intermediary may correct the HCPCS code and pay the claim. For example, if the reported diagnosis code is V04.81 and the narrative description (if annotated on the claim) says "flu shot" but the HCPCS code is incorrect, contractors may change the HCPCS code and pay for the flu vaccine. Effective October 1, 2006, carriers/AB MACs should follow the instructions in Pub. 100-04, Chapter 1, Section 80.3.2.1.1 (Carrier Data Element Requirements) for claims submitted without a HCPCS code.

Claims for hepatitis B vaccinations must report the I.D. Number of the referring physician. In addition, if a doctor of medicine or osteopathy does not order the influenza virus vaccine, the intermediary claims require:

- UPIN code SLF000 to be reported on claims submitted prior to May 23, 2008, when Medicare began accepting NPIs, only
- The provider's own NPI to be reported in the NPI field for the attending physician on claims submitted on or after May 23, 2008, when NPI requirements were implemented.

100-4, Chapter-18, 10.2.2.1

FI/AB MAC Payment for Pneumococcal Pneumonia Virus, Influenza Virus, and Hepatitis B Virus Vaccines and Their Administration

Payment for Vaccines

Payment for all of these vaccines is on a reasonable cost basis for hospitals, home health agencies (HHAs), skilled nursing facilities (SNFs), critical access hospitals (CAHs), and hospital-based renal dialysis facilities (RDFs). Payment for comprehensive outpatient rehabilitation facilities (CORFs), Indian Health Service hospitals (IHS), IHS CAHs and independent RDFs is based on 95 percent of the average wholesale price (AWP). Section 10.2.4 of this chapter contains information on payment of these vaccines when provided by RDFs or hospices. See §10.2.2.2 for payment to independent and provider-based Rural Health Centers and Federally Qualified Health Clinics.

Payment for these vaccines is as follows:

Facility	Type of Bill	Payment
Hospitals, other than Indian Health Service (IHS) Hospitals and Critical Access Hospitals (CAHs)	12x, 13x	Reasonable cost
IHS Hospitals	12x, 13x, 83x	95% of AWP
IHS CAHs	85x	95% of AWP
CAHs	85x	Reasonable cost
Method I and Method II		
Skilled Nursing Facilities	22x, 23x	Reasonable cost

Facility	Type of Bill	Payment
Home Health Agencies	34x	Reasonable cost
Comprehensive Outpatient Rehabilitation Facilities	75x	95% of AWP
Independent Renal Dialysis Facilities	72x	95% of AWP
Hospital-based Renal Dialysis Facilities	72x	Reasonable cost

Payment for Vaccine Administration

Payment for the administration of influenza virus and pneumococcal vaccines is as follows:

Facility	Type of Bill	Payment
Hospitals, other than IHS Hospitals and CAHs	12x, 13x	Outpatient Prospective Payment System (OPPS) for hospitals subject to OPPS Reasonable cost for hospitals not subject to OPPS
IHS Hospitals	12x, 13x, 83x	MPFS as indicated in guidelines below.
IHS CAHs	85x	MPFS as indicated in guidelines below.
CAHs	85x	Reasonable cost
Method I and II		
Skilled Nursing Facilities	22x, 23x	MPFS as indicated in guidelines below.
Home Health Agencies	35x	OPPS
Comprehensive Outpatient Rehabilitation Facilities	75x	MPFS as indicated in guidelines below.
Independent RDFs	72x	MPFS as indicated in guidelines below.
Hospital-based RDFs	72x	Reasonable cost

Guidelines for pricing pneumococcal and influenza virus vaccine administration under the MPFS.

Make reimbursement based on the rate in the MPFS associated with the CPT® code 90782 or 90471 as follows:

HCPCS code	Effective prior to March 1, 2003	Effective on and after March 1, 2003
G0008	90782	90471
G0009	90782	90471

See §10.2.2.2 for payment to independent and provider based Rural Health Centers and Federally Qualified Health Clinics.

Payment for the administration of hepatitis B vaccine is as follows:

Facility	Type of Bill	Payment
Hospitals other than IHS hospitals and CAHs	12x, 13x	Outpatient Prospective Payment System (OPPS) for hospitals subject to OPPS Reasonable cost for hospitals not subject to OPPS
IHS Hospitals	12x, 13x, 83x	MPFS as indicated in the guidelines below

Facility	Type of Bill	Payment
CAHs	85x	Reasonable cost
Method I and II		
IHS CAHs	85x	MPFS as indicated in the guidelines below
Skilled Nursing Facilities	22x, 23x	MPFS as indicated in the chart below
Home Health Agencies	34x	OPPS
Comprehensive Outpatient Rehabilitation Facilities	75x	MPFS as indicated in the guidelines below
Independent RDFs	75x	MPFS as indicated in the chart below
Hospital-based RDFs	72x	Reasonable cost

Guidelines for pricing hepatitis B vaccine administration under the MPFS.

Make reimbursement based on the rate in the MPFS associated with the CPT® code 90782 or 90471 as follows:

HCPCS code	Effective prior to March 1, 2003	Effective on and after March 1, 2003
G0010	90782	90471

See §10.2.2.2 for payment to independent and provider based Rural Health Centers and Federally Qualified Health Clinics.

100-4, Chapter-18, 10.2.5.2

Carrier/AB MAC Payment Requirements

Payment for pneumococcal, influenza virus, and hepatitis B vaccines follows the same standard rules that are applicable to any injectable drug or biological. (See chapter 17 for procedures for determining the payment rates for pneumococcal and influenza virus vaccines.)

Effective for claims with dates of service on or after February 1, 2001, §114, of the Benefits Improvement and Protection Act of 2000 mandated that all drugs and biologicals be paid based on mandatory assignment. Therefore, all providers of influenza virus and pneumococcal vaccines must accept assignment for the vaccine.

Prior to March 1, 2003, the administration of pneumococcal, influenza virus, and hepatitis B vaccines, (HCPCS codes G0008, G0009, and G0010), though not reimbursed directly through the MPFS, were reimbursed at the same rate as HCPCS code 90782 on the MPFS for the year that corresponded to the date of service of the claim.

Prior to March 1, 2003, HCPCS codes G0008, G0009, and G0010 are reimbursed at the same rate as HCPCS code 90471. Assignment for the administration is not mandatory, but is applicable should the provider be enrolled as a provider type "Mass Immunization Roster Biller," submits roster bills, or participates in the centralized billing program.

Carriers/AB MACs may not apply the limiting charge provision for pneumococcal, influenza virus vaccine, or hepatitis B vaccine and their administration in accordance with §§1833(a)(1) and 1833(a)(10)(A) of the Social Security Act (the Act.) The administration of the influenza virus vaccine is covered in the influenza virus vaccine benefit under §1861(s)(10)

(A) of the Act, rather than under the physicians' services benefit. Therefore, it is not eligible for the 10 percent Health Professional Shortage Area (HPSA) incentive payment or the 5 percent Physician Scarcity Area (PSA) incentive payment.

No Legal Obligation to Pay

Nongovernmental entities that provide immunizations free of charge to all patients, regardless of their ability to pay, must provide the immunizations free of charge to Medicare beneficiaries and may not bill Medicare. (See Pub. 100-02, Medicare Benefit Policy Manual, chapter 16.) Thus, for example, Medicare may not pay for influenza virus vaccinations administered to Medicare beneficiaries if a physician provides free vaccinations to all non-Medicare patients or where an employer offers free vaccinations to its employees. Physicians also may not charge Medicare beneficiaries more for a vaccine than they would charge non-Medicare patients. (See §1128(b)(6)(A) of the Act.) When an employer offers free vaccinations to its employees, it must also offer the free vaccination to an employee who is also a Medicare beneficiary. It does not have to offer free vaccinations to its non-Medicare employees.

Nongovernmental entities that do not charge patients who are unable to pay or reduce their charges for patients of limited means, yet expect to be paid if the patient has health insurance coverage for the services provided, may bill Medicare and expect payment.

Governmental entities (such as PHCs) may bill Medicare for pneumococcal, hepatitis B, and influenza virus vaccines administered to Medicare beneficiaries when services are rendered free of charge to non-Medicare beneficiaries.

100-4, Chapter-18, 10.3.1.1

Centralized Billing for Influenza Virus and Pneumococcal Vaccines to A/B MACs (B)

The CMS currently authorizes a limited number of providers to centrally bill for influenza virus and pneumococcal immunization claims. Centralized billing is an optional program available to providers who qualify to enroll with Medicare as the provider type "Mass Immunization Roster Biller," as well as to other individuals and entities that qualify to enroll as regular Medicare providers. Centralized billers must roster bill, must accept assignment, and must bill electronically.

To qualify for centralized billing, a mass immunizer must be operating in at least three payment localities for which there are three different contractors processing claims. Individuals and entities providing the vaccine and administration must be properly licensed in the State in which the immunizations are given and the contractor must verify this through the enrollment process.

Centralized billers must send all claims for influenza virus and pneumococcal immunizations to a single contractor for payment, regardless of the jurisdiction in which the vaccination was administered. (This does not include claims for the Railroad Retirement Board, United Mine Workers or Indian Health Services. These claims must continue to go to the appropriate processing entity.) Payment is made based on the payment locality where the service was provided. This process is only available for claims for the influenza virus and pneumococcal vaccines and their administration. The general coverage and coding rules still apply to these claims.

This section applies only to those individuals and entities that provide mass immunization services for influenza virus and pneumococcal vaccinations and that have been authorized

by CMS to centrally bill. All other providers, including those individuals and entities that provide mass immunization services that are not authorized to centrally bill, must continue to bill for these claims to their regular A/B MAC (B) per the instructions in §10.3.1 of this chapter.

The claims processing instructions in this section apply only to the designated processing contractor. However, all A/B MACs (B) must follow the instructions in §10.3.1.1.J, below, "Provider Education Instructions for All A/B MACs (B)."

A. Processing Contractor

The CMS central office will notify centralized billers of the appropriate contractor to bill when they receive their notification of acceptance into the centralized billing program.

B. Request for Approval

Approval to participate in the CMS centralized billing program is a two part approval process. Individuals and corporations who wish to enroll as a CMS mass immunizer centralized biller must send their request in writing. CMS will complete Part 1 of the approval process by reviewing preliminary demographic information included in the request for participation letter. Completion of Part 1 is not approval to set up vaccination clinics, vaccinate beneficiaries, and bill Medicare for reimbursement. All new participants must complete Part 2 of the approval process (Form CMS-855 Application) before they may set up vaccination clinics, vaccinate Medicare beneficiaries, and bill Medicare for reimbursement. If an individual or entity's request is approved for centralized billing, the approval is limited to 12 months from September to August 31 of the next year. It is the responsibility of the centralized biller to reapply for approval each year. The designated contractor shall provide in writing to CMS and approved centralized billers notification of completion and approval of Part 2 of the approval process. The designated contractor may not process claims for any centralized biller who has not completed Parts 1 and 2 of the approval process. If claims are submitted by a provider who has not received approval of Parts 1 and 2 of the approval process to participate as a centralized biller, the contractor must return the claims to the provider to submit to the A/B MAC (B) for payment.

C. Notification of Provider Participation to the Processing Contractor

Before September 1 of every year, CMS will provide the designated contractor with the names of the entities that are authorized to participate in centralized billing for the 12 month period beginning September 1 and ending August 31 of the next year.

D. Enrollment

Though centralized billers may already have a Medicare provider number, for purposes of centralized billing, they must also obtain a provider number from the processing contractor for centralized billing through completion of the Form CMS-855 (Provider Enrollment Application). Providers/suppliers are encouraged to apply to enroll as a centralized biller early as possible. Applicants who have not completed the entire enrollment process and received approval from CMS and the designated contractor to participate as a Medicare mass immunizer centralized biller will not be allowed to submit claims to Medicare for reimbursement.

Whether an entity enrolls as a provider type "Mass Immunization Roster Biller" or some other type of provider, all normal enrollment processes and procedures must be followed. Authorization from CMS to participate in centralized billing is dependent upon the entity's ability to qualify as some type of Medicare provider. In addition, as under normal enrollment procedures, the contractor must verify that the entity is fully qualified and certified per state requirements in each state in which they plan to operate.

The contractor will activate the provider number for the 12-month period from September 1 through August 31 of the following year. If the provider is authorized to participate in the centralized billing program the next year, the contractor will extend the activation of the provider number for another year. The entity need not re-enroll with the contractor every year. However, should there be changes in the states in which the entity plans to operate, the contractor will need to verify that the entity meets all state certification and licensure requirements in those new states.

E. Electronic Submission of Claims on Roster Bills

Centralized billers must agree to submit their claims on roster bills in an electronic media claims format. The processing contractor must provide instructions on acceptable roster billing formats to the approved centralized billers. Paper claims will not be accepted.

F. Required Information on Roster Bills for Centralized Billing

In addition to the roster billing instructions found in §10.3.1 of this chapter, centralized billers must provide on the claim the ZIP code (to determine the payment locality for the claim), and the provider of service/supplier's billing name, address, ZIP code, and telephone number. In addition, the NPI of the billing provider or group must be appropriately reported.

G. Payment Rates and Mandatory Assignment

The payment rates for the administration of the vaccinations are based on the Medicare Physician Fee Schedule (MPFS) for the appropriate year. Payment made through the MPFS is based on geographic locality. Therefore, payments vary based on the geographic locality where the service was performed.

The HCPCS codes G0008 and G0009 for the administration of the vaccines are not paid on the MPFS. However, prior to March 1, 2003, they must be paid at the same rate as HCPCS code 90782, which is on the MPFS. The designated contractor must pay per the correct MPFS file for each calendar year based on the date of service of the claim. Beginning March 1, 2003, HCPCS codes G0008, G0009, and G0010 are to be reimbursed at the same rate as HCPCS code 90471.

In order to pay claims correctly for centralized billers, the designated contractor must have the correct name and address, including ZIP code, of the entity where the service was provided.

The following remittance advice and Medicare Summary Notice (MSN) messages apply:

Claim adjustment reason code 16, "Claim/service lacks information which is needed for adjudication. At least one Remark Code must be provided (may be comprised of either the Remittance Advice Remark Code or NCPDP Reject Reason Code,

Remittance advice remark code MA114, "Missing/incomplete/invalid information on where the services were furnished."

MSN 9.4 - "This item or service was denied because information required to make payment was incorrect."

The payment rates for the vaccines must be determined by the standard method used by Medicare for reimbursement of drugs and biologicals. (See chapter 17 for procedures for determining the payment rates for vaccines.)

Effective for claims with dates of service on or after February 1, 2001, §114, of the Benefits Improvement and Protection Act of 2000 mandated that all drugs and biologicals be paid based on mandatory assignment. Therefore, all providers of influenza virus and pneumococcal vaccines must accept assignment for the vaccine. In addition, as a requirement for both centralized billing and roster billing, providers must agree to accept assignment for the administration of the vaccines as well. This means that they must agree to accept the amount that Medicare pays for the vaccine and the administration. Also, since there is no coinsurance or deductible for the influenza virus and pneumococcal benefit, accepting assignment means that Medicare beneficiaries cannot be charged for the vaccination.

H. Common Working File Information

To identify these claims and to enable central office data collection on the project, special processing number 39 has been assigned. The number should be entered on the HUBC claim record to CWF in the field titled Demonstration Number.

I. Provider Education Instructions for the Processing Contractor

The processing contractor must fully educate the centralized billers on the processes for centralized billing as well as for roster billing. General information on influenza virus and pneumococcal coverage and billing instructions is available on the CMS Web site for providers.

J. Provider Education Instructions for All A/B MACs (B)

By April 1 of every year, all A/B MACs (B) must publish in their bulletins and put on their Web sites the following notification to providers. Questions from interested providers should be forwarded to the central office address below. A/B MACs (B) must enter the name of the assigned processing contractor where noted before sending.

NOTIFICATION TO PROVIDERS

Centralized billing is a process in which a provider, who provides mass immunization services for influenza virus and pneumococcal pneumonia virus (PPV) immunizations, can send all claims to a single contractor for payment regardless of the geographic locality in which the vaccination was administered. (This does not include claims for the Railroad Retirement Board, United Mine Workers or Indian Health Services. These claims must continue to go to the appropriate processing entity.) This process is only available for claims for the influenza virus and pneumococcal vaccines and their administration. The administration of the vaccinations is reimbursed at the assigned rate based on the Medicare physician fee schedule for the appropriate locality. The vaccines are reimbursed at the assigned rate using the Medicare standard method for reimbursement of drugs and biologicals.

Individuals and entities interested in centralized billing must contact CMS central office, in writing, at the following address by June 1 of the year they wish to begin centrally billing.

Center for Medicare & Medicaid Services

Division of Practitioner Claims Processing

Provider Billing Group

7500 Security Boulevard

Mail Stop C4-10-07

Baltimore, Maryland 21244

By agreeing to participate in the centralized billing program, providers agree to abide by the following criteria.

CRITERIA FOR CENTRALIZED BILLING

- To qualify for centralized billing, an individual or entity providing mass immunization services for influenza virus and pneumococcal vaccinations must provide these services in at least three payment localities for which there are at least three different contractors processing claims.

- Individuals and entities providing the vaccine and administration must be properly licensed in the state in which the immunizations are given.

- Centralized billers must agree to accept assignment (i.e., they must agree to accept the amount that Medicare pays for the vaccine and the administration). Since there is no coinsurance or deductible for the influenza virus and pneumococcal benefit, accepting assignment means that Medicare beneficiaries cannot be charged for the vaccination, i.e., beneficiaries may not incur any out-of-pocket expense. For example, a drugstore may not charge a Medicare beneficiary $10 for an influenza virus vaccination and give the beneficiary a coupon for $10 to be used in the drugstore.

NOTE: The practice of requiring a beneficiary to pay for the vaccination upfront and to file their own claim for reimbursement is inappropriate. All Medicare providers are required to file claims on behalf of the beneficiary per §1848(g)(4)(A) of the Social Security Act and centralized billers may not collect any payment.

- The contractor assigned to process the claims for centralized billing is chosen at the discretion of CMS based on such considerations as workload, user-friendly software developed by the contractor for billing claims, and overall performance. The assigned contractor for this year is [Fill in name of contractor.]

- The payment rates for the administration of the vaccinations are based on the Medicare physician fee schedule (MPFS) for the appropriate year. Payment made through the MPFS is based on geographic locality. Therefore, payments received may vary based on the geographic locality where the service was performed. Payment is made at the assigned rate.

- The payment rates for the vaccines are determined by the standard method used by Medicare for reimbursement of drugs and biologicals. Payment is made at the assigned rate.

- Centralized billers must submit their claims on roster bills in an approved electronic format. Paper claims will not be accepted.

- Centralized billers must obtain certain information for each beneficiary including name, health insurance number, date of birth, sex, and signature. [Fill in name of contractor] must be contacted prior to the season for exact requirements. The responsibility lies with the centralized biller to submit correct beneficiary Medicare information (including the beneficiary's Medicare Health Insurance Claim Number) as the contractor will not be able to process incomplete or incorrect claims.

- Centralized billers must obtain an address for each beneficiary so that a Medicare Summary Notice (MSN) can be sent to the beneficiary by the contractor. Beneficiaries are sometimes confused when they receive an MSN from a contractor other than the contractor that normally processes their claims which results in unnecessary beneficiary inquiries to the Medicare contractor. Therefore, centralized billers must provide every beneficiary receiving an influenza virus or pneumococcal vaccination with the name of the processing contractor. This notification must be in writing, in the form of a brochure or handout, and must be provided to each beneficiary at the time he or she receives the vaccination.

- Centralized billers must retain roster bills with beneficiary signatures at their permanent location for a time period consistent with Medicare regulations. [Fill in name of contractor] can provide this information.

- Though centralized billers may already have a Medicare provider number, for purposes of centralized billing, they must also obtain a provider number from [Fill in name of contractor]. This can be done by completing the Form CMS-855 (Provider Enrollment Application), which can be obtained from [Fill in name of contractor].

- If an individual or entity's request for centralized billing is approved, the approval is limited to the 12 month period from September 1 through August 31 of the following year. It is the responsibility of the centralized biller to reapply to CMS CO for approval each year by June 1. Claims will not be processed for any centralized biller without permission from CMS.

- Each year the centralized biller must contact [Fill in name of contractor] to verify understanding of the coverage policy for the administration of the pneumococcal vaccine, and for a copy of the warning language that is required on the roster bill.

- The centralized biller is responsible for providing the beneficiary with a record of the pneumococcal vaccination.

- The information in items 1 through 8 below must be included with the individual or entity's annual request to participate in centralized billing:

1. Estimates for the number of beneficiaries who will receive influenza virus vaccinations;

2. Estimates for the number of beneficiaries who will receive pneumococcal vaccinations;

3. The approximate dates for when the vaccinations will be given;

4. A list of the states in which influenza virus and pneumococcal clinics will be held;

5. The type of services generally provided by the corporation (e.g., ambulance, home health, or visiting nurse);

6. Whether the nurses who will administer the influenza virus and pneumococcal vaccinations are employees of the corporation or will be hired by the corporation specifically for the purpose of administering influenza virus and pneumococcal vaccinations;

7. Names and addresses of all entities operating under the corporation's application;

8. Contact information for designated contact person for centralized billing program.

100-4, Chapter-18, 10.4.1

CWF Edits on FI/AB MAC Claims

In order to prevent duplicate payment by the same FI/AB MAC, CWF edits by line item on the FI/AB MAC number, the beneficiary Health Insurance Claim (HIC) number, and the date of service, the influenza virus procedure codes 90653, 90654, 90655, 90656, 90657, 90660, 90661, 90662, 90672, 90673,90685, 90686, 90687, or 90688 and the pneumococcal procedure codes 90669, 90670, or 90732, and the administration codes G0008 or G0009.

If CWF receives a claim with either HCPCS codes 90653, 90654, 90655, 90656, 90657, 90660, 90661, 90662, 90672, 90673,90685, 90686, 90687, or 90688 and it already has on record a claim with the same HIC number, same FI/AB MAC number, same date of service, and any one of those HCPCS codes, the second claim submitted to CWF rejects.

If CWF receives a claim with HCPCS codes 90669, 90670,or 90732 and it already has on record a claim with the same HIC number, same FI/AB MAC number, same date of service, and the same HCPCS code, the second claim submitted to CWF rejects when all four items match.

If CWF receives a claim with HCPCS administration codes G0008 or G0009 and it already has on record a claim with the same HIC number, same FI/AB MAC number, same date of service, and same procedure code, CWF rejects the second claim submitted when all four items match.

CWF returns to the FI/AB MAC a reject code "7262" for this edit. FIs/AB MACs must deny the second claim and use the same messages they currently use for the denial of duplicate claims.

100-4, Chapter-18, 10.4.2

CWF Edits on Carrier/AB MAC Claims

In order to prevent duplicate payment by the same carrier/AB MAC, CWF will edit by line item on the carrier/AB MAC number, the HIC number, the date of service, the influenza virus procedure codes 90653, 90654, 90655, 90656, 90657, 90660, 90661, 90662, 90672, 90673,90685, 90686, 90687, or 90688; the pneumococcal procedure codes 90669, 90670, or 90732; and the administration code G0008 or G0009.

If CWF receives a claim with either HCPCS codes 90653, 90654, 90655, 90656, 90657, 90660, 90661, 90662, 90672,90673,90685, 90686, 90687, or 90688 and it already has on record a claim with the same HIC number, same carrier/AB MAC number, same date of service, and any one of those HCPCS codes, the second claim submitted to CWF will reject.

If CWF receives a claim with HCPCS codes 90669, 90670,or 90732 and it already has on record a claim with the same HIC number, same carrier/AB MAC number, same date of service, and the same HCPCS code, the second claim submitted to CWF will reject when all four items match.

If CWF receives a claim with HCPCS administration codes G0008 or G0009 and it already has on record a claim with the same HIC number, same carrier/AB MAC number, same date of service, and same procedure code, CWF will reject the second claim submitted.

CWF will return to the carrier/AB MAC a specific reject code for this edit. Carriers/AB MACs must deny the second claim and use the same messages they currently use for the denial of duplicate claims.

In order to prevent duplicate payment by the centralized billing contractor and local carrier/AB MAC, CWF will edit by line item for carrier number, same HIC number, same date of service, the influenza virus procedure codes 90653, 90654, 90655, 90656, 90657, 90660, 90661, 90662, 90672, 90673, 90685, 90686, 90687, or 90688; the pneumococcal procedure codes

90669, 90670,or 90732; and the administration code G0008 or G0009.

If CWF receives a claim with either HCPCS codes 90653, 90654, 90655, 90656, 90657, 90660, 90661, 90662, 90672,90673, 90685, 90686, 90687, or 90688 and it already has on record a claim with a different carrier/AB MAC number, but same HIC number, same date of service, and any one of those same HCPCS codes, the second claim submitted to CWF will reject.

If CWF receives a claim with HCPCS codes 90669, 90670,or 90732 and it already has on record a claim with the same HIC number, different carrier/AB MAC number, same date of service, and the same HCPCS code, the second claim submitted to CWF will reject.

If CWF receives a claim with HCPCS administration codes G0008 or G0009 and it already has on record a claim with a different carrier/AB MAC number, but the same HIC number, same date of service, and same procedure code, CWF will reject the second claim submitted.

CWF will return a specific reject code for this edit. Carriers/AB MACs must deny the second claim. For the second edit, the reject code should automatically trigger the following Medicare Summary Notice (MSN) and Remittance Advice (RA) messages.

MSN: 7.2 –"This is a duplicate of a claim processed by another contractor. You should receive a Medicare Summary Notice from them."

Claim adjustment reason code 18 –duplicate claim or service

100-4, Chapter-18, 10.4.3

CWF A/B Crossover Edits for FI/AB MAC and Carrier/AB MAC Claims

When CWF receives a claim from the carrier/AB MAC, it will review Part B outpatient claims history to verify that a duplicate claim has not already been posted.

CWF will edit on the beneficiary HIC number; the date of service; the influenza virus procedure codes 90653, 90654, 90655, 90656, 90657, 90660, 90661, 90662, 90672, 90673,90685, 90686, 90687, or 90688; the pneumococcal procedure codes 90669, 90670, or 90732; and the administration code G0008 or G0009.

CWF will return a specific reject code for this edit. Contractors must deny the second claim and use the same messages they currently use for the denial of duplicate claims.

100-4, Chapter-18, 20

Mammography Services (Screening and Diagnostic)

A. Screening Mammography

Beginning January 1, 1991, Medicare provides Part B coverage of screening mammographies for women. Screening mammographies are radiologic procedures for early detection of breast cancer and include a physician's interpretation of the results. A doctor's prescription or referral is not necessary for the procedure to be covered. Whether payment can be made is determined by a woman's age and statutory frequency parameter. See Pub. 100-02, Medicare Benefit Policy Manual, chapter 15, section 280.3 for additional coverage information for a screening mammography.

Section 4101 of the Balanced Budget Act (BBA) of 1997 provides for annual screening mammographies for women over age 39 and waives the Part B deductible. Coverage applies as follows:

Age Groups	Screening Period
Under age 35	No payment allowed for screening mammography.
35-39	Baseline (pay for only one screening mammography performed on a woman between her 35th and 40th birthday)
Over age 39	Annual (11 full months have elapsed following the month of last screening

NOTE: Count months between screening mammographies beginning the month after the date of the examination. For example, if Mrs. Smith received a screening mammography examination in January 2005, begin counting the next month (February 2005) until 11 months have elapsed. Payment can be made for another screening mammography in January 2006.

B. Diagnostic Mammography

A diagnostic mammography is a radiological mammogram and is a covered diagnostic test under the following conditions:

- A patient has distinct signs and symptoms for which a mammogram is indicated;
- A patient has a history of breast cancer; or
- A patient is asymptomatic, but based on the patient's history and other factors the physician considers significant, the physician's judgment is that a mammogram is appropriate.
- Beginning January 1, 2005, Medicare Prescription Drug, Improvement, and Modernization Act (MMA) of 2003, §644, Public Law 108-173 has changed the way Medicare pays for diagnostic mammography. Medicare will pay based on the MPFS in lieu of OPPS or the lower of the actual change.

100-4, Chapter-18, 20.4

Billing Requirements –FI/A MAC Claims

Contractors use the weekly-updated MQSA file to verify that the billing facility is certified by the FDA to perform mammography services, and has the appropriate certification to perform the type of mammogram billed (film and/or digital). (See §20.1.) FIs/A/B MACs use the provider number submitted on the claim to identify the facility and use the MQSA data file to verify the facility's certification(s). FIs/A/B MACs complete the following activities in processing mammography claims:

- If the provider number on the claim does not correspond with a certified mammography facility on the MQSA file, then intermediaries/A/B MACs deny the claim.
- When a film mammography HCPCS code is on a claim, the claim is checked for a "1" film indicator.
- If a film mammography HCPCS code comes in on a claim and the facility is certified for film mammography, the claim is paid if all other relevant Medicare criteria are met.
- If a film mammography HCPCS code is on a claim and the facility is certified for digital mammography only, the claim is denied.
- When a digital mammography HCPCS code is on a claim, the claim is checked for "2" digital indicator.

- If a digital mammography HCPCS code is on a claim and the facility is certified for digital mammography, the claim is paid if all other relevant Medicare criteria are met.
- If a digital mammography HCPCS code is on a claim and the facility is certified for film mammography only, the claim is denied.

NOTE: The Common Working File (CWF) no longer receives the mammography file for editing purposes.

Except as provided in the following sections for RHCs and FQHCs, the following procedures apply to billing for screening mammographies:

The technical component portion of the screening mammography is billed on Form CMS-1450 under bill type 12X, 13X, 14X**, 22X, 23X or 85X using revenue code 0403 and HCPCS code 77057* (76092*).

The technical component portion of the diagnostic mammography is billed on Form CMS-1450 under bill type 12X, 13X, 14X**, 22X, 23X or 85X using revenue code 0401 and HCPCS code 77055* (76090*), 77056* (76091*).

Separate bills are required for claims for screening mammographies with dates of service prior to January 1, 2002. Providers include on the bill only charges for the screening mammography. Separate bills are not required for claims for screening mammographies with dates of service on or after January 1, 2002.

See separate instructions below for rural health clinics (RHCs) and federally qualified health centers (FQHCs).

* For claims with dates of service prior to January 1, 2007, providers report CPT® codes 76090, 76091, and 76092. For claims with dates of service January 1, 2007 and later, providers report CPT® codes 77055, 77056, and 77057 respectively.

** For claims with dates of service April 1, 2005 and later, hospitals bill for all mammography services under the 13X type of bill or for dates of service April 1, 2007 and later, 12X or 13X as appropriate. The 14X type of bill is no longer applicable. Appropriate bill types for providers other than hospitals are 22X, 23X, and 85X.

In cases where screening mammography services are self-referred and as a result an attending physician NPI is not available, the provider shall duplicate their facility NPI in the attending physician identifier field on the claim.

100-4, Chapter-18, 60.1

Payment

See the Medicare Benefit Policy Manual, Chapter 15, and the Medicare National Coverage Determinations (NCD) Manual, Chapter 1, Section 210.3 for Medicare Part B coverage requirements and effective dates of colorectal cancer screening services.

Effective for services furnished on or after January 1, 1998, payment may be made for colorectal cancer screening for the early detection of cancer. For screening colonoscopy services (one of the types of services included in this benefit) prior to July 2001, coverage was limited to high-risk individuals. For services July 1, 2001, and later screening colonoscopies are covered for individuals not at high risk.

The following services are considered colorectal cancer screening services:

- Fecal-occult blood test (FOBT),1-3 simultaneous determinations (guaiac-based);
- Flexible sigmoidoscopy;
- Colonoscopy; and,
- Barium enema

Effective for services on or after January 1, 2004, payment may be made for the following colorectal cancer screening service as an alternative for the guaiac-based FOBT, 1-3 simultaneous determinations:

- Fecal-occult blood test, immunoassay, 1-3 simultaneous determinations

Effective for claims with dates of service on or after October 9, 2014, payment may be made for colorectal cancer screening using the Cologuard™ multitarget stool DNA (sDNA) test:

- G0464 (this code has been deleted or 2017) (Colorectal cancer screening; stool-based DNA and fecal occult hemoglobin (e.g., KRAS, NDRG4 and BMP3).
- G0107 is discontinued and replaced with CPT® code 82270.

100-4, Chapter-18, 60.2

HCPCS Codes, Frequency Requirements, and Age Requirements (If Applicable)

Effective for services furnished on or after January 1, 1998, the following codes are used for colorectal cancer screening services:

- CPT® 82270* (HCPCS G0107*) - Colorectal cancer screening; fecal-occult blood tests, 1-3 simultaneous determinations;
- HCPCS G0104 - Colorectal cancer screening; flexible sigmoidoscopy;
- HCPCS G0105 - Colorectal cancer screening; colonoscopy on individual at high risk;
- HCPCS G0106 - Colorectal cancer screening; barium enema; as an alternative to HCPCS G0104, screening sigmoidoscopy;
- HCPCS G0120 - Colorectal cancer screening; barium enema; as an alternative to HCPCS G0105, screening colonoscopy.

Effective for services furnished on or after July 1, 2001, the following codes are added for colorectal cancer screening services:

- HCPCS G0121 - Colorectal cancer screening; colonoscopy on individual not meeting criteria for high risk.
- HCPCS G0122 - Colorectal cancer screening; barium enema (noncovered).

Effective for services furnished on or after January 1, 2004, the following code is added for colorectal cancer screening services as an alternative to CPT® 82270* (HCPCS G0107*):

- HCPCS G0328 - Colorectal cancer screening; immunoassay, fecal-occult blood test, 1-3 simultaneous determinations.

Effective for services furnished on or after October 9, 2014, the following code is added for colorectal cancer screening services:

- HCPCS G0464 – (this code has been deleted or 2017) Colorectal cancer screening; stool-based DNA and fecal occult hemoglobin (e.g., KRAS, NDRG4 and BMP3). Effective January 1, 2016, HCPCS G0464 is discontinued and replaced with CPT® 81528.

*NOTE: For claims with dates of service prior to January 1, 2007, physicians, suppliers, and providers report HCPCS G0107. Effective January 1, 2007, HCPCS G0107 is discontinued and replaced with CPT® 82270.

G0104 - Colorectal Cancer Screening; Flexible Sigmoidoscopy

Screening flexible sigmoidoscopies (HCPCS G0104) may be paid for beneficiaries who have attained age 50, when performed by a doctor of medicine or osteopathy at the frequencies noted below.

For claims with dates of service on or after January 1, 2002, contractors pay for screening flexible sigmoidoscopies (HCPCS G0104) for beneficiaries who have attained age 50 when these services were performed by a doctor of medicine or osteopathy, or by a physician assistant, nurse practitioner, or clinical nurse specialist (as defined in §1861(aa)(5) of the Social Security Act (the Act) and in the Code of Federal Regulations (CFR) at 42 CFR 410.74, 410.75, and 410.76) at the frequencies noted above. For claims with dates of service prior to January 1, 2002, Medicare Administrative Contractors (MACs) pay for these services under the conditions noted only when a doctor of medicine or osteopathy performs them.

For services furnished from January 1, 1998, through June 30, 2001, inclusive:

- Once every 48 months (i.e., at least 47 months have passed following the month in which the last covered screening flexible sigmoidoscopy was performed).

For services furnished on or after July 1, 2001:

- Once every 48 months as calculated above unless the beneficiary does not meet the criteria for high risk of developing colorectal cancer (refer to §60.3 of this chapter) and he/she has had a screening colonoscopy (HCPCS G0121) within the preceding 10 years. If such a beneficiary has had a screening colonoscopy within the preceding 10 years, then he or she can have covered a screening flexible sigmoidoscopy only after at least 119 months have passed following the month that he/she received the screening colonoscopy (HCPCS G0121).

NOTE: If during the course of a screening flexible sigmoidoscopy a lesion or growth is detected which results in a biopsy or removal of the growth; the appropriate diagnostic procedure classified as a flexible sigmoidoscopy with biopsy or removal along with modifier –PT should be billed and paid rather than HCPCS G0104.

HCPCS G0105 - Colorectal Cancer Screening; Colonoscopy on Individual at High Risk

Screening colonoscopies (HCPCS G0105) may be paid when performed by a doctor of medicine or osteopathy at a frequency of once every 24 months for beneficiaries at high risk for developing colorectal cancer (i.e., at least 23 months have passed following the month in which the last covered HCPCS G0105 screening colonoscopy was performed). Refer to §60.3 of this chapter for the criteria to use in determining whether or not an individual is at high risk for developing colorectal cancer.

NOTE: If during the course of the screening colonoscopy, a lesion or growth is detected which results in a biopsy or removal of the growth, the appropriate diagnostic procedure classified as a colonoscopy with biopsy or removal along with modifier –PT should be billed and paid rather than HCPCS G0105.

A. Colonoscopy Cannot be Completed Because of Extenuating Circumstances

1. A/B MACs (A)

When a covered colonoscopy is attempted but cannot be completed because of extenuating circumstances, Medicare will pay for the interrupted colonoscopy as long as the coverage conditions are met for the incomplete procedure. However, the frequency standards associated with screening colonoscopies will not be applied by the common working file (CWF). When a covered colonoscopy is next attempted and completed, Medicare will pay for that colonoscopy according to its payment methodology for this procedure as long as coverage conditions are met, and the frequency standards will be applied by CWF. This policy is applied to both screening and diagnostic colonoscopies. When submitting a facility claim for the interrupted colonoscopy, providers are to suffix the colonoscopy

Use of HCPCS codes with a modifier of –73 or –74 is appropriate to indicate that the procedure was interrupted. Payment for covered incomplete screening colonoscopies shall be consistent with payment methodologies currently in place for complete screening colonoscopies, including those contained in 42 CFR 419.44(b). In situations where a CAH has elected payment Method II for CAH patients, payment shall be consistent with payment methodologies currently in place as outlined in chapter 3 of this manual. As such, instruct CAHs that elect Method II payment to use modifier –53 to identify an incomplete screening colonoscopy (physician professional service(s) billed in revenue code 096X, 097X, and/or 098X). Such CAHs will also bill the technical or facility component of the interrupted colonoscopy in revenue code 075X (or other appropriate revenue code) using the -73 or -74 modifier as appropriate.

Note that Medicare would expect the provider to maintain adequate information in the patient's medical record in case it is needed by the contractor to document the incomplete procedure.

2. A/B MACs (B)

When a covered colonoscopy is attempted but cannot be completed because of extenuating circumstances (see chapter 12), Medicare will pay for the interrupted colonoscopy at a rate consistent with that of a flexible sigmoidoscopy as long as coverage conditions are met for the incomplete procedure. When a covered colonoscopy is next attempted and completed, Medicare will pay for that colonoscopy according to its payment methodology for this procedure as long as coverage conditions are met. This policy is applied to both screening and diagnostic colonoscopies. When submitting a claim for the interrupted colonoscopy, professional providers are to suffix the colonoscopy code with modifier of –53 to indicate that the procedure was interrupted. When submitting a claim for the facility fee associated with this procedure, ASCs are to suffix the colonoscopy code with modifier –73 or –74 as appropriate. Payment for covered screening colonoscopies, including that for the associated ASC facility fee when applicable, shall be consistent with payment for diagnostic colonoscopies, whether the procedure is complete or incomplete.

Note that Medicare would expect the provider to maintain adequate information in the patient's medical record in case it is needed by the contractor to document the incomplete procedure.

HCPCS G0106 - Colorectal Cancer Screening; Barium Enema; as an Alternative to HCPCS G0104, Screening Sigmoidoscopy

Screening barium enema examinations may be paid as an alternative to a screening sigmoidoscopy (HCPCS G0104). The same frequency parameters for screening sigmoidoscopies (see those codes above) apply. In the case of an individual aged 50 or over, payment may be made for a screening barium enema examination (HCPCS G0106) performed after at least 47 months have passed following the month in which the last screening barium enema or screening flexible sigmoidoscopy was performed. For example, the beneficiary received a screening barium enema examination as an alternative to a screening flexible sigmoidoscopy in January 1999. Start count beginning February 1999. The beneficiary is eligible for another screening barium enema in January 2003.

The screening barium enema must be ordered in writing after a determination that the test is the appropriate screening test. Generally, it is expected that this will be a screening double contrast enema unless the individual is unable to withstand such an exam. This means that in the case of a particular individual, the attending physician must determine that the estimated screening potential for the barium enema is equal to or greater than the screening potential that has been estimated for a screening flexible sigmoidoscopy for the same individual. The screening single contrast barium enema also requires a written order from the beneficiary's attending physician in the same manner as described above for the screening double contrast barium enema examination.

CPT® 82270* (HCPCS G0107*) - Colorectal Cancer Screening; Fecal-Occult Blood Test, 1-3 Simultaneous Determinations

Effective for services furnished on or after January 1, 1998, screening FOBT (CPT® 82270* (HCPCS G0107*) may be paid for beneficiaries who have attained age 50, and at a frequency of once every 12 months (i.e., at least 11 months have passed following the month in which the last covered screening FOBT was performed). This screening FOBT means a guaiac-based test for peroxidase activity, in which the beneficiary completes it by taking samples from two different sites of three consecutive stools. This screening requires a written order from the beneficiary's attending physician, or additionally, effective for dates of service on or after January 27, 2014, the beneficiary's attending physician assistant, nurse practitioner, or clinical nurse specialist. (The term "attending physician" is defined to mean a doctor of medicine or osteopathy (as defined in §1861(r)(1) of the Act) who is fully knowledgeable about the beneficiary's medical condition, and who would be responsible for using the results of any examination performed in the overall management of the beneficiary's specific medical problem.)

Effective for services furnished on or after January 1, 2004, payment may be made for an immunoassay-based FOBT (HCPCS G0328, described below) as an alternative to the guaiac-based FOBT, CPT® 82270* (HCPCS G0107*). Medicare will pay for only one covered FOBT per year, either CPT® 82270* (HCPCS G0107*) or HCPCS G0328, but not both.

*NOTE: For claims with dates of service prior to January 1, 2007, physicians, suppliers, and providers report HCPCS G0107. Effective January 1, 2007, HCPCS G0107 is discontinued and replaced with CPT® 82270.

HCPCS G0328 - Colorectal Cancer Screening; Immunoassay, Fecal-Occult Blood Test, 1-3 Simultaneous Determinations

Effective for services furnished on or after January 1, 2004, screening FOBT, (HCPCS G0328) may be paid as an alternative to CPT® 82270* (HCPCS G0107*) for beneficiaries who have attained age 50. Medicare will pay for a covered FOBT (either CPT® 82270* (HCPCS G0107*) or HCPCS G0328, but not both) at a frequency of once every 12 months (i.e., at least 11 months have passed following the month in which the last covered screening FOBT was performed).

Screening FOBT, immunoassay, includes the use of a spatula to collect the appropriate number of samples or the use of a special brush for the collection of samples, as determined by the individual manufacturer's instructions. This screening requires a written order from the beneficiary's attending physician, or, additionally, effective for claims with dates of service on or after January 27, 2014, the beneficiary's attending physician assistant, nurse practitioner, or clinical nurse specialist. (The term "attending physician" is defined to mean a doctor of medicine or osteopathy (as defined in §1861(r)(1) of the Act) who is fully knowledgeable about the beneficiary's medical condition, and who would be responsible for using the results of any examination performed in the overall management of the beneficiary's specific medical problem.)

HCPCS G0120 - Colorectal Cancer Screening; Barium Enema; as an Alternative to HCPCS G0105, Screening Colonoscopy

Screening barium enema examinations may be paid as an alternative to a screening colonoscopy (HCPCS G0105) examination. The same frequency parameters for screening colonoscopies (see those codes above) apply.

In the case of an individual who is at high risk for colorectal cancer, payment may be made for a screening barium enema examination (HCPCS G0120) performed after at least 23 months have passed following the month in which the last screening barium enema or the last screening colonoscopy was performed. For example, a beneficiary at high risk for developing colorectal cancer received a screening barium enema examination (HCPCS G0120) as an alternative to a screening colonoscopy (HCPCS G0105) in January 2000. Start counts beginning February 2000. The beneficiary is eligible for another screening barium enema examination (HCPCS G0120) in January 2002.

The screening barium enema must be ordered in writing after a determination that the test is the appropriate screening test. Generally, it is expected that this will be a screening double contrast enema unless the individual is unable to withstand such an exam. This means that in the case of a particular individual, the attending physician must determine that the estimated screening potential for the barium enema is equal to or greater than the screening potential that has been estimated for a screening colonoscopy, for the same individual. The screening single contrast barium enema also requires a written order from the beneficiary's attending physician in the same manner as described above for the screening double contrast barium enema examination.

HCPCS G0121 - Colorectal Screening; Colonoscopy on Individual Not Meeting Criteria for High Risk - Applicable On and After July 1, 2001

Effective for services furnished on or after July 1, 2001, screening colonoscopies (HCPCS G0121) performed on individuals not meeting the criteria for being at high risk for developing colorectal cancer (refer to §60.3 of this chapter) may be paid under the following conditions:

- At a frequency of once every 10 years (i.e., at least 119 months have passed following the month in which the last covered HCPCS G0121 screening colonoscopy was performed.)
- If the individual would otherwise qualify to have covered a HCPCS G0121 screening colonoscopy based on the above but has had a covered screening flexible sigmoidoscopy (HCPCS G0104), then he or she may have covered a HCPCS G0121 screening colonoscopy only after at least 47 months have passed following the month in which the last covered HCPCS G0104 flexible sigmoidoscopy was performed.

NOTE: If during the course of the screening colonoscopy, a lesion or growth is detected which results in a biopsy or removal of the growth, the appropriate diagnostic procedure classified as a colonoscopy with biopsy or removal along with modifier –PT should be billed and paid rather than HCPCS G0121.

HCPCS G0464 (Replaced with CPT® 81528) - Multitarget Stool DNA (sDNA) Colorectal Cancer Screening Test - Cologuard™

Effective for dates of service on or after October 9, 2014, colorectal cancer screening using the Cologuard™ multitarget sDNA test (G0464/81528) is covered once every 3 years for Medicare beneficiaries that meet all of the following criteria:

- Ages 50 to 85 years,
- Asymptomatic (no signs or symptoms of colorectal disease including but not limited to lower gastrointestinal pain, blood in stool, positive guaiac fecal occult blood test or fecal immunochemical test), and,
- At average risk of developing colorectal cancer (no personal history of adenomatous polyps, colorectal cancer, or inflammatory bowel disease, including Crohn's Disease and ulcerative colitis; no family history of colorectal cancers or adenomatous polyps, familial adenomatous polyposis, or hereditary nonpolyposis colorectal cancer).

See Pub. 100-03, Medicare National Coverage Determinations Manual, Chapter 1, Section 210.3, for complete coverage requirements.

Effective for claims with dates of service on or after October 9, 2014, providers shall report the following diagnosis codes when submitting claims for the Cologuard™ multitarget sDNA test:

ICD-9: V76.41 and V76.51, or,

ICD-10: Z12.11 and Z12.12

NOTE: Effective January 1, 2016, HCPCS G0464 is discontinued and replaced with CPT® 81528

HCPCS G0122 - Colorectal Cancer Screening; Barium Enema

The code is not covered by Medicare.

100-4, Chapter-18, 60.6

Billing Requirements for Claims Submitted to A/B MACs (A)

Follow the general bill review instructions in chapter 25. Hospitals use the ASC X12 837 institutional claim format to bill the A/B MAC (A) or the hardcopy Form CMS-1450 (UB-04). Hospitals bill revenue codes and HCPCS codes as follows:

Screening Test/ Procedure	Revenue Code	HCPCS Code	TOBs
FOBT	030X	82270*** (G0107***), G0328	12X, 13X, 14X**, 22X, 23X, 83X, 85X
Barium enema	032X	G0106, G0120, G0122	12X, 13X, 22X, 23X, 85X****
Flexible Sigmoidoscopy	*	G0104	12X, 13X, 22X, 23X, 85X****
Colonoscopy-high risk	*	G0105, G0121	12X, 13X, 22X, 23X, 85X****
Multitarget sDNA - CologuardTM	030X	(G0464*****), 81528*****	13X, 14X**, 85X

* The appropriate revenue code when reporting any other surgical procedure.

** 14X is only applicable for non-patient laboratory specimens.

*** For claims with dates of service prior to January 1, 2007, physicians, suppliers, and providers report HCPCS code G0107.

Effective January 1, 2007, HCPCS G0107, was discontinued and replaced with CPT® 82270.

**** CAHs that elect Method II bill revenue code 096X, 097X, and/or 098X for professional services and 075X (or other appropriate revenue code) for the technical or facility component.

***** Effective January 1, 2016, HCPCS G0464 is discontinued and replaced with CPT® 81528

Special Billing Instructions for Hospital Inpatients

When these tests/procedures are provided to inpatients of a hospital or when Part A benefits have been exhausted, they are covered under this benefit. However, the provider bills on TOB 12X using the discharge date of the hospital stay to avoid editing in the Common Working File (CWF) as a result of the hospital bundling rules.

100-4, Chapter-18, 80

Initial Preventive Physical Examination (IPPE)

(**NOTE:** For billing and payment requirements for the Annual Wellness Visit, see chapter 18, section 140, of this chapter.)

Background: Sections 1861(s)(2)(w) and 1861(ww) of the Social Security Act (and implementing regulations at 42 CFR 410.16, 411.15(a)(1), and 411.15(k)(11)) authorize coverage under Part B for a one-time initial preventive physical examination (IPPE) for new Medicare beneficiaries that meet certain eligibility requirements.

Coverage: As described in implementing regulations at 42 CFR 410.16, 411.15(a)(1), and 411.15(k)(11), the IPPE may be performed by a doctor of medicine or osteopathy as defined in section 1861 (r)(1) of the Social Security Act (the Act) or by a qualified nonphysician practitioner (NPP) (physician assistant, nurse practitioner, or clinical nurse specialist), not later than 12 months after the date the individual's first coverage begins under Medicare Part B. (See section 80.3 for a list of bill types of facilities that can bill A/B MACs for this service.)

The IPPE includes:

1. review of the individual's medical and social history with attention to modifiable risk factors for disease detection,

2. review of the individual's potential (risk factors) for depression or other mood disorders,

3. review of the individual's functional ability and level of safety;

4. an examination to include measurement of the individual's height, weight, body mass index, blood pressure, a visual acuity screen, and other factors as deemed appropriate, based on the beneficiary's medical and social history;

5. end-of-life planning, upon agreement of the individual.

6. education, counseling, and referral, as deemed appropriate, based on the results of the review and evaluation services described in the previous 5 elements, and

7. education, counseling, and referral including a brief written plan (e.g., a checklist or alternative) provided to the individual for obtaining appropriate screening and other preventive services, which are separately covered under Medicare Part B.

Medicare will pay for only one IPPE per beneficiary per lifetime. The Common Working File (CWF) will edit for this benefit.

The IPPE does not include other preventive services that are currently separately covered and paid under Medicare Part B. (That is: pneumococcal, influenza and hepatitis B vaccines and their administration, screening mammography, screening pap smear and screening pelvic examinations, prostate cancer screening tests, colorectal cancer screening tests, diabetes outpatient self-management training services, bone mass measurements, glaucoma screening, medical nutrition therapy for individuals with diabetes or renal disease, cardiovascular screening blood tests, diabetes screening tests, screening ultrasound for abdominal aortic aneurysms, an electrocardiogram, and additional preventive services covered under Medicare Part B through the Medicare national coverage determination process.)

For the physician/practitioner billing correct coding and payment policy, refer to chapter 12, section 30.6.1.1, of this manual.

100-4, Chapter-18, 80.1

Healthcare Common Procedure Coding System (HCPCS) Coding for the IPPE

The HCPCS codes listed below were developed for the IPPE benefit effective January 1, 2005, for individuals whose initial enrollment is on or after January 1, 2005.

G0344: Initial preventive physical examination; face-to-face visit, services limited to new beneficiary during the first 6 months of Medicare enrollment

Short Descriptor: Initial Preventive Exam

G0366: Electrocardiogram, routine ECG with 12 leads; performed as a component of the initial preventive examination with interpretation and report

Short Descriptor: EKG for initial prevent exam

G0367: tracing only, without interpretation and report, performed as a component of the initial preventive examination

Short Descriptor: EKG tracing for initial prev

G0368: interpretation and report only, performed as a component of the initial preventive examination

Short Descriptor: EKG interpret & report preve

The following new HCPCS codes were developed for the IPPE benefit effective January 1, 2009, and replaced codes G0344, G0366, G0367, and G0368 shown above beginning with dates of service on or after January 1, 2009:

G0402: Initial preventive physical examination; face-to-face visit, services limited to new beneficiary during the first 12 months of Medicare enrollment

>*Short Descriptor:* Initial Preventive exam

G0403: Electrocardiogram, routine ECG with 12 leads; performed as a screening for the initial preventive physical examination with interpretation and report

>*Short Descriptor:* EKG for initial prevent exam

G0404: Electrocardiogram, routine ECG with 12 leads; tracing only, without interpretation and report, performed as a screening for the initial preventive physical examination

>*Short Descriptor:* EKG tracing for initial prev

G0405: Electrocardiogram, routine ECG with 12 leads; interpretation and report only, performed as a screening for the initial preventive physical examination

>*Short Descriptor:* EKG interpret & report preve

100-4, Chapter-18, 80.2

A/B Medicare Administrative Contractor (MAC) (B)and Contractor Billing Requirements

Effective for dates of service on and after January 1, 2005, through December 31, 2008, contractors shall recognize the HCPCS codes G0344, G0366, G0367, and G0368 shown above in §80.1 for an IPPE. The type of service (TOS) for each of these codes is as follows:

G0344: TOS = 1

G0366: TOS = 5

G0367: TOS = 5

G0368: TOS = 5

Contractors shall pay physicians or qualified nonphysician practitioners for only one IPPE performed not later than 6 months after the date the individual's first coverage begins under Medicare Part B, but only if that coverage period begins on or after January 1, 2005.

Effective for dates of service on and after January 1, 2009, contractors shall recognize the HCPCS codes G0402, G0403, G0404, and G0405 shown above in §80.1 for an IPPE. The TOS for each of these codes is as follows:

G0402: TOS = 1

G0403: TOS = 5

G0404: TOS = 5

G0405: TOS = 5

Under the MIPPA of 2008, contractors shall pay physicians or qualified nonphysician practitioners for only one IPPE performed not later than 12 months after the date the individual's first coverage begins under Medicare Part B only if that coverage period begins on or after January 1, 2009.

Contractors shall allow payment for a medically necessary Evaluation and Management (E/M) service at the same visit as the IPPE when it is clinically appropriate. Physicians and qualified nonphysician practitioners shall use CPT® codes 99201-99215 to report an E/M with CPT® modifier 25 to indicate that the E/M is a significant, separately identifiable service from the IPPE code reported (G0344 or G0402, whichever applies based on the date the IPPE is performed). Refer to chapter 12, §30.6.1.1, of this manual for the physician/practitioner billing correct coding and payment policy regarding E/M services.

If the EKG performed as a component of the IPPE is not performed by the primary physician or qualified NPP during the IPPE visit, another physician or entity may perform and/or interpret the EKG. The referring physician or qualified NPP needs to make sure that the performing physician or entity bills the appropriate G code for the screening EKG, and not a CPT® code in the 93000 series. **Both the IPPE and the EKG should be billed in order for the beneficiary to receive the complete IPPE service.** Effective for dates of service on and after January 1, 2009, the screening EKG is optional and is no longer a mandated service of an IPPE if performed as a result of a referral from an IPPE.

Should the same physician or NPP need to perform an additional medically necessary EKG in the 93000 series on the same day as the IPPE, report the appropriate EKG CPT® code(s) with modifier 59, indicating that the EKG is a distinct procedural service.

Physicians or qualified nonphysician practitioners shall bill the contractor the appropriate HCPCS codes for IPPE. The HCPCS codes for an IPPE and screening EKG are paid under the Medicare Physician Fee Schedule (MPFS). See §1.3 of this chapter for waiver of cost sharing requirements of coinsurance, copayment and deductible for furnished preventive services available in Medicare.

100-4, Chapter-18, 80.3.3

Outpatient Prospective Payment System (OPPS) Hospital Billing

Hospitals subject to OPPS (TOBs 12X and 13X) must use modifier -25 when billing the IPPE G0344 along with the technical component of the EKG, G0367, on the same claim. The same is true when billing IPPE code G0402 along with the technical component of the screening EKG, code G0404. This is due to an OPPS Outpatient Code Editor (OCE) which contains an edit that requires a modifier -25 on any evaluation and management (E/M) HCPCS code if there is also a status "S" or "T" HCPCS procedure code on the claim.

100-4, Chapter-18, 80.4

Coinsurance and Deductible

The Medicare deductible and coinsurance apply for the IPPE provided before January 1, 2009.

The Medicare deductible is waived effective for the IPPE provided on or after January 1, 2009. Coinsurance continues to apply for the IPPE provided on or after January 1, 2009.

As a result of the Affordable Care Act, effective for the IPPE provided on or after January 1, 2011, the Medicare deductible and coinsurance (for HCPCS code G0402 only) are waived.

100-4, Chapter-18, 120.1

Coding and Payment of DSMT Services

The following HCPCS codes are used to report DSMT:

- G0108-Diabetes outpatient self-management training services, individual, per 30 minutes.
- G0109 -Diabetes outpatient self-management training services, group session (2 or more), per 30 minutes.

The type of service for these codes is 1.

Payment to physicians and providers for outpatient DSMT is made as follows:

Type of Facility	Payment Method	Type of Bill
Physician (billed to the carrier)	MPFS	NA
Hospitals subject to OPPS	MPFS	12X, 13X
Method I and Method II Critical Access Hospitals (CAHs) (technical services)	101% of reasonable cost	12X and 85X
Indian Health Service (IHS) providers billing hospital outpatient Part B	OMB-approved outpatient per visit all inclusive rate (AIR)	13X
IHS providers billing inpatient Part B	All-inclusive inpatient ancillary per diem rate	12X
IHS CAHs billing outpatient Part B	101% of the all-inclusive facility specific per visit rate	85X
IHS CAHs billing inpatient Part B	101% of the all-inclusive facility specific per diem rate	12X
FQHCs*	All-inclusive encounter rate with other qualified services. Separate visit payment available with HCPCS.	73X
Skilled Nursing Facilities **	MPFS non-facility rate	22X, 23X
Maryland Hospitals under jurisdiction of the Health Services Cost Review Commission (HSCRC)	94% of provider submitted charges in accordance with the terms of the Maryland Waiver	12X, 13X
Home Health Agencies (can be billed only if the service is provided outside of the treatment plan)	MPFS non-facility rate	34X

* Effective January 1, 2006, payment for DSMT provided in an FQHC that meets all of the requirements as above, may be made in addition to one other visit the beneficiary had during the same day, if this qualifying visit is billed on TOB 73X, with HCPCS G0108 or G0109, and revenue codes 0520, 0521, 0522, 0524, 0525, 0527, 0528, or 0900.

** The SNF consolidated billing provision allows separate part B payment for training services for beneficiaries that are in skilled Part A SNF stays, however, the SNF must submit these services on a 22 bill type. Training services provided by other provider types must be reimbursed by X the SNF.

NOTE: An ESRD facility is a reasonable site for this service, however, because it is required to provide dietician and nutritional services as part of the care covered in the composite rate, ESRD facilities are not allowed to bill for it separately and do not receive separate reimbursement. Likewise, an RHC is a reasonable site for this service, however it must be provided in an RHC with other qualifying services and paid at the all-inclusive encounter rate.

Deductible and co-insurance apply.

100-4, Chapter-18, 130.1

Healthcare Common Procedure Coding System (HCPCS) for HIV Screening Tests

Effective for claims with dates of service on and after December 8, 2009, implemented with the April 5, 2010, IOCE, the following HCPCS codes are to be billed for HIV screening:

- G0432- Infectious agent antibody detection by enzyme immunoassay (EIA) technique, HIV-1 and/or HIV-2, screening,
- G0433 - Infectious agent antibody detection by enzyme-linked immunosorbent assay (ELISA) technique, HIV-1 and/or HIV-2, screening, and,
- G0435 -Infectious agent antibody detection by rapid antibody test, HIV-1 and/or HIV-2, screening.

100-4, Chapter-18, 130.2

Billing Requirements

Effective for dates of service December 8, 2009, and later, contractors shall recognize the above HCPCS codes for HIV screening.

Medicare contractors shall pay for voluntary HIV screening as follows in accordance with Pub. 100-03, Medicare National Coverage Determinations Manual, sections 190.14 and 210.7:

- A maximum of once annually for beneficiaries at increased risk for HIV infection (11 full months must elapse following the month the previous test was performed in order for the subsequent test to be covered), and,
- A maximum of three times per term of pregnancy for pregnant Medicare beneficiaries beginning with the date of the first test when ordered by the woman's clinician.

Claims that are submitted for HIV screening shall be submitted in the following manner:

HCPCS code G0432, G0433, or G0435 is reported with the following diagnosis codes.

Diagnoses for beneficiaries reporting increased risk factors:

- If ICD-9-CM applies claims shall contain V73.89 (special screening for other specified viral disease) as primary, and V69.8 (other problems related to lifestyle), as secondary.
- If ICD-10-CM applies claims shall contain Z11.4 (encounter for screening for HIV) as primary, and Z72.89 (other problems related to lifestyle) as secondary.

Diagnoses for beneficiaries not reporting increased risk factors:

- If ICD-9-CM applies claims shall contain diagnosis code V73.89 only.
- If ICD-10-CM applies claims shall contain Z11.4 only.

Diagnoses for pregnant beneficiaries which allow for more frequent screening:

- If ICD-9-CM applies claims shall contain diagnosis code V73.89 as primary, and one of V22.0 (supervision of normal first pregnancy), V22.1 (supervision of other normal pregnancy), or V23.9 (supervision of unspecified high-risk pregnancy), as secondary
- If ICD-10-CM applies claims shall contain diagnosis code Z11.4 (encounter for screening for human immunodeficiency virus (HIV) as primary, and one of the following as secondary:

ICD-10-CM code	Description
Z34.00	Encounter for supervision of normal first pregnancy, unspecified trimester
Z34.01	Encounter for supervision of normal first pregnancy, first trimester

ICD-10-CM code	Description
Z34.02	Encounter for supervision of normal first pregnancy, second trimester
Z34.03	Encounter for supervision of normal first pregnancy, third trimester
Z34.80	Encounter for supervision of other normal pregnancy, unspecified trimester
Z34.81	Encounter for supervision of other normal pregnancy, first trimester
Z34.82	Encounter for supervision of other normal pregnancy, second trimester
Z34.83	Encounter for supervision of other normal pregnancy, third trimester
Z34.90	Encounter for supervision of normal pregnancy, unspecified, unspecified trimester
Z34.91	Encounter for supervision of normal pregnancy, unspecified, first trimester
Z34.92	Encounter for supervision of normal pregnancy, unspecified, second trimester
Z34.93	Encounter for supervision of normal pregnancy, unspecified, third trimester
O09.90	Supervision of high risk pregnancy, unspecified, unspecified trimester
O09.91	Supervision of high risk pregnancy, unspecified, first trimester
O09.92	Supervision of high risk pregnancy, unspecified, second trimester
O09.93	Supervision of high risk pregnancy, unspecified, third trimester

100-4, Chapter-18, 130.3

Payment Method

Payment for HIV screening is under the Medicare Clinical Laboratory Fee Schedule for TOBs 12X, 13X, 14X, 22X, and 23X beginning January 1, 2011. For TOB 85X payment is based on reasonable cost. Deductible and coinsurance do not apply. Between December 8, 2009, and April 4, 2010, these services can be billed with unlisted procedure code 87999. Between April 5, 2010, and January 1, 2011, the G codes will be contractor priced.

100-4, Chapter-18, 130.4

Types of Bill (TOBs) and Revenue Codes

The applicable bill types for HIV screening are: 12X, 13X, 14X, 22X, 23X, and 85X. (Effective April 1, 2006, TOB 14X is for non-patient laboratory specimens.)

Use revenue code 030X (laboratory, clinical diagnostic)

100-4, Chapter-18, 130, 130.5

Diagnosis Code Reporting

A claim that is submitted for HIV screening shall be submitted with one or more of the following diagnosis codes in the header and pointed to the line item:

A. Increased Risk Factor Reported

- ICD-9-CM - V73.89 as primary and V69.8, or V69.2 as secondary.

- ICD-10-CM - Z11.4 as primary and Z72.89, Z72.51, Z72.52, orZ72.53 as secondary

B. Increased risk factors are NOT reported:

- ICD-9-CM - V73.89 as primary only.
- ICD-10-CM - Z11.4 as primary only.

C. Pregnant Medicare beneficiaries:

- ICD-9-CM - The following diagnosis codes shall be submitted in addition to V73.89 to allow for more frequent screening than once per 12-month period:

    V22.0 - Supervision of normal first pregnancy, or,

    V22.1 - Supervision of other normal pregnancy, or,

    V23.9 - Supervision of unspecified high-risk pregnancy).

- ICD-10-CM - The following diagnosis codes shall be submitted in addition to Z11.4 to allow for more frequent screening than once per 12-month period:

Code	Description
Z34.00	Encounter for supervision of normal first pregnancy, unspecified trimester
Z34.01	Encounter for supervision of normal first pregnancy, first trimester
Z34.02	Encounter for supervision of normal first pregnancy, second trimester
Z34.03	Encounter for supervision of normal first pregnancy, third trimester
Z34.80	Encounter for supervision of other normal pregnancy, unspecified trimester
Z34.81	Encounter for supervision of other normal pregnancy, first trimester
Z34.82	Encounter for supervision of other normal pregnancy, second trimester
Z34.83	Encounter for supervision of other normal pregnancy, third trimester
Z34.90	Encounter for supervision of normal pregnancy, unspecified, unspecified trimester
Z34.91	Encounter for supervision of normal pregnancy, unspecified, first trimester
Z34.92	Encounter for supervision of normal pregnancy, unspecified, second trimester
Z34.93	Encounter for supervision of normal pregnancy, unspecified, third trimester
O09.90	Supervision of high risk pregnancy, unspecified, unspecified trimester
O09.91	Supervision of high risk pregnancy, unspecified, first trimester
O09.92	Supervision of high risk pregnancy, unspecified, second trimester
O09.93	Supervision of high risk pregnancy, unspecified, third trimester

100-4, Chapter-18, 140

Annual Wellness Visit (AWV)

Pursuant to section 4103 of the Affordable Care Act of 2010, the Centers for Medicare & Medicaid Services (CMS) amended section 411.15(a)(1) and 411.15(k)(15) of 42 CFR (list of examples of routine physical examinations excluded from coverage) effective for services furnished on or after January 1, 2011. This expanded coverage is subject to certain eligibility and other limitations that allow payment for an annual wellness visit (AWV), including personalized prevention plan services (PPPS), for an individual who is no longer within 12 months after the effective date of his or her first Medicare Part B coverage period, and has not received either an initial preventive physical examination (IPPE) or an AWV within the past 12 months.

The AWV will include the establishment of, or update to, the individual's medical/family history, measurement of his/her height, weight, body-mass index (BMI) or waist circumference, and blood pressure (BP), with the goal of health promotion and disease detection and encouraging patients to obtain the screening and preventive services that may already be covered and paid for under Medicare Part B. CMS amended 42 CFR §§411.15(a)(1) and 411.15(k)(15) to allow payment on or after January 1, 2011, for an AWV (as established at 42 CFR 410.15) when performed by qualified health professionals.

Coverage is available for an AWV that meets the following requirements:

1. It is performed by a health professional;

2. It is furnished to an eligible beneficiary who is no longer within 12 months after the effective date of his/her first Medicare Part B coverage period, and he/she has not received either an IPPE or an AWV providing PPPS within the past 12 months.

See Pub. 100-02,Medicare Benefit Policy Manual, chapter 15, section 280.5, for detailed policy regarding the AWV, including definitions of: (1) detection of cognitive impairment, (2) eligible beneficiary, (3) establishment of, or an update to, an individual's medical/family history, (4&5) first and subsequent AWVs providing PPPS, (6) health professional, and, (7) review of an individual's functional ability/level of safety.

100-4, Chapter-18, 140.1

Healthcare Common Procedure Coding System (HCPCS) Coding for the AWV

The HCPCS codes listed below were developed for the AWV benefit effective January 1, 2011, for individuals whose initial enrollment is on or after January 1, 2011.

G0438 -Annual wellness visit; includes a personalized prevention plan of service (PPPS); first visit

G0439 –Annual wellness visit; includes a personalized prevention plan of service (PPPS); subsequent visit

100-4, Chapter-18, 140.5

Coinsurance and Deductible

Sections 4103 and 4104 of the Affordable Care Act provide for a waiver of Medicare coinsurance/copayment and Part B deductible requirements for the AWV effective for services furnished on or after January 1, 2011.

100-4, Chapter-18, 140.6

Common Working File (CWF) Edits

Effective for claims with dates of service on and after January 1,2011, CWF shall reject:

- AWV claims for G0438 when a previous (first) AWV, HCPCS code G0438, is paid in history regardless of when it occurred.

- AWV claims when a previous AWV, G0438 or G0439, is paid in history within the previous 12 months.

- Beginning January 1, 2011, AWV claims when a previous IPPE, HCPCS code G0402, is paid in history within the previous 12 months.

- AWV claims (G0438 and G0439) billed for a date of service within 12 months after the effective date of a beneficiary's first Medicare PartB coverage period.

The following change shall be effective for claims processed on or after April 1, 2013. Typically, when a preventive service is posted to a beneficiary's utilization history, separate entries are posted for a "professional" service (the professional claim for the delivery of the service itself) and a "technical" service (the institutional claims for a facility fee). However, in the case of AWV services, since there is no separate payment for a facility fee, the AWV claim will be posted as the "professional" service only, regardless of whether it is paid on a professional claim or an institutional claim.

100-4, Chapter-18, 150

Counseling to Prevent Tobacco Use

Effective for claims with dates of service on and after August 25, 2010, the Centers for Medicare & Medicaid Services (CMS) will cover counseling to prevent tobacco use services for outpatient and hospitalized Medicare beneficiaries:

1. Who use tobacco, regardless of whether they have signs or symptoms of tobacco-related disease;

2. Who are competent and alert at the time that counseling is provided; and,

3. Whose counseling is furnished by a qualified physician or other Medicare-recognized practitioner.

These individuals who do not have signs or symptoms of tobacco-related disease will be covered under Medicare Part B when the above conditions of coverage are met, subject to certain frequency and other limitations.

Conditions of Medicare Part A and Medicare Part B coverage for counseling to prevent tobacco use are located in the Medicare National Coverage Determinations (NCD)Manual, Publication 100-3, chapter1, section 210.4.1.

100-4, Chapter-18, 150.1

Healthcare Common Procedure Coding System (HCPCS) and Diagnosis Coding

The CMS has created two new G codes for billing for tobacco cessation counseling services to prevent tobacco use for those individuals who use tobacco but do not have signs or symptoms of tobacco-related disease. These are in addition to the two CPT® codes 99406 and 99407 that currently are used for smoking and tobacco-use cessation counseling for symptomatic individuals.

The following HCPCS codes should be reported when billing for counseling to prevent tobacco use effective January 1, 2011:

G0436 (this code has been deleted or 2017)- Smoking and tobacco cessation counseling visit for the asymptomatic patient; intermediate, greater than 3 minutes, up to 10 minutes

Short descriptor: Tobacco-use counsel 3-10 min

G0437 (this code has been deleted or 2017)- Smoking and tobacco cessation counseling visit for the asymptomatic patient; intensive, greater than 10 minutes

Short descriptor: Tobacco-use counsel >10min

NOTE: The above G codes will not be active in contractors' systems until January 1, 2011. Therefore, contractors shall advise non-outpatient perspective payment system (OPPS) providers to use unlisted code 99199 to bill for counseling to prevent tobacco use and tobacco-related disease services during the interim period of August 25, 2010, through December 31, 2010.

On January 3, 2011, contractor's systems will accept the new G codes for services performed on or after August 25, 2010.

Two new C codes have been created for facilities paid under OPPS when billing for counseling to prevent tobacco use and tobacco-related disease services during the interim period of August 25, 2010, through December 31, 2010:

C9801 - Smoking and tobacco cessation counseling visit for the asymptomatic patient, intermediate, greater than 3 minutes, up to 10 minutes

Short descriptor: Tobacco-use counsel 3-10 min

C9802 - Smoking and tobacco cessation counseling visit for the asymptomatic patient, intensive, greater than 10 minutes

Short descriptor: Tobacco-use counsel >10min

Claims for smoking and tobacco use cessation counseling services G0436 (this code has been deleted or 2017) and G0437 (this code has been deleted or 2017) shall be submitted with the applicable diagnosis codes:

ICD-9-CM

V15.82, history of tobacco use, or

305.1, non-dependent tobacco use disorder

ICD-10-CM

F17.200, nicotine dependence, unspecified, uncomplicated,

F17.201, nicotine dependence, unspecified, in remission,

F17.210, nicotine dependence, cigarettes, uncomplicated,

F17.211, nicotine dependence, cigarettes, in remission,

F17.220, nicotine dependence, chewing tobacco, uncomplicated,

F17.221, nicotine dependence, chewing tobacco, in remission,

F17.290, nicotine dependence, other tobacco product, uncomplicated,

F17.291, nicotine dependence, other tobacco product, in remission, or

Z87.891, personal history of nicotine dependence, unspecified, uncomplicated.

Contractors shall allow payment for a medically necessary E/M service on the same day as the smoking and tobacco-use cessation counseling service when it is clinically appropriate. Physicians and qualified non-physician practitioners shall use an appropriate HCPCS code to report an E/M service with modifier -25 to indicate that the E/M service is a separately identifiable service from G0436 (this code has been deleted or 2017) or G0437 (this code has been deleted or 2017).

100-4, Chapter-18, 150.2

Carrier Billing Requirements

Carriers shall pay for counseling to prevent tobacco use services billed with code G0436 (this code has been deleted or 2017) or G0437 (this code has been deleted or 2017) for dates of service on or after January 1, 2011. Carriers shall pay for counseling services billed with code 99199 for dates of service performed on or after August 25, 2010 through December 31, 2010. The type of service (TOS) for each of the new codes is 1.

Carriers pay for counseling services billed based on the Medicare Physician Fee Schedule (MPFS). Deductible and coinsurance apply for services performed on August 25, 2010, through December 31, 2010. For claims with dates of service on and after January 1, 2011, coinsurance and deductible do not apply on G0436 (this code has been deleted or 2017) and G0437 (this code has been deleted or 2017).

Physicians or qualified non-physician practitioners shall bill the carrier for counseling to prevent tobacco use services on Form CMS-1500 or an approved electronic format.

NOTE: The above G codes will not be active in contractors' systems until January 1, 2011. Therefore, contractors shall advise providers to use unlisted code 99199 to bill for counseling to prevent tobacco use services during the interim period of August 25, 2010, through December 31, 2010.

100-4, Chapter-18, 150.2.1

Fiscal Intermediary (FI) Billing Requirements

The FIs shall pay for counseling to prevent tobacco use services with codes G0436 (this code has been deleted or 2017) and G0437 (this code has been deleted or 2017) for dates of service on or after January 1, 2011. FIs shall pay for counseling services billed with code 99199 for dates of service performed on or after August 25, 2010, through December 31, 2010. For facilities paid under OPPS, FIs shall pay for counseling services billed with codes C9801 and C9802 for dates of service performed on or after August 25, 2010, through December 31, 2010.

Claims for counseling to prevent tobacco use services should be submitted on Form CMS-1450 or its electronic equivalent.

The applicable bill types are 12X, 13X, 22X, 23X, 34X, 71X, 77X, and 85X.

Payment for outpatient services is as follows:

Type of Facility	Method of Payment
Rural Health Centers (RHCs) TOB 71X/Federally Qualified Health Centers (FQHCs)TOB 77X	All-inclusive rate (AIR) for the encounter
Hospitals TOBs 12X and 13X	OPPS for hospitals subject to OPPS MPFS for hospitals not subject to OPPS
Indian Health Services (IHS) Hospitals TOB 13X	AIR for the encounter
Skilled Nursing Facilities (SNFs) TOBs 22X and 23X	Medicare Physician Fee Schedule (MPFS)
Home Health Agencies (HHAs) TOB 34X	MPFS
Critical Access Hospitals (CAHs) TOB 85X	Method I: Technical services are paid at 101% of reasonable cost. Method II: technical services are paid at 101% of reasonable cost, and Professional services are paid at 115% of the MPFS Data Base
IHS CAHs TOB 85X	Based on specific rate
Maryland Hospitals	Payment is based according to the Health Services Cost Review Commission (HSCRC). That is 94% of submitted charges subject to any unmet deductible, coinsurance, and non-covered charges policies.

Deductible and coinsurance apply for services performed on August 25, 2010, through December 31, 2010. For claims with dates of service on and after January 1, 2011, coinsurance and deductible do not apply for G0436 (this code has been deleted or 2017) and G0437 (this code has been deleted or 2017).

100-4, Chapter-18, 150.4

Common Working File (CWF)

The Common Working File (CWF) shall edit for the frequency of service limitations of counseling to prevent tobacco use sessions and smoking and tobacco-use cessation counseling services (G0436 (this code has been deleted or 2017), G0437 (this code has been deleted or 2017), 99406, 99407) rendered to a beneficiary for a combined total of 8 sessions within a 12-month period. The beneficiary may receive another 8 sessions during a second or subsequent year after 11 full months have passed since the first Medicare covered counseling session was performed. To start the count for the second or subsequent 12-month period, begin with the month after the month in which the first Medicare covered counseling session was performed and count until 11 full months have elapsed.

By entering the beneficiary's health insurance claim number (HICN), providers have the capability to view the number of sessions a beneficiary has received for this service via inquiry through CWF.

100-4, Chapter-18, 160

Intensive Behavioral Therapy (IBT) for Cardiovascular Disease (CVD)

For services furnished on or after November 8, 2011, the Centers for Medicare & Medicaid Services (CMS) covers intensive behavioral therapy (IBT) for cardiovascular disease (CVD). See National Coverage Determinations (NCD) Manual (Pub. 100-03) §210.11 for complete coverage guidelines.

100-4, Chapter-18, 160.1

Coding Requirements for IBT for CVD Furnished on or After November 8, 2011

The following is the applicable Healthcare Procedural Coding System (HCPCS) code for IBT for CVD:

G0446: Annual, face-to-face intensive behavioral therapy for cardiovascular disease, individual, 15 minutes

Contractors shall not apply deductibles or coinsurance to claim lines containing HCPCS code G0446.

100-4, Chapter-18, 160.2.1

Correct Place of Service (POS) Codes for IBT for CVD on Professional Claims

Contractors shall pay for IBT CVD, G0446 only when services are provided at the following POS:

11- Physician's Office

22- Outpatient Hospital

49- Independent Clinic

72- Rural Health Clinic

Claims not submitted with one of the POS codes above will be denied.

The following messages shall be used when Medicare contractors deny professional claims for incorrect POS:

Claim Adjustment Reason Code (CARC) 58: "Treatment was deemed by the payer to have been rendered in an inappropriate or invalid place of service." **NOTE:** Refer to the 835 Healthcare Policy Identification Segment (loop 2110 Service Payment Information REF), if present.

Remittance Advice Remark Code (RARC) N428: "Not covered when performed in this place of service."

Medicare Summary Notice (MSN) 21.25: "This service was denied because Medicare only covers this service in certain settings."

Spanish Version: El servicio fue denegado porque Medicare solamente lo cubre en ciertas situaciones."

Group Code PR (Patient Responsibility) assigning financial liability to the beneficiary, if a claim is received with a GA modifier indicating a signed ABN is on file.

Group Code CO (Contractual Obligation) assigning financial liability to the provider, if a claim is received with a GZ modifier indicating no signed ABN is on file.

100-4, Chapter-18, 160.2.2

Provider Specialty Edits for IBT for CVD on Professional Claims

Contractors shall pay claims for HCPCS code G0446 only when services are submitted by the following provider specialty types found on the provider's enrollment record:

01= General Practice

08 = Family Practice

11= Internal Medicine

16 = Obstetrics/Gynecology

37= Pediatric Medicine

38 = Geriatric Medicine

42= Certified Nurse Midwife

50 = Nurse Practitioner

89 = Certified Clinical Nurse Specialist

97= Physician Assistant

Contractors shall deny claim lines for HCPCS code G0446 performed by any other provider specialty type other than those listed above.

The following messages shall be used when Medicare contractors deny IBT for CVD claims billed with invalid provider specialty types:

CARC 185: "The rendering provider is not eligible to perform the service billed."

NOTE: Refer to the 835 Healthcare Policy Identification Segment (loop 2110 Service Payment Information REF), if present.

RARC N95: "This provider type/provider specialty may not bill this service."

MSN 21.18: "This item or service is not covered when performed or ordered by this provider."

Spanish version: "Este servicio no esta cubierto cuando es ordenado o rendido por este proveedor."

Group Code PR (Patient Responsibility) assigning financial liability to the beneficiary, if a claim is received with a GA modifier indicating a signed ABN is on file.

Group Code CO (Contractual Obligation) assigning financial liability to the provider, if a claim is received with a GZ modifier indicating no signed ABN is on file.

100-4, Chapter-18, 160.3

Correct Types of Bill (TOB) for IBT for CVD on Institutional Claims

Effective for claims with dates of service on and after November 8, 2011, the following types of bill (TOB) may be used for IBT for CVD: 13X, 71X, 77X, or 85X. All other TOB codes shall be denied.

The following messages shall be used when Medicare contractors deny claims for G0446 when submitted on a TOB other than those listed above:

CARC 170: Payment is denied when performed/billed by this type of provider. *Note:* Refer to the 835 Healthcare Policy Identification Segment (loop 2110 Service Payment Information REF), if present.

RARC N428: Not covered when performed in this place of service."

MSN 21.25: "This service was denied because Medicare only covers this service in certain settings."

Spanish Version: El servicio fue denegado porque Medicare solamente lo cubre en ciertas situaciones."

Group Code PR (Patient Responsibility) assigning financial liability to the beneficiary, if a claim is received with a GA modifier indicating a signed ABN is on file.

Group Code CO (Contractual Obligation) assigning financial liability to the provider, if a claim is received with a GZ modifier indicating no signed ABN is on file.

100-4, Chapter-18, 160.4

Frequency Edits for IBT for CVD Claims

Contractors shall allow claims for G0446 no more than once in a 12-month period.

NOTE: 11 full months must elapse following the month in which the last G0446 IBT for CVD took place.

Contractors shall deny claims IBT for CVD claims that exceed one (1) visit every 12 months.

Contractors shall allow one professional service and one facility fee claim for each visit.

The following messages shall be used when Medicare contractors deny IBT for CVD claims that exceed the frequency limit:

CARC 119: "Benefit maximum for this time period or occurrence has been reached."

RARC N362: "The number of days or units of service exceeds our acceptable maximum."

MSN 20.5: "These services cannot be paid because your benefits are exhausted at this time."

Spanish Version: "Estos servicios no pueden ser pagados porque sus beneficios se hanagotado."

Group Code PR (Patient Responsibility) assigning financial liability to the beneficiary, if a claim is received with a GA modifier indicating a signed ABN is on file.

Group Code CO (Contractual Obligation) assigning financial liability to the provider, if a claim is received with a GZ modifier indicating no signed ABN is on file.

100-4, Chapter-18, 160.5

Common Working File (CWF) Edits for IBT for CVD Claims

When applying frequency, CWF shall count 11 full months following the month of the last IBT for CVD, G0446 before allowing subsequent payment of another G0446 screening.

When applying frequency limitations to G0446, CWF shall allow both a claim for the professional service and a claim for the facility fee. CWF shall identify the following institutional claims as facility fee claims for screening services: TOB 13X, TOB85X when the revenue code is not 096X, 097X, or 098X. CWF shall identify all other claims as professional service claims for screening services. *NOTE:* This does not apply to RHCs and FQHCs.

100-4, Chapter-18, 170.1

Healthcare Common Procedure Coding System (HCPCS) Codes for Screening for STIs and HIBC to Prevent STIs

Effective for claims with dates of service on and after November 8, 2011, the claims processing instructions for payment of screening tests for STI will apply to the following HCPCS codes:

- Chlamydia: 86631, 86632, 87110, 87270, 87320, 87490, 87491, 87810, 87800 (used for combined chlamydia and gonorrhea testing)
- Gonorrhea: 87590, 87591, 87850, 87800 (used for combined chlamydia and gonorrhea testing)
- Syphilis: 86592, 86593, 86780
- Hepatitis B: (hepatitis B surface antigen): 87340, 87341

Effective for claims with dates of service on and after November 8, 2011, implemented with the January 2, 2012, IOCE, the following HCPCS code is to be billed for HIBC to prevent STIs

- G0445 –high-intensity behavioral counseling to prevent sexually transmitted infections, face-to-face, individual, includes: education, skills training, and guidance on how to change sexual behavior, performed semi-annually, 30minutes.

100-4, Chapter-18, 170.2

Diagnosis Code Reporting

A claim that is submitted for screening chlamydia, gonorrhea, syphilis, and/or hepatitis B shall be submitted with one or more of the following diagnosis codes in the header and pointed to the line item:

a. For claims for screening for chlamydia, gonorrhea, and syphilis in women at increased risk who are not pregnant use the following ICD-9-CM diagnosis codes:

- V74.5 - Screening, bacterial - sexually transmitted; and
- V69.8 - Other problems related to lifestyle as secondary. (This diagnosis code is used to indicate high/increased risk for STIs).

Effective with the implementation of ICD-10, use the following ICD-10-CM diagnosis codes:

- Z11.3 - Encounter for screening for infections with a predominantly sexual mode of transmission; and
- any of o Z72.89 - Other problems related to lifestyle ,

- Z72.51 - High risk heterosexual behavior,
- Z72.52 - High risk homosexual behavior, or
- Z72.53 - High risk bisexual behavior. (These diagnosis codes are used to indicate high/increased risk for STIs).

b. For claims for screening for syphilis in men at increased risk use the following ICD-9-CM diagnosis codes:

- V74.5 - Screening, bacterial - sexually transmitted; and
- V69.8 - Other problems related to lifestyle as secondary.

Effective with the implementation of ICD-10, use the following ICD-10-CM diagnosis codes:

- Z11.3 - Encounter for screening for infections with a predominantly sexual mode of transmission; and
- any of
  - Z72.89 - Other problems related to lifestyle ,
  - Z72.51 - High risk heterosexual behavior,
  - Z72.52 - High risk homosexual behavior, or
  - Z72.53 - High risk bisexual behavior.

c. For claims for screening for chlamydia and gonorrhea in pregnant women at increased risk for STIs use the following ICD-9-CM diagnosis codes, if applicable:

- V74.5 - Screening, bacterial - sexually transmitted; and
- V69.8 - Other problems related to lifestyle, and
- one of,
  - V22.0 - Supervision of normal first pregnancy, or
  - V22.1 - Supervision of other normal pregnancy, or,
  - V23.9 - Supervision of unspecified high-risk pregnancy.

Effective with the implementation of ICD-10, use ICD-10-CM diagnosis code Z11.3 - Encounter for screening for infections with a predominantly sexual mode of transmission; and one of:

- Z72.89 - Other problems related to lifestyle ,
- Z72.51 - High risk heterosexual behavior,
- Z72.52 - High risk homosexual behavior, or
- Z72.53 - High risk bisexual behavior.

and also one of the following.

Code	Description
Z34.00	Encounter for supervision of normal first pregnancy, unspecified trimester
Z34.01	Encounter for supervision of normal first pregnancy, first trimester
Z34.02	Encounter for supervision of normal first pregnancy, second trimester
Z34.03	Encounter for supervision of normal first pregnancy, third trimester
Z34.80	Encounter for supervision of other normal pregnancy, unspecified trimester
Z34.81	Encounter for supervision of other normal pregnancy, first trimester
Z34.82	Encounter for supervision of other normal pregnancy, second trimester

Z34.83	Encounter for supervision of other normal pregnancy, third trimester
Z34.90	Encounter for supervision of normal pregnancy, unspecified, unspecified trimester
Z34.91	Encounter for supervision of normal pregnancy, unspecified, first trimester
Z34.92	Encounter for supervision of normal pregnancy, unspecified, second trimester
Z34.93	Encounter for supervision of normal pregnancy, unspecified, third trimester
O09.90	Supervision of high risk pregnancy, unspecified, unspecified trimester
O09.91	Supervision of high risk pregnancy, unspecified, first trimester
O09.92	Supervision of high risk pregnancy, unspecified, second trimester
O09.93	Supervision of high risk pregnancy, unspecified, third trimester

d. For claims for screening for syphilis in pregnant women use the following ICD-9-CM diagnosis codes:

- V74.5 - Screening, bacterial - sexually transmitted; and
- V22.0 - Supervision of normal first pregnancy, or,
- V22.1 - Supervision of other normal pregnancy, or,
- V23.9 - Supervision of unspecified high-risk pregnancy.

Effective with the implementation of ICD-10, use the following ICD-10-CM diagnosis codes:

- Z11.3 - Encounter for screening for infections with a predominantly sexual mode of transmission;
- and one of

Code	Description
Z34.00	Encounter for supervision of normal first pregnancy, unspecified trimester
Z34.01	Encounter for supervision of normal first pregnancy, first trimester
Z34.02	Encounter for supervision of normal first pregnancy, second trimester
Z34.03	Encounter for supervision of normal first pregnancy, third trimester
Z34.80	Encounter for supervision of other normal pregnancy, unspecified trimester
Z34.81	Encounter for supervision of other normal pregnancy, first trimester
Z34.82	Encounter for supervision of other normal pregnancy, second trimester
Z34.83	Encounter for supervision of other normal pregnancy, third trimester
Z34.90	Encounter for supervision of normal pregnancy, unspecified, unspecified trimester
Z34.91	Encounter for supervision of normal pregnancy, unspecified, first trimester
Z34.92	Encounter for supervision of normal pregnancy, unspecified, second trimester
Z34.93	Encounter for supervision of normal pregnancy, unspecified, third trimester
O09.90	Supervision of high risk pregnancy, unspecified, unspecified trimester
O09.91	Supervision of high risk pregnancy, unspecified, first trimester
O09.92	Supervision of high risk pregnancy, unspecified, second trimester
O09.93	Supervision of high risk pregnancy, unspecified, third trimester

e. For claims for screening for syphilis in pregnant women at increased risk for STIs use the following ICD-9-CM diagnosis codes:

- V74.5 - Screening, bacterial - sexually transmitted; and
- V69.8 - Other problems related to lifestyle, and,
- V22.0 - Supervision of normal first pregnancy, or
- V22.1 - Supervision of other normal pregnancy, or,
- V23.9 - Supervision of unspecified high-risk pregnancy.

Effective with the implementation of ICD-10, use the following ICD-10-CM diagnosis codes:

- Z11.3 - Encounter for screening for infections with a predominantly sexual mode of transmission;
- and any of:
  - Z72.89 - Other problems related to lifestyle, or
  - Z72.51 - High risk heterosexual behavior, or
  - Z72.52 - High risk homosexual behavior, or
  - Z72.53 - High risk bisexual behavior

and also one of the following:

Code	Description
Z34.00	Encounter for supervision of normal first pregnancy, unspecified trimester
Z34.01	Encounter for supervision of normal first pregnancy, first trimester
Z34.02	Encounter for supervision of normal first pregnancy, second trimester
Z34.03	Encounter for supervision of normal first pregnancy, third trimester
Z34.80	Encounter for supervision of other normal pregnancy, unspecified trimester
Z34.81	Encounter for supervision of other normal pregnancy, first trimester
Z34.82	Encounter for supervision of other normal pregnancy, second trimester
Z34.83	Encounter for supervision of other normal pregnancy, third trimester
Z34.90	Encounter for supervision of normal pregnancy, unspecified, unspecified trimester
Z34.91	Encounter for supervision of normal pregnancy, unspecified, first trimester
Z34.92	Encounter for supervision of normal pregnancy, unspecified, second trimester
Z34.93	Encounter for supervision of normal pregnancy, unspecified, third trimester
O09.90	Supervision of high risk pregnancy, unspecified, unspecified trimester
O09.91	Supervision of high risk pregnancy, unspecified, first trimester
O09.92	Supervision of high risk pregnancy, unspecified, second trimester
O09.93	Supervision of high risk pregnancy, unspecified, third trimester

f. CM diagnosis codes:

- V73.89 - Screening, disease or disorder, viral, specified type NEC; and
- V22.0 - Supervision of normal first pregnancy, or,
- V22.1 - Supervision of other normal pregnancy, or,
- V23.9 - Supervision of unspecified high-risk pregnancy.

Effective with the implementation of ICD-10, use the following ICD-10-CM diagnosis codes:

- Z11.59 - Encounter for screening for other viral diseases, and any of
- Z34.00 - Encounter for supervision of normal first pregnancy, unspecified trimester, or
- Z34.80 - Encounter for supervision of other normal pregnancy, unspecified trimester, or
- Z34.90 - Encounter for supervision of normal pregnancy, unspecified, unspecified trimester, or
- O09.90 - Supervision of high risk pregnancy, unspecified, unspecified trimester.

g. For claims for screening for hepatitis B in pregnant women at increased risk for STIs use the following ICD-9-CM diagnosis codes:

- V73.89 - Screening, disease or disorder, viral, specified type NEC; and
- V 69.8 - Other problems related to lifestyle, and,
- V22.0 - Supervision of normal first pregnancy, or,
- V22.1 - Supervision of other normal pregnancy, or,
- V23.9 - Supervision of unspecified high-risk pregnancy.

Effective with the implementation of ICD-10, use the following ICD-10-CM diagnosis codes:

- Z11.59 - Encounter for screening for other viral diseases, and
- Z72.89 - Other problems related to lifestyle, and
- any of
  - Z72.51 - High risk heterosexual behavior, or
  - Z72.52 - High risk homosexual behavior, or
  - Z72.53 - High risk bisexual behavior;
- and also one of the following:

Code	Description
Z34.00	Encounter for supervision of normal first pregnancy, unspecified trimester
Z34.01	Encounter for supervision of normal first pregnancy, first trimester
Z34.02	Encounter for supervision of normal first pregnancy, second trimester
Z34.03	Encounter for supervision of normal first pregnancy, third trimester
Z34.80	Encounter for supervision of other normal pregnancy, unspecified trimester
Z34.81	Encounter for supervision of other normal pregnancy, first trimester
Z34.82	Encounter for supervision of other normal pregnancy, second trimester
Z34.83	Encounter for supervision of other normal pregnancy, third trimester
Z34.90	Encounter for supervision of normal pregnancy, unspecified, unspecified trimester
Z34.91	Encounter for supervision of normal pregnancy, unspecified, first trimester
Z34.92	Encounter for supervision of normal pregnancy, unspecified, second trimester
Z34.93	Encounter for supervision of normal pregnancy, unspecified, third trimester
O09.90	Supervision of high risk pregnancy, unspecified, unspecified trimester

O09.91	Supervision of high risk pregnancy, unspecified, first trimester
O09.92	Supervision of high risk pregnancy, unspecified, second trimester
O09.93	Supervision of high risk pregnancy, unspecified, third trimester

100-4, Chapter-18, 170.3

Billing Requirements

- Effective for dates of service November 8, 2011, and later, contractors shall recognize HCPCS code G0445 for HIBC. Medicare shall cover up to two occurrences of G0445 when billed for IBC to prevent STIs. A claim that is submitted with HCPCS code G0445 for HIBC shall be submitted with ICD-9-CM diagnosis code V69.8 or ICD-10-CM diagnosis code Z72.89.

- Medicare contractors shall pay for screening for chlamydia, gonorrhea, and syphilis (as indicated by the presence of ICD-9-CM diagnosis code V74.5 or if ICD-10 is applicable, ICD-10-CM diagnosis code Z11.3); and/or hepatitis B (as indicated by the presence of ICD-9-CM diagnosis code V73.89 or ICD-10-CM diagnosis code Z11.59) as follows:

- One annual occurrence of screening for chlamydia, gonorrhea, and syphilis (i.e., 1 per 12-month period) in women at increased risk who are not pregnant,

- One annual occurrence of screening for syphilis (i.e., 1 per 12-month period) in men at increased risk,

- Up to two occurrences per pregnancy of screening for chlamydia and gonorrhea in pregnant women who are at increased risk for STIs and continued increased risk for the second screening,

- One occurrence per pregnancy of screening for syphilis in pregnant women,

- Up to an additional two occurrences per pregnancy of screening for syphilis in pregnant women if the beneficiary is at continued increased risk for STIs,

- One occurrence per pregnancy of screening for hepatitis B in pregnant women, and,

- One additional occurrence per pregnancy of screening for hepatitis B in pregnant women who are at continued increased risk for STIs.

100-4, Chapter-18, 170.4

Types of Bill (TOBs) and Revenue Codes

The applicable types of bill (TOBs) for HIBC screening, HCPCS code G0445, are: 13X, 71X, 77X, and 85X.

On institutional claims, TOBs 71X and 77X, use revenue code 052X to ensure coinsurance and deductible are not applied.

Critical access hospitals (CAHs) electing the optional method of payment for outpatient services report this service under revenue codes 096X, 097X, or 098X.

100-4, Chapter-18, 170.4.1

Payment Method

Payment for HIBC is based on the all-inclusive payment rate for rural health clinics (TOBs 71X) and federally qualified health centers (TOB 77X). Hospital outpatient departments (TOB 13X) are paid based on the outpatient prospective payment system and CAHs (TOB 85X) are paid based on reasonable cost. CAHs electing the optional method of payment for outpatient services are paid based on 115% of the lesser of the Medicare Physician Fee Schedule (MPFS) amount or submitted charge.

Effective for dates of service on and after November 8, 2011, deductible and coinsurance do not apply to claim lines with G0445.

HCPCS code G0445 may be paid on the same date of service as an annual wellness visit, evaluation and management (E&M) code, or during the global billing period for obstetrical care, but only one G0445 may be paid on any one date of service. If billed on the same date of service with an E&M code, the E&M code should have a distinct diagnosis code other than the diagnosis code used to indicate high/increased risk for STIs for the G0445 service. An E&M code should not be billed when the sole reason for the visit is HIBC to prevent STIs.

For Medicare Part B physician and non-practitioner claims, payment for HIBC to prevent STIs is based on the MPFS amount for G0445.

100-4, Chapter-18, 170.5

Specialty Codes and Place of Service (POS)

Medicare provides coverage for screening for chlamydia, gonorrhea, syphilis, and/or hepatitis B and HIBC to prevent STIs only when ordered by a primary care practitioner (physician or non-physician) with any of the following specialty codes:

- 01 –General Practice
- 08 –Family Practice
- 11 –Internal Medicine
- 16 –Obstetrics/Gynecology
- 37 –Pediatric Medicine
- 38 –Geriatric Medicine
- 42 –Certified Nurse Midwife
- 50 –Nurse Practitioner
- 89 –Certified Clinical Nurse Specialist
- 97 –Physician Assistant

Medicare provides coverage for HIBC to prevent STIs only when provided by a primary care practitioner (physician or non-physician) with any of the specialty codes identified above.

Medicare provides coverage for HIBC to prevent STIs only when the POS billed is 11, 22, 49, or 71.

100-4, Chapter-18, 180

Alcohol Screening and Behavioral Counseling Interventions in Primary Care to Reduce Alcohol Misuse

The United States Preventive Services Task Force (USPSTF) defines alcohol misuse as risky, hazardous, or harmful drinking which places an individual at risk for future problems with alcohol consumption. In the general adult population, alcohol consumption becomes risky or hazardous when consuming:

- Greater than 7 drinks per week or greater than 3 drinks per occasion for women and persons greater than 65 years old.
- Greater than 14 drinks per week or greater than 4 drinks per occasion for men 65 years old and younger.

100-4, Chapter-18, 180.1

Policy

Claims with dates of service on and after October 14, 2011, the Centers for Medicare & Medicaid Services (CMS) will cover annual alcohol misuse screening (HCPCS code G0442) consisting of 1 screening session, and for those that screen positive, upto 4 brief, face-to-face behavioral counseling sessions (HCPCS code G0443) per 12-month period for Medicare beneficiaries, including pregnant women.

Medicare beneficiaries that may be identified as having a need for behavioral counseling sessions include those:

- Who misuse alcohol, but whose levels or patterns of alcohol consumption do not meet criteria for alcohol dependence (defined as at least three of the following: tolerance, withdrawal symptoms, impaired control, preoccupation with acquisition and/or use, persistent desire or unsuccessful efforts to quit, sustains social, occupational, or recreational disability, use continues despite adverse consequences); and,
- Who are competent and alert at the time that counseling is provided; and,
- Whose counseling is furnished by qualified primary care physicians or other primary care practitioners in a primary care setting.

Once a Medicare beneficiary has agreed to behavioral counseling sessions, the counseling sessions are to be completed based on the 5As approach adopted by the United States Preventive Services Task Force (USPSTF.) The steps to the 5As approach are listed below.

1. **Assess:** Ask about/assess behavioral health risk(s) and factors affecting choice of behavior change goals/methods.
2. **Advise:** Give clear, specific, and personalized behavior change advice, including information about personal health harms and benefits.
3. **Agree:** Collaboratively select appropriate treatment goals and methods based on the patient's interest in and willingness to change the behavior.
4. **Assist:** Using behavior change techniques (self-help and/or counseling), aid the patient in achieving agreed-upon goals by acquiring the skills, confidence, and social/environmental supports for behavior change, supplemented with adjunctive medical treatments when appropriate.
5. **Arrange:** Schedule follow-up contacts (in person or by telephone) to provide ongoing assistance/support and to adjust the treatment plan as needed, including referral to more intensive or specialized treatment.

Institutional Billing Requirements

For claims with dates of service on and after October 14, 2011, Medicare will allow coverage for annual alcohol misuse screening, 15 minutes, G0442, and brief, face-to-face behavioral counseling for alcohol misuse, 15 minutes, G0443 for:

- Rural Health Clinics (RHCs) -type of bill (TOB) 71X only –based on the all-inclusive payment rate
- Federally Qualified Health Centers (FQHCs) -TOB 77X only –based on the all-inclusive payment rate
- Outpatient hospitals –TOB 13X -based on Outpatient Prospective Payment System (OPPS)

- Critical Access Hospitals (CAHs) -TOB 85X–based on reasonable cost
- CAH Method II –TOB 85X -based on 115% of the lesser of the Medicare Physician Fee Schedule (MPFS) amount or actual charge as applicable with revenue codes 096X, 097X, or 098X.

For RHCs and FQHCs the alcohol screening/counseling is not separately payable with another face-to-face encounter on the same day. This does not apply to the Initial Preventive Physical Examination (IPPE), unrelated services denoted with modifier 59, and 77X claims containing Diabetes Self Management Training (DSMT) and Medical Nutrition Therapy (MNT) services. DSMT and MNT apply to FQHCs only. However, the screening/counseling sessions alone when rendered as a face-to-face visit with a core practitioner do constitute an encounter and is paid based on the all-inclusive payment rate.

Note: For outpatient hospital settings, as in any other setting, services covered under this NCD must be provided by a primary care provider.

Claims submitted with alcohol misuse screening and behavioral counseling HCPCS codes G0442 and G0443 on a TOB other than 13X, 71X, 77X, and 85X will be denied.

Effective October 14, 2011, deductible and co-insurance should not be applied for line items on claims billed for alcohol misuse screening G0442 and behavioral counseling for alcohol misuse G0443.

100-4, Chapter-18, 180.3

Professional Billing Requirements

For claims with dates of service on and after October 14, 2011, CMS will allow coverage for annual alcohol misuse screening, 15 minutes, G0442, and behavioral counseling for alcohol misuse, 15 minutes, G0443, only when services are submitted by the following provider specialties found on the provider's enrollment record:

01 -General Practice

08 -Family Practice

11 -Internal Medicine

16 -Obstetrics/Gynecology

37 -Pediatric Medicine

38 -Geriatric Medicine

42 –Certified Nurse-Midwife

50 -Nurse Practitioner

89 -Certified Clinical Nurse Specialist

97 -Physician Assistant

Any claims that are not submitted from one of the provider specialty types noted above will be denied.

For claims with dates of service on and after October 14, 2011, CMS will allow coverage for annual alcohol misuse screening, 15 minutes, G0442, and behavioral counseling for alcohol misuse, 15 minutes, G0443, only when submitted with one of the following place of service (POS) codes:

11 -Physician's Office

22 -Outpatient Hospital

49 -Independent Clinic

71 -State or local public health clinic or

Any claims that are not submitted with one of the POS codes noted above will be denied.

The alcohol screening/counseling services are payable with another encounter/visit on the same day. This does not apply for IPPE.

100-4, Chapter-18, 180.4

Claim Adjustment Reason Codes, Remittance Advice Remark Codes, Group Codes, and Medicare Summary Notice Messages

Contractors shall use the appropriate claim adjustment reason codes (CARCs), remittance advice remark codes (RARCs), group codes, or Medicare summary notice (MSN) messages when denying payment for alcohol misuse screening and alcohol misuse behavioral counseling sessions:

- For RHC and FQHC claims that contain screening for alcohol misuse HCPCS code G0442 and alcohol misuse counseling HCPCS code G0443 with another encounter/visit with the same line item date of service, use group code CO and reason code:
  - Claim Adjustment Reason Code (CARC) 97 –The benefit for this service is included in the payment/allowance for another service/procedure that has already been adjudicated. *Note:* Refer to the 835 Healthcare Policy Identification Segment (loop 2110 Service Payment Information REF) if present
- Denying claims containing HCPCS code G0442 and HCPCS code G0443 submitted on a TOB other than 13X, 71X, 77X, and 85X:
  - Claim Adjustment Reason Code (CARC) 5 -The procedure code/bill type is inconsistent with the place of service. *Note:* Refer to the 835 Healthcare Policy Identification Segment (loop 2110 Service Payment Information REF) if present
  - Remittance Advice Remark Code (RARC) M77 – Missing/incomplete/invalid place of service
  - Group Code PR (Patient Responsibility) assigning financial liability to the beneficiary, if a claim is received with a GA modifier indicating a signed ABN is on file.
  - Group Code CO (Contractual Obligation) assigning financial liability to the provider, if a claim is received with a GZ modifier indicating no signed ABN is on file.
- Denying claims that contains more than one alcohol misuse behavioral counseling session G0443 on the same date of service:
  - Medicare Summary Notice (MSN) 15.6 –The information provided does not support the need for this many services or items within this period of time.
  - Claim Adjustment Reason Code (CARC) 151 – Payment adjusted because the payer deems the information submitted does not support this many/frequency of services.
  - Remittance Advice Remark Code (RARC) M86 – Service denied because payment already made for same/similar procedure within set time frame.
  - Group Code PR (Patient Responsibility) assigning financial liability to the beneficiary, if a claim is received with a GA modifier indicating a signed ABN is on file.
  - Group Code CO (Contractual Obligation) assigning financial liability to the provider, if a claim is received with a GZ modifier indicating no signed ABN is on file.

- Denying claims that are not submitted from the appropriate provider specialties:
  - Medicare Summary Notice (MSN) 21.18 –This item or service is not covered when performed or ordered by this provider.
  - Claim Adjustment Reason Code (CARC) 185 -The rendering provider is not eligible to perform the service billed. *NOTE:* Refer to the 835 Healthcare Policy Identification Segment (loop 2110 Service Payment Information REF), if present.
  - Remittance Advice Remark Code (RARC) N95 -This provider type/provider specialty may not bill this service.
  - Group Code PR (Patient Responsibility) assigning financial liability to the beneficiary, if a claim is received with a GA modifier indicating a signed ABN is on file.
  - Group Code CO (Contractual Obligation) assigning financial liability to the provider, if a claim is received with a GZ modifier indicating no signed ABN is on file.
- Denying claims without the appropriate POS code:
  - Medicare Summary Notice (MSN) 21.25 –This service was denied because Medicare only covers this service in certain settings.
  - Claim Adjustment Reason Code (CARC) 58 – Treatment was deemed by the payer to have been rendered in an inappropriate or invalid place of service. *Note:* Refer to the 835 Healthcare Policy Identification Segment (loop 2110 Service Payment Information REF) if present.
  - Remittance Advice Remark Code (RARC) N428 –Not covered when performed in this place of service.
  - Group Code PR (Patient Responsibility) assigning financial liability to the beneficiary, if a claim is received with a GA modifier indicating a signed ABN is on file.
  - Group Code CO (Contractual Obligation) assigning financial liability to the provider, if a claim is received with a GZ modifier indicating no signed ABN is on file.
- Denying claims for alcohol misuse screening HCPCS code G0442 more than once in a 12-month period, and denying alcohol misuse counseling sessions HCPCS code G0443 more than four times in the same 12-month period:
  - Medicare Summary Notice (MSN) 20.5 –These services cannot be paid because your benefits are exhausted at this time.
  - Claim Adjustment Reason Code (CARC) 119 –Benefit maximum for this time period or occurrence has been reached.
  - Remittance Advice Remark Code (RARC) N362 – The number of Days or Units of service exceeds our acceptable maximum.
  - Group Code PR (Patient Responsibility) assigning financial liability to the beneficiary, if a claim is received with a GA modifier indicating a signed ABN is on file.
  - Group Code CO (Contractual Obligation) assigning financial liability to the provider, if a claim is received with a GZ modifier indicating no signed ABN is on file.

100-4, Chapter-18, 180.5

CWF Requirements

When applying frequency, CWF shall count 11 full months following the month of the last alcohol misuse screening visit, G0442, before allowing subsequent payment of another G0442 screening. Additionally, CWF shall create an edit to allow alcohol misuse brief behavioral counseling, HCPCS G0443, no more than 4 times in a 12-month period and make this edit overridable. CWF shall also count four alcohol misuse counseling sessions HCPCS G0443 in the same 12-month period used for G0442 counting from the date the G0442 screening session was billed.

When applying frequency limitations to G0442 screening on the same date of service as G0443 counseling, CWF shall allow both a claim for the professional service and a claim for a facility fee. CWF shall identify the following institutional claims as facility fee claims for screening services: TOB 13X, TOB 85X when the revenue code is not 096X, 097X, or 098X. CWF shall identify all other claims as professional service claims for screening services. *NOTE:* This does not apply to RHCs and FQHCs.

100-4, Chapter-18, 190

Screening for Depression in Adults (Effective October 14, 2011)

A. Coverage Requirements

Effective October 14, 2011, the Centers for Medicare & Medicaid Services (CMS) will cover annual screening up to 15 minutes for Medicare beneficiaries in primary care settings that have staff-assisted depression care supports in place to assure accurate diagnosis, effective treatment, and follow-up. Various screening tools are available for screening for depression. CMS does not identify specific depression screening tools. Rather, the decision to use a specific tool is at the discretion of the clinician in the primary care setting. Screening for depression is non-covered when performed more than one time in a 12-month period. The Medicare coinsurance and Part B deductible are waived for this preventive service.

Additional information on this National Coverage Determination (NCD) for Screening for Depression in Adults can be found in Publication 100-03, NCD Manual, Section 210.9.

100-4, Chapter-18, 190.1

A/B MAC and Carrier Billing Requirements

Effective October 14, 2011, contractors shall recognize new HCPCS G0444, annual depression screening, 15 minutes.

100-4, Chapter-18, 190.2

Frequency

Medicare contractors shall pay for annual depression screening, G0444, no more than once in a 12-month period.

NOTE: 11 full months must elapse following the month in which the last annual depression screening took place.

100-4, Chapter-18, 190.3

Place of Service (POS)

Contractors shall pay for annual depression screening claims, G0444, only when services are provided at the following places of service (POS):

11 –Office

22 –Outpatient Hospital

49 –Independent Clinic

71 –State or Local Public Health Clinic

100-4, Chapter-18, 200

Intensive Behavioral Therapy for Obesity (Effective November 29, 2011)

The United States Preventive Services Task Force (USPSTF) found good evidence that body mass index (BMI) is a reliable and valid indicator for identifying adults at increased risk for mortality and morbidity due to overweight and obesity. It also good evidence that high intensity counseling combined with behavioral interventions in obese adults (as defined by a BMI ≥30 kg/m2) produces modest, sustained weight loss.

100-4, Chapter-18, 200.1

Policy

For services furnished on or after November 29, 2011, Medicare will cover Intensive Behavioral Therapy for Obesity. Medicare beneficiaries with obesity (BMI ≥30 kg/m2) who are competent and alert at the time that counseling is provided and whose counseling is furnished by a qualified primary care physician or other primary care practitioner in a primary care setting are eligible for:

- One face-to-face visit every week for the first month;
- One face-to-face visit every other week for months 2-6;
- One face-to-face visit every month for months 7-12, if the beneficiary meets the 3kg (6.6 lbs.) weight loss requirement during the first 6 months as discussed below.

The counseling sessions are to be completed based on the 5As approach adopted by the United States Preventive Services Task Force (USPSTF.) The steps to the 5As approach are listed below:

1. **Assess:** Ask about/assess behavioral health risk(s) and factors affecting choice of behavior change goals/methods.
2. **Advise:** Give clear, specific, and personalized behavior change advice, including information about personal health harms and benefits.
3. **Agree:** Collaboratively select appropriate treatment goals and methods based on the patient's interest in and willingness to change the behavior.
4. **Assist:** Using behavior change techniques (self-help and/or counseling), aid the patient in achieving agreed-upon goals by acquiring the skills, confidence, and social/environmental supports for behavior change, supplemented with adjunctive medical treatments when appropriate.
5. **Arrange:** Schedule follow-up contacts (in person or by telephone) to provide ongoing assistance/support and to adjust the treatment plan as needed, including referral to more intensive or specialized treatment.

Medicare will cover Face-to-Face Behavioral Counseling for Obesity, 15 minutes (G0447), Face-to-face behavioral counseling for obesity, group (2-10), 30 minute(s) (G0473), along with 1 of the ICD-9-CM codes for BMI 30.0-BMI 70 (V85.30-V85.39 and V85.41-V85.45), up to 22 sessions in a 12-month period for Medicare beneficiaries. The Medicare coinsurance and Part B deductible are waived for this preventive service.

NOTE: Effective for claims with dates of service on or after January 1, 2015, codes G0473 and G0447 can be billed for a total of no more than 22 sessions in a 12-month period.

Contractors shall note the appropriate ICD-10-CM code(s) that are listed below for future implementation. Contractors shall track the ICD-10-CM codes and ensure that the updated edit is turned on when ICD-10 is implemented.

ICD-10-CM	Description
Z68.30 BMI	30.0-30.9, adult
Z68.31 BMI	31.0-31.9, adult
Z68.32 BMI	32.0-32.9, adult
Z68.33 BMI	33.0-33.9, adult
Z68.34 BMI	34.0-34.9, adult
Z68.35 BMI	35.0-35.9, adult
Z68.36 BMI	36.0-36.9, adult
Z68.37 BMI	37.0-37.9, adult
Z68.38 BMI	38.0-38.9, adult
Z68.39 BMI	39.0-39.9, adult
Z68.41 BMI	40.0-44.9, adult
Z68.42 BMI	45.0-49.9, adult
Z68.43 BMI	50.0-59.9, adult
Z68.44 BMI	60.0-69.9, adult
Z68.45 BMI	70 or greater, adult

See Pub. 100-03, Medicare National Coverage Determinations Manual, §210.12 for complete coverage guidelines.

100-4, Chapter-18, 200.2

Institutional Billing Requirements

Effective for claims with dates of service on and after November 29, 2011, providers may use the following types of bill (TOB) when submitting HCPCS code G0447: 13x, 71X, 77X, or 85X. Service line items on other TOBs shall be denied.

Effective for claims with dates of service on and after January 1, 2015, providers may use the following types of bill (TOB) when submitting HCPCS code G0473: 13x or 85X. Service line items on other TOBs shall be denied.

The service shall be paid on the basis shown below:

- Outpatient hospitals – TOB 13X - based on Outpatient Prospective Payment System (OPPS)
- Critical Access Hospitals (CAHs) - TOB 85X – based on reasonable cost
- CAH Method II – TOB 85X - based on 115% of the lesser of the Medicare Physician Fee Schedule (MPFS) amount or actual charge as applicable with revenue codes 096X, 097X, or 098X.

NOTE: For outpatient hospital settings, as in any other setting, services covered under this NCD must be provided by a primary care provider.

100-4, Chapter-18, 200.3

Professional Billing Requirements

CMS will allow coverage for Face-to-Face Behavioral Counseling for Obesity, 15 minutes, (G0447), Face-to-face behavioral counseling for obesity, group (2-10), 30 minute(s) (G0473), along with 1 of the ICD-9-CM codes for BMI 30.0-BMI 70

(V85.30-V85.39 and V85.41-V85.45), or 1 of the ICD-10-CM codes for BMI 30.0-BMI 70 (Z68.30-Z68.39 and Z68.41-Z68.45) only when services are submitted by the following provider specialties found on the provider's enrollment record:

01 - General Practice

08 - Family Practice

11 - Internal Medicine

16 - Obstetrics/Gynecology

37 - Pediatric Medicine

38 - Geriatric Medicine

50 - Nurse Practitioner

89 - Certified Clinical Nurse Specialist

97 - Physician Assistant

Any claims that are not submitted from one of the provider specialty types noted above will be denied.

CMS will allow coverage for Face-to-Face Behavioral Counseling for Obesity, 15 minutes, (G0447), Face-to-face behavioral counseling for obesity, group (2-10), 30 minute(s) (G0473), along with 1 of the ICD-9-CM codes for BMI 30.0-BMI 70 (V85.30-V85.39 and V85.41-V85.45), or with 1 of the ICD-10-CM codes for BMI 30.0-BMI 70 (Z68.30-Z68.39 and Z68.41-Z68.45) only when submitted with one of the following place of service (POS) codes:

11 - Physician's Office

22 - Outpatient Hospital

49 - Independent Clinic

71 - State or Local Public Health Clinic

Any claims that are not submitted with one of the POS codes noted above will be denied.

NOTE: HCPCS Code G0447 is effective November 29, 2011. HCPCS Code G0473 is effective January 1, 2015.

100-4, Chapter-18, 200.4

Claim Adjustment Reason Codes (CARCs), Remittance Advice Remark Codes (RARCs), Group Codes, and Medicare Summary Notice (MSN) Messages

Contractors shall use the appropriate claim adjustment reason codes (CARCs), remittance advice remark codes (RARCs), group codes, or Medicare summary notice (MSN) messages when denying payment for obesity counseling sessions:

- Denying services submitted on a TOB other than 13X and 85X:

  CARC 171 - Payment is denied when performed by this type of provider on this type of facility. Note: Refer to the 835 Healthcare Policy Identification Segment (loop 2110 Service Payment Information REF), if present.

  RARC N428 - Not covered when performed in this place of service.

  MSN 16.2 - This service cannot be paid when provided in this location/facility.

  Group Code PR (Patient Responsibility) assigning financial responsibility to the beneficiary (if a claim is received with a GA modifier indicating a signed ABN is on file).

Group Code CO (Contractual Obligation) assigning financial liability to the provider (if a claim is received with a GZ modifier indicating no signed ABN is on file).

Note: For modifier GZ, use CARC 50 and MSN 8.81.

- Denying services for obesity counseling sessions HCPCS code G0473 or G0447 with 1 of the ICD-9-CM codes (V85.30-V85.39 or V85.41-V85.45) or with one of the ICD-10-CM codes (Z68.30-Z68.39 or Z68.41-Z68.45) when billed for a total of more than 22 sessions in the same 12-month period:

  CARC 119 - Benefit maximum for this time period or occurrence has been reached.

  RARC N362 - The number of days or units of service exceeds our acceptable maximum.

  MSN 20.5 - These services cannot be paid because your benefits are exhausted at this time.

  Spanish Version: "Estos servicios no pueden ser pagados porque sus beneficios se han agotado."

  Group Code PR (Patient Responsibility) assigning financial responsibility to the beneficiary (if a claim is received with a GA modifier indicating a signed ABN is on file).

  Group Code CO (Contractual Obligation) assigning financial liability to the provider (if a claim is received with a GZ modifier indicating no signed ABN is on file).

  Note: For modifier GZ, use CARC 50 and MSN 8.81.

- Denying claim lines for obesity counseling sessions HCPCS code G0473 or G0447 without 1 of the appropriate ICD-9-CM codes (V85.30-V85.39 or V85.41-V85.45) or 1 of the ICD-10-CM codes (Z68.30-Z68.39 or Z68.41-Z68.45):

  CARC 167 - "This (these) diagnosis(es) is (are) not covered. Note: Refer to the ASC X12 835 Healthcare Policy Identification Segment (loop 2110 Service Payment Information REF), if present."

  RARC N386 - This decision was based on a National Coverage Determination (NCD). An NCD provides a coverage determination as to whether a particular item or service is covered. A copy of this policy is available at www.cms.gov/mcd/search.asp. If you do not have web access, you may contact the contractor to request a copy of the NCD.

  MSN 14.9 - "Medicare cannot pay for this service for the diagnosis shown on the claim."

  Group Code PR (Patient Responsibility) assigning financial responsibility to the beneficiary (if a claim is received with a GA modifier indicating a signed ABN is on file).

  Group Code CO (Contractual Obligation) assigning financial liability to the provider (if a claim is received with a GZ modifier indicating no signed ABN is on file).

  NOTE: For modifier GZ, use CARC 50 and MSN 8.81.

- Denying claim lines without the appropriate POS code:

  CARC 5 - The procedure code/bill type is inconsistent with the place of service. Note: Refer to the 835 Healthcare Policy Identification Segment (loop 2110 Service Payment Information REF), if present.

RARC M77 - Missing/incomplete/invalid place of service.

MSN 21.25 - This service was denied because Medicare only covers this service in certain settings.

Group Code CO (Contractual Obligation) assigning financial liability to the provider (if a claim is received with a GZ modifier indicating no signed ABN is on file).

NOTE: For modifier GZ, use CARC 50 and MSN 8.81.

- Denying claim lines that are not submitted from the appropriate provider specialties:

  CARC 8 - "The procedure code is inconsistent with the provider type/specialty (taxonomy). NOTE: Refer to the 835 Healthcare Policy Identification Segment (loop 2110 Service Payment Information REF), if present."

  RARC N95 - "This provider type/provider specialty may not bill this service."

  MSN 21.18 - "This item or service is not covered when performed or ordered by this provider."

  Group Code CO (Contractual Obligation) assigning financial liability to the provider (if a claim is received with a GZ modifier indicating no signed ABN is on file).

  NOTE: For modifier GZ, use CARC 50 and MSN 8.81.

100-4, Chapter-18, 200.5

Common Working File (CWF) Edits

When applying frequency, CWF shall count 22 counseling sessions of any of G0473 and/or G0447 (for a total of no more than 22 sessions in the same 12-month period) along with 1 ICD-9-CM code from V85.30-V85.39 or V85.41-V85.45 in a 12-month period, or if ICD-10 is applicable with 1 ICD-10-CM code from Z68.30-Z68.39 or Z68.41-Z68.45. When applying frequency limitations to G0473 or G0447 counseling CWF shall allow both a claim for the professional service and a claim for a facility fee. CWF shall identify the following institutional claims as facility fee claims for this service: TOB 13X, TOB 85X when the revenue code is not 096X, 097X, or 098X. CWF shall identify all other claims as professional service claims.

100-4, Chapter-20, 30.1.2

Transcutaneous Electrical Nerve Stimulator (TENS)

In order to permit an attending physician time to determine whether the purchase of a TENS is medically appropriate for a particular patient, contractors pay 10 percent of the purchase price of the item for each of 2 months. The purchase price and payment for maintenance and servicing are determined under the same rules as any other frequently purchased item, except that there is no reduction in the allowed amount for purchase due to the two months rental.

Effective June 8, 2012, CMS will allow coverage for TENS use in the treatment of chronic low back pain (CLBP) only under specific conditions which are described in the NCD Manual, Pub. 100-03, chapter 1 Section 160.27.

100-4, Chapter-20, 100.2.2

Evidence of Medical Necessity for Parenteral and Enteral Nutrition (PEN) Therapy

The PEN coverage is determined by information provided by the treating physician and the PEN supplier. A completed certification of medical necessity (CMN) must accompany and support initial claims for PEN to establish whether coverage criteria are met and to ensure that the PEN therapy provided is consistent with the attending or ordering physician's prescription. Contractors ensure that the CMN contains pertinent information from the treating physician. Uniform specific medical data facilitate the review and promote consistency in coverage determinations and timelier claims processing.

The medical and prescription information on a PEN CMN can be most appropriately completed by the treating physician or from information in the patient's records by an employee of the physician for the physician's review and signature. Although PEN suppliers sometimes may assist in providing the PEN services, they cannot complete the CMN since they do not have the same access to patient information needed to properly enter medical or prescription information. Contractors use appropriate professional relations issuances, training sessions, and meetings to ensure that all persons and PEN suppliers are aware of this limitation of their role.

When properly completed, the PEN CMN includes the elements of a prescription as well as other data needed to determine whether Medicare coverage is possible. This practice will facilitate prompt delivery of PEN services and timely submittal of the related claim.

100-4, Chapter-20, 160.1

Billing for Total Parenteral Nutrition and Enteral Nutrition Furnished to Part B Inpatients

Inpatient Part A hospital or SNF care includes total parenteral nutrition (TPN) systems and enteral nutrition (EN).

For inpatients for whom Part A benefits are not payable (e.g., benefits are exhausted or the beneficiary is entitled to Part B only), total parenteral nutrition (TPN) systems and enteral nutrition (EN) delivery systems are covered by Medicare as prosthetic devices when the coverage criteria are met. When these criteria are met, the medical equipment and medical supplies (together with nutrients) being used comprise covered prosthetic devices for coverage purposes rather than durable medical equipment. However, reimbursement rules relating to DME continue to apply to such items.

When a facility supplies TPN or EN systems that meet the criteria for coverage as a prosthetic device to an inpatient whose care is not covered under Part A, the facility must bill one of the DME MACs. Additionally, HHAs, SNFs, and hospitals that provide PEN supplies, equipment and nutrients as a prosthetic device under Part B must use the ASC X12 837 professional claim format or if permissible the Form CMS-1500 paper form to bill the appropriate DME MAC. The DME MACis determined according to the residence of the beneficiary. Refer to §10 for jurisdiction descriptions.

A/B MACs (Aand HHH) return claims containing PEN charges for Part B services where the bill type is 12x, 13x, 22x, 23x, 32x, 33x, or 34x with instructions to the provider to bill the DME MAC.

100-4, Chapter-23, 60.3

Gap-filling DMEPOS Fees

The DME MACs and Part B MACs must gap-fill the DMEPOS fee schedule for items for which charge data were unavailable during the fee schedule data base year using the fee schedule amounts for comparable equipment, using properly calculated fee schedule amounts from a neighboring DME MAC or Part B MAC area, or using supplier price lists with prices in effect during the fee schedule data base year. Data base "year" refers to the time period mandated by the statute and/or regulations from which Medicare allowed charge data is to be extracted in order to compute the fee schedule amounts for the various DMEPOS payment categories. For example, the fee schedule base year for inexpensive or routinely purchased durable medical equipment is the 12 month period ending June 30, 1987. Mail order catalogs are particularly suitable sources of price information for items such as urological and ostomy supplies which require constant replacement. DME MACs will gap-fill based on current instructions released each year for implementing and updating the new year's payment amounts.

If the only available price information is from a period other than the base period, apply the deflation factors that are included in the current year implementation instructions against current pricing in order to approximate the base year price for gap-filling purposes.

The deflation factors for gap-filling purposes are:

Year*	OX	CR	PO	SD	PE	SC	IL
1987	0.965	0.971	0.974	n/a	n/a	n/a	n/a
1988	0.928	0.934	0.936	n/a	n/a	n/a	n/a
1989	0.882	0.888	0.890	n/a	n/a	n/a	n/a
1990	0.843	0.848	0.851	n/a	n/a	n/a	n/a
1991	0.805	0.810	0.813	n/a	n/a	n/a	n/a
1992	0.781	0.786	0.788	n/a	n/a	n/a	n/a
1993	0.758	0.763	0.765	0.971	n/a	n/a	n/a
1994	0.740	0.745	0.747	0.947	n/a	n/a	n/a
1995	0.718	0.723	0.725	0.919	n/a	n/a	n/a
1996	0.699	0.703	0.705	0.895	0.973	n/a	n/a
1997	0.683	0.687	0.689	0.875	0.951	n/a	n/a
1998	0.672	0.676	0.678	0.860	0.936	n/a	n/a
1999	0.659	0.663	0.665	0.844	0.918	n/a	n/a
2000	0.635	0.639	0.641	0.813	0.885	n/a	n/a
2001	0.615	0.619	0.621	0.788	0.857	n/a	n/a
2002	0.609	0.613	0.614	0.779	0.848	n/a	n/a
2003	0.596	0.600	0.602	0.763	0.830	n/a	n/a
2004	0.577	0.581	0.582	0.739	0.804	n/a	n/a
2005	0.563	0.567	0.568	0.721	0.784	n/a	n/a
2006	0.540	0.543	0.545	0.691	0.752	n/a	n/a
2007	0.525	0.529	0.530	0.673	0.732	n/a	n/a
2008	0.500	0.504	0.505	0.641	0.697	n/a	n/a
2009	0.508	0.511	0.512	0.650	0.707	n/a	n/a
2010	0.502	0.506	0.507	0.643	0.700	n/a	n/a
2011	0.485	0.488	0.490	0.621	0.676	n/a	n/a
2012	0.477	0.480	0.482	0.611	0.665	n/a	n/a
2013	0.469	0.472	0.473	0.600	0.653	n/a	0.983
2014	0.459	0.462	0.464	0.588	0.640	0.980	0.963

* Year price in effect

Payment Category Key:

OX	Oxygen & oxygen equipment (DME)
CR	Capped rental (DME)
IN	Inexpensive/routinely purchased (DME)
FS	Frequently serviced (DME)
SU	DME supplies
PO	Prosthetics & orthotics
SD	Surgical dressings
OS	Ostomy, tracheostomy, and urological supplies
PE	Parental and enteral nutrition
TS	Therapeutic Shoes
SC	Splints and Casts
IL	Intraocular Lenses inserted in a physician's office

IN, FS, OS and SU category deflation factors=PO deflation factors

After deflation, the result must be increased by 1.7 percent and by the cumulative covered item update to complete the gap-filling (e.g., an additional .6 percent for a 2002 DME fee).

Note that when gap-filling for capped rental items, it is necessary to first gap-fill the purchase price then compute the base period fee schedule at 10 percent of the base period purchase price.

For used equipment, establish fee schedule amounts at 75 percent of the fee schedule amount for new equipment.

When gap-filling, for those *DME MAC or Part B MAC* areas where a sales tax was imposed in the base period, add the applicable sales tax, e.g., five percent, to the gap-filled amount where the gap-filled amount does not take into account the sales tax, e.g., where the gap-filled amount is computed from pre-tax price lists or from another *DME MAC or Part B MAC* area without a sales tax. Likewise, if the gap-filled amount is calculated from another *DME MAC's or Part B MAC's* fees where a sales tax is imposed, adjust the gap-filled amount to reflect the applicable local sales tax circumstances.

Contractors send their gap-fill information to CMS. After receiving the gap-filled base fees each year, CMS develops national fee schedule floors and ceilings and new fee schedule amounts for these codes and releases them as part of the July update file each year and during the quarterly updates.

100-4, Chapter-32, 11.1

Electrical Stimulation

A. Coding Applicable to Carriers & Fiscal Intermediaries (FIs)

Effective April 1, 2003, a National Coverage Decision was made to allow for Medicare coverage of Electrical Stimulation for the treatment of certain types of wounds. The type of wounds overed are chronic Stage III or Stage IV pressure ulcers, arterial ulcers, diabetic ulcers and venous stasis ulcers. All other uses of electrical stimulation for the treatment of wounds are not covered by Medicare. Electrical stimulation will not be covered as an initial treatment modality.

The use of electrical stimulation will only be covered after appropriate standard wound care has been tried for at least 30 days and there are no measurable signs of healing. If electrical stimulation is being used, wounds must be evaluated periodically by the treating physician but no less than every

30 days by a physician. Continued treatment with electrical stimulation is not covered if measurable signs of healing have not been demonstrated within any 30-day period of treatment. Additionally, electrical stimulation must be discontinued when the wound demonstrates a 100% epithelialzed wound bed.

Coverage policy can be found in Pub. 100-03, Medicare National Coverage Determinations

Manual, Chapter 1, Section 270.1

(http://www.cms.hhs.gov/manuals/103_cov_determ/ncd103index.asp)

The applicable Healthcare Common Procedure Coding System (HCPCS) code for Electrical Stimulation and the covered effective date is as follows:

HCPSC	Definition	Effective Date
G0281	Electrical Stimulation, (unattended), to one or more areas for chronic Stage III and Stage IV pressure ulcers, arterial ulcers, diabetic ulcers and venous stasis ulcers not demonstrating measurable signs of healing after 30 days of conventional care as part of a therapy plan of care.	04/01/2003

B. FI Billing Instructions

The applicable types of bills acceptable when billing for electrical stimulation services are 12X, 13X, 22X, 23X, 71X, 73X, 74X, 75X, and 85X. Chapter 25 of this manual provides general billing instructions that must be followed for bills submitted to FIs. FIs pay for electrical stimulation services under the Medicare Physician Fee Schedule for a hospital, Comprehensive Outpatient Rehabilitation Facility (CORF), Outpatient Rehabilitation Facility (ORF), Outpatient Physical Therapy (OPT) and Skilled Nursing Facility (SNF). Payment methodology for independent Rural Health Clinic (RHC), provider-based RHCs, free-standing Federally Qualified Health Center (FQHC)and provider based FQHCs is made under the all-inclusive rate for the visit furnished to the RHC/FQHC patient to obtain the therapy service. Only one payment will be made for the visit furnished to the RHC/FQHC patient to obtain the therapy service. As of April 1, 2005, RHCs/FQHCs are no longer required to report HCPCS codes when billing for these therapy services.

Payment Methodology for a Critical Access Hospital (CAH) is on a reasonable cost basis unless the CAH has elected the Optional Method and then the FI pays115% of the MPFS amount for the professional component of the HCPCS code in addition to the technical component.

In addition, the following revenues code must be used in conjunction with the HCPCS code identified:

Revenue Code	Description
420	Physical Therapy
430	Occupational Therapy
520	Federal Qualified Health Center *
521	Rural Health Center *
977,978	Critical Access Hospital-method II CAH professional services only

* **NOTE:** As of April 1, 2005, RHCs/FQHCs are no longer required to report HCPCS codes when billing for these therapy services.

C. Carrier Claims

Carriers pay for Electrical Stimulation services billed with HCPCS codes G0281 based on the MPFS. Claims for Electrical Stimulation services must be billed on Form CMS-1500 or the electronic equivalent following instructions in chapter 12 of this manual

(http://www.cms.HHS.gov/manuals/104_claims/clm104c12.pdf).

D. Coinsurance and Deductible

The Medicare contractor shall apply coinsurance and deductible to payments for these therapy services except for services billed to the FI by FQHCs. For FQHCs, only co-insurance applies.

100-4, Chapter-32, 11.2

Electromagnetic Therapy

A. HCPCS Coding Applicable to A/B MACs (A and B)

Effective July 1, 2004, a National Coverage Decision was made to allow for Medicare coverage of electromagnetic therapy for the treatment of certain types of wounds. The type of wounds covered are chronic Stage III or Stage IV pressure ulcers, arterial ulcers, diabetic ulcers and venous stasis ulcers. All other uses of electromagnetic therapy for the treatment of wounds are not covered by Medicare. Electromagnetic therapy will not be covered as an initial treatment modality.

The use of electromagnetic therapy will only be covered after appropriate standard wound care has been tried for at least 30 days and there are no measurable signs of healing. If electromagnetic therapy is being used, wounds must be evaluated periodically by the treating physician but no less than every 30 days. Continued treatment with electromagnetic therapy is not covered if measurable signs of healing have not been demonstrated within any 30-day period of treatment. Additionally, electromagnetic therapy must be discontinued when the wound demonstrates a 100% epithelialzed wound bed.

Coverage policy can be found in Pub. 100-03, Medicare National Coverage Determinations Manual, Chapter 1 section 270.1.

(http://www.cms.hhs.gov/manuals/103_cov_determ/ncd103index.asp)

The applicable Healthcare Common Procedure Coding System (HCPCS) code for Electrical Stimulation and the covered effective date is as follows:

HCPCS	Definition	Effective Date
G0329	Electromagnetic Therapy, to one or more areas for chronic Stage III and Stage IV pressure ulcers, arterial ulcers, diabetic ulcers and venous stasis ulcers not demonstrating measurable signs of healing after 30 days of conventional care as part of a therapy plan of care.	07/01/2004

Medicare will not cover the device used for the electromagnetic therapy for the treatment of wounds. However, Medicare will cover the service. Unsupervised home use of electromagnetic therapy will not be covered.

B. A/B MAC (A) Billing Instructions

The applicable types of bills acceptable when billing for electromagnetic therapy services are 2X, 13X, 22X, 23X, 71X, 73X, 74X, 75X, and 85X. Chapter 25 of this manual provides general billing instructions that must be followed for bills submitted to A/B MACs (A). A/B MACs (A) pay for electromagnetic therapy services under the Medicare Physician Fee Schedule for a hospital, CORF, ORF, and SNF.

Payment methodology for independent (RHC), provider-based RHCs, free-standing FQHC and provider based FQHCs is made under the all-inclusive rate for the visit furnished to the RHC/FQHC patient to obtain the therapy service. Only one payment will be made for the visit furnished to the RHC/FQHC patient to obtain the therapy service. As of April 1, 2005, RHCs/FQHCs are no longer required to report HCPCS codes when billing for the therapy service.

Payment Methodology for a CAH is payment on a reasonable cost basis unless the CAH has elected the Optional Method and then the A/B MAC (A) pays pay 115% of the MPFS amount for the professional component of the HCPCS code in addition to the technical component.

In addition, the following revenues code must be used in conjunction with the HCPCS code identified:

Revenue Code	Description
420	Physical Therapy
430	Occupational Therapy
520	Federal Qualified Health Center *
521	Rural Health Center *
977,978	Critical Access Hospital-method II CAH professional services only

* **NOTE:** As of April 1, 2005, RHCs/FQHCs are no longer required to report HCPCS codes when billing for the therapy service.

C. A/B MAC (B) Claims

A/B MACs (B) pay for Electromagnetic Therapy services billed with HCPCS codes G0329 based on the MPFS. Claims for electromagnetic therapy services must be billed using the ASC X12 837 professional claim format or Form CMS-1500 following instructions in chapter 12 of this manual (www.cms.hhs.gov/manuals/104_claims/clm104index.asp).

Payment information for HCPCS code G0329 will be added to the July 2004 update of the Medicare Physician Fee Schedule Database (MPFSD).

D. Coinsurance and Deductible

The Medicare contractor shall apply coinsurance and deductible to payments for electromagnetic therapy services except for services billed to the A/B MAC (A) by FQHCs.

For FQHCs only co-insurance applies.

100-4, Chapter-32, 11.3.1

Policy

Effective for claims with dates of service on or after August 2, 2012, contractors shall accept and pay for autologous platelet-rich plasma (PRP) only for the treatment of chronic non-healing diabetic, venous and/or pressure wounds only in the context of an approved clinical study in accordance with the coverage criteria outlined in Pub. 100-03, chapter 1, section 270.3, of the NCD Manual.

100-4, Chapter-32, 11.3.2

Healthcare Common Procedure Coding System (HCPCS) Codes and Diagnosis Coding

HCPCS Code

Effective for claims with dates of service on or after August 2, 2012 Medicare providers shall report HCPCS code G0460 for PRP services.

If ICD-9 Diagnosis coding is applicable

For claims with dates of service on or after August 2, 2012, PRP, for the treatment of chronic non-healing diabetic, venous and/or pressure wounds only in the context of an approved clinical study must be billed using the following ICD codes:

- V70.7
- ICD-9 code from the approved list of diagnosis codes maintained by the Medicare contractor.

If ICD-10 Diagnosis coding is applicable

For claims with dates of service on or after the implementation of ICD-10, ICD-10 CM diagnosis coding is applicable.

- Z00.6
- ICD-10 code from the approved list of diagnosis codes maintained by the Medicare contractor.

Additional billing requirement:

The following modifier and condition code shall be reported when billing for PRP services only in the context of an approved clinical study:

- Q0 modifier
- Condition code 30 (for institutional claims only)
- Value Code D4 with an 8-digit clinical trial number. **NOTE:** This is optional and only applies to Institutional claims.

100-4, Chapter-32, 11.3.3

Types of Bill (TOB)

The applicable TOBs for PRP services are: 12X, 13X, 22X, 23X, 71X, 75X, 77X, and 85X.

100-4, Chapter-32, 11.3.4

Payment Method

Payment for PRP services is as follows:

- Hospital outpatient departments TOBs 12X and 13X – based on OPPS
- SNFs TOBs 22X and 23X –based on MPFS
- TOB 71X –based on all-inclusive rate
- TOB 75X –based on MPFS
- TOB 77X –based on all-inclusive rate
- TOB 85X –based on reasonable cost
- CAHs TOB 85X and revenue codes 096X, 097X, or 098X –based on MPFS

Contractors shall pay for PRP services for hospitals in Maryland under the jurisdiction of the Health Services Cost Review Commission (HSCRC) on an outpatient basis, TOB 13X, in accordance with the terms of the Maryland waiver.

100-4, Chapter-32, 11.3.5

Place of Service (POS) for Professional Claims

Effective for claims with dates of service on or after August 2, 2012, place of service codes 11, 22, and 49 shall be used for PRP services.

100-4, Chapter-32, 11.3.6

Medicare Summary Notices (MSNs), Remittance Advice Remark Codes (RARCs), Claim Adjustment Reason Codes (CARCs) and Group Codes

Contractors shall use the following messages when returning to provider/returning as unprocessable claims when required information is not included on claims for autologous platelet-rich plasma (PRP) for the treatment of chronic non-healing diabetic, venous and/or pressure wounds only in the context of an approved clinical study:

CARC 16 -Claim/service lacks information or has submission/billing error(s) which is (are) needed for adjudication. At least one Remark Code must be provided (may be comprised of either the NCPDP Reject Reason Code, or Remittance Advice Remark Code that is not an ALERT.)

NOTE: Refer to the 835 Healthcare Policy Identification Segment (loop 2110 Service Payment Information REF), if present.

RARC MA130 – Your claim contains incomplete and/or invalid information, and no appeal rights are afforded because the claim is unprocessable. Please submit a new claim with the complete/correct information.

Contractors shall deny claims for RPR services, HCPCS code G0460, when services are provided on other than TOBs 12X, 13X, 22X, 23X, 71X, 75X, 77X, and 85X using:

MSN 21.25: "This service was denied because Medicare only covers this service in certain settings."

Spanish Version: "El servicio fue denegado porque Medicare solamente lo cubre en ciertas situaciones."

CARC 58: "Treatment was deemed by the payer to have been rendered in an inappropriate or invalid place of service. **NOTE:** Refer to the 832 Healthcare Policy Identification Segment (loop 2110 Service payment Information REF), if present.

RARC N428: "Service/procedure not covered when performed in this place of service."

Group Code –CO (Contractual Obligation)

Contractors shall deny claims for PRP services for POS other than 11, 22, or 49 using the following:

MSN 21.25: "This service was denied because Medicare only covers this service in certain settings."

Spanish Version: "El servicio fue denegado porque Medicare solamente lo cubre en ciertas situaciones."

CARC 58: "Treatment was deemed by the payer to have been rendered in an inappropriate or invalid place of service. NOTE; Refer to the 835 Healthcare Policy Identification Segment (loop 2110 Service payment Information REF), if present.

RARC N428: "Service/procedure not covered when performed in this place of service."

Group Code –CO (Contractual Obligation)

100-4, Chapter-32, 30.1

Billing Requirements for HBO Therapy for the Treatment of Diabetic Wounds of the Lower Extremities

Hyperbaric Oxygen Therapy is a modality in which the entire body is exposed to oxygen under increased atmospheric pressure.

Effective April 1, 2003, a National Coverage Decision expanded the use of HBO therapy to include coverage for the treatment of diabetic wounds of the lower extremities. For specific coverage criteria for HBO Therapy, refer to the National Coverage Determinations Manual, Chapter 1, section 20.29.

NOTE: Topical application of oxygen does not meet the definition of HBO therapy as stated above. Also, its clinical efficacy has not been established. Therefore, no Medicare reimbursement may be made for the topical application of oxygen.

I. Billing Requirements for A/B MACs (A)

Claims for HBO therapy should be submitted using the ASC X12 837 institutional claim format or, in rare cases, on Form CMS-1450.

a. Applicable Bill Types

The applicable hospital bill types are 11X, 13X and 85X.

b. Procedural Coding

- 99183 – Physician attendance and supervision of hyperbaric oxygen therapy, per session.
- C1300 – Hyperbaric oxygen under pressure, full body chamber, per 30-minute interval.

NOTE: Code C1300 is not available for use other than in a hospital outpatient department.

In skilled nursing facilities (SNFs), HBO therapy is part of the SNF PPS payment for beneficiaries in covered Part A stays.

For hospital inpatients and critical access hospitals (CAHs) not electing Method I, HBO therapy is reported under revenue code 940 without any HCPCS code. For inpatient services, if ICD-9-is applicable, show ICD-9-CM procedure code 93.59. If ICD-10 is applicable, show ICD-10-PCS code 5A05121.

For CAHs electing Method I, HBO therapy is reported under revenue code 940 along with HCPCS code 99183.

c. Payment Requirements for A/B MACs (A)

Payment is as follows:

A/B MAC (A) payment is allowed for HBO therapy for diabetic wounds of the lower extremities when performed as a physician service in a hospital outpatient setting and for inpatients. Payment is allowed for claims with valid diagnosis codes as shown above with dates of service on or after April 1, 2003. Those claims with invalid codes should be denied as not medically necessary.

For hospitals, payment will be based upon the Ambulatory Payment Classification (APC) or the inpatient Diagnosis Related Group (DRG). Deductible and coinsurance apply.

Payment to Critical Access Hospitals (electing Method I) is made under cost reimbursement. For Critical Access Hospitals electing Method II, the technical component is paid under cost reimbursement and the professional component is paid under the Physician Fee Schedule.

II. A/B MAC (B) Billing Requirements

Claims for this service should be submitted using the ASC X12 837 professional claim format or

Form CMS-1500.

The following HCPCS code applies:

- 99183 –Physician attendance and supervision of hyperbaric oxygen therapy, per session.

a. Payment Requirements for A/B MACs (B)

Payment and pricing information will occur through updates to the Medicare Physician Fee

Schedule Database (MPFSDB). Pay for this service on the basis of the MPFSDB.

Deductible and coinsurance apply. Claims from physicians or other practitioners where assignment was not taken, are subject to the Medicare limiting charge.

III. Medicare Summary Notices (MSNs)

Use the following MSN Messages where appropriate:

In situations where the claim is being denied on the basis that the condition does not meet our coverage requirements, use one of the following MSN Messages:

"Medicare does not pay for this item or service for this condition." (MSN Message 16.48)

The Spanish version of the MSN message should read:

"Medicare no paga por este articulo o servicio para esta afeccion."

In situations where, based on the above utilization policy, medical review of the claim results in a determination that the service is not medically necessary, use the following MSN message:

"The information provided does not support the need for this service or item." (MSN Message 15.4)

The Spanish version of the MSN message should read:

"La informacion proporcionada no confirma la necesidad para este servicio o articulo."

IV. Remittance Advice Notices

Use appropriate existing remittance advice remark codes and claim adjustment reason codes at the line level to express the specific reason if you deny payment for HBO therapy for the treatment of diabetic wounds of lower extremities.

100-4, Chapter-32, 40.1

Coverage Requirements

Effective January 1, 2002, sacral nerve stimulation is covered for the treatment of urinary urge incontinence, urgency-frequency syndrome and urinary retention. Sacral nerve stimulation involves both a temporary test stimulation to determine if an implantable stimulator would be effective and a permanent implantation in appropriate candidates. Both the test and the permanent implantation are covered.

The following limitations for coverage apply to all indications:

- Patient must be refractory to conventional therapy (documented behavioral, pharmacologic and/or surgical corrective therapy) and be an appropriate surgical candidate such that implantation with anesthesia can occur.
- Patients with stress incontinence, urinary obstruction, and specific neurologic diseases (e.g., diabetes with peripheral nerve involvement) that are associated with secondary manifestations of the above three indications are excluded.
- Patient must have had a successful test stimulation in order to support subsequent implantation. Before a patient is eligible for permanent implantation, he/she must demonstrate a 50% or greater improvement through test stimulation. Improvement is measured through voiding diaries.

- Patient must be able to demonstrate adequate ability to record voiding diary data such that clinical results of the implant procedure can be properly evaluated.

100-4, Chapter-32, 50

Deep Brain Stimulation for Essential Tremor and Parkinson's Disease

Deep brain stimulation (DBS) refers to high-frequency electrical stimulation of anatomic regions deep within the brain utilizing neurosurgically implanted electrodes. These DBS electrodes are stereotactically placed within targeted nuclei on one (unilateral) or both (bilateral) sides of the brain. There are currently three targets for DBS --the thalamic ventralis intermedius nucleus (VIM), subthalamic nucleus (STN) and globus pallidus interna (GPi).

Essential tremor (ET) is a progressive, disabling tremor most often affecting the hands. ET may also affect the head, voice and legs. The precise pathogenesis of ET is unknown. While it may start at any age, ET usually peaks within the second and sixth decades. Beta-adrenergic blockers and anticonvulsant medications are usually the first line treatments for reducing the severity of tremor. Many patients, however, do not adequately respond or cannot tolerate these medications. In these medically refractory ET patients, thalamic VIM DBS may be helpful for symptomatic relief of tremor.

Parkinson's disease (PD) is an age-related progressive neurodegenerative disorder involving the loss of dopaminergic cells in the substantia nigra of the midbrain. The disease is characterized by tremor, rigidity, bradykinesia and progressive postural instability. Dopaminergic medication is typically used as a first line treatment for reducing the primary symptoms of PD. However, after prolonged use, medication can become less effective and can produce significant adverse events such as dyskinesias and other motor function complications. For patients who become unresponsive to medical treatments and/or have intolerable side effects from medications, DBS for symptom relief may be considered.

100-4, Chapter-32, 60.4.1

Allowable Covered Diagnosis Codes

For services furnished on or after July 1, 2002, the applicable ICD-9-CM diagnosis code for this benefit is V43.3, organ or tissue replaced by other means; heart valve.

For services furnished on or after March 19, 2008, the applicable ICD-9-CM diagnosis codes for this benefit are:

- V43.3 (organ or tissue replaced by other means; heart valve),
- 289.81 (primary hypercoagulable state),
- 451.0-451.9 (includes 451.11, 451.19, 451.2, 451.80-451.84, 451.89) (phlebitis & thrombophlebitis),
- 453.0-453.3 (other venous embolism & thrombosis),
- 453.40-453.49 (includes 453.40-453.42, 453.6,453.8-453.9) (venous embolism and thrombosis of the deep vessels of the lower extremity, and other specified veins/unspecified sites),
- 415.11-415.12, 415.19 (pulmonary embolism & infarction),or,
- 427.31 (atrial fibrillation (established) (paroxysmal)).

For services furnished on or after the implementation of ICD-10 the applicable ICD-10-CM diagnosis codes for this benefit are:

Heart Valve Replacement

- Z95.2 - Presence of prosthetic heart valve

Primary Hypercoagulable State

ICD-10-CM Code	Code Description
D68.51	Activated protein C resistance
D68.52	Prothrombin gene mutation
D68.59	Other primary thrombophilia
D68.61	Antiphospholipid syndrome
D68.62	Lupus anticoagulant syndrome

Phlebitis & Thrombophlebitis

ICD-10-CM Code	Code Description
I80.00	Phlebitis and thrombophlebitis of superficial vessels of unspecified lower extremity
I80.01	Phlebitis and thrombophlebitis of superficial vessels of right lower extremity
I80.02	Phlebitis and thrombophlebitis of superficial vessels of left lower extremity
I80.03	Phlebitis and thrombophlebitis of superficial vessels of lower extremities, bilateral
I80.10	Phlebitis and thrombophlebitis of unspecified femoral vein
I80.11	Phlebitis and thrombophlebitis of right femoral vein
I80.12	Phlebitis and thrombophlebitis of left femoral vein
I80.13	Phlebitis and thrombophlebitis of femoral vein, bilateral
I80.201	Phlebitis and thrombophlebitis of unspecified deep vessels of right lower extremity
I80.202	Phlebitis and thrombophlebitis of unspecified deep vessels of left lower extremity
I80.203	Phlebitis and thrombophlebitis of unspecified deep vessels of lower extremities, bilateral
I80.209	Phlebitis and thrombophlebitis of unspecified deep vessels of unspecified lower extremity
I80.221	Phlebitis and thrombophlebitis of right popliteal vein
I80.222	Phlebitis and thrombophlebitis of left popliteal vein
I80.223	Phlebitis and thrombophlebitis of popliteal vein, bilateral
I80.229	Phlebitis and thrombophlebitis of unspecified popliteal vein
I80.231	Phlebitis and thrombophlebitis of right tibial vein
I80.232	Phlebitis and thrombophlebitis of left tibial vein
I80.233	Phlebitis and thrombophlebitis of tibial vein, bilateral
I80.239	Phlebitis and thrombophlebitis of unspecified tibial vein
I80.291	Phlebitis and thrombophlebitis of other deep vessels of right lower extremity
I80.292	Phlebitis and thrombophlebitis of other deep vessels of left lower extremity
I80.293	Phlebitis and thrombophlebitis of other deep vessels of lower extremity, bilateral
I80.299	Phlebitis and thrombophlebitis of other deep vessels of unspecified lower extremity
I80.3	Phlebitis and thrombophlebitis of lower extremities, unspecified
I80.211	Phlebitis and thrombophlebitis of right iliac vein
I80.212	Phlebitis and thrombophlebitis of left iliac vein
I80.213	Phlebitis and thrombophlebitis of iliac vein, bilateral
I80.219	Phlebitis and thrombophlebitis of unspecified iliac vein

ICD-10-CM Code	Code Description
I80.8	Phlebitis and thrombophlebitis of other sites
I80.9	Phlebitis and thrombophlebitis of unspecified site

Other Venous Embolism & Thrombosis

ICD-10-CM Code	Code Description
I82.0	Budd- Chiari syndrome
I82.1	Thrombophlebitis migrans
I82.211	Chronic embolism and thrombosis of superior vena cava
I82.220	Acute embolism and thrombosis of inferior vena cava
I82.221	Chronic embolism and thrombosis of inferior vena cava
I82.291	Chronic embolism and thrombosis of other thoracic veins
I82.3	Embolism and thrombosis of renal vein

Venous Embolism and thrombosis of the deep vessels of the lower extremity, and other specified veins/unspecified sites

ICD-10-CM Code	Code Description
I82.401	Acute embolism and thrombosis of unspecified deep veins of right lower extremity
I82.402	Acute embolism and thrombosis of unspecified deep veins of left lower extremity
I82.403	Acute embolism and thrombosis of unspecified deep veins of lower extremity, bilateral
I82.409	Acute embolism and thrombosis of unspecified deep veins of unspecified lower extremity
I82.411	Acute embolism and thrombosis of right femoral vein
I82.412	Acute embolism and thrombosis of left femoral vein
I82.413	Acute embolism and thrombosis of femoral vein, bilateral
I82.419	Acute embolism and thrombosis of unspecified femoral vein
I82.421	Acute embolism and thrombosis of right iliac vein
I82.422	Acute embolism and thrombosis of left iliac vein
I82.423	Acute embolism and thrombosis of iliac vein, bilateral
I82.429	Acute embolism and thrombosis of unspecified iliac vein
I82.431	Acute embolism and thrombosis of right popliteal vein
I82.432	Acute embolism and thrombosis of left popliteal vein
I82.433	Acute embolism and thrombosis of popliteal vein, bilateral
I82.439	Acute embolism and thrombosis of unspecified popliteal vein
I82.4Y1	Acute embolism and thrombosis of unspecified deep veins of right proximal lower extremity
I82.4Y2	Acute embolism and thrombosis of unspecified deep veins of left proximal lower extremity
I82.4Y3	Acute embolism and thrombosis of unspecified deep veins of proximal lower extremity, bilateral
I82.4Y9	Acute embolism and thrombosis of unspecified deep veins of unspecified proximal lower extremity
I82.441	Acute embolism and thrombosis of right tibial vein
I82.442	Acute embolism and thrombosis of left tibial vein
I82.443	Acute embolism and thrombosis of tibial vein, bilateral
I82.449	Acute embolism and thrombosis of unspecified tibial vein
I82.491	Acute embolism and thrombosis of other specified deep vein of right lower extremity

ICD-10-CM Code	Code Description
I82.492	Acute embolism and thrombosis of other specified deep vein of left lower extremity
I82.493	Acute embolism and thrombosis of other specified deep vein of lower extremity, bilateral
I82.499	Acute embolism and thrombosis of other specified deep vein of unspecified lower extremity
I82.4Z1	Acute embolism and thrombosis of unspecified deep veins of right distal lower extremity
I82.4Z2	Acute embolism and thrombosis of unspecified deep veins of left distal lower extremity
I82.4Z3	Acute embolism and thrombosis of unspecified deep veins of distal lower extremity, bilateral
I82.4Z9	Acute embolism and thrombosis of unspecified deep veins of unspecified distal lower extremity
I82.501	Chronic embolism and thrombosis of unspecified deep veins of right lower extremity
I82.502	Chronic embolism and thrombosis of unspecified deep veins of left lower extremity
I82.503	Chronic embolism and thrombosis of unspecified deep veins of lower extremity, bilateral
I82.509	Chronic embolism and thrombosis of unspecified deep veins of unspecified lower extremity
I82.591	Chronic embolism and thrombosis of other specified deep vein of right lower extremity
I82.592	Chronic embolism and thrombosis of other specified deep vein of left lower extremity
I82.593	Chronic embolism and thrombosis of other specified deep vein of lower extremity, bilateral
I82.599	Chronic embolism and thrombosis of other specified deep vein of unspecified lower extremity
I82.511	Chronic embolism and thrombosis of right femoral vein
I82.512	Chronic embolism and thrombosis of left femoral vein
I82.513	Chronic embolism and thrombosis of femoral vein, bilateral
I82.519	Chronic embolism and thrombosis of unspecified femoral vein
I82.521	Chronic embolism and thrombosis of right iliac vein
I82.522	Chronic embolism and thrombosis of left iliac vein
I82.523	Chronic embolism and thrombosis of iliac vein, bilateral
I82.529	Chronic embolism and thrombosis of unspecified iliac vein
I82.531	Chronic embolism and thrombosis of right popliteal vein
I82.532	Chronic embolism and thrombosis of left popliteal vein
I82.533	Chronic embolism and thrombosis of popliteal vein, bilateral
I82.539	Chronic embolism and thrombosis of unspecified popliteal vein
I82.5Y1	Chronic embolism and thrombosis of unspecified deep veins of right proximal lower extremity
I82.5Y2	Chronic embolism and thrombosis of unspecified deep veins of left proximal lower extremity
I82.5Y3	Chronic embolism and thrombosis of unspecified deep veins of proximal lower extremity, bilateral
I82.5Y9	Chronic embolism and thrombosis of unspecified deep veins of unspecified proximal lower extremity
I82.541	Chronic embolism and thrombosis of right tibial vein
I82.542	Chronic embolism and thrombosis of left tibial vein

ICD-10-CM Code	Code Description	ICD-10-CM Code	Code Description
I82.543	Chronic embolism and thrombosis of tibial vein, bilateral	I82.B29	Chronic embolism and thrombosis of unspecified subclavian vein
I82.549	Chronic embolism and thrombosis of unspecified tibial vein	I82.C11	Acute embolism and thrombosis of right internal jugular vein
I82.5Z1	Chronic embolism and thrombosis of unspecified deep veins of right distal lower extremity	I82.C12	Acute embolism and thrombosis of left internal jugular vein
I82.5Z2	Chronic embolism and thrombosis of unspecified deep veins of left distal lower extremity	I82.C13	Acute embolism and thrombosis of internal jugular vein, bilateral
I82.5Z3	Chronic embolism and thrombosis of unspecified deep veins of distal lower extremity, bilateral	I82.C19	Acute embolism and thrombosis of unspecified internal jugular vein
I82.5Z9	Chronic embolism and thrombosis of unspecified deep veins of unspecified distal lower extremity	I82.C21	Chronic embolism and thrombosis of right internal jugular vein
I82.611	Acute embolism and thrombosis of superficial veins of right upper extremity	I82.C22	Chronic embolism and thrombosis of left internal jugular vein
I82.612	Acute embolism and thrombosis of superficial veins of left upper extremity	I82.C23	Chronic embolism and thrombosis of internal jugular vein, bilateral
I82.613	Acute embolism and thrombosis of superficial veins of upper extremity, bilateral	I82.C29	Chronic embolism and thrombosis of unspecified internal jugular vein
I82.619	Acute embolism and thrombosis of superficial veins of unspecified upper extremity	I82.210	Acute embolism and thrombosis of superior vena cava
I82.621	Acute embolism and thrombosis of deep veins of right upper extremity	I82.290	Acute embolism and thrombosis of other thoracic veins
I82.622	Acute embolism and thrombosis of deep veins of left upper extremity	I82.701	Chronic embolism and thrombosis of unspecified veins of right upper extremity
I82.623	Acute embolism and thrombosis of deep veins of upper extremity, bilateral	I82.702	Chronic embolism and thrombosis of unspecified veins of left upper extremity
I82.629	Acute embolism and thrombosis of deep veins of unspecified upper extremity	I82.703	Chronic embolism and thrombosis of unspecified veins of upper extremity, bilateral
I82.601	Acute embolism and thrombosis of unspecified veins of right upper extremity	I82.709	Chronic embolism and thrombosis of unspecified veins of unspecified upper extremity
I82.602	Acute embolism and thrombosis of unspecified veins of left upper extremity	I82.711	Chronic embolism and thrombosis of superficial veins of right upper extremity
I82.603	Acute embolism and thrombosis of unspecified veins of upper extremity, bilateral	I82.712	Chronic embolism and thrombosis of superficial veins of left upper extremity
I82.609	Acute embolism and thrombosis of unspecified veins of unspecified upper extremity	I82.713	Chronic embolism and thrombosis of superficial veins of upper extremity, bilateral
I82.A11	Acute embolism and thrombosis of right axillary vein	I82.719	Chronic embolism and thrombosis of superficial veins of unspecified upper extremity
I82.A12	Acute embolism and thrombosis of left axillary vein	I82.721	Chronic embolism and thrombosis of deep veins of right upper extremity
I82.A13	Acute embolism and thrombosis of axillary vein, bilateral	I82.722	Chronic embolism and thrombosis of deep veins of left upper extremity
I82.A19	Acute embolism and thrombosis of unspecified axillary vein	I82.723	Chronic embolism and thrombosis of deep veins of upper extremity, bilateral
I82.A21	Chronic embolism and thrombosis of right axillary vein	I82.729	Chronic embolism and thrombosis of deep veins of unspecified upper extremity
I82.A22	Chronic embolism and thrombosis of left axillary vein	I82.811	Embolism and thrombosis of superficial veins of right lower extremities
I82.A23	Chronic embolism and thrombosis of axillary vein, bilateral	I82.812	Embolism and thrombosis of superficial veins of left lower extremities
I82.A29	Chronic embolism and thrombosis of unspecified axillary vein	I82.813	Embolism and thrombosis of superficial veins of lower extremities, bilateral
I82.B11	Acute embolism and thrombosis of right subclavian vein	I82.819	Embolism and thrombosis of superficial veins of unspecified lower extremities
I82.B12	Acute embolism and thrombosis of left subclavian vein	I82.890	Acute embolism and thrombosis of other specified veins
I82.B13	Acute embolism and thrombosis of subclavian vein, bilateral	I82.891	Chronic embolism and thrombosis of other specified veins
I82.B19	Acute embolism and thrombosis of unspecified subclavian vein	I82.90	Acute embolism and thrombosis of unspecified vein
I82.B21	Chronic embolism and thrombosis of right subclavian vein	I82.91	Chronic embolism and thrombosis of unspecified vein
I82.B22	Chronic embolism and thrombosis of left subclavian vein		
I82.B23	Chronic embolism and thrombosis of subclavian vein, bilateral		

Pulmonary Embolism & Infarction

ICD-10- CM Code	Code Description
I26.90	Septic pulmonary embolism without acute cor pulmonale
I26.99	Other pulmonary embolism without acute cor pulmonale
I26.01	Septic pulmonary embolism with acute cor pulmonale
I26.90	Septic pulmonary embolism without acute cor pulmonale
I26.09	Other pulmonary embolism with acute cor pulmonale
I26.99	Other pulmonary embolism without acute cor pulmonale

Atrial Fibrillation

ICD-10-CM Code	Code Description
I48.0	Paroxysmal atrial fibrillation
I48.2	Chronic atrial fibrillation
I48	-91 Unspecified atrial fibrillation Other
I23.6	Thrombosis of atrium, auricular appendage, and ventricle as current complications following acute myocardial infarction
I27.82	Chronic pulmonary embolism
I67.6	Nonpyogenic thrombosis of intracranial venous system
O22.50	Cerebral venous thrombosis in pregnancy, unspecified trimester
O22.51	Cerebral venous thrombosis in pregnancy, first trimester
O22.52	Cerebral venous thrombosis in pregnancy, second trimester
O22.53	Cerebral venous thrombosis in pregnancy, third trimester
O87.3	Cerebral venous thrombosis in the puerperium
Z79.01	Long term (current) use of anticoagulants

100-4, Chapter-32, 80

Billing of the Diagnosis and Treatment of Peripheral Neuropathy with Loss of Protective Sensation in People with Diabetes

Coverage Requirements -Peripheral neuropathy is the most common factor leading to amputation in people with diabetes. In diabetes, peripheral neuropathy is an anatomically diffuse process primarily affecting sensory and autonomic fibers; however, distal motor findings may be present in advanced cases. Long nerves are affected first, with symptoms typically beginning insidiously in the toes and then advancing proximally. This leads to loss of protective sensation (LOPS), whereby a person is unable to feel minor trauma from mechanical, thermal, or chemical sources. When foot lesions are present, the reduction in autonomic nerve functions may also inhibit wound healing.

Peripheral neuropathy with LOPS, secondary to diabetes, is a localized illness of the feet and falls within the regulation's exception to the general exclusionary rule (see 42 C.F.R. §411.15(l)(l)(i)). Foot exams for people with diabetic peripheral neuropathy with LOPS are reasonable and necessary to allow for early intervention in serious complications that typically afflict diabetics with the disease.

Effective for services furnished on or after July 1, 2002, Medicare covers, as a physician service, an evaluation (examination and treatment) of the feet no more often than every 6 months for individuals with a documented diagnosis of diabetic sensory neuropathy and LOPS, as long as the beneficiary has not seen a foot care specialist for some other reason in the interim. LOPS shall be diagnosed through

sensory testing with the 5.07 monofilament using established guidelines, such as those developed by the National Institute of Diabetes and Digestive and Kidney Diseases guidelines. Five sites should be tested on the plantar surface of each foot, according to the National Institute of Diabetes and Digestive and Kidney Diseases guidelines. The areas must be tested randomly since the loss of protective sensation may be patchy in distribution, and the patient may get clues if the test is done rhythmically. Heavily callused areas should be avoided. As suggested by the American Podiatric Medicine Association, an absence of sensation at two or more sites out of 5 tested on either foot when tested with the 5.07 Semmes-Weinstein monofilament must be present and documented to diagnose peripheral neuropathy with loss of protective sensation.

100-4, Chapter-32, 80.2

Applicable HCPCS Codes

G0245 - Initial physician evaluation and management of a diabetic patient with diabetic sensory neuropathy resulting in a loss of protective sensation (LOPS) which must include:

1. The diagnosis of LOPS;
2. A patient history;
3. A physical examination that consists of at least the following elements:
   a. visual inspection of the forefoot, hindfoot, and toe web spaces,
   b. evaluation of a protective sensation,
   c. evaluation of foot structure and biomechanics,
   d. evaluation of vascular status and skin integrity,
   e. evaluation and recommendation of footwear, and
4. Patient education.

G0246 -Follow-up physician evaluation and management of a diabetic patient with diabetic sensory neuropathy resulting in a loss of protective sensation (LOPS) to include at least the following:

1. a patient history;
2. a physical examination that includes:
   a. (a) visual inspection of the forefoot, hindfoot, and toe web spaces,
   b. evaluation of protective sensation,
   c. evaluation of foot structure and biomechanics,
   d. evaluation of vascular status and skin integrity,
   e. evaluation and recommendation of footwear, and 3.patient education.

G0247 -Routine foot care by a physician of a diabetic patient with diabetic sensory neuropathy resulting in a LOPS to include if present, at least the following:

1. local care of superficial (i.e., superficial to muscle and fascia) wounds;
2. debridement of corns and calluses; and
3. trimming and debridement of nails.

NOTE: Code G0247 must be billed on the same date of service with either G0245 or G0246 in order to be considered for payment.

The short descriptors for the above HCPCS codes are as follows:

G0245 – INITIAL FOOT EXAM PTLOPS

G0246 – FOLLOW-UP EVAL OF FOOT PT LOP

G0247 – ROUTINE FOOTCARE PT W LOPS

100-4, Chapter-32, 80.8

CWF Utilization Edits

<u>Edit 1</u>- Should CWF receive a claim from an FI for G0245 or G0246 and a second claim from a contractor for either G0245 or G0246 (or vice versa) and they are different dates of service and less than 6 months apart, the second claim will reject. CWF will edit to allow G0245 or G0246 to be paid no more than every 6 months for a particular beneficiary, regardless of who furnished the service. If G0245 has been paid, regardless of whether it was posted as a facility or professional claim, it must be 6 months before G0245 can be paid again or G0246 can be paid. If G0246 has been paid, regardless of whether it was posted as a facility or professional claim, it must be 6 months before G0246 can be paid again or G0245 can be paid. CWF will not impose limits on how many times each code can be paid for a beneficiary as long as there has been 6 months between each service.

The CWF will return a specific reject code for this edit to the contractors and FIs that will be identified in the CWF documentation. Based on the CWF reject code, the contractors and FIs must deny the claims and return the following messages:

MSN 18.4 -- This service is being denied because it has not been __ months since your last examination of this kind (**NOTE:** Insert 6 as the appropriate number of months.)

RA claim adjustment reason code 96 – Non-covered charges, along with remark code M86 – Service denied because payment already made for same/similar procedure within set time frame.

<u>Edit 2</u>

The CWF will edit to allow G0247 to pay only if either G0245 or G0246 has been submitted <u>and accepted as payable</u> on the same date of service. CWF will return a specific reject code for this edit to the contractors and FIs that will be identified in the CWF documentation. Based on this reject code, contractors and FIs will deny the claims and return the following messages:

MSN 21.21 - This service was denied because Medicare only covers this service under certain circumstances.

RA claim adjustment reason code 107 – The related or qualifying claim/service was not identified on this claim.

<u>Edit 3</u>

Once a beneficiary's condition has progressed to the point where routine foot care becomes a covered service, payment will no longer be made for LOPS evaluation and management services. Those services would be considered to be included in the regular exams and treatments afforded to the beneficiary on a routine basis. The physician or provider must then just bill the routine foot care codes, per Pub 100-02, Chapter 15, §290.

The CWF will edit to reject LOPS codes G0245, G0246, and/or G0247 when on the beneficiary's record it shows that one of the following routine foot care codes were billed and paid within the prior 6 months: 11055, 11056, 11057, 11719, 11720, and/or 11721.

The CWF will return a specific reject code for this edit to the contractors and FIs that will be identified in the CWF documentation. Based on the CWF reject code, the contractors and FIs must deny the claims and return the following messages:

MSN 21.21 - This service was denied because Medicare only covers this service under certain circumstances.

The RA claim adjustment reason code 96 –Non-covered charges, along with remark code M86 –Service denied

because payment already made for same/similar procedure within set time frame.

100-4, Chapter-32, 100

Billing Requirements for Expanded Coverage of Cochlear Implantation

Effective for dates of services on and after April 4, 2005, the Centers for Medicare & Medicaid Services (CMS) has expanded the coverage for cochlear implantation to cover moderate-to-profound hearing loss in individuals with hearing test scores equal to or less than 40% correct in the best aided listening condition on tape-recorded tests of open-set sentence recognition and who demonstrate limited benefit from amplification. (See Publication 100-03, chapter 1, section 50.3, for specific coverage criteria).

In addition CMS is covering cochlear implantation for individuals with open-set sentence recognition test scores of greater than 40% to less than or equal to 60% correct but only when the provider is participating in, and patients are enrolled in, either:

- A Food and Drug Administration (FDA)-approved category B investigational device exemption (IDE) clinical trial; or
- A trial under the CMS clinical trial policy (see Pub. 100-03, section 310.1); or

A prospective, controlled comparative trial approved by CMS as consistent with the evidentiary requirements for national coverage analyses and meeting specific quality standards.

100-4, Chapter-32, 110.5

DMERC Billing Instructions

Effective for dates of service on or after April 27, 2005, DMERCs shall allow payment for ultrasonic osteogenic stimulators with the following HCPCS codes:

E0760 for low intensity ultrasound (include modifier "KF"), or;

E1399 for other ultrasound stimulation (include modifier "KF")

100-4, Chapter-32, 120.1

Payment for Services and Supplies

For an IOL inserted following removal of a cataract in a hospital, on either an outpatient or inpatient basis, that is paid under the hospital Outpatient Prospective Payment System (OPPS) or the Inpatient Prospective Payment System (IPPS), respectively; or in a Medicare-approved ambulatory surgical center (ASC) that is paid under the ASC fee schedule:

- Medicare does not make separate payment to the hospital or ASC for an IOL inserted subsequent to extraction of a cataract. Payment for the IOL is packaged into the payment for the surgical cataract extraction/lens replacement procedure.
- Any person or ASC, who presents or causes to be presented a bill or request for payment for an IOL inserted during or subsequent to cataract surgery for which payment is made under the ASC fee schedule, is subject to a civil money penalty.
- For a P-C IOL or A-C IOL inserted subsequent to removal of a cataract in a hospital, on either an outpatient or inpatient basis, that is paid under the OPPS or the IPPS, respectively; or in a Medicare-approved ASC that is paid under the ASC fee schedule:

- The facility shall bill for the removal of a cataract with insertion of a conventional IOL, regardless of whether a conventional, P-C IOL, or A-C IOL is inserted. When a beneficiary receives a P-C or A-C IOL following removal of a cataract, hospitals and ASCs shall report the same CPT® code that is used to report removal of a cataract with insertion of a conventional IOL. Physicians, hospitals and ASCs may also report an additional HCPCS code, V2788, to indicate any additional charges that accrue when a P-C IOL or A-C IOL is inserted in lieu of a conventional IOL until January 1, 2008. Effective for A-C IOL insertion services on or after January 1, 2008, physicians, hospitals and ASCs should use V2787 to report any additional charges that accrue. On or after January 1, 2008, physicians, hospitals, and ASCs should continue to report HCPCS code V2788 to indicate any additional charges that accrue for insertion of a P-C IOL. See Section 120.2 for coding guidelines.

- There is no Medicare benefit category that allows payment of facility charges for services and supplies required to insert and adjust a P-C or A-C IOL following removal of a cataract that exceed the facility charges for services and supplies required for the insertion and adjustment of a conventional IOL.

- There is no Medicare benefit category that allows payment of facility charges for subsequent treatments, services and supplies required to examine and monitor the beneficiary who receives a P-C or A-C IOL following removal of a cataract that exceeds the facility charges for subsequent treatments, services and supplies required to examine and monitor a beneficiary after cataract surgery followed by insertion of a conventional IOL.

A -For a P-C IOL or A-C IOL inserted in a physician's office

-A physician shall bill for a conventional IOL, regardless of a whether a conventional, P-C IOL, or A-C IOL is inserted (see section 120.2, General Billing Requirements)

-There is no Medicare benefit category that allows payment of physician charges for services and supplies required to insert and adjust a P-C or A-C IOL following removal of a cataract that exceed the physician charges for services and supplies for the insertion and adjustment of a conventional IOL.

-There is no Medicare benefit category that allows payment of physician charges for subsequent treatments, service and supplies required to examine and monitor a beneficiary following removal of a cataract with insertion of a P-C or A-C IOL that exceed physician charges for services and supplies to examine and monitor a beneficiary following removal of a cataract with insertion of a conventional IOL.

B - For a P-C IOL or A-C IOL inserted in a hospital

-A physician may not bill Medicare for a P-C or A-C IOL inserted during a cataract procedure performed in a hospital setting because the payment for the lens is included in the payment made to the facility for the surgical procedure.

-There is no Medicare benefit category that allows payment of physician charges for services and supplies required to insert and adjust a P-C or A-C IOL following removal of a cataract that exceed the physician charges for services and supplies required for the insertion of a conventional IOL.

C - For a P-C IOL or A-C IOL inserted in an Ambulatory Surgical Center

-Refer to Chapter 14, Section 40.3 for complete guidance on payment for P-C IOL or A-C IOL in Ambulatory Surgical Centers.

100-4, Chapter-32, 120.2

Coding and General Billing Requirements

Physicians and hospitals must report one of the following Current Procedural Terminology (CPT®) codes on the claim:

- 66982 - Extracapsular cataract removal with insertion of intraocular lens prosthesis (one stage procedure), manual or mechanical technique (e.g., irrigation and aspiration or phacoemulsification), complex requiring devices or techniques not generally used in routine cataract surgery (e.g., iris expansion device, suture support for intraocular lens, or primary posterior capsulorrhexis) or performed on patients in the amblyogenic development stage.

- 66983- Intracapsular cataract with insertion of intraocular lens prosthesis (one stage procedure)

- 66984 - Extracapsular cataract removal with insertion of intraocular lens prosthesis (one stage procedure), manual or mechanical technique (e.g., irrigation and aspiration or phacoemulsification)

- 66985 - Insertion of intraocular lens prosthesis (secondary implant), not associated with concurrent cataract extraction

- 66986 - Exchange of intraocular lens

In addition, physicians inserting a P-C IOL or A-C IOL in an office setting may bill code V2632 (posterior chamber intraocular lens) for the IOL. Medicare will make payment for the lens based on reasonable cost for a conventional IOL. Place of Service (POS) = 11.

Effective for dates of service on and after January 1, 2006, physician, hospitals and ASCs may also bill the non-covered charges related to the P-C function of the IOL using HCPCS code V2788. Effective for dates of service on and after January 22, 2007 through January 1, 2008, non-covered charges related to A-C function of the IOL can be billed using HCPCS code V2788. The type of service indicator for the non-covered billed charges is Q. (The type of service is applied by the Medicare carrier and not the provider). Effective for A-C IOL insertion services on or after January 1, 2008, physicians, hospitals and ASCs should use V2787 rather than V2788 to report any additional charges that accrue.

When denying the non-payable charges submitted with V2787 or V2788, contractors shall use an appropriate Medical Summary Notice (MSN) such as 16.10 (Medicare does not pay for this item or service) and an appropriate claim adjustment reason code such as 96 (non-covered charges) for claims submitted with the non-payable charges.

Hospitals and physicians may use the proper CPT® code(s) to bill Medicare for evaluation and management services usually associated with services following cataract extraction surgery, if appropriate.

A - Applicable Bill Types

The hospital applicable bill types are 12X, 13X, 83X and 85X.

B - Other Special Requirements for Hospitals

Hospitals shall continue to pay CAHs method 2 claims under current payment methodologies for conditional IOLs.

100-4, Chapter-32, 130

External Counterpulsation (ECP) Therapy

Commonly referred to as enhanced external counterpulsation, is a non-invasive outpatient treatment for coronary artery disease refractory medical and/or surgical therapy. Effective for dates of service July 1, 1999, and after, Medicare will cover ECP when its use is in patients with stable angina (Class III or Class IV, Canadian Cardiovascular Society Classification or equivalent classification) who, in the opinion of a cardiologist or cardiothoracic surgeon, are not readily amenable to surgical intervention, such as PTCA or cardiac bypass, because:

- Their condition is inoperable, or at high risk of operative complications or post-operative failure;
- Their coronary anatomy is not readily amenable to such procedures; or
- They have co-morbid states that create excessive risk.

(Refer to Publication 100-03, section 20.20 for further coverage criteria.)

100-4, Chapter-32, 130.1

Billing and Payment Requirements

Effective for dates of service on or after January 1, 2000, use HCPCS code G0166 (External counterpulsation, per session) to report ECP services. The codes for external cardiac assist (92971), ECG rhythm strip and report (93040 or 93041), pulse oximetry (94760 or 94761) and plethysmography (93922 or 93923) or other monitoring tests for examining the effects of this treatment are not clinically necessary with this service and should not be paid on the same day, unless they occur in a clinical setting not connected with the delivery of the ECP. Daily evaluation and management service, e.g., 99201-99205, 99211-99215, 99217-99220, 99241-99245, cannot be billed with the ECP treatments. Any evaluation and management service must be justified with adequate documentation of the medical necessity of the visit. Deductible and coinsurance apply.

100-4, Chapter-32, 140.2.2.1

Correct Place of Service (POS) Code for CR and ICR Services on Professional Claims

Effective for claims with dates of service on and after January 1, 2010, place of service (POS) code 11 shall be used for CR and ICR services provided in a physician's office and POS 22 shall be used for services provided in a hospital outpatient setting. All other POS codes shall be denied. Contractors shall adjust their prepayment procedure edits as appropriate.

The following messages shall be used when contractors deny CR and ICR claims for POS:

Claim Adjustment Reason Code (CARC) 171 –Payment is denied when performed/billed by this type of provider in this type of facility.

NOTE: Refer to the 832 Healthcare Policy Identification Segment (loop 2110 Service payment Information REF), if present.

Remittance Advice Remark Code (RARC) N428 - Service/procedure not covered when performed in this place of service.

Medicare Summary Notice (MSN) 21.25 -This service was denied because Medicare only covers this service in certain settings.

Group Code PR (Patient Responsibility) -Where a claim is received with the GA modifier indicating that a signed ABN is on file.

Group Code CO (Contractor Responsibility) –Where a claim is received with the GZ modifier indicating that no signed ABN is on file.

100-4, Chapter-32, 140.3

Intensive Cardiac Rehabilitation Program Services Furnished On or After January 1, 2010

As specified at 42 CFR 410.49, Medicare covers intensive cardiac rehabilitation items and services for patients who have experienced one or more of the following:

- An acute myocardial infarction within the preceding 12 months; or
- A coronary artery bypass surgery; or
- Current stable angina pectoris; or
- Heart valve repair or replacement; or
- Percutaneous transluminal coronary angioplasty (PTCA) or coronary stenting; or
- A heart or heart-lung transplant; or
- A stable, chronic heart failure defined as patients with left ventricular ejection fraction of 35% or less and New York Heart Association (NYHA) class II to IV symptoms despite being on optimal heart failure therapy for at least 6 weeks(effective February 18, 2014).

Intensive cardiac rehabilitation programs must include the following components:

- Physician-prescribed exercise each day cardiac rehabilitation items and services are furnished;
- Cardiac risk factor modification, including education, counseling, and behavioral intervention at least once during the program, tailored to patients' individual needs;
- Psychosocial assessment;
- Outcomes assessment; and
- An individualized treatment plan detailing how components are utilized for each patient.

Intensive cardiac rehabilitation programs must be approved by Medicare. In order to be approved, a program must demonstrate through peer-reviewed published research that it has accomplished one or more of the following for its patients:

- Positively affected the progression of coronary heart disease;
- Reduced the need for coronary bypass surgery; and
- Reduced the need for percutaneous coronary interventions.

An intensive cardiac rehabilitation program must also demonstrate through peer- reviewed published research that it accomplished a statistically significant reduction in five or more of the following measures for patients from their levels before cardiac rehabilitation services to after cardiac rehabilitation services:

- Low density lipoprotein;
- Triglycerides;
- Body mass index;
- Systolic blood pressure;
- Diastolic blood pressure; and
- The need for cholesterol, blood pressure, and diabetes medications.

Intensive cardiac rehabilitation items and services must be furnished in a physician's office or a hospital outpatient setting. All settings must have a physician immediately available and accessible for medical consultations and emergencies at all times items and services are being furnished under the program. This provision is satisfied if the physician meets the requirements for direct supervision of physician office services as specified at 42 CFR 410.26 and for hospital outpatient therapeutic services as specified at 42 CFR 410.27.

As specified at 42 CFR 410.49(f)(2), intensive cardiac rehabilitation program sessions are limited to 72 1-hour sessions, up to 6 sessions per day, over a period of up to 18 weeks.

100-4, Chapter-32, 140.3.1

Coding Requirements for Intensive Cardiac Rehabilitation Services Furnished On or After January 1, 2010

The following are the applicable HCPCS codes for intensive cardiac rehabilitation services:

G0422 (Intensive cardiac rehabilitation; with or without continuous ECG monitoring, with exercise, per hour, per session)

G0423 (Intensive cardiac rehabilitation; with or without continuous ECG monitoring, without exercise, per hour, per session)

Effective for dates of service on or after January 1, 2010, hospitals and practitioners may report a maximum of 6 1-hour sessions per day. In order to report one session of cardiac rehabilitation services in a day, the duration of treatment must be at least 31 minutes.

Additional sessions of intensive cardiac rehabilitation services beyond the first session may only be reported in the same day if the duration of treatment is 31 minutes or greater beyond the hour increment. In other words, in order to report 6 sessions of intensive cardiac rehabilitation services on a given date of service, the first five sessions would account for 60 minutes each and the sixth session would account for at least 31 minutes. If several shorter periods of intensive cardiac rehabilitation services are furnished on a given day, the minutes of service during those periods must be added together for reporting in 1-hour session increments.

Example: If the patient receives 20 minutes of intensive cardiac rehabilitation services in the day, no intensive cardiac rehabilitation session may be reported because less than 31 minutes of services were furnished.

Example: If a patient receives 20 minutes of intensive cardiac rehabilitation services in the morning and 35 minutes of intensive cardiac rehabilitation services in the afternoon of a single day, the hospital or practitioner would report 1 session of intensive cardiac rehabilitation services under 1 unit of the appropriate HCPCS G-code for the total duration of 55 minutes of intensive cardiac rehabilitation services on that day.

Example: If the patient receives 70 minutes of intensive cardiac rehabilitation services in the morning and 25 minutes of intensive cardiac rehabilitation services in the afternoon of a single day, the hospital or practitioner would report two sessions of intensive cardiac rehabilitation services under the appropriate HCPCS G-code(s) because the total duration of intensive cardiac rehabilitation services on that day of 95 minutes exceeds 90 minutes.

Example: If the patient receives 70 minutes of intensive cardiac rehabilitation services in the morning and 85 minutes of intensive cardiac rehabilitation services in the afternoon of a single day, the hospital or practitioner would report three sessions of intensive cardiac rehabilitation services under the appropriate HCPCS G-code(s) because the total duration of intensive cardiac rehabilitation services on that day is 155 minutes, which exceeds 150 minutes and is less than 211 minutes.

100-4, Chapter-32, 140.4

Pulmonary Rehabilitation Program Services Furnished On or After January 1, 2010

As specified in 42 CFR 410.47, Medicare covers pulmonary rehabilitation items and services for patients with moderate to very severe COPD (defined as GOLD classification II, III and IV), when referred by the physician treating the chronic respiratory disease.

Pulmonary rehabilitation programs must include the following components:

- Physician-prescribed exercise. Some aerobic exercise must be included in each pulmonary rehabilitation session;
- Education or training closely and clearly related to the individual's care and treatment which is tailored to the individual's needs, including information on respiratory problem management and, if appropriate, brief smoking cessation counseling;
- Psychosocial assessment;
- Outcomes assessment; and,
- An individualized treatment plan detailing how components are utilized for each patient.

Pulmonary rehabilitation items and services must be furnished in a physician's office or a hospital outpatient setting. All settings must have a physician immediately available and accessible for medical consultations and emergencies at all time items and services are being furnished under the program. This provision is satisfied if the physician meets the requirements for direct supervision of physician office services as specified at 42 CFR 410.26 and for hospital outpatient therapeutic services as specified at 42 CFR 410.27.

As specified at 42 CFR 410.47(f), pulmonary rehabilitation program sessions are limited to a maximum of 2 1-hour sessions per day for up to 36 sessions, with the option for an additional 36 sessions if medically necessary. Contractors shall accept the inclusion of the KX modifier on the claim lines as an attestation by the provider of the service that documentation is on file verifying that further treatment beyond the 36 sessions is medically necessary up to a total of 72 sessions for that beneficiary.

100-4, Chapter-32, 140.4.1

Coding Requirements for Pulmonary Rehabilitation Services Furnished On or After January 1, 2010

The following is the applicable HCPCS code for pulmonary rehabilitation services:

G0424 (Pulmonary rehabilitation, including exercise (includes monitoring), per hour, per session)

Effective for dates of service on or after January 1, 2010, hospitals and practitioners may report a maximum of 2 1-hour sessions per day. In order to report one session of pulmonary rehabilitation services in a day, the duration of treatment must be at least 31 minutes. Two sessions of pulmonary rehabilitation services may only be reported in the same day if the duration of treatment is at least 91 minutes. In other words, the first session would account for 60 minutes and the second session would account for at least 31 minutes, if two sessions are reported. If several shorter periods of pulmonary rehabilitation services are furnished on a given day, the minutes of service during those periods must be added together for reporting in 1-hour session increments.

Example: If the patient receives 20 minutes of pulmonary rehabilitation services in the day, no pulmonary rehabilitation session may be reported because less than 31 minutes of services were furnished.

Example: If a patient receives 20 minutes of pulmonary rehabilitation services in the morning and 35 minutes of pulmonary rehabilitation services in the afternoon of a single day, the hospital or practitioner would report 1 session of pulmonary rehabilitation services under 1 unit of the HCPCS G-code for the total duration of 55 minutes of pulmonary rehabilitation services on that day.

Example: If the patient receives 70 minutes of pulmonary rehabilitation services in the morning and 25 minutes of pulmonary rehabilitation services in the afternoon of a single day, the hospital or practitioner would report two sessions of pulmonary rehabilitation services under the HCPCS G-code because the total duration of pulmonary rehabilitation services on that day of 95 minutes exceeds 90 minutes.

Example: If the patient receives 70 minutes of pulmonary rehabilitation services in the morning and 85 minutes of pulmonary rehabilitation services in the afternoon of a single day, the hospital or practitioner would report two sessions of pulmonary rehabilitation services under the HCPCS G-code for the total duration of pulmonary rehabilitation services of 155 minutes. A maximum of two sessions per day may be reported, regardless of the total duration of pulmonary rehabilitation services.

100-4, Chapter-32, 250.1

Coverage Requirements

Effective August 3, 2009, pharmacogenomic testing to predict warfarin responsiveness is covered only when provided to Medicare beneficiaries who are candidates for anticoagulation therapy with warfarin; i.e., have not been previously tested for CYP2C9 or VKORC1 alleles; and have received fewer than five days of warfarin in the anticoagulation regimen for which the testing is ordered; and only then in the context of a prospective, randomized, controlled clinical study when that study meets certain criteria as outlined in Pub 100-03, section 90.1, of the NCD Manual.

NOTE: A new temporary HCPCS Level II code effective August 3, 2009, G9143, warfarin responsiveness testing by genetic technique using any method, any number of specimen(s), was developed to enable implementation of CED for this purpose.

100-4, Chapter-32, 250.2

Billing Requirements

Institutional clinical trial claims for pharmacogenomic testing for warfarin response are identified through the presence of all of the following elements:

- Value Code D4 and 8-digit clinical trial number (when present on the claim) -Refer to Transmittal 310, Change Request 5790, dated January 18, 2008;
- ICD-9 diagnosis code V70.7 -Refer to Transmittal 310, Change Request 5790, dated January 18, 2008;
- Condition Code 30 -Refer to Transmittal 310, Change Request 5790, dated January 18, 2008;
- HCPCS modifier Q0: outpatient claims only -Refer to Transmittal 1418, Change Request 5805, dated January18, 2008; and,
- HCPCS code G9143 (mandatory with the April 2010 Integrated Outpatient Code Editor (IOCE) and the January 2011 Clinical Laboratory Fee Schedule (CLFS) updates. Prior to these times, any trials should bill FIs for this test as they currently do absent these instructions, and the FIs should process and pay those claims accordingly.)

Practitioner clinical trial claims for pharmacogenomic testing for warfarin response are identified through the presence of all of the following elements:

- ICD-9 diagnosis code V70.7;
- 8-digit clinical trial number(when present on the claim);
- HCPCS modifier Q0; and
- HCPCS code G9143 (to be carrier priced for claims with dates of service on and after August 3, 2009, that are processed prior to the January 2011 CLFS update.)

100-4, Chapter-32, 260.1

Policy

The Centers for Medicare & Medicaid Services (CMS) received a request for national coverage of treatments for facial lipodystrophy syndrome (LDS) for human immunodeficiency virus (HIV)-infected Medicare beneficiaries. Facial LDS is often characterized by a loss of fat that results in a facial abnormality such as severely sunken cheeks. This fat loss can arise as a complication of HIV and/or highly active antiretroviral therapy. Due to their appearance and stigma of the condition, patients with facial LDS may become depressed, socially isolated, and in some cases may stop their HIV treatments in an attempt to halt or reverse this complication.

Effective for claims with dates of service on and after March 23, 2010, dermal injections for facial LDS are only reasonable and necessary using dermal fillers approved by the Food and Drug Administration for this purpose, and then only in HIV-infected beneficiaries who manifest depression secondary to the physical stigmata of HIV treatment.

See Pub. 100-03, National Coverage Decision manual, section 250.5, for detailed policy information concerning treatment of LDS.

100-4, Chapter-32, 260.2.1

Hospital Billing Instructions

A -Hospital Outpatient Claims

For hospital outpatient claims, hospitals must bill covered dermal injections for treatment of facial LDS by having all of the required elements on the claim:

- A line with HCPCS codes Q2026 or Q2027 with a Line Item Date of service (LIDOS) on or after March 23, 2010,
- A line with HCPCS code G0429 with a LIDOS on or after March 23, 2010,

- If ICD-9-CM is applicable,ICD-9-CM diagnosis codes 042 (HIV) and 272.6 (Lipodystrophy)or,
- If ICD-10-CM is applicable, ICD-10-CM diagnosis codes B20 Human Immunodeficiency Virus (HIV) disease and E88.1 Lipodystrophy, not elsewhere classified

The applicable NCD is 250.5 Facial Lipodystrophy.

B - Outpatient Prospective Payment System (OPPS) Hospitals or Ambulatory Surgical Centers (ASCs):

For line item dates of service on or after March 23, 2010, and until HCPCS codes Q2026 and Q2027 are billable, facial LDS claims shall contain a temporary HCPCS code C9800 (this code has been deleted or 2017), instead of HCPCS G0429 and HCPCS Q2026/Q2027, as shown above.

C -Hospital Inpatient Claims

Hospitals must bill covered dermal injections for treatment of facial LDS by having all of the required elements on the claim:

- Discharge date on or after March 23, 2010,

If ICD-9-CM is applicable,

- ICD-9-CM procedure code 86.99 (other operations on skin and subcutaneous tissue, i.e., injection of filler material), or
- ICD-9-CM diagnosis codes 042 (HIV) and 272.6 (Lipodystrophy)
- If ICD-10-PCS is applicable,
- ICD-10-PCS procedure code 3E00XGC Introduction of Other Therapeutic Substance into Skin and Mucous Membranes, External Approach, or
- ICD-10-CM diagnosis codes B20 Human Immundodeficiency Virus [HIV] disease and E88.1 Lipodystrophy not elsewhere classified.

A diagnosis code for a comorbidity of depression may also be required for coverage on an outpatient and/or inpatient basis as determined by the individual Medicare contractor's policy.

100-4, Chapter-32, 260.2.2

Practitioner Billing Instructions

Practitioners must bill covered claims for dermal injections for treatment of facial LDS by having all of the required elements on the claim:

Performed in a non-facility setting:

- A line with HCPCS codes Q2026 or Q2027 with a LIDOS on or after March 23, 2010,
- A line with HCPCS code G0429 with a LIDOS on or after March 23, 2010,
- If ICD-9-CM applies,diagnosis codes 042 (HIV) and 272.6 (Lipodystrophy) or,
- If ICD-10-CM applies, diagnosis codes B20 Human Immunodeficiency Virus(HIV) disease and E88.1 (Lipodystrophy not elsewhere classified).

NOTE: A diagnosis code for a comorbidity of depression may also be required for coverage based on the individual Medicare contractor's policy.

Performed in a facility setting:

- A line with HCPCS code G0429 with a LIDOS on or after March 23, 2010,
- If ICD-9 applies,ICD-9-CM diagnosis codes 042 (HIV) and 272.6 (Lipodystrophy)or

- If ICD-10 applies, ICD-10-CM diagnosis codes B20 Human Immundodeficiency Virus (HIV) disease and E88.1 (Lipodystrophy not elsewhere classified).

NOTE: A diagnosis code for a comorbidity of depression may also be required for coverage based on the individual Medicare contractor's policy.

100-4, Chapter-32, 280.1

Policy

Effective for services furnished on or after June 30, 2011, a National Coverage Determination (NCD) provides coverage of sipuleucel-T (PROVENGE®) for patients with asymptomatic or minimally symptomatic metastatic, castrate-resistant (hormone refractory) prostate cancer. Conditions of Medicare Part A and Medicare Part B coverage for sipuleucel-T are located in the Medicare NCD Manual, Publication 100-03, section 110.22.

100-4, Chapter-32, 280.2

Healthcare Common Procedure Coding System (HCPCS) Codes and Diagnosis Coding

HCPCS Codes

Effective for claims with dates of service on June 30, 2011, Medicare providers shall report one of the following HCPCS codes for PROVENGE®:

- C9273 - Sipuleucel-T, minimum of 50 million autologous CD54+ cells activated with PAP-GM-CSF, including leukapheresis and all other preparatory procedures, per infusion, or
- J3490 –Unclassified Drugs, or
- J3590 –Unclassified Biologics.

NOTE: Contractors shall continue to process claims for HCPCS code C9273, J3490, and J3590, with dates of service June 30, 2011, as they do currently.

Effective for claims with dates of service on and after July 1, 2011, Medicare providers shall report the following HCPCS code:

Q2043 – Sipuleucel-T, minimum of 50 million autologous CD54+ cells activated with PAP-

GM-CSF, including leukapheresis and all other preparatory procedures, per infusion; short descriptor, Sipuleucel-T auto CD54+.

ICD-9 Diagnosis Coding

For claims with dates of service on and after July 1, 2011, for PROVENGE®, the on-label indication of asymptomatic or minimally symptomatic metastatic, castrate-resistant (hormone refractory) prostate cancer, must be billed using ICD-9 code 185 (malignant neoplasm of prostate) and at least one of the following ICD-9 codes:

ICD-9 Code	Description
196.1	Secondary and unspecified malignant neoplasm of intrathoracic lymph nodes
196.2	Secondary and unspecified malignant neoplasm of intra-abdominal lymph nodes
196.5	Secondary and unspecified malignant neoplasm of lymph nodes of inguinal region and lower limb
196.6	Secondary and unspecified malignant neoplasm of intrapelvic lymph nodes

ICD-9 Code	Description
196.8	Secondary and unspecified malignant neoplasm of lymph nodes of multiple sites
196.9	Secondary and unspecified malignant neoplasm of lymph node site unspecified -The spread of cancer to and establishment in the lymph nodes.
197.0	Secondary malignant neoplasm of lung –Cancer that has spread from the original (primary) tumor to the lung. The spread of cancer to the lung. This may be from a primary lung cancer, or from a cancer at a distant site.
197.7	Malignant neoplasm of liver secondary -Cancer that has spread from the original (primary) tumor to the liver. A malignant neoplasm that has spread to the liver from another (primary) anatomic site. Such malignant neoplasms may be carcinomas (e.g., breast, colon), lymphomas, melanomas, or sarcomas.
198.0	Secondary malignant neoplasm of kidney -The spread of the cancer to the kidney.This may be from a primary kidney cancer involving the opposite kidney, or from a cancer at a distant site.
198.1	Secondary malignant neoplasm of other urinary organs
198.5	Secondary malignant neoplasm of bone and bone marrow –Cancer that has spread from the original (primary) tumor to the bone. The spread of a malignant neoplasm from a primary site to the skeletal system. The majority of metastatic neoplasms to the bone are carcinomas.
198.7	Secondary malignant neoplasm of bone and bone marrow –Cancer that has spread from the original (primary) tumor to the bone. The spread of a malignant neoplasm from a primary site to the skeletal system. The majority of metastatic neoplasms to the bone are carcinomas.
198.82	Secondary malignant neoplasm of genital organs

Coding for Off-Label PROVENGE® Services

The use of PROVENGE® off-label for the treatment of prostate cancer is left to the discretion of the Medicare Administrative Contractors. Claims with dates of service on and after July 1, 2011, for PROVENGE® paid off-label for the treatment of prostate cancer must be billed using either ICD-9 code 233.4 (carcinoma in situ of prostate), or ICD-9 code 185 (malignant neoplasm of prostate) in addition to HCPCS Q2043. Effective with the implementation date for ICD-10 codes, off-label PROVENGE® services must be billed with either ICD-10 code D075(carcinoma in situ of prostate), or C61 (malignant neoplasm of prostate) in addition to HCPCS Q2043.

ICD-10 Diagnosis Coding

Contractors shall note the appropriate ICD-10 code(s) that are listed below for future implementation. Contractors shall track the ICD-10 codes and ensure that the updated edit is turned on as part of the ICD-10 implementation effective October 1, 2013.

ICD-10	Description
C61	Malignant neoplasm of prostate (for on-label or off-label indications)
D075	Carcinoma in situ of prostate (for off-label indications only)
C77.1	Secondary and unspecified malignant neoplasm of intrathoracic lymph nodes
C77.2	Secondary and unspecified malignant neoplasm of intra-abdominal lymph nodes

ICD-10	Description
C77.4	Secondary and unspecified malignant neoplasm of inguinal and lower limb lymph nodes
C77.5	Secondary and unspecified malignant neoplasm of intrapelvic lymph nodes
C77.8	Secondary and unspecified malignant neoplasm of lymph nodes of multiple regions
C77.9	Secondary and unspecified malignant neoplasm of lymph node, unspecified
C78.00	Secondary malignant neoplasm of unspecified lung
C78.01	Secondary malignant neoplasm of right lung
C78.02	Secondary malignant neoplasm of left lung
C78.7	Secondary malignant neoplasm of liver
C79.00	Secondary malignant neoplasm of unspecified kidney and renal pelvis
C79.01	Secondary malignant neoplasm of right kidney and renal pelvis
C79.02	Secondary malignant neoplasm of left kidney and renal pelvis
C79.10	Secondary malignant neoplasm of unspecified urinary organs
C79.11	Secondary malignant neoplasm of bladder
C79.19	Secondary malignant neoplasm of other urinary organs
C79.51	Secondary malignant neoplasm of bone
C79.52	Secondary malignant neoplasm of bone marrow
C79.70	Secondary malignant neoplasm of unspecified adrenal gland
C79.71	Secondary malignant neoplasm of right adrenal gland
C79.72	Secondary malignant neoplasm of left adrenal gland
C79.82	Secondary malignant neoplasm of genital organs

100-4, Chapter-32, 280.4

Payment Method

Payment for PROVENGE® is as follows:

- TOBs 12X, 13X, 22X and 23X -based on the Average Sales Price (ASP) + 6%,
- TOB 85X –based on reasonable cost,
- TOBs 71X and 77X –based on all-inclusive rate.

For Medicare Part B practitioner claims, payment for PROVENGE® is based on ASP + 6%.

Contractors shall not pay separately for routine costs associated with PROVENGE®, HCPCS Q2043, except for the cost of administration. (Q2043 is all-inclusive and represents all routine costs except for its cost of administration).

100-4, Chapter-32, 280.5

Medicare Summary Notices (MSNs), Remittance Advice Remark Codes (RARCs), Claim Adjustment Reason Codes (CARCs), and Group Codes

Contractors shall use the following messages when denying claims for the on-label indication for PROVENGE®, HCPCS Q2043, submitted without ICD-9-CM diagnosis code 185 and at least one diagnosis code from the ICD-9 table in Section 280.2 above:

MSN 14.9 - Medicare cannot pay for this service for the diagnosis shown on the claim.

Spanish Version -Medicare no puede pagar por este servicio debido al diagnóstico indicado en la reclamación.

RARC 167 - This (these) diagnosis (es) are not covered. *Note:* Refer to the 835 Healthcare Policy Identification segment (loop 2110 Service Payment Information REF), if present.

Group Code – CO (Contractual Obligation)

Contractors shall use the following messages when denying claims for the off-label indication for PROVENGE®, HCPCS Q2043, submitted without ICD-9-CM diagnosis code 233.4:

MSN 14.9 - Medicare cannot pay for this service for the diagnosis shown on the claim.

Spanish Version - Medicare no puede pagar por este servicio debido al diagnóstico indicado en la reclamación.

RARC 167 - This (these) diagnosis (es) are not covered. *Note:* Refer to the 835 Healthcare Policy Identification segment (loop 2110 Service Payment Information REF), if present.

Group Code –CO (Contractual Obligation)

For claims with dates of service on or after July 1, 2012, processed on or after July 2, 2012, when denying claims for PROVENGE®, HCPCS Q2043® that exceed three (3) services in a patient's lifetime, contractors shall use the following messages:

MSN 20.5 - These services cannot be paid because your benefits are exhausted at this time.

Spanish Version - Estos servicios no pueden ser pagados porque sus beneficios se han agotado.

RARC N362 - The number of Days or Units of Service exceeds our acceptable maximum.

CARC 149 -Lifetime benefit maximum has been reached for this service/benefit category.

Group Code – CO (Contractual Obligation)

100-4, Chapter-32, 300

Billing Requirements for Ocular Photodynamic Therapy (OPT) with Verteporfin

Ocular Photodynamic Therapy (OPT) is used in the treatment of ophthalmologic diseases; specifically, for age-related macular degeneration (AMD), a common eye disease among the elderly. OPT involves the infusion of an intravenous photosensitizing drug called Verteporfin, followed by exposure to a laser. For complete Medical coverage guidelines, see National Coverage Determinations (NCD) Manual (Pub 100-03) § 80.2 through 80.3.1.

100-4, Chapter-32, 300.1

Coding Requirements for OPT with Verteporfin

The following are applicable Current Procedural Terminology (CPT®) codes for OPT with Verteporfin:

67221- Destruction of localized lesion of choroid (e.g. choroidal neovascularization); photodynamic therapy (includes intravenous infusion)

67225- Destruction of localized lesion of choroid (e.g. choroidal neovascularization); photodynamic therapy, second eye, at single session (List separately in addition to code for primary eye treatment)

The following are applicable Healthcare Common Procedure Coding System (HCPCS) code for OPT with Verteporfin:

J3396- Injection, Verteporfin, 0.1 mg

100-4, Chapter-32, 300.2

Claims Processing Requirements for OPT with Verteporfin Services on Professional Claims and Outpatient Facility Claims

OPT with Verteporfin is a covered service when billed with ICD-9-CM code 362.52 (Exudative Senile Macular Degeneration of Retina (Wet)) or ICD-10-CM code H35.32 (Exudative Age-related Macular Degeneration).

Coverage is denied when billed with either ICD-9-CM code 362.50 (Macular Degeneration (Senile), Unspecified) or 362.51 (Non-exudative Senile Macular Degeneration) or their equivalent ICD-10-CM code H35.30 (Unspecified Macular Degeneration) or H35.31 (Non-exudative Age-Related Macular Degeneration).

OPT with Verteporfin for other ocular indications are eligible for local coverage determinations through individual contractor discretion.

Payment for OPT service (CPT® code 67221/67225) must be billed on the same claim as the drug (J3396) for the same date of service.

Claims for OPT with Verteporfin for dates of service prior to April 3,2013 are covered at the initial visit as determined by a fluorescein angiogram (FA) CPT® code 92235. Subsequent follow-up visits also require a FA prior to treatment.

For claims with dates of service on or after April 3, 2013, contractors shall accept and process claims for subsequent follow-up visits with either a FA, CPT® code 92235, or optical coherence tomography (OCT), CPT® codes 92133 or 92134, prior to treatment.

Regardless of the date of service of the claim, the FA or OCT is not required to be submitted on the claim for OPT and can be maintained in the patient's file for audit purposes.

100-4, Chapter-32, 310

Transesophageal Doppler Used for Cardiac Monitoring

Effective May 17, 2007, Transesophageal Doppler used for cardiac monitoring is covered for ventilated patients in the ICU and operative patients with a need for intra-operative fluid optimization was deemed reasonable and necessary. See National Coverage Determinations Manual (Pub. 100-03)§220.5, for complete coverage guidelines.

A new Healthcare Common Procedure Coding System (HCPCS) code, G9157, Transesophageal Doppler used for cardiac monitoring, will be made effective for use for dates of service on or after January 1, 2013.

100-4, Chapter-32, 310.2

Coding Requirements for Transesophageal Doppler Cardiac Monitoring Furnished On or After January 1, 2013

After January 1, 2013, the applicable HCPCS code for Transesophageal Doppler cardiac monitoring is:

HCPCS G9157: Transesophageal Doppler used for cardiac monitoring

Contractors shall allow HCPCS G9157 to be billed when services are provided in POS 21 for ventilated patients in the ICU or for operative patients with a need for intra-operative fluid optimization.

Contractors shall deny HCPCS 76999 when billed for Esophageal Doppler for ventilated patients in the ICU or for operative patients with a need for intra-operative fluid optimization using the following messages:

CARC 189: "'Not otherwise classified' or 'unlisted' procedure code (CPT®/HCPCS) was billed when there is a specific procedure code for this procedure/service."

RARC M20: "Missing/incomplete/invalid HCPCS."

MSN 16.13: "The code(s) your provider used is/are not valid for the date of service billed." (English version) or "El/los código(s) que usó su proveedor no es/son válido(s) en la fecha de servicio facturada." (Spanish version).

Group Code: Contractual Obligation (CO)

100-4, Chapter-32, 310.3

Correct Place of Service (POS) Code for Transesophageal Doppler Cardiac Monitoring Services on Professional Claims

Contractors shall pay for Transesophageal Doppler cardiac monitoring, G9157, only when services are provided at POS 21.

Contractors shall deny HCPCS G9157 when billed globally in any POS other than 21 for ventilated patients in the ICU or for operative patients with a need for intra-operative fluid optimization using the following messages:

CARC 58:"Treatment was deemed by the payer to have been rendered in an inappropriate

or invalid place of service. *Note:* Refer to the 835 Healthcare Policy Identification Segment (loop 2110 Service Payment Information REF), if present.

MSN 16.2: This service cannot be paid when provided in this location/facility.

Group Code: CO

100-4, Chapter-36, 50.14

Purchased Accessories & Supplies for Use With Grandfathered Equipment

Non-contract grandfathered suppliers must use the KY modifier on claims for CBA-residing beneficiaries with dates of service on or after January 1, 2011, for purchased, covered accessories or supplies furnished for use with rented grandfathered equipment. The following HCPCS codes are the codes for which use of the KY modifier is authorized:

- Continuous Positive Airway Pressure Devices, Respiratory Assistive Devices, and Related Supplies and Accessories – A4604, A7030, A7031, A7032, A7033, A7034, A7035, A7036, A7037, A7038, A7039, A7044, A7045, A7046, E0561, and E0562
- Hospital Beds and Related Accessories – E0271, E0272, E0280, and E0310
- Walkers and Related Accessories – E0154, E0156, E0157 and E0158

Grandfathered suppliers that submit claims for the payment of the aforementioned purchased accessories and supplies for use with grandfathered equipment should submit the applicable single payment amount for the accessory or supply as their submitted charge on the claim. Non-contract grandfathered suppliers should be aware that purchase claims submitted for these codes without the KY modifier will be

denied. In addition, claims submitted with the KY modifier for HCPCS codes other than those listed above will be denied.

After the rental payment cap for the grandfathered equipment is reached, the beneficiary must obtain replacement supplies and accessories from a contract supplier. The supplier of the grandfathered equipment is no longer permitted to furnish the supplies and accessories once the rental payment cap is reached.

100-4, Chapter-36, 50.15

Hospitals Providing Walkers and Related Accessories to Their Patients on the Date of Discharge

Hospitals may furnish walkers and related accessories to their own patients for use in the home during an admission or on the date of discharge and receive payment at the applicable single payment amount, regardless of whether the hospital is a contract supplier or not. Separate payment is not made for walkers furnished by a hospital for use in the hospital, as payment for these items is included in the Part A payment for inpatient hospital services.

To be paid for walkers as a non-contract supplier, the hospital must use the modifier J4 in combination with the following HCPCS codes: A4636; A4637; E0130; E0135; E0140; E0141; E0143; E0144; E0147; E0148; E0149; E0154; E0155; E0156; E0157; E0158; and E0159. Under this exception, hospitals are advised to submit the claim for the hospital stay before or on the same day that they submit the claim for the walker to ensure timely and accurate claims processing.

Hospitals that are located outside a CBA that furnish walkers and/or related accessories to travelling beneficiaries who live in a CBA must affix the J4 modifier to claims submitted for these items.

The J4 modifier should not be used by contract suppliers.

NOTES